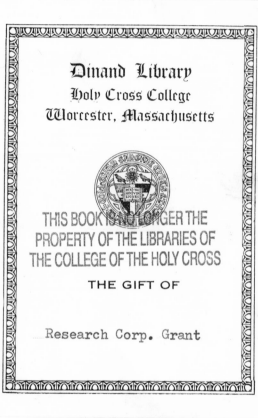

Group Theory
and Its Applications

Contributors

R. E. BEHRENDS

L. C. BIEDENHARN

A. J. COLEMAN

STIG FLODMARK

W. J. HOLMAN, III

J. M. JAUCH

B. R. JUDD

DIRK KLEIMA

P. KRAMER

F. A. MATSEN

M. MOSHINSKY

L. O'RAIFEARTAIGH

T. O. PHILIPS

O. R. PLUMMER

EUGENE P. WIGNER

Group Theory and Its Applications

Edited by ERNEST M. LOEBL
POLYTECHNIC INSTITUTE
BROOKLYN, NEW YORK

1968

ACADEMIC PRESS New York and London

ACADEMIC PRESS INC.
111 Fifth Avenue, New York, New York 10003

United Kingdom Edition published by
ACADEMIC PRESS INC. (LONDON) LTD.
Berkeley Square House, London W.1

LIBRARY OF CONGRESS CATALOG CARD NUMBER: 67-23166

PRINTED IN THE UNITED STATES OF AMERICA

To the memory of
G. RACAH
pioneer and teacher

List of Contributors

Numbers in parentheses indicate the pages on which the authors' contributions begin.

R. E. BEHRENDS (541), Belfer Graduate School of Science, Yeshiva University, New York

L. C. BIEDENHARN (1), Physics Department, Duke University, Durham, North Carolina

A. J. COLEMAN (57), Department of Mathematics, Queen's University, Kingston, Ontario, Canada

STIG FLODMARK (265), Institute of Theoretical Physics, University of Stockholm, Stockholm, Sweden

W. J. HOLMAN, III (1), Physics Department, Duke University, Durham, North Carolina

J. M. JAUCH (131), University of Geneva, Geneva, Switzerland

B. R. JUDD (183), Department of Physics, The Johns Hopkins University, Baltimore, Maryland

DIRK KLEIMA* (1), Physics Department, Duke University, Durham, North Carolina

P. KRAMER† (339), Instituto de Física, Universidad de México, México

F. A. MATSEN (221), Department of Chemistry, University of Texas, Austin, Texas

M. MOSHINSKY (339), Instituto de Física, Universidad de México, México

L. O'RAIFEARTAIGH‡ (469), Syracuse University, Syracuse, New York

T. O. PHILIPS (631), Bell Telephone Laboratories, Incorporated, Whippany, New Jersey

O. R. PLUMMER (221), University of Arkansas, Fayetteville, Arkansas

EUGENE P. WIGNER (119, 631), Princeton University, Princeton, New Jersey

*Present address: Twente Institute of Technology, Enschede, The Netherlands.
†Present address: Institut für Theoretische Physik, Tübingen, Germany.
‡Permanent address: Dublin Institute for Advanced Studies, Dublin, Ireland.

Preface

The importance of group theory and its utility in applications to various branches of physics and chemistry is now so well established and universally recognized that its explicit use needs neither apology nor justification. Matters have moved a long way since the time, just thirty years ago, when Condon and Shortley, in the introduction to their famous book, "The Theory of Atomic Spectra", justified their doing "group theory without group theory" by the statement that ". . . the theory of groups . . . is not . . . part of the ordinary mathematical equipment of physicists." The somewhat adverse, or at least sceptical, attitude toward group theory illustrated by the telling there of the well-known anecdote concerning the Weyl-Dirac exchange,* has been replaced by an uninhibited and enthusiastic espousal. This is apparent from the steadily increasing number of excellent textbooks published in this field that seek to instruct ever widening audiences in the nature and use of this tool. There is, however, a gap between the material treated there and the research literature and it is this gap that the present treatise is designed to fill. The articles, by noted workers in the various areas of group theory, each review a substantial field and bring the reader from the level of a general understanding of the subject to that of the more advanced literature.

The serious student and beginning research worker in a particular branch should find the article or articles in his specialty very helpful in acquainting him with the background and literature and bringing him up to the frontiers of current research; indeed, even the seasoned specialist in a particular branch will still learn something new. The editor hopes also to have the treatise serve another useful function: to entice the specialist in one area into becoming acquainted with another. Such ventures into novel fields might be facilitated by the recognition that similar basic techniques are applied throughout; e.g., the use of the Wigner-Eckart theorem can be recognized as a unifying thread running through much of the treatise.

The applications of group theory can be subdivided generally into two broad areas: one, where the underlying dynamical laws (of interactions) and therefore all the resulting symmetries are known exactly; the other, where

*After a seminar on spin variables and exchange energy which Dirac gave at Princeton in 1928, Weyl protested that Dirac had promised to derive the results without use of group theory. Dirac replied: "I said I would obtain the results without previous knowledge of group theory" (Condon and Shortley, "The Theory of Atomic Spectra", pp. 10–11. Cambridge Univ. Press, 1953).

these are as yet unknown and only the kinematical symmetries (i.e. those of the underlying space-time continuum) can serve as a certain guide.

In the first area, group theoretical techniques are used essentially to exploit the known symmetries, either to simplify numerical calculations or to draw exact, qualitative conclusions. All (extra-nuclear) atomic and molecular phenomena are believed to belong to this category; the central chapters in this book deal with such applications, which, until relatively recently, formed the bulk of all uses of group theory.

In the second major area, application of group theory proceeds essentially in the opposite direction: It is used to discover as much as possible of the underlying symmetries and, through them, learn about the physical laws of interaction. This area, which includes all aspects of nuclear structure and elementary particle theory, has mushroomed in importance and volume of research to an extraordinary degree in recent times; the articles in the second half of the treatise are devoted to it.

In part as a consequence of these developments, physical scientists have been forced to concern themselves more profoundly with mathematical aspects of the theory of groups that previously could be left aside; questions of topology, representations of noncompact groups, more powerful methods for generating representations as well as a systematic study of Lie groups and their algebras in general belong in this category. They are treated in the earlier chapters of this book.

Considerations of both space and timing have forced omission from this volume of articles dealing with several important areas of applied group theory like molecular spectra, hidden symmetry and "accidental" degeneracy, group theory and computers, and others. These will be included in a second volume, currently in preparation.

Complete uniformity and consistency of notation is an ideal to be striven for but difficult to attain; it is especially hard to achieve when, as in the present case, many different and widely separated specialities are discussed, each of which usually has a well-established notational system of its own which may not be reconcilable with an equally well-established one in another area. In the present book uniformity has been carried as far as possible, subject to these restrictions, except where it would impair clarity.

The glossary of symbols included is expected to be of help; a few general remarks about notation follow: different mathematical entities are generally distinguished by different type fonts: vectors in bold face ($\mathbf{A}, \mathbf{H}, \mathbf{M}, \mathbf{u}, \boldsymbol{\alpha}, \boldsymbol{\Sigma}$), matrices in bold face sans serif ($\boldsymbol{\mathsf{A}}, \boldsymbol{\mathsf{M}}, \boldsymbol{\mathsf{R}}, \boldsymbol{\mathsf{u}}$), operators in script ($\mathscr{C}, \mathscr{H}, \mathscr{R}$) (though certain special Hamiltonians are indicated by italic sans serif $\boldsymbol{\mathsf{H}}$); spaces, fields, etc., by bold face German ($\mathfrak{C}, \mathfrak{H}, \mathfrak{R}, \mathfrak{B}$). The asterisk (*) denotes the complex conjugate, the dagger (†) the adjoint, and the tilde ($\sim$) the transpose. Different product signs are used as follows: $\times$, number product; $\boldsymbol{\times}$, vector cross product; X, the general (Cartesian) product of sets, the (outer) direct product of groups and representations; $\boxtimes$, the inner direct product of groups and representations (of the same group), and $\wedge$, the semidirect product; $\oplus$ denotes the direct sum.

It would be highly presumptuous for the editor to commend the authors for the quality of their contributions; however, I would like to thank them publicly and most sincerely for the spirit in which they cooperated in matters of selection of subject matter or emphasis, notation, style, etc., often sacrificing or modifying individual preferences for the sake of greater unity for the work as a whole. This made the task of the editor a much more enjoyable and less harassing one than it might otherwise have been.

It is also a great pleasure to thank the publisher, Academic Press, Inc., and the printers for the patience, devotion, diligence, and consummate skill with which they handled the uncommonly complex manuscripts. In spite of this diligence and skill misprints and errors undoubtedly still exist and the editor expresses his gratitude in advance to any reader who will point them out.

The dedication of this volume to the late G. Racah is a mark of appreciation for the monumental contribution he has made to group theory and its applications and a token of the esteem in which his person and his work is held by the editor and the contributors. It also symbolizes the sorrow and sense of loss which his tragic and untimely death caused. His contribution to this volume, which had been solicited, would have added luster and its absence leaves a void. On a more personal note, Professor Racah was the first to teach me theoretical physics and to stimulate my interest in it and in group theory. I owe him a debt of gratitude which cannot adequately be expressed, much less repaid.

ERNEST M. LOEBL

Brooklyn, New York
April 1968

Contents

Projective Representation of the Poincaré Group in a Quaternionic Hilbert Space

J. M. JAUCH

Group Theory in Atomic Spectroscopy

B. R. JUDD

Group Lattices and Homomorphisms

F. A. MATSEN and O. R. PLUMMER

Group Theory in Solid State Physics

STIG FLODMARK

Group Theory of Harmonic Oscillators and Nuclear Structure

P. KRAMER AND M. MOSHINSKY

Broken Symmetry

L. O'RAIFEARTAIGH

Broken $SU(3)$ as a Particle Symmetry

R. E. BEHRENDS

De Sitter Space and Positive Energy

T. O. PHILIPS AND E. P. WIGNER

Glossary of Symbols and Abbreviations

Where a symbol is substantially restricted to only one or two chapters or where the same symbol has a different meaning in different chapters, the chapters are identified by the first letters of the authors' names.

$\mathbf{a}$	annihilation operator; components a_μ
$\mathbf{a}^\dagger$	creation operator; components $a_\mu^\dagger$
$A(n)$	group of unitary diagonal matrices (K & M)
$A(G)$	Frobenius algebra of G (M & P)
$\mathbf{A}$	Lenz vector
$\mathscr{A}$	antisymmetrizer (F)
$\mathscr{A}_\ell$	Cartan notation for the special unitary groups $SU(\ell + 1)$
$\mathfrak{A}_{jk}$	generator of $U(r)$ (K & M)
APW	augmented plane wave
$\mathbf{b}_i$	reciprocal lattice vector (F)
B^ν	basis of $\mathfrak{B}$ (M & P)
$B^{\nu S}$	symmetry adapted basis (M & P)
B	baryon number operator
$\mathscr{B}_\ell$	Cartan notation for odd-dimensional rotation groups $O^+(2\ell + 1)$
$\mathscr{B}$	Borel structure (C)
BIR	bases for irreducible representations
$c^\mu_{\tau\lambda}$, C^k_{ij}	structure constants of Lie groups
C^μ_{rr}	Wigner projection operator (K & M)
C	charge conjugation operator (O'R)
C^{st}	generator of $U(n)$ (K & M)
$\hat{C}^{st}$	generator of $U(n)$ in spin-isospin space (K & M)
C^γ	γth chain of subgroup (M & P)
C^α_{rs}	matric basis element of $A(G)$ (M & P)
$\mathbf{C}^{st}_{ij}$	generator of $\mathbf{U}(3n)$ (K & M)
$\hat{\mathbf{C}}^{st}_{ij}$	generator of $\mathbf{U}(4n)$ (in spin-isospin space) (K & M)
$\mathscr{C}$	center of lattice (Ja); charge conjugation operator (B)
$\mathscr{C}_\ell$	Cartan notation for symplectic groups $Sp(2\ell)$
$\mathscr{C}_n$	rotation through $2\pi/n$ (F)
$\mathscr{C}_{jk}$	generator of $\mathscr{U}(3)$ (K & M)
$\hat{\mathscr{C}}_{jk}$	generator of $\mathscr{U}(4)$ (in spin-isospin space) (K & M)

$\mathfrak{C}$	complex field
C-G	Clebsch-Gordan
crp	completely reducible primary
CVC	conserved vector current
$\mathscr{D}$	representations of $SU(2)$ (C)
$\mathscr{D}_k$	representations of $O^+(3)$ (Ju)
$\mathscr{D}_\ell$	Cartan notation for even-dimensional rotation groups $O^+(2\ell)$
e (sub- or superscript)	even
e_i	imaginary unit of quaternions (Ja)
$\mathbf{e}_i$	unit vector in weight space
e_{rs}	matric basis elements of Dirac algebra (M & P)
E	elements of equivalence class (P & W)
E_α	generator of $SU(3)$ with root $\mathbf{r}(\alpha)$
$\mathbf{E}$	electric field with components E_x, E_y, E_z
$\mathscr{E}$	total energy (B)
E^{st}	operator related to lowering operators of $U(n)$ (K & M)
$f=\{f_1 f_2 \ldots f_n\}$	partition characterizing IR of $S(n)$ (K & M)
$f_w=f^1 f^2 \ldots f^j$	set of partitions characterizing IR of $W=S(n_1)\oplus S(n_2)\oplus\ldots\oplus S(n_j)$ (K & M)
$\mathfrak{F}$	field
fpc	fractional parentage coefficient
FPT	function of positive type
FRT	Frobenius reciprocity theorem
$g_{\mu\nu}$	metric sensor
$g_{NN\pi}$	strong coupling constant
G	Poincaré group (Ja); unspecified group (M & P); weak coupling constant (B)
G_a	element of G (M & P)
$G_{\hat{a}}$	little group (Ja)
${}^dG$	double group (M & P)
G_e	connected component of Poincaré group (Ja)
$G^h(G^t)$	head (tail) group in chain (M & P)
G_i	Casimir invariants of $SU(3)$
$G_{\mathbf{k}}$	group of $\mathbf{k}$ vector (F)
G_N	non-symmorphic group (F)
G_p	projective geometry (Ja)
G_P	point group (F)

G_S	symmorphic group (F)
$G^{\gamma j}$	jth group in γth lattice (M & P)
$[G_a]^\nu$	matrix representing G_a in representation Γ^ν (M & P)
$\mathscr{G}_2$	Cartan notation for exceptional group of order 14
$\mathscr{h}$	effective Fock Hamiltonian (F)
H_i	(diagonal) $SU(3)$ group generators
$\mathbf{H}$	magnetic field with components H_x, H_y, H_z
$\boldsymbol{H}$	truncated Hamiltonian (M & P)
$\boldsymbol{H}_0$	reduced ho Hamiltonian (K & M)
$\mathscr{H}$	Hamiltonian
$\boldsymbol{\mathscr{H}}$	Heisenberg Hamiltonian (B)
$\mathscr{H}_0$	ho Hamiltonian (K & M)
$\mathfrak{H}$	Hilbert space
$\mathfrak{H}_{\mathfrak{C}}^{(i)}$	complex Hilbert space with imaginary quaternion (Ja)
hfpc	ho fractional parentage coefficient
ho	harmonic oscillator
(ij^k)	structure constants of Lie group (K, H & B)
$i(\Delta)$	self intertwining number of representation Δ
I	identity
I_i	generators of isospin
I	nuclear spin quantum number (M & P)
I_p	Talmi integral (K & M)
$\mathscr{I}$	inversion operator (F)
$\mathfrak{I}$	moment of inertia
$\boldsymbol{\mathfrak{I}}$	integers
IR	irreducible representation
IRT	induced representation theorem
$\mathbf{J}$	total angular momentum (operator), with components J_x, J_y, J_z and eigenvalue J
J_α	weak current component (B)
$\mathscr{J}$	unitary anti-Hermitian operator (Ja); exchange operator (F)
$\mathscr{J}_\mu^e(X)$	hadron electromagnetic current density (O'R)
$\mathscr{J}_\mu^w(X)$	hadron weak current density (O'R)
J-T	Johnson-Treiman
K	conjugation of $\mathfrak{H}_{\mathfrak{C}}$
$\mathbf{K}$	primitive zone vector (F); K-meson multiplet (O'R)
$\mathscr{K}$	complex conjugation operator (F); Coulomb operator (F)

l	azimuth quantum number; leptons (B)
l^t	orbital angular momentum of particle t (K & M)
$l^{s,t}$	relative orbital angular momentum of particles s and t (K & M)
$\mathbf{l}$, $\mathbf{L}$	orbital angular momentum with components l_x, L_x, etc., and eigenvalue L
ℓ	group rank
L	Lorentz group (Ja)
L_A	Hermitian generator of infinitesimal Lie algebra
L_e	connected component of Lorentz group
L^{st}	lowering operator for the group $U(m)$ (K & M)
$L_{\alpha\beta}$	generator of $U(3)$ (O'R)
$\mathscr{L}$	linear transformation (C); lattice (Ja); Lagrangian density
$\mathscr{L}_+$, $\mathscr{L}_-$, $\mathscr{L}_z$	operators of $O^+(3)$ (Ju)
$\mathscr{L}_{kj}$	lowering operators for the group $\mathscr{U}(k)$ (K & M)
$\boldsymbol{\mathscr{L}}$	interaction Lagrangian (O'R)
LCAO	linear combination of atomic orbitals
$m(\ )$	morphism (Ja)
m_l, m_s	(magnetic) quantum numbers
$\mathbf{m}$	weight vector of representation, components m_i
M	mass (operator)
$\mathbf{M}$	highest weight vector of representation (B)
$\mathscr{M}$	magnetic group element (F)
$\mathscr{M}_i$	class operator (F)
n	neutron
n	main quantum number
N	dimension of representation (B); anti-self-adjoint infinitesimal element (P & W)
N'	self-adjoint infinitesimal element (P & W)
$N_\epsilon(e)$	ϵ-neighborhood (of e) (Ja)
$\mathbf{N}$	nucleon multiplet (O'R)
N	normalization coefficient of highest weight (K & M)
$\mathscr{N}$	normalization coefficient (K & M)
$\mathfrak{N}$	natural numbers
NFPT	normalized function of positive type
o (sub- or superscript)	odd
$O(n)$	orthogonal (rotation-reflection) group
$O^+(n)$	proper orthogonal (rotation) group

$O_L(n)$	orthogonal group in orbital space (Ju)
$O_S(n)$	orthogonal group in spin space (Ju)
$\mathscr{O}$	spinor interaction (B)
$\mathscr{O}(n)$	orthogonal group in component space (K & M)
OPW	orthogonalized plane waves
p	proton
p	four-momentum (B)
$\mathbf{p}$	three-momentum
$\mathfrak{p}$	eigenvalue of clustering operator (K & M)
$P_{\mathbf{k}}$	little point group (F)
$\mathbf{P}$	element of permutation (K & M)
$\mathbf{P}_{\mathbf{m}}$	momentum of lattice vibration (F)
$\mathscr{P}$	Poincaré group (C); improper rotation operator (F); parity operator (B)
$\mathscr{P}_{ij}$	transposition operator (F)
${}^{jm}\mathscr{P}_{\mathbf{k}}$	projection operator of $Q_{\mathbf{k}}$ (F)
$\mathscr{P}_{\mu}$	prong operator (F)
$\mathfrak{P}$	clustering operator with eigenvalue $\mathfrak{p}$ (K & M)
PW	plane wave
q	electric charge; quaternion (Ja)
$\mathbf{q}$	three-momentum in center-of-mass system (B)
$\mathfrak{q}$	eigenvalue of Wheeler operator
Q	electric charge operator
$Q_{\mathbf{k}}$	little group (F)
Q_q	quadrupole operator (K & M)
$Q_{\alpha\beta}$	generators of $U(3)$ (O'R)
$\mathbf{Q}$	quasispin (Ju)
$\mathfrak{Q}$	Wheeler operator with eigenvalue $\mathfrak{q}$ (K & M)
$\boldsymbol{\mathfrak{Q}}$	quaternion field
r	Yamanouchi symbol
$\mathbf{r}(\alpha)$	root associated with $SU(3)$ generator E_{α}
R	hypercharge reflection operator (O'R); outer automorphism of $SU(3)$ (B); radius of universe (P & W)
$\mathbf{R}$	rotation matrix
$\mathscr{R}$	rotation operator (F)
$\mathscr{R}_{ql}$	radial part of one-particle ho state (K & M)
${}^{j}\mathscr{R}_{m}$	symmetry type operator (F)
$\mathfrak{R}$	field of reals

s	strangeness eigenvalue (B)
s, **S**	spin (operators) with components s_z, S_z, etc., and eigenvalues s, S
s(**r**)	spin density at **r** (F)
$\mathbf{s}_x, \mathbf{s}_y, \mathbf{s}_z$	Pauli spin matrices (F)
S, S_α	Weyl reflections (B)
$S(n)$	symmetric group of degree n
$\mathscr{S}\mathscr{U}(k)$	special unitary group related to space or spin components (K & M)
$\mathscr{S}\mathscr{U}^\sigma(2)$	special unitary group related to total spin (K & M)
$\mathscr{S}\mathscr{U}^\tau(2)$	special unitary group related to total isospin (K & M)
${}^j\mathbf{S}_{mm}$	projection matrix (F)
$\mathscr{S}$	symmetric group (C)
$\mathscr{S}_n$	improper rotation through $2\pi/n$ (F)
${}^j\mathscr{S}_{mm}$	projection operator (F)
${}^{jm}\mathscr{S}_{\mathbf{k}}$	projection operator of G_S (F)
$\mathfrak{S}_{jk}$	generator of $U(r)$ (K & M)
SG	Special Gelfand
Sh	sinh
SNAG	Stone-Neumark-Ambrose-Godement
t	single particle isospin (K & M)
$\mathbf{t}_\mu$	column of reduction matrix (F)
${}^j\mathbf{t}_m$	symmetry reduction matrix (F)
T	translation (Ja); eigenvalue of total isospin (K & M)
T_1	space reflection operator (P & W)
T^μ_ν	νth component of tensor operator belonging to μth representation (B)
T_t	time displacement operator (P & W)
T	index of tensor interaction (K & M)
T	Erikson time reversal matrix (F)
T	total isospin with eigenvalue T (K & M)
$\mathscr{T}$	topological structure (C); time inversion
$\mathscr{T}_{\mathbf{n}}$	primitive lattice translation (F)
$\mathscr{T}(\mathbf{k})$	projection operator of translation group
$\mathscr{T}^\mu_\nu$	νth component of multipole operator belonging to μth representation (B)
Th	tanh
$u(i)$	one-electron energy operator (F)
u	two-dimensional spin rotation matrix (F)
U	unitary representation (C); representations for $\mathscr{G}_2$ (Ju)

$U(n)$	unitary group (with respect to particle indices in K & M)
$U(\mathbf{Q})$	potential energy for lattice vibrations (F)
$\mathbf{U}^{(k)}$	tensor operators with components $U_q^{(k)}$ (Ju)
$\mathbf{U}(3n)$	unitary group with respect to particle and space component indices (K & M)
$\mathbf{U}(4n)$	unitary group with respect to particle and spin-isospin indices (K & M)
$\mathbf{U}$	Erikson rotation matrix (F)
$\mathscr{U}(\tau, \mathbf{r})$	time displacement operator (F)
$\mathscr{U}(3)$	unitary group with respect to space component indices (K & M)
$\mathscr{U}(4)$	unitary group with respect to spin-isospin component indices (K & M)
UIR	unitary irreducible representation
v	seniority
$\mathfrak{V}$	vector space
$\mathfrak{V}^E$	Euclidean three-space (M & P)
$\mathfrak{V}^S$	spin space (M & P)
$\mathfrak{V}^D$	Dirac four-space (M & P)
(w)	representations for $O^+(8l+4)$ (Ju)
$\mathbf{w}$	weight representation (K & M)
W	representation for $O^+(7)$ (Ju); nuclear and ion core energy (F)
$W(abcd; ef)$	Racah coefficients
W-E	Wigner-Eckart
$\mathbf{x}$	Wannier lattice operator (F)
X_μ	Lie group generators
Y	hypercharge operator with eigenvalue y
z	element of $\mathfrak{C}$
Z_1	partition function for one-particle states (F)
$\boldsymbol{\alpha}$	root with components α_i (Ju); basis with state vector components $\|\alpha_i\rangle$ (F)
${}^j\boldsymbol{\alpha}_m$	unreduced symmetry adapted basis (F)
${}^j\boldsymbol{\beta}_m$	reduced symmetry adapted basis (F)

γ	sublattice (Ja); photon
$\boldsymbol{\gamma}_\alpha$	Dirac matrices
Γ	decay rate (B); electromagnetic vertex operator
${}^j\Gamma$	irreducible representation
δ	modular function
$\boldsymbol{\Delta}$	metric or overlap matrix (F)
ϵ	small number
ϵ_b	band energy (F)
ϵ_i	Fock energy eigenvalue (F)
ζ	spin-orbit coupling constant
$\boldsymbol{\eta}$	η-meson multiplet (O'R)
$\boldsymbol{\eta}^s$	creation operator of particle s (K & M)
ϑ, θ	angles
Θ	time reversal operator (F; P & W)
$\Theta^{\alpha_1 \dots}_{\beta_1 \dots}$	spin projection operator (B)
ι	isospin (B)
λ_i	component of weight for $U(3)$ (Ju)
Λ	element of Lorentz group (Ja)
Λ^{st}	generator of $O^+(m)$ (K & M)
$\boldsymbol{\Lambda}$	Λ-particle multiplet (O'R)
μ	measure
$\xi(r)$	spin orbit coupling constant (Ju)
$\boldsymbol{\xi}^s$	annihilation operator of particle s (K & M)
$\boldsymbol{\Xi}$	Ξ-particle multiplet (O'R)
$\boldsymbol{\pi}$	π-meson multiplet (O'R)
σ	space inversion (Ja); single particle spin projection (K & M)
σ_h, σ_v	space reflection (F)
$\boldsymbol{\sigma}$	electron spin (F); Pauli matrices (O'R)
$\boldsymbol{\Sigma}$	Σ-particle multiplet (O'R)
τ	single particle isospin projection (K & M)
$\boldsymbol{\tau}$	Pauli matrices

ϕ	angle; absurd proposition (Ja)
φ	function; multiplicity index in the chain $K(n) \supset S(n)$ (K & M)
$\varphi_\alpha(x)$	meson field (O'R)
Φ	potential
Φ^c	core potential (M & P)
χ	(class) character; multiplicity index in the group chain $U(n) \supset K(n)$ or $U(n) \supset S(n)$ (K & M)
ψ	Euler rotation angle (F); time independent wave function; function
$\|\psi\rangle$	time independent state vector
$\psi_\alpha(x)$	baryon field (O'R)
$\Psi(\mathbf{r}, t)$	time dependent wave function
ω	quaternion of norm 1 (Ja); frequency of harmonic oscillator (K & M)
$\mathbf{\Omega}$	operator appearing in chain $\mathscr{U}(3) \supset \mathscr{O}^+(3)$ with eigenvalue Ω (K & M)
$\mathbf{\Omega}^-$	Ω^- particle multiplet
$\cup$	union
$\cap$	intersection
$\subset$	proper subset
$\subseteq$	subset; partial ordering (Ja)
$\in$	element of
$\forall$	for every
$\Rightarrow$	logical implication
$\leftrightarrow$	compatibility
$\oplus$	direct sum
$\times$	number product
$\mathbf{\times}$	vector product
$\times$	Cartesian set product; (outer) direct product of groups or representations
$\boxtimes$	(inner) direct product of groups or representations
$\wedge$	semidirect product
$\varnothing$	null set
$\langle \|, \| \rangle$	state vectors (bra, ket)
$\|0\rangle$	vacuum state
$\langle\|\rangle$	Wigner coefficient
$\langle\| \|\rangle$	matrix element

$\langle \Vert \Vert \rangle$	reduced matrix element
$(\Vert \Vert)$	reduced matrix element, Nielson & Koster
$\langle \vert \} \rangle$, $(\{ \vert)$	fractional parentage coefficient
$\{ \}$	determinantal product state (Ju)
$\to$	reduction of groups and branching rules (Ju)
$\{,\}$	invariant scalar product (P & W)
$[ ]$	weight of $U(n)$ (Ju)
$\mathbf{[ ]}$	partition of $\mathscr{U}(3)$, Gelfand pattern (K & M)
$\mathbf{\{ \}}$	partition of $U(n)$, Gelfand pattern (K & M)
$\varDelta \uparrow G$	representation of G induced by $\varDelta$
$\varGamma \downarrow H$	representation of H subduced by $\varGamma$
$\mathbf{I}$	unit matrix

Group Theory
and Its Applications

The Algebras of Lie Groups and Their Representations

DIRK KLEIMA, W. J. HOLMAN, III, and L. C. BIEDENHARN*

PHYSICS DEPARTMENT, DUKE UNIVERSITY, DURHAM, NORTH CAROLINA

I. Introduction

A Lie group is defined as a topological group whose identity element has a neighborhood that is homeomorphic to a subset of an r-dimensional Euclidean space, where r is then called the order or dimension of the Lie group (*1*). Thus, a Lie group combines in one entity two distinct structures, a topological structure and a group-theoretic structure. The topological properties of the Lie group have far-reaching implications for the algebraic, or group-theoretic, structure. These implications are largely contained in the theorem that states that a Lie group (and in fact any topological group) is *homogeneous*, that is, for any given pair of points X, Y in the group manifold G there exists a homeomorphism $f\colon G \to G$ such that $f(X) = Y$. Thus, we need state and examine the local properties of a Lie group only in the neighborhood of a single point, e.g., the identity element; the homogeneity of the manifold then enables us to derive the same properties at any other point. Let us consider an analytic function $F(X)$ defined over the group manifold and examine $F(X)$ in a small neighborhood of the identity $X = 0$ where it takes the form

$$F(X) = F(0) + \sum_{i,j=1}^{r} \mu_j^i \left[\frac{\partial F(X)}{\partial X^i}\right]_{X=0} X^j \equiv F(0) + \sum_{j=1}^{r} X^j [x_j F(X)]_{X=0} \quad (1.1)$$

* *Present address:* Twente Institute of Technology, Enschede, The Netherlands.

where the x_i are linearly independent differential operators over the parameter space. These differential operators act as the generators of infinitesimal transformations and obey the commutation relations

$$[x_i, x_j] = (ij^k)\, x_k, \tag{1.2}$$

which serve to define the *structure constants* (ij^k). In order to assure that an infinitesimal transformation of the group can be integrated to obtain a finite transformation, it can be shown that the generators must also obey the Jacobi condition

$$[[x_i, x_j], x_k] + [[x_j, x_k], x_i] + [[x_k, x_i], x_j] = 0. \tag{1.3}$$

This set of generators, then, which is closed under the operation of commutation, and the set of all their linear combinations is called the *Lie algebra* of the group, and there exists a Lie algebra for every Lie group. The conditions (1.2) and (1.3) can be expressed as conditions on the structure constants:

$$(ij^k) = -(ji^k), \tag{1.4}$$

$$(ij^k)(kl^m) + (li^k)(kj^m) + (jl^k)(ki^m) = 0 \qquad \text{(Jacobi condition)}. \tag{1.5}$$

Lie further demonstrated that if we are given any r^3 constants (ij^k) that satisfy the relations (1.4) and (1.5), then we can integrate the generators that specify the infinitesimal transformations of a group and so determine the group itself, that is, the structure constants *alone* determine a group of continuous transformations. This group, however, is determined only up to a local isomorphism; the integration of the generators gives us a representation of the universal covering group, while other groups that are multiply connected may have the same local properties, that is, the same Lie algebra and the same structure constants.

In the study of Lie groups, then, we achieve an enormous simplification by restricting our attention to the Lie algebra and its representations. We need deal only with a finite number of elements, the Lie algebra, rather than a continuous infinity in order to establish a system of basis vectors for a representation space for the group. The algebra, because of its integrability, determines all the structures that have the desired properties of transformation under the finite elements of the group. In particular, we can determine all the irreducible unitary representations of a group by performing only the much easier construction of all the Hermitian representations and sets of basis vectors for the Lie algebra. Hence it is worth our while to study Lie algebras in some detail.

In the present chapter we shall restrict our attention to the problem of the classification of the compact real semisimple Lie algebras and review the work originally done by Killing (*2*) and Cartan (*3*). In a continuation of this chapter, which will be published in a subsequent volume, we shall apply this apparatus to a systematic treatment of the representation theory of the groups of n-dimensional unitary matrices and to a determination of all tensor operators in $U(n)$, using the techniques of the boson calculus and the Gel'fand and Weyl systems of basis vectors (*4*).

A Lie algebra is defined abstractly as a linear space of elements x_i with coefficients in any field (for our purposes the real or complex numbers) and a product defined by the foregoing relations (1.2) that satisfies (1) the condition of antisymmetry (or equivalently $[x,x]=0$); (2) the Jacobi condition (1.3); and, of course, (3) the usual conditions of linearity:

$$[ax_i, x_j] = a[x_i, x_j],$$
$$[x_i + x_j, x_k] = [x_i, x_k] + [x_j, x_k]. \tag{1.6}$$

Hence a Lie algebra is a particular instance of a nonassociative algebra; the Jacobi condition holds instead of the property of associativity. The property of antisymmetry and that provided by the Jacobi condition are expressed by conditions on the structure constants given earlier by (1.4) and (1.5).

We wish to show now that there exists a Lie algebra for every set of structure constants that satisfy these conditions, and we shall do this by the explicit construction of a model. A linear correspondence $x \to X$ of a Lie algebra L into a set of linear transformations X of a vector space S is called a *representation* of the Lie algebra if $[x,y] \to XY - YX$, where $x, y \in L$ and X and Y are transformations of S. We shall write $XY - YX = [X, Y]$. These linear transformations, or matrices, are called representations, and the vector space S is called the carrier space of the representation. The vectors in the carrier space then span the representation space, and the set of matrices X itself is loosely called a representation. Since physics is concerned with Lie groups that are themselves groups of linear transformations and therefore representations of themselves, the concept of matrix representation of Lie groups and their Lie algebras is of fundamental importance.

We remark now that the particular linear mappings of L into L that we define as $x \to x' = [y,x]$, where $x, y \in L$, and that we shall denote as $x' = [y,x] \equiv (\text{ad}\, y)\, x$, have the property

$$(\text{ad}\, y_1\, \text{ad}\, y_2 - \text{ad}\, y_2\, \text{ad}\, y_1)\, x = [y_1, [y_2, x]] - [y_2, [y_1, x]]$$
$$= [[y_1, y_2], x] = (\text{ad}[y_1, y_2])\, x, \tag{1.7}$$

which can be written as

$$[\text{ad}\, y_1, \text{ad}\, y_2] = \text{ad}[y_1, y_2]. \tag{1.7a}$$

(We have made use here of the Jacobi condition.) It follows from (1.7a), then, that the linear transformations ad y are a (faithful) representation of L, which we call ad L, the *adjoint representation.* The reader should note that the idea of a representation of the Lie algebra by transformations induced in the algebra itself as a carrier space, though easy to grasp and seemingly trivial, is nonetheless very important and underlies the entire treatment to follow. In fact, the theory of the classification of semisimple Lie algebras *is* nothing more than the theory of the adjoint representation.

When we introduce a coordinate system in L, it becomes possible to specify matrix elements of ad y explicitly. Let x_i be the generators of L which we now take to define the basis (specified by the index i) and let $x = r^i x_i$ be an arbitrary element of L. Then

$$(\mathrm{ad}\, x_j)\, x = r^i [x_j, x_i] = r^i (ji^k)\, x_k, \tag{1.8}$$

and we note that the r^i and the x_j transform contragrediently to each other. The matrix elements of the adjoint representation are then seen to be simply the structure constants of L which are specified by our chosen basis

$$(\mathrm{ad}\, x_j)_{ki} = (ji^k). \tag{1.9}$$

These, then, are the desired matrices for our model, since we can write the Jacobi identity for the structure constants as

$$-(ij^a)(\mathrm{ad}\, x_a)_{lk} + (\mathrm{ad}\, x_j)_{ak}(\mathrm{ad}\, x_i)_{la} + (-\mathrm{ad}\, x_i)_{ak}(\mathrm{ad}\, x_j)_{la} = 0, \tag{1.10}$$

and this relation proves that structure constants that satisfy antisymmetry and the Jacobi condition "belong" to a Lie algebra.

The transformations of the adjoint representation of the Lie algebra (which, by Lie's fundamental theorem, can be integrated to yield the *adjoint group*), can be regarded as acting either on the abstract elements x or on the coordinates r^i, and we shall write indiscriminately $f(r^i) = f(x)$ for a fixed basis, i.e., the generators x_i. More complicated functions of x than linear ones, in fact polynomials, are defined indirectly (through $x \equiv r^i x_i$) as functions of r^i. [Note that only the operation of "commutation," Eq. (1.2), is defined for the elements x, and no other; in a representation, however, there exist two multiplication operations: one is the ordinary associative matrix multiplication AB, and the other, the commutation operation $[A, B] = AB - BA$, is expressed in terms of the former, but only this operation has a counterpart in the abstract Lie algebra.]

From Eq. (1.7) it follows that

$$\begin{aligned}
[\mathrm{ad}\, y, \mathrm{ad}\, x] &= \mathrm{ad}((\mathrm{ad}\, y)\, x), \\
[\mathrm{ad}\, y, [\mathrm{ad}\, y, \mathrm{ad}\, x]] &= \mathrm{ad}((\mathrm{ad}\, y)(\mathrm{ad}\, y)\, x) \equiv \mathrm{ad}((\mathrm{ad}\, y)^2 x),
\end{aligned} \tag{1.11}$$

hence we may apply the Baker-Campbell-Hausdorff formula

$$\exp(\theta A)\beta\exp(-\theta A) = \beta + \frac{\theta}{1!}[A,\beta] + \frac{\theta^2}{2!}[A,[A,\beta]] + \cdots \tag{1.12}$$

to obtain the transformations of the adjoint group:

$$[\exp(\theta\,\mathrm{ad}\,y)](\mathrm{ad}\,x)[\exp(-\theta\,\mathrm{ad}\,y)] = \mathrm{ad}(\exp(\theta\,\mathrm{ad}\,y)\,x). \tag{1.13}$$

The essential point of Lie's theory is that the conditions that are necessary for the integrability of a Lie algebra, namely, antisymmetry and the Jacobi condition, are also in general sufficient for integration in the neighborhood of the identity. The integration of representations is not a problem and proceeds directly by matrix exponentiation.

We turn now to the problem of the explicit classification of Lie algebras and their representations. First we introduce some definitions: the subset $x_{\bar{a}}$ of generators span a Lie *subalgebra* $\bar{L}$ if and only if $[x_{\bar{a}}, x_{\bar{b}}] \in \bar{L}$. In terms of the structure constants, $(\bar{a}, \bar{b}^k) = 0$ unless $k = \bar{c}$ also designates a member of the subalgebra. The condition for an *invariant subalgebra* is $[x_{\bar{a}}, x_b] \in \bar{L}$ for any $x_b \in L$. We can also write, in this case, $[\bar{L}, x] \in \bar{L}$. Note that an invariant subalgebra is therefore an *ideal* in L under the commutation operation. The condition for the invariance of a subalgebra in terms of the structure constants is then $(\bar{a}b^k) = 0$ unless $k = \bar{k}$ denotes a member of the subalgebra. Further, $\bar{L}$ is an Abelian subalgebra if $(\bar{a}\bar{b}^k) = 0$ for all $\bar{a}, \bar{b}, k$, and is an *invariant Abelian subalgebra* if both conditions hold; that is, if $(\bar{a}j^k) \neq 0$ only if $x_j \in L$, $x_k \in \bar{L}$.

A Lie algebra that possesses no invariant subalgebras at all is called *simple*, and simple Lie algebras belong to simple Lie groups. It is important here to note that a simple Lie group is one that possesses no invariant Lie subgroups; it may possess invariant *finite* subgroups, since these have no elements in a sufficiently small neighborhood of the identity except the identity itself. A Lie algebra (group) that possesses no invariant Abelian subalgebra (invariant Abelian Lie subgroup) is called *semisimple*. Of course, the property of simplicity implies that of semisimplicity. It will be seen later that a semisimple Lie algebra (group) can be represented as a direct sum (direct product) of simple Lie algebras (groups).

In order to establish a criterion for semisimplicity, which was first introduced by Cartan, let us construct the tensor (to be interpreted later as a *metric* tensor):

$$g_{ab} \equiv \mathrm{tr}(\mathrm{ad}\,x_a\,\mathrm{ad}\,x_b) = \sum_{ik}(ai^k)(bk^i). \tag{1.14}$$

Cartan's criterion states that *a Lie algebra is semisimple if and only if g_{ab} is nonsingular*.

Proof. The proof of necessity is easy. Suppose that L is not semisimple and hence has an Abelian invariant subalgebra $\bar{L}$ whose elements are $x_{\bar{a}}$. Then

$$g_{\bar{a}b} = \sum_{ik} (\bar{a}i^k)(bk^i) = \sum_{i\bar{k}} (\bar{a}i^{\bar{k}})(b\bar{k}^i) = \sum_{\bar{i}\bar{k}} (\bar{a}\bar{i}^{\bar{k}})(b\bar{k}^{\bar{i}}) = 0, \qquad (1.15)$$

where we have used the conditions on the structure constants that characterize an Abelian invariant subalgebra. This expression vanishes; hence g_{ab} has an entire row $g_{\bar{a}b}$ of zeros and thus is singular. The proof of the sufficiency of the Cartan criterion is more difficult and makes use of Cartan's second criterion of solvability, which we shall discuss in Section IV. We shall defer consideration of the sufficiency proof until Section IV, then, when we shall have developed the necessary tools. At present we shall merely prove the trivial theorem: If g_{ab} is singular, then L has an invariant subalgebra; that is, L is not simple.

Proof. We can construct the linear space L^* of all $x^* = w^a x_a$ such that $\mathrm{tr}(\mathrm{ad}\, x^* \,\mathrm{ad}\, x_b) = w^a \,\mathrm{tr}(\mathrm{ad}\, x_a \mathrm{ad}\, x_b) = w^a g_{ab} = 0$ for all $x_b \in L$. Since g_{ab} is singular, L^* is not empty. For any x_b, $x_c \in L$ we can write

$$\mathrm{tr}(\mathrm{ad}[x_c, x^*]\,\mathrm{ad}\, x_b) = \mathrm{tr}([\mathrm{ad}\, x_c, \mathrm{ad}\, x^*]\,\mathrm{ad}\, x_b) = \mathrm{tr}(\mathrm{ad}\, x^*[\mathrm{ad}\, x_b, \mathrm{ad}\, x_c])$$
$$= (bc^d)\,\mathrm{tr}(\mathrm{ad}\, x^* \,\mathrm{ad}\, x_d) = 0, \qquad (1.16)$$

by the definition of x^*. Hence all $[x_c, x^*]$ belong to L^* and L^* is an invariant subalgebra. Note that for any two elements x^*, $y^* \in L^*$ we have in particular

$$\mathrm{tr}(\mathrm{ad}\, x^* \,\mathrm{ad}\, y^*) = 0, \qquad (1.17)$$

a fact that we shall need later in our treatment of the second solvability criterion of Cartan.

In this study we shall restrict our attention to compact Lie algebras defined over the field of real numbers. We say that a Lie algebra is compact if it is isomorphic to the Lie algebra of a Lie group whose manifold is a compact set. It can be shown that for a compact Lie group all irreducible matrix representations are finite-dimensional and equivalent to unitary representations (Peter-Weyl theorem); hence all representations of their Lie algebras are similarly finite-dimensional and equivalent to Hermitian representations. These properties are not shared by noncompact groups. For noncompact groups all† the faithful irreducible unitary representations are infinite-dimensional and there exists a nondenumerable infinity of them, that is, there exist series of irreducible unitary representations that are labeled by continuous values of the invariants. For compact groups, on the other hand, all irreducible unitary representations are finite-dimensional and occur only in discrete series. For both

† Except of course the identity representation.

compact and noncompact groups, of course, the unitarity of a representation implies its complete reducibility. Any unitary representation of a compact (noncompact) Lie group can be expressed as a direct sum (direct sum plus direct integral) of irreducible unitary representations.

A necessary and sufficient condition for the compactness of a semisimple Lie algebra is that the quadratic form $g^{ab}x_a x_b$, called the Casimir invariant (it is invariant under transformations of the adjoint group) be positive definite. We shall not prove this result, but merely refer to Pontrjagin (*5*, Sect. 61). It is important to note that a Lie group that is noncompact may still possess a compact Lie algebra if it is not a semisimple group: for example, the Abelian group of all vectors in r-dimensional Euclidean space, whose Lie algebra is Abelian, hence isomorphic to the Lie algebras of the (compact) toroidal groups, and therefore compact. A semisimple Lie group, however, may have a compact Lie algebra only if it is itself compact.

We establish one more formal result: We can use the metric tensor g_{ab} to lower the superscript in the structure constant (ij^k), with the result that the object $(ijk) \equiv g_{kl}(ij^l)$ is antisymmetric in all three subscripts.

Proof.

$$(ijk) \equiv g_{kl}(ij^l) = \mathrm{tr}(\mathrm{ad}\,x_k\,\mathrm{ad}\,x_l\,(ij^l)) = \mathrm{tr}(\mathrm{ad}\,x_k[\mathrm{ad}\,x_i,\,\mathrm{ad}\,x_j]),$$
$$= \mathrm{tr}(\mathrm{ad}\,x_i[\mathrm{ad}\,x_j,\,\mathrm{ad}\,x_k]), \qquad (1.18)$$

which is antisymmetric in j and k. Since Eq. (1.4) establishes the antisymmetry of (ij^k) in i and j, our result follows immediately. [We can also obtain this result by expressing (1.18) completely in terms of the structure constants and then using the Jacobi condition.]

II. Preliminary Survey

Our ultimate goal is to find all possible compact semisimple Lie algebras, and the principal tool of our investigation will be the adjoint algebra. To each element $h = h^i x_i \in L$ of the Lie algebra there corresponds the linear transformation $[h, y] \equiv (\mathrm{ad}\,h)\,y$ of L into itself, and the study of the dependence of the eigenvalues and eigenvectors of $(\mathrm{ad}\,h)$ on h constitutes the fundamental method of analysis of the structure of the algebra. In other words, since the x_i may be subjected to any linear transformation, the structure constants(ij^k) are similarly determined only up to a linear transformation; hence, we approach the entire structure problem of the Lie algebra by way of invariant theory [the invariant theory of the tensor (ij^k), which satisfies (1.4) and (1.5) above], posing it as a suitable eigenvalue problem. Since the structure constants are the matrix elements of the adjoint representation, we try to find all elements y which, for a fixed element h, satisfy

$$(\mathrm{ad}\,h)y = wy \qquad (2.1)$$

Since the eigenvalues w are, in general, complex, it becomes necessary to extend the real vector space L to a complex space L^* that is composed of all elements $z^a x_a$, with z^a complex. Thus, we are unavoidably involved in the study of complex Lie algebras. The space L^* is called the *complex extension* of L and is uniquely determined by it; L, in turn, is called the *real form* of L^*. In this connection it is essential to note that nonisomorphic real Lie algebras may possess isomorphic complex extensions and, consequently, that a complex Lie algebra may possess several distinct real forms. A complex semisimple Lie algebra, however, admits one and, up to an isomorphism, only one real form that is compact.

Now, (2.1) has solutions only for values of w that satisfy the characteristic equation

$$\det[\operatorname{ad} h - w\mathbf{1}] \equiv \Delta(h, w) = 0. \tag{2.2}$$

The eigenvalues of (2.2) are also called *roots* of h. Since $(\operatorname{ad} h)h = 0$, then $y = h$ is a solution of (2.1) with $w = 0$, hence $w = 0$ is always a root of Δ. The multiplicity of this root depends on h; the minimal value l of this multiplicity is called the *rank* of L. Every element $y \in L$ for which $(\operatorname{ad} h)y$ has zero as a root with multiplicity l is called a *regular element* of L. In order to construct the entire root system we select a particular element h, then find the set L_0 of those $h_0 \in L$ such that $[h, h_0] = 0$ forms an l-dimensional commutative subalgebra of L, a so-called *regular* or *Cartan subalgebra*, or (following Freudenthal) a *trunk*. We will eventually show that all linear transformations $(\operatorname{ad} h)$, $h \in L_0$, possess common eigenvectors and that the eigenvalues of these transformations are linear forms in the vector h which we call *roots*. The roots, considered as functions of h as h varies in L_0, will be called *root forms*. The collection of all root forms constitutes a *root system* of L; the root system then depends on the initial choice of a regular element h. We state without proof the converse result: a root system completely determines the Lie algebra in the following sense. Any two root systems of the same compact semisimple algebra are isometric to one another (since any two regular subalgebras of L can be mapped onto one another by some automorphism of L); and when two compact semisimple algebras have isometric root systems, the algebras themselves are isomorphic. Hence, the classification problem of the compact semisimple Lie algebras becomes the classification problem of all possible root systems.

Our first step toward the classification problem is to distinguish two broad classes of Lie algebras that possess, in a sense, complementary properties. These are, on the one hand, the semisimple algebras and, on the other, the *solvable* algebras. The latter we define using the *derived series*

$$L, \quad L' = [L, L], \quad L'' = [L', L'], \quad L^{(3)} = [L'', L''], \ldots, \quad L^{(h)} = [L^{(h-1)}, L^{(h-1)}], \ldots, \tag{2.3}$$

which for a finite Lie algebra must terminate, at least in the sense that $L^{(k)} = L^{(k-1)}$ for some k. When it terminates in zero, $L^{(k)} = 0$, then the algebra L is called solvable. It is easily seen that any $L^{(h)}$ is an invariant subalgebra not only of $L^{(h-1)}$ but also of all preceding members of the derived series as well, including L itself. For example, in a natural extension of our notation, we have (from the Jacobi condition), for any $x \in L$

$$[x, L''] = [x, [L', L']] = [L', [L', x]] + [L', [x, L']] \subset [L', L'] = L'', \qquad (2.4)$$

and the proof is easily completed by induction. Since $L^{(k)} = 0$ implies that $L^{(k-1)}$ is Abelian, we might also have defined a semisimple Lie algebra as one that has no solvable invariant subalgebra. A nonsemisimple Lie algebra, however, does not need to be solvable. The group of Euclidean motions in three dimensions has a Lie algebra that satisfies $L' = L$, but has the generators of translations as an invariant subalgebra. The solvable algebras are those that can be constructed stepwise out of Abelian Lie algebras, while the semisimple algebras are less closely related to commutative algebras. It turns out (and this is the content of a theorem initially proved by Levi and sharpened by Malcev) that an arbitrary Lie algebra is made up of a solvable part and a semisimple part, in the sense that it contains a solvable ideal, and the algebra of cosets modulo that ideal is semisimple. In this limited sense the study of an arbitrary Lie algebra reduces to the study of a solvable algebra and a semisimple algebra. There is as yet no classification of solvable algebras; the classification problem for semisimple algebras has, however, been solved by Killing and Cartan, and it is this classification that we shall review in the present work.

As we have mentioned, we must deal with complex semisimple Lie algebras, which can be resolved into the direct sum of simple noncommutative algebras, all of which are known. In a series of papers that appeared during the years 1888–1890, Killing (*2*) defined the rank of a Lie group and used this concept as well as the characteristic equation [our Eq. (2.2)] as the starting point and basis for his classification of Lie algebras. He rediscovered the four series of simple Lie algebras, $\mathscr{A}_\ell$, $\mathscr{B}_\ell$, $\mathscr{C}_\ell$, and $\mathscr{D}_\ell$, which were known to Lie, and established that in addition to these the only possible simple Lie algebras are $\mathscr{G}_2$, $\mathscr{F}_4$, $\mathscr{E}_6$, $\mathscr{E}_7$, and $\mathscr{E}_8$. Furthermore, he proved that every Lie algebra that is not solvable is composed of the direct product of an invariant solvable subalgebra and a subalgebra that is either simple or composed of invariant simple subalgebras, and we shall present his proof in Section IV. In his doctoral thesis (*3*) Cartan significantly improved the work of Killing from the standpoint of mathematical rigor and filled some essential gaps in the proofs, but at that point the classification program for complex simple Lie algebras was complete. Improvements in exposition have been made since Cartan's thesis—chiefly Dynkin's (*6*) method of simple root vectors and his idea of a lexical ordering on a Euclidean vector space—but the work stands substantially unchanged to this day.

But the transition to the problem of the classification of real semisimple Lie algebras, that is, those Lie algebras that belong to Lie groups, presents as many difficulties as the original classification in the complex case. It must be shown that every complex semisimple Lie algebra possesses real forms, that the number of distinct real forms is finite, and that they can all be found and classified. This problem was first attacked by Cartan (*7*), who made extensive use of homology theory in determining all the real forms of the simple Lie groups. Subsequently, Weyl (*8*) pointed out the significance of the compact real Lie algebras and the importance of the distinction between the compact and noncompact real forms of a complex Lie algebra. He showed that each Lie algebra possesses one and only one real form that is compact and that hence there exists a one-to-one correspondence between the complex simple Lie algebras and the compact real simple Lie algebras. Hence the entire structure of classification can be carried over isomorphically from the former to the latter set of algebras. Subsequently Cartan (*9*) was able to simplify his previous work on real Lie algebras by means of the techniques of Riemannian geometry and to show that the determination of all real forms of the complex simple Lie algebras can be reduced to the search for the involutory automorphisms of the compact real forms, and that in consequence the determination of these real forms and that of the corresponding Riemannian spaces are equivalent problems. Also, he applied this method to the construction of all the real forms of the four classical algebras $\mathscr{A}_\ell$, $\mathscr{B}_\ell$, $\mathscr{C}_\ell$, and $\mathscr{D}_\ell$. This work has been ably reviewed by Helgason (*10*).

In expositions of Lie algebras by physicists it is customary to neglect these phases of the development. The present writers claim a prescriptive right to do likewise and to restrict their attention to a derivation of the root and weight structure of complex Lie algebras and the program of their classification. In addition to the original papers of Killing and Cartan, this work has been treated by Pontrjagin (*5*), Helgason (*10*), Jacobson (*11*), Freudenthal (*12*), Mostow (*13*), Weyl (*14*), and O'Raifeartaigh (*15*), to whom we refer the reader for details and elaboration. We also call attention to an article by Kaplansky (*16*) that contains many interesting perspectives on the entire program

Let us return to the determinantal equation (2.2), which we expand:

$$\Delta(h, w) = (-1)^r\{w^r - \varphi_1(h^i)w^{r-1} + \varphi_2(h^i)w^{r-2} + \cdots + (-1)^{r-1}\varphi_{r-1}(h^i)w\} \quad (2.5)$$

where r denotes the number of generators in the algebra L. The coefficients $\varphi_k(h^i)$, which are polynomials in the h^i, will often be regarded as functions of $h = h^i x_i$; we write therefore also $\varphi_k(h)$. These functions are invariant under all transformations $A = \exp(\theta \operatorname{ad} x)$ of the adjoint group. Under the transformation $h \to h' = AhA^{-1}$, $\Delta(h, w)$ has the following behavior:

$$\begin{aligned}\det(\operatorname{ad} h - w\mathbf{1}) &= \det(\operatorname{ad} h' - w\mathbf{1}) \\ &= \det(\exp(\theta \operatorname{ad} x) \operatorname{ad} h \exp(-\theta \operatorname{ad} x) - w\mathbf{1}) \\ &= \det(\exp(\theta \operatorname{ad} x)(\operatorname{ad} h - w\mathbf{1}) \exp(-\theta \operatorname{ad} x)) \\ &= \det(\operatorname{ad} h - w\mathbf{1}). \end{aligned} \tag{2.6}$$

Hence $\Delta(h, w)$ and therefore all the $\varphi_k(h)$ are invariant under the adjoint group. [This proof is still straightforward, although more involved, if we regard the $\varphi_k(h)$ as functions $\varphi_k(h^i)$ of the variables h^i and write the ad x as explicit differential operators $\operatorname{ad} x_i = \sum_{jk} (ij^k) h^j \partial/\partial h^k$.] It is clear from their definition that the $\varphi_k(h)$ can be expressed in traces of powers of ad h. For example:

$$(\varphi_1(h))^2 - 2\varphi_2(h) = \operatorname{tr}(\operatorname{ad} h)^2. \tag{2.7}$$

Applying now the infinitesimal operation ad x to $\operatorname{tr}(\operatorname{ad} h)^2$ gives us

$$\begin{aligned} &\operatorname{tr}(\operatorname{ad}[x, h] \operatorname{ad} h) + \operatorname{tr}(\operatorname{ad} h \operatorname{ad}[x, h] \\ &\quad = \operatorname{tr}([\operatorname{ad} x, \operatorname{ad} h] \operatorname{ad} h) + \operatorname{tr}(\operatorname{ad} h [\operatorname{ad} x, \operatorname{ad} h]) = 0. \end{aligned} \tag{2.8}$$

The $\varphi_k(h)$ appear explicitly as polynomials only when they are written out in terms of their components h^i $(h = h^i x_i)$.

It is evident that with the $\varphi_k(h)$ we have found all the independent invariants of the adjoint group, because the group of differential operators $\sum_{jk} A_{ij}^k h^j \partial/\partial h^k$ that leave invariant the functions $\varphi_k(h^i)$ is again the adjoint group.

Example. For $SU(2)$ we have the commutation relations $[x_i, x_j] = e_{ijk} x_k$, $i, j, k = 1, 2, 3$, where e_{ijk} is the totally antisymmetric unit tensor. The matrices of the adjoint representation can be given as

$$\operatorname{ad} x_1 = \begin{pmatrix} 0 & 0 & 0 \\ 0 & 0 & -1 \\ 0 & 1 & 0 \end{pmatrix}, \quad \operatorname{ad} x_2 = \begin{pmatrix} 0 & 0 & 1 \\ 0 & 0 & 0 \\ -1 & 0 & 0 \end{pmatrix}, \quad \operatorname{ad} x_3 = \begin{pmatrix} 0 & -1 & 0 \\ 1 & 0 & 0 \\ 0 & 0 & 0 \end{pmatrix}, \tag{2.9}$$

and the characteristic polynomial becomes

$$\begin{aligned} \Delta(w) &= \det(X \operatorname{ad} x_1 + Y \operatorname{ad} x_2 + Z \operatorname{ad} x_3 - w\mathbf{1}) \\ &= \begin{pmatrix} -w & -Z & Y \\ Z & -w & -X \\ -Y & X & -w \end{pmatrix} \\ &= -[w^3 + (X^2 + Y^2 + Z^2)w]. \end{aligned} \tag{2.10}$$

The only invariant is the Euclidean distance $X^2 + Y^2 + Z^2 = \varphi_2$, which is indeed invariant under the differential operators $X\,\partial/\partial Y - Y\,\partial/\partial X$, etc. In this case, as in most cases of interest to us, the nonzero roots occur in pairs $\alpha, -\alpha$, and the characteristic polynomial is either odd or even.

We note that, in the general case,

$$\varphi_1(h^i) = \sum_{i,p} h^i(ip^p) = \operatorname{tr}(\operatorname{ad} h)$$

$$\varphi_2(h^i) = \tfrac{1}{2}\{(\varphi_1(h^i))^2 - h^i h^j (ip^q)(jq^p)\}$$

$$= \tfrac{1}{2}\{(\operatorname{tr}\operatorname{ad} h)^2 - h^i h^j g_{ij}\} = \tfrac{1}{2}\{\operatorname{tr}\operatorname{ad} h)^2 - \operatorname{tr}(\operatorname{ad} h)^2\}. \tag{2.11}$$

According to Newton's formulas the sum of the squares of the roots w_j of $\Delta(h, w) = 0$ can be expressed in terms of φ_1 and φ_2 alone:

$$\varphi_1^2 - 2\varphi_2 = h^i h^j g_{ij} = \operatorname{tr}((\operatorname{ad} h)^2) = \sum_j w_j^2. \tag{2.12}$$

Since the trace of a commutator is zero, any ad x_i that can be expressed as a linear combination of commutators has zero trace.

The first member of the derived series that we defined earlier in (2.3) is again a Lie algebra, which we called the *derived algebra* L'; it is the linear space spanned by all commutators $[x_i, x_j]$. This algebra is then the infinitesimal analog of the derived or commutator group. As we have seen, L' is an invariant subalgebra of L since any product $[x', x]$ for which $x' \in L'$, $x \in L$, again belongs to L' by definition. Now, if $L' = L$, then $\varphi_1 = 0$; but the converse does not hold, as the following example demonstrates.

Example. An instance is the group of Euclidean motions in the plane, which consists of the linear transformations

$$\begin{pmatrix} \cos\theta & \sin\theta & a_x \\ -\sin\theta & \cos\theta & a_y \\ 0 & 0 & 1 \end{pmatrix}$$

where θ indicates an angle of rotation and a_x and a_y are parameters of translation along the x and y axes, respectively. This group has the infinitesimal generators

$$x_0 = \begin{pmatrix} 0 & 1 & 0 \\ -1 & 0 & 0 \\ 0 & 0 & 0 \end{pmatrix}, \qquad x_1 = \begin{pmatrix} 0 & 0 & 1 \\ 0 & 0 & 0 \\ 0 & 0 & 0 \end{pmatrix}, \qquad x_2 = \begin{pmatrix} 0 & 0 & 0 \\ 0 & 0 & 1 \\ 0 & 0 & 0 \end{pmatrix}, \tag{2.13}$$

and the Lie algebra is, accordingly, defined by the commutation relations

$$[x_0, x_1] = -x_2, \qquad [x_0, x_2] = x_1, \qquad [x_1, x_2] = 0. \tag{2.14}$$

Hence the adjoint representation becomes

$$\operatorname{ad} x_0 = \begin{pmatrix} 0 & 0 & 0 \\ 0 & 0 & 1 \\ 0 & -1 & 0 \end{pmatrix}, \quad \operatorname{ad} x_1 = \begin{pmatrix} 0 & 0 & 0 \\ 0 & 0 & 0 \\ 1 & 0 & 0 \end{pmatrix}, \quad \operatorname{ad} x_2 = \begin{pmatrix} 0 & 0 & 0 \\ -1 & 0 & 0 \\ 0 & 0 & 0 \end{pmatrix}, \tag{2.15}$$

and the characteristic equation becomes

$$\det(h^i \operatorname{ad} x_i - w\mathbf{1}) = \left| \begin{pmatrix} -w & 0 & 0 \\ -h^2 & -w & h^0 \\ h^1 & -h^0 & -w \end{pmatrix} \right| = -(w^3 + (h^0)^2 w). \tag{2.16}$$

Hence $\varphi_1 = 0$. Nevertheless the derived algebra L' is the proper invariant subgroup of translations, not the whole group L, as the converse would require.

Example. An instance is the non-Abelian group of linear transformations

$$\begin{pmatrix} a_1 & 0 & b_1 \\ 0 & a_2 & b_2 \\ 0 & 0 & 1 \end{pmatrix},$$

in which the a_i and b_i are all real. This group has both an invariant and a noninvariant Abelian subgroup. The generators are

$$x_1 = \begin{pmatrix} 1 & 0 & 0 \\ 0 & 0 & 0 \\ 0 & 0 & 0 \end{pmatrix}, \quad x_2 = \begin{pmatrix} 0 & 0 & 0 \\ 0 & 1 & 0 \\ 0 & 0 & 0 \end{pmatrix}, \quad x_3 = \begin{pmatrix} 0 & 0 & 1 \\ 0 & 0 & 0 \\ 0 & 0 & 0 \end{pmatrix}, \quad x_4 = \begin{pmatrix} 0 & 0 & 0 \\ 0 & 0 & 1 \\ 0 & 0 & 0 \end{pmatrix}, \tag{2.17}$$

and the commutation relations are

$$[x_1, x_3] = x_3, \qquad [x_2, x_4] = x_4, \tag{2.18}$$

and other commutators equal to zero. The matrices of the adjoint representation are:

$$\begin{aligned} \operatorname{ad} x_1 &= \begin{pmatrix} 0 & 0 & 0 & 0 \\ 0 & 0 & 0 & 0 \\ 0 & 0 & 1 & 0 \\ 0 & 0 & 0 & 0 \end{pmatrix}, & \operatorname{ad} x_2 &= \begin{pmatrix} 0 & 0 & 0 & 0 \\ 0 & 0 & 0 & 0 \\ 0 & 0 & 0 & 0 \\ 0 & 0 & 0 & 1 \end{pmatrix}, \\ \operatorname{ad} x_3 &= \begin{pmatrix} 0 & 0 & 0 & 0 \\ 0 & 0 & 0 & 0 \\ -1 & 0 & 0 & 0 \\ 0 & 0 & 0 & 0 \end{pmatrix}, & \operatorname{ad} x_4 &= \begin{pmatrix} 0 & 0 & 0 & 0 \\ 0 & 0 & 0 & 0 \\ 0 & 0 & 0 & 0 \\ 0 & -1 & 0 & 0 \end{pmatrix}. \end{aligned} \tag{2.19}$$

Hence,

$$\Delta(h_1 w) = \left|\begin{pmatrix} -w & 0 & 0 & 0 \\ 0 & -w & 0 & 0 \\ -h^3 & 0 & h^1 - w & 0 \\ 0 & -h^4 & 0 & h^2 - w \end{pmatrix}\right| = w^2(w^2 - (h^1 + h^2)w + h^1 h^2). \quad (2.20)$$

There is another series of invariant subalgebras that can be extracted from a given Lie algebra, the *lower central series*

$$L, \quad L_{(1)} = [L, L], \quad L_{(2)} = [L, L_{(1)}], \ldots \quad (2.21)$$

If this series ends, that is, if $L_{(k)} = [L, [L, \ldots, [L, L], \ldots]] = 0$, then L is called (*Lie*) *nilpotent*, and any multiple commutator that has at least $k + 1$ elements is zero. The elements of the adjoint algebra are nilpotent in the usual (associative) sense, since $[y_1, x] = (\text{ad } y_1)x$, $[y_2, [y_1, x]] = (\text{ad } y_2)(\text{ad } y_1)x_1, \ldots$. It is extremely important to note that in this way an associative algebra (ad L, in this case) has been related to the abstract structure of a nonassociative Lie algebra. (We recall here that an associative algebra is defined as nilpotent when any product $abcd \cdots$ with sufficiently many factors vanishes.)

Note also that the Lie algebras of the two examples just given, (2.14) and (2.18), are solvable but not nilpotent. On the other hand, nilpotency directly implies solvability. An example of a nilpotent Lie algebra arises from the non-Abelian group of matrices

$$\begin{pmatrix} 1 & a & b \\ 0 & 1 & c \\ 0 & 0 & 1 \end{pmatrix}, \qquad a, b, c \text{ real.}$$

The Lie algebra has the elements

$$x_1 = \begin{pmatrix} 0 & 1 & 0 \\ 0 & 0 & 0 \\ 0 & 0 & 0 \end{pmatrix}, \qquad x_2 = \begin{pmatrix} 0 & 0 & 1 \\ 0 & 0 & 0 \\ 0 & 0 & 0 \end{pmatrix}, \qquad x_3 = \begin{pmatrix} 0 & 0 & 0 \\ 0 & 0 & 1 \\ 0 & 0 & 0 \end{pmatrix}, \quad (2.22)$$

which obey the commutation relations

$$[x_1, x_2] = 0, \qquad [x_1, x_3] = x_2, \qquad [x_2, x_3] = 0. \quad (2.23)$$

Hence any double commutator $[x_p, [x_q, x_r]]$ vanishes; and so the Jacobi condition is fulfilled automatically. The adjoints are

$$\text{ad } x_1 = \begin{pmatrix} 0 & 0 & 0 \\ 0 & 0 & 1 \\ 0 & 0 & 0 \end{pmatrix}; \quad \text{ad } x_2 = \begin{pmatrix} 0 & 0 & 0 \\ 0 & 0 & 0 \\ 0 & 0 & 0 \end{pmatrix}; \quad \text{ad } x_3 = \begin{pmatrix} 0 & 0 & 0 \\ -1 & 0 & 0 \\ 0 & 0 & 0 \end{pmatrix}. \quad (2.24)$$

The determinantal equation is merely

$$(h^1 \operatorname{ad} x_1 + h^2 \operatorname{ad} x_2 + h^3 \operatorname{ad} x_3 - w\mathbf{1}) = \left|\begin{pmatrix} -w & 0 & 0 \\ -h^3 & -w & h^1 \\ 0 & 0 & -w \end{pmatrix}\right| = -w^3. \quad (2.25)$$

This group is a subgroup of the unimodular linear group in three dimensions, and its Lie algebra is a subalgebra of the Lie algebra of $SU(n)$, $n \geqq 3$, but the group itself is not a subgroup of any $SU(n)$.

III. Lie's Theorem, the Rank Theorem, and the First Criterion of Solvability

We now proceed to a proof of Lie's theorem, upon which we shall subsequently base proofs of the Cartan criteria for the solvability of a Lie algebra, which will in turn be necessary for a demonstration of the theorem that any semisimple algebra is the direct sum of simple non-Abelian algebras. We shall also have occasion to use Lie's theorem in the consideration of the root system of the algebra. Lie's theorem states: *A solvable Lie algebra L of linear transformations has a simultaneous eigenvector V; that is,*

$$x_a V = \lambda(a) V, \qquad \text{for all} \quad x_a \in L. \quad (3.1)$$

First we shall prove as a lemma the weaker theorem for the case that $L' = 0$, that is, that a set of commuting matrices has a simultaneous eigenvector.

Proof of Lemma. Let the set of commuting matrices be called $A_1, A_2, \ldots$. Since every matrix has a nonzero eigenvector, then A_1 has one, which we shall denote V. Hence $A_1 V = \lambda_1 V$; hence $A_1 A_2 V = A_2 A_1 V = \lambda A_2 V$ and it follows that $A_2 V$ is also an eigenvector of A_1 which belongs to the same eigenvalue λ_1. The space Γ_{λ_1} of all eigenvectors V of A_1 that belong to λ_1 is therefore invariant under A_2. Hence there is a subspace Γ_{λ_2} of Γ_{λ_1} that has dimension greater than or equal to one and which consists of all vectors in Γ_{λ_1} that belong to an eigenvalue λ_2 of the linear transformation that A_2 induces in Γ_{λ_1}. The vectors in Γ_{λ_2} are simultaneous eigenvectors of A_1, A_2. The completion of the proof of the lemma by induction is now straightforward.

Proof of Lie's Theorem. We note that the lemma proves the theorem for the member $L^{(p-1)}$, which is Abelian, of the derived series

$$L, L', L'', \ldots, L^{(p)} = 0.$$

Hence we need prove only that the elements of a Lie algebra L of linear transformations have a simultaneous eigenvector when the elements of L' have a simultaneous eigenvector. The proof then holds by induction. We shall give this proof for Lie *groups* of linear transformations, but shall forego the proof of the extended Lie theorem, that any linear Lie algebra can be integrated to a connected and simply connected Lie group. Trivially, of course, the Lie group has the same set of eigenvectors that the Lie algebra has. The theorem can be proved directly for linear Lie algebras, but the proof for groups is more transparent. We shall prove, then, that if the matrices of a representation of the derived group G', whose elements consist of all commutators $g_1 g_2 g_1^{-1} g_2^{-1}$ and their products (where $g_1, g_2 \in G$, the Lie group whose algebra is L), have a simultaneous eigenvector, then the matrices of G itself have a simultaneous eigenvector.

By hypothesis the space K_λ of all vectors V that are simultaneous eigenvectors of the matrices $g' \in G'$ with the same "eigenvalue function" $\lambda(g')$, that is,

$$g'V = \lambda(g')V, \qquad \text{for all} \quad g' \in G', \tag{3.2}$$

has dimension greater than or equal to one. We show first that K_λ is invariant under the operations $g \in G$: Consider the vector $w = gV$ of gK_λ; for any element $h' \in G'$ we have

$$h'w = h'gV = g(g^{-1}h'g)V. \tag{3.3}$$

Since G' is an invariant subgroup, the element $g^{-1}h'g$ is also in G', and this element therefore has V as an eigenvector:

$$(g^{-1}h'g)V = \lambda(g^{-1}h'g)V. \tag{3.4}$$

Hence for any $h' \in G'$,

$$h'w = g\lambda(g^{-1}h'g)V = \lambda(g^{-1}h'g)gV = \lambda(g^{-1}h'g)w, \tag{3.5}$$

that is, the vectors $w = gV$ are simultaneous eigenvectors of the elements G'. When we can show that $\lambda(g^{-1}h'g) = \lambda(h')$, then we may conclude that the vectors $w = gV$ belong to K_λ also. This is in fact the case, since the function $\lambda(g^{-1}h'g)$ is a continuous function of g which is at the same time an eigenvalue of h' which has a discrete spectrum. Therefore, $\lambda(g^{-1}h'g) = \lambda(h')$ when we make the additional hypothesis that g is connected to the unit element.

This proves that $gK_\lambda \subset K_\lambda$; that is, K_λ is an invariant subspace of all matrices g. We may suppose the matrices g of G to be reduced with respect to K_λ, and the linear transformations induced in K_λ will be called g_K. Since K_λ is spanned by the simultaneous eigenvectors of the $g' \in G'$, with the eigenvalue $\lambda(g')$ depending only on g' and not on the particular eigenvector, then the matrices g_K' are multiples $\lambda(g')$ of the unit matrix. Since any g' is a product of commutators $g_1 g_2 g_1^{-1} g_2^{-1}$, it follows that $\det(g') = 1$, and it may easily be seen that the same result holds for $\det(g'_K)$. But the latter determinant is also equal to $(\lambda(g'))^{\dim K_\lambda}$, and therefore $\lambda(g')$ is a root of unity and hence takes on only a discrete set of values. Now $\lambda(g')$ must remain constant as g' varies over G', since $\lambda(g')$ must be continuous, and since g' is connected to the identity by hypothesis, $\lambda(g') = \lambda(e) = 1$.

Since all g'_K are subspaces of the unit matrix, the matrices g_K are a representation of the factor group G/G', which is Abelian. Hence the matrices g_K commute and have a common eigenvector in K_λ, which is also a simultaneous eigenvector of the g since K_λ is invariant under g. This result establishes Lie's theorem; only a straightforward induction remains.

It is easily seen now by induction that the matrices of a solvable linear Lie group (or Lie algebra) can be transformed simultaneously into triangular form, i.e.,

$$\begin{pmatrix} \cdot & \cdot & \cdot \\ 0 & \cdot & \cdot \\ 0 & 0 & \cdot \end{pmatrix},$$

where the elements on the principal diagonal need not be zero, but all elements below it are. The converse statement, that a Lie group or Lie algebra of triangular matrices is solvable, is trivial, since the commutator of two triangular matrices is also triangular and in fact has zeros on the principal diagonal. Such matrices, which are triangular and also have only zeros as elements along the principal diagonal and hence have only zero roots, are called *nil triangular*. Nil triangular matrices are both Lie nilpotent and associatively nilpotent. From these considerations it follows directly that a solvable Lie algebra of matrices has a nilpotent (in both senses) derived algebra. Trivially, an abstract Lie algebra is solvable (Lie nilpotent) if and only if its adjoint representation, or any other faithful representation, is solvable (Lie nilpotent), and hence we have the theorem that a solvable Lie algebra L has a Lie nilpotent derived algebra L'. Since nil triangular matrices have only zero roots, and since $\operatorname{ad} L'$ is nil triangular when L is solvable, we also have it that if L is solvable, then $\operatorname{ad} L'$ has only zero roots. This theorem and its converse constitute *Cartan's first criterion of solvability*; we shall return to the proof of the converse when we have first introduced the notion of rank and the rank theorem, which are necessary to the proof.

We define the *rank* l of a Lie algebra (and, correspondingly, of the Lie group associated with it) as the number of algebraically independent roots of the characteristic equation (2.2). It is equal to the number of independent coefficients φ_i in $\Delta(w)$, and is therefore equal to the number of independent invariants of the adjoint group, which is again (by local isomorphism) equal to the number of independent invariants of the corresponding Lie group. The rank of a Lie algebra, then, is zero if and only if all roots are equal to zero.

The rank theorem states that *the number of zero roots of* $\Delta(w) = 0$ *is at least equal to the rank* l.

Proof. We consider the parameter space of the adjoint group. In it we define the variety V which consists of all points q^a $(a = 1, \ldots, r)$ such that the invariants $\varphi_i(q^a)$ (considered as functions of the coordinates of the element $q = q^a x_a$ in the space of the Lie algebra) assume constant values α_i. The dimension of this variety is equal to the difference between the number of parameters q^a and the number of independent coefficients φ_i in $\Delta(w)$, that is, $\dim V = r - l$. In the case of $SU(2)$, for example, $r = 3$ and $l = 1$, so that V becomes the surface of a three-dimensional sphere $(q^1)^2 + (q^2)^2 + (q^3)^2 = \alpha_1$.

Since the conditions $\varphi_i(q^a) = \alpha_i$ are invariant under the operations of the adjoint group, the variety V is also invariant. Now, $\dim V$ is equal to the number of linearly independent tangent vectors that can be drawn at any point q^a. This number in turn is not smaller (and may be much larger) than the number of linearly independent "directions" in which one can move the point q^a by applying the infinitesimal operations of the adjoint group. These directions do not leave the variety, which is invariant. The operation of ad y on q^a is just the commutation of $q = q^a x_a$ with y, and the number of linearly independent directions is therefore equal to the number of independent elements among the $[q, y]$, as q is held fixed and y is varied throughout the Lie algebra L. This number is equal to the dimension of the space L, which is r, minus the dimension of the space of all y such at $[q, y] = 0$ (i.e., the number of zero roots that belong to q). Therefore, $r - l \geqq r - l_0$, where l_0 is the number of zero roots that belong to q. Thus the rank theorem is proven.

Note that nil triangular matrices have only zero eigenvalues, hence the presence of a solvable invariant subgroup in a Lie algebra will especially give rise to surplus zero roots, since they produce nil triangular submatrices in the adjoint representation. Later we shall show that for groups without solvable invariant subgroups the number of zero roots is equal to the rank, that is, $l_0 = l$.

We are now ready to resume our study of Cartan's first criterion of solvability and demonstrate the proposition that if L' has zero rank [i.e., all roots of $\Delta(h, w) = 0$ are zero if $h \in L'$], then L is solvable.

Proof. Let M be a maximal solvable subalgebra of L', and then let us consider the mappings ad m, where $m \in M$, of L' into L'. Obviously the mappings $x \to (\text{ad } m)x = [m, x]$ map commutators into commutators; hence for $x \in L'$ they map L' into itself. Since $[M, M] \subset M$, the mappings ad m leave M invariant. They can therefore be considered as mappings of the (nonempty) factor space L'/M; that is, for any equivalence class $x + M$, where $x \in L'$, we have $x + M \to (\text{ad } m)x + (\text{ad } m)M = (\text{ad } m)x + M$. Since these mappings are a homomorphic image of the solvable M, these mappings constitute a solvable algebra of linear transformations and have therefore (by Lie's theorem) a common eigenvector, say, $y + M$, which satisfies $y + M \to (\text{ad } m)y + M \equiv \lambda(m)y + M$, or, in other terms, $[m, y] \equiv \lambda(m)y \pmod{M}$, for all $m \in M$. Note that $y + M$ is not the zero vector of L'/M, hence $y \neq 0 \pmod{M}$. Since L' has rank zero, every element $m \in M$ has only vanishing eigenvalues. Hence $\lambda(m) = 0$, and $[m, y] \in M$ for all $m \in M$. Therefore the subalgebra $M \oplus \{y\}$ (the direct sum of M and the set of all $y \in L'$) is still solvable. Hence the maximal solvable subalgebra of L' is L' itself, and L' is solvable, hence L is also solvable.

This theorem can also be shown in the following manner: If L is not solvable, then we prove that any element ad x contained in ad L' has at least one nonzero root, hence that L' has nonzero rank. Let us suppose, then, that L is not solvable, and hence the derived series L, $L' = [L, L]$, $L'' = [L', L']$, ... ends in $L^{(p)}$ such that $[L^{(p)}, L^{(p)}] = L^{(p)}$, that is, the sum of all image spaces $(\text{ad } x^i)L^{(p)}$, for all $x^i \in L^{(p)}$, coincides with the whole $L^{(p)}$. Therefore a general element $h_i \text{ ad } x^i$ of $L^{(p)}$, with indeterminate coefficients h_i, has at least one nonzero eigenvalue. A fortiori, therefore, a general element of ad L' has at least one nonzero eigenvalue, or root. Hence L' is of nonzero rank. Of course, under our hypothesis L, L', $L^{(2)}$, ..., $L^{(p)}$ all have rank greater than zero. When L is solvable, the first derived subalgebra L' is already nilpotent and therefore of rank zero; the useful criterion is that L' has rank zero (nonzero) if L is solvable (nonsolvable).

IV. The Cartan Subalgebra and Root Systems

We now proceed to a decomposition of the carrier space of a representation of the adjoint Lie algebra into its constituent eigenspaces, each of which corresponds to a particular root of the characteristic equation $\det(\text{ad } h - w\mathbf{1}) = 0$. First, however, we introduce a few definitions.

A *module* M is a linear (vector) space of vectors x that can be operated upon by the elements A of a ring of operators $\mathscr{A}$ such that the following laws hold:

$$\begin{aligned} A(x_1 + x_2) &= Ax_1 + Ax_2, \\ (A_1 + A_2)x &= A_1x + A_2x, \\ \alpha(Ax) &= A(\alpha x) = (A\alpha)x, \qquad \alpha \text{ a complex number}, \\ (A_1A_2)x &= A_1(A_2x). \end{aligned} \tag{4.1}$$

A linear subspace $N \subset M$ is a *submodule* when N is invariant under all operations A. The carrier space of a group representation becomes a module when we allow operations upon it by the ring that is generated by the representation matrices. We call the carrier space in this case the *representation module.* Any submodule of the representation module again spans a representation of the group, and the irreducible representations are those that are spanned by the minimal submodules. We now state the following *decomposition theorem*: Let A be a linear transformation (matrix) in the linear space M and let

$$P(W) = \prod_{i=1}^{k} [p_i(w)]^{n_i}, \tag{4.2}$$

where $p_i(w) = w - w_i$ and w_i is an eigenvalue of $\Delta(h, w) = 0$, be the minimal polynomial $P(w)$ of A. [That is, $P(w)$ is the polynomial of lowest degree such that $P(A) = 0$.] Then our theorem asserts that the space M that is annihilated by $P(A)$ $(P(A)M = 0)$ can be decomposed into the direct sum of linear subspaces M_i, each of which is annihilated by a polynomial $[p_i(w)]^{n_i}$. That is,

$$\begin{aligned} M_i &= \{x | [p_i(A)]^{n_i} x = 0\}, \\ M &= M_1 \oplus M_2 \oplus \cdots \oplus M_k. \end{aligned} \tag{4.3}$$

Since A commutes with $p_i(A)$, each of the spaces M_i is invariant under A. We shall not prove this theorem since it is only a coordinate-free version (and trivial consequence) of the familiar theorem that every matrix can be transformed into Jordan normal form.

Example.

$$A = \begin{pmatrix} \lambda & 1 & 0 & 0 & 0 \\ 0 & \lambda & 0 & 0 & 0 \\ 0 & 0 & \mu & 0 & 0 \\ 0 & 0 & 0 & \mu & 0 \\ 0 & 0 & 0 & 0 & \nu \end{pmatrix} \tag{4.4}$$

The partition in this case corresponds to the subspace decomposition $M = M_\lambda \oplus M_\mu \oplus M_\nu$. Clearly,

$$(A - \lambda\mathbf{1})^2 (A - \mu\mathbf{1})(A - \nu\mathbf{1}) = 0 = (p_\lambda(A))^2 p_\mu(A) p_\nu(A) = 0.$$

We now apply the decomposition theorem to the matrix ad h, where h is any element of L, and find that to each root $w_0 = 0, w_1, w_2, \ldots, w_q$ of $\Delta(h, w) = 0$ there corresponds an invariant subspace L_{w_i}, $0 \leqq i \leqq q$, of L which we call a *root space*. Of course the root space L_{w_i} is an eigenvector of ad h when $n_i = 1$. The entire Lie algebra can be decomposed into the direct sum $L = L_{w_0} \oplus L_{w_1} \oplus \cdots \oplus L_{w_q}$; hence we have already an (incomplete) canonical form of the Lie algebra L. We shall often write the roots as $w_i(h)$ to emphasize their dependence on h.

Since the roots w_i can be complex, the root spaces L_{w_i} can also be complex, and so we are necessarily dealing with the space of all $x = r^a x_a$ where r_a is an arbitrary complex coefficient, i.e., with the complex extension of the Lie algebra L. The functions $w_i(h)$ are analytic functions of $h = h^a x_a$ on the whole complex manifold of L.

We now choose a *fixed* $h_0 = h_0^a x_a \in L$ such that as few roots $w_i(h_0)$ as possible coalesce. Then $w_0(h_0) = 0$ is at least l-fold and the number of nonzero roots is at least l; at any rate, only l of the nonzero roots are functionally independent when h_0 is varied. Since the functions $w_i(h)$ are analytic in h, we may also suppose h_0 to be chosen in such a way that all roots $w_i(h)$ can be determined from their values $w_i(h_0)$ at h_0, that is, we perform the analytic continuation from h_0 to h in such a way as to avoid branch points in the complex planes of the coordinates h^a.

Example. For $SU(2)$ we have the Lie algebra $L = xx_1 + yx_2 + zx_3$, where the generators x_α obey the commutation rules given earlier in Eq. (2.9). As the element h_0 it is traditional to choose $x = y = 0$, $z = 1$ for the roots

$$w_0 = 0, \qquad w_1 = -w_2 = (x^2 + y^2 + z^2)^{1/2}. \tag{4.5}$$

In defining values of the roots for other elements $h \neq h_0$ of L, we must then avoid those points that lie on the surface $x^2 + y^2 + z^2 = 0$.

We choose h_0 in such a way that the roots that are zero for the point h_0 are also zero everywhere in L, and so that any linear relations with integral coefficients of the form $\sum p^a w_a(h_0) = 0$ that hold at h_0 also hold for all h throughout L. It can easily be seen that it is possible to choose h_0 so that this latter condition holds; we refer to the work of Freudenthal (*12*) for a proof. When these two conditions are met, the element h_0 is called a *regular element*. The values $w_i(h_0)$ then "distinguish between" the functions $w_i(h)$, that is, for h_0 there is minimal degeneracy among the w_i, and conversely the subspaces $L_{w_i(h_0)}$ are commonly called simply L_{w_i}. We shall show now that the restriction of ad h to the subspace L_{w_0} has only zero eigenvalues, and that L_{w_0} is hence solvable by the first criterion of solvability. In fact, L_{w_0} is the largest solvable subalgebra that contains the original regular element h_0 and constitutes the familiar *Cartan subalgebra*, and is the maximal Abelian subalgebra that is commutative with h_0. First we prove a multiplication property of the root spaces.

Let α, β be two of the roots $w_i(h_0)$. By definition, the root space L_α consists of all vectors $x \in L$ such that

$$(\operatorname{ad} h_0 - \alpha \mathbf{1})^m x = 0 \tag{4.6}$$

for sufficiently large m (we do not need to know a bound for m); the other root spaces are similarly defined. We shall show that

$$[L_\alpha, L_\beta] \subset L_{\alpha+\beta} \tag{4.7}$$

if $\alpha + \beta$ is again one of the roots $w_i(h_0)$, and

$$[L_\alpha, L_\beta] = 0 \tag{4.8}$$

if $\alpha + \beta$ is not among these roots. Now let $x \in L_\alpha$, $y \in L_\beta$. We compute first the expression

$$(\mathrm{ad}\, h_0 - (\alpha + \beta)\mathbf{1})\,[x, y]. \tag{4.9}$$

By use of the Jacobi condition we have

$$\begin{aligned}(\mathrm{ad}\, h_0 - (\alpha + \beta)\mathbf{1})\,[x, y] &= (\mathrm{ad}\, h_0)\,[x, y] - (\alpha + \beta)\,[x, y] \\ &= [h_0, [x, y]] - (\alpha + \beta)\,[x, y] \\ &= -[y, [h_0, x]] - [x, [y, h_0]] - (\alpha + \beta)\,[x, y] \\ &= [(\mathrm{ad}\, h_0)x, y] + [x, (\mathrm{ad}\, h_0)y] - (\alpha + \beta)\,[x, y] \\ &= [(\mathrm{ad}\, h_0 - \alpha\mathbf{1})x, y] + [x, (\mathrm{ad}\, h_0 - \beta\mathbf{1})y]. \end{aligned} \tag{4.10}$$

Hence, by iteration

$$(\mathrm{ad}\, h_0 - (\alpha + \beta)\mathbf{1})^k[x, y] = \sum_p \binom{k}{p} [(\mathrm{ad}\, h_0 - \alpha\mathbf{1})^p x, (\mathrm{ad}\, h_0 - \beta\mathbf{1})^{k-p} y], \tag{4.11}$$

and the right-hand side becomes zero for sufficiently large k, hence $[x, y] \in L_{\alpha+\beta}$ and $\alpha + \beta$ is a root unless all x and y commute.

Example. For $SU(2)$ we have chosen $h_0 = x_3 = J_z$, and the corresponding adjoint matrix is

$$\mathrm{ad}\, h_0 = \begin{pmatrix} 0 & -1 & 0 \\ 1 & 0 & 0 \\ 0 & 0 & 0 \end{pmatrix}. \tag{4.12}$$

The vectors that are annihilated by $(\mathrm{ad}\ h_0 - w\mathbf{1})$ are, for $w = 0, -i, i$, proportional to

$$\begin{pmatrix} 0 \\ 0 \\ 1 \end{pmatrix}, \quad \begin{pmatrix} i \\ -1 \\ 0 \end{pmatrix}, \quad \begin{pmatrix} i \\ 1 \\ 0 \end{pmatrix},$$

respectively. The corresponding elements of the Lie algebra are $x_3 = J_z$, $ix_1 - x_2 = iJ_x - J_y$, $ix_1 + x_2 = iJ_x + J_y$, which span the one-dimensional root spaces L_0, L_{+i}, L_{-i}. It is easily checked that in this case $[L_\alpha, L_\beta] = L_{\alpha+\beta}$ when $\alpha \neq \beta$.

From the multiplication property follow two important consequences. First,

$$[L_0, L_0] \subset L_0, \tag{4.13}$$

where $L_0 = L_{w_0}$. Hence L_0 is a (possibly Abelian) subalgebra that of course contains our regular element h_0. Second, since

$$[L_0, L_\alpha] \subset L_\alpha \tag{4.14}$$

[i.e., for all $x \in L_\alpha$, either $(\text{ad } h)x = 0$ or $(\text{ad } h)x \in L_\alpha$], it follows that each L_α is invariant under the operations ad h, where $h \in L_0$. In other words, the representation module of the adjoint representation of L_0 can be reduced into invariant (not necessarily irreducible) subspaces L_0, L_α, ..., which form submodules under the operation of commutation with elements of L_0, but not under commutation with an arbitrary element of L.

It will be convenient to write $(\text{ad } h)_\alpha$ for the restriction of ad h to the root space L_α. Hence, if we denote P_α as the projection operator corresponding to L_α,

$$\begin{aligned} P_\alpha L &= L_\alpha, \\ P_\alpha^2 &= P_\alpha, \\ P_\alpha L' &= L' \cap L_\alpha, \qquad L' \text{ any subspace of } L, \end{aligned} \tag{4.15}$$

and finally $(\text{ad } h)_\alpha = P_\alpha (\text{ad } h) P_\alpha$. The elements of L_0 are traditionally called h. The root spaces $L_{\alpha(h_0)}$, of course, depend on the particular choice of element h_0. We shall show that $L_{\alpha(h_0)}$ does not change as long as h_0 remains in L_0, hence, that $L_{\alpha(h)} = L_{\alpha(h_0)}$. Since $L_{\alpha(h_0)}$ is invariant under ad h, where $h \in L_0$, then $L_{\alpha(h_0)}$ consists of complete root spaces $L_{\beta(h)}$, which are eigenspaces of ad h:

$$L_{\alpha(h_0)} = \bigcup L_{\beta(h)}. \tag{4.16}$$

Since h_0 is a regular element, the set of root spaces $L_{\beta(h)}$ of h cannot be a refinement of the $L_{\alpha(h_0)}$, hence $L_{\alpha(h_0)} = L_{\beta(h)}$. Evidently $\alpha(h_0) = \beta(h_0)$. By the property of regularity different roots have different values in h_0, hence $\alpha(h) = \beta(h)$, therefore we can write $L_{\alpha(h_0)} = L_{\alpha(h)} = L_\alpha$ by definition. Of course, in general $\alpha(h_0) \neq \alpha(h)$.

Since $(\text{ad } h)_\alpha$ has $\alpha(h)$ as its single root, which may perhaps be multiple [i.e., occur more than once as eigenvalue of the determinantal equation $\Delta(h, w) = 0$], we have, for $h \in L_0$,

$$((\text{ad } h)_\alpha - \alpha(h)\mathbf{1})^{m_\alpha} L_\alpha = 0, \tag{4.17}$$

where m_α indicates the dimension of L_α. This relation then implies

$$(\operatorname{ad} h - \alpha(h)\mathbf{1})^{m_\alpha} L_\alpha = 0 \tag{4.18}$$

for $h \in L_0$. Of course, (4.18) might also hold if m_α were replaced by a smaller value.

Note that what holds for L_α also holds for the zero root; in particular,

$$(\operatorname{ad} h)^{m_0} L_0 = 0 \tag{4.19}$$

for all $h \in L_0$. It follows that the $(\operatorname{ad} h)_0$ have zero eigenvalues only, hence L_0 is solvable by the first criterion of solvability. It is in fact the largest solvable subalgebra that contains the original regular element h_0, and such a maximal solvable subalgebra is called a *Cartan subalgebra* or, in Freudenthal's terminology, a *trunk*. We shall subsequently see that L_0 is also Abelian.

It will be useful, as implied by the notation, to consider the roots $\alpha(h)$ as functions on L_0 alone instead of as functions on the whole L. Because the restrictions $(\operatorname{ad} h)_\alpha$ constitute a representation of the solvable subalgebra L_0, the operators $(\operatorname{ad} h)_k$ are solvable and have a common eigenvector x that by Lie's theorem is contained in the representation space L_α:

$$((\operatorname{ad} h)_\alpha - \alpha(h)\mathbf{1})x = 0 \tag{4.20}$$

for all $h \in L_0$. Since $x \in L_\alpha$, it follows that

$$(\operatorname{ad} h - \alpha(h)\mathbf{1})x = 0 \tag{4.21}$$

for all $h \in L_0$ and some $x \in L_\alpha$. Since ad h depends linearly on h, it follows that $\alpha(h)x$ and hence $\alpha(h)$ itself depend *linearly* on h as long as h varies in L_0. This is a crucial point and the whole reason for our considering the roots as functions on L_0. The roots in their aspect of functions of $h \in L_0$ will be called *root forms*, and they are indeed linear forms, i.e., homogeneous polynomials.

Up to this point we have established the following results:

(a) Let L be a complex Lie algebra and h_0 a regular element. Then the trunk L_0 that consists of all $h \in L$ that are eventually annihilated by ad h_0 [i.e., $(\operatorname{ad} h_0)^m h = 0$ for some m] is a *solvable subalgebra*.

(b) To each root $\alpha(h)$ of $\det(\operatorname{ad} h - \alpha(h)\mathbf{1}) = 0$ belongs a space

$$L_\alpha = \{x \mid (\operatorname{ad} h - \alpha(h)\mathbf{1})^m x = 0 \text{ for some } m \leqq m_\alpha\},$$

hence $(\operatorname{ad} h - \alpha(h)\mathbf{1})^{m_\alpha} L_\alpha = 0$.

(c) The L_α have the property that $[L_\alpha, L_\beta] \subset L_{\alpha+\beta}$ if $\alpha + \beta$ is a root, and $[L_\alpha, L_\beta] = 0$ if $\alpha + \beta$ is not a root.

(d) The subspaces L_0, L_α, L_β, ..., exhaust L: $L = L_0 \oplus L_\alpha \oplus L_\beta \oplus \cdots$.
(e) The functions $\alpha(h)$ are *linear* on h and are called root forms.

Since $\alpha + \beta = 0$ only if $\beta = -\alpha$, the elements of L_0 that can be written as commutators of elements not in L_0 can arise only as, say, $[y_+, y_-]$, where $y_+ \in L_\alpha$ and $y_- \in L_{-\alpha}$. Clearly when L_μ is a root space we have

$$(\operatorname{ad} y_+)L_\mu \equiv [y_+, L_\mu] \subset L_{\mu+\alpha}, \tag{4.22}$$

and

$$(\operatorname{ad} y)L_\mu \equiv [y_-, L_\mu] \subset L_{\mu-\alpha}. \tag{4.23}$$

Therefore

$$H = \sum_j \oplus L_{\mu+j\alpha}, \tag{4.24}$$

where the sum is taken over all integral values of j such that $\mu + j\alpha$ is a root form, is invariant under transformation by any ad y_+, any ad y_-, and any ad $h = [\text{ad } y_+, \text{ad } y_-]$, where $y_+ \in L_{+\alpha}$ and $y_- \in L_{-\alpha}$. Writing as usual $(\text{ad } x)_H$ for the restriction of ad x to H, we note that the invariance of H under ad y_+ and ad y_- implies

$$(\operatorname{ad} h)_H = [(\operatorname{ad} y_+)_H, (\operatorname{ad} y_-)_H], \tag{4.25}$$

which, since it is a commutator, has trace zero; hence,

$$\operatorname{tr}(\operatorname{ad} h)_H = 0, \qquad h = [y_+, y_-]. \tag{4.26}$$

Since on the other hand $L_{\mu+j\alpha}$ is an eigenspace that belongs to the root $\mu(h) + j\alpha(h) = (\mu + j\alpha)(h)$ for any ad h, $h \in L_0$, then $(\text{ad } h)_H$ has the eigenvalue $(\mu + j\alpha)(h)$ with a multiplicity equal to the dimension of $L_{\mu+j\alpha}$. Hence

$$\operatorname{tr}(\operatorname{ad} h)_H = \sum \operatorname{tr}(\operatorname{ad} h)L_{\mu+j\alpha} = \sum m_{\mu+j\alpha}(\mu + j\alpha)(h) = 0 \tag{4.27}$$

where $m_{\mu+j\alpha}$ is the dimension of the eigenspace that belongs to the eigenvalue $(\mu + j\alpha)(h)$.

We now define the elements of $[L_\alpha, L_{-\alpha}]$ as α-*nodes*. Then formula (4.27) shows that if h is an α-node, then $\mu(h)$ is a rational multiple of $\alpha(h)$ for every root form μ. Note that the factor of proportionality depends only on μ and α, not on the particular $y_+ \in L_\alpha$ and $y_- \in L_{-\alpha}$ that define $h = [y_+, y_-]$.

We now return to an object defined previously, the metric tensor

$$g_{ab} = \operatorname{tr}(\operatorname{ad} x_a \operatorname{ad} x_b),$$

which we shall also write in the form

$$g(x, y) = \operatorname{tr}(\operatorname{ad} x \operatorname{ad} y).$$

It is of course possible to restrict the summation implicit in the definition of a trace to a subspace M of L. We shall write such a restriction as

$$g_M(x, y) = \operatorname{tr}_M(\operatorname{ad} x \operatorname{ad} y).$$

If the operator of which the trace is taken is such that it transforms L into M, then both traces are equal, i.e., $\operatorname{tr}_M = \operatorname{tr} \equiv \operatorname{tr}_L$. This is the case when M is an invariant subalgebra and $x, y \in M$. Hence $g_M(x, y)$ when x and y are both contained in the invariant subalgebra M.

We are now ready to prove the *second criterion of solvability*. We have seen that L is solvable when all roots of the derived algebra L' vanish (first criterion of solvability). Hence $g(x, x)$ which is equal to the sum of the squares of all roots of x [Eq. (2.12)], is zero when $x \in L'$. The converse is also true and is the statement of the second criterion of solvability: L is solvable if and only if $g(x, x) = 0$ for all $x \in L'$. In order to prove this assertion we need now prove only that $g(x, x)$ is not identically zero on L' when L is not solvable. Now when L is not solvable there is an *invariant* subgroup M [the last member of the derived series, Eq. (2.3)] that has the property that $M' = M$. We shall prove that $g_M(x, x)$ is not identically zero for $x \in M$, and this will be a sufficient proof for our criterion. Let h be a regular element of M and let M_0 be the corresponding trunk. Since $M' = M$, not all roots of h vanish (by the first criterion of solvability), and there exist nonzero root spaces M_α. Since $M' = M$, any element, including h, is a sum of commutators. Hence h is a sum of nodes, $h = \sum_\alpha [y_\alpha, y_{-\alpha}]$, and at least one of the terms, say $h_\alpha \equiv [y_\alpha, y_{-\alpha}]$, has a nonzero root $\mu(h_\alpha)$.

Since h_α is an α-node, its nonzero root $\mu(h_\alpha)$ is a rational multiple of $\alpha(h_\alpha)$. And since $(\operatorname{ad} h_\alpha)^2$ has eigenvalue $(\mu(h_\alpha))^2$ in L_μ, then

$$g(h_\alpha, h_\alpha) = \operatorname{tr}(\operatorname{ad} h_\alpha)^2 = \sum m_\mu(\mu(h_\alpha))^2, \tag{4.28}$$

where the summation is performed over all nonzero roots. Hence $g(h_\alpha, h_\alpha)$ is a nonzero multiple of $(\alpha(h_\alpha))^2$, which is not equal to zero.

We are now in a position to complete the proof of Cartan's criterion of semisimplicity that we introduced earlier in Section I. In Eq. (1.15) we established the necessity for the condition that g_{ab} be nonsingular if L is to be semisimple, but we proceeded to demonstrate only that if g_{ab} is singular, then L has an invariant subalgebra $\bar{L}$, that is, L is not simple. We can now complete the proof of sufficiency and show that L is also not semisimple. This result, in fact, now follows immediately from the second criterion of solvability; we now have it that the invariant subalgebra $\bar{L}$ is solvable and hence contains an Abelian invariant subalgebra.

We are also now in a position to prove that any semisimple Lie algebra is a direct sum of simple Lie algebras.

Proof. Let M, with elements y, be a minimal invariant subalgebra of the semisimple algebra L, and consider the set N of all z such that $\mathrm{tr}(\mathrm{ad}\, y \,\mathrm{ad}\, z) = 0$ for all $y \in M$. Then immediately, for any $x \in L$,

$$\begin{aligned}\mathrm{tr}(\mathrm{ad}\, y\, \mathrm{ad}[z, x]) &= \mathrm{tr}(\mathrm{ad}\, y\, [\mathrm{ad}\, z, \mathrm{ad}\, x]) = \mathrm{tr}([\mathrm{ad}\, x, \mathrm{ad}\, y]\, \mathrm{ad}\, z) \\ &= \mathrm{tr}(\mathrm{ad}[x, y]\, \mathrm{ad}\, z) = 0 \end{aligned} \tag{4.29}$$

because M is an invariant subalgebra, i.e., $[x, y] \in M$. Since y is an arbitrary member of M, it follows that $[z, x] \in N$. Therefore N is an invariant subalgebra. Now let the number of dimensions of L, M, and N be λ, μ, and ν, respectively. Since the conditions $\mathrm{tr}(\mathrm{ad}\, y\, \mathrm{ad}\, z) = 0$ imposed on the elements $z = r^a x_a$, $x_a \in L$, such that z be a member of N amount to a system of μ linear equations, the dimension ν of N is at least $\nu \geqq \lambda - \mu$. Hence $\lambda \leqq \nu + \mu$.

We now show that the intersection of N and M is zero. The elements z of $N \cap M$ satisfy the condition $\mathrm{tr}(\mathrm{ad}\, z)^2 = 0$. By the second criterion of solvability, $N \cap M$ is then a solvable invariant subalgebra. Since L is semisimple it has no such subalgebra, and thus $N \cap M = 0$. Hence $\lambda = \nu + \mu$ and $L = N \oplus M$. M is simple by definition, and N is clearly semisimple; so we can repeat this procedure, i.e., decompose N into the direct sum of its minimal invariant (simple) subalgebra and a semisimple invariant subalgebra, and continue until all semisimplicity is exhausted and we have obtained only subalgebras of N that are themselves simple. We may show in an exactly similar manner that any semisimple Lie group is the direct product of simple Lie subgroups.

We shall now consider semisimple Lie algebras only, and for these we know, by the Cartan criterion of semisimplicity, that the metric form $g(x, y) = \mathrm{tr}(\mathrm{ad}\, x\, \mathrm{ad}\, y)$ is nondegenerate. Since

$$(\mathrm{ad}\, x)(\mathrm{ad}\, y)z = [x, [y, z]] \in L_{\alpha+\beta+\gamma} \tag{4.30}$$

when $x \in L_\alpha$, $y \in L_\beta$, and $z \in L_\gamma$, it is clear that $g(x, y)$ can be nonzero only when $\beta = -\alpha$, and by the nondegeneracy of $g(x, y)$ we have it that L_α is orthogonal to L_β, for $\beta \neq -\alpha$, with respect to $g(x, y)$ as our metric.

Because the metric form is nondegenerate, we obtain two consequences: (1) For any $h \in L_0$ there exists an $h' \in L_0$ such that $g(h, h') \neq 0$. Hence the restriction g_0 of the metric g to L_0 is also nondegenerate. (2) For any $e_\alpha \in L_\alpha$ there exists an $e_{-\alpha} \in L_{-\alpha}$ such that $g(e_\alpha, e_{-\alpha}) \neq 0$.

We derive now an expression for $g(h, h')$. Since L_0 is solvable, ad h and ad h' can be simultaneously put in triangular form as we have already seen. Hence $\mathrm{tr}(\mathrm{ad}\, h\, \mathrm{ad}\, h')$ becomes a sum of products of a root form that is a function of h and another that is the analytic continuation of the latter evaluated at h', i.e.,

$$g(h, h') = \sum_\mu (\dim L_\mu)\mu(h)\mu(h').$$

Hence the root forms $\mu(h)$ cannot all vanish unless $h = 0$.

Now a 0-node $[h_1, h_2]$, where $h_1, h_2 \in L_0$, has, by a theorem previously demonstrated, only roots that are rational multiples of the root to which the node belongs; hence $[h_1, h_2]$, which belongs to L_0, has only zero root forms, and is therefore equal to zero. This result establishes that L_0 is Abelian.

We shall now prove that the dimension of L_0 is equal to the rank l of the group, which is also equal to the number of independent root forms. We consider the *dual space* $\bar{L}_0$ which consists of all linear functions on L_0, and hence has dimension equal to that of L_0. The linear space spanned by all root forms $\alpha(h)$, $h \in L_0$, is a subspace of $\bar{L}_0$ which has dimension l, hence the dimension of L_0 is greater than or equal to the rank l. Now, when $\dim L_0 > l$, there must exist a vector $k \in L_0$ such that all root forms $\alpha(k)$ are zero. This would imply that $g(h, k) = \sum (\dim L_\alpha)\alpha(h)\alpha(k) = 0$ for all $h \in L_0$, but this condition would violate the nondegeneracy of the restriction of g to L_0. Hence $\dim L_0 = l$.

We shall now show that an α-node $[e_\alpha, e_{-\alpha}]$, where $e_\alpha \in L_\alpha$, $e_{-\alpha} \in L_{-\alpha}$, is never zero. Let us suppose the contrary; then by Lie's theorem ad e_α and ad $e_{-\alpha}$ can be transformed simultaneously to triangular form. Because $(\text{ad } e_\alpha)L_\mu \subset L_{\mu+\alpha}$, it follows that all diagonal elements, hence all eigenvalues of the triangular ad e_α, are zero. The same result holds for ad $e_{-\alpha}$, hence $\text{tr}(\text{ad } e_\alpha)(\text{ad } e_{-\alpha}) = g(e_\alpha, e_{-\alpha}) = 0$, and the Cartan criterion of semisimplicity is not fulfilled.

Hence all nodes are nonzero. Since the number of nodes is at least equal to the number l of independent roots, and since the nodes that correspond to independent roots have themselves independent roots and are therefore different, each node $[e_\alpha, e_{-\alpha}]$ is one-dimensional (hence *unique*), and the nodes corresponding to l independent roots exhaust L_0.

We shall now probe the structure of the root-forms somewhat more deeply and finally prove that the root spaces L_α are also one-dimensional. Except for normalization and choice of a basis in L_0, we shall then have found a canonical basis for the whole L.

Since the elements $x \in L_\alpha$ are defined by the condition that

$$(\text{ad } h - \alpha(h)\mathbf{1})^m x = 0$$

for some m, we can choose an element $e_\alpha \in L_\alpha$ such that

$$(\text{ad } h - \alpha(h)\mathbf{1})e_\alpha = 0. \tag{4.31}$$

This is

$$[h, e_\alpha] = \alpha(h)e_\alpha, \qquad \text{for all} \quad h \in L_0. \tag{4.32}$$

We can also find an element e_α in L_α such that the node $h_\alpha \equiv [e_\alpha, e_{-\alpha}]$ is not zero. Note that we do not yet know whether $e_{-\alpha}$ is also an eigenvector of ad h.

We use now our key formula (4.7), which tells us that $[L_\alpha, L_\beta]$ either is contained in the root space $L_{\alpha+\beta}$ or is equal to zero (in the case that $\alpha+\beta$ is not a root). This formula can also be written as $(\mathrm{ad}\, L_\alpha)L_\beta \subset L_{\alpha+\beta}$. Since the series of subspaces

$$(\mathrm{ad}\, e_{-\alpha})L_\beta, \quad (\mathrm{ad}\, e_{-\alpha})^2 L_\beta, \ldots \tag{4.33}$$

that correspond to root forms $\beta-\alpha$, $\beta-2\alpha$, ... must surely end, since we are dealing only with compact Lie algebras, we can find an L_μ such that $(\mathrm{ad}\, e_{-\alpha})L_\mu = 0$. In L_μ we can find a vector x that is even an eigenvector of ad h; hence

$$\begin{aligned} &(\mathrm{ad}\, e_{-\alpha})x = 0 \\ &(\mathrm{ad}\, h)x = \mu(h)x, \qquad \text{for all} \quad h \in L_0. \end{aligned} \tag{4.34}$$

We construct a *ladder* by operating with the *raising operator* ad e_α on x:

$$x^{(j)} = (\mathrm{ad}\, e_\alpha)^j x, \qquad \text{for all positive integers} \quad j. \tag{4.35}$$

The vector $x^{(j)}$ belongs to $L_{\mu+j\alpha}$ if $\mu+j\alpha$ is a root form. Because both $x \equiv x^{(0)}$ and e_α are eigenvectors of ad h, $x^{(j)}$ is an eigenvector also. The proof goes by induction:

$$\begin{aligned} (\mathrm{ad}\, h)x^{(j)} &= (\mathrm{ad}\, h)(\mathrm{ad}\, e_\alpha)x^{(j-1)} \\ &= [\mathrm{ad}\, h, \mathrm{ad}\, e_\alpha]x^{(j-1)} + (\mathrm{ad}\, e_\alpha)(\mathrm{ad}\, h)x^{(j-1)} \\ &= (\mathrm{ad}\, [h, e_\alpha])x^{(j-1)} + (\mathrm{ad}\, e_\alpha)(\mu(h) + (j-1)\alpha(h))x^{(j-1)} \\ &= \mathrm{ad}(\alpha(h)e_\alpha)x^{(j-1)} + (\mathrm{ad}\, e_\alpha)(\mu(h) + (j-1)\alpha(h))x^{(j-1)} \\ &= (\mu(h) + j\alpha(h))(\mathrm{ad}\, e_\alpha)x^{(j-1)} = (\mu(h) + j\alpha(h))x^{(j)}. \end{aligned} \tag{4.36}$$

We have worked here with eigenvectors of ad h, but note that we have not obtained a greater generality than we would have by using a particular element ad h_α, where $h_\alpha \equiv [e_\alpha, e_{-\alpha}]$.

Let us see now what happens when we apply the *lowering operator* ad $e_{-\alpha}$ to $x^{(j+1)}$:

$$\begin{aligned} (\mathrm{ad}\, e_{-\alpha})x^{(j+1)} &= (\mathrm{ad}\, e_{-\alpha})(\mathrm{ad}\, e_\alpha)x^{(j)} \\ &= [\mathrm{ad}\, e_{-\alpha}, \mathrm{ad}\, e_\alpha]x^{(j)} + (\mathrm{ad}\, e_\alpha)(\mathrm{ad}\, e_{-\alpha})x^{(j)}, \\ &= -(\mathrm{ad}\, h_\alpha(x^{(j)} + (\mathrm{ad}\, e_\alpha)(\mathrm{ad}\, e_{-\alpha})x^{(j)}. \end{aligned} \tag{4.37}$$

Hence $(\mathrm{ad}\, e_{-\alpha})x^{(j+1)}$ is a multiple of $x^{(j)}$ if $(\mathrm{ad}\, e_{-\alpha})x^{(j)}$ is a multiple of $x^{(j-1)}$.

Further, we note that

$$(\operatorname{ad} e_{-\alpha})x^{(1)} = -(\operatorname{ad} h_\alpha)x^{(0)} + (\operatorname{ad} e_\alpha)(\operatorname{ad} e_{-\alpha})x^{(0)} = -(\operatorname{ad} h_\alpha)x^{(0)}. \tag{4.38}$$

Hence the induction is completed, that is, $(\operatorname{ad} e_{-\alpha})x^{(j)}$ is a multiple of $x^{(j-1)}$ for $j \geqq 1$, and we may put

$$(\operatorname{ad} e_{-\alpha})x^{(j+1)} = \rho_j\, x^{(j)}, \tag{4.39}$$

and we find by substitution

$$\rho_j x^{(j)} = -(\operatorname{ad} h_\alpha)x^{(j)} + (\operatorname{ad} e_\alpha)\rho_{j-1}x^{(j-1)}. \tag{4.40}$$

Equation (4.36) now gives us, with h_α instead of h,

$$\rho_j = -(\mu(h_\alpha) + j\alpha(h_\alpha)) + \rho_{j-1}. \tag{4.41}$$

Since

$$-(\operatorname{ad} h_\alpha)x^{(0)} = \rho_0 x^{(0)}, \tag{4.42}$$

we have

$$\rho_0 = -\mu(h_\alpha). \tag{4.43}$$

Summation gives

$$\rho_l = -\sum_{j=0}^{l} (\mu(h_\alpha) + j\alpha(h_\alpha)) = -(l+1)\mu(h_\alpha) - \tfrac{1}{2}l(l+1)\alpha(h_\alpha). \tag{4.44}$$

Since the sequence $x^{(0)}, x^{(1)}, \ldots$ is bound to end with, say, an $x^{(p)}$ such that $(\operatorname{ad} e_\alpha)x^{(p)} = 0$, the equation

$$(\operatorname{ad} e_{-\alpha})x^{(p+1)} = \rho_p x^{(p)} \tag{4.45}$$

implies that $\rho_p = 0$; hence

$$-\rho_p = (p+1)\mu(h_\alpha) + \tfrac{1}{2}p(p+1)\alpha(h_\alpha) = 0. \tag{4.46}$$

Therefore

$$-\frac{2\mu(h_\alpha)}{\alpha(h_\alpha)} = p, \tag{4.47}$$

and p is a positive integer that is equal to the length (number of interspaces) of the ladder $x^{(0)}, x^{(1)}, \ldots, x^{(p)}$. Thus we find anew that $\mu(h_\alpha)$ is a rational multiple of $\alpha(h_\alpha)$. Eliminating $\mu(h_\alpha)$ from our expression for ρ_l, we obtain

$$\begin{aligned}\rho_l &= \tfrac{1}{2}p(l+1)\alpha(h_\alpha) - \tfrac{1}{2}l\,(l+1)\alpha(h_\alpha)\\ &= \tfrac{1}{2}(p-l)(l+1)\alpha(h_\alpha).\end{aligned} \tag{4.48}$$

We note: Beginning with any $x^{(j)}$, which corresponds to a root form $\lambda = \mu + j\alpha$, we can complete the ladder by applying the raising operators e_α and the lowering operators $e_{-\alpha}$. We find then

$$-\frac{2(\lambda(h_\alpha) - j\alpha(h_\alpha))}{\alpha(h_\alpha)} = p;$$

hence

$$-\frac{2\lambda(h_\alpha)}{\alpha(h_\alpha)} = p - 2j, \tag{4.49}$$

and this integer, $p - 2j$, is equal to the total number of steps needed to reach the upper limit of the ladder minus the number of steps necessary to reach its lower limit. But regardless of our starting point, we find the same sequence $x^{(0)}, x^{(1)}, \ldots, x^{(p)}$ (except for nonzero numerical coefficients). In particular the upward α-ladder is identical with the downward $(-\alpha)$-ladder.

Note also that the center of the sequence of root forms, where this center is defined as half the sum of the upper and lower limits of the sequence, that is,

$$\tfrac{1}{2}(\mu(h) + \mu(h) + p\alpha(h))$$

(which of course is not necessarily itself a root form), can be written as

$$\mu(h) - \frac{\mu(h_\alpha)}{\alpha(h_\alpha)}\alpha(h) \equiv c. \tag{4.50}$$

This expression is translation invariant; it does not change when $\mu(h)$ and $\mu(h_\alpha)$ are replaced by $\mu(h) + \sigma\alpha(h)$ and $\mu(h_\alpha) + \sigma\alpha(h_\alpha)$, for any σ, since

$$\mu(h) + \sigma\alpha(h) - \frac{\mu(h_\alpha) + \sigma\alpha(h_\alpha)}{\alpha(h_\alpha)}\alpha(h) = \mu(h) - \frac{\mu(h_\alpha)}{\alpha(h_\alpha)}\alpha(h). \tag{4.51}$$

Therefore all α-ladders [or $(-\alpha)$-ladders] of which the root forms are

$$\mu(h) + \sigma\alpha(h), \quad \mu(h) + (\sigma + 1)\alpha(h), \quad \mu(h) + (\sigma + 2)\alpha(h), \ldots \tag{4.52}$$

have the same center.

We prove now that L_α is one-dimensional for $\alpha \neq 0$. We choose e_α, $e_{-\alpha}$ and $h_\alpha = [e_\alpha, e_{-\alpha}]$ as before and suppose that L_α has dimension > 1. Then ad h_α possesses an eigenvector in the factor space $L_\alpha/\{e_\alpha\}$, that is, there is an element $f_\alpha \in L_\alpha$ such that

$$(\operatorname{ad} h_\alpha) f_\alpha \equiv \alpha(h_\alpha) f_\alpha \qquad (\operatorname{mod} e_\alpha). \tag{4.53}$$

Since the nodes are one-dimensional, we must have

$$[f_\alpha, e_{-\alpha}] = \zeta h_\alpha. \tag{4.54}$$

We can therefore find a linear combination of f_α and e_α that commutes with $e_{-\alpha}$, namely,

$$x = e_\alpha - \frac{1}{\zeta} f_\alpha \quad \text{or} \quad x = f_\alpha \quad \text{if} \quad \zeta = 0. \tag{4.55}$$

Then

$$(\operatorname{ad} e_{-\alpha})x = [e_{-\alpha}, x] = 0, \tag{4.56}$$

and we construct a ladder as before:

$$x = x^{(0)}, \qquad (\operatorname{ad} e_\alpha)x = x^{(1)}, \qquad (\operatorname{ad} e_\alpha)^2 x = x^{(2)}, \ldots, \tag{4.57}$$

which now has root forms α, 2α, ... instead of μ, $\mu + \alpha$, ...

Now $x = x^{(0)}$ is not an eigenvector of ad h_α but instead satisfies

$$(\operatorname{ad} h_\alpha)x^{(0)} = \alpha(h_\alpha)x^{(0)} + \eta e_\alpha. \tag{4.58}$$

Since, however, $(\operatorname{ad} e_\alpha)e_\alpha = [e_\alpha, e_\alpha] = 0$, we still have

$$(\operatorname{ad} h_\alpha)x^{(j)} = (\operatorname{ad} h_\alpha)(\operatorname{ad} e_\alpha)^j x^{(0)} = (j+1)\alpha(h_\alpha)x^{(j)}, \qquad \text{for all} \quad j \geqq 1. \tag{4.59}$$

Again, the sequence must end, the last member being $x^{(p)}$, and $(\operatorname{ad} e_\alpha)x^{(p)} = x^{(p+1)} = 0$.

We can try, as before, to recover $x^{(j)}$ from $x^{(j+1)}$ by application of $e_{-\alpha}$. We find, for the step from $x^{(1)}$ to $x^{(0)}$,

$$\begin{aligned}(\operatorname{ad} e_{-\alpha})x^{(1)} &= (\operatorname{ad} e_{-\alpha})(\operatorname{ad} e_\alpha)x^{(0)} \\ &= [\operatorname{ad} e_{-\alpha}, \operatorname{ad} e_\alpha]x^{(0)} + (\operatorname{ad} e_\alpha)(\operatorname{ad} e_{-\alpha})x^{(0)} \\ &= -(\operatorname{ad} h_\alpha)x^{(0)} + (\operatorname{ad} e_\alpha)(\operatorname{ad} e_{-\alpha})x^{(0)}.\end{aligned} \tag{4.60}$$

Since $x^{(0)}$ is an eigenvector modulo e_α by Eq. (4.58), and since $(\operatorname{ad} e_{-\alpha})x^{(0)} = 0$, we find

$$(\operatorname{ad} e_{-\alpha})x^{(1)} = -\alpha(h_\alpha)x^{(0)} - \eta e_\alpha.$$

The next step, however, is

$$(\operatorname{ad} e_{-\alpha})x^{(2)} = -(\operatorname{ad} h_\alpha)x^{(1)} + (\operatorname{ad} e_\alpha)(\operatorname{ad} e_{-\alpha})x^{(1)}, \tag{4.61}$$

and by the previous formula and (4.59) we have

$$(\mathrm{ad}\, e_{-\alpha})x^{(2)} = -2\alpha(h_\alpha)x^{(1)} + (\mathrm{ad}\, e_\alpha)(-\alpha(h_\alpha)x^{(0)} - \eta e_\alpha). \tag{4.62}$$

Since $(\mathrm{ad}\, e_\alpha)e_\alpha = [e_\alpha, e_\alpha] = 0$, we find

$$(\mathrm{ad}\, e_{-\alpha})x^{(2)} = -3\alpha(h_\alpha)x^{(1)}. \tag{4.63}$$

We can then prove by induction that

$$(\mathrm{ad}\, e_{-\alpha})x^{(j+1)} = \eta_j x^{(j)}, \qquad j \geqq 1,$$

where the coefficients η_i follow from

$$\begin{aligned}(\mathrm{ad}\, e)_{-\alpha} x^{(j+1)} &= -(\mathrm{ad}\, h_\alpha)x^{(j)} + (\mathrm{ad}\, e_\alpha)(\mathrm{ad}\, e_{-\alpha})x^{(j)} \\ &= -(j+1)\alpha(h_\alpha)x^{(j)} + (\mathrm{ad}\, e_\alpha)\eta_{j-1}x^{(j-1)} \\ &= \{-(j+1)\alpha(h_\alpha) + \eta_{j-1}\}x^{(j)} = \eta_j x^{(j)}.\end{aligned} \tag{4.64}$$

Since $\eta_1 = -3\alpha(h_\alpha)$, we find

$$\begin{aligned}\eta_l &= \eta_1 - \sum_{j=2}^{l} (j+1)\alpha(h_\alpha), \\ &= -\sum_{j=0}^{l} (j+1)\alpha(h_\alpha), \\ &= -\tfrac{1}{2}(l+2)(l+1)\alpha(h_\alpha).\end{aligned} \tag{4.65}$$

And because $x^{(p+1)} = 0$, we must have

$$\eta_p = -\tfrac{1}{2}(p+2)(p+1)\alpha(h_\alpha) = 0;$$

hence $\alpha(h_\alpha) = 0$, which is impossible. Therefore f_α does not exist, and L_α is one-dimensional.

We have seen that all ladders of root forms

$$\mu + \sigma\alpha, \quad \mu + (\sigma+1)\alpha, \ldots, \quad \mu + (\sigma + p)\alpha \tag{4.66}$$

have the same center. A ladder with an odd number of elements contains its center as a member of the ladder, while a ladder with an even number of elements has its center between two consecutive root forms; therefore there exist at most two α-ladders of root forms $\lambda \equiv \mu \bmod \alpha$, one that contains an odd number of elements and one with an even number.

It is clear also that the *reflection* with respect to the center that is defined as

$$\lambda \to \lambda' = 2c - \lambda \tag{4.67}$$

for any λ in a $\{\mu + (\sigma + j)\alpha\}$-ladder, maps root forms into root forms [c here is defined as in (4.50)]. Using the translational invariance of the expression (4.50) for the center, we find

$$\lambda(h) \to \lambda'(h) = 2\left\{\lambda(h) - \frac{\lambda(h_\alpha)}{\alpha(h_\alpha)}\alpha(h)\right\} - \lambda(h), \tag{4.68}$$

or, calling these reflections S_α,

$$S_\alpha\colon \quad \lambda(h) \to \lambda'(h) = \lambda(h) - \frac{2\lambda(h_\alpha)}{\alpha(h_\alpha)}\alpha(h). \tag{4.69}$$

The operations S_α (all roots α), together with their products, constitute a group that is called the *kaleidoscope* or *Weyl group*. This group plays a fundamental role in the theory of Lie groups.

Now let $\alpha(h)$ and $\beta(h)$ be two root forms and let $\beta(h)$ be a multiple of $\alpha(h)$

$$\beta(h) = t\alpha(h).$$

By a previous theorem, Eq. (4.49), both

$$\frac{2\alpha(h_\beta)}{\beta(h_\beta)} = 2t \qquad \text{and} \qquad \frac{2\beta(h_\alpha)}{\alpha(h_\alpha)} = \frac{2}{t}$$

are integers; hence the only allowed values of t are $\pm\frac{1}{2}$, ± 1, and ± 2. If $\beta = 2\alpha$, there is an α-ladder of root forms

$$-2\alpha, \quad -\alpha, \quad 0, \quad \alpha, \quad +2\alpha. \tag{4.70}$$

But the element $x^{(4)} \in L_{2\alpha}$ could arise only as

$$x^{(4)} = (\operatorname{ad} e_\alpha)x^{(3)}, \qquad x^{(3)} \in L_\alpha. \tag{4.71}$$

Hence $x^{(4)} = (\operatorname{ad} e_\alpha)x^{(3)} = (\operatorname{ad} e_\alpha)e_\alpha = 0$; but a ladder that contains 0 is necessarily of the form

$$\alpha(h), \quad 0, \quad -\alpha(h), \tag{4.72}$$

and no such ladder as (4.70) exists. Hence the only allowed values of t are ± 1. Hence, if $\alpha(h)$ is a root form, then so is $-\alpha(h)$, but no other nonvanishing multiple of $\alpha(h)$ is a root form.

We can now compute the components of the metric tensor $g(x, y) = \mathrm{tr}(\mathrm{ad}\, x\ \mathrm{ad}\, y)$. We have seen already that the only nonzero components of this tensor are

$$g(e_\alpha, e_{-\alpha}) \qquad \text{(any root } \alpha\text{)},$$

and

$$g(h_\alpha, h_\beta) \qquad \text{(any two } h_\alpha, h_\beta \in L_0\text{)}.$$

Since, for $x^{(l+1)} \in L_{\mu+(l+1)\alpha}$,

$$(\mathrm{ad}\, e_\alpha)(\mathrm{ad}\, e_{-\alpha})x^{(l+1)} = (\mathrm{ad}\, e_\alpha)\rho_l x^{(l)} = \rho_l x^{(l+1)}, \tag{4.73}$$

we find for the restriction to a $(\mu + l\alpha)$-ladder [i.e., the α-ladder that contains the root forms $(\mu + l\alpha)$]

$$g_{\mu+l\alpha}(e_\alpha, e_{-\alpha}) = \mathrm{tr}((\mathrm{ad}\, e_\alpha)(\mathrm{ad}\, e_{-\alpha}))_{\text{ladder}} = \sum_l \rho_l,$$

which becomes, by Eq. (4.48),

$$\begin{aligned}\mathrm{tr}((\mathrm{ad}\, e_\alpha)(\mathrm{ad}\, e_{-\alpha}))_{\text{ladder}} &= \sum_{l=0}^{p-1} \tfrac{1}{2}(p-l)(l+1)\alpha(h_\alpha) \\ &= \tfrac{1}{12}p(p+1)(p+2)\alpha(h_\alpha).\end{aligned} \tag{4.74}$$

Hence

$$\begin{aligned} g(\alpha, -\alpha) \equiv g(e_\alpha, e_{-\alpha}) &= \mathrm{tr}((\mathrm{ad}\, e_\alpha)(\mathrm{ad}\, e_{-\alpha})) \\ &= \sum_{\alpha\text{-ladders}} \mathrm{tr}((\mathrm{ad}\, e_\alpha)(\mathrm{ad}\, e_{-\alpha}))_{\text{ladder}} \\ &= \tfrac{1}{12}\alpha(h_\alpha) \sum_p p(p+1)(p+2), \end{aligned} \tag{4.75}$$

where the sum runs over all α-ladders, and p is the corresponding length, equal to the number of *spaces* between members of an α-ladder. Of course, p—as is expressed by (4.49)—depends on λ.

Finally, as we have noticed before, since L_0 is solvable (and even Abelian) we have

$$g(h, h') = \mathrm{tr}((\mathrm{ad}\, h)(\mathrm{ad}\, h')) = \sum \mu(h)\mu(h') \tag{4.76}$$

where the sum is taken over all root forms μ.

Summary

We shall now summarize what we have found up to this point:

(a) For a semisimple Lie algebra L there exists a Cartan subalgebra or trunk $H = L_0$ that is Abelian. Its elements are called h; it is l-dimensional, where l is equal to the rank of the algebra.

(b) The roots w of

$$\det(\mathrm{ad}\, h - w\mathbf{1}) = 0$$

depend linearly on $h \in H$. The nonzero roots are simple and are called root forms. They are written $\alpha(h)$, $\beta(h)$, ...

(c) There are l root forms that are *linearly independent.*

(d) When $\alpha(h)$ is a root form, then so is $-\alpha(h)$, but no other nonvanishing multiple of $\alpha(h)$ is a root form.

(e) The root 0 occurs with multiplicity l.

(f) To every root form $\alpha(h)$ corresponds a unique branch e_α, and to $-\alpha$ a branch $e_{-\alpha}$, such that (1) $[h, e_\alpha] = (\mathrm{ad}\, h)e_\alpha = \alpha(h)e_\alpha$, for any $h \in H$, and (2) $[e_\alpha, e_{-\alpha}]$ is an element of H, called h_α.

(g) The elements h_α (α-*nodes*) span H, but need not all be independent.

(h) The elements $e_\alpha, e_{-\alpha}, e_\beta, e_{-\beta}, \ldots, h_\alpha, h_\beta, \ldots$ together span L.

(i) $[e_\alpha, e_\beta] = N_{\alpha\beta}e_{\alpha+\beta}$ if $\alpha + \beta$ is nonzero, where $N_{\alpha\beta}$ is nonzero, and $[e_\alpha, e_\beta] = 0$ if $\alpha + \beta$ is not a root form.

(j) When $\lambda(h)$ and $\alpha(h)$ are root forms, the α-ladder $\lambda(h) - j\alpha(h), \ldots, \lambda(h), \ldots, \lambda(h) + k\alpha(h)$ consists of root forms also, and the nonnegative integers j and k satisfy

$$\frac{-2\lambda(h_\alpha)}{\alpha(h_\alpha)} = k - j,$$

which is equal to the number of upward steps in the ladder from the element $\lambda(h)$ minus the number of downward steps, and this relation holds no matter what element of the ladder is chosen as a starting point.

(k) The quadratic form $g(x, y) = \mathrm{tr}(\mathrm{ad}\, x)(\mathrm{ad}\, y))$, $x, y \in L$, is nondegenerate on L (hence on H).

(ℓ) The nonzero elements of $g(x, y)$ are (1) $g(h, h') = \sum \mu(h)\mu(h')$ (where the sum is taken over all root forms) and (2) $g(e_\alpha, e_{-\alpha}) = (1/12)\alpha(h_\alpha) \sum p(p+1) \times (p+2) \equiv N_\alpha$, where the sum is taken over all α-ladders, and $p = k + j$ is the number of elements of a ladder minus one. Also, p is a function of λ [Eq. (4.49)].

We now look for connections between the root forms, which are linear functions on H, and the $g(h, h')$, which are bilinear functions on H. Since we have, as a formal identity that expresses the invariance of $g(h_\lambda, e_{-\mu})$ under ad e_μ,

$$\mathrm{tr}([\mathrm{ad}\, e_\mu, \mathrm{ad}\, h_\lambda]\, \mathrm{ad}\, e_{-\mu}) + \mathrm{tr}(\mathrm{ad}\, h_\lambda[\mathrm{ad}\, e_\mu, \mathrm{ad}\, e_{-\mu}] \equiv 0, \tag{4.77}$$

it follows from our result (f) given earlier

$$\operatorname{tr}(-\mu(h_\lambda)\operatorname{ad} e_\mu \operatorname{ad} e_{-\mu}) + \operatorname{tr}(\operatorname{ad} h_\lambda \operatorname{ad} h_\mu) = 0. \tag{4.78}$$

Using (ℓ,2) from the foregoing summary, we have

$$g(h_\lambda, h_\mu) = \mu(h_\lambda)N_\mu. \tag{4.79}$$

Because the branches e_μ are linearly independent, we can renormalize them (i.e., provide them with a suitable numerical coefficient) such that all N_μ equal one; then

$$g(e_\alpha, e_{-\alpha}) = 1, \qquad \text{for all root forms.} \tag{4.80}$$

The elements h_λ (which have in consequence also been renormalized since they are defined as $[e_\lambda, e_{-\lambda}]$) then satisfy

$$g(h_\lambda, h_\mu) = \mu(h_\lambda). \tag{4.81}$$

And this is the connection that we wished to find.

Since the h_λ span H, and both sides of (4.81) are (bi-) linear and non-degenerate, it follows that

$$g(h, h_\mu) = \mu(h). \tag{4.82}$$

Equation (4.82) can be used to provide the dual space $\bar{H}$ (defined as the space of linear functions on H) with a metric. We simply define, for any two root forms $\lambda(h)$ and $\mu(h)$ (which are contained in $\bar{H}$), a symmetric nonsingular scalar product, which we write as (λ, μ).

$$(\lambda, \mu) = g(h_\lambda, h_\mu) = \mu(h_\lambda) = \lambda(h_\mu). \tag{4.83}$$

The ladder-length formula (4.49) can now be written

$$\frac{-2(\lambda, \alpha)}{(\alpha, \alpha)} = k - j. \tag{4.84}$$

We note that (ℓ,1) can be written as

$$g(h_\lambda, h_\mu) = \sum_\alpha \alpha(h_\lambda)\alpha(h)_\mu, \tag{4.85}$$

where the sum is taken over all root forms. Hence

$$(\lambda, \mu) = \sum_\alpha (\alpha, \lambda)(\alpha, \mu). \tag{4.86}$$

We wish to emphasize that the set of all root forms is a set of vectors in $\bar{H}$ which as a rule has more members than the dimension l of $\bar{H}$.

Since we have made $N_\alpha = 1$, then (ℓ,2) implies that

$$(\alpha, \alpha) = \alpha(h_\alpha)$$

is rational and real. Since $-2(\alpha, \beta)/(\alpha, \alpha)$ is an integer, we see that (α, β) is also rational and real for any two root forms. Hence, using (4.86), we see that

$$(\lambda, \lambda) = \sum_\alpha (\alpha, \lambda)^2$$

is a sum of positive terms; therefore

$$(\lambda, \lambda) > 0 \tag{4.87}$$

for any root form h_λ. The metric space of the real linear combinations of the root forms, $\bar{H}$, is therefore a real Euclidean space.

Because both $2(\alpha, \beta)/(\alpha, \alpha)$ and $2(\alpha, \beta)/(\beta, \beta)$ are integers, it follows that

$$\frac{2(\alpha, \beta)}{(\alpha, \alpha)} \frac{2(\alpha, \beta)}{(\beta, \beta)} = 4\cos^2 \measuredangle (\alpha, \beta) < 4 \tag{4.88}$$

is the product of two integers. We have used the Euclidean property of the metric; $\cos \measuredangle (\alpha, \beta) = \pm 1$ would imply that α is a multiple of β, and this is impossible as we have seen. Let us suppose for a moment that $2(\alpha, \beta)/(\alpha, \alpha) \leqq 2(\alpha, \beta)/(\beta, \beta)$. Then the only possible solutions are specified by

$$\frac{2(\alpha, \beta)}{(\alpha, \alpha)} = \frac{2(\alpha, \beta)}{(\beta, \beta)} = 0, \qquad \measuredangle (\alpha, \beta) = 90^\circ \tag{4.89}$$

and

$$\frac{2(\alpha, \beta)}{(\alpha, \alpha)} = 1, \qquad \frac{2(\alpha, \beta)}{(\beta, \beta)} = 1, 2, 3. \tag{4.90}$$

We obtain, then, Table I. Hence if

$$\cos \measuredangle (\alpha, \beta) = \pm \frac{j^{1/2}}{2}, \qquad j = 0, 1, 2, 3, \tag{4.91}$$

then the ratio of the length of the vectors α and β is undetermined in the case $j = 0$, and

$$\left[\frac{(\alpha, \alpha)}{(\beta, \beta)}\right]^{\pm 1/2} = j^{1/2}, \qquad j = 1, 2, 3. \tag{4.92}$$

These two properties, then, determine all possible systems of root forms, and all roots are generated from ladders and Weyl reflections.

We shall now state without proof that isomorphic Lie algebras have the same system of root forms. Furthermore, the metric structure of a root system determines the Lie algebra uniquely, hence the classification of semisimple Lie algebras can be reduced to the classification of root systems. For proof of these propositions we refer the reader to Pontrjagin (*5*) or Freudenthal (*12*).

TABLE I

$\cos \measuredangle(\alpha, \beta)$	$\measuredangle(\alpha, \beta)$	$[(\alpha, \alpha)/(\beta, \beta)]^{1/2}$
$\frac{0}{2}$	90°	Undetermined
$\pm\frac{1}{2}$	60°, 120°	1
$\pm\frac{\sqrt{2}}{2}$	45°, 135°	$\sqrt{\frac{1}{2}}$ or $\sqrt{2}$
$\pm\frac{\sqrt{3}}{2}$	30°, 150°	$\sqrt{\frac{1}{3}}$ or $\sqrt{3}$

We have not exhausted all the freedom available to us in respect to normalization. As an example, let us consider the linear Lie algebra generated by the two-by-two matrices

$$\begin{pmatrix} 0 & p \\ 0 & 0 \end{pmatrix}, \quad \begin{pmatrix} 0 & 0 \\ 1/p & 0 \end{pmatrix}, \quad \begin{pmatrix} 1 & 0 \\ 0 & -1 \end{pmatrix}.$$

This algebra has structure constants that are independent of p, hence the algebra of generators contains an undetermined constant. The structure constants here are those of $SU(2)$. As a less trivial example, let us consider the algebra of the eight generators

$$\begin{pmatrix} 0 & p & 0 \\ 0 & 0 & 0 \\ 0 & 0 & 0 \end{pmatrix}, \quad \begin{pmatrix} 0 & 0 & 0 \\ 1/p & 0 & 0 \\ 0 & 0 & 0 \end{pmatrix}, \quad \begin{pmatrix} 0 & 0 & pq \\ 0 & 0 & 0 \\ 0 & 0 & 0 \end{pmatrix}, \quad \begin{pmatrix} 0 & 0 & 0 \\ 0 & 0 & 0 \\ 1/pq & 0 & 0 \end{pmatrix},$$

$$\begin{pmatrix} 0 & 0 & 0 \\ 0 & 0 & q \\ 0 & 0 & 0 \end{pmatrix}, \quad \begin{pmatrix} 0 & 0 & 0 \\ 0 & 0 & 0 \\ 0 & 1/q & 0 \end{pmatrix}, \quad \begin{pmatrix} 1 & 0 & 0 \\ 0 & -1 & 0 \\ 0 & 0 & 0 \end{pmatrix}, \quad \begin{pmatrix} 1 & 0 & 0 \\ 0 & 0 & 0 \\ 0 & 0 & -1 \end{pmatrix},$$

which has structure constants [essentially those of $SU(3)$] that are independent of p and q. We can resolve this indeterminacy, as is apparent from the examples, by imposing some relation between e_α and $e_{-\alpha}$, such as

$$\begin{pmatrix} 0 & p & 0 \\ 0 & 0 & 0 \\ 0 & 0 & 0 \end{pmatrix}^\dagger = \begin{pmatrix} 0 & 0 & 0 \\ 1/p & 0 & 0 \\ 0 & 0 & 0 \end{pmatrix}.$$

We state without proof (cf. Freudenthal): When L is a linear Lie algebra and L^* its complex extension, then there exists a group of unitary matrices G such that its *Hermitian linear Lie algebra* L_u has the same complex extension, $L_u^* = L^*$, that L has. The Hermitian linear Lie algebra of a group is simply a linear representation of the Lie algebra of the group in terms of Hermitian matrices. We can therefore always resolve the normalization difficulty. The only indeterminacies that remain are in the signs of the elements of the algebra. That is, the coefficients $N_{\alpha\beta}$ of (i) are determined up to a sign, so that the standard Lie algebra [Eq. (5.2) following] becomes determined by its system of root forms.

V. The Classification of Semisimple Lie Algebras in Terms of Their Root Systems

We now introduce a set of orthogonal operators as a basis for the Cartan subalgebra H, a basis that consists of operators h_i, $i = 1, 2, \ldots, l$, such that $\mathrm{tr}(\mathrm{ad}\, h_i\, \mathrm{ad}\, h_j) = \delta_{ij}$. This is obviously possible since g is positive definite on H. Thus, we can write for an element h_α,

$$h_\alpha = \sum_{i=1}^{l} C_{\alpha i} h_i, \tag{5.1}$$

where, by the definition of the h_i and Eq. (4.82), $C_{\alpha i} = \alpha(h_i)$. Hence the commutation relations for the Lie algebra can be written in the standard form

$$\begin{aligned} [e_\alpha, e_{-\alpha}] &= \sum_i \alpha(h_i) h_i, \\ [h_i, e_\alpha] &= \alpha(h_i)\, e_\alpha, \\ [e_\alpha, e_\beta] &= N_{\alpha\beta} e_{\alpha+\beta}. \end{aligned} \tag{5.2}$$

The scalar product in root space becomes

$$(\lambda, \mu) = \mathrm{tr}(\mathrm{ad}\, h_\lambda\, \mathrm{ad}\, h_\mu) = \sum_{ij} \lambda(h_i)\mu(h_j)\, \mathrm{tr}(\mathrm{ad}\, h_i\, \mathrm{ad}\, h_j) = \sum_i \lambda(h_i)\mu(h_i); \tag{5.3}$$

hence the *root vector* λ has components $\lambda(h_i)$.

We can choose the h_i such that the coordinate plane $\lambda(h_1) = 0$ contains no root vectors. We call now all root vectors λ that have $\lambda(h_1) > 0$ *positive root vectors*. We can also define an *ordering*: $\lambda > \mu$ when $\lambda - \mu$ is a positive vector. A positive vector is a vector on the same side of the hyperplane $\lambda(h_1) = 0$ as the positive root vectors. We call the set of all roots Γ and the set of all positive roots Γ^+. Since $-\alpha$ is a negative root when α is a positive root, the set Γ can be separated into the positive root set Γ^+ and the negative root set Γ^-, which are mirror images of each other under reflections at the origin. It is clear that the notion of positive root vectors can be defined without reference to a special coordinate system, since every hyperplane that contains none of the root vectors immediately separates Γ into two sets Γ^+ and Γ^- with the required properties.

Since there is a process for making new root vectors out of old ones (ladders and Weyl reflections), it is natural to try to generate Γ, or Γ^+, from a subset of Γ^+. It is natural also to include in this subset the starting points or end points of ladders. We therefore define: A *positive* root α is called a *simple* root if it cannot be written as a sum of two positive roots; $\alpha \neq \beta + \gamma$. The set of simple roots will be called Γ^{++}. It can also be defined in a coordinate-free manner.

The linear combinations of positive roots with nonnegative coefficients form a *convex cone*. We consider all *root vectors* that lie on its boundary. These boundary vectors still span the space of all vectors of the cone. We can discard all boundary vectors that can be written as linear combinations of boundary vectors with nonnegative coefficients, and then the set Λ that remains still subtends the convex cone, has exactly l members, and coincides with Γ^{++}. We must prove these statements, but first we need the following lemma.

Lemma. If a set of positive vectors $\lambda_1, \lambda_2, \ldots, \lambda_k$ satisfies $(\lambda_i, \lambda_j) \leqq 0$ for all $i, j = 1, 2, \ldots, k$, $i \neq j$, then the k vectors span a k-dimensional space, that is, they are linearly independent. The lemma is trivially true for $k = 2$ and for $k = 3$: If three vectors $\lambda_1, \lambda_2, \lambda_3$, all lie in a plane and satisfy the condition $(\lambda_i, \lambda_j) \leqq 0$ for all $i \neq j$, then $270^\circ \geqq \measuredangle(\lambda_i, \lambda_j) \geqq 90^\circ$, and the vectors cannot all three be positive; that is, they cannot all lie on the same side of some given line through the origin, because the sum of two angles larger than 90° is larger than 180°. We now reduce the general case to the case $k = 3$. Suppose λ_k depends on $\lambda_1, \ldots, \lambda_{k-1}$; hence

$$\lambda_k = \sum_{i=1}^{k-1} p_i \lambda_i \tag{5.4}$$

for some nontrivial set of coefficients p_i. We collect the positive terms $p_{i'}\lambda_{i'}$ and the negative terms $p_{i''}\lambda_{i''}$ and write

$$\lambda_k = \sum_{i'} p_{i'}\lambda_{i'} - \sum_{i''} (-p_{i''})\lambda_{i''} \equiv \xi - \eta \tag{5.5}$$

where $\xi \equiv \sum_{i'} p_{i'}\lambda_{i'}$ and $\eta \equiv \sum_{i''} (-p_{i''})\lambda_{i''}$. Now ξ and η are both positive vectors, and since they belong to convex cones of positive vectors constructed from the *disjoint* sets $\lambda_{i'}$ and $\lambda_{i''}$, they satisfy

$$(\xi, \eta) \leqq 0.$$

Since, moreover, $(\lambda_k, \xi) \leqq 0$ and $(\lambda_k, \eta) \leqq 0$, we have found three positive vectors λ_k, ξ, and η that satisfy the condition of the lemma but are linearly dependent, and this is impossible.

We prove now that any two different root vectors $\alpha, \beta \in \Lambda$ or $\in \Gamma^{++}$ have the following three fundamental properties.

(1) $\alpha - \beta$ is not a root. If it were, then either it or $\beta - \alpha$ would be a positive root and either $\alpha = (\alpha - \beta) + \beta$ or $\beta = (\beta - \alpha) + \alpha$ would be a sum of two positive roots, and this is contrary to the definition of both Λ and Γ^{++}.

(2) $(\alpha, \beta) \leqq 0$. The α-ladder that passes through β has the form $\beta, \beta + \alpha, \ldots, \beta + k\alpha$, since $\beta - \alpha$ is not a root. Then, Eq. (4.84) gives us the result (since $j = 0$ for this case):

$$\frac{2(\beta, \alpha)}{(\alpha, \alpha)} = -k \leqq 0; \tag{5.6}$$

and our proposition is demonstrated.

Since the root vectors of Λ subtend the convex cone of all positive vectors, they span the l-dimensional root space. The foregoing lemma therefore implies that there are exactly l root vectors in Λ, and that these root vectors are linearly independent. Since any vector of Λ is by definition simple, then $\Lambda \subset \Gamma^{++}$. Since, by the lemma, Γ^{++} also has at most l elements, it follows that $\Lambda = \Gamma^{++}$, and we drop the name Λ; Γ^{++} is unique once we have defined positive root vectors. It follows from the original construction of Λ that any positive root can be written uniquely as a linear combination, with non-negative coefficients, of the l root vectors in Γ^{++}. We show that the coefficients are integers:

(3) If $\lambda \in \Gamma^+$, then $\lambda = \sum_{\alpha \in \Gamma^{++}} n_\alpha \alpha$, where n_α is a nonnegative integer. Let the elements of Γ^{++} be called $\alpha_1, \alpha_2, \ldots, \alpha_i, \ldots \alpha_l$, and let $\lambda = \sum p_i \alpha_i$, $p_i \geqq 0$, be an element of Γ^+. We show that we can always find an $\alpha \in \Gamma^{++}$, say α_j, such that $\lambda - \alpha_j = \sum_i (p_1 - \delta_{ij})\alpha_i$ is also in Γ^+. The sequence λ, $\lambda - \alpha_j$, $\lambda - \alpha_j - \alpha_{j'}$, ..., which is not necessarily a ladder, must terminate at the boundary, and this is possible only if all p_i are positive integers. (The elements on the boundary are of the required form by the same argument.) If none of the vectors $\lambda - \alpha_j$ were roots, it would follow, as in (2), that $(\lambda, \alpha_j) \leqq 0$, $j = 1, \ldots, l$, and by the lemma λ would be independent of the α_j.

We have now shown that any root vector $\lambda \in \Gamma$ is a sum of α'_is with positive or negative integer coefficients:

$$\lambda = \sum_{i=1}^{l} n_i \alpha_i, \qquad n_i \text{ integer}, \quad \text{all } n_i \geqq 0 \text{ or all } n_i \leqq 0. \tag{5.7}$$

Of course the α_i are also a basis for the linear space $\bar{H}$. In $\bar{H}$ we use the α_i to define an ordering; a vector

$$\xi = w_1\alpha_1 + w_2\alpha_2 + \cdots, \qquad w_l\alpha_l \in \bar{H},$$

is called positive ($\xi > 0$) if the first nonvanishing coefficient, w_h, say, is positive. No α_i is a sum of positive roots, hence the α_i are simple and form the systems of simple root vectors (root forms) that are defined by the ordering. The new ordering need not be the same as the old one in $\bar{H}$, but it is equivalent for the root vectors.

The matrix

$$A_{ij} = \frac{2(\alpha_i, \alpha_j)}{(\alpha_i, \alpha_i)} \tag{5.8}$$

is called a *Cartan matrix* for L (relative to the simple root system $\Gamma^{++} \equiv \{\alpha_i\}$). Since the off-diagonal elements are nonpositive, we have as possible values

$$A_{ij} = 0, -1, -2, \text{or} -3 \qquad \text{if} \quad i \neq j, \tag{5.9}$$
$$A_{ii} = 2.$$

According to previous considerations [Eq. (4.88)], we have for $i \neq j$

$$0 \leqq A_{ij}A_{ji} < 4; \tag{5.10}$$

hence either

$$A_{ij} = A_{ji} = 0,$$

or

$$A_{ij}A_{ji} = 1, 2, \text{ or } 3;$$

hence

$$A_{ij} = -1, \qquad A_{ji} = -1, -2, -3, \tag{5.11}$$

or conversely. The determinant of A_{ij} is a nonzero multiple of the determinant of the (α_i, α_j), which is the Gram determinant of the independent vectors α and hence is nonzero.

The significance of the Cartan matrix is that we can now determine which of the linear combinations $\lambda = \sum_{i=1}^{l} n_i \alpha_i$, where the n_i are all integers that have the same sign, are root vectors solely from the Cartan matrix and the length of the simple root vectors α_i. We shall show this by induction on the *level*

$$N(\lambda) = \sum_{i=1}^{l} |n_i| \tag{5.12}$$

of the vector λ. We need consider only positive roots. The root vectors of level $N(\lambda) = 1$ are obviously known. Let us suppose that we know which of the vectors of level $N(\lambda) \leqq M$ are root vectors. Let λ be a positive root vector of level M. We must find out which of the vectors $\lambda + \alpha_r$ are root vectors. Since 2α is never a root vector when α is one, the case of $\lambda = \alpha_r$ is trivial. Excluding this trivial case, we may assume that there is at least one positive coefficient n_i, $i \neq r$, in the sum for λ.

Hence all vectors

$$\lambda - \alpha_r, \quad \lambda - 2\alpha_r, \quad \lambda - 3\alpha_r, \ldots$$

have at least one positive coefficient; therefore those among them that are root vectors have coefficients only of positive sign, and are consequently positive root vectors of level less than M. We therefore know the number of steps downward in the α_r-ladder. Now

$$j - k = \frac{2(\lambda, \alpha_r)}{(\alpha_r, \alpha_r)} = \frac{2 \sum_i n_i(\alpha_i, \alpha_r)}{(\alpha_r, \alpha_r)} = \sum_i n_i A_{ri} \tag{5.13}$$

is known; hence we can find the total number of steps upward in the ladder, and we know whether

$$\lambda + \alpha_r, \quad \lambda + 2\alpha_r, \ldots$$

are root vectors. This completes the induction step.

Since it has appeared that all the root vectors, and hence the complete Lie algebra, are determined by the (α_i, α_i) and the A_{ij}, then we may attempt to make a picture of the polygon of which the simple root vectors are end points by means of the known length of the α_i and the angles between them. First, we must devise a simple way to indicate both the angles and the lengths. The discussion following Eq. (5.8) shows that it is enough for us to give the (α_i, α_i) and (for symmetry!) the value (either 1, 2, or 3) of

$$A_{ij} A_{ji} = \frac{4 \cos^2 \sphericalangle (\alpha_i, \alpha_j)}{(\alpha_i, \alpha_i)(\alpha_j, \alpha_j)}. \tag{5.14}$$

We define the *Dynkin diagram* as a set of l dots that we label $\alpha_1, \alpha_2, \ldots, \alpha_l$. To each dot α_i is attached a "weight" (α_i, α_i) and each two dots α_i and α_j are connected by $A_{ij}A_{ji}$ (i.e., 1, 2, or 3) lines. For example,

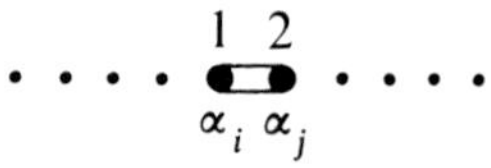

We shall now prove a number of lemmas that show that the number of possible diagrams is quite small. For convenience the possible values A_{ij}, A_{ji}, the angle between α_i and α_j, its cosine, the number of lines $A_{ij}A_{ji}$, and the ratio of the squares of the length of α_i and α_j are given in Table II. It is clear

TABLE II

A_{ij}	A_{ji}	Angle	Cosine	$A_{ij}\,A_{ji}$	$(\alpha_i, \alpha_i)/(\alpha_j, \alpha_j)$
0	0	90°	0	0	Undetermined
−1	−1	120°	$-\frac{1}{2}$	1	1
−1	−2	135°	$-\frac{\sqrt{2}}{2}$	2	2
−1	−3	150°	$-\frac{\sqrt{3}}{2}$	3	3

that in a *connected diagram* the "weights" (α_i, α_i) are determined to a very large extent by the angles $\sphericalangle(\alpha_i, \alpha_j)$, and the lemmas that we shall prove really depend on the values of the possible angles. The algebraic proofs that we shall give could be replaced by more transparent, but also more cumbersome, geometric proofs. For example, the diagrams

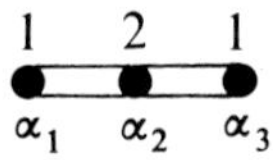

and

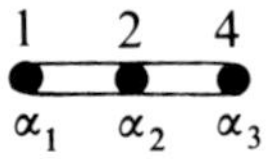

are impossible because the angle between α_1 and α_3 would be less than $360° - 270° = 90°$, and this is not allowed.

We will use, instead of the vectors α_i, a set of *unit vectors* u_i proportional to the α_i. Since the angle between any two of these unit vectors is restricted to the values 90° (for a disconnected dot), 120° (one line), 135° (two lines), and 150° (three lines), we have it that (u_i, u_j) is either equal to zero or less than or equal to $-\frac{1}{2}$. Also,

$$(u_i, u_j)^2 = 1/4, \qquad \text{for one connecting line,}$$
$$(u_i, u_j)^2 = 2/4, \qquad \text{for two connecting lines,}$$
$$(u_i, u_j)^2 = 3/4, \qquad \text{for three connecting lines.}$$

Note that $4(u_i, u_j)^2$ is equal to the number of connecting lines between u_i and u_j.

Lemma 1. For l vectors u_i (or α_i) there are less than l connected pairs, hence a connected diagram has exactly $l-1$ connected pairs.

Proof. For $u \equiv \sum_{i=1}^{l} u_i$ we have

$$0 < (u, u) = \sum_i (u_i, u_i) + 2 \sum_{i>j} (u_i, u_j) = l + 2 \sum_{i>j} (u_i, u_j).$$

We recall that $u \neq 0$ by the linear independence of the vectors u_i. Since $2(u_i, u_j) \leqq -1$ for each connected pair, the number of connected pairs is less than l. Because the same reasoning holds for any subset of a diagram, and because a closed cycle must have at least as many connecting lines as there are elements in the cycle, we have:

Lemma 2. There are no cycles. Therefore we need not concern ourselves with the length of the root vectors; the lengths do not give rise to any additional restrictions.

We shall appeal to the reader's intuition for acceptance of

Lemma 3. We may remove any number of dots, together with the lines attached to them, and we are left with a diagram for a set of vectors from which the vectors that correspond to the removed dots have been deleted.

Alternatively, the diagrams can be constructed recursively; for example, we may construct an $(l+1)$-dot diagram by adding a dot to a diagram that has l dots.

Lemma 4. The total number of lines that are attached to any dot is at most 3.

Proof. Let the unit vector (dot) u be connected to $v_1, v_2, \ldots, v_k$. Since $4(u, v_i)^2$ is the number of connecting lines between u and v_i, the number of lines attached to u is

$$4 \sum_{i=1}^{k} (u, v_i)^2.$$

Since there are no closed cycles, and since by hypothesis u is connected to all the v_i, then no v_i is connected to any other, and the v_i are therefore mutually orthogonal. The (u, v_i) therefore are the components of u with respect to the axes v_i. Since u is a unit vector that has a component outside of the space spanned by the v_i (by virtue of the linear independence of the u_i), we find that

$$\sum_i (u, v_i)^2 < 1;$$

hence the total number of lines in our diagram becomes

$$4 \sum_i (u, v_i)^2 \leqq 3. \tag{5.15}$$

Trivially, Lemma 4 implies

Lemma 5. The only connected diagram with a triple line is

which is called $\mathscr{G}_2$.

Let us now suppose that a diagram contains a simple chain, a set of dots each of which is connected to the next by a simple line:

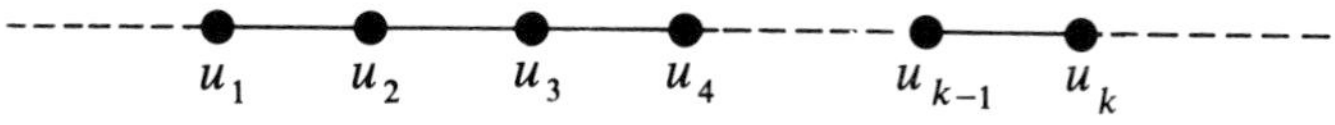

The parts of the diagram that are connected by the simple chain are not connected in any other way since there can be no cycles. Therefore the vectors in the part connected to u_1 are orthogonal to the vectors in the part connected to u_k. A Euclidean motion that carries u_1 into u_k is therefore possible which leaves the two parts orthogonal. Since dots from which two lines emerge can be connected only by a simple chain we would have simple chains in the following cases:

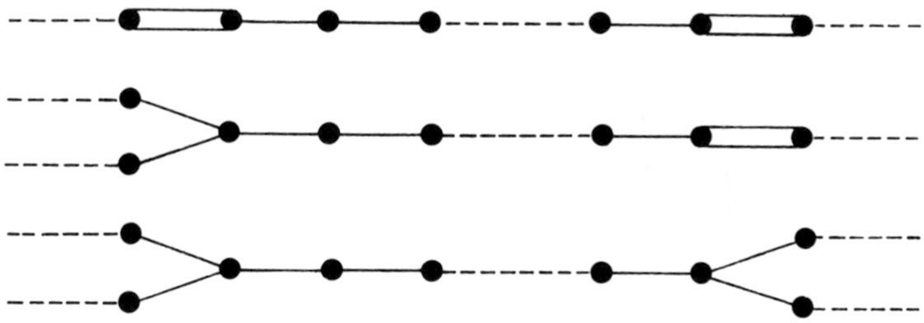

We have just shown that we can "shrink" the simple chain, that is, carry u_1 into u_k by a Euclidean motion. Hence the following diagrams

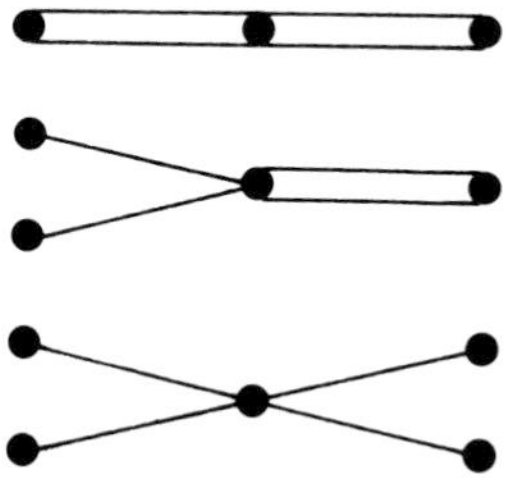

would also be admissible, but they are ruled out by Lemma 4. Hence a connected diagram has at most either one fork

or at most one double line

Except for the diagram $\mathscr{G}_2$ that we have already mentioned, the only possible diagrams that remain are the following three general types.

$\mathscr{A}_\ell$:

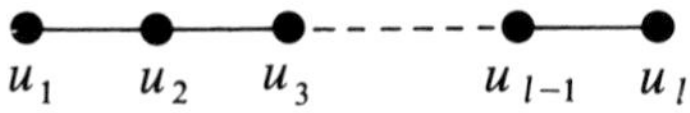

Second type:

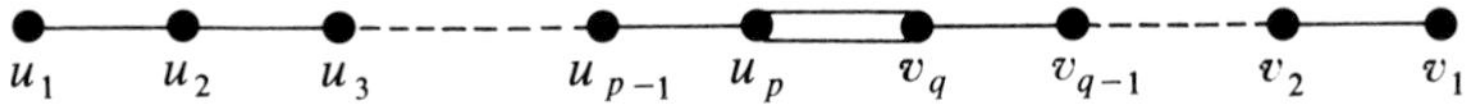

Third type:

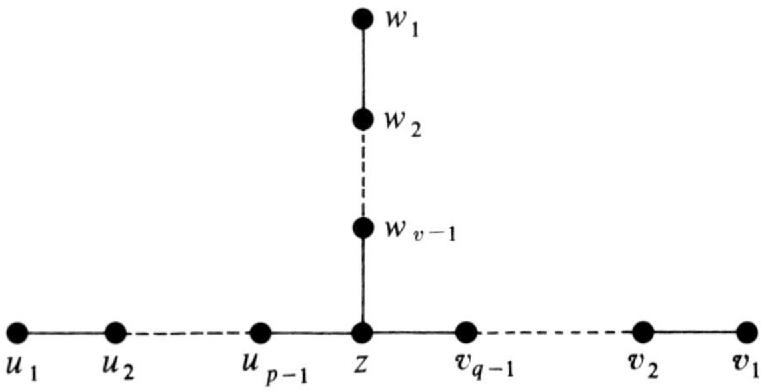

It is evident that the type $\mathscr{A}_l$ is general in that it can be realized for any $l = 1, 2, 3, \ldots$. We shall now investigate whether there are any limitations on the p and q for the second type and on the p, q, r for the third type.

For the second type we define:

$$u \equiv \sum_{i=1}^{p} iu_i \qquad \text{and} \qquad v \equiv \sum_{j=1}^{q} jv_j.$$

When we construct explicitly a set of unit vectors $u_1, \ldots, u_p$ under the requirement that $(u_i, u_{i+1}) = -\frac{1}{2}$ for $i = 1, \ldots, p-1$, with all other (u_i, u_k) equal to zero, we find the following realization for them:

$$u_1 = (1, 0, 0, \ldots, \ldots),$$
$$u_2 = (-\tfrac{1}{2}\sqrt{1}, \tfrac{1}{2}(\tfrac{1}{2}\cdot 2\cdot 3)^{1/2}, 0, \ldots),$$
$$u_3 = (0, -\tfrac{1}{3}(\tfrac{1}{2}\cdot 2\cdot 3)^{1/2}, \tfrac{1}{3}(\tfrac{1}{2}\cdot 3\cdot 4)^{1/2}, 0, \ldots),$$
$$\ldots,$$
$$u_n = \left(0, \ldots, 0, -\frac{1}{n}[\tfrac{1}{2}(n-1)n]^{1/2}, \frac{1}{n}[\tfrac{1}{2}n(n+1)]^{1/2}, 0, \ldots\right),$$
$$\ldots,$$

where the first $(n-2)$ components of u_n are equal to zero. Then the first $p-1$ components of $u = \sum iu_i$ are zero. Thus the introduction of u and v effectively eliminates these components of u_i and v_i, which are consequently irrelevant to the question whether the simple chains $u_1, \ldots, u_p$ and $v_q, \ldots, v_1$ can be joined with a "double bond." The necessary condition that we shall find will also be sufficient. We find now

$$(u, u) = \sum_{ij} ij(u_i, u_j) = \sum i^2 - \sum i(i+1) = p^2 - \tfrac{1}{2}p(p-1) = \tfrac{1}{2}p(p+1) \tag{5.16}$$

and

$$(v, v) = \tfrac{1}{2}q(q+1). \tag{5.17}$$

And since, except for the component at their common joint, the u-chain and the v-chain are orthogonal, we have it that

$$(u, v) = pq(u_p, u_q) = pq[-(2)^{-1/2}]. \tag{5.18}$$

Hence by Schwarz's inequality, $(u, v)^2 < (u, u)(v, v)$, we have

$$\frac{p^2q^2}{2} < \frac{p(p+1)}{2}\frac{q(q+1)}{2}, \tag{5.19}$$

or, since p and q are positive,

$$2pq < (p+1)(q+1) = pq + p + q + 1, \qquad (p-1)(q-1) < 2. \tag{5.20}$$

The only integral solutions are (i) $p = 1$, q arbitrary (the case $q = 1$ with p arbitrary, of course, merely gives us another chain of the same type), and (ii) $p = 2, q = 2$.

The possible diagrams of the second type are therefore

(i) 

The possible "weights" are evidently as in:

$\mathscr{B}_\ell$: 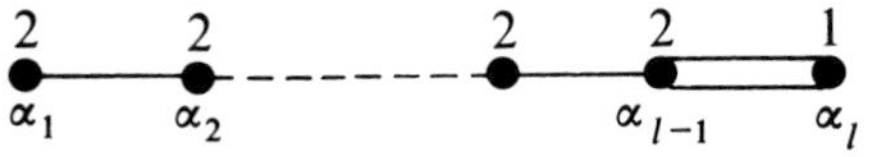

and

$\mathscr{C}_\ell$: 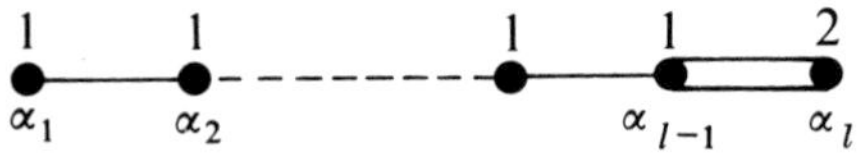

And, for the solution (ii),

$\mathscr{F}_4$: 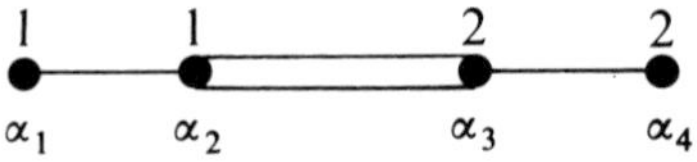

It remains now only to investigate the third type. We define again

$$u = \sum_{i=1}^{p-1} i u_i, \qquad v = \sum_{j=1}^{q-1} j v_j, \qquad w = \sum_{k=1}^{r-1} k w_k. \tag{5.21}$$

The vectors u, v, w are mutually orthogonal and z is independent of them. Therefore, defining $\theta_u = \measuredangle(z, u), \ldots$, we have

$$\cos^2\theta_u + \cos^2\theta_v + \cos^2\theta_w < 1. \tag{5.22}$$

And since

$$(u_{p-1}, z) = -\tfrac{1}{2}, \tag{5.23}$$

we have

$$(u, z) = -\tfrac{1}{2}(p-1). \tag{5.24}$$

And since

$$(u, u) = \tfrac{1}{2}p(p-1), \tag{5.25}$$

we find

$$\cos^2\theta_u = \frac{(u, z)^2}{(u, u)} = \frac{(p-1)^2}{2p(p-1)} = \frac{1}{2}\left(1 - \frac{1}{p}\right). \tag{5.26}$$

Therefore

$$\frac{1}{2}\left(1-\frac{1}{p}+1-\frac{1}{q}+1-\frac{1}{r}\right)<1, \tag{5.27}$$

or

$$\frac{1}{p}+\frac{1}{q}+\frac{1}{r}>1. \tag{5.28}$$

We may suppose $p \geqq q \geqq r \geqq 2$ (otherwise we have no diagrams distinct from type $\mathscr{A}_\ell$); then $r=3$ is impossible, hence $r=2$. It is clear then, since $(1/p)+(1/q)>\frac{1}{2}$, that either $p=2$ and q is arbitrary, or $q=3$ and p is equal to 3, 4, or 5. The corresponding diagrams are

$\mathscr{D}_\ell$:

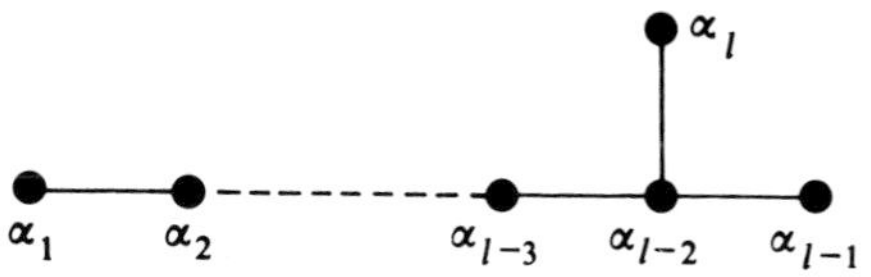

and

$\mathscr{E}_6$:

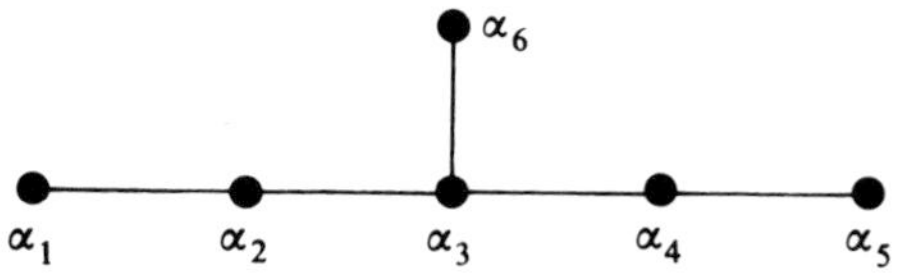

$\mathscr{E}_7$:

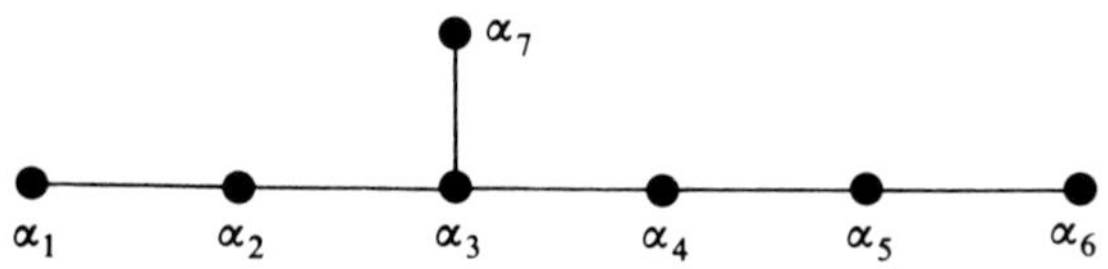

$\mathscr{E}_8$:

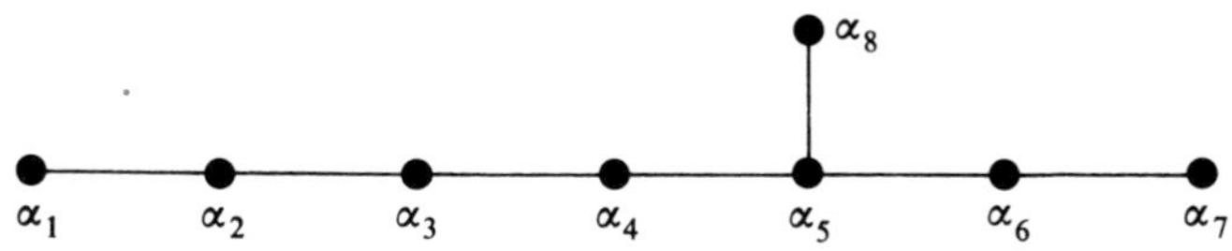

There is clearly only one way to allot the "weights": the weight one is associated with each dot of each of these four diagrams.

We now note the following three isomorphisms between our given simple Lie algebras, which can be read off directly from the Dynkin diagrams.

$$\begin{aligned} \mathscr{A}_1 &\cong \mathscr{B}_1 \cong \mathscr{C}_1, \\ \mathscr{B}_2 &\cong \mathscr{C}_2, \\ \mathscr{A}_3 &\cong \mathscr{D}_3. \end{aligned} \tag{5.29}$$

There are no other possible isomorphisms between the simple Lie algebras. This completes the classification of all the possible simple Lie algebras.

VI. Representations and Weights for Semisimple Lie Algebras

The theory of the representations of semisimple Lie algebras serves two purposes. It provides us with a proof of the existence of Lie algebras that correspond to the Dynkin diagrams that we have found, and it classifies the objects that have nice transformation properties under the operation of elements of the Lie group, i.e., appropriate basis vectors for the representation space.

We shall now present only the results of the Cartan classification program, omitting the proofs of the following statements, which relate the specific Lie algebras that we have discovered to their Lie groups.

$\mathscr{A}_l$ belongs to $SU(l+1)$, the group of $(l+1)$-dimensional unitary unimodular matrices.

$\mathscr{B}_l$ belongs to $O(2l+1)$, the orthogonal group in $(2l+1)$-dimensional space.

$\mathscr{C}_l$ belongs to the symplectic group in $(2l)$-dimensional space.

$\mathscr{D}_l$ belongs to $O(2l)$, the orthogonal group in $(2l)$-dimensional space.

The exceptional algebras $\mathscr{G}_2$, $\mathscr{F}_4$, $\mathscr{E}_6$, $\mathscr{E}_7$, $\mathscr{E}_8$ belong to certain special geometries, for which we refer to the literature [Freudenthal (*17*)].

The representation theory can in principle use the same (more abstract) tools as the classification theory, since the latter is in principle nothing but the theory of the adjoint representation. We shall be content, however, with a more superficial account. We are looking for matrices H_i, E_α, $E_{-\alpha}$, which satisfy the standard commutation relations (5.2). We demand in addition that H_i be Hermitian and that $E_{-\alpha}$ be the Hermitian conjugate of E_α. We know beforehand that commuting matrices and Hermitian matrices each have complete sets of (in general degenerate) eigenvectors. Now let u be an eigenvector of H_i in the representation space $\mathscr{R}$ (which is a representation module; the associative algebra is then the enveloping algebra of the representing matrices H, E). We have

$$H_i u = m_i u \qquad (i = 1, \ldots, l), \tag{6.1}$$

and the vector m_i is called a *weight vector*. (It is a vector, since H_i is a vector in the space of the Cartan subalgebra). The space spanned by the weight vectors is called *weight space*; it is (since the H_i are linearly independent) l-dimensional. For any linear combination $H = \lambda^i H_i$ we have

$$\lambda^i H_i u = \lambda^i m_i u \equiv (\lambda, m) u. \tag{6.2}$$

A weight vector m_i will be called *simple* if it is nondegenerate. Note that the *roots* are the *weights* of the adjoint representation; the nonzero ones are simple.

We shall prove a number of easy lemmas.

Lemma 1. Every representation has at least one weight.

Proof. Obviously, the set of the H_i is solvable, even Abelian; hence the lemma follows immediately from Lie's theorem.

Lemma 2. Vectors in $\mathscr{R}$ that belong to different weights are linearly independent.

Proof. We shall prove that a vector $u \in \mathscr{R}$ that belongs to a weight vector $m(u)$ cannot be a linear combination of vectors $u^{(k)}$ that all belong to weight vectors $m(k)$, which differ from $m(u)$. By "differ" we mean that the linear form $\sum_i \lambda^i m_i(u) \neq \sum_i \lambda^i m_i(k)$ for all k (i.e., the λ^i are "indeterminate"). We assume that, on the contrary,

$$u = \sum_k a_k u^{(k)}, \tag{6.3}$$

and then we construct an operator W that transforms each $u^{(k)}$ into zero without transforming u into zero. Using the summation convention, we define

$$W = \prod_l \{\lambda^i H_i - \lambda^i m_i(l)\}. \tag{6.4}$$

Clearly, since u belongs to the weight m,

$$Wu = \prod_l \{\lambda^i m_i(u) - \lambda^i m_i(l)\} u \neq 0, \tag{6.5}$$

since no factor is zero. On the other hand

$$W \sum_k a_k u^{(k)} = \sum_k (a_k \prod_l \{\lambda^i m_i(k) - \lambda^i m_i(l)\} u^{(k)}) = 0, \tag{6.6}$$

and we have a contradiction. Hence

$$u \neq \sum a_k u^{(k)}. \tag{6.7}$$

Hence we have

Lemma 3. The number of different weights is at most equal to the degree of the representation, i.e., the dimension of $\mathscr{R}$, but it may be less.

The important result is the following.

Lemma 4. If u is a vector of weight m, then $H_i u$ is of weight m, and $E_\alpha u$ is of weight $m + \alpha$.

Proof. The first part of the lemma is trivial since the H_i commute; the second part follows from the standard commutation relations:

$$H_i E_\alpha u = [H_i, E_\alpha]u + E_\alpha H_i u = \alpha(h_i)E_\alpha u + E_\alpha m_i u, \\ = (m_i + \alpha(h_i))E_\alpha u. \tag{6.8}$$

We can now prove

Lemma 5. If a representation is irreducible, the H_i can be diagonalized simultaneously.

Proof. There is a vector $u \in \mathscr{R}$ that has a definite weight. We then construct all possible products

$$\cdots E_\gamma E_\beta E_\alpha u.$$

They all have a definite weight according to the preceding lemma and evidently span an irreducible representation that then cannot fail to be the one with which we started. Since all the vectors that we constructed have a weight, all the H_i are diagonal on any basis selected from these vectors.

We now state a "reflection theorem" which is essentially the same as that for root vectors.

Theorem. For any weight m and any root vectors α, $2(m, \alpha)/(\alpha, \alpha)$ is an integer and $m - [2(m, \alpha)/(\alpha, \alpha)]\alpha$ is a weight.

Proof. The proof is exactly the same as for roots. The reflections generate again the Weyl group or kaleidoscope group W. They are reflections with respect to the hyperplanes through the origin perpendicular to the root vectors.

Weights obtained from each other by such reflections are called *equivalent* weights. It will again be expedient to introduce an *ordering*: A vector in weight space $(u_1, u_2, \ldots, u_l)$ will be called *positive* if its first nonvanishing component is positive. A weight vector $m(u)$ will be said to be *higher* than a weight vector $m(v)$ when the vector $m(u) - m(v) = (m_1(u) - m_1(v),\ m_2(u) - m_2(v),\ \ldots,\ m_l(u) - m_l(v))$ is positive. A weight is called *dominant* when it is higher than all its equivalent weights.

We shall now prove the

Main Theorem I. The highest weight of an irreducible representation is simple.

Proof. Let u be a vector belonging to the highest weight $m(u)$. According to the proof of Lemma 5 we must prove that any product

$$v = \cdots E_\delta E_\gamma E_\beta E_\alpha u$$

that has the same weight $m(u)$ as u is a multiple of u. Since v has the weight $\cdots + \delta + \gamma + \beta + \alpha + m(u) = m(u)$, then at least one of the roots $\cdots \delta, \gamma, \beta, \alpha$ is positive. Let us suppose that it is γ. Commuting E_γ with E_β and E_α, that is, substituting $[E_\gamma, E_\beta] + E_\beta E_\gamma$ for $E_\gamma E_\beta$, etc., we can move E_γ to the position in front of u at the expense of getting some additional terms with, however, fewer factors E. Since $m(u)$ is the highest weight, $E_\gamma u = 0$; hence we are left with nothing but the additional terms. We apply the same procedure to each of these additional terms, but the process must end. It ends when there are no more E's that belong to positive root vectors. We have then arrived at a sum of H's that operate on u, hence v is indeed a multiple of u.

We now prove the

Main Theorem 2. Two irreducible representations with the same highest weights are equivalent.

Proof. Let $\mathscr{R}$ and $\mathscr{R}'$ be two irreducible representations. Let u_0 and u_0' be the (unique) vectors with equal highest weight, and let $E_\alpha, \ldots$ and $E_\alpha', \ldots$ be the respective representation matrices of the operators. By the proof of Lemma 4 the linear correspondence

$$\cdots E_\gamma E_\beta E_\alpha u_0 \to \cdots E_{\gamma'} E_{\beta'} E_{\alpha'} u_0'$$

maps the whole space $\mathscr{R}$ into $\mathscr{R}'$. Since the representations are both irreducible, the image, by Schur's lemma, must be either the null element or the whole space $\mathscr{R}'$. Since it cannot be the null element, it must be $\mathscr{R}'$, and the representations are equivalent.

REFERENCES

1. For a brief survey of the topological background to this chapter we refer to Professor Coleman's article, p. 62 *et seq.*

2. W. Killing, *Math. Ann.* **31**, 252 (1888); **33**, 1 (1889); **34**, 57 (1889); **36**, 161 (1890).

3. E. Cartan, "Sur la structure des groupes de transformations finis et continus." Thesis. Paris, 1894.

4. G. E. Baird and L. C. Biedenharn, *J. Mathematical Phys.* **4**, 1449 (1963); other references quoted there.

5. L. S. Pontryagin, "Topological Groups," 2nd ed., Chapter 11. Gordon and Breach, New York, 1966.

6. E. B. Dynkin, *Uspehi Mat. Nauk* **2**, 59 (1947) [*Amer. Math. Soc. Transl.* Ser. 1, No. 17 (1950)].

7. E. Cartan, *Ann. Ecole Norm.* **31**, 263 (1914).

8. H. Weyl, *Math. Z.* **23**, 271 (1925); **24**, 238 (1925).

9. E. Cartan, *J. Math. Pures Appl.* **8**, 1 (1929); F. Gantmacher, *Mat. Sb.* **5** (**47**), 217 (1939).

10. S. Helgason, "Differential Geometry and Symmetric Spaces." Academic Press, New York, 1962.

11. N. Jacobson, "Lie Algebras." Wiley (Interscience), New York, 1962.

12. H. Freudenthal, Lie groups. Unpublished notes. Yale Univ., New Haven, Connecticut, 1961.

13. G. D. Mostow, Lectures on Lie groups and Lie algebra. Unpublished notes. Yale Univ., New Haven, Connecticut.

14. H. Weyl, The structure and representation of continuous groups. Unpublished notes. Princeton Univ., Princeton, New Jersey, 1935.

15. L. O'Raifeartaigh, Lectures on local Lie groups and their representations. Matscience Rept. 25. Inst. Math. Sci., Madras, India, 1964.

16. I. Kaplansky, Lie algebras. *In* "Lectures on Modern Mathematics" (T. L. Saaty, ed.), Vol. I. Wiley, New York, 1963.

17. H. Freudenthal, Lie groups in the foundations of geometry. *Advan. Math.* **1**, 145 (1965).

Induced and Subduced Representations

A. J. COLEMAN

DEPARTMENT OF MATHEMATICS, QUEEN'S UNIVERSITY
KINGSTON, ONTARIO, CANADA

I. Introduction

The topic of *induced representations* of groups is now all the rage among physicists and mathematicians as a result of a sudden general awakening to the extraordinary power and simplicity of this notion. The concept was discovered by Frobenius (*1*) seventy years ago. It was used in the late 1920's by Weyl in his famous book on group theory and quantum mechanics (*2*), though few readers noticed this because even today his Chapter V is still largely terra incognita. Suddenly, however, the *kairos* for induced representations occurred in the early 1950's and, with the abruptness of the transition of a superconductor, has radically changed our approach to all topics in which the theory of group representations plays an essential role.

In the present chapter we attempt (i) to assemble the basic ideas and theorems related to induced and subduced representations, and (ii) to describe a few applications of these notions to problems of current interest in theoretical physics. We have not attempted to expound the most general theory currently available. Even if the author were capable of doing this, such an attempt would require too much space and would go beyond the aims of the present book. In any case, Mackey's masterful surveys (*3*,*4*) provide a definitive introduction to the more recondite reaches of the mathematical literature.

We have attempted to provide the background necessary for a reader who wishes to approach, without too great trepidation, the many papers, in the *Journal of Mathematical Physics* for example, dealing with helicity, the Galilei and Poincaré groups, Wigner's theorem, and similar topics. However, to achieve even this modest aim has forced us to, at least, touch upon a considerable body of mathematical ideas that most chemists and physicists regard as highly esoteric, such as Haar measure, direct integral decomposition, the generalized Schur lemma, and the Murray-von Neumann typology, to mention only a few. Of necessity, therefore, the next five sections contain a multitude of definitions and unproved assertions. Even though we wished to avoid overburdening the text with formal definitions, we have put in italic type the key concepts at their first occurrence, accompanying this with a descriptive phrase sufficiently precise to serve effectively as a definition. A few words are treated in this way even though they are not used subsequently in the chapter in order to prepare the reader for more ambitious forays into the literature of our subject.

A major lacuna in our treatment is the absence, except for one passing reference, of any discussion of fiber bundles. Hermann (*5*, p. 57) rightly asserts that the theory of fiber bundles can "be strongly recommended to physicists as an appropriate mathematical language with which to understand the true nature of the relation between symmetries and fields." Indeed, Mackey (*4*) has shown that the essential simplicity of induced representations is most easily seen when they are viewed as acting on a fiber bundle. However, a single chapter cannot contain everything and the reader who wishes to pursue this topic is directed to the work of Mackey (*4*) and Hermann (*5*).

In practice, groups arise most often as sets of automorphisms G of a physical or mathematical structure, such as the symmetry group of a crystal, the 1:1 mappings of a quantum system onto itself under which the Hamiltonian is invariant, the Galois group of a field, or the linear transformations of a cubic surface into itself. The list of instances is almost endless. In order to master a particular system, we normally study its "parts." We think of the system as being made up of subsystems: lines consist of points; nuclei are composed of nucleons; molecules are built of atoms. The automorphisms of the system that change a subsystem into itself form a subgroup of the group G of all automorphisms of the system.

It is therefore a subject of great practical interest, even of urgency, to study the relation between a group and its subgroups. This study cannot be restricted merely to abstract groups. In practice, the same abstract group appears in a variety of guises or representations, so we are led to consider the interrelations among the representations of a group and the representations of each of its subgroups. Such interrelations are the focal point of the present article.

If Γ is a representation of a group G, then restricting the domain of Γ to a subgroup H of G results in or *subduces* a representation of H that we denote by $\Gamma \downarrow H$ and describe as *the representation of H subduced by* Γ. That is simple, indeed trivial. However, given a representation Δ of H, it is possible, by a well-defined process that is described later, to construct a representation of G. The recipe is almost as simple as for subducing, but seventy years were needed from its first vague formulation, by Frobenius, until it emerged clearly and powerfully in the early 1950's. The resulting representation of G, which we denote by $\Delta \uparrow G$, is called *the representation of G induced by* Δ. That subducing and inducing are intimately related processes is apparent from one of the central theorems of representation theory, known as the Frobenius reciprocity theorem. In the case of finite groups this theorem states that if Δ and Γ are irreducible representations of H and G respectively, then the frequency of Γ in $\Delta \uparrow G$ is equal to the frequency of Δ in $\Gamma \downarrow H$.

The reciprocity theorem was formulated originally (*1*) in terms not of *representations* but of *characters* of a representation. In the hands of Frobenius, Littlewood, and Murnaghan it was a useful, but somewhat recherché, tool for digging up formulas for the characters of the symmetric and full linear groups by obscure, painful, and unenlightening methods. Speiser (*6*), in his famous textbook on finite groups, was perhaps the first writer to publish an explicit expression for the matrix of the induced representation. In 1939, Wigner (*7*) published his now justly famous paper on the representations of the inhomogeneous Lorentz group. In this paper he manufactured representations of the full group from representations of the translation subgroup by what he called "the method of Frobenius." In the past few years there has been an avalanche of articles, in physics journals, that attempt to exploit or extend Wigner's paper in the hope of classifying elementary particles. These papers have been motivated by the belief that the inhomogeneous Lorentz group is here to stay. Therefore, the group of symmetries of the mathematical theory describing any (or all) fundamental particles must contain the inhomogeneous Lorentz group $\mathscr{P}$ as a subgroup. Thus the representation Γ of the full symmetry group $\mathscr{S}$ relevant to the system under study must *subduce* an appropriate representation of $\mathscr{P}$. Whence, by Frobenius's theorem, Γ must occur as a constituent of the representation of $\mathscr{S}$ *induced* from the representation of $\mathscr{P}$ in question.

It was shown by Weil (*8*) that Frobenius's theory of induced representations of finite groups could be extended, essentially unaltered, to compact groups.

However, it was not until the appearance of Mackey's papers (*9*) in 1952–1953 that *inducing* was revealed as an indispensable tool for discussing representations of noncompact groups. It has even been stated that inducing is the *only* method that has so far been employed to obtain nontrivial representations of such groups. Mackey's articles triggered a host of other mathematical papers, clarifying, simplifying, and generalizing the basic theory of induced representations. Even before Mackey's articles, Gelfand and his school in the Soviet Union had used the method of inducing to obtain explicit representations of Lie groups.

In the early 1930's several gallant physicists, among whom Dirac was perhaps the most illustrious, donned armor of various ingenious patterns, mounted their silver chargers, and contended resolutely against the "group pest." It was a lost cause. Dyson (*10*) has rightly asserted "now in the 1960's we are faced with a multitude of particles, having a rich internal structure which is manifested in their observed behavior but which resists any attempt at concrete description. We seem to have come up against what Eddington (*11*) called 'unknowable actors executing unknowable actions.' In response to this crisis, group-theoretical ideas have come into full flower in particle physics during the last five years, and have succeeded to a remarkable extent in imposing order upon the chaos of experimental discoveries." Eddington, whose foresight and prophetic genius we can only now begin to appreciate, had realized very early (*11*) that "We must seek a knowledge which is neither of actors nor of actions, but of which the actors and actions are a vehicle. The knowledge we can acquire is knowledge of a structure or pattern contained in the actions. In mathematics we describe such knowledge as knowledge of group structure."

Now we know that *inducing* and *subducing* are key tools in unraveling the intricacies of $SU(3)$, the Lorentz group, the Poincaré group, the theory of little groups, space groups, and the symmetric groups. A mere glance at the *Physical Review* or the *Journal of Experimental and Theoretical Physics* reveals that this list encompasses a large portion of contemporary physics—a portion that is growing steadily.

Another remark of Dyson (*10*) was to the effect that Wigner, Weyl, and van der Waerden "developed the theory in a style of great generality and mathematical polish, which delayed for about 25 years its acceptance as a working tool by the majority of physicists, although the chemists during the same period found no great difficulty in adapting it to their needs."

It might be fairly alleged that the "discovery" of induced representations in the 1950's is the most important event in the theory of the representations of groups since Schur's Berlin dissertation (*11a*) at the opening of the twentieth century. The author hopes that this chapter will open a door through which some readers may glimpse the power and beauty of the method of Frobenius.

II. Group, Topological, Borel, and Quotient Structures

In his famous satire, Orwell (*11b*) remarked that "All animals are equal, but some are more equal than others." All share in a common animality and yet are distinguished by their power, prestige, or purpose. So it is with mathematical *structures*. Any such structure has a *set* as a substratum, but usually it possesses an extra something.

Sets, as such, are the plebeians among structures. The theory of sets contains only one basic relation, usually denoted by $\in$ and expressed in English as "belongs to." All other ideas, relations, and definitions in the pure *theory of sets* must be expressible in terms of $\in$. For example, $A \subset B$ means the same as $x \in A \Rightarrow x \in B$. Here $\Rightarrow$ stands for "implies." Similarly, $\tilde{A}$, the complement of A in S, is the set, $\{x|x \in S, x \notin A\}$, of all x that belong to S and do not belong to A.

We shall adopt the common notation $f: A \to B$ to indicate that f is the name of a *function* or *mapping* that assigns to *each* element of its *domain* A an unambiguous *image* or *value* in B. Alternatively, by $x \to f(x)$ where $x \in A$, $f(x) \in B$; we indicate that f is a function with domain A that maps elements of A onto elements of B. The *range* of f, which is the set of all images of elements of A, can be denoted by $f(A)$ so that $f(A) = \{y|y = f(x)$ for some $x \in A\}$. The words *function* and *mapping* are synonymous. A function that sends distinct elements of the domain into distinct elements of the range is *injective* or *monic*. If $f(A) = B$, that is, if every element y of B has at least one *preimage* x such that $f(x) = y$, then f is *surjective*, *epic*, or *onto*. A mapping that is both injective and surjective is *bijective* or *one-to-one*.

A *group* is a more interesting structure than a set. Perhaps it is best to think of a group G as a *pair* $(S,*) = G$, consisting of a set S *together with* a binary operation defined on S such that the following well-known *group properties* are satisfied: for all a, b, c belonging to S

GP I (Closed) $a * b$ is an element of S;
GP II (Associative) $a * (b * c) = (a * b) * c$;
GP III (Neuter) There is an element n such that $a * n = n * a = a$;
GP IV (Inverse) To each element a there corresponds an element a^{-1} such that $a^{-1} * a = a * a^{-1} = n$.

It can easily be proved that n is unique. It is called the *neuter*, or *neutral element*, of G. It is customary to speak of an element as belonging to a group when, strictly, what is intended is that the element belongs to the set S that is the substratum of the group. To insist on the more correct usage is unnecessary pedantry, so that we shall feel free to write $a \in S$ *or* $a \in G$ as equivalent statements. It should be noted, however, that two groups differing in the properties of their binary operations might quite well have the same set substratum—a possibility that is blurred by the common usage just noted.

All groups satisfy the four group properties. Particular classes of groups can be specified by the imposition of further restrictions. For example, *commutative* or *Abelian* groups satisfy

$$\text{GP V} \quad \text{(Abelian)} \quad a * b = b * a.$$

The group, consisting of a set and one binary operation, is one of the simplest and most powerful instances of an *algebraic* structure. These are characterized by the presence of one or more operations mapping a *finite* number of elements of the substratum set into itself. There are other kinds of mathematical structures. We shall discuss briefly three such that are widely used in the applications of mathematics: topological, Borel, and quotient structures. *Topology* is often described as a generalization of geometry; however, it could also be regarded as a generalization of calculus, since it was in freshman calculus that most of us first met the idea of limit. Armed with this idea we were able to formulate precise definitions of *continuity*, *derivative*, etc. The most general definition of *topological space* has been contrived by mathematicians (perhaps, following the advice of Sylvester as to the ideal conditions for mathematical creativity, at 3 A.M. with a decanter of ripe port at hand) to provide the widest possible framework within which the concept of *limit* makes sense. Similarly, a *Borel* structure is the broadest arena to which we can extend our intuitive notions of area and volume and is therefore the natural habitat for integration theory. The notions of topological and Borel structures, though distinct, are very similar. If they are regarded as raw materials that the mathematician uses, then the concept of *quotient structure* is a tool with which he shapes his materials into startling, even grotesque, forms.

Given a set S we can use such words as *neighborhood*, *open set*, *limit*, *continuous* only if S has been provided with a *topology*. This may be done by specifying a family $\mathscr{T}$ of special *subsets* of S that we shall call the *open sets* of the *topological space* $(S, \mathscr{T})$. If in a given context only one topology $\mathscr{T}$ is being considered, it is usual to abbreviate and refer to the *topological space* S. In most of classical analysis (before 1920, say) the topology was accepted unconsciously, as God-given, so that the foregoing concept was not made explicit. Now there are important parts of analysis in which the chief skill needed is the ability to switch adroitly from one topology to another as rapidly as a quick-change artist exchanges personalities. In such situations the old notations and habits of mind are very inhibiting—at least, such is the experience of the author, who is incredibly old-fashioned.

In a group the binary operation is subject to certain properties, so $\mathscr{T}$ must satisfy a number of conditions if it is to be dignified by the designation a *topology*. The basic properties common to all topologies are the following. (Recall that an *element* of $\mathscr{T}$ is a *subset* of S.)

TP I (Arbitrary Unions) The union of any collection of elements of $\mathscr{T}$ belongs to $\mathscr{T}$.

TP II (Finite Intersection) The intersection of any finite collection of elements of $\mathscr{T}$ belongs to $\mathscr{T}$.

TP III The empty set $\emptyset$ and the set S belong to $\mathscr{T}$.

An element of $\mathscr{T}$ is called an *open* set. A *closed* set is the complement in S of an open set. A function f from one topological space $(S_1, \mathscr{T}_1)$ into another topological space $(S_2, \mathscr{T}_2)$ is *continuous* if and only if for every open set $U_2 \in \mathscr{T}_2$ the inverse image of U_2 under f is an open set in S_1 or, in other words, $f^{-1}(U_2) \in \mathscr{T}_1$. If f is bijective, then f^{-1} is a function. If both f and f^{-1} are continuous, f is a *homeomorphism* and the topological spaces $(S_1, \mathscr{T}_1)$ and $(S_2, \mathscr{T}_2)$ are abstractly identical. Thus homeomorphisms play a role in topology analogous to that of isomorphisms in group theory.

A topology satisfying only TP I–III is rather too general for most purposes, so that we usually demand further properties of $(S, \mathscr{T})$. In this chapter we always assume that our topological spaces have the Hausdorff property:

TP IV (Hausdorff) If x and y are distinct points of S, then $\mathscr{T}$ contains nonempty elements U_x and U_y such that $U_x \cap U_y$ is empty and $x \in U_x$, $y \in U_y$.

This Hausdorff axiom is one of the strongest of several so-called *separation axioms* that have been widely studied by mathematicians, and appears to be the most useful. A topological space satisfying TP I–IV is called a *Hausdorff space*.

We shall make frequent reference to one other topological property, *compactness*. For our purposes the most useful property of a compact set C is that every continuous function from C into the real numbers (with the normal topology) is *bounded*. This property characterizes compactness and we shall take it as the definition. Alternative definitions can be found in textbooks on topology. A closed interval such as $[0, 1]$ in the real line and the circumference of a circle are compact sets in the usual topologies. However, the whole of the real line is not compact. This distinction between a closed interval and the whole line explains (to a topologist) why we can use Fourier *series* on the interval but resort to the Fourier *integral* on the line. It explains why we cannot merely contemplate direct sum decompositions of reducible representations of groups but must also study direct *integral* decompositions. If all groups were compact, the Murray-von Neumann typology would be irrelevant to group theory. Though not compact, the real line is really quite well-behaved—it is *locally compact*.

Most subsets of S are neither closed nor open. If $A \subset S$, the largest open subset of A is called the *interior* of A, and the smallest closed set containing A is called the *closure* of A. A topological space is *locally compact* if every point is contained in an open set that has compact closure. Locally compact topological groups admit a particularly regular Lebesgue measure that has been used extensively so that the theory of locally compact groups is in a relatively advanced and satisfactory state in comparison with the theory of arbitrary topological groups.

It is possible to provide the same substratum set S with several mathematical structures. Indeed the objects with which this book is largely concerned are examples of *topological groups*. As the name implies, this is a structure $(S, *, \mathcal{T})$ consisting of a set S, a binary operation, and a topology satisfying the group *and* topological properties. However, a topological group has a further key property, which assures the harmonious cohabitation of the group and topological structures:

TGP The mappings $(a, b) \to a * b$ and $a \to a^{-1}$ are continuous.

Notice that of all the properties of a topological group, TGP is the only one involving both the group operation and the topology (through the word *continuous*).

As suggested by etymology, a *homomorphism* is a structure-preserving mapping of one mathematical structure into another. If the homomorphism is one-to-one (injective and surjective), it is called an *isomorphism*. When several structures are involved, some care may be necessary to specify precisely which properties are preserved by the mapping. By a homomorphism h of a topological group $G_1 = (S_1, *, \mathcal{T}_1)$ into a topological group $G_2 = (S_2, \Delta, \mathcal{T}_2)$ we shall normally mean a *continuous* mapping of S_1 into S_2 such that $h(a * b) = h(a)\Delta h(b)$ for all $a, b \in S_1$.

Whenever the idea of *integration* is defined on a set S, implicitly or explicitly, a *Borel structure* is present. A Borel structure is similar to a topological structure in being specified by the designation of a special family $\mathcal{B}$ of subsets of S. We speak of a Borel space $(S, \mathcal{B})$, or simply S, if there is no danger of confusion with other structures. Borel and topological structures are distinguished by satisfying different properties.

BP I (Denumerable Union) The union of a denumerable collection of elements of $\mathcal{B}$ belongs to $\mathcal{B}$.

BP II (Denumerable Intersection) The intersection of a denumerable collection of elements of $\mathcal{B}$ belongs to $\mathcal{B}$.

BP III The set S and the empty set Ø belong to $\mathcal{B}$.

BP IV (Complementation) The complement in S of any element of $\mathcal{B}$ belongs to $\mathcal{B}$.

It is easy to verify that, in the presence of properties III and IV, I $\Leftrightarrow$ II.

If $(S, \mathscr{B}_1)$ and $(S, \mathscr{B}_2)$ are two Borel structures on the same set S, we say that $\mathscr{B}_1$ is *finer* than $\mathscr{B}_2$, or that $\mathscr{B}_2$ is coarser than $\mathscr{B}_1$, if $\mathscr{B}_1 \supset \mathscr{B}_2$. The same usage applies to topologies.

Currently, there are two common approaches to the definition of *integral*. One, associated with the names Daniell and Radon, takes as starting point the fact that the integral is a linear mapping from functions into a vector space; the other, associated with the name Lebesgue, starts from our intuitive concepts of length, area, and volume. In the latter approach it is assumed that a Borel structure $(S, \mathscr{B})$ is given and that μ is a nonnegative real function on $\mathscr{B}$ such that μ is *countably additive* in the sense that if $E_i \in \mathscr{B}$ form a countable set of mutually disjoint Borel sets, then $\mu(\bigcup_i E_i) = \sum \mu(E_i)$; that is, the measure of the *union* of the *disjoint* sets E_i equals the *sum* of the measures of the sets.

A *measure space* $(S, \mathscr{B}, \mu)$ is a Borel space equipped with a countably additive measure. A *set* $E \in \mathscr{B}$ has *finite* measure if $\mu(E)$ is finite; whereas the measure of E is *σ-finite* if there exists a *countable* partition $\{E_i\}$ of E such that $E_i \in \mathscr{B}$ and $\mu(E_i)$ is finite. (Recall that a *partition* exhausts E by mutually disjoint subsets.)

In the case that S is a G space, we can define the idea of an *invariant measure*. To say that S is a G space means that the group G acts on the set S in such a way that to each pair (s, g) where $s \in S$, $g \in G$ there is associated an element of S, say sg. Examples of G space include (i) the straight line under translations, (ii) the plane under Euclidean transformations, (iii) a group G under left or right multiplication by the elements of G. This third example is most important for our present purposes. Any group G can be given *two* G space structures, according to whether we use *right* multiplication $(s, g) \rightarrow sg$ or *left* multiplication $(s, g) \rightarrow gs$ to define the "action" of G on itself. A measure μ on a G space S is *right invariant* if $\mu(Eg) = \mu(E)$ for all $g \in G$ and all Borel sets E. G is said to act *transitively* on S if for any two elements s_1 and s_2 of S there is at least one element g of G such that $s_2 = s_1 g$. When G acts transitively on S, a right invariant measure is unique to within a multiplicative factor. This unique measure is called the *right Haar measure* (*12*) on the G space S. For a locally compact group there are both right and left Haar measures μ_R and μ_L. For any $E \in \mathscr{B}$, $\mu_R(Eg) = \mu_R(E)$ and $\mu_L(gE) = \mu_L(E)$. It is a necessary property of Haar measure that $\mathscr{B}$ is invariant under G, that is $E \in \mathscr{B} \Rightarrow Eg \in \mathscr{B}$. Hence it is easily seen that for fixed g if we define $\tilde{\mu}$ by $\tilde{\mu}(E) = \mu_R(gE)$, then $\tilde{\mu}$ is a right Haar measure, but from the uniqueness property, $\tilde{\mu}(E)$ must be a constant positive multiple of $\mu_R(E)$. The constant depends on g, so we call it $\delta(g)$ and have the result

$$\mu_R(gE) = \delta(g)\mu_R(E).$$

The mapping $g \to \delta(g)$ is called the *modular* function of G and is a homomorphism of G into the multiplicative positive reals. It can be proved that for compact, Abelian, and simple groups $\delta(g) = 1$. A group for which $\delta(g) = 1$ is *unimodular*. Clearly if a group is unimodular, the right Haar measure is also left invariant. Thus, for compatible normalizations, $\mu_R = \mu_L$ on a unimodular group. This circumstance causes the theory of induced representations of unimodular groups to be slightly simpler than is that of general locally compact groups.

The last idea that we shall discuss in this section is that of *quotient structure*. It is probably the device used most frequently by the mathematician in defining new objects. It is at once so powerful and so little appreciated by chemists and physicists that it is sometimes called the mathematician's secret weapon in the academic one-upmanship battle.

If S is the substratum of any mathematical structure, the first step in defining a quotient structure is to *partition* S into a family of exhaustive mutually disjoint subsets. The subsets become *elements* of the new *quotient set*. In favorable circumstances it is possible to provide the new set with a mathematical structure derived from, or subduced by, the primal structure given on S.

Conceptually, the main obstacle for anyone approaching the idea for the first time already occurs in the abstraction "a set of sets." This phrase fixes attention on a set each of whose *elements* is a set. This possibility occurs commonly in day-to-day affairs. Thus Canada can be thought of as a set of provinces, each province as a set of counties, and each county as a set of townships. Does Canada consist of provinces, counties, or townships? This is largely a matter of convenience. For some purposes it is best regarded as one, for others as another.

Assuming that the natural numbers $\mathfrak{N} = \{1,2,3,\ldots\}$ have been defined, it is an old trick of mathematicians to *define* the *integer* $^{+}2$ as the *set* of all ordered pairs (n,m) of natural numbers n,m such that $n = m + 2$. Similarly, the integer $^{-}2$ is the *set* of ordered pairs (n,m) such that $n + 2 = m$. Once the integers $\mathfrak{J}$ have been defined, a *rational* may be *defined* as a *set* of ordered pairs (n,m) of *integers* such that (n,m) and (n',m') belong to the same rational if $nm' = n'm$. If the notion of a Cauchy sequence of rationals is understood, it is possible to *define* a real number as a *set* of Cauchy sequences. The Cauchy sequences $\{a_n\}$ and $\{b_n\}$ are "contained in" the same real number if $a_n - b_n \to 0$ as $n \to \infty$.

The preceding examples illustrate different quotient sets. In each of these cases it is possible to superimpose algebraic structure on the new set and, for example, to give a meaning to the addition of two rationals or the multiplication of two reals.

The set $xH = \{y \mid y = xh,\ h \in H\}$ is sometimes called a right coset of H, because H is on the right of x, and sometimes a left coset of H, because x is on the left of H. We shall call it a *left* coset of H. Similarly, Hx is a *right* coset. The reader should prove that if H is a *subgroup* of G, then $Hx = Hy \Leftrightarrow yx^{-1} \in H$; that is, the two right cosets are identical if and only if yx^{-1} belongs to H. Further, if H is a subgroup, then *either* the intersection $Hx \cap Hy$ is empty *or* $Hx = Hy$. Thus the right cosets of H in G constitute a partition of G into a set of exhaustive mutually disjoint subsets. We denote this partition by G/H. An *element* of G/H is a right coset of H in G. In particular, $\alpha = Hx \in G/H$ and $\alpha y = Hxy \in G/H$. Thus for each y of G, the so-called *right translation* $\alpha \to \alpha y$ effects a permutation of the elements of G/H among themselves. Thus if we set $S = G/H$, then under right translations S becomes a G space in the sense defined earlier. When G acts transitively on S, then S is said to be a *homogeneous G space*. Thus G/H is a homogeneous G spaçe under the action of G resulting from right translation.

The G-space structure of G/H follows merely from the assumption that H is a subgroup of G. If H is a *normal* subgroup (i.e., $gH = Hg$ for all $g \in G$), then it is possible to impose on G/H a group structure $(G/H, *)$ by defining $(Hx) * (Hy) = Hxy$. The resulting group is called the *quotient group of G with respect to H*.

The mapping $c: G \to G/H$ defined by $c(x) = Hx$ for each $x \in G$, is so important that it is generally known as the *canonical mapping*. If H is normal, then c is a homomorphism of G onto G/H. If G is a topological group, so that there is given a distinguished family of subsets called *open* sets, we can employ the canonical mapping c to endow the homogeneous space G/H with a topology by decreeing that a subset $\Omega \subset G/H$ will be called open if and only if its inverse image $c^{-1}(\Omega)$ is open in G. The resulting topology on G/H is the finest (i.e., it has the most open sets) topology for which c is a *continuous* function. This topology is often called the *quotient topology* and is always presupposed in discussions of quotient sets of topological spaces unless explicit mention is made to the contrary. If G is a topological group and H is a normal subgroup, then G/H, endowed with the quotient topology, is a topological group and the canonical mapping is a *continuous* homomorphism of G onto G/H.

III. The Generalized Schur Lemma and Type I Representations

In this section we first recall the notion of linear space extended to allow the scalars to belong to a noncommutative field. This extension is necessary in order that our discussion encompass the recent tendency (*13*) to contemplate representations of the Lorentz group over quaternions. We then study representations of a group, the intertwining space of two representations, irreducible and completely reducible representations, and finally, a class of representations of great importance for applications called completely reducible Type I primary representations.

Suppose that $(L, +)$ is an additive group and that $\mathfrak{F}$ is a field. $\mathfrak{F}$ can be finite or infinite, commutative or noncommutative. Then $(L, +, \mathfrak{F})$, or simply L, is a *linear space over* $\mathfrak{F}$ if there is a mapping $m: L \times \mathfrak{F} \to L$, called scalar multiplication, such that for $x, y \in L$ and $a, b \in \mathfrak{F}$: (i) $m(x,a) \in L$; (ii) $m(x,1) = x$; (iii) $m(x+y,a) = m(x,a) + m(y,a)$; (iv) $m(x,ab) = m(m(x,b),a)$.

The unique element $m(x,a)$ is usually denoted by ax, and then the foregoing properties are more simply expressed as $ax \in L$, $1x = x$, $a(x+y) = ax + ay$, $(ab)x = a(bx)$. Sometimes it is convenient to replace (iv) by (iv'): $m(x,ab) = m(m(x,a),b)$; and to denote $m(x,a)$ by xa.

The elements of L are called vectors. The familiar notions such as linear dependence and independence, basis, linear transformation, dimension, linear subspace, and matrix can be introduced as usual. If $\mathfrak{F}$ is noncommutative, care must be exercised with respect to the order of scalars in the terms arising in matrix products.

Supposing that $(M, +, \mathfrak{F})$ is a subspace of L, we could form the quotient of the group $(L, +)$ with respect to $(M, +)$ and denote it by L/M. Thus if $\zeta \in L/M$ and $z \in \zeta$, then $\zeta = \{x | x \in L,\ x - z \in M\} = \{z + m | m \in M\}$. If $y \in \xi \in L/M$, and $a \in \mathfrak{F}$, then we define $\zeta + \xi = \{z + y + m | m \in M\}$ and $a\zeta = \{az + m | m \in M\}$. It can be shown that, thus equipped, $(L/M, +, \mathfrak{F})$ is a linear space. Naturally, we call it the quotient space of L with respect to M. If L and M have dimensions $d(L)$ amd $d(M)$, respectively, then $d(L/M) = d(L) - d(M)$.

If L_1 and L_2 are distinct or identical linear spaces over $\mathfrak{F}$, we can consider various mappings of L_1 into L_2, that is, functions $f: L_1 \to L_2$ such that for $x \in L_1, f(x) \in L_2$. For a concrete example, suppose that L_1 is a two-dimensional space over the complex numbers $\mathfrak{C}$ consisting of pairs (z_1, z_2) of complex numbers, whereas L_2 is the one-dimensional space $\mathfrak{C}$ itself. Contrast the following three mappings, defined by their effect on $z = (z_1, z_2)$.

$$
\begin{aligned}
&f_1: z \to z_1, \\
&f_2: z \to z_1^*, \quad \text{(the complex conjugate of } z_1\text{)}, \\
&f_3: z \to z_1^2.
\end{aligned}
$$

If $y = (y_1, y_2)$, the reader should verify that

$$
\begin{aligned}
\text{(i)}\ & f_1(y+z) = f_1(y) + f_1(z), \\
& f_1(az) = af(z); \\
\text{(ii)}\ & f_2(y+z) = f_2(y) + f_2(z), \\
& f_2(az) = a^* f_2(z); \\
\text{(iii)}\ & f_3(y+z) = f_3(y) + f_3(z) + 2y_1 z_1, \\
& f_3(az) = a^2 f(z).
\end{aligned}
$$

A mapping $f\colon L_1 \to L_2$ such that $f(y+z) = f(y) + f(z)$ for all $y, z \in L_1$ is said to be *additive*; one such that $f(az) = af(z)$ for all $a \in \mathfrak{F}$, *homogeneous.* A function that is both additive and homogeneous is said to be a *linear function.* It is well known that linear functions are very important in mathematics. Their significance derives from the fact that they preserve *linear space structure* Of the three mappings just described, only f_1 is linear. In fact, f_1 is merely the projection of the vector onto its first component. The second function, f_2, has the great virtue of being additive, but instead of being homogeneous it replaces the factor a by the complex conjugate (i.e., its image under an automorphism of $\mathfrak{F}$). Thus f_2 is "almost" linear. A mapping of a linear space over $\mathfrak{C}$ with the properties (ii) is variously styled *antilinear*, *conjugate linear*, or *sesquilinear.* (This last term, due to Bourbaki, is also applicable when $\mathfrak{F}$ is a field possessing automorphisms, $a \to \bar{a}$, other than conjugation). Finally, our third mapping, f_3, is neither additive nor homogeneous, but from the second property of (iii) we see that it has a quadratic character.

A *linear representation* A of a group G on a linear space L is a function $A\colon g \to A(g)$ where $A(g)$ is a linear mapping of L into itself such that $A(g_1 g_2) = A(g_1)A(g_2)$ for all $g_1, g_2 \in G$. To be more explicit, we could describe a representation as a *triple* (G, A, L) where A is the homomorphism just described. It is also possible to consider *sesquilinear representations* $g \to A(g)$ for which $A(g)$ is a sesquilinear transformation of L. These play a role in the TCP theorem.

An alternative description of a linear representation is preceded by the definition of the set $\mathscr{L}(L_1, L_2)$ of all linear transformations of L_1 into L_2. In particular, let $\mathscr{L}(L) = \mathscr{L}(L, L)$. Then, the function $A\colon G \to \mathscr{L}(L)$ of G into the set of linear transformations of L itself is a linear representation of G if $A(g_1 g_2) = A(g_1)A(g_2)$ for all $g_1, g_2 \in G$. If L has finite dimension, m say, then by fixing a basis, we can associate a unique matrix to each element of $\mathscr{L}(L)$ and the representation A can be described as a mapping of each element g onto a matrix belonging to $GL(m, \mathfrak{F})$, the so-called *general linear group of degree m over the field* $\mathfrak{F}$.

If a subspace M of L has the property that for all $x \in M$, $A(g)x \in M$ for all $g \in G$, then M is *invariant under* A. Denote by $B(g)$ the mapping of $M \to M$ such that $B(g)x = A(g)x$ for all $x \in M$. Then, if $B\colon g \to B(g)$, it is easily seen that (G, B, M) is also a representation of G. We shall call it a *subrepresentation* of A. Thus, to each subspace M of L, invariant under A, there corresponds a unique subrepresentation of A. If M is neither L nor empty, the corresponding subrepresentation is *proper* and A is *reducible.* If A has no proper subrepresentation it is *irreducible.*

If M is an invariant subspace of L, we can also manufacture a representation of G for which L/M is the carrier space. If B is the subrepresentation of A described in the foregoing, we shall define a representation $B^{\perp}$ of G as follows.

For $\xi \in L/M$, $g \in G$, $x \in \xi$, let $B^{\perp}(g)\xi = \{A(g)x + m | m \in M\}$. From this definition we see immediately that $B^{\perp}(g)\xi$ is an element of L/M. However, does it really depend only on ξ and not on the particular x that was chosen in ξ? Yes! Because suppose $y \in \xi$, then $y = x + m'$ where $m' \in M$. Thus $A(g)y = A(g)x + A(g)m'$. However, we assumed that M was invariant so that $A(g)m' \in M$. Thus $\{(A(g)m') + m | m \in M\} = M$, so that $\{A(g)y + m | m \in M\} = \{A(g)x + m | m \in M\}$ and $B^{\perp}(g)\colon \xi \to B^{\perp}(g)\xi$ is a well-defined map of L/M into itself. The reader should verify that $B^{\perp}(g)$ is a linear transformation of $(L/M, +, \mathfrak{F})$ and that $B^{\perp}: g \to B^{\perp}(g)$ is a homomorphism of G so that $(G, B^{\perp}, L/M)$ is a representation of G manufactured from A and B. We may think of $B^{\perp}$ as the complement of B in A or as the quotient A/B of A with respect to B.

If L is a Hilbert space with scalar product $\langle x | y \rangle$, it is meaningful to require that A be a *unitary* representation. In other words, we could ask that, for all $g \in G$, $A(g)$ be a unitary transformation of L; that is, $\langle A(g)x | A(g)y \rangle = \langle x | y \rangle$ for all $x, y \in L$. In this case, the subspace $M^{\perp}$ of L, which is orthogonal to M, is also invariant under A. Then $B^{\perp}$ is isomorphic to, and may be identified with, the subrepresentation of A corresponding to $M^{\perp}$. More generally, a representation A is *completely reducible* if to *every* invariant subspace M of L there corresponds an *invariant* complementary subspace $M^{\perp}$ such that $L = M \oplus M^{\perp}$ is the direct sum of M and $M^{\perp}$. In this event, we say that A is the direct sum of B and $B^{\perp}$ and symbolize this situation by $A = B \oplus B^{\perp}$. From the preceding remark, *unitary representations are completely reducible.*

In studying the interrelation of two different representations of a group, their intertwining space is extremely useful. Suppose A_1 and A_2 are representations of G on linear spaces L_1 and L_2 over the same field $\mathfrak{F}$. Consider the set $[A_1, A_2]$ of all linear mappings $T\colon L_1 \to L_2$ such that $TA_1(g) = A_2(g)T$ for all $g \in G$. We easily see that $[A_1, A_2]$ is a linear space over $\mathfrak{F}$. It is called the *intertwining space* of the representations A_1 and A_2. In the case that $A_1 = A_2$ and $T\colon L_1 \to L_1$, the space $[A_1, A_1] = [A_1]$ becomes an associative algebra over $\mathfrak{F}$ if we define multiplication as the composition of mappings. Then $[A_1]$ is called either the *intertwining algebra of* A_1 or the *commutant of* A_1. If L_1 or L_2, or both, are infinite-dimensional and have a topological structure, the elements of the intertwining space are usually restricted to *continuous* linear maps. If two representations A_1 and A_2 are such that $[A_1, A_2] = [A_2, A_1] = 0$, we say that A_1 *and* A_2 *are disjoint*. Otherwise, A_1 *and* A_2 *intertwine.*

If A_1 *and* A_2 *are completely reducible*, it may be shown that the spaces $[A_1, A_2]$ and $[A_2, A_1]$ are isomorphic. Their common dimension is the *intertwining number of* A_1 *and* A_2. For any representation A with subrepresentation B, we could ask whether or not A/B intertwines with B. A representation A for which the answer is affirmative for *every* proper subrepresentation B is called a *primary* representation.

It can be shown that *intertwining is an equivalence relation among completely reducible primary representations.* Two representations A_1 and A_2 are *similar* if there exists an invertible T such that $TA_1(g) = A_2(g)T$ for all g. Clearly, similar representations intertwine. However, since similarity is also an equivalence relation, we can still seek to partition an intertwining class of completely reducible primary representations into similarity classes.

The reader is doubtless aware that the notion of irreducible representation, defined earlier, plays an important role in the theory of group representations. Its importance is linked closely to the famous result known as Schur's lemma, which is somewhat more general than is usually suggested by elementary discussions. For the generalized Schur lemma it is not necessary to assume that G is a group, but merely that it is an arbitrary set. Suppose that A and B associate to each $g \in G$ transformations $A(g)$ and $B(g)$ of the linear spaces L and M, respectively. We assume that L and M have the same field of scalars. Suppose further that there is a nonzero linear (or sesquilinear) mapping $T: L \to M$ that intertwines A and B; that is, $TA(g) = B(g)T$ for all $g \in G$. Recall that by the kernel of T is meant the set $K = \{x | x \in L, Tx = 0\}$. Then the essence of Schur's lemma consists of the assertions (i) K is a linear subspace of L invariant under A, and (ii) TL, the image of L under T, is a linear subspace of M invariant under B.

Proof. (i) We first show that K is a linear subspace of L. If $x, y \in K$, then $T(x+y) = Tx + Ty = 0$, hence $x + y \in K$. For any $a \in \mathfrak{F}$, $x \in K$ implies $T(ax) = aTx = 0$ if T is linear, and $T(ax) = \bar{a}Tx = 0$ if T is sesquilinear and $a \to \bar{a}$ is an automorphism of the field of scalars. In either case $ax \in K$. Thus K is a linear space.

For any $x \in K$, consider $y = A(g)x$. Since T intertwines A and B, $Ty = TA(g)x = B(g)Tx = 0$. Thus $y \in K$. Hence K is invariant under A.

(ii) If T is linear, it is well known that TL is a linear space. If T is sesquilinear, the only novelty in the proof is to show that if $y \in TL$, then $ay \in TL$ for any $a \in \mathfrak{F}$. But $y \in TL \Rightarrow$ there is an $x \in L$ such that $y = Tx$. For any $a \in \mathfrak{F}$ there is a b such that $\bar{b} = a$. Therefore $T(bx) = \bar{b}(Tx) = ay \in TL$.

Now suppose that $y = Tx$ is an arbitrary element of TL, then $B(g)y = B(g)Tx = TA(g)x \in TL$. Thus TL is invariant under B.

If we *assume that A is irreducible* so that L has no proper invariant subspace other than $\{0\}$, it follows that $K = \{0\}$ so that T is injective—that is, T effects a one-to-one mapping of L onto TL.

Since $TL = M'$ is invariant under B, we may restrict the domain of $B(g)$ to M'. Calling the restricted mapping $B'(g)$, we see that $T: L \to M'$ intertwines A and B'. Since T is 1:1, we can define on inverse map $T^{-1}: M' \to L$ and conclude that $B'(g) = TA(g)T^{-1}$ for all g where T is independent of g. Thus $\{B'(g)\}$ and $\{A(g)\}$ are sets of similar operators.

We recapitulate this important result. If $\{A(g)\}_{g \in G}$ is an *irreducible* set of operators that intertwines the set of operators $\{B(g)\}_{g \in G}$, then the $B(g)$ are extensions of operators $B'(g)$ that are similar to $A(g)$.

In particular, *if A and B are both irreducible and intertwine, then they are similar*. Notice that in the preceding discussion we did not assume that G was a group, but merely used it as an index set to effect a correspondence between $A(g)$ and $B(g)$. Indeed, the argument is valid if A and B are linear, quasilinear, or projective representations of a group.

Armed with Schur's lemma, we return to the study of $[A, B]$, the intertwining space of two *linear representations* of a group G. Suppose A and B are irreducible and that they intertwine. Let $T, S \in [A, B]$ so that $TA(g) = B(g)T$, and $SA(g) = B(g)S$ for all $g \in G$. Both T and S are invertible so that $S^{-1}B(g) = A(g)S^{-1}$. Thus $S^{-1}TA(g) = S^{-1}B(g)T = A(g)S^{-1}T$. Hence, $S^{-1}T \in [A]$ and $T = SU$ where $U \in [A]$; that is, $UA(g) = A(g)U$ for all g. It follows that if S is fixed, we obtain all elements T of $[A, B]$ by setting $T = SU$ and allowing U to assume all values in $[A]$.

As was noted earlier in this section, even if A is reducible, $[A]$ is an algebra over $\mathfrak{F}$. *If A is irreducible*, however, every nonzero element of $[A]$ is invertible, *so* $[A]$ *is a field*. For most applications of representation theory in physics, $\mathfrak{F}$ is either the reals $\mathfrak{R}$ or the complex numbers $\mathfrak{C}$. If the $A(g)$ are linear, $a \in \mathfrak{F}$, and I is the identity operator, then $aI \in [A]$, so that the field $[A]$ contains a subfield isomorphic to $\mathfrak{F}$. There is a famous theorem of Frobenius that the only algebraic fields of finite dimension over the reals are (i) the reals, (ii) the complex numbers, or (iii) the real quaternions. Arens (*14*), generalizing ideas of Mazur and Gelfand, has reached the same conclusion when the hypothesis that $\mathfrak{F}$ is finite-dimensional is replaced by the assumption that the field $[A]$ can be given a topological structure for which addition, multiplication, and inversion are continuous. The Frobenius conclusion is always valid also if the representation A is finite-dimensional.

Thus for situations arising in physics the field $[A]$ is either real, complex, or quaternionic. Since quaternions over $\mathfrak{C}$ are not a field, the quaternions cannot occur if the scalars include the complex numbers. In the latter case $[A]$ is necessarily isomorphic to the complex numbers.

Among completely reducible primary (crp) representations intertwining is an equivalence relation. If a crp representation intertwines an irreducible representation, we shall say that it is of Type I. By Schur's lemma, two irreducible representations can belong to the same intertwining class only if they are similar. Thus a Type I intertwining class of crp representations is uniquely determined by any one of its irreducible members.

Suppose that (G, B, M) is a crp representation of Type I and that (G, A, L) is an *irreducible* representation of G that intertwines with B. We shall say that B is of *intertwining class A*. Thus there exists a nonzero $T_1 \colon L \to M$ such that

$T_1A(g) = B(g)T_1$ for all $g \in G$. Let $T_1L = M_1 \subset M$. Then T_1 is a 1:1 mapping of L onto M_1. Since M_1 is invariant under B, and B is completely reducible, M is the direct sum of M_1 and a complementary subspace $M_1^{\perp}$ invariant under B. Then it can be shown that $B \downarrow M_1^{\perp}$, the restriction of B to $M_1^{\perp}$, is also primary of class A. As before, $M_1^{\perp}$ contains an invariant subspace $M_2 = T_2L$ isomorphic to L and a complementary invariant subspace $M_1^{\perp}$. Proceeding by induction (transfinite, if necessary) we find that M is a direct sum of the spaces M_i where $M_i = T_iL$ and i belongs to some index set Ω. Denote by T_i^{-1} the inverse map $T_i^{-1}: M_i \to L$ such that $T_i^{-1}T_ix = x$ for all $x \in L$. The cardinality of Ω is called the *multiplicity* or *frequency of A in B*. This frequency uniquely determines the *similarity* class of B in the *intertwining* class A.

Let us now determine $[B]$, the commutant of B. Since M is a direct sum of M_i, any linear operator V on M can be expressed as a matrix (V_{ij}) where V_{ij} is a linear mapping of M_j into M_i such that if $m_j \in M_j$, then $V_{ij}m_j$ is the i component of Vm_j. If $V \in [B]$, then $B(g)Vm_j = VB(g)m_j$. Since $M_j = T_jL$, there is an $l_j \in L$ such that $m_j = T_jl_j$, $l_j = T_j^{-1}m_j$. Thus $VB(g)m_j = VB(g)T_jl_j = VT_jA(g)l_j = B(g)VT_jl_j$. Since the M_k are invariant under B, the i component of this last equality gives $V_{ij}T_jA(g) = B(g)V_{ij}T_j$, since it is valid for all $l_j \in L$. But $T_i^{-1}B(g) = A(g)T_i^{-1}$. Hence, $T_i^{-1}V_{ij}T_jA(g) = A(g)T_i^{-1}V_{ij}T_j$ for all g. Thus, $T_i^{-1}V_{ij}T_j = U_{ij} \in [A]$.

Thus $V = (V_{ij})$ is a matrix in which V_{ij}: $M_j \to M_i$ is a linear operator given by

$$V_{ij} = T_iU_{ij}T_j^{-1},$$

where $U_{ij} \in [A]$. Conversely, we see that for arbitrary $U_{ij} \in [A]$, V of the form just given belongs to $[B]$. Since the T_i and T_i^{-1} are fixed mappings, the "freedom" in the choice of V is that of choosing all the U_{ij} arbitrarily in the field $[A]$. Thus when the multiplicity n of A in B is finite, $[B]$ *is equivalent to the algebra of all* $n \times n$ *matrices with coefficients in the field* $[A]$. In the case that $[A]$ is the complex field, we have obtained a famous result of Schur's thesis (*11a*).

We have now discussed the basic facts about completely reducible primary linear representations of Type I. Each such intertwines a fixed *irreducible* representation, say A, which may be of finite or infinite dimension. If the field $\mathfrak{F}$ of scalars is the complex numbers $\mathfrak{C}$ or the quaternions $\mathfrak{Q}$, then $[A]$, the commutant of A, is isomorphic to $\mathfrak{C}$ or to $\mathfrak{Q}$, respectively. If $\mathfrak{F}$ is the reals, then $[A]$ may be isomorphic to $\mathfrak{R}$, to $\mathfrak{C}$, or to $\mathfrak{Q}$. A crp representation B of type A is determined, to within a similarity, by the frequency of A in B. If this frequency is n, then the dimension of the commutant $[B]$ over the field $[A]$ is equal to n^2.

IV. Direct Integrals of Representations

Linear representations, over the complex numbers, of *finite* or *compact* groups are completely reducible into a direct sum of irreducible subrepresentations. As we saw in the previous section, such is also the case for Type I completely reducible *primary* representations. However, there are reducible representations that possess no irreducible subrepresentations. We illustrate this possibility by means of the regular representation of the one-parameter group of translations of the real line $\mathfrak{R}$.

We construct the *regular* representation of $\mathfrak{R}$ with the help of the set L^2 of square-integrable functions on $\mathfrak{R}$. Recall that a complex-valued function f defined on $\mathfrak{R}$ belongs to L^2 if $\int |f(x)|^2 dx$ is finite, where we are using the Lebesgue integral on the real line. The set L^2 is a linear space and we can introduce into it a scalar product by setting

$$\langle f | g \rangle = \int f^*(x) g(x)\, dx.$$

This does not make L^2 a Hilbert space, since there are nonzero functions for which $\langle f | f \rangle = 0$—for example, any function that equals 1 at a finite number of points and zero elsewhere. The set $\mathcal{N}$ of all functions f for which $\langle f | f \rangle = 0$ is a linear subspace of L^2. Defining $\mathfrak{H} = L^2/\mathcal{N}$, it can be shown that, with the scalar product subduced from that on L^2, $\mathfrak{H}$ is a Hilbert space. It is customary to use the same notation, f, for an element of L^2 and the class in $\mathfrak{H}$ to which f belongs. We supinely follow this questionable practice.

To each element s of $\mathfrak{R}$ we associate a mapping T_s of $\mathfrak{H}$ into itself by the definition $T_s : f \to T_s f$ where $T_s f(x) = f(x + s)$. Thus $T_s f$ is the translate of f through a distance s. It is trivial to verify that $T_{r+s} = T_r T_s$. Hence the mapping $s \to T_s$ effects a homomorphism of the additive reals into the multiplicative group of translations of $\mathfrak{H}$. It is called the *regular representation of* $\mathfrak{R}$.

It is a famous result of the classical theory of the Fourier integral that the Fourier transform effects a unitary mapping, F, of $\mathfrak{H}$ onto itself. We denote by $\hat{f} = Ff$ the function such that

$$f(x) = (2\pi)^{-1/2} \int \hat{f}(p) e^{ipx}\, dp,$$

$$\hat{f}(p) = (2\pi)^{-1/2} \int f(x) e^{-ipx}\, dx.$$

Thus

$$T_s f(x) = f(x + s) = (2\pi)^{-1/2} \int \hat{f}(p) e^{ip(x+s)}\, dp$$

$$= (2\pi)^{-1/2} \int \hat{f}(p) e^{ips} e^{ipx}\, dp$$

and

$$F(T_s f)(p) = e^{ips} \hat{f}(p).$$

Define $\hat{T}_s : f \to \hat{T}_s f$ where $\hat{T}_s f(p) = e^{ips} f(p)$. It follows from these definitions that

$$F(T_s f) = \hat{T}_s \hat{f} = \hat{T}_s Ff.$$

Thus

$$\hat{T}_s = FT_s F^{-1}$$

so that the representations T and $\hat{T}$ of the additive reals are similar.

Suppose that M is a subspace of $\mathfrak{H}$ that is invariant under $\hat{T}$, then $f \in M$ implies that $\hat{T}_s f \in M$ for all s. Thus all finite linear sums of the form $\sum_s a(s)\hat{T}_s f$ belong to M and so does $\int a(s)\hat{T}_s f\,ds$ for suitable functions $s \to a(s)$. At any $p \in \mathfrak{R}$, this last function assumes the value $\int a(s)e^{ips} f(p)\,ds = g(p)f(p)$ where $g(p)$ is arbitrary except that gf must be square integrable. The only obvious restriction on gf is that it vanishes whenever f vanishes. Suppose U is a Borel subset of $\mathfrak{R}$, then it is clear that the set $\mathfrak{H}(U)$ of all functions in $\mathfrak{H}$ that vanish on U is a linear subspace of $\mathfrak{H}$ invariant under $\hat{T}$. By an extension of the foregoing argument it can be shown that any subspace of $\mathfrak{H}$ invariant under $\hat{T}$ is a $\mathfrak{H}(U)$ for some measurable set U. Suppose that $\bar{U}$ the complement of U is not of measure zero, then there is a measurable subset V of $\mathfrak{R}$ such that $V \supset U$ and the measure of $\bar{V}$ is not zero. Hence $\mathfrak{H}(V) \subset \mathfrak{H}(U)$. It follows that *every* $\hat{T}$-invariant subspace is reducible. Note that $\hat{T}$ is completely reducible since $\mathfrak{H}(U)$ and $\mathfrak{H}(\bar{U})$ are both invariant, span the whole of $\mathfrak{H}$, and are disjoint.

Suppose that the above function $p \to f(p)$ were the *characteristic* function of the half open-closed interval $U_0 = \{p | 0 \leqq p < 1\}$, that is, $f(p) = 1$ if $p \in U_0$ and $f(p) = 0$ if $p \notin U_0$. Then $\mathfrak{H}(\bar{U}_0)$ would consist of all square-integrable functions that vanish in $\bar{U}_0$. The Fourier transform $F\mathfrak{H}(\bar{U}_0)$ would consist of all square-integrable functions in whose harmonic analysis the only circular frequencies that occur belong to U_0. In other words, f is a *band-pass filter*! The representation space $\mathfrak{H}(\bar{U}_0)$ is completely determined by the one function, or vector, f. It is the smallest closed subspace of L^2 containing f and all $\hat{T}_s f$. Such a space, generated by a *single* vector f, is called *cyclic*, and denoted by $\mathfrak{H}_f$. The representation of $\mathfrak{R}$ carried by $\mathfrak{H}_f$ is a cyclic representation and the vector f is a *cyclic vector*. Cyclic vectors of a given cyclic space are far from unique. In our example, f could be any function that vanishes only on $\bar{U}_0$. If we define $U_n = \{p | n \leqq p < n + 1\}$ where n is a natural number, it is clear that L^2 is a direct sum of $\mathfrak{H}(\bar{U}_n)$. This implies the fact, familiar to electrical engineers, that any signal can be expressed as a sum of signals whose bandwidths partition the total bandwidth of the signal. Thus the regular representation on L^2 is a direct sum of cyclic representations. A simple proof by induction shows that *any completely reducible representation of an arbitrary group can be expressed as a direct sum of cyclic representations*. In general this reduction is fantastically nonunique! In the preceding example there are distinct direct cyclic decompositions for *each partition* of the reals by means of Borel sets.

Since $\mathfrak{R}$ is Abelian and we are working over the complex numbers, any irreducible representation is one-dimensional. A function g with the property that $T_s g = \lambda(s)g$ is such that $g(x+s) = \lambda(s)g(x) = \lambda(x)g(s)$. Thus $g(s) = c\lambda(s)$, where c is a constant and $\lambda(x+s) = \lambda(x)\lambda(s)$. The only continuous functions satisfying this functional equation are $x \to e^{\alpha x}$ where $\alpha \in \mathfrak{C}$. Our representation T is unitary. In order for $s \to \lambda(s)$ to be unitary, α must be a pure imaginary, say $\alpha = ip$, $p \in \mathfrak{R}$. Indeed, if $g_p(x) = e^{ipx}$, then $T_s g_p = e^{ips} g_p$, giving a one-dimensional unitary representation for *each* choice of $p \in \mathfrak{R}$. Unfortunately, the function g_p *does not belong to* L^2. However, any function $f \in L^2$ can be expressed in the form

$$f(x) = (2\pi)^{-1/2} \int \hat{f}(p) e^{ipx}\, dp$$

or

$$f = (2\pi)^{-1/2} \int \hat{f}(p) g_p\, dp.$$

Thus an element of L^2 is expressed as an *integral* that can be thought of as the limit of a weighted sum of the g_p. Each g_p spans an irreducible representation space of the additive group $\mathfrak{R}$. We may therefore think of the Fourier integral as effecting a decomposition of the Hilbert space L^2 into a *direct integral* of irreducible representation spaces of $\mathfrak{R}$.

For fixed p and different $\hat{f}$, $\hat{f}(p)g_p$ constitute a one-dimensional space—the multiples of the function g_p—that spans an irreducible representation of $\mathfrak{R}$. Being irreducible it is necessarily primary of Type I. For a given f, the corresponding $\hat{f}$ is essentially unique, that is, it is determined except on a set of measure zero. It is a natural extension of our previous definition to say that a representation is of Type I if it can be expressed as a direct sum *or* as a direct integral of Type I primary representations in an essentially unique manner.

The example of the regular representation of the additive group of reals is the prototype for von Neumann's notion of the *direct integral of Hilbert spaces*. Suppose $(S, \mathscr{B}, \mu)$ is a measure space and that to each $s \in S$ there corresponds a Hilbert space $\mathfrak{H}_s$ with scalar product $\langle \cdot | \cdot \rangle_s$. Consider the set of all functions f with domain S such that $f(s) \in \mathfrak{H}_s$ and $\int \langle f(s) | f(s) \rangle_s\, d\mu(s)$ is finite. The set $\mathfrak{H}$ of all such functions constitutes a Hilbert space when provided with the scalar product

$$\langle f | g \rangle = \int \langle f(s) | g(s) \rangle_s\, d\mu(s).$$

As before, we must take the quotient with respect to the set of functions f such that $\langle f | f \rangle = 0$.

As in our example, so in general, $\mathfrak{H}$ will *not* contain any particular $\mathfrak{H}_s$ as a subspace. Exceptions occur if $\mu(t)$ is finite for a particular $t \in S$. Indeed, if $(S, \mathscr{B}, \mu)$ is discrete in that every point of S has finite measure, the direct integral $\mathfrak{H}$ reduces to the direct sum $\oplus \mathfrak{H}_s$. This possibility justifies the adjective *direct* in the name *direct integral* for $\mathfrak{H}$.

If each $\mathfrak{H}_s$ is the carrier space for a representation $g \to T_s(g)$ of a group G, we may construct a mapping $T(g): \mathfrak{H} \to \mathfrak{H}$ by defining $T(g): f \to T(g)f$ such that $(T(g)f)(s) = T_s(g)f(s)$. The new function $T(g)f$ will belong to $\mathfrak{H}$ if $\int \langle T_s(g)f(s)|T_s(g)f(s)\rangle_s \, d\mu(s)$ is finite. This will certainly be the case if all of the T_s are unitary representations of G, but might well obtain more generally. It is natural to symbolize the situation described here by the equation

$$T = \int^{\oplus} T_s \, d\mu(s)$$

and to say that the representation T has been decomposed into a *direct integral of the representations* T_s.

V. Murray-von Neumann Typology

A simple atomistic view of physics regards matter as built up of *elementary* particles. Thus hydrogen is made up of a proton and an electron. We like to think that in some "true" sense a hydrogen atom *contains* an electron. How are we to define elementary particle? One attempt says that the wave function of an elementary particle will belong to the carrier space of an irreducible representation of the group of symmetries of the type of particle in question. The wave function of a composite function would then belong to the carrier space of a representation that decomposed into a direct sum of irreducible representations corresponding to the elementary building-blocks of the composite particle. For any advocate of such an analysis of physical systems it is obviously disconcerting that there are groups that possess reducible representations that *contain* no irreducible subrepresentations! Such representations are especially intractable at the present stage of our knowledge of representation theory, so it is a question of considerable interest whether such Type II and Type III monsters need actually be taken into account in a reasonable physical theory. In the present section we give a brief description of the classification of intertwining classes of completely reducible primary representations due to Murray and von Neumann.*

A completely reducible primary (crp) representation has the property that any two subrepresentations intertwine. If it is of Type I, it possesses an *irreducible*

* A good discussion can be found in chapter VII of M. A. Naimark's book "Normed Rings", Noordhoff, Groningen, 1959.

subrepresentation A. Two Type I crp representations in the intertwining class A are similar if and only if A occurs in them with the same frequency. Type I representations are also called *discrete*.

Recall that a set S is of *infinite* or *finite* cardinality depending on whether it is *possible* or *impossible* to establish a one-to-one correspondence between S and a *proper* subset of S. By analogy with this terminology, we shall say that a primary representation is *infinite* or *finite* depending on whether the representation is or is not similar to a proper subrepresentation. Thus a Type I crp representation B, which intertwines the irreducible A, is *finite* if the frequency of A in B is finite and *infinite* otherwise.

It is a remarkable and exciting fact, whose discovery we owe to Murray and von Neumann, that there are crp representations that are not of Type I. Thus there are intertwining classes of crp representations that contain no irreducible representation. A family of such classes, called Type III or *completely infinite*, is such that if B is a Type III crp representation, then B is reducible and B is similar to *all* its subrepresentations.

A crp representation B that is neither of Type I nor III does not intertwine an irreducible representation and does have subrepresentations that are not similar to B. All such are said to be of Type II. If B is of Type II, it may or may not contain proper subrepresentations that *are* similar to B. If it does, it is said to be of *infinite* Type II or of Type II_∞ and the similarity classes of its subrepresentations may be put into one-to-one correspondence with the non-negative real numbers. If B is of Type II and contains no proper subrepresentation similar to itself, it is of *finite* Type II or of Type II_1 and the similarity classes of its subrepresentation may be put into one-to-one correspondence with the real numbers of the closed interval [0, 1].

It can be shown that any completely reducible representation B of a group can be expressed as a direct sum

$$B = B(\mathrm{I}) \oplus B(\mathrm{II}_1) \oplus B(\mathrm{II}_\infty) \oplus B(\mathrm{III})$$

of summands $B(\mathrm{J})$ such that $B(\mathrm{J})$ intertwines only with crp representations of Type J. Each of the summands $B(\mathrm{J})$ can be further decomposed into a direct sum or a direct integral of crp representations of Type J. In the Type I case this latter decomposition is essentially unique. In other cases the theory is still rather obscure. There are examples of Type II representations expressible as direct integrals of irreducible representations in two distinct manners with no irreducibles common to the two direct integrals.

In view of the latter remarks, it is fortunate that most of the groups that are currently employed in physics possess only Type I primary representations. This is true, for example, of the following classes of groups: (1) compact and finite groups; (2) locally compact commutative groups; (3) semisimple Lie groups; (4) nilpotent Lie groups; (5) connected real algebraic groups; (6) the rigid motions of Euclidean n-space; (7) the Poincaré group (that is, the group of translations and Lorentz transformations of Minkowski four-space).

There are solvable Lie groups and infinite discrete groups that possess crp representations not of Type I. However, all locally compact groups possess some Type I representations, since Gelfand and Raikov (*21*) proved that every locally compact group has a sufficient supply of irreducible representations to separate any two of its elements. That is, if $g_1 \neq g_2$, there is at least one irreducible representation A of G for which $A(g_1) \neq A(g_2)$.

Indeed every unitary representation of a locally compact group can be expressed as a direct integral of irreducible representations (direct sums are subsummed as the particular case of direct integral with discrete measure). For Type I primary representations this decomposition is unique to within a similarity transformation. Indeed, Dixmier (*15*, Theorem 8.6.6) asserts that for any separable Type I representation the foregoing direct integral decomposition into irreducibles is essentially unique. However, there are astonishing examples known of the nonuniqueness for Type II representations. But even for these there is always a well-defined decomposition into *primary*, rather than irreducible, direct integral summands. We remark, parenthetically, that the decomposition involves direct *sums* or direct *integrals* according as the summand representations are or are not subrepresentations.

The primary decomposition can be understood in terms familiar to quantum physicists for whom the *summum bonum* is that eschatological concept: a complete set of commuting observables whose eigenvalues could serve to name the possible states of a system. This is an idea basic to Dirac's famous book (*15a*). For a given representation A, a maximal Abelian subalgebra M of the commutant $[A]$ would come close to the idea just expressed. This notion has not been exploited in the mathematical literature and perhaps deserves more attention. In the simplest case in which M is generated by a set of operators $\{M_i\}$ with discrete spectrum, A would be a direct *sum* of irreducible representations for which the eigenvalues of M_i would serve as names. If some of the M_i had continuous spectra, the decomposition of A into irreducibles would necessarily involve direct *integrals*. Presumably, the abovementioned nonuniqueness of decomposition by irreducibles corresponds to the existence of distinct similarity classes of maximal commutative subalgebras of $[A]$.

However, there is a uniquely defined commutative subalgebra of $[A]$, not necessarily maximal, that is used to effect the *central decomposition* of A. The bicommutant of A, namely, the commutant $[[A]]$ of $[A]$, is an algebra over the scalars, the so-called *von Neumann algebra generated by A*, which obviously contains A. The intersection $Z = [A] \cap [[A]]$ is the center of $[[A]]$ and is a commutative subalgebra of $[A]$. The set S of projectors in Z can be given a

Borel structure and a measure μ, and to each $s \in S$ may be associated a Hilbert space $\mathfrak{H}_s$ that carries a *primary* representation A_s of G such that

$$\mathfrak{H}(A) = \int^{\oplus} \mathfrak{H}_s \, d\mu(s)$$

and

$$A = \int^{\oplus} A_s \, d\mu(s)$$

where the equality is to be interpreted as "similar to."

Clearly Z is common to *all* maximal commutative subalgebras of $[A]$. The measure μ is not unique, but its null sets are uniquely determined. *Any* other measure μ' with the same null sets could equally well be used in the foregoing integrals and would give rise to direct integrals similar to them. It follows from the foregoing considerations that, for Type II and III, the nonuniqueness for direct integral decomposition by irreducibles pertains only to the decomposition of *primary* representations by irreducibles.

VI. Induced Representations of Finite Groups

An induced representation (G, H, Δ) of group G is a representation manufactured with the help of a representation Δ of a subgroup H and the permutations of the homogeneous space G/H engendered by the action of elements of G. The mathematical and physical literature contains many different examples of induced representations. For given G, H, and Δ the definition of the induced representation varies somewhat from one author to another. For representations of finite or compact groups over a field of scalars that is algebraically closed and of characteristic zero, all good definitions of (G, H, Δ) are equivalent. For these cases the basic ideas were discovered by Frobenius (*1*) and are expounded by Weyl (*2*, Chapter V), in the author's Uppsala and Oxford lectures (*16*), and by Bradley (*17*).

Induced representations of finite groups over *arbitrary* fields, which involve greater complications, have been given a masterful, possibly definitive, treatment by Curtis and Reiner (*18*, Chapter 6, 7).

Weil (*8*) showed that Frobenius's theory for finite groups applies, almost unchanged, to compact groups. For noncompact groups, however, the situation is not so tidy. Only for unitary representations of locally compact groups is there currently anything like a systematic theory. Even for this case, different authors have employed inequivalent definitions of induced representation and associated concepts. The restriction to unitary representations ensures complete reducibility and is often desirable in quantum mechanics. However, even the smallest simple noncommutative noncompact group,

$SL(2, \mathfrak{R})$, has no finite-dimensional unitary representations other than the trivial one, nor do all its irreducible representations occur in the direct irreducible decomposition of the regular representation. The necessity of studying infinite-dimensional representations brings, almost inevitably, topological and measure-theoretic complications. Of course, such complications should not be deplored since they make life interesting and bearable for pure mathematicians! The variety of definitions of induced representation is related to the variety of topological and Borel structures employed by different authors.

Very recently (*4*, *5*) it has been realized that an induced representation of G is a particular case of the notion of a fiber bundle under the action of G. Hermann emphasizes that this is the natural context in which to consider induced representations with a view to applications in physics. For example, the transformation properties of the electromagnetic field F_{rs} under the inhomogeneous Lorentz group $\mathscr{P}$ involve the behavior of the field at any one point under the homogeneous Lorentz group L. The six-dimensional linear space of possible F_{rs} at a point is a *fiber*. Space-time is the *base* space of a fiber bundle. The whole fiber bundle is transformed into itself under the action of $\mathscr{P}$. But space-time is homeomorphic to $\mathscr{P}/L$. If we take Δ to be the six-dimensional representation of L spanned by F_{rs}, that is, $\Delta = D(1, 0) \oplus D(0, 1)$, it follows that a particular value of the electromagnetic field is a vector in the carrier space of the induced representation $(\mathscr{P}, L, \Delta)$.

In order to be on terms of easy intimacy with induced representations, we begin with the simplest case of representations of finite groups over the complex numbers. The only esoteric knowledge presupposed concerns the orthogonality relations for the character of irreducible representations of a finite group and the notion of block matrix. In the following sections we discuss unitary representations of locally compact groups with the aid of functions of positive type, finally applying our theory to specific examples of current interest in physics.

We begin with the simplest examples of the induced representation $\Delta \uparrow G$. We shall assume that H is a subgroup of G and that Δ is a finite-dimensional representation of H, possibly reducible. It is a classic theorem of Maschke that, over the complex numbers, $\mathfrak{C}$, all representations of a *finite* group are completely reducible (*18a*). Maschke's theorem is equivalent to the statement that the *Frobenius* or *group algebra* over $\mathfrak{C}$ is semisimple. Hence the induced representation will be completely reducible.

Notations in our topic are not yet established. Mackey employs the notation U^{Δ} for the representation of G induced from the representation Δ of H. The symbol U is appropriate in Mackey's context since he deals always with unitary representations. In this instance and others, however, the author has frequently found that Mackey's notations are more of an obstacle than an aid to understanding, so he hopes the subject will not stabilize on Mackey's notation. The symbol $\Delta \uparrow G$ or $\Delta(H) \uparrow G$ for the representation of G induced from Δ of H was employed by Robinson (*18b*). It is especially serviceable in the statement of theorems, but we shall often use other symbols incidentally in the course of proofs.

There is one very familiar example of $\Delta \uparrow G$, namely, the case in which Δ is the identity representation of H, that is, the one-dimensional representation $J(H)$, which maps every group element on the one-dimensional identity matrix. If H is the subgroup containing only the neutral element n, then we shall see that the induced representation coincides with the regular representation. There are two common ways of defining the regular representation of a finite group.

For the *first* definition, the carrier space consists of the vector space substructure of the Frobenius algebra. The latter consists of all formal linear combinations of group elements over a field $\mathfrak{F}$ equipped with the obvious definition of addition and with a multiplication consisting of the linear extension of group multiplication. Thus if $x = \sum_{g \in G} x(g)g$ and $y = \sum_{g \in G} y(g)g$ where $x(g), y(g) \in \mathfrak{F}$, then

$$x + y = \sum_{g} (x(g) + y(g))g,$$

$$xy = \sum_{g,s} x(g)y(s)gs = \sum_{g,s} x(s)y(s^{-1}g)g,$$

$$= \sum_{g} x * y(g)g.$$

Here $x * y$ is the *convolution* of the functions x and y, which is a new function such that $x * y(g) = \sum_s x(s)y(s^{-1}g)$. If V is the linear space substructure of the Frobenius algebra, the *left regular representation* of G is a mapping $L: g \to L_g$ where L_g is a linear transformation of V defined by $x \to L_g x = gx$. It follows that for any two $g, h \in G$,

$$L_{gh}x = ghx = gL_h x = L_g L_h x;$$

$$\therefore L_{gh} = L_g L_h.$$

Further, $L_g = I$ implies $L_g x = x$ for all x, so that $gs = s$ for all $s \in G$ and hence $g = n$, the neuter of G. Hence the left regular representation L is an isomorphism of G onto a group of linear transformations of G. It is possible to define a second bijective representation of G, called the *right regular representation*, as follows. Let $R_g: g \to R_g$ be defined by $R_g x = xg^{-1}$ for all $x \in V$. Then

$$R_{gh}x = x(gh)^{-1} = (xh^{-1})g^{-1} = R_g(xh^{-1}) = R_g R_h x.$$

Thus

$$R_{gh} = R_g R_h.$$

And again we easily show that R is bijective.

The regular representations of a group, as defined in the foregoing, have played an extraordinarily important role in the development of modern algebra. As the reader doubtlessly realizes, the left and right regular representations are similar, the dimension of each equals the order $|G|$ of the finite group, each is a direct sum of irreducibles with each irreducible representation Γ_α occurring with frequency $f_\alpha = \dim(\Gamma_\alpha)$. Burnside's famous theorem asserts that $|G| = \sum_\alpha f_\alpha^2$, a result that can be intepreted as stating that any complex-valued function on G is a linear combination of the functions occurring as components in the matrices corresponding to the irreducible representations.

One reason that the regular representations are so useful is that each is contained in the commutant of the other and, indeed, suffices to generate this commutant. The proof of the first part of this statement is trivial.

$$R_g L_h x = R_g(hx) = hxg^{-1} = L_h(xg^{-1}) = L_h R_g x.$$

Thus $R_g L_h = L_h R_g$ for all $g, h \in G$. Hence $L \subset [R]$ and $R \subset [L]$. That any $A \in [R]$ can be expressed in the form $A = \sum_s a(s) L_s$ follows, essentially, from the completeness property expressed by Burnside's theorem.

The preceding definition of the regular representation is straightforward and effective for finite groups; it is not so useful, however, for the study of continuous representations of topological groups. In this case, it is more usual to employ as the carrier space of the regular representation a class of complex-valued functions defined on the group. When interest is focused on unitary representations, it is usual for the *second* definition of the regular representation to take as carrier space W the set $L^2(G)$ of square-integrable complex-valued functions on G. (There are three other spaces of complex functions defined on G that play a considerable role in representation theory: (i) $C(G)$, the continuous functions; (ii) $C_0(G)$, the continuous functions of compact support that vanish outside a compact set; (iii) $L^1(G)$, the functions f for which the $\int |f| \, d\mu(g)$ is finite where μ is a Haar measure on G.) The *right regular representation* ρ is now defined as the mapping $\rho: g \to \rho_g$ where ρ_g is the linear transformation on W defined by $f \to \rho_g f$ for all $f \in W$ where $\rho_g f(s) = f(sg)$ for all $s \in G$. Similarly, the *left regular representation* λ is such that $\lambda_g f(s) = f(g^{-1}s)$. The reader may be surprised to note that where in the definition of R_g the product sg^{-1} occurred it seems that sg appears at the corresponding point of ρ_g. However, in the first definition the carrier space V *contained* G, in the second definition the carrier space W contains *functions* on G. That is, W is a dual object to V. As is universal, objects and dual objects transform contragrediently.

By considering the characteristic function c_g, such that $c_g(s)$ equals 1 if $s = g$ and zero otherwise, we easily see that for finite groups the dimensions of V and W are equal to the order of G. Two linear spaces of the same dimension are isomorphic, and it can be shown that for finite groups the two definitions of the regular representation are equivalent. The second has the advantage of immediate applicability to topological groups.

The regular representation is a tool of such crucial importance in representation theory as to more than justify our apparent digression from the main theme of induced representations. For the moment, we simply reiterate the bald assertion that $J(\{n\}) \uparrow G$ *is* the right regular representation of G if $J(\{n\})$ is the identity representation of the neuter subgroup of G. Then the description given earlier of the right regular representation provides a first example of the construction of an "induced representation."

The next simplest case arises if we again induce from the identity representation, but of a subgroup H other than $\{n\}$. The representation $J(H) \uparrow G$ is simply a representation by the permutations of the right cosets of H belonging to G/H. For $\sigma \in G/H$ and $s_\sigma \in \sigma$, $\sigma = Hs_\sigma$. Denote by σg the coset to which $s_\sigma g$ belongs. Then $A(g)\colon \sigma \to \sigma g^{-1}$ is a permutation of the elements of G/H. If V is the linear space spanned by formal sums $x = \sum_\sigma x(\sigma)\sigma$ where $\sigma \in G/H$ and $x(\sigma) \in \mathfrak{C}$, then the permutation $A(g)$ can be extended to a linear transformation V by the definition $A(g)x = \sum_\sigma x(\sigma)\sigma g^{-1} = \sum_\sigma x(\sigma g)\sigma$. The induced representation $J(H) \uparrow G$ is defined as $A\colon g \to A(g)$. It is thus a linear representation of dimension equal to the index of H in G, that is, to $|G|/|H|$. It can be exhibited very simply as a mapping from G onto *matrices* if we take the cosets as a basis. For $\tau \in G/H$, if we set $x(\sigma) = \delta(\sigma, \tau)$ where $\delta(\sigma, \tau)$ is the Kronecker delta, then $x = \sum_\sigma \delta(\sigma, \tau)\sigma = \tau$. Thus $A(g)\tau = \sum_\sigma \delta(\sigma g, \tau)\sigma$ and we easily verify that $g \to (\delta(\sigma g, \tau))$, that is, the mapping of g onto the matrix that has $\delta(\sigma g, \tau)$ in the σ row and τ column is a matrix representation of G.

There is one remaining simple case. Suppose $H = G$, then we shall find that $\Delta(G) \uparrow G = \Delta$!

Let us finally consider the general case of a representation $\Delta(H)$ of a subgroup $H \subset G$. The induced representation $A = \Delta \uparrow G$ will have dimension equal to the product of the $\dim(\Delta)$ and the index of H in G. It can be described most concretely as a matrix representation such that $A(g)$ is a $|G|/|H|$ block matrix where each block is a square matrix of dimension equal to $\dim(\Delta)$. We use the elements of G/H as indices for the blocks so that $A(g) = (A_{\sigma\tau}(g))$ is a block matrix. We define

$$A_{\sigma\tau}(g) = \Delta(s_\sigma g s_\tau^{-1})\delta(\sigma g, \tau)$$

where $\sigma, \tau \in G/H$ and $\sigma = Hs_\sigma$ where the $s_\sigma \in G$ are a fixed set of representatives of the cosets. In order for $A_{\sigma\tau}(g)$ to be defined, $s_\sigma g s_\tau^{-1}$ must lie in H.

However, because of the delta factor, the only case that actually occurs has $\tau = \sigma g$. Since $s_\sigma g \in \sigma g$, it follows that $s_\sigma g s_{\sigma g}^{-1} \in H$. We claim that

$$A: g \to A(g) = (A_{\sigma\tau}(g))$$

is a matrix representation of G. As promised, it is manufactured with the help of the given representation Δ of the subgroup H and the homogeneous space G/H. It is called *the representation of G induced by $\Delta(H)$ and denoted by $\Delta \uparrow G = A$.*

Theorem 1. For a finite group G and the representation Δ of a subgroup H, the foregoing mapping A into matrices defines a representation of G of dimension equal to $|G|\dim(\Delta)/|H|$.

The proof, given by Coleman (*16*), involves a straightforward verification. Notice that if $\Delta = J$, our general definition of $\Delta \uparrow G$ reduces to the permutation representation given earlier.

Theorem 2. If $h \to \psi(h)$ is the character of the representation Δ, then the character $g \to \chi(g)$ of $\Delta \uparrow G$ is given by the formula

$$\chi(g) = \sum \psi(s_\sigma g s_\sigma^{-1})$$

where the summation is over precisely those σ for which $\sigma g = \sigma$.

Proof.

$$\chi(g) = \operatorname{tr} A(g) = \sum_\sigma \operatorname{tr}(A_{\sigma\sigma}(g))$$

$$= \sum_\sigma \psi(s_\sigma g s_\sigma^{-1})\delta(\sigma g, \sigma)$$

$$= \sum \psi(s_\sigma g s_\sigma^{-1}), \qquad \text{where} \quad \sigma g = \sigma.$$

Notice that in general $\psi(s_\sigma g s_\sigma^{-1}) \neq \psi(g)$ even when $g \in H$ since for $s \notin H$, h and shs^{-1} could belong to distinct conjugate classes of H. From Theorem 2 we see that $\chi(g) = 0$ unless g is conjugate to an element of H; even in this case, however, it does not necessarily follow that $\chi(g) \neq 0$.

If Γ and Λ are representations of a group G, then $\Gamma \times \Lambda$ will denote the usual tensor product representation, which is a representation of the outer product $G \times G$, whereas $\Gamma \boxtimes \Lambda$ will denote the representation of G obtained by restricting $\Gamma \times \Lambda$ to the diagonal $D = \{(g, g) | g \in G\}$ of $G \times G$. Thus

$$\Gamma \boxtimes \Lambda = \Gamma \times \Lambda \downarrow D.$$

Here, as always, we interpret "=" between representations to indicate that they are *similar*.

Theorem 3. For Δ a representation of H, and Γ a representation of G,

$$\Gamma \boxtimes (\Delta \uparrow G) = ((\Gamma \downarrow H) \boxtimes \Delta) \uparrow G.$$

The proof of this and the following two theorems can be effected by comparing the characters of the representations on either side of the equality sign. Alternative proofs are given by Coleman (*16*).

Theorem 4. (Inducing in Stages). If Δ is a representation of the subgroup H and $H \subset K$ where K is a subgroup of G, then

$$(\Delta \uparrow K) \uparrow G = \Delta \uparrow G.$$

Theorem 5. If Δ_i is a representation of a subgroup H_i of a group G_i, then

$$\Delta_1 \times \Delta_2 \uparrow G_1 \times G_2 = (\Delta_1 \uparrow G_1) \times (\Delta_2 \uparrow G_2).$$

Theorems 4 and 5 reveal that there is a preestablished harmony between the concept of induced representation and the subgroup structure of groups which is a chief source of the power and usefulness of this particular method of manufacturing group representations. We come now to the Frobenius reciprocity theorem (FRT), first proved by Frobenius (*1*) in 1898. The scope and elegance of this theorem is such that it may justly be regarded as the most important single result in the theory of group representations. We state the FRT here only for finite groups. Later we shall report on attempts to reformulate the FRT so that it will remain valid for infinite groups. As always, $H \subset G$.

Theorem 6 (Frobenius Reciprocity Theorem). If Δ and Γ are *irreducible* representations of H and G respectively, then the frequency of Γ in $\Delta \uparrow G$ is equal to the frequency of Δ in $\Gamma \downarrow H$.

Again, the proof is a simple exercise in the use of characters and can be found in the work of Coleman (*16*) or Bradley (*17*).

The FRT expresses in vivid form the reciprocal relation between inducing and subducing. It has the immediate consequence that *every* irreducible representation of G will occur as an irreducible summand in the decomposition of one or more of the representations of G obtained by inducing from the irreducible representations of *any* fixed subgroup H. We stated the FRT only for finite groups; however, that the theorem in the foregoing formulation holds for compact groups was proved by Weil (*8*).

Corollary I. An irreducible representation Γ_α of G of dimension f_α occurs in the regular representation f_α times and $\sum_\alpha f_\alpha^2 = |G|$, the order of G.

Proof. For $H = \{n\}$, $J(\{n\}) \uparrow G$ is the right regular representation of G. But $\Gamma_\alpha \downarrow \{n\}$ contains $J(\{n\})$ with frequency f_α, so the first statement follows from the FRT.

Since a representation of a finite group over the complex numbers is completely reducible, it follows that the dimension of the regular representation is $\sum_\alpha f_\alpha^2$, but it also equals the order of the group $|G|$, as required.

We have thus obtained Burnside's completeness theorem as an immediate consequence of the Frobenius reciprocity theorem. All the properties of induced representations discussed so far are classical. We turn now to a series of important results first obtained by Mackey for topological groups (*18c*). Since we restrict attention here to finite groups, it will be possible to greatly simplify Mackey's proofs and, in consequence, we hope to make his elegant theory more widely appreciated.

We must first recall a few basic properties of double cosets. Suppose H and K are subgroups of G, possibly identical. It is not difficult to see that if two double cosets Hg_1K and Hg_2K have a single element d in common, then they are each identical with the double coset HdK. It then follows, as for ordinary cosets, that the H, K double cosets are a family of mutually disjoint subsets that exhaust G. The particular double coset $\delta = HdK$ can be partitioned into a family of right cosets of H, that is, there are elements k_i of K such that $Hdk_i \cap Hdk_j$ is empty if $k_i \neq k_j$ and $\delta = \bigcup_i (Hdk_i)$. Since $Hdk_1 = Hdk_2$ if and only if $k_1k_2^{-1} \in d^{-1}Hd$, it follows that the k_i are a set of representatives of the right cosets of $L^d = d^{-1}Hd \cap K$ in K. Thus the number of right cosets of H in δ is equal to $|K|/|L^d|$. We denote the group $d^{-1}Hd$ by H^d.

If Δ is a representation of H, then $\Delta^d(s) = \Delta(dsd^{-1})$ is defined if $s \in H^d$ and so $s \to \Delta^d(s)$ is a representation of H^d. The character ψ^d of Δ^d is given by $\psi^d(s) = \psi(dsd^{-1})$ where ψ is the character of Δ. The representations Δ and Δ^d are said to be *conjugate*. Even if $H = H^d$, Δ and Δ^d need not be similar.

Theorem 7 (Mackey's Subgroup Theorem). With notation fixed as in the foregoing

$$(\Delta \uparrow G) \downarrow K = \sum_\delta (\Delta^d \downarrow L^d) \uparrow K.$$

A proof of Theorem 7 using characters may be found in the work of Bradley (*17*), and an alternative proof is given by Coleman (*16*).

Suppose G contains only one double coset so that in Theorem 7 we may choose d to be the neuter n. Thus $(\Delta \uparrow G) \downarrow K = (\Delta \downarrow L^n) \uparrow K$. An important instance of this situation which includes the case of a subdirect product is dealt with in the following:

Theorem 8. If $G = HK$, $H \cap K = \{n\}$ and if Δ has dimension f, then

$$(\Delta \uparrow G) \downarrow K = f \times \text{(the regular representation of } K).$$

Proof. Since $L^n = \{n\}$, $\Delta \downarrow L^n = fJ(\{n\})$ and Theorem 8 is an immediate consequence of Theorem 7.

Theorem 8 provides a clue to the success of the method of *little groups* for obtaining representations of the space groups.

Theorem 9 (Product Theorem). Suppose Λ is a representation of K; then, employing the notation of Theorem 7, we have

$$(\Delta \uparrow G) \boxtimes (\Lambda \uparrow G) = \sum_{\delta} ((\Delta^d \boxtimes \Lambda) \downarrow L^d) \uparrow G.$$

Proof. By Theorem 3 the left-hand side is similar to $(((\Delta \uparrow G) \downarrow K) \boxtimes \Lambda) \uparrow G$. The required result follows by a straightforward application of Theorems 7, 3, and 4.

The final theorem of this section characterizes induced representations. Mackey calls it the imprimitivity theorem, but Loomis (*18d*), justly, refers to it as Mackey's induced representation theorem (IRT). Its statement involves the concept of *spectral measure*. Recall that a positive measure μ on a Borel space $(S, \mathscr{B})$ is a function from $\mathscr{B}$ into the nonnegative reals. A spectral measure P on $(S, \mathscr{B})$ differs from this chiefly in that P is a function from $\mathscr{B}$ into the set of projectors on a Hilbert space. Thus if $E, F \in \mathscr{B}$, $P(E)$ and $P(F)$ are projectors, that is, Hermitian idempotent operators. Thus P is a projector-valued set function. As a spectral measure it satisfies the following conditions: if $E \cap F = \varnothing$, then $P(E \cup F) = P(E) + P(F)$, $P(\varnothing) = 0$, $P(S) = I$. Further, for arbitrary $E, F \in \mathscr{B}$, $P(E \cap F) = P(E)P(F)$.

For a discrete measure space for which $\mathscr{B}$ contains *all* subsets of S, a measure can be described by specifying its value at each point. For example, if $S = G/H$ for $\alpha \in G/H$, we could define $P(\alpha)$ as a block matrix such that $(P(\alpha))_{\sigma\tau} = \delta(\sigma, \alpha)\delta(\tau, \alpha)I_f$ where f is the dim(Δ) and $\sigma, \tau \in G/H$. Then $P(\alpha)$ is a square matrix of the same dimension as $A = \Delta \uparrow G$. It will be a good exercise for the reader to verify that P is a spectral measure and that $(P(\alpha)A(g))_{\sigma\tau} = (A(g)P(\alpha g))_{\sigma\tau} = \Delta(s_\sigma g s_{\overline{\sigma g}}^{-1})\delta(\sigma, \alpha)\delta(\alpha g, \tau)$. Hence, with the foregoing definition, P is a spectral measure on G/H such that $P(\alpha)A(g) = A(g)P(\alpha g)$ or $P(\alpha g) = A^{-1}(g)P(\alpha)A(g)$. For any representation A of a group G, a spectral measure defined on S satisfying this last equation is called, by Mackey, an *imprimitivity system* of A based on S. Thus every induced representation $\Delta(H) \uparrow G$ possesses a system of imprimitivity based on G/H. *Mackey's induced representation theorem* asserts the converse.

Theorem 10. A representation A of a group G possesses an imprimitivity system P based on G/H if and only if A is similar to $\Delta \uparrow G$ where Δ is a representation of H.

Proof. We have already seen that $\Delta \uparrow G$ possesses such a system of imprimitivity. Suppose that A is a representation of G and that $P(\alpha)$ is a projector on the carrier space of A such that $P(\alpha)A(g) = A(g)P(\alpha g)$ for all $\alpha \in G/H$ and $g \in G$.

For $\eta = H$, $\eta h = \eta$ for each $h \in H$, so that $P(\eta)A(h) = A(h)P(\eta)$. If V is the carrier space of A, then $P(\eta)V$ is invariant under $A(h)$ for $h \in H$. We denote by Δ the representation of H obtained by restricting the domain of $A(h)$ to $P(\eta)V$, and set $\psi(h) = \mathrm{tr}(\Delta(h)) = \mathrm{tr}(P(\eta)A(h)P(\eta))$. That is, ψ is the character of $\Delta(H)$.

Since P is a spectral measure $\sum_\sigma P(\sigma)$ equals I, the identity on V. Thus $A(g) = \sum_{\sigma,\tau} P(\sigma)A(g)P(\tau)$, and χ, the character of A, is given by

$$\chi(g) = \sum_{\sigma,\tau} \mathrm{tr}(P(\sigma)A(g)P(\tau)),$$

$$= \sum_{\sigma} \mathrm{tr}(P(\sigma)A(g)P(\sigma)),$$

since $\mathrm{tr}(P(\sigma)A(g)P(\tau)) = \mathrm{tr}(A(g)P(\tau)P(\sigma))$, which vanishes if $\tau \neq \sigma$. Since P is a spectral measure, $P(\sigma)A(g)P(\sigma) = A(g)P(\sigma g)P(\sigma)$, which vanishes unless $\sigma g = \sigma$.

Now $s_\sigma \in \sigma$, $\sigma = \eta s_\sigma$; hence $P(\sigma) = P(\eta s_\sigma) = A^{-1}(s_\sigma)P(\eta)A(s_\sigma)$, and it follows that $\chi(g) = \sum_\sigma \mathrm{tr}(A^{-1}(s_\sigma)P(\eta)A(s_\sigma)A(g)A(s_\sigma^{-1})P(\eta)A(s_\sigma))$, where $\sigma g = \sigma$. Thus $\chi(g) = \sum_\sigma \mathrm{tr}(P(\eta)A(s_\sigma g s_\sigma^{-1})P(\eta))$, where the condition $\sigma g = \sigma$ on the summation implies that $s_\sigma g s_\sigma^{-1} \in H$. Hence

$$\chi(g) = \sum_{\sigma} \psi(s_\sigma g s_\sigma^{-1}), \qquad \text{where} \quad \sigma g = \sigma.$$

Comparing this with Theorem 2, we see that A is similar to $\Delta \uparrow G$.

Mackey's IRT provides a necessary and sufficient condition that a representation of a group is induced from a representation of a subgroup. Our proof, in which characters play a key role, is valid for finite-dimensional representations of finite groups. Using a more sophisticated approach to characters, the proof could be adapted to a somewhat wider situation. However, Blattner (*19*), using functions of positive type, has shown that the IRT is valid for arbitrary unitary representations of arbitrary locally compact groups. Mackey (*20*) has also generalized his theorem to a form applicable to projective representations.

The preceding discussion has followed fairly closely the author's Oxford lectures (*16*), which in turn were largely based on the lecture notes of Mackey

(*20a*). If we followed these precedents, we would next discuss Mackey's intertwining number theorem and the idea of little groups for finite groups. However, these are topics which are extremely important for current applications in physics but in which the essential difficulties do not appear in connection with finite groups. Therefore, instead of immediately proceeding further in this line, we turn to the discussion of a new concept which will enable us to define induced representations from arbitrary representations of arbitrary locally compact groups.

VII. Orthogonality Relations for Square-Integrable Representations

If $g \to U(g)$ is any *unitary* representation of a group G on a Hilbert space $\mathfrak{H}$, for any fixed vector $\xi \in \mathfrak{H}$ we could construct the smallest closed subspace $\mathfrak{H}(\xi)$ of $\mathfrak{H}$ containing $U(g)\xi$ for all $g \in G$. It is clear that $\mathfrak{H}(\xi)$ is invariant under U and carries a *cyclic* subrepresentation of U. The subspace of $\mathfrak{H}$ orthogonal to $\mathfrak{H}(\xi)$ also carries a subrepresentation of U. If this latter space is not empty, we can take any vector η in it and generate another cyclic subspace $\mathfrak{H}(\eta)$ orthogonal to $\mathfrak{H}(\xi)$. It is apparent that $\mathfrak{H}$ is a direct sum of mutually orthogonal subspaces, each of which carries a cyclic representation of G. This is a fact of capital importance. The analysis of *any* completely reducible representation can be reduced to the study of *cyclic* representations. It is clear that *an irreducible representation is cyclic* and that every vector in its carrier space is cyclic.

A cyclic representation U of G on a cyclic space $\mathfrak{H}(\xi)$ is determined to within a similarity by the function $g \to \varphi(g) = \langle \xi | U(g)\xi \rangle$. This fact has been known for some years, but only recently, through the work of Weil, Godement, Gelfand, and Raikov, has its full importance for the theory of representations become apparent. The function φ is a complex-valued function of *positive type*. Loomis and Blattner have used such functions to simplify the theory of induced representations. In this section, we study the particular case when φ is square integrable with respect to Haar measure on G. This covers many of the problems that arise in applications. In order to avoid a few complications we shall also assume that G is unimodular or, in other words, that the Haar measure μ is both left and right invariant. Thus if E is any Borel set of G, $\mu(E) = \mu(gE) = \mu(Eg)$ for all $g \in G$. All compact, Abelian, simple, or semisimple groups are unimodular, so that the theory of the present section has wide applications.

It is easy to convince oneself that $\varphi(g) = \langle \xi | U(g)\xi \rangle$ does indeed determine the cyclic representation U. Since ξ is cyclic, there exist $g_i \in G$ such that the vectors $U(g_i)\xi = \xi_i$ constitute a basis for $\mathfrak{H}(\xi)$. Consider the matrix $(\varphi(g_i^{-1}gg_j)) = A(g)$. Since U is unitary, $\varphi(g_i^{-1}gg_j) = \langle \xi | U(g_i^{-1}gg_j)\xi \rangle = \langle U(g_i)\xi | U(g)U(g_j)\xi \rangle = \langle \xi_i | U(g)\xi_j \rangle$. Thus, if dim $\mathfrak{H}(\xi)$ is finite or denumerable, $A(g)$, which is completely determined by the function φ, is a matrix representation of the operator $U(g)$. Dixmier (*15*, Section 13.3), shows that there is a one-to-one correspondence between continuous unitary representations of a locally compact group G and representations of an associated algebra of integrable functions $L^1(G)$, with convolution as product. The cyclic representations of this algebra are determined by continuous bounded functions φ of positive type (*15*, Theorem 13.4.5). If the function φ is square integrable with respect to Haar measure, that is, $\int |\varphi(g)|^2 \, d\mu(g)$ is finite, we shall say that the corresponding *representation* U_φ on $\mathfrak{H}(\xi)$ is *square integrable.* The square-integrable representations are precisely those that occur as *subrepresentations*, that is, as direct *summands*, of the regular representations λ and ρ of G (*15*, 14.1.1). We shall prove this result later when U_φ is irreducible. In contrast to this result, recall that none of the irreducibles $x \to e^{ipx}$ that occur in direct *integral* reduction of the regular representation $\rho(\mathfrak{R})$ of the additive reals is square integrable, though $\rho(\mathfrak{R})$ contains an uncountable number of square-integrable reducible subrepresentations.

Suppose that $\varphi(g) = \langle \xi | U(g)\xi \rangle \in L^2(G, \mu)$; then, with the foregoing notation, since G is unimodular,

$$\int |\langle \xi_i | U(g)\xi_j \rangle|^2 \, d\mu(g) = \int |\langle \xi | U(g_i^{-1} g g_j)\xi \rangle|^2 \, d\mu(g) = \int |\varphi(g)|^2 \, d\mu(g).$$

Thus $\langle \xi_i | U(g)\xi_j \rangle \in L^2(G, \mu)$ where ξ_i span the Hilbert space $\mathfrak{H}(\xi)$. It follows that $g \to \langle \zeta | U(g)\eta \rangle$ *is a square-integrable function on G for any two vectors* $\zeta, \eta \in \mathfrak{H}(\zeta)$. We could perfectly well have taken this last property as the definition of a square-integrable representation $(G, U, \mathfrak{H})$.

Square-integrable representations of unimodular groups are especially tractable because the intertwining space $[U_1, U_2]$ of two such representations $(G, U_1, \mathfrak{H}_1)$ and $(G, U_2, \mathfrak{H}_2)$ is rather easy to describe. Let ξ_i be an arbitrary vector in $\mathfrak{H}_i$. We shall consider operators $T(\xi_1, \xi_2): \mathfrak{H}_1 \to \mathfrak{H}_2$ defined, in Dirac's notation, by

$$T = T(\xi_1, \xi_2) = \int |U_2(s)\xi_2\rangle \langle U_1(s)\xi_1| \, d\mu(s).$$

A meaning is attached to the right-hand side by agreeing that for *any* vectors $\eta_i \in \mathfrak{H}_i$

$$\langle \eta_2 | T\eta_1 \rangle_2 = \int \langle \eta_2 | U_2(s)\xi_2 \rangle_2 \langle U_1(s)\xi_1 | \eta_1 \rangle_1 \, d\mu(s)$$

where $\langle \cdot | \cdot \rangle_i$ denotes scalar product in $\mathfrak{H}_i$. That this equation defines a bounded linear operator T from $\mathfrak{H}_1$ to $\mathfrak{H}_2$ may be proved by the following classic argument. Note that the integral is finite, since $fg^* \in L^2$ if $f, g \in L^2$, by the Schwarz inequality. Further, for fixed η_1 the right-hand side is an antilinear functional in η_2. By the Riesz representation theorem, there exists an unique element of $\mathfrak{H}_2$, η say, such that the foregoing integral equals $\langle \eta_2 | \eta \rangle_2$. Define $T\eta_1 = \eta$. But η_1 was any vector of $\mathfrak{H}_1$, so that we have succeeded in defining a mapping from $\mathfrak{H}_1$ into $\mathfrak{H}_2$. It is easy to verify that T, so defined, is linear. By a similar argument we can see that there also exists an adjoint mapping $T^\dagger$ from $\mathfrak{H}_2$ into $\mathfrak{H}_1$ with the property $\langle T^\dagger \eta_2 | \eta_1 \rangle_1 = \langle \eta_2 | T\eta_1 \rangle_2$ for any vectors $n_i \in \mathfrak{H}_i$.

Theorem II. The operators $T(\xi_1, \xi_2)$ defined earlier belong to the intertwining space $[U_1, U_2]$.

Proof.

$$\langle \eta_2 | TU_1(g)\eta_1 \rangle_2 = \int \langle \eta_2 | U_2(s)\xi_2 \rangle_2 \langle U_1(s)\xi_1 | U_1(g)\eta_1 \rangle_1 \, d\mu(s)$$

$$= \int \langle \eta_2 | U_2(s)\xi_2 \rangle_2 \langle U_1(g^{-1}s)\xi_1 | \eta_1 \rangle_1 \, d\mu(s), \qquad \text{since } U_1 \text{ is unitary,}$$

$$= \int \langle \eta_2 | U_2(gs)\xi_2 \rangle_2 \langle U_1(s)\xi_1 \rangle \eta_1 \, d\mu(s), \qquad \text{since } \mu \text{ is left invariant,}$$

$$= \langle U_2(g^{-1})\eta_2 | T\eta_1 \rangle_2, \qquad \text{since } U_2 \text{ is unitary,}$$

$$= \langle \eta_2 | U_2(g)T\eta_1 \rangle_2.$$

This equality is true for all η_1, η_2 if and only if

$$TU_1(g) = U_2(g)T.$$

Hence T intertwines U_1 and U_2, as required.

We can employ Schur's lemma to obtain the following important generalization of the orthogonality conditions, which are well known for finite and compact groups.

Corollary I. If U_1 and U_2 are inequivalent, irreducible, square-integrable representations, then

$$\int \langle \eta_2 | U_2(s)\xi_2 \rangle_2 \langle \eta_1 | U_1(s)\xi_1 \rangle_1^* \, d\mu(s) = 0.$$

Proof. Immediate, since $T = 0$ and hence $\langle \eta_2 | T\eta_1 \rangle_2 = 0$.

Thus these famous orthogonality conditions are valid for any irreducible representation that can occur as a direct summand in the regular representation of G. However, the foregoing proof does not cover the case of e^{ipx}, e^{iqx}, $p \neq q$, on the additive group of reals. For this purpose we would need to have the theory of distributions at our disposal. Presumably, there is an orthogonality theorem, involving distributions, that reduces to Corollary 1 for distributions arising from square-integrable functions.

Corollary 2. If U is an irreducible square-integrable unitary representation of G on a complex Hilbert space $\mathfrak{H}$, and ξ_i, η_i are arbitrary vectors in $\mathfrak{H}$, then

$$\int \langle \eta_2 | U(s)\xi_2 \rangle \langle \eta_1 | U(s)\xi_1 \rangle^* \, d\mu(s) = f^{-1} \langle \eta_2 | \eta_1 \rangle \langle \xi_1 | \xi_2 \rangle$$

where f is a real constant greater than zero.

Proof. Since U is irreducible and $T \in [U]$, by the Frobenius-Mazur-Gelfand-Arens theorem of Section III, $T = aI$ where $a \in \mathfrak{C}$. Thus $\langle \eta_2 | T\eta_1 \rangle = a\langle \eta_2 | \eta_1 \rangle$ However,

$$\langle \eta_2 | T\eta_1 \rangle = \int \langle U(s^{-1})\eta_2 | \xi_2 \rangle \langle U(s^{-1})\eta_1 | \xi_1 \rangle^* \, d\mu(s)$$

$$= \int \langle \xi_1 | U(s)\eta_1 \rangle \langle U(s)\eta_2 | \xi_2 \rangle \, d\mu(s),$$

since $\mu(s^{-1}) = \mu(s)$ because G is unimodular. The argument by which Theorem 11 was proved shows that

$$\langle \eta_2 | T\eta_1 \rangle = b\langle \xi_1 | \xi_2 \rangle \qquad \text{where} \quad b \in \mathfrak{C}.$$

Comparing this with the previous equation, we note that it follows that

$$\int \langle \eta_2 | U(s)\xi_2 \rangle \langle \eta_1 | U(s)\xi_1 \rangle^* \, d\mu(s) = c\langle \eta_2 | \eta_1 \rangle \langle \xi_1 | \xi_2 \rangle$$

where c is a complex constant independent of ξ_i and η_i. Choose $\xi_i = \eta_i = \xi$ where $\|\xi\| = 1$. Then

$$c = \int |\langle \xi | U(s)\xi \rangle|^2 \, d\mu(s) \geq 0.$$

Now $\langle \xi | U(s)\xi \rangle$ is a continuous function of s that equals $\langle \xi | \xi \rangle$ for s equal to the neuter n of G. Since G is locally compact, there will be a neighborhood of n with positive measure on which $|\langle \xi | U(s)\xi \rangle|^2 > \frac{1}{2}\langle \xi | \xi \rangle$, say. Thus the last integral is actually greater than zero. We set $f = c^{-1} > 0$, giving the statement of the corollary.

The reader will be correct if he suspects us of an ulterior aim in introducing the *reciprocal* of c into the formulation of the foregoing corollary. As we shall see in the next section, for compact groups, f is a positive *integer* equal to the dimension of the representation space if μ is so normalized that $\mu(G) = 1$.

The significance of $T(\xi, \eta)$ can be illuminated by an example. Perhaps the simplest involves the finite group of two elements $G = \{n, a\}$ where $a^2 = n$. G has two representations, both one-dimensional: (i) the identity, and (ii) the alternating; which we call U_1 and U_2, respectively. Thus

$$U_1(n)\xi = \xi, \qquad U_1(a)\xi = \xi,$$

$$U_2(n)\eta = \eta, \qquad U_2(a)\eta = -\eta,$$

$$\mu(n) = \mu(a) = \tfrac{1}{2},$$

$$T(\xi, \eta) = \int |U_2(s)\eta\rangle\,\langle U_1(s)\xi|\, d\mu(s)$$

$$= \tfrac{1}{2}|\eta\rangle\,\langle\xi| + \tfrac{1}{2}| - \eta\rangle\,\langle\xi| = 0,$$

whereas

$$T(\eta, \eta) = \int |U_2(s)\eta\rangle\,\langle U_2(s)\eta|\, d\mu(s)$$
$$= \tfrac{1}{2}|\eta\rangle\,\langle\eta| + \tfrac{1}{2}| - \eta\rangle\,\langle -\eta| = |\eta\rangle\,\langle\eta|.$$

Corollary 3. An irreducible square-integrable representation of a unimodular locally compact group G is similar to a subrepresentation of the regular representation of G.

Proof. Suppose $(G, U, \mathfrak{H}(\xi))$ is irreducible. Here, ξ is any unit vector in the carrier space and therefore necessarily cyclic. We shall inject $\mathfrak{H}(\xi)$ into $L^2(G, \mu)$ by the mapping

$$T\colon \eta \to f_\eta \qquad \text{where} \quad \eta \in \mathfrak{H}(\xi), \quad f_\eta \in L^2(G, \mu),$$

and for any $s \in G$,

$$f_\eta(s) = c^{-1/2}\langle\eta|U(s)\xi\rangle$$

where c, the positive constant of Corollary 2, is such that

$$\|\eta\|^2 = \int f_\eta(s) f_\eta^*(s)\, d\mu(s),$$

so that

$$\|\eta\| = 0 \Rightarrow f_\eta = 0$$

and T is an injective isometry. Furthermore, $TU(g)\eta$ is the function that at s takes the value

$$c^{-1/2}\langle U(g)\eta | U(s)\xi\rangle = c^{-1/2}\langle \eta | U(g^{-1}s)\xi\rangle = f_\eta(g^{-1}s) = \lambda(g) f_\eta(s).$$

Thus

$$TU(g)\eta = \lambda(g)T\eta, \qquad \text{for all } \eta$$

and

$$TU(g) = \lambda(g)T$$

so that T injects U isometrically into the left regular representation λ of G on $L^2(G, \mu)$.

The reader is aware of the value of the projectors onto the carrier space of irreducible representations, which were employed by Wigner, in his writings on group theory, as early as 1930. They effect the symmetry adaptation of a wave function. The most common such operation is that which projects out the antisymmetric part of a function. Löwdin and his associates (*20b*) have been especially assiduous in recent years in exploiting the elegant properties of projectors for a wide variety of calculations in chemistry and physics. Wigner's formula for these projectors for finite groups are a particular case of the well-known extension to compact groups. It is not generally appreciated that the same techniques are applicable to square-integrable representations of locally compact groups.

Suppose U_α is an irreducible square-integrable unitary representation of the unimodular group G and that ξ_α is a unit vector in the carrier space of U_α. Suppose A is any continuous representation of G. Let

$$P_\alpha = f_\alpha \int \langle U_\alpha(s)\xi_\alpha | \xi_\alpha\rangle A(s)\, d\mu(s)$$

where $f_\alpha^{-1} = \int |\langle U_\alpha(s)\xi_\alpha|\xi_\alpha\rangle|^2 \, d\mu(s)$. This operator P_α can be given a meaning, as was done for T in the proof of Theorem 11, if $A(s)$ is a square-integrable unitary representation; however, possibly for other cases also, for example, for certain representations on a Banach space.

Theorem 12. With the preceding notation, whenever P_α, P_β are meaningful, then

$$P_\alpha P_\beta = \delta_{\alpha\beta}\langle \xi_\alpha | \xi_\beta\rangle P_\alpha$$

where $\delta_{\alpha\beta}$ equals 0 if U_α and U_β are not similar, and 1 if $U_\alpha(s) = U_\beta(s)$. In the latter case, ξ_α and ξ_β may be different but they both belong to the carrier space of $U_\alpha = U_\beta$.

Proof.

$$
\begin{aligned}
P_\alpha P_\beta &= f_\alpha f_\beta \int d\mu(s) \int d\mu(t) \langle U_\alpha(s)\xi_\alpha|\xi_\alpha\rangle \langle U_\beta(t)\xi_\beta|\xi_\beta\rangle A(st) \\
&= f_\alpha f_\beta \int d\mu(s) \int d\mu(r) \langle U_\alpha(s)\xi_\alpha|\xi_\alpha\rangle \langle U_\beta(s^{-1}r)\xi_\beta|\xi_\beta\rangle A(r) \\
&= f_\alpha f_\beta \int d\mu(r) \int d\mu(s) \langle U_\beta(r)\xi_\beta| U_\beta(s)\xi_\beta\rangle \langle U_\alpha(s)\xi_\alpha|\xi_\alpha\rangle A(r) \\
&= f_\alpha \int d\mu(r)\, \delta_{\alpha\beta}\langle \xi_\alpha|\xi_\beta\rangle \langle U_\alpha(r)\xi_\alpha|\xi_\alpha\rangle A(r)
\end{aligned}
$$

by Theorem 11 and its corollaries. Whence,

$$P_\alpha P_\beta = \delta_{\alpha\beta}\langle \xi_\alpha|\xi_\beta\rangle P_\alpha,$$

as required.

Much of the representation theory of compact and finite groups is an immediate consequence of the simple conclusion of Theorem 12. We see immediately that $P_\alpha^2 = P_\alpha$. Also, if A is a unitary representation, the reader will easily prove [using $\mu(s) = \mu(s^{-1})$] that P_α is Hermitian and, in an obvious notation, that $A(g)P_\alpha(\xi_\alpha) = P_\alpha(U_\alpha(g)\xi_\alpha)A(g)$. If we associate with a finite-dimensional irreducible representation U_α an orthonormal basis $\{\xi_i\}$ of its carrier space, it follows from the theorem that $P_\alpha(\xi_i)P_\alpha(\xi_j) = \delta_{ij}P_\alpha(\xi_i)$ and, letting $Q_\alpha = \sum_i P_\alpha(\xi_i)$, we see that $Q_\alpha^2 = Q_\alpha$. Substituting in the definition of P_α gives

$$Q_\alpha = f_\alpha \int \chi_\alpha(s^{-1})A(s)\, d\mu(s)$$

where $\chi_\alpha(s) = \mathrm{tr}(U_\alpha(s))$ is the character of the irreducible U_α. When the foregoing integral for Q_α is valid, we can easily prove that $A(g)Q_\alpha = Q_\alpha A(g)$, so that Q_α projects out of the carrier space of A an invariant subspace. For compact groups, we know that this subspace carries a primary representation of Type I of similarity class U_α.

VIII. Functions of Positive Type and Compact Groups

Functions $g \to \varphi(g) = \langle \xi|U(g)\xi\rangle$ occur on the diagonal of matrices of a unitary representation U of a group G. In the case that φ is square integrable we have employed such functions in Section VII to define projectors associated with the irreducible representations. From the Schwarz inequality, $|\varphi(g)| \leqslant \|\xi\|^{1/2}\|U(g)\xi\|^{1/2}$, and hence, since U is unitary, $|\varphi(g)| \leqslant \|\xi\| = \varphi(n)$. Thus φ is a continuous bounded function on G. It has the additional property that for

g_i, an arbitrary set of elements of G, the matrix $(\varphi(g_i^{-1}g_j))$ is positive semi-definite. For consider,

$$\sum_{i,j} \varphi(g_i^{-1}g_j)z_i^* z_j = \sum_{i,j} \langle U(g_i)\xi | U(g_j)\xi \rangle z_i^* z_j = \langle \zeta | \zeta \rangle \geqslant 0$$

where $\zeta = \sum_i z_i U(g_i)\xi$. A continuous function on G with this last property will be called a *function of positive type* (FPT) or a *positive definite function.*

An alternative equivalent definition discussed by Dixmier (*15*, Section 13.4.4) is that a function φ is an FPT if

$$\int\int \varphi(st^{-1})\, f^*(s) f(t)\, d\mu(s)\, d\mu(t) \geqslant 0$$

for all continuous complex-valued functions f that vanish outside a compact set.

Suppose that U is a finite-dimensional irreducible unitary representation of a compact group and that $\varphi(s) = u_{11}(s)$, a diagonal element of a matrix representation of U. Then $\varphi(st^{-1}) = u_{11}(st^{-1}) = \sum_j u_{1j}(s)u_{j1}(t^{-1}) = \sum_j u_{1j}(s)u_{1j}^*(t)$ since U is unitary. Thus the foregoing integral will vanish if and only if f is orthogonal to all functions u_{1j} in the first row of (u_{ij}). Thus the quotient of *all* the continuous functions on the compact group by the set of *those* functions that make the foregoing integral vanish is a linear space isomorphic to the finite-dimensional space spanned by u_{1j}. This example will, we hope, make the following definition appear fairly natural.

Given an FPT φ on a locally compact group G, let $\mathfrak{H}'$ consist of all measurable functions f for which

$$\int\int \varphi(st^{-1}) f^*(s) f(t)\, d\mu(s)\, d\mu(t)$$

is finite. Let $\mathcal{N}$ consist of the subset of functions for which the integral above vanishes. Let $\mathfrak{H}_\varphi' = \mathfrak{H}'/\mathcal{N}$ and set

$$\langle f_1 | f_2 \rangle_\varphi = \int\int \varphi(st^{-1}) f_1^*(s) f_2(t)\, d\mu(s)\, d\mu(t).$$

It can be shown that $\langle f_1' | f_2' \rangle_\varphi = \langle f_1 | f_2 \rangle_\varphi$ if $f_1' - f_i \in \mathcal{N}$, so that with the foregoing definition of scalar product $\mathfrak{H}_\varphi'$ is a pre-Hilbert space. The *completion* of $\mathfrak{H}_\varphi'$ is a Hilbert space that we denote by $\mathfrak{H}_\varphi$. Let ρ be the mapping $g \to \rho(g)$ where $\rho(g) f$ is the function such that $\rho(g) f(s) = f(sg)$. Then

$$\begin{aligned}\langle \rho(g) f_1 | \rho(g) f_2 \rangle_\varphi &= \int\int \varphi(st^{-1}) f_1^*(sg) f_2(tg)\, d\mu(s)\, d\mu(t)\\ &= \int\int \varphi(st^{-1}) f_1^*(s) f_2(t)\, d\mu(sg^{-1})\, d\mu(tg^{-1})\\ &= \langle f_1 | f_2 \rangle_\varphi.\end{aligned}$$

Thus $\mathcal{N}$ is invariant under $\rho(g)$. If c is the canonical mapping from $\mathfrak{H}'$ to $\mathfrak{H}'_\varphi$ that maps a function f into the set $c(f)$ of $\mathfrak{H}'/\mathcal{N}$ to which f belongs, then the equation $U_\varphi(g)(c(f)) = c(\rho(g)f)$ defines a unitary representation U_φ of G on the Hilbert space $\mathfrak{H}_\varphi$. The capital fact, proved, for example, by Dixmier (*15*, Section 13.4), is that *every* unitary *cyclic* representation *of a locally compact* group is similar to such a representation U_φ for a proper choice of φ. Here, at last, we have an important theorem valid for arbitrary locally compact groups!

Since φ is bounded, we may normalize it by multiplying by a positive real number to ensure that $\varphi(n) = 1$. Call such a φ a normalized FPT, or an NFPT. The set of NFPT is convex. By a rather subtle argument it can be shown that a topology can be imposed on this set for which it is a compact set. Hence by the Krein-Milman (*21a*) theorem any NFPT can be approximated by linear combinations of *extreme* NFPT with nonnegative real coefficients. It can be proved (*15*, Section 13.6), that an extreme NFPT corresponds to an irreducible representation of G. Thus, *any unitary representation of a locally compact group is a direct sum or a direct integral of irreducibles.* Furthermore, Gelfand and Raikov (*21*) showed that there are enough irreducibles to separate any two elements of G. That is, if $s \neq t$, there is at least one irreducible A for which $A(s) \neq A(t)$.

If φ and ψ are FPT, then so is $\varphi\psi$. It can be shown (*15*, Section 13.4), that $U_{\varphi\psi}$ is the inner direct product $U_\varphi \boxtimes U_\psi$.

The preceding theory has a particularly simple and beautiful application to compact groups, permitting a direct proof of the Peter-Weyl theorem without recourse to the theory of integral equations. Since the Haar measure of a compact group is finite and can be normalized so that $\mu(G) = 1$, every continuous function on G is square integrable. Every irreducible representation of G can be shown to be similar to a unitary representation and is contained in the regular representation. The finiteness of $\mu(G)$ has the further consequence that the dimension of an irreducible is finite. The following proof is generally attributed to Nachbin (*22*).

Theorem 13. An irreducible unitary representation of a compact group on a Hilbert space $\mathfrak{H}$ is finite-dimensional. When $\mu(G) = 1$, the dimension is equal to the constant f of Theorem 11, Corollary 2.

Proof. Suppose η_i, $i \in \{1,2,\ldots,m\}$, are orthonormal vectors in $\mathfrak{H}$, then in the notation of Corollary 2, Theorem 11, and with $\mu(G) = 1 = \langle\xi|\xi\rangle$,

$$1 = \int \langle\xi|\xi\rangle \, d\mu(s) = \int \langle U(s)\xi | U(s)\xi\rangle \, d\mu(s) \geqq \sum_i \int |\langle\eta_i | U(s)\xi\rangle|^2 \, d\mu(s) = \frac{m}{f},$$

since the square of a vector is not less than the sum of the squares of a set of its components in an orthonormal basis. Therefore $m \leqslant f$ and the dim($\mathfrak{H}$) $\leqslant f$. if m equals dim($\mathfrak{H}$), the inequality in the argument just presented becomes an equality and we have $m = f$, as required.

The representation theory of a compact group is rather well known and has had several elegant presentations, notably by Weil (*8*). We therefore summarize some key results that can be derived fairly easily from the foregoing. Let G be compact with $\mu(G) = 1$.

(i) Every continuous irreducible representation Γ_α of G is of finite dimension, say f_α, and occurs f_α times in the two regular representations.

(ii) (Peter-Weyl). The regular representation is the direct sum of irreducible representations and any continuous function on G can be approximated arbitrarily closely by linear combinations of the coefficients $g \to u_{ij}^\alpha(g)$ of irreducible representations. Since any representation of G is square integrable, these coefficients satisfy the orthogonality and normality conditions of Theorem 11, Corollaries 1 and 2.

(iii) The characters χ_α of Γ_α satisfy the conditions

$$f_\alpha f_\beta \int \chi_\alpha(s)\chi_\beta(s^{-1}t)\, ds = \delta_{\alpha\beta} f_\alpha \chi_\alpha(t)$$

where $\delta_{\alpha\beta}$ is unity or zero according as Γ_α and Γ_β are or are not similar. The foregoing equation expresses the fact that $\varphi_\alpha = f_\alpha \chi_\alpha$ are idempotents in the convolution algebra satisfying the equation $\varphi_\alpha * \varphi_\beta = \delta_{\alpha\beta}\varphi_\alpha$, where the asterisk denotes convolution. Again, these equations are equivalent to the relations

$$Q_\alpha Q_\beta = \delta_{\alpha\beta} Q_\alpha$$

among the projectors introduced in the discussion following Theorem 12.

(iv) The space $L^2(G,\mu)$ is a representation space for the outer product $G \times G$ under the action of $\lambda \times \rho$, where λ and ρ are the left and right regular representation, respectively. Under $\lambda \times \rho$, $L^2(G,\mu)$ decomposes into a direct sum of irreducibles $\Gamma_\alpha \times \Gamma_\alpha^c$, where Γ_α^c is the representation contragredient to Γ_α, characterized by $\chi_\alpha^c(g) = \chi_\alpha^*(g) = \chi_\alpha(g^{-1})$. The corresponding irreducible carrier space has dimension f_α^2. Each $\Gamma_\alpha \times \Gamma_\alpha^c$ occurs in $\lambda \times \rho$ once.

We conclude this section by proving an extremely useful variation of the Peter-Weyl theorem that does not seem to be widely known. For finite groups the following theorem was known to Burnside. Wigner (*22a*) attributes the main idea of the following proof to a private communication from M. H. Stone.

Theorem 14. If G is a compact group that possesses a *faithful* finite-dimensional representation $A: g \to A(g) = (a_{ij}(g))$, *then* all irreducible representations of G over the complex numbers occur in the decomposition of the various direct products of A and its complex conjugate representation A^*.

This theorem generalizes and "explains" our familiar experience of manufacturing the representations $\mathscr{D}_j$ of $SU(2)$ from direct products of $\mathscr{D}_{1/2}$; or, the irreducible representations of the rotation group from direct products of $\mathscr{D}_1$; or the irreducible representations of $SL(n, \mathfrak{C})$ from direct products of $SL(n, \mathfrak{C})$. Indeed, since most compact groups in physics originally occur explicitly as faithful linear groups, Theorem 14 has wide application.

Proof. Consider all polynomials homogeneous of degree 0, 1, 2, ... in the coefficients $a_{ij}(g)$ and $a_{ij}^*(g)$ of A and A^*. Let $\{\varphi_n\}$ denote an orthonormal set of functions obtained by the Schmidt process from the foregoing ordered set. If f is any continuous function on G, let $c_n = \int f(s)\varphi_n^*(s)\,d\mu(s)$ so that $\sum c_n\varphi_n$ is the least-squares approximation to f with respect to the set $\{\varphi_n\}$. Let

$$\mathring{f} = f - \sum c_n\varphi_n.$$

We claim that $\mathring{f} = 0$.

To prove this we introduce the functions

$$\delta_N(s, t) = B_N \exp(-N \sum_{ij} |a_{ij}(s) - a_{ij}(t)|^2).$$

Since A is faithful, the foregoing exponent vanishes only if $s = t$. The normalization constant B_N is chosen so that $\int \delta_N(s,t)\,d\mu(s) = 1$. As $N \to \infty, \delta_N$ approaches the Dirac delta function δ. If the exponential function is expressed as a series, it may be expanded in terms of φ_n so $s \to \mathring{f}(s)$ is orthogonal to $s \to \delta_N(s,t)$ for every value of t. Suppose $\mathring{f}(t) \neq 0$, then $\int \mathring{f}(s)\delta(s, t)\,d\mu(s) = \mathring{f}(t) \neq 0$. By considering the limit, as $N \to \infty$, of $\int \mathring{f}(s)\delta_N(s,t)\,d\mu(s)$, we see that this is impossible.

Thus every continuous function on G is contained in the set of functions spanned by the φ_n. In particular, the coefficients of every continuous irreducible representation must occur in at least one of the Kronecker products of A and A^*.

IX. Inducing for Locally Compact Groups

In Section VI we gave a definition of induced representation for finite groups and derived several properties of inducing. It is not difficult to show that with a suitable definition of $\Delta \uparrow G$ all of the results of Section VI remain valid for compact groups. For finite and compact groups all representations are *similar* to unitary square-integrable representations, so that for such groups it is not an essential generalization to consider other than unitary representations. However, a representation of a *simple* noncompact group is either faithful or is trivial. If it is faithful and bicontinuous onto a compact group, for example, a group of unitary finite-dimensional matrices, it is necessarily compact. Thus *a simple non-compact group has no finite unitary representations other than the trivial one.* Many noncompact groups occur in physics as finite-dimensional matrix groups, so we must consider nonunitary representations. On the other hand, we frequently need unitary representations in quantum mechanics, so we are also forced to consider infinite-dimensional representations.

Most definitions of $\Delta(H) \uparrow G$ employ a set of functions as carrier space. The functions have as *domain* either G or G/H and as *range* the complex numbers or the carrier space of Δ. Depending on the purpose of the particular author, the carrier space of $\Delta \uparrow G$ may be a convex topological vector space, a Banach space, or a Hilbert space, and the resulting representation Borelian, differentiable, unitary, or nonunitary. In order to effect the decomposition of $\Delta \uparrow G$ a knowledge of its commutant is desirable, so much effort has been devoted to the study of intertwining spaces and intertwining numbers between induced representations. Even so, this is currently one of the most confused areas of our subject since there are many different intertwining number theorems with different hypotheses and different conclusions. Their intersection is approximately vacuous and their least upper bound apparently nonexistent! In the present brief note we can only hope to pick our way delicately through this maze while bringing to the notice of the attentive reader a few of the more attractive blossoms.

We shall *restrict discussion to unimodular groups* for which the Haar measure μ satisfies $\mu(gs) = \mu(sg) = \mu(s)$. However, recall that in general the *modulus* $\delta_G(g)$ of the group is defined by $\mu(gs) = \delta_G(g)\mu(s)$ if μ is the right invariant Haar measure, and that $\delta_G\colon g \to \delta_G(g)$ is a homomorphism of G into the *positive* reals. (Note that $\delta_G(g) \neq 0$.) Unimodular groups for which $\delta_G(g) = 1$ include all Abelian, compact, and semisimple Lie groups. The theory we describe later for unimodular groups can be readily adapted to the general case by judiciously introducing factors involving $\delta_G(h)$ and $\delta_H(h)$, $(h \in H \subset G)$ at strategic points. These factors greatly complicate the formalism and inhibit comprehension of the main ideas. A reader who is dealing with a group that is not unimodular should consult the writings of Mackey or Blattner (*18c, 19*) for these details.

The ingredients of our definition of $\Delta(H) \uparrow G$ in the finite case were (i) the representation $h \to \Delta(h)$ of the subgroup H and (ii) the space G/H of right cosets acted on by right multiplication by the elements of G. Let us consider functions $f\colon G/H \to V$ where V is the carrier space of Δ. By varying f for *fixed* $\sigma \in G/H, f(\sigma)$ can range over the whole of V, providing a stage for the action of Δ, that is, one of the blocks in our previous block matrix. As σ ranges over

G/H, we obtain $|G|/|H|$ such blocks. Recall that s_σ are fixed coset representatives, set $A = \Delta \uparrow G$, and consider the mapping

$$A(g): f \to A(g)f$$

where

$$A(g)f(\sigma) = \Delta(s_\sigma g s_{\sigma g}^{-1}) f(\sigma g).$$

We claim that $g \to A(g)$ is a representation of G, and leave the reader to verify that $A(g_1 g_2) = A(g_1)A(g_2)$. Note that the "objects" being transformed are *functions* with domain G/H and range V. The preceding definition of $\Delta \uparrow G$ was used in the author's Oxford lectures (*16*). It has the advantage of being the most obvious reformulation in function language of the matrix definition of Section VI. All definitions of $\Delta \uparrow G$ known to the author contain a kernel that is equivalent to the foregoing definition. However, the definition is not yet finished, since if we allowed f to be *any* function from $G/H \to V$, we would be admitting within the pale such horrible objects as discontinuous non-measurable functions. The suppression of such extreme deviates is the point at which different authors part company. In order to have a carrier space for A we need a set of functions that is *invariant under the action of all* $A(g)$. If it satisfies this one condition, we will have a representation of G, possibly not unitary or Borelian, but at least linear. Our assumption that G and H are unimodular assures the existence of a right-invariant measure ν on G/H. The most common restriction on f is to insist that $\int \|f(\sigma)\|_V^2 d\nu(\sigma)$ is finite. It is then possible to impose a Hilbert space structure on the allowed set of functions and to ensure that $\Delta \uparrow G$ is unitary if Δ is unitary. This is the route pursued by Mackey, Loomis, Blattner, and many other authors. However, Moore (*22b*) found that the Frobenius Reciprocity Theorem has a natural generalization if, instead of defining $\Delta \uparrow G$ on a Hilbert space, it is defined on the Banach space consisting of functions f such that $\sigma \to \|f(\sigma)\|$ is *integrable*. Alternatively, Bruhat (*36*), with a view to applications to Lie groups restricted f to belong to a set of *differentiable* functions.

There is a *second* method of defining $\Delta \uparrow G$ which has formal advantages over the first naive approach above even though it is logically equivalent. We take G as the domain of our functions f with V again as range. There are obviously many more functions $G \to V$ than for $G/H \to V$, so we must restrict attention to a special class of such functions. This is done by demanding that $\lambda(h^{-1}) f(s) = f(hs) = \Delta(h) f(s)$ for all $h \in H$, $s \in G$. If $\Delta(h)$ is regarded as given, the effect of this condition is that the value of $f(g)$ is determined for *all* $g \in \sigma$ by its value at *one* $s_\sigma \in \sigma$. Thus the degree of freedom in our choice of these functions on G is the same as for the foregoing functions on G/H. In the sequel we shall consider only unitary representations, so we further restrict the allowed functions f with the aim of manufacturing a Hilbert space. For the sake of definiteness, we settle on the following:

Definition. Given a subgroup H of a locally compact unimodular group G and a unitary representation Δ of H with carrier space V, the induced representation $\Delta \uparrow G = U$ of G from H is defined as follows:

(i) Consider every function $f\colon G \to V$ satisfying $f(hg) = \Delta(h) f(g)$ for all $h \in H$, $g \in G$.

(ii) For functions restricted as in (i) and with μ denoting the Haar measure on G, define

$$\langle f_1 | f_2 \rangle = \int \langle f_1(s) | f_2(s) \rangle_V \, d\mu(s).$$

Let $\mathcal{N} = \{f \mid \langle f | f \rangle = 0\}$, $\mathfrak{H}' = \{f \mid \langle f | f \rangle < \infty\}$. In the usual manner, denote by $\mathfrak{H}$ the completion of $\mathfrak{H}'/\mathcal{N}$ in the norm $\langle f | f \rangle$. $\mathfrak{H}$ is the carrier space of $\Delta \uparrow G$.

(iii) For $f \in \mathfrak{H}$, $g \in G$, $U(g) f$ is a function in $\mathfrak{H}$ defined by $U(g) f(s) = f(sg)$ for all $s \in G$.

It follows immediately from this definition that $U(g_1 g_2) = U(g_1) U(g_2)$. The basic properties of Theorems 3, 4, and 5 also follow without difficulty. However, to pursue the theory beyond this point with the foregoing definition seems to necessitate involvement in troublesome denumerability issues. These have been circumvented by Loomis (*18d*) and Blattner (*19*) by another approach, which is very efficient in the case of unitary representations.

For this *third* definition we employ functions of positive type as the main tool. We shall also need a simple property of the product of measures. Just as an integral over a plane region can be evaluated as a repeated integral, so an integral with respect to Haar measure μ_G on G can be effected as a repeated integral with respect to Haar measure μ_H on the subgroup H and with respect to a measure ν on G/H. With the right coset representatives s_σ fixed as in Section VI any element $g \in G$ has a unique factorization as $g = hs_\sigma$ where $h \in H$. The possibility of replacing integration on G by repeated integration on H and G/H is suggested by the symbolic equation $\mu_G(g) = \mu_H(h)\nu(\sigma)$. If μ_G and μ_H are right invariant, it does not necessarily follow that ν is right invariant. It will be, however, if G and H are unimodular, which is our chief reason for considering only unimodular groups. Associated with the *function* ψ on H we define *the injection of* ψ *in* G as the *distribution* φ on G defined by $\varphi(g) = \psi(h)\delta(\sigma)$, where $g = hs_\sigma$ and where δ is the Dirac distribution such that for any continuous function f on G/H

$$\int \delta(\sigma) f(\sigma) \, d\nu(\sigma) = f(\eta) \qquad \text{where} \quad \eta = H.$$

As remarked previously, it is sufficient to discuss cyclic representations from which any other unitary representation can be obtained as a direct sum. Recall that associated with an FPT ψ on the group H there is a well-defined unitary representation $U_\psi(H)$ on a Hilbert space $\mathfrak{H}_\psi$ constructed from functions f such that $\iint \psi(st^{-1}) f^*(s) f(t) d\mu_H(s) d\mu_H(t)$ is finite. Let φ be the distribution obtained by injecting ψ into G as in the foregoing. It is not difficult to see that we may associate to φ a representation $U_\varphi(G)$ on $\mathfrak{H}_\varphi$ for which the carrier space is manufactured from functions f on G for which $\iint \varphi(st^{-1}) f^*(s) f(t) d\mu_G(s) d\mu_G(t)$ is finite. The resulting representation is $\Delta \uparrow G$, and Blattner (*19*) has proved that it is similar to the representations obtained from our second definition for the case studied by Mackey in which G and G/H are separable. Observe that for $J(\{n\}) \uparrow G$, we may take $\psi(n) = 1$ and $\varphi(g) = \delta(g)$, so that the functions $f \in \mathfrak{H}_\varphi$ are restricted by the condition

$$\int\int \delta(st^{-1}) f^*(s) f(t)\, d\mu(s)\, d\mu(t) = \int |f(s)|^2\, d\mu(s) < \infty.$$

Thus $J(\{n\}) \uparrow G$ is the right regular representation on $L^2(G, \mu)$. In the other, extreme case, $H = G$, $G/H = \eta$, $\nu(\eta) = 1$, and $\Delta \uparrow G = \Delta$, as we would expect.

Theorem 15. If $\Delta(H)$ is square integrable, so is $\Delta \uparrow G$.

Proof. Because $(\Delta_1 \oplus \Delta_2) \uparrow G = \Delta_1 \uparrow G \oplus \Delta_2 \uparrow G$, it is sufficient to assume that Δ is cyclic. We proved that an *irreducible* representation is square integrable if and only if it is a subrepresentation of the reguiar representations and remarked (*15*, Section 14.1) that this is true of any *cyclic* representation. Thus Δ is contained in $J(\{n\}) \uparrow H$ and hence $\Delta \uparrow G$ is a subrepresentation of $J(\{n\}) \uparrow H \uparrow G = J(\{n\}) \uparrow G$, that is, of $\rho(G)$. Hence $\Delta \uparrow G$ is square integrable.

In the following theorem we presuppose our *second* definition of $\Delta \uparrow G$ and use λ to denote the left regular representation of G such that $\lambda(g) f(s) = f(g^{-1}s)$.

Theorem 16. For H compact and $\Delta(H)$ square integrable, the commutant of $\Delta \uparrow G$, $[\Delta \uparrow G]$, is generated by operators of the form $\int a(g) \lambda(g)\, d\mu(g)$, where $a(g)$ is a linear transformation on V that vanishes outside a compact subset of G and is such that for any vectors $\xi, \eta \in V$, $g \to \langle \xi | a(g) \eta \rangle_V$ is a continuous function, and where

$$a(hgh') = \Delta(h) a(g) \Delta(h') \qquad \text{for} \quad h, h' \in H.$$

Proof. Our theorem is due to Mautner (*23*). We sketch the proof.

By Theorem 15, $\Delta \uparrow G$ is similar to a subrepresentation, (G, A, W) say, of the right regular representation ρ where $W \subset L^2(G, \mu)$. Any element of the commutant $[A]$ is the restriction to W of an element of the commutant of ρ. But the latter, for a unimodular group, is known (*24*) to be generated by $\lambda(G)$. Thus $[A]$ is generated by all the linear combinations of $\lambda(g)$, $g \in G$, that leave W invariant. The corresponding operators on the carrier space of $\Delta \uparrow G$ are of the form $\alpha = \int a(g)\lambda(g)\,d\mu(g)$ where $a(g)$ is a linear operator on V, and for $f \in \mathfrak{H}$ we interpret αf as the function such that $\alpha f(s) = \int a(g) f(g^{-1}s)\,d\mu(g)$, which is meaningful since $f(g^{-1}s) \in V$. For any function $g \to a(g)$, it is clear that $\rho(g)\alpha f = \alpha\rho(g) f$, so that α commutes with $\Delta \uparrow G$.

However, α must be restricted, so that $f \in \mathfrak{H} \Rightarrow \alpha f \in \mathfrak{H}$. The restriction that $a(g)$ vanishes outside a compact set ensures that $\langle f \mid f \rangle < \infty \Rightarrow \langle \alpha f \mid \alpha f \rangle < \infty$.

If $\alpha f \in \mathfrak{H}$, then

$$\begin{aligned} \alpha f(hs) &= \Delta(h)\alpha f(s) \\ &= \int \Delta(h) a(g) f(g^{-1}s)\,d\mu(g). \end{aligned}$$

But, using the left invariance of μ,

$$\begin{aligned} \alpha f(hs) &= \int a(g) f(g^{-1}hs)\,d\mu(g) \\ &= \int a(hg) f(g^{-1}s)\,d\mu(g). \end{aligned}$$

For these equations to be valid for all $f \in \mathfrak{H}$ we must have $a(hg) = \Delta(h)a(g)$ for *almost* all g, and therefore for *all* g, *if* we assume that Δ and $g \to a(g)$ are continuous. Furthermore, since μ is left invariant

$$\begin{aligned} \alpha f(s) &= \int a(g) f(g^{-1}s)\,d\mu(g) = \int a(gh) f(h^{-1}g^{-1}s)\,d\mu(g) \\ &= \int a(gh)\Delta(h^{-1}) f(g^{-1}s)\,d\mu(g). \end{aligned}$$

By the same argument as before $a(gh) = a(g)\Delta(h)$, so that $a(hgh') = \Delta(h)a(g)\Delta(h')$ for $h, h' \in H$, as required.

This theorem provides the clue to the key role of double cosets in the theory of induced representations. We met them before in Mackey's Subgroup Theorem, Theorem 7. If we specify $a(g)$ for one value of g in the double coset $\delta = HdH$, it is completely determined on δ by the functional equation $a(hdh') = \Delta(h)a(d)\Delta(h')$. Thus the freedom of choice of a is limited to that of a transformation-valued function on the family D of H, H double cosets of G. There is evidence that the restriction of H to compact subgroups in Theorem 16 can be lifted if $g \to a(g)$ is interpreted as a distribution.

Notice that if $dhd^{-1} \in H$, or if $h \in d^{-1}Hd$, $a(d)\Delta(h) = a(dh) = a(dhd^{-1}d) = \Delta(dhd^{-1})a(d)$. Thus, denoting $\Delta(dhd^{-1})$ by $\Delta^d(h)$ so that Δ^d is a representation of $H^d = d^{-1}Hd$, if $t \in L^d = H \cap H^d$ we have $a(d)\Delta(t) = \Delta^d(t)a(d)$. We have thus proved the following:

Corollary 1. $a(d) \in [\Delta \downarrow L^d, \Delta^d \downarrow L^d]$, where $L^d = H \cap d^{-1}Hd$, and $\Delta^d(s) = \Delta(dsd^{-1})$ for $s \in d^{-1}Hd$.

Defining, $i[\Delta, \delta] = \dim[\Delta \downarrow L^d, \Delta^d \downarrow L^d]$ where $d \in \delta = HdH$, and setting $i[\Delta \uparrow G]$ equal to the *self-intertwining number of* $\Delta \uparrow G$, that is, $i[\Delta \uparrow G] = \dim[\Delta \uparrow G, \Delta \uparrow G]$, we have the following:

Corollary 2. $i[\Delta \uparrow G] \leqq \sum_{\delta \in D} i[\Delta, \delta]$ where D is the family of H, H double cosets.

As mentioned in the introduction of this section, much effort has been devoted to the problem of deciding when equality obtains in this last formula and, if it does not obtain, to the problem of improving the upper bound that the corollary provides for $i[\Delta \uparrow G]$. Clearly if the right-hand side equals 1, then $\Delta \uparrow G$ is irreducible. This is the case of greatest practical interest, since a chief application of inducing has been to the manufacture of infinite-dimensional irreducible unitary representations. It is known that the *equality* in Corollary 2 certainly obtains *if the index of H in G is finite.*

It will perhaps be helpful to illustrate Theorem 16 and Corollary 2 by means of finite groups. We shall assume that the reader is familiar with the association of Young diagrams with irreducible representations of the symmetric group $\mathcal{S}_n$.

Example. The branching theorem for $\mathcal{S}_n$ asserts that when an irreducible representation is restricted to $\mathcal{S}_{n-1}$, the subduced representation decomposes into a direct sum of irreducibles whose Young diagrams are obtained from that of the original diagram by removing one node. Thus

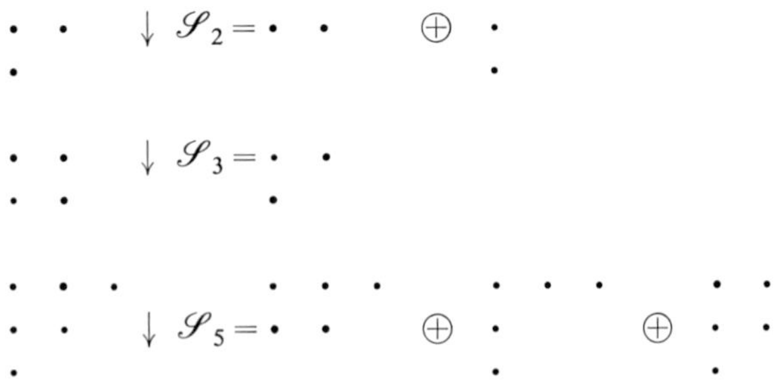

By an application of the Frobenius Reciprocity Theorem, it follows that inducing from an irreducible of $\mathcal{S}_n$ to $\mathcal{S}_{n+1}$ gives rise to a direct sum of the irreducibles corresponding to adding one node to the original Young diagram.

Thus

$$\begin{array}{l}\cdot\ \cdot\\ \cdot\end{array} \uparrow \mathscr{S}_4 = \begin{array}{l}\cdot\ \cdot\ \cdot\\ \cdot\end{array} \oplus \begin{array}{l}\cdot\ \cdot\\ \cdot\ \cdot\end{array} \oplus \begin{array}{l}\cdot\ \cdot\\ \cdot\\ \cdot\end{array}$$

Here $G = \mathscr{S}_4(1,2,3,4)$, the symmetric group on the symbols 1, 2, 3, and 4, and $H = \mathscr{S}_3(1,2,3)$, say; Δ is a two-dimensional representation corresponding to the partition $[2,1]$ of 3. From the explicit decomposition above $i[\Delta \uparrow \mathscr{S}_4] = 3$. There are two H, H double cosets: $G = H + H(34)H$. We may take $\{n, (34)\}$ as double coset representatives.

With $d = n$, $\delta = H$, $L^d = H$, $i[\Delta, \delta] = 1$.

With $d = (34)$, $\delta = H(34)H$, $H^d = \mathscr{S}_3(1,2,4)$, $L^d = \mathscr{S}_2(1,2)$; hence $\Delta \downarrow L^d = [2] \oplus [1^2]$, $\Delta^d \downarrow L^d = [2] \oplus [1^2]$, so that $i[\Delta, \delta] = 2$.

$$3 = 1 + 2.$$

Thus for this simple example equality obtains in the statement of Corollary 2. The symmetric group can be used along the lines just shown to construct a great many simple examples of Theorem 16. It will be found that for finite groups the *equality* always holds in Corollary 2. *Successive* induction gives rise to more interesting situations. Thus

$$[2] \uparrow \mathscr{S}_4 = [2, 1^2] \oplus [2^2] \oplus 2[3, 1] \oplus [4]$$

for which the self-intertwining number is $1^2 + 1^2 + 2^2 + 1^2 = 7$, since it equals $\sum \nu_\alpha^2$ where ν_α is the frequency of the irreducible Γ_α.

The argument that led to Theorem 16 can be extended to deal with the intertwining of two induced representations. For $i \in \{1,2\}$ suppose that H_i are compact, that (H_i, Δ_i, V_i) are *square-integrable* representations, and that $\mathfrak{H}_i$ is the carrier space of $\Delta_i \uparrow G$; then we can prove the following theorem:

Theorem 17. The intertwining space $[\Delta_1 \uparrow G, \Delta_2 \uparrow G]$ is spanned by operators of the form $\alpha = \int a(g)\lambda(g)\,d\mu(g)$ where λ is the left regular representation on $\mathfrak{H}_1$. The linear transformation $a(g)$ from V_1 to V_2 vanishes outside a compact set of G and satisfies the equation

$$a(h_2 d h_1) = \Delta_2(h_2) a(d) \Delta_1(h_1)$$

for all $h_i \in H_i$.

As before, we define $H_2^d = d^{-1} H_2 d$, $L^d = H_1 \cap H_2^d$, $\Delta_2^d(s) = \Delta_2(dsd^{-1})$ for $s \in H_2^d$ and have the following:

Corollary 1. $a(d) \in [\Delta_1 \downarrow L^d, \Delta_2^d \downarrow L^d]$.

Corollary 2. $i[\Delta_1 \uparrow G, \Delta_2 \uparrow G] \leqslant \sum_\delta i[\Delta_1, \Delta_2, \delta]$ where $i[\Delta_1, \Delta_2, \delta] = \dim[\Delta_1 \downarrow L^d, \Delta_2^d \downarrow L^d]$ with $d \in \delta = H_2 d H_1$.

It is clear that Theorem 16 is the particular case of Theorem 17 for which $H_2 = H_1$ and $\Delta_2 = \Delta_1$.

Theorems 16 and 17 immediately imply the following properties about the irreducibility of induced representations.

Theorem 18. For Δ a square-integrable representation of the compact group H, $\Delta \uparrow G$ will be irreducible if (i) Δ is irreducible and (ii) $i(\Delta, \delta) = 0$ for $\delta \neq H$. Further, if $\Delta_1 \uparrow G$ and $\Delta_2 \uparrow G$ are irreducible, they will be inequivalent if $i[\Delta_1, \Delta_2, \delta] = 0$ for all δ.

The H, H double cosets are especially easy to describe when H is a normal subgroup since $HdH = Hd$ for all d. The double cosets coincide with ordinary cosets and they correspond to elements of the quotient group G/H. Further, for all d, $H^d = H = L^d$, so that Δ^d is a representation of H that we call a *conjugate* of Δ. Thus for Δ irreducible $i[\Delta, \delta] = 1$ or 0 according as Δ^d is or is not similar to Δ. The set of all elements d of G for which Δ^d is similar to Δ form a subgroup that we shall call the *little group of* Δ and denote by K. A set of representatives of each of the similarity classes of representations conjugate to Δ will be called a *star of* Δ. The number of elements of a star equals the index of K in G. The group H is a normal subgroup of K, and K/H is the *little co-group of* Δ. The foregoing language originated in the study of space groups, in which a vector of the reciprocal lattice names a representation, the little group leaves the vector fixed, and its star is a set of vectors equivalent to it under the action of the point group of the lattice.

Suppose H is a normal subgroup of G and Γ an *irreducible* representation of G with carrier space V, and that $\Gamma \downarrow H$ decomposes into a direct sum of irreducible representations of H. Suppose that in this direct sum the irreducible representation Δ of H occurs with carrier space $V_1 \subset V$. We assert that *the only other irreducibles of H that occur are conjugates of* Δ, *that all conjugates actually occur and each with the same frequency*. For any $g \in G$, $\Gamma(g^{-1})V_1$ is a subspace of V which, under the action of $\Gamma(h)$, $h \in H$, becomes $\Gamma(h)\Gamma(g^{-1})V_1 = \Gamma(g^{-1})\Gamma(g)\Gamma(h)\Gamma(g^{-1})V_1 = \Gamma(g^{-1})\Gamma(ghg^{-1})V_1 = \Gamma(g^{-1})(\Delta^g(h)V_1) \subset \Gamma(g^{-1})V_1$. Thus $\Gamma(g^{-1})V_1$ is the carrier space of Δ^g, under the action of $\Gamma \downarrow H$. Hence all the conjugates of Δ actually occur. Let $M = \{m | \Gamma(m)V_1 \subset V_1, m \in G\}$. M is a subgroup that contains H. M is contained in K, for V_1 is irreducible under $\Gamma \downarrow H$ giving the subrepresentation Δ; hence Δ^m must be similar to Δ for $m \in M$ and thus $M \subset K$. If $M \neq K$, there are elements $k \in K$ such that $\Gamma(k)V_1 \not\subset V_1$, yet $\Gamma(k)V_1$ is the carrier space of an irreducible representation of H that is similar to Δ. It is fairly obvious that *Δ occurs in $\Gamma \downarrow H$ with frequency*

$|K|/|M|$ and that the dimension of Γ equals the dim(Δ) $\times$ ($|K|/|M|$) $\times$ ($|G|/|K|$), that is, the dim(Δ) *multiplied by the index of M in G.*

As remarked earlier, for Δ irreducible and H normal, $i[\Delta, \delta] = 1$ if Δ^d is similar to Δ; otherwise it is zero. Thus $i[\Delta \uparrow G] = |K|/|H|$. Hence if $K = H$, $\Delta \uparrow G$ is irreducible. Suppose that Λ_α is an irreducible representation of K such that $\Lambda_\alpha \downarrow H$ contains Δ with frequency f_α. It must contain the star of Δ under K which, by definition, is Δ. We claim that $\Lambda_\alpha \uparrow G$ is irreducible. For by Corollary 2 of Theorem 16, $i[\Lambda_\alpha \uparrow G] \leqq \sum i[\Lambda_\alpha, \delta]$ where the summation is over all double cosets $\delta = KdK$. $L^d = K \cap K^d$ always contains H, which is normal, and it easily follows that $i[\Lambda_\alpha, \delta] = 0$ except for $\delta = K$, and in this case $L^d = K$, and $i[\Lambda_\alpha \downarrow K] = 1$ since Λ_α is irreducible. Hence $\Lambda_\alpha \uparrow G$ is irreducible. We are thus led to the *key result of the theory of little groups.*

Theorem 19. If Δ is a square-integrable representation of the compact normal subgroup H of the locally compact unimodular group G and Λ_α is an irreducible representation of K, the little group of Δ, then

(i) $\Lambda_\alpha \uparrow G = \Gamma_\alpha$ is irreducible.
(ii) $\Lambda_\alpha \downarrow H = f_\alpha \Delta$.
(iii) $\Delta \uparrow G = \sum f_\alpha \Gamma_\alpha$.
(iv) All square-integrable irreducible representations of G may be obtained by this process.

We thus have the following recipe, familiar from the study of space groups, for finding irreducible representations of a group G containing a normal subgroup H. *First*, collect the irreducible representations of H into conjugate classes under G, that is, into stars. *Second*, from a star choose one representation Δ and find its little group K. *Third*, obtain the irreducible subrepresentations Λ_α of $\Delta \uparrow K$. *Finally*, construct $\Lambda_\alpha \uparrow K = \Gamma_\alpha$. By following this prescription for all stars we obtain each irreducible representation of G once.

Unfortunately, the exact scope of the procedure just presented is somewhat in doubt. In the cases of greatest practical interest, the space groups and the inhomogeneous Lorentz group, the normal subgroup H is not compact and so its irreducible representations are not square integrable so our proof does not apply. However, Mackey has proved that if, in Theorem 19, we take for Λ_α a *primary* representation of the little group, then the foregoing method produces all the primary representations of G for any Type I group. Thus, in fact, Theorem 19 applies to space groups and Lorentz groups. Furthermore, the Λ_α are simply related to the representation Δ of H and the irreducible projective representations of the little co-group K/H. When H is Abelian, Mackey has even dealt with cases of non-Type I groups. The method is therefore of sufficiently wide scope to cover most current applications in physics. The reader is referred to Mackey (*4*, Section 6) for precise details.

X. Applications

To pursue all the applications of induced and subduced representations of groups would lead us through huge tracts of contemporary mathematics and physics. The present section consists of brief notes dealing with a sampling of topics of current interest and importance together with a few references to the literature.

A. Galilei and Poincaré Groups

The current appreciation of inducing as a convenient method of obtaining representations of groups is probably due to its use by Wigner in his classic paper (*7*) on the inhomogeneous Lorentz group more than to any other single factor. Essentially, Wigner's approach involves a straightforward use of Theorem 19. We first illustrate the method in a simpler situation.

1. Rigid Motions in Euclidean n *Space*, E_n

The group G of motions of E_n contains the n-dimensional translation group T_n as a normal subgroup, and the homogeneous group of rotations and reflections O_n that leave the origin fixed. Indeed G is a semidirect product of T_n and O_n, $G = T_n \wedge O_n$ and any $g \in G$ has a unique factorization $g = \mathbf{t}s$ where $\mathbf{t} \in T_n$ and $s \in O_n$. To apply Theorem 19, we choose $H = T_n$. An irreducible representation Δ of H is necessarily one-dimensional and can be expressed as $\mathbf{t} \to \exp(i\mathbf{p}\cdot\mathbf{t})$ where $\mathbf{p}$ is a fixed real n vector characterizing Δ, $\mathbf{t}$ is an n vector corresponding to an arbitrary translation so that $\mathbf{t} \in H$, and $\mathbf{p}\cdot\mathbf{t}$ is the Euclidean scalar product. K, the little group of Δ, consists of all elements of G leaving $\mathbf{p}$ unchanged and therefore contains H and, if $|\mathbf{p}| > 0$, a subgroup O_{n-1} of O_n; indeed K is a semidirect product $H \wedge O_{n-1}$. When $|\mathbf{p}| = 0$, $K = G$. The conjugate representations Δ^d are all the representations characterized by vectors of the same length as $\mathbf{p}$, thus a star is simply a sphere of radius $|\mathbf{p}| = p$, say. If $s \to D_\alpha(s)$ is an irreducible representation of O_{n-1}, then, if $k = \mathbf{t}s$, $k \to \exp(i\mathbf{p}\cdot\mathbf{t}) \times D_\alpha(s)$ is an irreducible representation of K, which we call $\Lambda_{\alpha,p}$. It can be shown that *any* irreducible representation Λ of K such that $\Lambda \downarrow H$ contains Δ is of the type $\Lambda_{\alpha,p}$. Thus by choosing *one* Δ for $|\mathbf{p}| = p > 0$, $\Lambda_{\alpha,p} \uparrow G = \Gamma_{\alpha,p}$ is irreducible. When $p = 0$, Δ is the identity representation of H, and $\Gamma_{\alpha,0}(g) = \Lambda_\alpha(s)$, where $g = \mathbf{h}s$, $\mathbf{h} \in H$, $s \in O_n$. All irreducible representations of G are obtained in this way.

The simplicity of the preceding application of Theorem 19 resulted from two properties of G: (i) H is Abelian, so the candidates for Δ are all one-dimensional; (ii) G is a semidirect product. These two properties permitted us to obtain the irreducible representations of the little group immediately from representations of H and representations of the little co-group K/H. Happily this same situation obtains for the space groups and the Poincaré group.

2. Extended Poincaré Group

By the Poincaré group we understand the affine isomorphisms of Minkowski space. It contains a four-dimensional translation group H and the extended Lorentz group, which leaves the origin fixed. As in (1), an irreducible representation of H, Δ, is characterized by a linear form in the translations $\mathbf{t}$. Since the Minkowski scalar product $\mathbf{a}\cdot\mathbf{b} = a^0b^0 - a^1b^1 - a^2b^2 - a^3b^3$ is nonsingular, we may express this linear form as $\mathbf{p}\cdot\mathbf{t}$ where $\mathbf{p}$ is a real four-vector and $\mathbf{t}$ is an arbitrary translation. The argument proceeds exactly as in (1), except that instead of *two* kinds of stars, depending on whether $p = 0$ or $p > 0$, there are *four*. They result from the fact that the Lorentz group leaves the *Minkowski* magnitude of $\mathbf{p}$ fixed so that spacelike, null, and timelike vectors cannot belong to the same star. However, within each of the four classes a star is characterized, as in (1), by $|\mathbf{p}|^2 = p^2$. The little group in the four cases is a semidirect product of H and: (i) the full Lorentz group, when $\mathbf{p} = 0$; (ii) the three-dimensional homogeneous Euclidean group O_3, when $\mathbf{p}$ is timelike or for $p^2 > 0$; (iii) the homogeneous Lorentz group in Minkowski three-space when $\mathbf{p}$ is spacelike or for $p^2 < 0$; and (iv) the Euclidean group in two dimensions, O_2, when $\mathbf{p}$ is a null vector or for $p = 0$.

If we do not allow time reflection, the class (ii) of stars will partition into the past and future subclasses (a) $p^2 > 0$, $p^0 < 0$; (b) $p^2 > 0$, $p^0 > 0$. In order to allow fermions it is necessary to admit double-valued representations, or to consider, instead of the Poincaré group, its two-sheeted simply connected covering group. For this, the groups (ii) and (iii) described in the preceding paragraphs are replaced by $SU(2, \mathfrak{C})$ and $SL(2, \mathfrak{R})$ respectively.

The physical literature abounds in discussion of the topic of the present section. The preceding note depends heavily on Mackey (*20a*, pp. 171–173) and the article of Moussa and Stora in the Boulder lectures (*24a*). The author has also found the following articles especially lucid or interesting (Wigner, *25*; Shirokov, *26*; Kummer, *27*). That the physical interpretation of the irreducible representations is somewhat in doubt is apparent from Wigner (*25*) and Pursey (*28*).

3. Galilei Group

According to a theorem of Wigner, for the Poincaré group it is sufficient for quantum-mechanical purposes to consider ordinary representations. In general, however, since a pure state corresponds not to a vector but to a *ray* obtained from a vector by arbitrary changes of phase, it is to be expected that projective representations should play a key role in quantum mechanics. These are such that the rule $A(g_1g_2) = A(g_1)A(g_2)$ for ordinary representations is replaced by $A(g_1g_2) = \omega(g_1, g_2)A(g_1)A(g_2)$ where $\omega(g_1, g_2)$ is a complex number of unit modulus, called the *multiplier* of the representation. Because $A((g_1g_2)g_3) = A(g_1(g_2g_3))$, ω satisfies the functional equation

$$\omega(g_1, g_2g_3)\omega(g_2, g_3) = \omega(g_1g_2, g_3)\omega(g_1, g_2).$$

Mackey (*20*) showed that the ordinary theory of inducing can be extended to projective representations. This is necessary for the ten-parameter Galilei group G of rotations, translations, time dilations, and uniform motions. Bargmann (*28a*) has shown that the projective representations of G may be readily obtained from the ordinary representations of an eleven-parameter group G_M. Voisin (*29*) has given an elegant treatment of the representations of G_M by a straightforward application of the little group theorem.

B. Products of Representations and Branching Laws

To study the symmetry of a complex system composed of simpler parts it is frequently essential to analyze the inner direct product $\Gamma \boxtimes \Lambda$ of two representations of a group G. To express the carrier spaces of the direct summands in terms of the product of the spaces of the components requires a knowledge of the Clebsch-Gordan coefficients. When a product of more than two components is involved, Racah coefficients, fractional parentage coefficients, $3j$-, $6j$-, $9j$-symbols, etç., enter into play. Sometimes these generalized Clebsch-Gordan coefficients can be obtained recursively by analyzing $\Gamma \boxtimes (\Lambda \downarrow H)$ where H is an appropriate subgroup of G. To decompose $\Lambda \downarrow H$ into its irreducible constituents is to obtain a branching law. The prototype for all such laws is the one due to Young that we quoted in Section IX for $[\lambda] \downarrow \mathscr{S}_{N-1}$, where $[\lambda]$ is an irreducible representation of the symmetric group of permutations of N symbols, $\mathscr{S}_N$. Thus to find a branching law is equivalent to an act of subducing and this, by the Frobenius reciprocity theorem, is to decompose a corresponding induced representation. Thus, endemic among theoretical physicists today are acts of induction and subduction!

1. The Poincaré Group

When we are concerned with the product of two induced representations $\Delta_1 \uparrow G \boxtimes \Delta_2 \uparrow G$ where Δ_i is a representation of $H_i \subset G$, Theorem 9 of Section VI may be of use. That this indeed is an ideal tool for application to the Poincaré group is shown very clearly by the article of Moussa and Stora (*24a*). The central core of their method of deriving the formulas of Jacob and Wick (*29a*) for the product of two irreducible representations of the Poincaré group is precisely Theorem 9.

2. Representations of $\mathscr{S}_N$

The author showed (*16*) that if we take the product H_1 of certain symmetric groups associated with a partition λ of N, and the similar group H_2 associated with the conjugate partition $\bar{\lambda}$, then

$$i[J(H_1) \uparrow \mathscr{S}_N, \bar{J}(H_2) \uparrow \mathscr{S}_N] = 1$$

where J is the identity and $\bar{J}$ the alternating representation. Thus there is a unique irreducible representation of $\mathscr{S}_N$ common to $J(H_1) \uparrow \mathscr{S}_N$ and $\bar{J}(H_2) \uparrow \mathscr{S}_N$. It is the representation of $\mathscr{S}_N$ commonly denoted by $[\lambda]$. A mixture of the approaches of Frobenius and Young leads quickly to the principal results of the theory of the representation of $\mathscr{S}_N$. Schur's relation, which asserts that the commutant of the N-fold inner product of $GL(n, \mathfrak{C})$ is generated by $\mathscr{S}_N$, may then be used to obtain a considerable generalization of Weyl's branching law for $GL(n, \mathfrak{C})$.

A comprehensive summary of known branching laws for simple Lie groups is provided by Whippman (*30*).

C. Irreducible Representations of Compact Lie Groups

Let Δ_m denote the one-dimensional representation $\theta \to \exp(im\theta)$ of a maximal one-parameter subgroup H of $SU(2, \mathfrak{C}) = G$, where θ is a parameter such that $\theta = 0$ and $\theta = 4\pi$ correspond to the identity operation so that $2m$ is an integer. How does $\Delta_j \uparrow G$ decompose? We know that the irreducible representations are the $\mathscr{D}_j$ of dimension $2j+1$. Further, $\mathscr{D}_j \downarrow H$ contains Δ_m once if and only if $j \geqq |m|$. Thus,

$$\Delta_j \uparrow G = \mathscr{D}_j \oplus \mathscr{D}_{j+1} \oplus \mathscr{D}_{j+2} \oplus \cdots = \sum_{s=0}^{\infty} \mathscr{D}_{j+s}.$$

We may thus write, symbolically

$$\mathscr{D}_j = (\Delta_j \uparrow G) - (\Delta_{j+1} \uparrow G)$$

or

$$\mathscr{D}_j = (\Delta_j \uparrow G)/(\Delta_{j+1} \uparrow G).$$

This suggests that the irreducible representations of $SU(2)$ can be manufactured from representations induced from its maximal Abelian subgroups. We are led to consider whether or not some analogous procedure would apply to any compact Lie group.

A compact connected Abelian group of dimension n is merely an n-dimensional torus, that is, the product of n circle groups. The characters of such a torus, H, maximal in G are specified by n integers $(m_1, m_2, \ldots, m_n) = \mathbf{m}$ and correspond to one-dimensional irreducible representations $\Delta_{\mathbf{m}}$, say. The analysis of $\Delta_{\mathbf{m}} \uparrow G$ is as simple as before. It proves sufficient to consider only $\mathbf{m}$ for which $m_i \geqq 0$. These may be ordered by the definition: $\mathbf{m}' \geqslant \mathbf{m}$ is equivalent to $\Delta_{\mathbf{m}'}$ in $\Gamma \downarrow H \Rightarrow \Delta_{\mathbf{m}}$ in $\Gamma \downarrow H$ for all irreducible representations Γ. In the decomposition of $\Delta_{\mathbf{m}} \uparrow G$ there is an irreducible representation Γ such that

$\Gamma \downarrow H$ contains $\Delta_{\mathbf{m}'}$ only if $\mathbf{m}' \leqq \mathbf{m}$ and in which $\Delta_{\mathbf{m}}$ occurs with frequency one. Denote this unique irreducible representation by Γ_m. Then

$$\Delta_{\mathbf{m}} \uparrow G = \sum f_{\mathbf{mm}'} \Gamma_{\mathbf{m}'}$$

where $f_{\mathbf{mm}'}$, by FRT, is the frequency of $\Delta_{\mathbf{m}}$ in $\Gamma_{\mathbf{m}'} \downarrow H$. A knowledge of $f_{\mathbf{mm}'}$ for $\mathbf{m}' \leqq \mathbf{m}$ is equivalent to the knowledge of the character of $\Gamma_{\mathbf{m}}$.

The value of $f_{\mathbf{mm}'}$, also called the multiplicity of a weight of a representation, is implicit in Weyl's formula for the character, as is shown by Cartier (*31*). These multiplicities were applied by Steinberg (*32*) to effect the decomposition of the product of two irreducible representations.

D. Space Groups

We remarked that the language adopted in connection with Theorem 19 is familiar to solid state physicists from its occurrence in the study of space groups. This topic is treated elsewhere in this volume.

The analysis of the product of three irreducible representations of a space group results in selection rules for allowed transitions. This problem has been discussed by Bradley in an elegant paper (*17*), using the methods of the present chapter.

E. Examples of Type II Representations

Type II and Type III representations are so startlingly different from those of Type I, which are the only ones that occur for finite groups, that it is of great interest to have specific examples upon which to meditate. Kleppner (*33*) has shown that Type II_1 always occur in representations $\Delta(H) \uparrow G$ when Δ is irreducible and H is a normal subgroup of a discrete group G for which the index of H in G is infinite.

F. Magnetic Translation Group

In the de Haas-van Alphen effect in metals there are observations that can be interpreted as due to a broadening of the Landau levels of the electrons in the uniform external magnetic field. In certain cases this broadening is considerably greater than has been explained by theory hitherto. In searching for an explanation we are led to study the Bloch levels in a uniform magnetic field $\mathbf{B}$. Since in a uniform magnetic field the physical situation is unchanged by a lattice translation $\mathbf{R} = \sum_i n^i \mathbf{a}_i$ (n^i are integers, $\mathbf{a}_i$ generate the lattice translation group G), from analogy with the usual theory of space groups we would expect that to any $\mathbf{R} \in G$ corresponds an operator $T(\mathbf{R})$ such that $\mathbf{R} \to T(\mathbf{R})$ is a representation of G. However, it gives rise, not to an ordinary representation, but rather to a projective or ray representation such that

$$T(\mathbf{R}_1)T(\mathbf{R}_2) = T(\mathbf{R}_2)T(\mathbf{R}_1)\exp(-i\mathbf{R}_1 \times \mathbf{R}_2 \cdot \boldsymbol{\beta})$$

where $\hbar c\boldsymbol{\beta} = e\mathbf{B}$ with e equal to the electronic charge. These representations have been discussed by Brown (*34*) and Zak (*35*), who refer to several other papers.

We mention this magnetic translation group not because any immediate application of inducing has been made to it, but because it illustrates behavior possible for projective representations which is unheard of for ordinary representations.

For example, since G is Abelian, we naturally expect irreducible representations to be one-dimensional. Far from it! Because of the multiplier $\omega(\mathbf{R}_1, \mathbf{R}_2) = \exp(-i\mathbf{R}_1 \times \mathbf{R}_2 \cdot \boldsymbol{\beta})$ the operators $T(\mathbf{R})$ do not commute. Brown and Zak obtain the irreducible projective representations of G. For the applications to solids they have large dimension, most often infinite. If the magnetic field satisfies certain rationality conditions determined by the lattice constants, an irreducible ω representation is finite-dimensional but otherwise infinite. The author is unaware of any other function associated with a simple physical problem that is so utterly discontinuous. If we consider the dependence of the dimension of an irreducible representation of G on the magnitude of the field $\mathbf{B}$, then within any finite interval of values of $|\mathbf{B}|$ there is a denumerable set for which the dimension is finite and a continuous infinity of values at which the dimension is infinite!

G. Representations of Noncompact Lie Groups

An irreducible representation of a compact group is necessarily of finite dimension and is similar to a unitary representation. An irreducible representation of a compact Lie group may be designated by a character of a maximal Abelian subgroup.

If a simple group is not compact, then any unitary representation other than the trivial one has infinite dimension. Thus, for example, in the case $\mathbf{p} = 0$ for the Poincaré group discussed in Section X. A, we face the problem of obtaining the infinite-dimensional unitary representations of the homogeneous Lorentz group—a simple noncompact group of six real parameters.

All the infinite-dimensional representations of such groups that are effectively known were constructed by inducing from a representation of a solvable subgroup. Soviet mathematicians, particularly Gelfand, Naimark, and Graev were pioneers in this area. A review of their work and related papers is given by Mackey (*3*, Section 9). Perhaps the most important single reference is to the thesis of Bruhat (*36*).

The clue to the methods of these various authors is Iwasawa's theorem, which, for a connected semisimple Lie group G, asserts the existence of a maximal compact subgroup K and a corresponding solvable subgroup S such that $G = KS$ while $K \cap S$ contains only the neuter of G. *Suppose* it were possible, as is the case for $SL(n, \mathfrak{C})$, to embed S in a larger solvable subgroup $\tilde{S} \supset S$, such that $\tilde{S} \cap K = A$, then A, as a solvable subgroup of a compact group, is necessarily Abelian. In G there is only one $\tilde{S}, K$ double coset, so that, if Theorem 17 applies, for a one-dimensional representation Δ of $\tilde{S}$ and an irreducible representation Λ of K, it follows that $i = i[\Delta \uparrow G, \Lambda \uparrow G] = i[\Delta \downarrow A, \Lambda \downarrow A]$. But $\Delta \downarrow A$ is merely a character of the Abelian group A so that i equals the frequency of $\Delta \downarrow A$ in $\Lambda \downarrow A$, and is therefore necessarily finite. *Suppose* A is a maximal Abelian subgroup of K, which is the case for $SL(n, \mathfrak{C})$, and that $\Delta \downarrow A$ is the character that designates the irreducible Λ then $i = 1$. Thus a unique irreducible of G is isolated as common to $\Delta \uparrow G$ and $\Lambda \uparrow G$. Compare this with our earlier definition of the representation $[\lambda]$ of $\mathscr{S}_N$. Indeed, Bruhat has shown, under somewhat general circumstances, that $\Delta \uparrow G$ is itself irreducible. These cases admit the simplest explicit treatment.

For $\alpha, \beta, z \in \mathfrak{C}$ and $\alpha_i, \beta_i, z_i \in \mathfrak{R}$, notice that $z \rightarrow \varphi(z) = \exp(\alpha z + \beta \bar{z}) = \exp[(\alpha_1 + \beta_1)z_1 + i(\alpha_2 - \beta_2)z_2]$ is a homomorphism of the additive into the multiplicative group of complex numbers. If $|\varphi(z)| = 1$, $\alpha_1 + \beta_1 = i\rho$ is a pure imaginary, whereas $\alpha_2 - \beta_2 = m$ is a real number. If, for $z_1 = 0$, $0 \leqq z_2 < 2\pi$, we want $\varphi(z)$ to be the circle group then m must be an integer. *Suppose* that the unitary character Δ depends on n such complex numbers z in such a way that restricting them to their pure imaginary parts gives $\Delta \downarrow A$, then Δ will be characterized by n integers m_i and n pure imaginaries $i\rho_i$. Granting the foregoing unbelievable four suppositions, it follows that there is a unique unitary irreducible representation of G characterized by n integers (m_i) and n pure imaginaries $(i\rho_i)$. This is indeed the case for what Gelfand and Naimark (*37*) call the *nondegenerate principal series* of irreducible representations of $SL(n, \mathfrak{C})$!

In a somewhat similar manner other series of representations of $SL(n, \mathfrak{C})$ and of various real simple Lie groups may be defined. The subject is still under active study and, to the author's knowledge, only for $SL(2, \mathfrak{C})$ and $SL(2, \mathfrak{R})$ is it certain that all irreducible unitary representations have been discovered.

Kirillov (*38*) has shown that the little group theory is also the key to the study of representations of nilpotent Lie groups.

REFERENCES

1. G. Frobenius, Über Relationen zwischen den Charakteren einer Gruppe und denen ihrer Untergruppen. *Sitzber. Akad. Wiss. Berlin* **36**, 501–515 (1898).

2. H. Weyl, "The Theory of Groups and Quantum Mechanics." Dutton, New York, 1931.

3. G. W. Mackey, Infinite dimensional group representations. *Bull. Amer. Math. Soc.* **69**, 628–668 (1963).

4. G. W. Mackey, "Group Representations and Non-Commutative Harmonic Analysis." Univ. of California Press, Berkeley, California, 1965.

5. R. Hermann, "Lie Groups for Physicists." Benjamin, New York, 1966.

6. A. Speiser, "Theorie der Gruppen von endlicher Ordnung." Springer, Berlin, 1927 [Reprinted by Dover, New York, 1945].

7. E. P. Wigner, *Ann. of Math.* **40**, 149–204 (1939).

8. A. Weil, "L'Intégration dans les Groupes Topologiques." Hermann, Paris, 1940.

9. G. W. Mackey, Induced representations of locally compact groups, I and II. *Ann. of Math.* **55**, 101–139 (1952); **58**, 193–221 (1953).

10. F. J. Dyson, Applications of group theory in particle physics *SIAM Rev.* **8**, 1–10 (1966).

11. A. S. Eddington, "New Pathways in Science." Cambridge Univ. Press, London and New York, 1935.

11a. I. Schur, Ueber eine Klasse von Matrizen. Thesis. Berlin, 1901.

11b. G. Orwell, "Animal Farm." Harcourt, Brace, New York, 1946.

12. P. R. Halmos, "Measure Theory." Van Nostrand, Princeton, New Jersey, 1950.

13. J. M. Jauch, Projective representation of the Poincaré group in quaternionic Hilbert space, this volume; G. Emch, Representations of the Lorentz group in quaternionic quantum mechanics. *In* "Lectures in Theoretical Physics" (W. E. Brittin and A. O. Barut, eds.), Vol. VIIa, Chapter 1. Univ. of Colorado Press, Boulder, Colorado, 1964.

14. R. Arens, *Bull. Amer. Math. Soc.* **53**, 623–632 (1947).

15. J. Dixmier, "Les C*-algèbres et leurs représentations." Gauthier-Villars, Paris, 1964.

15a. P. A. M. Dirac, "The Principles of Quantum Mechanics." Oxford Univ. Press, London and New York, 1930.

16. A. J. Coleman, "Induced Representations with Applications to GL(n) and $\mathscr{S}_N$." Queen's Papers in Pure Appl. Math. No. 4, Tech. Supplies. Queen's Univ., Kingston, Ontario, 1966.

17. C. J. Bradley, Space groups and selection rules. *J. Mathematical Phys.* **7**, 1145–1152 (1966).

18. C. W. Curtis and I. Reiner, "Representation Theory of Finite Groups and Associative Algebras." Wiley (Interscience), New York, 1962.

18a. H. Maschke, *Math. Ann.* **50**, 482–498 (1898).

18b. G. de B. Robinson, Lectures. Univ. of Toronto, Toronto, Ontario, 1950–1965.

18c. G. W. Mackey, Induced representations of locally compact groups I, II. *Ann. of Math.* **55**, 101–139; **58**, 193–220 (1952).

18d. L. H. Loomis, Positive definite functions of induced representations. *Duke Math. J.* **27**, 564–579 (1960).

19. R. J. Blattner, Positive definite measures. *Proc. Amer. Math. Soc.* **14**, 423–428 (1963).

20. G. W. Mackey, Unitary representations of group extensions, I. *Acta Math.* **99**, 265–311 (1958).

20a. G. W. Mackey, Lecture notes, Chapter III, Sect. 3. Univ. of Chicago, Chicago, Illinois, 1955.

20b. P. O. Löwdin, Angular momentum wave functions constructed by projection operators. *Rev. Mod. Phys.* **36**, 966–976 (1964).

21. I. M. Gelfand and D. A. Raikov, Irreducible unitary representations of arbitrary locally compact groups, *Mat. Sb.* **13**, (*55*), 301–316 (1943).

21a. M. Krein and D. Milman, *Studia Math.* **9**, 133–138 (1940).

22. L. Nachbin, On the finite dimensionality of every irreducible representation of a compact group. *Proc. Amer. Math. Soc.* **12**, 11–12 (1961).

22a. E. P. Wigner, Lectures on group theory. Princeton Univ., Princeton, New Jersey, 1955.

22b. C. C. Moore, On the Frobenius reciprocity theorem for locally compact groups. *Pacific J. Math.* **12**, 359–365 (1962).

23. F. I. Mautner, *Proc. Nat. Acad. Sci. U.S.A.* **37**, 431–435 (1951).

24. I. Segal, The two-sided regular representations of a unimodular locally compact group. *Ann. of Math.* **51**, 293–298 (1950).

24a. P. Moussa and R. Stora, Some remarks on the product of irreducible representations of the inhomogeneous Lorentz group. *In* "Lectures in Theoretical Physics" (W. E. Brittin and A. O. Barut, eds.), Vol.VIIa. Univ. of Colorado Press, Boulder, Colorado, 1964.

25. E. P. Wigner, *in* "Group Theoretical Concepts and Methods in Elementary Particle Physics" (F. Gürsey, ed.), Chapter 2. Gordon and Breach, New York, 1964.

26. I. M. Shirokov, Group-theoretical consideration of the basis of relativistic quantum mechanics. *Soviet Physics JETP* **6**, 664–673, 911–928, 929–935 (1958).

27. M. Kummer, The most general Clebsch-Gordan coefficients of the universal covering group of the inhomogeneous Lorentz group. *J. Mathematical Phys.* **7**, 997–1015 (1966).

28. D. Pursey, *Ann. Physics* **32**, 157–191 (1965).

28a. V. Bargmann, Unitary ray representations of continuous groups. *Ann. of Math.* **59**, 1–46 (1954).

29. J. Voisin, On some Unitary representations of the Galilei group. I. Irreducible representations. *J. Mathematical Phys.* **6**, 1519–1529 (1965).

29a. M. Jacob and G. C. Wick, *Ann. Physics* **7**, 404 (1959).

30. M. L. Whippman, Branching rules for simple Lie groups. *J. Math. and Phys.* **6**, 1534–1539 (1965).

31. P. Cartier, On H. Weyl's character formula. *Bull. Amer. Math. Soc.* **67**, 228–230 (1961).

32. R. Steinberg, A general Clebsch-Gordan theorem. *Bull. Amer. Math. Soc.* **67**, 401–407 (1961).

33. A. Kleppner, The structure of some induced representations. *Duke Math. J.* **29**, 555–572 (1962).

34. E. Brown, Bloch electrons in a uniform magnetic field. *Phys. Rev.* **133**, 1038–1044 (1964).

35. J. Zak, Group-Theoretical consideration of Landau level branching in crystals. *Phys. Rev.* **136**, 776–780 (1964).

36. F. Bruhat, Sur les représentations induites des groupes de Lie. *Bull. Soc. Math. France* **84**, 97–205 (1956).

37. I. M. Gelfand and M. A. Naimark, "Unitäre Darstellungen der Klassischen Gruppen." Akademie Verlag, Berlin, 1957 (Translated from original Russian of 1950).

38. A. A. Kirillov, Unitary representations of nilpotent Lie groups. *Russian Math. Surveys* **17**, 53–104 (1962).

On a Generalization of Euler's Angles

EUGENE P. WIGNER

PRINCETON UNIVERSITY, PRINCETON, NEW JERSEY

I. Origin of the Problem

The considerations to be presented arose from an attempt to extend **R** matrix theory so as to account for peripheral reactions more generally.

As is well known, **R** matrix theory deals principally with nuclear reactions. It divides the configuration space into an internal and an external region. It introduces on the boundary B separating these two regions a suitable orthogonal set of functions. The **R** matrix itself provides a relation

$$v_s = \sum_t R_{st} d_t \tag{1}$$

between the expansion coefficients v_s of the value of a wave function on B and the expansion coefficients d_t of the normal derivative of that same wave function. The validity of Eq. (1) is the condition that the wave function can be continued into the internal region.

The purpose of the theory is to obtain a relation

$$e_s = \sum_t S_{st} i_t \tag{2}$$

between the amplitudes of the outgoing waves e_s, and those of the incoming waves i_t, in those parts of the configuration space in which the distance between colliding or separating particles is large. In the standard form of the theory,*

* There are several excellent reviews of this theory, including those by Lane and Thomas (*1*), by Vogt (*2*), and by Breit (*3*). For the standard theory of direct reactions, see, for instance, the article by Austern (*4*).

we assume a one-to-one correspondence between "channels" (which characterize the type, state of excitation, and relative angular momentum of the colliding or separating particles) and the aforementioned orthogonal system on B in such a way that each pair of expansion coefficients v_s, d_s depends only on the corresponding e_s, i_s

$$\begin{aligned} v_s &= \mathscr{E}_s e_s + \mathscr{I}_s i_s \\ d_s &= \mathscr{E}'_s e_s + \mathscr{I}'_s i_s. \end{aligned} \tag{3}$$

$\mathscr{E}_s$ and $\mathscr{E}'_s$ are the value and the derivative, at the boundary B, of the radial part of the outgoing wave carrying unit current in channel s. $\mathscr{I}_s$ and $\mathscr{I}'_s$ have the same significance with respect to the incoming wave. Equation (3) implies that the interaction in the external region is very simple; according to the usual assumption it can be represented by a potential acting between the colliding or separating particles as entities. It causes no change in the structure of the particles nor a transformation between them.

If interactions do cause such changes at considerable separation of these particles, and if we do not wish to extend the internal region to a correspondingly large part of the configuration space, we can take into account the interaction at larger distances as peripheral reactions by generalizing Eq. (3). This will render the usual properties of the **R** of Eq. (1) more pronounced. Hence, we shall write, instead of Eq. (3),

$$\begin{aligned} i_s &= \sum_t \alpha_{st} d_t + \beta_{st} v_t, \\ e_s &= \sum_t \gamma_{st} d_t + \delta_{st} v_t, \end{aligned} \tag{4}$$

expressing, this time, **i** and **e** in terms of **v** and **d**. Actually, because of time-inversion invariance, there are some relations between the matrices that enter (4) ($\boldsymbol{\alpha} = \boldsymbol{\gamma}^*$, $\boldsymbol{\beta} = \boldsymbol{\delta}^*$), but we shall disregard these. The problem that prompted the considerations to be presented is the determination of those relations between the matrices $\boldsymbol{\alpha}$, $\boldsymbol{\beta}$, $\boldsymbol{\gamma}$, $\boldsymbol{\delta}$ that follow from the unitary nature of the theory. This can be expressed by the postulate that the probability current entering the external region from the internal one be equal to the current flowing out from it at very large distances.

The aforementioned unitarity condition gives the equation

$$\sum i(v_s d_s^* - d_s v_s^*) = \sum |e_s|^2 - |i_s|^2. \tag{5}$$

If the **e** and **i** satisfy the relations (4), this must be valid for arbitrary **v** and **d**. The **v**, **d**, **e**, **i** can be considered to be vectors with the scalar product

$$(\mathbf{v}, \mathbf{d}) = \sum v_s^* d_s \tag{6}$$

so that (5) can be given the form

$$i(\mathbf{d}, \mathbf{v}) - i(\mathbf{v}, \mathbf{d}) = (\mathbf{e}, \mathbf{e}) - (\mathbf{i}, \mathbf{i}). \tag{7}$$

This equation can be further simplified if we unite **d** and **v** into a vector **D** with twice the dimension of **v** or **d**, and similarly, unite **i** and **e** into a vector **I** of the same dimension as **D**. Then, (7) becomes

$$(\mathbf{D}, \mathbf{s}_y \mathbf{D}) = (\mathbf{I}, \mathbf{s}_z \mathbf{I}) \tag{8}$$

where

$$\mathbf{s}_y = \begin{pmatrix} 0 & i\mathbf{1} \\ -i\mathbf{1} & 0 \end{pmatrix}, \qquad \mathbf{s}_z = \begin{pmatrix} -\mathbf{1} & 0 \\ 0 & \mathbf{1} \end{pmatrix}, \tag{8a}$$

the matrices $\mathbf{1}$ in (8a) having the same dimension as the vectors **d**, **v**, etc. Finally, we write

$$\mathbf{D} = \mathbf{T}\mathbf{D}', \qquad \mathbf{T} = 2^{-1/2}\begin{pmatrix} \mathbf{1} & i\mathbf{1} \\ i\mathbf{1} & \mathbf{1} \end{pmatrix}, \tag{9}$$

the unitary $\mathbf{T}$ having been so chosen that (the dagger denotes Hermitian adjoint)

$$\mathbf{T}^\dagger \mathbf{s}_y \mathbf{T} = \mathbf{s}_z, \tag{9a}$$

which then gives, instead of Eq. (8)

$$(\mathbf{D}', \mathbf{s}_z \mathbf{D}') = (\mathbf{I}, \mathbf{s}_z \mathbf{I}). \tag{9b}$$

According to (4) **i** and **e** depend linearly on **v** and **d**. Hence, we can write

$$\mathbf{I} = \mathbf{A}\mathbf{D} = \mathbf{A}\mathbf{T}\mathbf{D}', \qquad \mathbf{A} = \begin{pmatrix} \alpha & \beta \\ \gamma & \delta \end{pmatrix}, \tag{10}$$

so that if we write $\mathbf{A}\mathbf{T} = \mathbf{U}$, (9b) implies that $\mathbf{U}$ leaves the form $\mathbf{s}_z$ invariant: $\mathbf{U}^\dagger \mathbf{s}_z \mathbf{U} = \mathbf{s}_z$. It is also clear that in order to return from the relation

$$\mathbf{I} = \mathbf{U}\mathbf{D}' = \mathbf{U}\mathbf{T}^\dagger \mathbf{D} \tag{10a}$$

between **I** and **D** to a relation between **i**, **e**, **v**, and **d**, we will need $\mathbf{U}$ in the form decomposed into submatrices with half the dimension of $\mathbf{U}$.

The problem to be considered further is somewhat more general than the one, just outlined, to which the generalization of $\mathbf{R}$ matrix theory leads. Instead of giving a normal form of the submatrices of the $\mathbf{U}$ that satisfies the equation $\mathbf{U}^\dagger \mathbf{s}_z \mathbf{U} = \mathbf{s}_z$, we shall consider the matrices $\mathbf{U}$

$$\mathbf{U}^\dagger \mathbf{F} \mathbf{U} = \mathbf{F}, \tag{11}$$

which leave the form

$$\mathbf{F} = \begin{pmatrix} +\mathbf{1}_n & 0 \\ 0 & -\mathbf{1}_m \end{pmatrix} \tag{12}$$

invariant where $\mathbf{1}_n$ and $\mathbf{1}_m$ are unit matrices that may have different dimensions n and m, and we assume $n \geqslant m$. The dagger denotes Hermitian adjoint, the tilde (~) will denote the transpose. Similarly, we shall consider real matrices $\mathbf{R}$ that leave $\mathbf{F}$ invariant

$$\tilde{\mathbf{R}}\mathbf{F}\mathbf{R} = \mathbf{F}. \tag{13}$$

The matrices $\mathbf{U}$ and $\mathbf{R}$ that satisfies Eqs. (2) and (3) form, of course, well-known groups. The $\mathbf{R}$ here is, of course, not the $\mathbf{R}$-matrix of (1).

II. Summary of Results

The representations of $\mathbf{U}$ and $\mathbf{R}$ that will be arrived at show a great similarity to Euler's representation of rotations in three-dimensional space and the corresponding representation of two-dimensional unitary matrices

$$\mathbf{U} = \begin{pmatrix} u_1 & 0 \\ 0 & u_2 \end{pmatrix} \begin{pmatrix} c & s \\ -s & c \end{pmatrix} \begin{pmatrix} v_1 & 0 \\ 0 & v_2 \end{pmatrix} \tag{14}$$

where u_1, u_2, v_1, v_2 are numbers of modulus 1, c and s are real $c^2 + s^2 = 1$. It will be shown that there is a corresponding representation for unitary matrices of arbitrary dimensions, that is, for matrices that satisfy Eq. (11) with an $\mathbf{F}$ that is an $(n+m)$-dimensional unit matrix. The generalization of Eq. (14) reads in this case

$$\mathbf{U} = \begin{pmatrix} \mathbf{u}_1 & \mathbf{0} \\ \mathbf{0} & \mathbf{u}_2 \end{pmatrix} \begin{pmatrix} \mathbf{c} & \mathbf{s} \\ -\tilde{\mathbf{s}} & \mathbf{c}' \end{pmatrix} \begin{pmatrix} \mathbf{v}_1 & \mathbf{0} \\ \mathbf{0} & \mathbf{v}_2 \end{pmatrix} \tag{15}$$

where $\mathbf{u}_1$ and $\mathbf{v}_1$ are n-dimensional unitary matrices, $\mathbf{u}_2$ and $\mathbf{v}_2$ are m-dimensional and unitary, $\mathbf{c}$ and $\mathbf{c}'$ are real diagonal matrices, the last $n - m$ diagonal elements of $\mathbf{c}$ being 1, the first m identical with those of $\mathbf{c}'$. The $\mathbf{s}$ of Eq. (15) is a real $n \times m$ matrix. We shall call such a matrix diagonal if, for $n > m$, the last $n - m$ rows are 0, and if the matrix formed by the first m rows is diagonal. Similarly, an $m \times n$ matrix will be called diagonal if its transpose is diagonal; its last $n - m$ columns are then 0. In this sense, $\mathbf{s}$ is diagonal, as is also $\tilde{\mathbf{s}}$, and they satisfy the equation

$$\mathbf{c}^2 + \mathbf{s}\tilde{\mathbf{s}} = \mathbf{1}_n \tag{15a}$$

and hence

$$(\mathbf{c}')^2 + \tilde{\mathbf{s}}\mathbf{s} = \mathbf{1}_m. \tag{15b}$$

However, we shall be more interested in the $\mathbf{U}$ that satisfy Eq. (11) with the $\mathbf{F}$ of Eq. (12). For these, the representation to be obtained is

$$\mathbf{U} = \begin{pmatrix} \mathbf{u}_1 & \mathbf{0} \\ \mathbf{0} & \mathbf{u}_2 \end{pmatrix} \begin{pmatrix} \mathbf{C} & \mathbf{S} \\ \tilde{\mathbf{S}} & \mathbf{C}' \end{pmatrix} \begin{pmatrix} \mathbf{v}_1 & \mathbf{0} \\ \mathbf{0} & \mathbf{v}_2 \end{pmatrix}; \tag{16}$$

$\mathbf{u}_1$, $\mathbf{v}_1$, $\mathbf{u}_2$, $\mathbf{v}_2$ are again unitary with dimensions n and m, the $\mathbf{C}$, $\mathbf{C}'$ again real and diagonal, $\mathbf{C}'$ is m-dimensional, and the first m diagonal elements of $\mathbf{C}$ are identical with the corresponding elements of $\mathbf{C}'$, the rest 1. The $\mathbf{S}$ is again $n \times m$, again real and diagonal, and instead of (15a) and (15b) we now have

$$\mathbf{C}^2 - \mathbf{S}\tilde{\mathbf{S}} = \mathbf{1}_n \tag{16a}$$

$$\mathbf{C}'^2 - \tilde{\mathbf{S}}\mathbf{S} = \mathbf{1}_m. \tag{16b}$$

Evidently, the constituents of the right side of (16) are not uniquely determined by $\mathbf{U}$. This remains unchanged if the first and last factors are changed as follows:

$$\begin{aligned} \mathbf{u}_1 &\to \mathbf{u}_1 \boldsymbol{\omega}, & \mathbf{v}_1 &\to \boldsymbol{\omega}^\dagger \mathbf{v}_1, \\ \mathbf{u}_2 &\to \mathbf{u}_2 \boldsymbol{\omega}', & \mathbf{v}_2 &\to \boldsymbol{\omega}'^\dagger \mathbf{v}_2, \end{aligned} \tag{17}$$

where $\boldsymbol{\omega}$ and $\boldsymbol{\omega}'$ are unitary, $\boldsymbol{\omega}$ commutes with $\mathbf{C}$ (every diagonal matrix does), and $\boldsymbol{\omega}'$ is equal to $\boldsymbol{\omega}$ in those rows and columns in which the diagonal element of $\mathbf{C}$ is not 1, arbitrary otherwise. If no diagonal element of $\mathbf{S}$ is zero, only the last $n - m$ diagonal elements of $\mathbf{C}$ are 1 and $\boldsymbol{\omega}$ will split up into an $m \times m$ unitary matrix and an $(n - m) \times (n - m)$ unitary matrix, the remaining matrix elements being 0. In this case, $\boldsymbol{\omega}'$ is identical with the $m \times m$ submatrix of $\boldsymbol{\omega}$.

The representation to be obtained for the real matrices $\mathbf{R}$ is the same as (16) except that $\mathbf{u}_1$, $\mathbf{u}_2$, $\mathbf{v}_1$, $\mathbf{v}_2$ are real orthogonal matrices in this case. If the $-\mathbf{1}_m$ in (12) is replaced by $\mathbf{1}_m$ and $n = 2$, $m = 1$, we recognize Euler's original formula

$$\mathbf{R} = \begin{pmatrix} \cos\alpha & \sin\alpha & 0 \\ -\sin\alpha & \cos\alpha & 0 \\ 0 & 0 & 1 \end{pmatrix} \begin{pmatrix} \cos\beta & 0 & -\sin\beta \\ 0 & 1 & 0 \\ \sin\beta & 0 & \cos\beta \end{pmatrix} \begin{pmatrix} \cos\gamma & \sin\gamma & 0 \\ -\sin\gamma & \cos\gamma & 0 \\ 0 & 0 & 1 \end{pmatrix}; \tag{14a}$$

$\mathbf{u}_2$ and $\mathbf{v}_2$ are, in this case, 1; $\mathbf{u}_1$ and $\mathbf{v}_1$ rotations by α and γ in the plane of $\mathbf{1}_2$; the diagonal elements of $\mathbf{C}$ are $\cos\beta$ and 1, whereas the only diagonal element of $\mathbf{C}'$ is $\cos\beta$. The $\mathbf{S}$ is a 2×1 matrix, the second row of which is 0; $\tilde{\mathbf{S}}$ is its transpose, a 1×2 matrix.

It may be worthwhile to state explicitly the similarities, as well as the differences, between Euler's formulas (14) and (14a) and their generalizations (15) and (16). The first factors are in both cases elements of a subgroup. However, this subgroup is commutative in Euler's formulas (14) and (14a), and noncommutative in the generalizations (15) and (16). The elements of the same subgroup appear also as the last factor in both cases. The middle factors are elements of another subgroup; this is commutative in both cases.* Naturally, the generalized formulas apply to a much greater variety of groups than the original formulas.

III. Proof

Let us subdivide $\mathbf{U}$ in the same fashion in which $\mathbf{F}$ in (12) is subdivided

$$\mathbf{U} = \begin{pmatrix} \mathbf{U}_{11} & \mathbf{U}_{12} \\ \mathbf{U}_{21} & \mathbf{U}_{22} \end{pmatrix} \tag{18}$$

where $\mathbf{U}_{11}$ is an $n \times n$ matrix, $\mathbf{U}_{12}$ has n rows and m columns, etc. Equation (11) then reads

$$\mathbf{U}_{11}^{\dagger} \mathbf{U}_{11} = \mathbf{1}_n + \mathbf{U}_{21}^{\dagger} \mathbf{U}_{21} \tag{18a}$$

$$\mathbf{U}_{11}^{\dagger} \mathbf{U}_{12} = \mathbf{U}_{21}^{\dagger} \mathbf{U}_{22} \tag{18b}$$

$$\mathbf{U}_{12}^{\dagger} \mathbf{U}_{11} = \mathbf{U}_{22}^{\dagger} \mathbf{U}_{21} \tag{18c}$$

$$\mathbf{U}_{22}^{\dagger} \mathbf{U}_{22} = \mathbf{1}_m + \mathbf{U}_{12}^{\dagger} \mathbf{U}_{12}. \tag{18d}$$

Equation (18c) is just the adjoint to (18b) and need not be considered separately. Since $\mathbf{U}_{21}^{\dagger} \mathbf{U}_{21}$ is self-adjoint and positive semidefinite, it can be written as

$$\mathbf{U}_{21}^{\dagger} \mathbf{U}_{21} = \mathbf{v}_1^{\dagger} \mathbf{S}^2 \mathbf{v}_1 \tag{19}$$

where $\mathbf{S}$ is a diagonal matrix with real, nonnegative diagonal elements; $\mathbf{v}_1$ is unitary. Further, it can be assumed that the diagonal elements of $\mathbf{S}$ form a nonincreasing sequence. Since the rank of $\mathbf{U}_{21}$ is at most m, at least $n - m$ of

* One can recognize a certain similarity between the decompositions considered here and Iwasawa's decomposition of an arbitrary matrix into a product of *two* matrices, one orthogonal, the other triangular. Cf., e.g., Helgason (*5*). In Iwasawa's decomposition also the matrices which can appear as the first factor are elements of a subgroup; the same applies to the matrices which can appear as the second factor.

the characteristic values of $\mathbf{U}_{21}^{\dagger}\,\mathbf{U}_{21}$ vanish. As a result, at least the last $n-m$ diagonal elements of $\mathbf{S}^2$ are zero, and as a rule only these diagonal elements will vanish. At any rate, $\mathbf{S}$ can be replaced by an $n \times m$ matrix and $\mathbf{S}\tilde{\mathbf{S}}$ substituted for $\mathbf{S}^2$ in (19). It follows from (18a) that

$$\mathbf{U}_{11}^{\dagger}\,\mathbf{U}_{11} = \mathbf{v}_1^{\dagger}(\mathbf{1}_n + \mathbf{S}\tilde{\mathbf{S}})\,\mathbf{v}_1 = \mathbf{v}_1^{\dagger}\,\mathbf{C}^2\,\mathbf{v}_1 \tag{19a}$$

where $\mathbf{C}$ is defined by (16a). Evidently, the diagonal elements of $\mathbf{C}$ also form a nondecreasing sequence, the last $n-m$ of them are 1.

Since $\mathbf{C}\mathbf{v}_1$ is nonsingular, we can write

$$\mathbf{U}_{11} = \mathbf{u}_1\,\mathbf{C}\mathbf{v}_1 \tag{20}$$

and, inserting this into (19a), we find that $\mathbf{u}_1$ is unitary. It now follows from (19) that the ranks of $\tilde{\mathbf{S}}\mathbf{v}_1$ and of $\mathbf{U}_{21}$ are the same. In fact, if $\tilde{\mathbf{S}}\mathbf{v}_1\boldsymbol{\varphi} = \mathbf{0}$, where $\boldsymbol{\varphi}$ is an n-dimensional vector, it follows from (19) that $\mathbf{U}_{21}^{\dagger}\,\mathbf{U}_{21}\boldsymbol{\varphi} = \mathbf{0}$, or

$$(\boldsymbol{\varphi}, \mathbf{U}_{21}^{\dagger}\,\mathbf{U}_{21}\,\boldsymbol{\varphi}) = (\mathbf{U}_{21}\,\boldsymbol{\varphi}, \mathbf{U}_{21}\,\boldsymbol{\varphi}) = 0$$

so that $\mathbf{U}_{21}\boldsymbol{\varphi} = 0$ also. Hence, the ranges of $\tilde{\mathbf{S}}\mathbf{v}_1$ and of $\mathbf{U}_{21}$ have equal dimensions and there is an $m \times m$ matrix $\mathbf{u}_2$ such that

$$\mathbf{U}_{21} = \mathbf{u}_2\,\tilde{\mathbf{S}}\mathbf{v}_1. \tag{20a}$$

Insertion of this into (19) shows that $\mathbf{u}_2$ is length preserving on the range of $\tilde{\mathbf{S}}\mathbf{v}_1$ and since it is arbitrary on the perpendicular complement of this range, it can be assumed to be unitary. It will then map the perpendicular complement of the range of $\tilde{\mathbf{S}}\mathbf{v}_1$ into the perpendicular complement of the range of $\mathbf{U}_{21}$.

The same argument that was just applied to (18a) can be applied to (18d). It gives, instead of (20) and (20a),

$$\mathbf{U}_{22} = \mathbf{u}_p\,\mathbf{C}'\,\mathbf{v}_2 \tag{21}$$

and

$$\mathbf{U}_{12} = \mathbf{u}_p'\,\tilde{\mathbf{S}}_p\,\mathbf{v}_2 \tag{21a}$$

where $\mathbf{u}_p$ and $\mathbf{v}_2$ are unitary, $\mathbf{C}'$ real diagonal, all three $m \times m$ matrices. $\mathbf{S}_p$ is $m \times n$, its last $n-m$ columns being 0, and it is real and diagonal in its first m columns; $\mathbf{u}_p'$ is $n \times n$ and can be assumed to be unitary. Instead of (16b) we now have

$$(\mathbf{C}')^2 - \mathbf{S}_p\,\tilde{\mathbf{S}}_p = \mathbf{1}_m. \tag{21b}$$

We assume again that the diagonal elements of $\mathbf{S}_p$ and $\mathbf{C}'$ form a nonincreasing sequence. The only difference from the preceding case is that, even if $n > m$, no diagonal element of $\mathbf{C}'$ needs to be 1.

We have so far reduced $\mathbf{U}$ to the form

$$\mathbf{U} = \begin{pmatrix} \mathbf{u}_1 \mathbf{C} \mathbf{v}_1 & \mathbf{u}_p' \tilde{\mathbf{S}}_p \mathbf{v}_2 \\ \mathbf{u}_2 \tilde{\mathbf{S}} \mathbf{v}_1 & \mathbf{u}_p \mathbf{C}' \mathbf{v}_2 \end{pmatrix}. \tag{22}$$

In order to verify (16) completely, we have yet to show that $\tilde{\mathbf{S}}_p = \mathbf{S}$, $\mathbf{u}_p = \mathbf{u}_2$, $\mathbf{u}_p' = \mathbf{u}_1$, and that the first m diagonal elements of $\mathbf{C}$ are the same as the diagonal elements of $\mathbf{C}'$. This must follow from (18b), which becones

$$\mathbf{v}_1^\dagger \mathbf{C} \mathbf{u}_1^\dagger \mathbf{u}_p' \tilde{\mathbf{S}}_p \mathbf{v}_2 = \mathbf{v}_1^\dagger \mathbf{S} \mathbf{u}_2^\dagger \mathbf{u}_p \mathbf{C}' \mathbf{v}_2 \tag{22a}$$

or

$$\mathbf{u}_1^\dagger \mathbf{u}_p' \tilde{\mathbf{S}}_p \mathbf{C}'^{-1} = \mathbf{C}^{-1} \mathbf{S} \mathbf{u}_2^\dagger \mathbf{u}_p. \tag{22b}$$

Let us denote $\mathbf{u}_1^\dagger \mathbf{u}_p' = \mathbf{w}_1$, $\mathbf{u}_2^\dagger \mathbf{u}_p = \mathbf{w}_2$; these are unitary. Similarly, we set $\tilde{\mathbf{S}}_p(\mathbf{C}')^{-1} = \mathbf{T}_1$, $\mathbf{C}^{-1}\mathbf{S} = \mathbf{T}$. These are $n \times m$ real diagonal matrices with non-negative diagonal elements. Furthermore, if s_p is a diagonal element of $\mathbf{S}_p$, the corresponding diagonal element of $\mathbf{C}'$ is, because of (21b), $(1 + s_p^2)^{1/2}$ and hence the corresponding diagonal element to $\mathbf{T}_1$ is $s_p(1 + s_p^2)^{-1/2}$. Since the diagonal elements s_p form a nonincreasing sequence, the same is true of the diagonal elements $s_p(1 + s_p^2)^{-1/2}$ of $\mathbf{T}_1$. The same applies to $\mathbf{T}$, because of (16a) which was established by (19a), and because the diagonal elements of $\mathbf{S}$ were also assumed to form a nonincreasing sequence.

In terms of the $\mathbf{w}$ and $\mathbf{T}$, (22b) becomes

$$\mathbf{w}_1 \mathbf{T}_1 = \mathbf{T} \mathbf{w}_2 \tag{23}$$

and the adjoint of this is

$$\mathbf{T}_1^\dagger \mathbf{w}_1^\dagger = \mathbf{w}_2^\dagger \mathbf{T}^\dagger. \tag{23a}$$

The product of the last two equations is

$$\mathbf{T}_1^\dagger \mathbf{T}_1 = \mathbf{w}_2^\dagger \mathbf{T}^\dagger \mathbf{T} \mathbf{w}_2. \tag{23b}$$

The left side is an $m \times m$ real diagonal matrix; the right side is the transform, by the unitary matrix $\mathbf{w}_2$, of a similar diagonal matrix. It follows that the diagonal elements of $\mathbf{T}_1^\dagger \mathbf{T}_1$ and $\mathbf{T}^\dagger \mathbf{T}$ are pairwise equal and, since both form a nonincreasing sequence, the two diagonal matrices are equal:

$$\mathbf{T}_1^\dagger \mathbf{T}_1 = \mathbf{T}^\dagger \mathbf{T}. \tag{24}$$

Since, furthermore, the diagonal element of $\mathbf{T}_1^\dagger \mathbf{T}_1$ that corresponds to the diagonal element s_p of $\tilde{\mathbf{S}}_p$ is $s_p^2/(1+s_p^2)$, and the diagonal element of $\mathbf{T}^\dagger \mathbf{T}$ that corresponds to the diagonal element s of $\mathbf{S}$ is $s^2/(1+s^2)$, these two are equal. Since both s_p and s were assumed to be nonnegative, they are pairwise equal and we conclude

$$\tilde{\mathbf{S}}_p = \mathbf{S}. \tag{24a}$$

It then follows from (16a) and (21b) that the first m diagonal elements of $\mathbf{C}$ and $\mathbf{C}'$ (all of which are positive) are equal. The preceding is a somewhat roundabout version of the argument that, because of the positive semidefinite nature of $\mathbf{S}_p$, $\mathbf{C}'$, $\mathbf{T}_1$, and $\mathbf{T}_1^\dagger \mathbf{T}_1$, these are all single-valued functions of each other and the same applies to the quartet $\mathbf{S}$, $\mathbf{C}$, $\mathbf{T}$, and $\mathbf{T}^\dagger \mathbf{T}$. The argument was made in detail because $\mathbf{S}_p$, $\mathbf{T}_1$, $\mathbf{S}$, and $\mathbf{T}$ are not square matrices.

We have yet to prove that $\mathbf{u}_p = \mathbf{u}_2$, $\mathbf{u}_p' = \mathbf{u}_1$ or, rather, that $\mathbf{u}_p$ can be replaced by $\mathbf{u}_2$, $\mathbf{u}_p'$ by $\mathbf{u}_1$ without affecting the validity of (21) and (21a). For this purpose, we rewrite (23b) by means of (24)

$$\mathbf{w}_2 \mathbf{T}_1^\dagger \mathbf{T}_1 = \mathbf{T}_1^\dagger \mathbf{T}_1 \mathbf{w}_2; \tag{25}$$

that is, $\mathbf{w}_2$ commutes with $\mathbf{T}_1^\dagger \mathbf{T}_1$. It therefore also commutes with $\mathbf{C}'$ and $\tilde{\mathbf{S}}_p = \mathbf{S}$. Hence, (21) and (21a) will remain valid if we replace

$$\mathbf{u}_p \to \mathbf{u}_p \mathbf{w}_2^{-1}, \qquad \mathbf{v}_2 \to \mathbf{w}_2 \mathbf{v}_2, \qquad \mathbf{u}_p' \to \mathbf{u}_p' \mathbf{w}_2^{-1}. \tag{25a}$$

Since $\mathbf{w}_2 = \mathbf{u}_2^\dagger \mathbf{u}_p$, the new $\mathbf{u}_p$ will be $\mathbf{u}_p \mathbf{u}_p^\dagger \mathbf{u}_2 = \mathbf{u}_2$ and we now have

$$\mathbf{u}_p = \mathbf{u}_2. \tag{25b}$$

We next return to (22b). We note that since the last $n-m$ rows of $\mathbf{S}$ are 0, the first m rows of $\mathbf{C}$ are equal to those of $\mathbf{C}'$, all of them diagonal.

$$\mathbf{S}(\mathbf{C}')^{-1} = \mathbf{C}^{-1}\mathbf{S} = \mathbf{T}. \tag{26}$$

Hence, (22b) reads, with (24a), (25b), and (26),

$$\mathbf{u}_1^\dagger \mathbf{u}_p' \mathbf{T} = \mathbf{w}_1 \mathbf{T} = \mathbf{T}. \tag{26a}$$

We recall that $\mathbf{w}_1 = \mathbf{u}_1^\dagger \mathbf{u}_p'$. Let us assume that the first k diagonal elements of $\mathbf{S}$, and hence of $\mathbf{T}$, are different from 0. Then, (26a) means that the first k columns of $\mathbf{w}_1$ contain a 1 at the diagonal, the rest is 0. Since $\mathbf{w}_1$ is unitary, the same applies to the first k rows:

$$\mathbf{w}_1 = \begin{pmatrix} \mathbf{1}_k & \mathbf{0} \\ \mathbf{0} & \mathbf{w}_1' \end{pmatrix}. \tag{27}$$

The subdivision in (27) is k ($k \leqslant m$) and $n-k$. Since $\mathbf{S}$ is diagonal and only its first k diagonal elements are different from 0, we have

$$\mathbf{w}_1 \mathbf{S} = \mathbf{S}, \qquad \tilde{\mathbf{S}} \mathbf{w}_1^\dagger = \tilde{\mathbf{S}}, \tag{27a}$$

and multiplying the last equation by $\mathbf{w}_1$, we obtain

$$\tilde{\mathbf{S}} = \tilde{\mathbf{S}} \mathbf{w}_1. \tag{27b}$$

Since the diagonal elements of $\mathbf{C}$ are 1 wherever those of $\mathbf{S}$ are 0, with the same subdivision as in (27)

$$\mathbf{C} = \begin{pmatrix} \mathbf{C}_k & \mathbf{0} \\ \mathbf{0} & \mathbf{1}_{n-k} \end{pmatrix}. \tag{27c}$$

It follows that

$$\mathbf{w}_1 \mathbf{C} = \mathbf{C} \mathbf{w}_1. \tag{27d}$$

Hence, (20) and (20a) will remain valid if we replace

$$\begin{aligned} \mathbf{u}_1 &\to \mathbf{u}_1 \mathbf{w}_1, \\ \mathbf{v}_1 &\to \mathbf{w}_1^\dagger \mathbf{v}_1, \end{aligned} \tag{28}$$

as a result of which

$$\mathbf{u}_1 = \mathbf{u}_p'. \tag{28a}$$

As a result of (24a), (25b), (28a), the form (22) is now identical with (16).

The proofs of (15) and the modification of (16) in which $\mathbf{U}$ is real (and the $\mathbf{u}$ and $\mathbf{v}$ are also real) can be carried out in the same way. Actually, the proof carried out is very simple and the apparent complication arises only from the fact that the $\mathbf{S}$ is not a square matrix and we are less used to operating with general rectangular matrices than with square ones. For this reason also, the case $m = n$ originally considered by this writer, appears to be simpler.

IV. Corollary

As was mentioned before, the original objective of the preceding considerations concerned the theory of peripheral nuclear reactions, which will not be dealt with here. There is, however, one immediate consequence of the form (16) for complex and real matrices that leave $\mathbf{F}$ invariant that is worth mentioning. It relates to the characteristic values of $\mathbf{U}^\dagger \mathbf{U}$ (or of $\mathbf{U}\mathbf{U}^\dagger$). We obtain from (16)

$$\mathbf{U}^\dagger \mathbf{U} = \begin{pmatrix} \mathbf{v}_1^\dagger & \mathbf{0} \\ \mathbf{0} & \mathbf{v}_2^\dagger \end{pmatrix} \begin{pmatrix} \mathbf{C} & \mathbf{S} \\ \tilde{\mathbf{S}} & \mathbf{C}' \end{pmatrix}^2 \begin{pmatrix} \mathbf{v}_1 & \mathbf{0} \\ \mathbf{0} & \mathbf{v}_2 \end{pmatrix}. \tag{29}$$

Hence, $\mathbf{U}^\dagger \mathbf{U}$ is the unitary transform of

$$\begin{pmatrix} \mathbf{C} & \mathbf{S} \\ \tilde{\mathbf{S}} & \mathbf{C}' \end{pmatrix}^2 = \begin{pmatrix} \mathbf{C}^2 + \mathbf{S}\tilde{\mathbf{S}} & \mathbf{C}\mathbf{S} + \mathbf{S}\mathbf{C}' \\ \tilde{\mathbf{S}}\mathbf{C} + \mathbf{C}'\tilde{\mathbf{S}} & \tilde{\mathbf{S}}\mathbf{S} + (\mathbf{C}')^2 \end{pmatrix}. \tag{29a}$$

Since the first m diagonal elements of $\mathbf{C}$ and $\mathbf{C}'$ are identical, if we subdivide (29a) into sections m, $n-m$, and m, it assumes the form

$$\begin{pmatrix} (\mathbf{C}')^2 + \mathbf{S}_m^2 & \mathbf{0} & 2\mathbf{S}_m\mathbf{C}' \\ \mathbf{0} & \mathbf{1} & \mathbf{0} \\ 2\mathbf{S}_m\mathbf{C}' & \mathbf{0} & (\mathbf{C}')^2 + \mathbf{S}_m^2 \end{pmatrix} \tag{29b}$$

where $\mathbf{S}_m$ is the upper $m \times m$ section of $\mathbf{S}$. The secular equation of (29b) decomposes into m two-dimensional parts of the form

$$\begin{pmatrix} c^2 + s^2 & 2sc \\ 2sc & c^2 + s^2 \end{pmatrix} \tag{29c}$$

where s is a diagonal element of $\mathbf{S}$, $c = (1 + s^2)^{1/2}$, the corresponding diagonal element of $\mathbf{C}'$ (or of $\mathbf{C}$). Hence, $\mathbf{U}^\dagger \mathbf{U}$ has m pairs of characteristic values that are reciprocals of each other. It also has $n-m$ characteristic values 1. For $m = 0$ this is, or course, a trivial result.

In the case of real $\mathbf{U}$, we can further infer from (29), since the $\mathbf{v}$ are real, that the characteristic vectors of $\mathbf{U}^\dagger \mathbf{U}$ (or of $\mathbf{U}\mathbf{U}^\dagger$) can be assumed to be real.

REFERENCES

1. A. M. Lane and R. G. Thomas, *Rev. Mod. Phys.* **30**, 257 (1958).
2. E. Vogt, *in* "Nuclear Reactions," p. 215. North-Holland Publ., Amsterdam, 1959.
3. G. Breit, *in* "Encyclopedia of Physics," Vol. 41/1, p. 274. Springer Verlag, Berlin, 1959.
4. N. Austern, *in* "Fast Neutron Physics," Vol. IV, p. 1113. Wiley (Interscience), New York, 1963.
5. S. Helgason, "Differential Geometry and Symmetric Spaces," p. 219 ff. Academic Press, New York, 1962.

Projective Representation of the Poincaré Group in a Quaternionic Hilbert Space

J. M. JAUCH

UNIVERSITY OF GENEVA, GENEVA, SWITZERLAND

I. Introduction

A. Relativistic Quantum Mechanics

Theoretical physics in the first half of the twentieth century is dominated by two major developments: the discovery of the theory of relativity and the discovery of quantum mechanics. Both have led to profound modifications of basic concepts. Relativity in its special form proclaimed the invariance of physical laws with respect to Lorentz transformations and led to the inevitable consequence of the relativity of spatial and temporal relationships. Quantum mechanics, on the other hand, recognizes as basic the complementarity of certain measurable quantities for microsystems (uncertainty relations) and the concomitant indeterminism of physical measurements.

From the mathemetical point of view the central object in the special theory of relativity is a group, the Lorentz group, or more generally, the *Poincaré group*. For quantum mechanics the most important mathematical object is the *Hilbert space* and its linear operators. It is therefore not surprising that the most important mathematical problem in relativistic quantum mechanics is the representation theory of the Poincaré group in infinite-dimensional Hilbert space.

The representation theory of groups was first developed, at about the turn of the century, as a branch of algebra for the finite groups. The extension to compact Lie groups was a relatively easy generalization. However, these theories are too restrictive for the representation theory required by relativistic quantum mechanics. Two generalizations are needed in this case. First, not the vector representations but only representations up to a factor of modulus one are important in quantum mechanics. Such representations are called projective representations because they are encountered in projective geometry. Second, the Poincaré group is a noncompact group, and the faithful unitary representations of such groups are necessarily of infinite dimensions.

Until 1940 the unitary representation theory of noncompact groups in infinite-dimensional spaces was practically nonexistent. The first important results were obtained by Wigner (*1*) in 1939, and later by Bargmann (*2*). Wigner was able to adapt a method of Frobenius to the Poincaré group, and in this way he obtained a classification of all physically interesting irreducible representations of this group. Many questions of a mathematical nature remained unanswered by this work. A more complete and more general theory was given much later by Mackey, who generalized Frobenius's theorem to the case of noncompact groups of a certain class (*3*, *4*).

The study of projective representations led to the theory of the classes of equivalent factors developed especially by Bargmann (*5*). Thus the local and global theories of factors, together with the Mackey-Frobenius theory of the irreducible vector representations, constitute the main building blocks of the quantum-mechanical representation theory of the Poincaré group. They will be used in this article for a classification of elementary particles in quaternionic quantum mechanics.

B. General Quantum Mechanics

Quantum mechanics as it was discovered in connection with the problems in atomic physics has the peculiar feature that it is a theory that uses as its main tool a *complex* Hilbert space. The appearance of complex numbers in a basic physical theory can be of a rather trivial nature, such as, for instance, the representation in the complex plane of a periodic motion. In such a case the use of complex numbers is a matter of convenience, and it can be just as well avoided if we are willing to pay the price of more cumbersome formulas.

In quantum mechanics, however, the appearance of complex numbers seems to have a more fundamental significance, which has never been understood very well.

The question concerning the role of complex numbers was expressed early by Ehrenfest (*6*) and an answer was attempted by Pauli (*7*), for at least a special case. The question can be placed in a broader context if we examine more carefully just what properties of the complex Hilbert space are actually used in quantum mechanics. One way to do this is to reformulate quantum mechanics on an axiomatic basis as an algebraic structure, as was done by Birkoff and von Neumann (*8*) in 1936. In this formulation there is no need to introduce Hilbert space at all. The primary object is instead a lattice of the elementary propositions (yes–no experiment) pertaining to a given physical system. In conventional quantum mechanics this lattice is realized as the lattice of all the subspaces of a complex Hilbert space. In the abstract formulation of the proposition system the nature of the Hilbert space in a possible realization is left open. There is no obvious physical property that would force us to choose the complex numbers for the field of coefficients.

There is, however, one property of the field that one can motivate to some extent with physical considerations: the field should contain the reals as a subfield so that the representation of continuous quantities, such as the position of a particle, does not cause any difficulties. With this restriction the number of possible realizations of the abstract lattices is greatly reduced because, according to a celebrated theorem (*9*), there exist only three fields that contain the real numbers as a subfield, namely, the real numbers themselves, the complex numbers, and the quaternions. Thus it suffices to examine in detail quantum mechanics in real and in quaternionic Hilbert spaces.

Quantum mechanics in a real Hilbert space was studied by Stueckelberg in a number of papers (*10*, *11*). The result of these investigations is that the theory is in contradiction with the uncertainty relations unless we postulate the existence of a nontrivial operator $\mathcal{J}$ that commutes with all the observables. This operator $\mathcal{J}$ must in addition be antisymmetrical ($\mathcal{J}^\dagger = -\mathcal{J}$) and must satisfy $\mathcal{J}^2 = -I$. The latter property says that $\mathcal{J}$ is the square root of the negative identity operator. This implies that the theory is identical with conventional quantum mechanics in complex Hilbert spaces.

The situation is a little different for quaternion quantum mechanics. In fact, experience with real Hilbert spaces has shown that the question of the field is certainly connected with the question of superselection rules. The choice of the "wrong" field (for instance, the reals) can be compensated by restricting the number of operators that are admitted as observables. Such restrictions are called *superselection rules*. It was therefore natural to believe that the occurrence of superselection rules in nature might somehow find a natural explanation by a suitable choice of the number field. For this reason the study of quaternion quantum mechanics was undertaken by Finkelstein *et al.* in a number of publications (*12*, *13*). In spite of some interesting formal possibilities these attempts yielded no essentially new results that could be connected with the empirical facts of elementary particle physics, and the deeper significance of the complex numbers in quantum mechanics remains obscure.

In order to progress further it seemed natural to return to the lattice-theoretical approach of Birkhoff and von Neumann and to try to recover the number field from the structure properties of the lattice itself. It was especially emphasized by Finkelstein *et al.* that the abstract algebraic properties of the lattice are essentially nothing other than the formalization of the fundamental empirically given properties of the physical systems. On the other hand, from the experience we have had with the coordinate representations of projective geometries we expect that the nature of the field is essentially (that is, up to automorphisms) determined by this lattice structure.

This program of research was undertaken by Piron (*14*), who succeeded in formulating, in the precise mathematical language of lattice theory, a set of general quantum-mechanical axioms that embodied the basic empirical facts of quantum systems. He went beyond the work of Birkhoff and von Neumann by showing that for certain systems the axiom of modularity favored by these authors is in contradiction with the facts, and by supplying the correct axiom of *weak modularity*. He then stated and proved a representation theorem for the lattices encountered in Nature. For systems of finite dimensions this theorem is the well-known representation theorem of projective geometries; for infinite-dimensional systems it is a generalization of this theorem.

With Piron's result it became possible to affirm the representation of the lattice of a physical proposition system as subspaces in a Hilbert space with coefficients from a field. But still nothing was known about the physical properties that reflect the nature of the field.

C. Intervention of Group Theory

A new aspect was introduced with the study of the symmetry groups of proposition systems. It is known from examples that these symmetry groups have quite different structures for the different lattices. Since physical symmetries are often more easily recognized in Nature than, for instance, other detailed mechanical properties of the systems, this seemed a promising line of research to pursue.

The symmetries of a proposition system have two aspects. There is (as we shall show in detail in Section III, A, 3) a symmetry group of the proposition system that we shall call M. It consists of all automorphisms of the lattice. There is, in addition, the symmetry group G, which arises from the space-time frame of physical events. For relativistic quantum mechanics this group G is the Poincaré group. The study of elementary systems and their properties leads to the question of the isomorphisms (or homomorphisms) between G and the subgroups of M. In other words, we have here a representation problem of the Poincaré group.

The representation of groups as automorphisms of a lattice structure is a natural generalization of the representation of groups by unitary transformation of vectors in a complex Hilbert space. An intermediate stage in this generalization consists of the projective representations, which can be reduced to the vector representations via the theory of factors. There is virtually nothing known about representations of groups as automorphisms of lattices.

A special aspect of the problem could be revealed by studying the projective representations of the Poincaré group in quaternionic Hilbert space. This is essentially the same problem that Wigner had solved in 1939 for complex space, transferred and adapted to the situation in quaternionic space. The work of Mackey (*3*) and Bargmann (*5*) that intervened simplified the task considerably and made it possible to solve this problem with complete mathematical rigor. This was dome by Emch (*15*) in a thesis published in 1963. The result, which will be reported here, shows that the physical content of quaternionic Hilbert space is identical with that of complex space when it is combined with the principle of relativity. This result revealed, a little better than most previous attempts, why complex Hilbert space plays such an exceptional role in quantum mechanics. It is a good example of the efficacy of group-theoretical considerations in answering profound questions of fundamental physical theory.

II. The Lattice Structure of General Quantum Mechanics

A. The Proposition System

1. *The Elementary Propositions (Yes–No Experiments)*

All the information concerning the properties of a physical system is obtained by measurements. The results of such measurements depend on two things: the nature of the physical system and the state of that system. Although this distinction cannot always be carried through consistently in all cases, it is quite useful for most situations. Roughly speaking, the nature of the system is incorporated in all those measurable properties that are independent of the history of the system. We shall call then *intrinsic properties*. For instance, if the system consists of an elementary particle, the mass, charge, spin, and magnetic moment are some of the intrinsic properties. On the other hand, the position, energy, and orientation of the spin are some of the properties that depend on the state of the system.

The nature of the system can be characterized completely by specifying all the intrinsic properties of the system. In order to do this in the simplest and most systematic way, it is convenient to introduce a special class of experiments the yes–no experiments. These are experiments with equipment that can only respond with one of two alternatives. A typical example of such equipment is the *counter*, which is either triggered or remains silent. Every measurement of a measurable quantity can be broken up into a suitable set of yes–no experiments by the simple device of measuring only whether the quantity in question belongs to a given subset or not. For instance, the measurement of the position of a particle is accomplished if we know whether the values of its position coordinates belong to any given subset of the possible values of these coordinates.

We shall refer to the two alternatives of a yes–no experiment as (elementary) propositions for the system, which we denote in the following by $\mathscr{L}$. The determination of the nature and the state of a system is accomplished if we know the truth or falsehood of all propositions for the system.

2. *The Partial Ordering of Propositions*

One of the most important intrinsic properties of a physical system is expressed in a partial ordering of its proposition system. Certain pairs of propositions are not independent of each other. For instance, let proposition a locate a particle in a volume element V_a and proposition b locate the particle in volume element V_b. If $V_a \subseteq V_b$, then the two propositions clearly depend on each other because whenever a is true, b must be true too. Furthermore whenever b is false, a must be false too. We express this by the relation $a \subseteq b$ and recognize easily that it is a *partial ordering* of the proposition system that satisfies the following fundamental properties:

$$
\begin{aligned}
&\text{(a)}\quad a \subseteq a && \forall\ a \in \mathscr{L};\\
&\text{(b)}\quad a \subseteq b \quad \text{and} && b \subseteq a \Leftrightarrow a = b;\\
&\text{(c)}\quad a \subseteq b \quad \text{and} && b \subseteq c \Rightarrow a \subseteq c. \qquad \text{(I)}
\end{aligned}
$$

Property (b) may be considered as the definition of the equality of two propositions.

The fact that the ordering is only partial is very important. It gives rise to the existence of nontrivial symmetry groups for proposition systems.

3. *Intersection, Union, and Orthocomplement of Proposition*

In a partially ordered system it is natural to define the operations of intersection and union of its elements. If the system is a system of propositions, then we can give these operations a physical interpretation that enables us to verify in individual cases a system of axioms concerning them.

For these axioms the following have been found consistent with the empirically verifiable proposition systems.

Let I be an index set containing at least two elements and a_i $(i \in I)$ any subset of $\mathscr{L}$, $a_i \in \mathscr{L}$. Then there exists a proposition, denoted by $\bigcap_I a_i$, with the property

$$x \subseteq a_i \quad \forall \quad i \in I \;\Leftrightarrow\; x \subseteq \bigcap_I a_i \quad (\forall \quad x \in \mathscr{L}). \tag{II}$$

It is called the *greatest lower bound*, or *intersection*, of the elements a_i. In the particular case that the index set I contains exactly two elements, we denote the intersection of two elements a and b by $a \cap b$.

In a similar way we define the *least upper bound*, or *union*, of an arbitrary subset of $\mathscr{L}$ by $\bigcup_I a_i$ with the property

$$a_i \subseteq x \quad \forall \quad i \in I \;\Leftrightarrow\; \bigcup_I a_i \subseteq x \quad (\forall \quad x \in \mathscr{L}). \tag{III}$$

If the subset $\{a_i\}$ is identical with $\mathscr{L}$, we obtain two special elements of the set $\mathscr{L}$

$$\phi = \bigcap_{\mathscr{L}} a, \qquad I = \bigcup_{\mathscr{L}} a. \tag{1}$$

The element ϕ represents the *absurd* proposition, which is always false, while I is the *trivial* proposition, which is always true.

The next axiom (IV) asserts the existence of a unique *orthocomplement*: For every $a \in \mathscr{L}$ there exists another $a' \in \mathscr{L}$ such that

$$\begin{aligned} (a')' &= a, \\ a' \cap a &= \phi, \\ a \subseteq b &\Leftrightarrow b' \subseteq a'. \end{aligned} \tag{IV}$$

From the axioms stated so far follows immediately that for every subset $\{a_i\}$ $(i \in I)$ of $\mathscr{L}$ we have

$$\bigcup_I a_i = \Big(\bigcap_I a_i'\Big)'. \tag{2}$$

In particular, by taking for $\{a_i\}$ the set $\mathscr{L}$ itself, we obtain

$$\begin{aligned} \phi' &= I, \\ I' &= \phi. \end{aligned} \tag{3}$$

For every $x \in \mathscr{L}$ we verify also

$$x' \cup x = I. \tag{4}$$

If two elements a and b satisfy the symmetrical relation $a \subset b'$, we call them *disjoint* and we denote it by $a \perp b$.

The four axioms (I), (II), (III), and (IV) define an *orthocomplemented* and *complete lattice*.

4. *The States of a Physical System*

The properties that define the lattice structure of $\mathscr{L}$ contain the formalization of the intrinsic properties of a physical system. We shall now turn our attention to those properties that refer to the state of the system.

A state is the result of a set of physical manipulations that constitute the preparation of the system. The state can be determined by measuring the truth or falsehood of all the propositions of the system. In contradistinction to classical systems, however, not every proposition is necessarily true or false. The result of measurements on ensembles of identically prepared systems will yield the result that a given proposition may be true with a certain probability only. We are thus led to the following axiom.

A state is a function from $\mathscr{L}$ onto the interval $[0, 1]$ that satisfies

(i) $p(\phi) = 0, \qquad p(I) = 1.$

(ii) For every sequence a_i of pairwise disjoint elements we have

$$p\left(\bigcup_i a_i\right) = \sum_i p(a_i).$$

(iii) $p(a) = 1 = p(b) \Rightarrow p(a \cap b) = 1.$

If p_1 and p_2 are two different states, then $\lambda_1 p_1 + \lambda_2 p_2 \equiv p$ with $\lambda_1 + \lambda_2 = 1$, $\lambda_i > 0$ is also a state. Such a state p which can be constructed from two different states is called a *mixture*. A state that is not a mixture is said to be *pure*.

The states are thus a convex set of functionals over $\mathscr{L}$. The pure states are the boundary of this convex set.

The functional $\sigma_p(a) \equiv p(a) - p^2(a)$ measures the *dispersion* of a state. If $\sigma_p(a) \equiv 0 \ \forall \in \mathscr{L}$, we call the state *dispersion free*. A mixture always has dispersion, but a pure state is not necessarily dispersion free. For certain simple quantum-mechanical systems, such as a spin or an elementary particle, we can even show that there does not exist any dispersion-free state.

B. Distributivity, Modularity, and Atomicity

1. *Distributivity*

The lattice of propositions exists for any physical system, be it classical or quantal. The distinction between these two kinds of systems requires an additional structure property that is compatible with axioms (I)–(IV); a classical system has a proposition system that satisfies the axiom of *distributivity* as well as axioms (I)–(IV).

A lattice is distributive if for every triple $a, b, c \in \mathscr{L}$, the relations

$$\begin{aligned} a \cap (b \cup c) &= (a \cap b) \cup (a \cap c), \\ a \cup (b \cap c) &= (a \cup b) \cap (a \cup c) \end{aligned} \tag{D}$$

hold.

Such a lattice is called a Boolean lattice (or a Boolean algebra). If a lattice is not Boolean, it may at least contain Boolean sublattices. A sublattice $\mathscr{L}_0 \subset \mathscr{L}$ is a subset of $\mathscr{L}$ that satisfies all the axioms (I)–(IV). If $\mathscr{L}_i \subset \mathscr{L}$ is a famile of sublattices, then the set intersection $\mathscr{L}_0 \equiv \bigcap_i \mathscr{L}_i$ is also a sublattice.

Let $\gamma \subset \mathscr{L}$ be an arbitrary subset of $\mathscr{L}$. We may then consider the class of all sublattices $\mathscr{L}_i$ that contain γ. The intersection $\mathscr{L}_0 \equiv \bigcap_i \mathscr{L}_i$ will then also contain γ, and it is the smallest sublattice of $\mathscr{L}$ with this property. We call it the sublattice *generated* by γ and denote it by $\mathscr{L}(\gamma) \equiv \mathscr{L}_0$.

Of particular interest in the following are the subsets γ for which $\mathscr{L}(\gamma)$ is a Boolean sublattice of $\mathscr{L}$. We say then that the set γ is *classical*, or γ consists of pairwise *compatible elements*. If the set γ consists of exactly two elements $\gamma = \{a, b\}$, then these elements are compatible if and only if $\mathscr{L}(\{a, b\})$ is Boolean.

We have thus arrived at the important notion of *compatibility*, for which we introduce the special notation $a \leftrightarrow b$, which indicates that it is a symmetrical relation. It is clear from the preceding that in a classical system every pair of propositions is compatible. The converse is also true (*14*). The notion of compatibility defined here was first introduced in a slightly different way by Jordan (*16*) and it is discussed extensively in the mathematical literature (*17*, *18*).

2. *Modularity and Weak Modularity*

It was clearly recognized by Birkhoff and von Neumann (*8*) that the distribution law is violated in Nature and that it has to be replaced by a weaker law. For this weakened structure property these authors proposed the so-called *modular law*.

It is an elementary exercise to show that in any lattice we have

$$x \cup (y \cap z) \subseteq (x \cup y) \cap z$$

for $x \subseteq z$.

If the lattice is such that for all $x \subseteq z$ the equality sign holds in this relation, then it is said to be modular. The modular law is thus expressed by

$$x \subseteq z \Rightarrow x \cup (y \cap z) = (x \cup y) \cap z. \tag{M}$$

It is clear that a Boolean lattice is always modular, but the converse is not true. Simple examples are found, for instance, in the work of Piron (*14*).

As was pointed out by Birkhoff (*19*), the modular lattices have many properties that make them quite attractive for the description of propositions in general quantum mechanics. It was established by Piron, however, that the notion of localizability, which is implied by that of an elementary particle, is incompatible with modularity (*14*, Proposition on p. 452). Piron also supplied the weaker axiom that is needed to describe the actually known physical systems. It is called the *weak modularity* axiom and can be stated in many equivalent forms. We choose the following, which lends itself most easily to a physical interpretation:

$$a \subseteq b \Rightarrow a \leftrightarrow b. \tag{P}$$

It is not difficult to verify that (M) implies (P) for a complete orthocomplemented lattice. The converse is not true. The most important example is the lattice of closed linear subspaces in an infinite-dimensional Hilbert space. This lattice satisfies (P) but is not modular (*14*).

Concluding this subsection, we state a theorem that is a rich source of alternative formulations of compatibility:

In a weakly modular lattice the following relations are equivalent [cf. (*14*, Theorem VII)].

(1) $a \leftrightarrow b$.
(2) $a \leftrightarrow b'$.
(3) $(a \cap b') \cup b \supseteq a$.
(4) $(a \cup b') \cap b \subseteq a$.
(5) Any three of the four elements a, b, a', b' satisfy a distributive law
$$x \cap (y \cup z) = (x \cap y) \cup (x \cap z).$$
(6) $(a \cap b) \cup (a \cap b') \cup (a' \cap b) \cup (a' \cap b') = I$.
(7) $(a \cup b) \cap (a \cup b') \cap (a' \cup b) \cap (a' \cup b') = \phi$.

3. *Atomicity*

The axion of atomicity consists of two parts. The first part expresses the existence of minimal propositions $P \in \mathscr{L}$ (called points) with the property

$$x \subset P \Rightarrow x = \phi. \tag{A.1}$$

The second part affirms the existence of minimal propositions over any other proposition.

For any point $P \in \mathscr{L}$

$$a \subseteq x \subseteq a \cup P \Rightarrow x = a \qquad \text{or} \qquad x = a \cup P. \tag{A.2}$$

We say then the proposition $a \cup P$ *covers* a.

The postulate of atomicity has the character of a technical axiom that is perhaps not indispensable for the description of actual physical systems, but that is mathematically useful. Recent experience, however, suggests that it may be possible to dispense with the axiom altogether (*20*). Work is now in progress to study the possibility in relation to weakly modular lattices.

For the rest of this chapter we shall designate as a *proposition system* a lattice that satisfies axioms (I)–(IV); (P); and (A.1) and (A.2).

C. Superposition Principle and Superselection Rules

1. *Reducible and Irreducible Lattices*

Consider two proposition systems $\mathscr{L}_1$ and $\mathscr{L}_2$. We can construct a third one, the elements of which are the pairs of elements (x_1, x_2) $x_1 \in \mathscr{L}_1$, $x_2 \in \mathscr{L}_2$ (the Cartesian product $\mathscr{L}_1 \times \mathscr{L}_2$). The partial ordering is defined by the rule

$$(x_1, x_2) \subseteq (y_1, y_2) \Leftrightarrow x_1 \subseteq y_1 \qquad \text{and} \qquad x_2 \subseteq y_2. \tag{5}$$

If we define further

$$(x_1, x_2)' = (x_1', x_2'), \tag{6}$$

$$(x_1, x_2) \cap (y_1, y_2) = (x_1 \cap y_1, x_2 \cap y_2), \quad \text{etc.}, \tag{7}$$

we obtain a new lattice, which we call the *direct union* of $\mathscr{L}_1$ and $\mathscr{L}_2$.

Any lattice that can thus be written as a direct union of two or more other lattices is called *reducible.* If this is not the case, it is called *irreducible* or *coherent.*

Every Boolean lattice is reducible except the trivial lattice consisting of only two elements ϕ and I. The occurrence of nontrivial irreducible lattices is thus an essential property of quantum systems.

Whenever a lattice is reducible, there exist nontrivial elements that are compatible with every other element in the lattice. The set of all such elements is called the *center* $\mathscr{C}$ of the lattice.

2. *The Superposition Principle*

An irreducible lattice $\mathscr{L}$ satisfies the *superposition principle*, which can be expressed as follows:

For every pair of distinct P, $Q \in \mathscr{L}$ there exists a third point $R \in \mathscr{L}$ such that

$$P \cup Q = P \cup R = R \cup Q. \tag{8}$$

Every proposition system can be decomposed in an essentially unique manner (except for the order of the irreducible parts) into a direct union of irreducible lattices (*14*). This theorem allows the reduction of the study of general proposition systems to that of irreducible ones. For an irreducible lattice the center is trivial (that is, it consist of only two elements ϕ and I). For any Boolean lattices it is identical with the entire lattice.

The lattices that actually occur in Nature are in general reducible. When this is the case, the superposition principle has only restricted validity. We say then that the system allows *superselection rules*, a notion introduced by P. Destouches-Février (*21*), and later again by Wick *et al.* (*22*)

III. The Group of Automorphisms in a Proposition System

A. Morphisms

1. *Definition of Morphisms*

Let $\mathscr{L}_1$, $\mathscr{L}_2$ be two proposition systems and m a bijective mapping with domain $\mathscr{L}_1$ and range $\mathscr{L}_2$ with the properties

$$\begin{aligned} &\text{(i)} \quad x \subseteq y \Leftrightarrow m(x) \subseteq m(y) \\ &\text{(ii)} \quad m(x') = m(x)' \end{aligned} \tag{9}$$

for every $x, y \in \mathscr{L}_1$.

Such a mapping is called a *morphism* of $\mathscr{L}_1$ onto $\mathscr{L}_2$. Every morphism admits an inverse m^{-1} with domain $\mathscr{L}_2$ and range $\mathscr{L}_1$ defined by

$$m^{-1}(m(x)) = x. \tag{10}$$

The inverse of a morphism is also a morphism.

2. *Various Invariance Properties*

The following properties are simple consequences of this definition. For the detailed proofs we refer to the work of Emch and Piron (*23*). If m is a morphism from $\mathscr{L}_1$ to $\mathscr{L}_2$ and $\{x_i\}$ any subset of $\mathscr{L}_1$, then

$$m\Big(\bigcup_i x_i\Big) = \bigcup_i m(x_i). \tag{11}$$

Similarly, we have

$$m\left(\bigcap_i x_i\right) = \bigcap_i m(x_i). \tag{12}$$

From this follows immediately

$$m(I_1) = I_2, \qquad m(\phi_1) = \phi_2, \tag{13}$$

and

$$x_1 \leftrightarrow x_2 \Leftrightarrow m(x_1) \leftrightarrow m(x_2). \tag{14}$$

If $P_1 \in \mathscr{L}_1$ is a point, then $m(P_1) = P_2 \in \mathscr{L}_2$ is also a point.

Furthermore, if x and y are contained in the same coherent component of $\mathscr{L}_1$, then $m(x)$ and $m(y)$ are also contained in the same coherent component of $\mathscr{L}_2$ [cf. Emch and Piron (*23*, Lemma 4)].

3. *Automorphisms*

If $\mathscr{L}_1 = \mathscr{L}_2 = \mathscr{L}$, then a morphism with domain and range $\mathscr{L}$ is called an *automorphism*. It is a permutation of the lattice that leaves the lattice structure invariant. An automorphism will also be called a *symmetry* of the lattice $\mathscr{L}$.

The set of all the automorphisms are a group, the symmetry group of the lattice. We shall denote it by M. The composition law of this group is defined by setting for the product of two automorphisms m_1 and m_2

$$m_1 m_2(x) = m_1(m_2(x)). \tag{15}$$

The identity element e of the group is represented by the trivial automorphism, which leaves every element of the lattice invariant: $e(x) = x$; and the inverse automorphism m^{-1} is the group inverse.

Every automorphism induces a transformation $p \to p^m$ of the states of a system through the formula

$$p^m(x) \equiv p(m^{-1}(x)) \qquad \forall \quad x \in \mathscr{L}. \tag{16}$$

It can easily be verified that if p is a state, then p^m, defined by Eq. (16), is a state too. If p is a pure state, then p^m is pure too.

B. The Symmetry Group of a Proposition System

1. *Topology in a Group of Automorphisms*

The group of automorphisms of a proposition system reflects many of the structure properties of the lattice. The study of these properties can therefore be reduced to some extent to the study of the group of its automorphisms. In this section we define the topology in the group of automorphisms so as to make this group a topological group.

A topology in an abstract space M is given by specifying a certain class of subsets, designated as the *open* sets of that space. In order to define them it is sufficient to give a *complete system* of *neighborhoods* of the set M. They form a *basis* in the sense that every open set can be represented as the union of such neighborhoods.

In the case of groups it suffices to designate only the neighborhoods of the identity element $e \in M$. Neighborhoods at other points $m_0 \neq e$ are then obtained by left or right translations of the neighborhoods at the identity. Thus if U is such a neighborhood, then the sets

$$m_0 U = \{m' | m' = m_0 m, m \in U\}$$
$$U m_0 = \{m' | m' = m_0 m, m \in U\}$$

are neighborhoods of the point m_0.

For the definition of the neighborhoods at $e \in M$ we look for a motivation in the physical interpretation of the lattice. The measurable quantities are the states, and proximity of two transformations of the lattice is therefore expressed most naturally in terms of the transformation of the states. Thus we define an ϵ neighborhood $N_\epsilon(e)$ of e as the set of automorphisms m such that

$$|p^m(x) - p(x)| < \epsilon \qquad \forall \quad x \in \mathscr{L} \text{ and all states } p. \tag{17}$$

It is easy to verify that this system of ϵ neighborhoods satisfies the five conditions of Theorem 10 of Pontrjagin (*9*, Section 17). Thus they define a topology in the group such that the group operations are continuous functions of its arguments. From now on we shall consider the group of automorphisms equipped with this topology so that it may be considered a topological group.

We may now consider various properties that depend on that topology. The following will be used frequently:

(a) *Closure:* A subset of M is *closed* if its complement in M is open.

(a) *Limit point:* A point m_0 is a *limit point* of a subset $A \subset M$ if every neighborhood of m_0 has at least one point $\neq m_0$ in common with A. A subset $A \subset M$ is closed if and only if it contains all its limit points.

(c) *Connectedness:* The space M is *connected* if there does not exist a subset A of M that is both open and closed. If such a set exists, then its complement $A' = M - A$ is also open and closed. It follows then that A is the union of two open sets and also the union of two closed sets.

(*d*) *Discreteness:* The space M is *discrete* if every subset of M is both open and closed.

(*e*) *Compactness:* The space M is *compact* if from every countable family of open sets in M we can select a finite subfamily that also covers M. In that case every infinite subset of M contains at least one limit point in M. If this is not the case, then the space is called noncompact.

If a space is not connected it may contain connected components. A closed subset M_0 of M is a connected component if it cannot be represented as the union of two nonintersecting closed sets.

The largest connected subset $M_0 \subset M$ that contains the element $e \in M$ is called the connected component of the unit element. It is easy to see that M_0 is an invariant subgroup of M.

2. *The Connected Component and Superselection Rules*

We shall here first examine the effect of the automorphisms in the connected component of a proposition system with superselection rules. We consider only the case of *discrete* superselection rules for which the lattice $\mathscr{L}$ is a direct union of a finite or countably infinite set of lattices $\mathscr{L}_i$.

We denote by $I_i = \{\phi_1, \phi_2, \ldots, I_i, \phi_{i+1}, \ldots\}$ the element that has the zero element at every position except at the ith position, where it has the unit element I_i of the lattice $\mathscr{L}_i$. The lattice $\mathscr{L}_i$ is then isomorphic with the segment $[\phi, I_i]$ that is the set of elements x such that $\phi \subseteq x \subseteq I_i$. So we may identify $\mathscr{L}_i$ with this segment. The elements I_i are all disjoint elements of the center of $\mathscr{L}$.

Let us now consider a state p_1 such that $p_1(I_i) = 1$. Because the I_i are disjoint, we have for any state $p(I_1) + p(I_i) = p(I_1 \cup I_i)$. It follows that $p_1(I_i) = 0$ for $i \neq 1$. Let us next choose a sufficiently small $\epsilon > 0$ and consider $m \in N_\epsilon(e)$ so that

$$|p_1(m^{-1}(I_1)) - p_1(I_1)| \lesssim \epsilon.$$

Since m^{-1} is an automorphism, $m^{-1}(I_1) = I_i$. But we have already shown that $p_1(I_i) = 0$ for $i \neq 1$. Hence $m^{-1}(I_i) = I_1$ (if $\epsilon < 1$, for instance) or $m(I_1) = I_1$ for all $m \in N_\epsilon(e)$.

We have thus established that for all $m \in N_\epsilon(e) = U$ we must have $m(I_1) = I_1$. It is now easy to extend this invariance of I_1 to the entire connected component $M_0 \subset M$ by using a theorem of Pontrjagin (*9*, Theorem 15) according to which every element in M can be written as a finite product of elements from U. With this we have proved the following

Theorem I. If a lattice $\mathscr{L}$ is a direct union of coherent lattices $\mathscr{L}_i$, then every morphism from the connected component that contains the unit element leaves every sublattice $\mathscr{L}_i$ invariant.

3. *Representations of Symmetry Groups*

The group of automorphisms M is in general much too large a group for the description of physical symmetries. The physical symmetry groups satisfy additional properties that are related to the physical content of the theory.

We shall say that the topological group G is a *symmetry group* of the system if there exists a homomorphism U of G into M. Such a homomorphism will be called a *projective representation* of the group G.

We remark here that by a projective representation we mean always a homomorphism as far as the group structure is concerned, and a homomorphism with respect to the topologies of G and M. A projective representation is thus always the continuous image of G in M.

We can now easily establish

Theorem 2. If the lattice $\mathscr{L}$ is a direct union of lattices $\mathscr{L}_i$ and if it admits a connected symmetry group G, then every $U_x \in M$ that is an image of $x \in G$ in the representation M leaves every component $\mathscr{L}_i$ invariant.

The proof follows from the remark that connectedness is invariant under a homeomorphism, hence all $U_x \in M_0$. We shall say the projective representation U in $\mathscr{L}$ (denoted by $(\mathscr{L}, U)$) of the group G is *irreducible* if

$$U_x a = a \qquad \forall \quad x \in G \Rightarrow a = \phi \qquad \text{or} \qquad a = I, \tag{18}$$

and we call such a pair $(\mathscr{L}, U)$ an *elementary system* with respect to the symmetry group G. We see immediately that every elementary system with respect to a symmetry group G is necessarily coherent. Indeed if it were not, it would have a nontrivial center and we have just seen that the elements of the center are all invariant under M_0. Since $U_x \in M_0$ for all $x \in G$, the conclusion follows that $\mathscr{L}$ is coherent.

The foregoing remarks contain the germ of a theory of elementary particles based on the phenomenology of physical systems. The idea is this: The phenomenology of a physical system is essentially contained in the lattice structure of the proposition system $\mathscr{L}$. This structure in turn determines the group M of its automorphisms, including all its subgroups. The irreducible representations of the group G in M are the possible elementary systems that are compatible with this lattice structure.

Unfortunately the representation theory of groups in lattices is a branch of mathematics that is not yet developed. Therefore the foregoing sketch of a program cannot yet be carried out. It is possible to pursue another road, however. Instead of working with abstract lattices, we can seek a representation of proposition systems and then study the automorphisms of such representations.

It is known that the closed linear subspaces (henceforth just called subspaces) of a Hilbert space have a lattice structure that satisfies all the axioms of a proposition system. These subspaces do furnish us, therefore, with a representation of a proposition system. This is, however, not the only representation possible. The task of finding all the representations of irreducible proposition systems was accomplished by Piron (*14*) and in the following subsection we shall give a brief outline of his and some related results.

C. Irreducible Proposition Systems as Subspaces of a Hilbert Space

1. *Proposition Systems and Projective Geometries*

There is a remarkable similarity between the proposition system of a quantum-mechanical system and the lattices that arise in the set of axioms of projective geometries. It is thus not surprising that representation theorems for proposition systems are modeled after those for projective geometries. In fact, the essence of the general representation theory of proposition systems is an embedding theorem that says that every proposition system can be embedded in a canonical way into a projective geometry. This theorem, then, establishes the link to the representation theory of the projective geometries and in this manner the representations of proposition systems can all be found.

The essential difference between projective geometries and proposition systems is that the former satisfy the modular law, whereas the latter, as we have seen, do not necessarily do so. If they do, they are, according to a theorem of Piron (*14*, Theorem V), direct unions of projective geometries of *finite dimensions*, where the dimension of a lattice is defined as the maximum of a chain $\phi \subset c \cdots \subset a \subset b \subset \cdots \subset I$ in the lattice.

In the case of infinite dimensions modularity is incompatible with the other axioms of a proposition system. This fact has been known for a long time, and for this reason von Neumann has expressed the conjecture that the *continuous geometries* discovered by him might give the mathematical frame of a generalized quantum mechanics. The continuous geometries do not contain any minimal elements ("point-less" geometries, as von Neumann called them) and thus they do not satisfy axiom (A.1).

Since there are proposition systems in Nature that are not modular (*14*, Proposition on p. 452), the strong constraint of modularity can be replaced by weak modularity and in that case it is possible to retain all the axioms of a proposition system, even for infinite systems, without contradiction. Projective geometries *are* modular, as we have seen. If they are infinite, the other axioms of a proposition system cannot hold for such projective geometries. The axiom that is violated for infinite projective geometries is axiom (IV), which affirms the existence of an orthocomplement. Infinite projective geometries are never orthocomplemented.

A standard example of an infinite projective geometry is the not necessarily closed linear manifolds of a Hilbert space. If union and intersection are defined as linear space and intersection, then the linear manifolds of such a space *are* modular (*18*, Theorem 9, p. 370; *24*). The complement is still defined. If a is not a closed linear manifold, we have $a \subset (a')'$. This violates axiom (IV).

For Boolean lattices representation theorems have been known for a long time: Every Boolean lattice may be realized as the lattice of subsets of some set (*25*, *26*).

2. *The Representation Theorem for Proposition Systems*

In subsection C, 1 we quoted the theorem that says that every reducible proposition system is the unique direct union of irreducible ones (*14*). The general representation problem of the lattices of proposition systems can thus be reduced to that of irreducible lattices. The following theorem is true for reducible or irreducible lattices (*14*, Theorem XVIII, p. 462).

Theorem 3 (Piron). If $\mathscr{L}$ is any lattice of propositions, then there exists always a projective geometry G_p and a canonical mapping α of $\mathscr{L}$ into G_p that satisfies the following properties.

(1) The restriction of α to the points of $\mathscr{L}$ is a one-to-one mapping onto the points of G_p.

(2) $a \subseteq b \Leftrightarrow \alpha(a) \subseteq \alpha(b)$.

(3) $\alpha\left(\bigcap_i a_i\right) = \bigcap_i \alpha(a_i)$.

(4) $\alpha(a \cup P) = \alpha(a) \cup \alpha(P) \qquad \forall \quad \text{points } P \in \mathscr{L}$.

It follows from these properties that if $\mathscr{L}$ is irreducible, then the canonically defined projective geometry G_p is irreducible, too.

This theorem establishes the bridge between the abstract proposition systems and the projective geometries. For the latter there exist well-known representation theorems that will yield similar theorems for the proposition systems. In order to formulate the fundamental representation theorem we need the following three concepts.

(a) A *chain* in $\mathscr{L}$ is a sequence of elements $\phi, \ldots, a, b, \ldots, I$ that satisfies $\phi \subset \cdots \subset a \subset b \subset \cdots \subset I$, where the inclusions are all proper. The number of elements in the chain is called its *length*.

(b) An *antiautomorphism* of a field $\mathfrak{F}$ is an involution $\alpha \to \alpha^*$ $(\alpha \in \mathfrak{F})$ with the property

$$
\begin{aligned}
(\alpha + \beta)^* &= \alpha^* + \beta^* \\
(\alpha\beta)^* &= \beta^* \alpha^* \\
(\alpha^*)^* &= \alpha \qquad \forall \quad \alpha, \beta \in \mathfrak{F}.
\end{aligned} \tag{19}
$$

An example of an antiautomorphism in the field of complex numbers is the complex conjugation. There are many others. But we can show that complex conjugation is the only one that is also continuous in the natural topology of these numbers. For the quaternions, on the other hand, every automorphism is continuous [cf. remark after Eq. (31)].

(c) A sesquilinear form over a vector space $\mathfrak{B}$ with coefficients from a field is a mapping f of $\mathfrak{B} \times \mathfrak{B}$ into $\mathfrak{F}$ such that

$$\begin{aligned} f(x+\alpha y, z) &= f(x,z) + f(y,z)\,\alpha^* \\ f(x, y+\alpha z) &= f(x,y) + \alpha f(y,z) \\ \forall \quad x, y \in \mathfrak{B} \quad &\text{and} \quad \forall \quad \alpha \in \mathfrak{F}. \end{aligned} \tag{20}$$

Such a form is called *Hermitian* if $f(x,y) = f^*(y,x)$, and it is *definite* if $f(x,x) = 0 \Rightarrow x = 0$. An example of such a form is the scalar product in a Hilbert space. The representation theorem of proposition systems can now be stated in the following form.

Theorem 4. Every irreducible proposition system that contains a chain of length at least equal to four can be realized by a linear vector space $\mathfrak{B}$ over a field $\mathfrak{F}$, an antiautomorphism of $\mathfrak{F}$, and a definite Hermitian sesquilinear form in $\mathfrak{B}$. Every proposition $a \in \mathscr{L}$ is represented by a subspace of vectors $x \in \mathfrak{B}$ that satisfy $f(x, y_i) = 0$ for some $y_i \in \mathfrak{B}$. If $a \in \mathscr{L}$ is represented by the subspace $M \subset \mathfrak{B}$ than a' is represented by the subspace $M^{\perp} \equiv N$ consisting of all $x \in \mathfrak{B}$ that satisfy $f(x,y) = 0$, $\forall\ y \in M$.

For the proof of this theorem we refer to Piron (*14*, Theorem XXI. [The proof of Theorem XXII in Piron (*14*) is incomplete. A corrected proof has been given by Amemiya and Araki (*29*).

We remark here that for irreducible proposition systems the field is essentially uniquely determined by the structure of the lattice. This is no longer the case for reducible lattices. This fact is at the origin of the connection between the field $\mathfrak{F}$ and the superselection rules mentioned in Section I, B.

If irreducibility is dropped, other representations are possible. We mention here particularly the representation of proposition systems by algebraic Hilbert spaces where the coefficients are no longer a field but only a matrix algebra. Such representations give an elegant and compact formulation of lattices with certain types of superselection rules (*27*, *28*).

D. Projective Representations of Symmetry Groups

1. *The Semilinear Transformations*

Let $\mathfrak{B}$ be a vector space over a field $\mathfrak{F}$ and let $\alpha \in \mathfrak{F}$. An *automorphism* $\alpha \to \alpha^s$ of the field $\mathfrak{F}$ is a permutation of the elements of $\mathfrak{F}$ that satisfies

$$\begin{aligned} (\alpha\beta)^s &= \alpha^s \beta^s, \\ (\alpha+\beta)^s &= \alpha^s + \beta^s. \end{aligned} \tag{21}$$

A nonsingular *semilinear* transformation of $\mathfrak{V}$ is a one-to-one mapping S of $\mathfrak{V}$ onto itself that has the properties

$$\begin{aligned} S(u+v) &= Su + Sv \qquad \forall \quad u, v \in \mathfrak{V}, \\ S(\alpha u) &= \alpha^s Su, \\ Su = 0 &\Rightarrow u = 0. \end{aligned} \tag{22}$$

If $u = \sum_i u_i$ is a finite linear combination of vectors $u_i \in \mathfrak{V}$, then it follows from (22) that $Su = \sum Su_i$. Thus the lattice structure of the linear manifolds of $\mathfrak{V}$ is left invariant under a semilinear transformation. According to the so-called first fundamental theorem of projective geometry (*24*), the converse is true, too. That is, we have

Theorem 5. Every automorphism of the lattice of linear manifolds of a vector space $\mathfrak{V}$ over a field is induced by a nonsingular semilinear transformation S of the vectors in $\mathfrak{V}$.

2. *Automorphisms of Subspaces*

Let us now consider the vectór space $\mathfrak{V}$ associated with an irreducible proposition system $\mathscr{L}$. This space is endowed with the positive definite Hermitian form $f(x,y)$ of Theorem 4. We shall from now on write $f(x,y) = (x,y)$ and $f(x,x) = \|x\|^2$. The vector space $\mathfrak{V}$ then becomes a Hilbert space $\mathfrak{H}_{\mathfrak{F}}$ over the field $\mathfrak{F}$. The subspaces, images of the propositions in $\mathscr{L}$, are the closed linear manifolds in the norm topology of this space.

If S is a nonsingular bounded semilinear transformation, then there exists an inverse S^{-1} that is also such a transformation. Furthermore, is S_1 and S_2 are two such transformations, the $S_1 S_2$ is one, too. They are thus a group that is closely related to the group of automorphisms of the subspaces in $\mathfrak{H}_{\mathfrak{F}}$.

The precise nature of this relation is obtained if we consider the subgroup $M_0 \subset M_1$, which leaves all the subspaces of $\mathfrak{H}_{\mathfrak{F}}$ invariant. A transformation $T \in M_0$ is then of the form $Tx = \lambda x \ \forall \ x \in \mathfrak{H}_{\mathfrak{F}}$ for some fixed $\lambda \in \mathfrak{F}$. It is easily verified that M_0 is an invariant subgroup of M_1 and that the factor group M_1/M_0 is isomorphic to the group M of automorphisms.

Among the semilinear transformations there are the semiunitary transformations. Such a transformation satisfies, in addition to (22), the relation

$$\|Ux\| = \|x\| \qquad \forall \quad x \in \mathfrak{H}_{\mathfrak{F}}. \tag{23}$$

Consider now any semilinear transformation $S \in M_1$ and define for any pair of elements $x, y \in \mathfrak{H}_{\mathfrak{F}}$ the Hermitian form $g(x,y) = (Sx, Sy)^{S^{-1}}$. Because S is also an automorphism of the subspaces of $\mathfrak{H}_{\mathfrak{F}}$ this form defines the same orthocomplementation in $\mathfrak{H}_{\mathfrak{F}}$ as the scalar product. According to a theorem of Baer (*30*) there exists then a number $\gamma \in \mathfrak{F}$ such that

$$g(x, y) = (x, y)\gamma \qquad \forall \quad x, y \in \mathfrak{H}_{\mathfrak{F}}. \tag{24}$$

Since g is Hermitian, γ is real and is in fact equal to $\gamma = g(x,x)/\|x\|^2$. If we define now $U = \gamma^{-1/2} S$, we find that U is semiunitary and is in the same equivalence class as S modulo M_0.

Thus we have shown: In every equivalence class modulo M_0 of semilinear transformations there exist semiunitary transformations. Two such transformations in the same class differ at most by a factor of modulus 1.

We shall now change the notation and designate henceforth as U the entire class of equivalent semiunitary transformations and as $u = U$ an element from this class.

We can then represent any automorphism $m \in M$ by one of these classes U_m and if E is a projection of $\mathfrak{H}_{\mathfrak{F}}$, $m(E)$ its image under the automorphism m, then we have the explicit formula

$$m(E) = u_m E u_m^{-1} \tag{25}$$

where $u_m \in U_m$ is any element from the class U_m.

3. *Wigner's Theorem*

Consider now a transformation in $\mathfrak{H}_{\mathfrak{C}}$ that maps unit rays into unit rays and conserves the magnitude of the scalar product for the unit vectors in the rays. Such a transformation preserves the order relation of subspaces and transforms orthogonal rays into orthogonal ones. It thus satisfies the two conditions of Eq. (9) for an automorphism. According to the preceding sections it is thus generated by a semiunitary transformation u. Since complex conjugation is the only continuous automorphism of the complex numbers, u is either unitary or antiunitary. Thus we have proved

Theorem 6 (Wigner). Every mapping of unit rays of a complex Hilbert space $\mathfrak{H}_{\mathfrak{C}}$ that preserves the magnitude of the scalar product between such rays can be induced by a unitary or antiunitary vector transformation of $\mathfrak{H}_{\mathfrak{C}}$.
We see from the proof we have given for this theorem that the hypotheses of Wigner's theorem are stronger than needed for the affirmation of the theorem. The only assumption we have used is that orthogonal rays are transformed into orthogonal ones. This generalization of the theorem was first given by Uhlhorn (*31*).

There exist many so-called elementary proofs of this theorem, beginning with the original (incomplete) proof of Wigner (*32*). Not all of these proofs were without error, as can be seen from the critical discussion by Uhlhorn (*31*); to complete the list given there, the elementary proofs that have appeared since (*33–35*) should be added. A more general theorem was proved by Emch and Piron (*23*).

4. *Unitary Projective Representations of Symmetry Groups*

Let G be a symmetry group of an irreducible physical system. There exists thus an isomorphism of G to a subgroup of M. Let $x \in G$ and $U_x \in M$ be the corresponding automorphism of the lattice $\mathscr{L}$ of subspaces. We say that we have a unitary projective representation of G if in every class U_x of semiunitary transformations there exists a unitary transformation.

Let U_x be such a representation and let $u_x \in U_x$ be a unitary transformation. It follows then that

$$u_x u_y = \omega(x, y)\, u_{xy} \qquad \text{where } |\omega(x, y)| = 1, \qquad \omega(x, y) \in \mathfrak{F}. \tag{26}$$

The function $\omega(x, y)$ is called a *factor* of the unitary projective representation of the symmetry group G.

The theory of unitary projective representations can thus be divided into two parts. The first part is the theory of factors, which reduces the problem to the second part, the theory of unitary vector representations.

The theory of factors is quite different for the three different fields. For connected groups it can itself be subdivided into the theory of local factors and global theory. For complex Hilbert spaces and Lie groups the local theory and global theory of factors was developed by Bargmann (*36*). For quaternionic Hilbert spaces the theory of factors was given by Emch (*15*). It is interesting that the result for this case is much simpler than that for the complex case. We shall discuss it in Section IB, B, 1 and 2.

IV. Projective Representation of the Poincaré Group in Quaternionic Hilbert Space

A. Quaternionic Hilbert Space

1. *Quaternions*

The quaternions are an algebraic field endowed with a norm and a topology. As such they are a nontrivial but natural extension of the real numbers and the complex numbers. The central position occupied by the last two fields in all branches of mathematics and physics makes it desirable to understand the possible role of quaternions in fundamental physical theory, especially in quantum mechanics. This is all the more true since it can be shown that the complex numbers and the quaternions are the only possible algebraic fields endowed with a topology such that the algebraic operations are continuous in that topology and that they contain the real numbers as a subfield (*9*).

The quaternions contain three imaginary units, denoted by e_1, e_2, and e_3, which are assumed to satisfy the fundamental relations

$$\begin{aligned} e_i e_j &= e_k = -e_j e_i, \\ e_i^2 &= -1, \end{aligned} \tag{27}$$

where i, j, k are a cyclic permutation of 1, 2, 3.

A general quaternion q is then defined as a linear form

$$q = a_0 + a_1 e_1 + a_2 e_2 + a_3 e_3$$

with real coefficients a_r. We write sometimes $e_0 = 1$ and set $q = \sum_{r=0} a_r e_r$.

The sum and product of quaternions are defined by assuming the associative and distributive law with respect to both of these operations. Thus

$$q + q' = \sum_r (a_r + a_r') e_r \qquad \text{if} \quad q = \sum a_r e_r,\, q' = \sum a_r' e_r \tag{28}$$

and

$$qq' = \sum b_r e_r$$

with

$$\begin{aligned} b_0 &= a_0 a_0' - a_1 a_1' - a_2 a_2' - a_3 a_3' \\ b_1 &= a_0 a_1' + a_0 a_1' + a_2 a_3' - a_3 a_2' \\ b_2 &= a_0 a_2' + b_0 a_2' + a_3 a_1' - a_1 a_3' \\ b_3 &= a_0 a_3' + a_0 a_3' + a_1 a_2' - a_2 a_1'. \end{aligned} \tag{29}$$

We verify immediately that this product is *not* commutative: $qq' \neq q'q$.

The *norm* of quaternions is $|q| = [a_0^2 + a_1^2 + a_2^2 + a_3^2]^{1/2}$. It satisfies $|q + q'| \leqq |q| + |q'|$ and $|qq'| = |q|\,|q'|$ and it defines a topology by setting for the ϵ neighborhood of the element q_0 the quaternions q with $|q - q_0| < \epsilon$. With such a set of neighborhoods as a fundamental set, we have defined a topology for which the two operations of addition and multiplication are continuous operations (*q*).

The conjugation is defined by $q^{\Omega} = a_0 - a_1 e_1 - a_2 e_2 - a_3 e_3$. It follows that the norm is defined also by $|q|^2 = qq^{\Omega} = q^{\Omega} q$. Every quaternion $q \neq 0$ has an inverse given explicitly by

$$q^{-1} = (|q|)^{-1} q^{\Omega}. \tag{30}$$

The field of the quaternions thus defines two topological groups. The additive group is isomorphic to the group of vector addition in a four-dimensional real space. It is thus Abelian.

The multiplicative group is isomorphic to the covering group of $U(2, \mathfrak{C})$ the complex unitary group in two dimensions. It is thus not Abelian.

The quaternions ω of magnitude 1 are the invariant subgroup $SU(2, \mathfrak{C})$ of the multiplicative group. We denote these quaternions by Ω.

The center of the multiplicative group are the real quaternions $\mathfrak{R} \subset \mathfrak{Q}$. The center of Ω consists of the two elements ± 1. It is thus the cyclic group of order 2.

For every $\omega \in \Omega$ we can define an automorphism of the quaternions $\mathfrak{Q}$ by setting

$$q \to q^{\omega} = \omega q \omega^{-1}. \tag{31}$$

We prove in algebra that conversely every automorphism of the quaternions is of this form. The automorphisms are thus themselves a group that is isomorphic to the factor group $O^{+}(3) = SU(2, \mathfrak{Q})/Z_2$.

It is sometimes convenient to represent quaternions as pairs of complex numbers by setting

$$q = z_1 + e_2 z_2 = (z_1, z_2) \tag{32}$$

where

$$\begin{aligned} z_1 &= a_0 + a_3 e_3, \\ z_2 &= a_2 + a_1 e_3. \end{aligned} \tag{33}$$

We then identify e_3 with the imaginary unit i of the complex numbers. The multiplication law is then expressible by

$$\begin{gathered} q = (z_1, z_2), \qquad q' = (z_1', z_2'), \\ qq' = (z_1 z_1' - z_2^* z_2', z_2 z_1' + z_1^* z_2'). \end{gathered} \tag{34}$$

We shall call this representation of the quaternions by pairs of complex numbers the *symplectic decomposition.*

The symplectic decomposition furnishes us with a representation of the quaternions by 2×2 matrices in a complex space as follows. For any fixed quaternion $a \in \mathfrak{Q}$ with symplectic decomposition $a = (\alpha_1, \alpha_2)$ we set

$$q \to q' = aq. \tag{35}$$

We then interpret the quaternions q and q' as two component vectors with complex coefficients. Equation (35) is then equivalent with the linear transformation

$$q' = Aq,$$

where

$$A = \begin{pmatrix} \alpha_1 & -\alpha_2^* \\ \alpha_2 & \alpha_1^* \end{pmatrix}. \tag{36}$$

We shall refer to this as the *symplectic representation* of the quaternions. For the particular case that $a = e_r$ $(r = 1, 2, 3)$ we obtain in the symplectic representation

$$e_r = -i\sigma_r \qquad (r = 1, 2, 3) \tag{37}$$

where σ_r are the three Pauli spin matrices. We should remark here that the symplectic decomposition can be made in a coordinate-free manner as follows: Let i be any fixed pure imaginary quaternion of magnitude 1 so that $i^{\mathfrak{Q}} = -i$, $i^2 = -1$. We write, for every quaternion $q = q_+ + q_-$, where $q_\pm = \frac{1}{2}(q \mp iqi)$, and define $q_+ = z_1$ and $q_- = iz_2$. The pair z_1 and z_2 can be considered as complex numbers with i as the imaginary unit. The correspondence $q \leftrightarrow (z_1, z_2)$ is unique in both directions and satisfies the rules (32). This is the symplectic decomposition with respect to i.

The symplectic decomposition will be very useful in the following because it can be extended to quaternionic Hilbert spaces, and it permits a certain reduction of quaternionic Hilbert spaces to pairs of complex spaces.

2. *Elementary Properties of Quaternionic Hilbert Space*

A quaternionic Hilbert space $\mathfrak{H}_{\mathfrak{Q}}$ is a linear vector space over the field of the quaternions. This means that in addition to the usual rule of vector addition there is also a left multiplication with scalars that associates with every $q \in \mathfrak{Q}$ and every $f \in \mathfrak{H}_{\mathfrak{Q}}$ an element $qf \in \mathfrak{H}_{\mathfrak{Q}}$.

This scalar multiplication shall satisfy the usual rules of distributivity and associativity, such as

$$\begin{aligned} q_1(q_2 f) &= (q_1 q_2) f, \\ q(f + g) &= qf + qg, \\ (q_1 + q_2) f &= q_1 f + g_2 f, \end{aligned} \tag{38}$$

for $q_r \in \mathfrak{Q}$ and $\forall\, f, g \in \mathfrak{H}_{\mathfrak{Q}}$.

Furthermore, we define a quaternion-valued scalar product $(f,g) \in \mathfrak{Q}$ by the axioms

$$\begin{aligned}
&\text{(i)} \quad (qf,g)=(f,g)q^*.\\
&\text{(ii)} \quad (f+g,h)=(f,h)+(g,h).\\
&\text{(iii)} \quad (f,g)=(g,f)^*. \qquad (39)\\
&\text{(iv)} \quad \|f\|^2=(f,f)>0;\\
&\qquad \|f\|^2=0 \Rightarrow f=0.
\end{aligned}$$

Just as in the case of ordinary (complex) Hilbert space, we demonstrate then the inequalities of Cauchy and Minkowski:

$$\begin{aligned}
&\text{(i)} \quad |(f,g)| \leqq \|f\|\,\|g\|,\\
&\text{(ii)} \quad \|f+g\| \leqq \|f\|+\|g\|.
\end{aligned} \qquad (40)$$

With the scalar product, strong and weak convergence can be defined in the usual manner.

3. *Linear and Semilinear Operators*

We define a semilinear operator t as a function tf, with a linear manifold as domain and values in $\mathfrak{H}_{\mathfrak{Q}}$, that satisfies the conditions

$$\begin{aligned}
t(f+g)&=tf+tg,\\
t(qf)&=q^t(tf).
\end{aligned} \qquad (41)$$

Here q^t designates an automorphism of the quaternions independent of f. It follows that the range of a semilinear operator is also a linear manifold. We shall consider only nonsingular transformations such that $tf=0 \Rightarrow f=0$. The inverse t^{-1} then exists and it is also semilinear. The operator t is *linear* if $q^t=q \;\forall\, q \in \mathfrak{Q}$.

The Hermitian conjugate $t^\dagger$ of t is defined by the relation

$$(f,tg)=(t^\dagger f,g)^t.$$

We can verify that $t^\dagger$ is semilinear if t is, and if the automorphism associated with t is $q \to q^t$, then the automorphism associated with $t^\dagger$ is $q \to ((q^{\mathfrak{Q}})^s)^{\mathfrak{Q}}$ where $(q^s)^t=q$.

A semiunitary operator u is semilinear and in addition satisfies $\|uf\|^2=\|f\|^2$ $\forall$ f $\in \mathfrak{H}_{\mathfrak{Q}}$. It is called unitary if it is also linear.

A simple example of a semilinear operator is a multiplication with a fixed quaternion $a \in \mathfrak{Q}$. Indeed, let

$$tf \equiv af \qquad a \in \mathfrak{Q}.$$

It follows that $t(qf) = a(qf) = (aq)f = aqa^{-1}af = q^a tf$. Thus we see that left multiplication with a fixed quaternion a induces a semilinear transformation that leaves every ray invariant.

4. *Ray Transformations*

Every semilinear transformation induces a ray transformation or, more generally, an automorphism of subspaces. A ray is defined as the set of vectors of the form qf with variable $q \in \mathfrak{Q}$ and fixed $f \in \mathfrak{H}_{\mathfrak{Q}}$. The image ray is given by the set of vectors ptf for all $p \in \mathfrak{Q}$.

We denote by F a ray that contains the vector f and by TF the mapping of the ray induced by a semilinear transformation t. We shall say that two semilinear transformations are *equivalent* if they induce the same ray transformation. This is clearly an equivalence relation. We can therefore identify the class $[t]$ of all equivalent transformations t with the ray transformation T.

We now have the following important property:

Theorem 7. Every equivalence class T of semilinear transformations in a Hilbert space $\mathfrak{H}_{\mathfrak{Q}}$ contains at least one linear transformation t_0.

Proof. Let $q \to q^t$ be the automorphism induced in $\mathfrak{Q}$ by the semilinear transformation t. Since every such automorphism is inner, there exists an $\omega \in \Omega$ (quaternions of norm 1) such that

$$q^t = \omega q \omega^{-1}. \tag{42}$$

Define $t_0 = \omega^{-1} t$. It is equivalent to t and we find $t_0(qf) = \omega^{-1} t(qf) = \omega^{-1} \omega q \omega^{-1} tf = q t_0 f$. Thus t_0 is linear. This proves Theorem 7.

If t_0' is another linear transformation in the same class than $t_0^{-1} t_0'$ is a linear transformation that leaves every ray invariant. Such a transformation is of the form

$$f \to \lambda f \qquad \text{with} \quad \lambda \in \mathfrak{R} \quad \text{and} \quad \lambda \neq 0.$$

In the particular case that t is also unitary we must have $\lambda^2 = 1$ or $\lambda = \pm 1$. If we combine this result with the result of subsection D, 2, we obtain the following

Corollary. Every equivalence class T of semilinear transformations of a quaternionic Hilbert space contains exactly two unitary transformations. They differ only by a sign.

B. Projective Representations of Symmetry Groups in Quaternionic Hilbert Space

1. *Local Lifting of Factors*

We consider now a topological group G and a projective representation that associates with every $x \in G$ a ray transformation U_x. According to the preceding subsection, every such transformation can be represented by two unitary operators $u_x \in U_x$ that differ only by a sign. If we choose in an arbitrary manner in each class U_x one of the two representatives u_x then we obtain a projective representation of the symmetry group G by unitary operators that satisfies

$$u_x u_y = \omega(x, y)\, u_{xy} \tag{43}$$

where $\omega(x,y) = \pm 1$. From the foregoing it is clear that every ray representation of a topological group in a quaternionic Hilbert space can be brought into this form. If we choose $u_e = I$, then the factors $\omega(x,y)$ also satisfy

$$\omega(e, y) = \omega(x, e) = 1 \tag{44}$$

for all x, y in G.

It is natural to ask at this point whether it is possible to choose in a suitable neighborhood of the identity $e \in G$ the representatives u_x in such a way that the factors $\omega(x,y) = 1$. This is indeed the case. The relevant theorem is due to Bargmann (*36*), and it states that for every representation of a topological group in a complex Hilbert space there exists a suitable neighborhood $N(e)$ of the identity so that $\omega(x,y)$ is a *continuous* function of its two arguments. This theorem is also valid in quaternionic Hilbert spaces. The proof for this case was given by Emch (*15*).

The application of this result to the representation $x \to U_x$ leads to

Theorem 8 (Emch). Every ray representation $x \to U_x$ of a topological group G in a quaternionic Hilbert space can be induced by a strongly continuous unitary representation $x \to u_x \in U_x$ in a suitable neighborhood of the identity.

It is worth pointing out here that this theorem is false for complex Hilbert spaces. The deeper reason for this fundamental difference of the two spaces has been analyzed by Emch (*15*) and is due to the fact that $SU(2, \mathfrak{C}) = \Omega$ of the quaternions of magnitude 1 is semisimple, whereas the corresponding group of phase transformations in a complex space is not (it is in fact Abelian).

Theorem 8 leads to a considerable simplification of the theory of projective representations of groups. It suffices to study the locally unitary vector representations.

2. *Global Lifting of Factors*

We must next examine the question whether it is possible to extend the vector representation $x \to u_x$ to the entire group G. For simply connected groups the answer is easy. We have in fact

Theorem 9. Every ray representation $x \to U_x$ of a simply connected topological group in a quaternionic Hilbert space can be induced by a unitary vector representation $x \to u_x$.

Proof. According to Theorem 8 there exists a neighborhood $N(e)$ of the identity and a local lifting of the factors such that $u_x u_y = u_{xy}$ $\forall$ $x, y \in N(e)$. According to Theorem 15 of Pontrjagin (*9*) every element $x \in G$ admits a representation $x = \prod_{i=1}^{n} x_i$, $x_i \in N(e)$ and $n < \infty$. Since the correspondence $x \to u_x$ is a vector representation for all $x \in N(e)$, this theorem permits us to conclude that it remains true for all $x \in G$. This proves Theorem 9. [For the details of this part of the proof we refer to Bargmann (*36*).]

The case of multiply connected groups can be reduced to the case of simply connected groups via the theory of the universal covering group. In the application that constitutes the main topic of this article we need only the result for doubly connected groups, which we shall state with

Theorem 10. Every ray representation of a doubly connected topological group G in a quaternionic Hilbert space can be induced by a unitary vector representation $x \to u_x$ of its simply connected covering group G. There are two and only two distinct cases possible. Either $x \to u_x$ is also a vector representation of G or it is a double-valued vector representation that satisfies only

$$u_x u_y = \pm u_{xy}.$$

The proof of this theorem is exactly the same as in the case of complex spaces. We can therefore omit it here (*15*).

3. *Schur's Lemma and Its Corollary*

The lemma of Schur plays a fundamental role in the representation theory of groups. For the quaternionic case we shall need its generalization, which can be stated as follows.

Lemma (Schur). Let $\mathfrak{H}_{\mathfrak{Q}}^{(r)}$ $(r = 1, 2)$ be two quaternionic Hilbert spaces, G a topological group, and $u_x^{(r)}$ irreducible unitary representations of G in $\mathfrak{H}_{\mathfrak{Q}}^{(r)}$. Furthermore, let t be a bounded colinear mapping of $\mathfrak{H}_{\mathfrak{Q}}^{(1)}$ into $\mathfrak{H}_{\mathfrak{Q}}^{(2)}$ such that

$$t u_x^{(1)} = u_x^{(2)} t \qquad \forall \quad x \in G;$$

then t either admits an inverse or it is zero.

The proof of this lemma requires only small adaptations to be valid for the case of quaternionic spaces as well, and we shall omit it here [for details cf. Emch (*15*)].

Although Schur's lemma is identical in the quaternionic and complex cases, the situation is quite different for its corollary. We state it in the form of

Theorem 11. Let u_x be an irreducible representation of the group G in a quaternionic Hilbert space $\mathfrak{H}_{\mathfrak{Q}}$ and t a bounded linear operator in $\mathfrak{H}_{\mathfrak{Q}}$ such that $tu_x = u_x t\ \forall\ x \in G$; then t is of the form $t = rI + s\mathscr{J}$ where r, s are real, I is the identity in $\mathfrak{H}_{\mathfrak{Q}}$ and $\mathscr{J}$ is a unitary and anti-Hermitian operator in $\mathfrak{H}_{\mathfrak{Q}}$.

If we compare this theorem with the corollary of Schur's lemma in $\mathfrak{H}_{\mathfrak{Q}}$, we note that the essential difference is the appearance of a linear operator $\mathscr{J}$ that is unitary and anti-Hermitian. Such a $\mathscr{J}$ satisfies $\mathscr{J}^\dagger = -\mathscr{J}$ and $\mathscr{J}^\dagger = \mathscr{J}^\dagger \mathscr{J} = -\mathscr{J}^2 = I$.

In a complex space such an operator is always of the form $\mathscr{J} = \pm iI$ where $i = (-1)^{1/2}$ and it is seen that in this case the corollary reduces to the corollary for complex spaces.

Before giving a formal proof of the theorem, let us verify it for the case of a one-dimensional space. The vectors in this space are the quaternions q. Linear operators are multiplication from the right with another quaternion. The unitary operators are multiplication from the right with a quaternion of magnitude 1. Thus we may write $uq = q\omega$, $q \in \mathfrak{Q}$, $\omega \in \Omega$.

A linear operator t that commutes with u must have the form

$$tq = qa \qquad a \in \mathfrak{Q} \quad \text{and} \quad \omega a = a\omega.$$

Let us write for $\omega = \omega_0 + \omega \cdot e$. We define $e_\omega = |\omega|^{-1} \omega \cdot e$ so that $\omega = \omega_0 + |\omega| e_\omega$. We find then easily that a must have the form $a = r + se_\omega$ with r and s real. Thus t is of the form

$$tq = rq + sqe_\omega$$

and we have verified the theorem for this case if we show that $\mathscr{J}q = qe_\omega$ is unitary and anti-Hermitian. This is indeed the case, since $e_\omega^\dagger = -e_\omega$ and $e_\omega^2 = -1$, so that $\mathscr{J}^\dagger q = -qe_\omega$ and $\mathscr{J}^2 = -I$.

Let us now prove Theorem 11. Assume first that t is Hermitian, so that $t^\dagger = t$. In that case not only t but also every function of t commutes with u. In particular, the spectral projections associated with t do the same. Since u is irreducible, all these spectral projections are either 0 or I. From this follows that t is a multiplum of $I : t = r \cdot I$ with r real. This proves the theorem for Hermitian t.

Let us now examine the case of anti-Hermitian $t : t^\dagger = -t$. It follows then that $t^\dagger t$ is a positive operator, since $(f, t^\dagger tf) = 0 \Rightarrow (tf, tf) = 0$ or $tf = 0$. By

Schur's lemma this is only possible if $f = 0$. Hence $t^\dagger t$ is positive and Hermitian. According to a well-known theorem (*37*) there exists then a unique positive square root $(t^\dagger t)^{1/2} = |t|$ that is Hermitian, possesses an inverse, and commutes with t. We define then

$$\mathscr{I} = t|t|^{-1} = |t|^{-1} t$$

so that

$$\mathscr{I}^\dagger = -\mathscr{I} \quad \text{and} \quad \mathscr{I}^2 = -I.$$

We verify then that t also commutes with u, so according to the preceding paragraph it is of the form $s \cdot I$. Thus we have proved that $t = s \cdot \mathscr{I}$ with $\mathscr{I}^2 = -I$, $\mathscr{I}^\dagger = -\mathscr{I}$ if $t^\dagger = -t$.

The general case, where t is neither Hermitian nor anti-Hermitian, is now easily reduced to the preceding two special cases. We write $t = t_1 + t_2$, where $t_1 = \frac{1}{2}(t + t^\dagger)$, $t_2 = \frac{1}{2}(t - t^\dagger)$, so that $t_1^\dagger = t_1$, $t_2^\dagger = -t_2$. Moreover, both t_1 and t_2 commute separably with u. Thus $t_1 = r \cdot I$, $t_2 = s \cdot \mathscr{I}$, and $t = r \cdot I + s \cdot \mathscr{I}$. This proves the theorem.

It should have become obvious by now that the operator $\mathscr{I}$ is related to the symplectic decomposition of the complex numbers. Indeed the $\mathscr{I}$ plays the role of an imaginary unit in the quaternionic Hilbert space. This will be discussed in detail in the following subsection.

4. *The Symplectic Decomposition of* $\mathfrak{H}_\mathfrak{Q}$

We recall that the symplectic decomposition for quaternions (cf. Section IV, A, 1) was obtained by distinguishing one of the quaternionic units and decomposing the quaternions into two distinct classes, those that commute with this unit and those that anticommute. This process can be extended to Hilbert spaces.

Let $\mathscr{I}$ be a linear operator in $\mathfrak{H}_\mathfrak{Q}$ such that

$$\mathscr{I}\mathscr{I}^\dagger = \mathscr{I}^\dagger \mathscr{I} = I, \qquad \mathscr{I}^\dagger = -\mathscr{I}. \tag{45}$$

We observe first that every vector $f \in \mathfrak{H}_\mathfrak{Q}$ is an eigenvector of $\mathscr{I}$ and every pure imaginary quaternion of magnitude 1 is an eigenvalue.

To see this let $f \in \mathfrak{H}_\mathfrak{Q}$ be an arbitrary vector and define $g = \mathscr{I}f$. We decompose f with respect to the ray $F = \{f\}$, which is a one-dimensional subspace of $\mathfrak{H}_\mathfrak{Q}$:

$$\mathscr{I}f = g = qf + h, \qquad \text{where} \quad (h, f) = 0. \tag{46}$$

It follows from this and the properties (45) that

$$(f, \mathscr{I}h) = (f, \mathscr{I}(\mathscr{I}f - qf)) = -(f, f) - q(f, (qf + h)) = -(1 + q^2)(f, f). \tag{47}$$

On the other hand

$$(f, \mathscr{J} h) = -(\mathscr{J} f, h) = -(h,h) = -(1 - |q|^2)(f, f). \tag{48}$$

From this we obtain

$$q^2 = -|q|^2 \quad \text{and} \quad |q|^2 \leqq 1. \tag{49}$$

Using $\mathscr{J}^2 = -I$, we obtain further

$$0 = \mathscr{J}^2 f + f = (1 + q^2) f + \mathscr{J} h = (1 - |q|^2) f + \mathscr{J} h,$$

so that

$$(h, h) = (\mathscr{J} h, \mathscr{J} h) = (1 - |q|^2)^2 (f, f). \tag{50}$$

Comparing Eq. (50) with Eq. (48) we find

$$|q|^2 = 1, \qquad q^2 = -1, \qquad h = 0. \tag{51}$$

Thus we have proved: every vector $f \in \mathfrak{H}_{\mathfrak{Q}}$ is an eigenvector of $\mathscr{J}$ and the eigenvalue is a pure imaginary quaternion of magnitude 1.

Consider now any $f \in \mathfrak{H}_{\mathfrak{Q}}$ and assume $\mathscr{J} f = if$ where i is pure imaginary and $i^2 = -1$. Let $\omega \in \Omega$ and evaluate

$$\mathscr{J} \omega f = \omega \mathscr{J} f = \omega i f = \omega i \omega^{-1} \omega f.$$

Thus we see: If f is an eigenvector of $\mathscr{J}$ with eigenvalue i, then ωf is an eigenvector of $\mathscr{J}$ with eigenvalue $\omega i \omega^{-1}$. If ω runs through Ω, we obtain with $\omega i \omega^{-1}$ every imaginary quaternion of norm 1. Thus we have proved

Theorem 12. Every vector f in a ray F is an eigenvector of the operator $\mathscr{J}$. The eigenvalues are pure imaginary quaternions of magnitude 1. As f runs through the ray, the eigenvalues run through all such quaternions.

Let us now select an arbitrary but fixed pure imaginary quaternion i of magnitude 1. In every ray F we select the ensemble of vectors f such that $\mathscr{J} f = if$. The totality of such vectors from all rays defines a subset of $\mathfrak{H}_{\mathfrak{Q}}$ that we denote by $\mathfrak{H}_{\mathfrak{C}}^{(i)}$; thus

$$\mathfrak{H}_{\mathfrak{C}}^{(i)} = \{ f \in \mathfrak{H}_{\mathfrak{Q}} | \mathscr{J} f = if \}.$$

We verify without effort that $\mathfrak{H}_{\mathfrak{C}}^{(i)}$ is a complex Hilbert space when the complex numbers $\mathfrak{C}$ are defined by $z = x + iy$ (x, y real). Thus for instance if we have $f,\ g \in \mathfrak{H}_{\mathfrak{C}}^{(i)}$, then $\mathscr{J}(f+g) = \mathscr{J} f + \mathscr{J} g = if + ig$; $i(f+g)$. If $z \in \mathfrak{C}$, then $\mathscr{J}(zf) = z \mathscr{J} f = zif = i(zf)$. Furthermore, if $f, g \in \mathfrak{H}_{\mathfrak{C}}^{(i)}$, then $i(f,g) = (-if, g) = (-\mathscr{J} f, g) = (f, \mathscr{J} g) = (f, ig) = (f,g)i$. Hence $(f,g) \in \mathfrak{C}$.

Finally, if $f_n \in \mathfrak{H}_{\mathfrak{C}}^{(i)}$ is a sequence such that $\|f_n - f_m\| \to 0$ for $n, m \to \infty$, then there exists a limit $f \in \mathfrak{H}_{\mathfrak{Q}}$ such that $f_n \to f$. For this element f we find $\|\mathscr{J}f - \mathscr{J}f_n\| = \|f - f_n\|$, so that $\mathscr{J}f$ is also the limit of $\mathscr{J}f = if_n$. This means $\mathscr{J}f = if$ and $f \in \mathfrak{H}_{\mathfrak{C}}^{(i)}$. With this we have verified that $\mathfrak{H}_{\mathfrak{C}}^{(i)}$ is indeed a complex Hilbert space.

We remark also that the space $\mathfrak{H}_{\mathfrak{C}}^{(i)}$ is total in $\mathfrak{H}_{\mathfrak{C}}$ in the sense that every $f \in \mathfrak{H}_{\mathfrak{C}}$ can be written as linear combinations of vectors $f_+ \in \mathfrak{H}_{\mathfrak{C}}^{(i)}$ with coefficients from $\mathfrak{Q}$. Indeed, let $f \in \mathfrak{H}_{\mathfrak{Q}}$. We define $f_\pm = \frac{1}{2}(I \mp i\mathscr{J})f$ and then choose an arbitrary imaginary quaternion j that anticommutes with i. By setting $f'_+ = -jf_-$ we find

$$\mathscr{J}f_+ = if_+,$$
$$\mathscr{J}f'_+ = if'_+, \tag{52}$$

and

$$f = f'_+ + jf'_+.$$

Thus every vector $f \in \mathfrak{H}_{\mathfrak{Q}}$ admits a decomposition into pairs of vectors f_+, $f'_+ \in \mathfrak{H}_{\mathfrak{C}}^{(i)}$ such that f is a linear combination of such a pair with coefficients from $\mathfrak{Q}$. This is the symplectic decomposition of the quaternionic Hilbert space.

We summarize the results of this subsection with

Theorem 13. Every unitary anti-Hermitian operator $\mathscr{J}$ in a quaternionic Hilbert space defines for each imaginary quaternion i of magnitude 1 a family $\mathfrak{H}_{\mathfrak{C}}^{(i)}$ of vectors f all of which satisfy $\mathscr{J}f = if$. They are a complex Hilbert space that is total in $\mathfrak{H}_{\mathfrak{Q}}$.

5. *Restriction and Extension of Representations*

As before, let $\mathscr{J}$ denote a unitary anti-Hermitian operator in $\mathfrak{H}_{\mathfrak{Q}}$, $\mathfrak{H}_{\mathfrak{C}}^{(i)}$ the complex Hilbert space associated with an imaginary quaternion, and t a bounded linear operator that commutes with $\mathscr{J}$. If $f \in \mathfrak{H}_{\mathfrak{C}}^{(i)}$, then $\mathscr{J}tf = t\mathscr{J}f = t(if) = itf$. Thus $tf \in \mathfrak{H}_{\mathfrak{C}}^{(i)}$. We may therefore define the *restriction* $t_{(i)}$ of the operator as the operator with domain $\mathfrak{H}_{\mathfrak{C}}^{(i)}$. For all $f \in \mathfrak{H}_{\mathfrak{C}}^{(i)}$ it is defined by $t^{(i)}f = tf$.

Conversely, if $t_{(i)}$ is any bounded linear operator in $\mathfrak{H}_{\mathfrak{C}}^{(i)}$, we define its extension t to $\mathfrak{H}_{\mathfrak{Q}}$ by the conditions

(i) t is linear

(ii) $tf = t^{(i)}f \quad \forall \quad f \in \mathfrak{H}_{\mathfrak{C}}^{(i)}$. (53)

Let us show that this extension is always possible and that is is unique. This can be seen directly from the symplectic decomposition (52). Thus we *define* tf by

$$tf = t^{(i)} f_+ + j t^{(i)} f'_+. \tag{54}$$

Let t' be any other extension. Because it is linear we have for any f

$$t' f = t^{(i)} f_+ + j t^{(i)} f'_+ = tf. \tag{55}$$

This proves that the extension is unique.

Let us now consider the Hermitian conjugate of t. It is defined by the relation $(f, tg) = (t^\dagger f, g)\ \forall\ f, g \in \mathfrak{H}_{\mathfrak{Q}}$. Since $\mathscr{J}$ commutes with t we have also for $t^{(i)}$ $(f, t^{(i)} g) = (t^{(i)\dagger} f, g)\ \forall\ f, g \in \mathfrak{H}_{\mathfrak{C}}^{(i)}$. If in the first of these two relations we restrict f, g to $\mathfrak{H}_{\mathfrak{C}}^{(i)}$, we evidently obtain $(t^{\dagger(i)} f, g) = (f, t^{(i)} g)$, from which we conclude that $t^{\dagger(i)} = t^{(i)\dagger}$.

The following assertions are immediate consequences of this.

(a) If t is Hermitian, then $t^{(i)}$ is Hermitian, too.
(b) If t is a projection, then $t^{(i)}$ is a projection, too.
(c) If $t = u$ is unitary, then $u^{(i)}$ is unitary, too.
(d) If $t_1 t_2$ commute, then $t_1^{(i)} t_2^{(i)}$ commute.
(e) If t is an irreducible system all commuting with $\mathscr{J}$, then $t^{(i)}$ is an irreducible system, too.
(f) If t_n is a sequence of t_n all of which commute with $\mathscr{J}$ and tending weakly, strongly, or uniformly to a limit t, then t commutes with $\mathscr{J}$ too, and $t_n^{(i)}$ tends weakly, strongly, or uniformly to $t^{(i)}$.

We retain the part that is relevant for the group representations in

Theorem 14. If $x \to u_x$ is a unitary representation of the topological group G in a quaternionic Hilbert space $\mathfrak{H}_{\mathfrak{Q}}$ that commutes with a unitary and anti-Hermitian linear operator $\mathscr{J}$, then for each pure imaginary quaternion the restriction $u_x^{(i)}$ is defined and

(a) the $u_x^{(i)}$ are a unitary representation of G in $\mathfrak{H}_{\mathfrak{C}}^{(i)}$;
(b) if u_x is irreducible in $\mathfrak{H}_{\mathfrak{Q}}$, then $u_x^{(i)}$ is irreducible in $\mathfrak{H}_{\mathfrak{C}}^{(i)}$.

This theorem gives us complete information as to the properties of the restriction of a representation that commutes with a unitary anti-Hermitian operator. It is natural to ask the question about the converse problem: If we extend a representation from $\mathfrak{H}_{\mathfrak{C}}^{(i)}$ with the unique process described at the beginning of this subsection, what happens to a representation? The answer is contained in

Theorem 15. If $x \to u_x^{(i)}$ is a representation of a topological group G in a complex Hilbert space $\mathfrak{H}_{\mathfrak{C}}^{(i)}$ and it is of class $+1$ or 0 in the sense of Frobenius and Schur, then x_x is an irreducible representation of G in $\mathfrak{H}_{\mathfrak{Q}}$. On the other hand, if $u_x^{(i)}$ is of class -1, then u^x is reducible.

The classification of Frobenius and Schur that is needed here is defined in the following way.

Let $\mathfrak{H}_x$ be a complex Hilbert space, and K a conjugation of $\mathfrak{H}_{\mathfrak{C}}$, that is, an antiunitary involutive mapping of $\mathfrak{H}_{\mathfrak{C}}$ onto itself. If $x \to u_x$ is an irreducible representation of a group G, we can define a conjugate representation $\tilde{u}_x = Ku_xK$. Then Frobenius and Schur have observed that exactly three cases may occur.

(a) $\tilde{u}$ is equivalent to u. There exists then a unitary operator C such that $u_x = C^{-1}u_xC$. If $CKCK = I$, then the representation is of class $+1$.

(b) $\tilde{u}$ is equivalent to u and $CKCK = I$. The representation is then of class -1.

(c) $\tilde{u}$ is not equivalent to u. It is then said to be of class 0.

The proof of Theorem 15 is given by Finkelstein *et al.* (*12*) and Emch (*15*). [The second part (concerning the class -1) is, however, proved only for compact groups by Finkelstein *et al.* (*12*).]

6. *Representation of Abelian Groups*

It is well known that the only irreducible vector representations of an Abelian group in a complex Hilbert space are one-dimensional. Let us now establish this same theorem for the quaternionic vector representation. Assume $x \to u_x$ to be such a representation. It follows, then, from the corollary of Schur's lemma, that $u_x = r(x)I + s(x)\mathscr{I}(x)$ where the $\mathscr{I}(x)$ are unitary and anti-Hermitian operators that all commute with one another. The operators $\mathscr{I}(x)\mathscr{I}(y)$ are thus Hermitian and they all commute with each other and with all the u_x. Thus all the $\mathscr{I}(x)$ are multiples of one another. We can thus write $u_x = r(x)I + s(x)\mathscr{I}$. According to Section IV, A, 4, every vector is an eigenvector of $\mathscr{I}$. Thus u_x leaves every ray invariant, and since the u_x are irreducible, the representation $x \to u_x$ is one-dimensional.

Let us now examine the properties of these irreducible representations of G. Every vector f in a one-dimensional quaternionic Hilbert space may be represented by a quaternion $q \in \mathfrak{Q}$. The operator I is then multiplication with 1 and the linear operator $\mathscr{I}$ is multiplication from the right with an arbitrary pure imaginary quaternion i, so that

$$u_x q = q(r(x) + s(x)\, i). \tag{56}$$

The unitarity of u_x implies $r(x)^2 + s(x)^2 = 1$. We may thus write

$$u_x q = qe^{i\theta(x)} \tag{57}$$

with

$$tg\theta(x) = \frac{s(x)}{r(x)} \qquad (0 \leqq \theta(x) < 2\pi).$$

The representation property $u_x u_y = u_{xy}$ leads then to the relation

$$\theta(x) + \theta(y) = \theta(xy) \qquad (\text{mod}\, 2\pi). \tag{58}$$

The correspondence $u_x \to \theta(x)$ is thus a continuous homomorphism of the group G onto the additive group of real numbers modulo 2π, called the *circle group*. The image $\theta(x)$ of such a homomorphism is called a *character* of the group G.

The characters of an Abelian group G are themselves a group, the character group X, and there exists a natural procedure to define a topology in X such that this group becomes a topological group. The group operations in X are defined by setting for any two characters $\theta_1(x)$ and $\theta_2(x)$

$$(\theta_1\,\theta_2)(x) = \theta_1(x) + \theta_2(x) \qquad (\text{mod}\, 2\pi). \tag{59}$$

Just as in the complex case so we can here, too, characterize the inequivalent irreducible representations of the Abelian group G by their characters. In order to see this, let us assume that $u_x^{(1)}$ and $u_x^{(2)}$ are two equivalent irreducible representations. There exists then a unitary (hence linear) operator u such that $u_x^{(1)} = u u_x^{(2)} u^{-1}$. Recalling that unitary operators in a one-dimensional quaternionic Hilbert space are multiplication from the *right* with a quaternion $\omega \in \Omega$, we see that

$$u_x^{(1)} q = q \exp(i_1\,\theta_1(x)) = u u_x^{(2)} u^{-1} q = q\omega^{-1} \exp(i_2\,\theta_2(x))\,\omega.$$

Thus

$$\omega^{-1} \exp(i_2\,\theta_2(x))\,\omega = \exp(i_1\,\theta_1(x)), \tag{60}$$

which implies

$$\omega^{-1}\, i_2\,\omega = i_1 \qquad \text{and} \qquad \theta_1(x) = \theta_2(x) \qquad (\text{mod}\, 2\pi). \tag{61}$$

The second part of Eq. (61) says that the two characters are equal. Conversely, if the two characters are equal, then we can always choose an $\omega \in \Omega$ such that for any two pure imaginary quaternions i_1 and i_2 we have $i_1 = \omega^{-1}\, i_2\,\omega$. This ω interpreted as a right multiplication in $\mathfrak{Q}$ furnishes us with the unitary operator u that establishes the equivalence between the two representations.

This result enables us to reduce the problem of finding all irreducible representations of an Abelian group G to that of finding all the characters of G.

The group that interests us in the following is the group of translations in the four-dimensional Minkowski space. For this case all the characters are known. They are of the form

$$\theta(x) = p \cdot x \qquad (\mathrm{mod}\ 2\pi) \tag{62}$$

where p is a fixed four-component vector in Minkowski space, x is the four-vector of the translation x, and $p \cdot x$ is the scalar product in the Minkowski metric of these two four-vectors.

Let us now proceed to the discussion of reducible representations. In the complex case the structure of the reducible representations of a locally compact Abelian group can be characterized by a projection-valued measure on the group of characters θ. This is the theorem of Stone-Neumark-Ambrose-Godement [in the following referred to as the SNAG theorem; (*38–41*)], which may be stated as follows.

Every unitary representation of a locally compact connected Abelian topological group G defines a unique projection valued measure dE on the character group X such that

$$u_x = \int_X e^{i\theta(x)}\,\mathrm{dE}. \tag{63}$$

This result can be described as a kind of generalization of the spectral resolution of unitary operators.

This theorem can be transferred to the quaternionic case. The only problem is to construct the analog of the imaginary unit i that appears in the expression (63). It is clear that this analog must be replaced by a unitary anti-Hermitian operator $\mathcal{J}$ that commutes with all u_x. The construction of such an operator is always possible (*15*, Lemma 4.2, p. 766).

In order to establish the SNAG theorem for the quaternionic representations, we proceed as follows. We are given a representation $x \to u_x$ in $\mathfrak{H}_{\mathfrak{Q}}$. We choose a unitary anti-Hermitian $\mathcal{J}$ that commutes with all u_x and select an arbitrary pure imaginary quaternion i. According to Theorem 13 this defines a complex Hilbert space $\mathfrak{H}_{\mathfrak{C}}^{(i)}$ that is invariant under all u_x. The restriction of u_x to $\mathfrak{H}_{\mathfrak{C}}^{(i)}$ is denoted by $u_x^{(i)}$. It satisfies the hypotheses of the SNAG theorem. Hence there exists a unique projection-valued measure $dE^{(i)}$ on the character group X so that for this $u_x^{(i)}$ we have a formula

$$u_x^{(i)} = \int_X e^{i\theta(x)}\,dE^{(i)}. \tag{64}$$

The unique extension procedure described in subsection 5 defines projections dE in $\mathfrak{H}_{\mathfrak{Q}}$ and an operator $\mathscr{I}$ such that

$$u_x = \int_X e^{\mathscr{I}\theta(x)}\, dE. \tag{65}$$

Thus we have established

Theorem 16. Let $x \to u_x$ be a representation of a locally compact connected Abelian group G in a quaternionic Hilbert space $\mathfrak{H}_{\mathfrak{Q}}$. Then there exists a unitary anti-Hermitian operator $\mathscr{I}$ and a projection-valued measure dE on the character group X of G such that u_x can be represented by formula (65).

We remark here that the uniqueness of the measure cannot be affirmed as in the complex case because the operator $\mathscr{I}$ need not be unique. There is a trivial ambiguity for $\mathscr{I}$ because, on the subspace $M = \{f \,|\, u f_x = f \quad \forall\ x \in G\}$ that reduces u_x, $\mathscr{I}$ is completely arbitrary. This situation already exists in the complex case, but in neither case has it any consequences for the definition of the spectral measure.

In the quaternionic case there is a further ambiguity for $\mathscr{I}$, even for the part of $\mathscr{I}$ that belongs to the space $M^{\perp}$.

For the case of the Poincaré group it is relatively easy to formulate physically motivated conditions on the representation that imply uniqueness of the operator $\mathscr{I}$ in that case. This will be done in the subsection C, 2.

C. Representation Theory of the Poincaré Group

1. *The Poincaré Group*

The Poincaré group G is defined as the group of real linear transformations in four variables that leave the metric of Minkowski space invariant. We shall choose for this metric the tensor $g_{00} = +1$, $g_{ii} = -1$ for $i = 1, 2, 3$ and $g_{\mu\nu} = 0$ for $\mu \neq \nu$.

The translations T are an Abelian invariant subgroup. The homogeneous transformations constitute another subgroup L, called the Lorentz group. This subgroup consists of four disconnected components that contain, respectively, the identity e, space inversion σ, time reversal $\mathscr{T}$, and combined inversion $\vartheta = \sigma\mathscr{T}$. The connected component of the Poincaré group will be denoted by G_e and that of the Lorentz group by L_e.

The composition law can be expressed in terms of the translation vector $a \in T$ and an arbitrary Lorentz transformation by

$$(a, \Lambda)(a', \Lambda') = (a'', \Lambda'') \tag{67}$$

where

$$a'' = a + \Lambda a',$$
$$\Lambda'' = \Lambda\Lambda'. \tag{68}$$

The subgroup T consists of the elements of the form (a, I) while L is represented by the elements of the form $(0, \Lambda)$. The connected component L_e is doubly connected. Its simply connected covering group is the group $S(2,\mathfrak{C})$.

2. *Physical Heuristics*

It is now time to consider some of the physical aspects of the representation problem of the Poincaré group. If we compare the representation theory of groups in complex and quaternionic Hilbert spaces, then we observe that up to a certain point the two theories run more or less parallel without, however, being exactly identical. The point where the two theories begin to differ in a deeper way is met when we introduce the unitary anti-Hermitian operator $\mathcal{J}$. In a complex Hilbert space such an operator is always the direct sum of $\pm i$ times the identity operator.

In a quaternionic space such an operator has a much richer structure because there exist an infinity of different square roots of -1. Consequently we expect that the representation of groups in a quaternionic space will depart from the complex case in an essential way if we admit for the operators $\mathcal{J}$ the most general possibilities.

Instead of studying the most general possibilities for the operator $\mathcal{J}$, we want to examine the problem from a physical point of view and see whether we can find in the physical interpretation a motive for restricting the possibilities for the operator $\mathcal{J}$. The operator $\mathcal{J}$ is met when the Abelian subgroups of the Poincaré group are studied. Such groups are, for instance, the one-parameter subgroups. If $s \to u_s$ is the representation of such a one-parameter subgroup, then we can always define in a unique manner [cf. Finkelstein *et al.* (*13*)] an anti-Hermitian operator A by setting

$$A = s - \lim_{s \to 0} (1/s)(u_s - I).$$

This limit always exists on a dense linear manifold of vectors that is the domain for this operator A.

In complex quantum mechanics the self-adjoint operator $P = -iA$ is always an observable. Thus the reconstruction of an observable from the generator of an infinitesimal one-parameter symmetry transformation is a unique process in complex quantum mechanics. In quaternion quantum mechanics any operator $\mathcal{J}$ can be used for defining a self-adjoint operator P by setting, for instance, $P(\mathcal{J}) = -\mathcal{J}A$. However, only A is determined uniquely by the group, but A is not an observable, because it is not self-adjoint. The $P(\mathscr{J})$ *is* self-adjoint, but is is not unique. Since only self-adjoint operators can represent observables, we cannot associate observables in this manner with the infinitesimal generators of symmetry transformations without restricting the operator $\mathscr{J}$ in some way.

The simplest way to restrict the operator $\mathscr{J}$ is to require that it commute with all the transformations of the Poincaré group. Let us examine whether this condition can by physically motivated.

The infinitesimal generators A of the translation group behave under Lorentz transformations like a four-vector. We can make a good case that the self-adjoint momentum operators $P = -\mathscr{J}A$ associated with these operators should have the same property. This means physically that the measured values of these operators transform like a four-vector under Lorentz transformations. This is only possible if the operator $\mathscr{J}$ commutes with all the u_x of the given representation.

A further restriction is obtained by requiring the energy operator P_0 to have a positive definite spectrum. It is interesting to note that in quaternion quantum mechanics this can always be accomplished by a suitable choice of $\mathscr{J}$ (*13*).

We formulate therefore the following two postulates:

Postulate 1. The observables P associated with the translations in Minkowski space (momentum operators) transform under Lorentz transformations like a four-vector.

Postulate 2. The energy P_0 has a positive definite spectrum.

It is seen that these postulates are quite reasonable from the point of view of physics. We want to point out, however, that there are possible representations of the Poincaré group that do not satisfy these requirements. In view of recent developments in fundamental particle physics there might even be some interest in these representations, for instance, for a relativistic theory of the recently discussed hypothetical units called *quarks*. That the infinitesimal generators for the translations do not give rise to unique observables is not such a compelling objection to quarks, which do not seem to be observable in the usual sense of the word. In fact, they reveal their presence (if present they are) only through a structure of partial symmetries for strongly interacting particles.

In the rest of this chapter we shall not dwell, however, on these speculative aspects of the unknown quaternionic representations of the Poincaré group. We now proceed to the classification of the irreducible representations that satisfy Postulates 1 and 2; we shall call these the *physical representations*.

3. *The Physical Representations of the Connected Component*

We denote by G_e the connected component of the Poincaré group and we shall determine all the physical ray representations of this group in a quaternionic Hilbert space. The theory of the preceding section (notably Section IV, B, 5 and 6) permits us to reduce this problem to the complex case, where it is already solved. The steps in this reduction can be outlined as follows.

(a) We assume that we have an irreducible ray representation $x \to U_x$ of the connected Poincaré group G_e into the ray transformations of the quaternionic Hilbert space $\mathfrak{H}_{\mathfrak{Q}}$. Theorem 8 tells us that this representation can be induced by a unitary vector representation $x \to u_x$ by a suitable choice of the factors. Because the group G_e is doubly connected, $x \to u_x$ is a unitary representation of the simply connected covering group $\tilde{G}_e$. The representation of G_e is thus either unitary (if the kernel of the homomorphism $\tilde{G}_e \to G_e$ is represented by the unit operators), or unitary but double valued (if it is represented by $\pm I$; Theorem 10).

(b) According to Theorem 16 there exists a unitary anti-Hermitian operator $\mathscr{J}$ and a projection-valued measure on the characters of the translation group $T \subset G_e$ such that

$$u_x = \int_X e^{J\theta(x)}\, dE \tag{69}$$

where $x \in T$, $\theta(x)$ is the character, and the integral is extended over the entire character group X. Every character $\theta(x)$ has the form (62) where x is the translation vector and p is an arbitrary fixed vector in Minkowski space.

(c) According to Postulate 1 the operator $\mathscr{J}$ commutes with all operators u_x with $x \in G_e$. According to Theorems 18 and 14 we can, for each arbitrary but fixed pure imaginary quaternion i, define a complex Hilbert space $\mathfrak{H}_{\mathfrak{C}}^{(i)}$ and a restriction $u_x^{(i)}$ of the representation u_x to this space. According to Section IV, B, 5, this restriction is an irreducible single- or double-valued unitary vector representation of G_e in the complex space $\mathfrak{H}_{\mathfrak{C}}^{(i)}$.

(d) Conversely, if $x \to u_x^{(i)}$ is an irreducible (possibly double-valued) representation of G_e and if it is not of type -1 then it can, according to Theorem 15, be extended in a unique way to a unitary representation in $\mathfrak{H}_{\mathfrak{Q}}$.

The problem of finding all the physically meaningful representations of the Poincaré group in a quaternionic space $\mathfrak{H}_{\mathfrak{Q}}$ is thus reduced to that of finding these representations in the complex space. This problem is solved and all these representations are known.

We shall summarize the method and results for the complex case in the following subsections.

4. *Induced Representations* (*Discrete Case*)

Herein we review briefly the theory of induced representations in a complex

Hilbert space for the case of finite groups. Although finite groups are not our primary concern, they serve as a useful example for the discussion of the purely *algebraic* aspects of the theory. The application of these results to the infinite Poincaré group is then possible by supplementing this algebraic part by some *measure*-theoretical and *topological* considerations.

The notion of *induced* representations is a generalization of that of the *regular* representations. Characteristic for both is that the group plays a double role: First, it is the group to be represented and second it is also a Hilbert space. For finite groups this space is finite-dimensional; in fact, its dimension is equal to the order of the group.

This space is defined as the set of all functions $f(x)$ from the group G to the complex numbers $\mathfrak{C}$. If we define the norm of such functions by

$$\|f\|^2 = \sum_{x \in G} |f(x)|^2, \tag{70}$$

we evidently obtain a Hilbert space $\mathfrak{H}(R)$.

The regular representation is then obtained by defining for any $s \in G$ the unitary operator R_s:

$$(R_s f)(x) = f(xs). \tag{71}$$

If s_1 and s_2 are two elements from G, we have evidently

$$(R_{s_1}(R_{s_2} f))(x) = (R_{s_2} f)(xs_1) = f(xs_1 s_2).$$

Therefore we may set

$$R_{s_1} R_{s_2} = R_{s_1 s_2}. \tag{72}$$

The correspondence $s \to R_s$ is a unitary representation of the abstract group in the Hilbert space $\mathfrak{H}(R)$. This is the *regular* representation of the group G.

We shall now generalize this notion in successive steps until we arrive at the induced representation in sufficient generality for use in connection with the Poincaré group.

Let $H \subset G$ be a subgroup of G. We can then decompose G into its right cosets by the formula

$$G = H + Hx_1 + Hx_2 + \cdots \qquad x_1 \notin H,\ x_2 \notin H,\ x_2 \notin Hx, \text{ etc.} \tag{73}$$

We denote the set of right cosets of G by G_H. Two elements x and y in the same coset are said to be equivalent modulo H, and we write

$$x \equiv y(H). \tag{74}$$

We consider now functions $f(x)$ defined on right cosets G_H. If the number of right cosets G_H is j, then these functions define a j-dimensional vector space, which can be made into a Hilbert space by defining the norm

$$\|f\|^2 = \sum_{x \in G_H} |f(x)|^2 \tag{75}$$

where the summation is (as indicated) extended only over the cosets. Since $f(x)$ is assumed to be constant in a coset, it suffices to select from each coset one x and carry out the sum (75).

The induced representation is now obtained by setting for all $s \in G$

$$(U_s f)(x) = f(xs). \tag{76}$$

We remark here that this definition is meaningful; that is, the right-hand side is again a function on the cosets because as x runs through one coset the image xs runs through another.

We again easily verify that this is indeed a representation in a j-dimensional space and that it is unitary.

For the special case where H consists only of the unit element, we obtain the regular representation. Thus U_s is seen to be a generalization of the regular representation. For the other extreme case where $H = G$, we obtain the trivial unit representation for which every $s \in G$ is represented by 1.

In the next step we consider functions $f(x)$ that are not necessarily constant in the cosets. Let, for instance, $\chi(s)$ be a one-dimensional representation of G so that

$$\begin{gathered} \chi(s_1)\,\chi(s_2) = \chi(s_1 s_2) \\ |\chi(s)| = 1 \end{gathered} \tag{77}$$

and define

$$f(\xi x) = \chi(\xi) f(x) \qquad \forall \quad \xi \in H, x \in G. \tag{78}$$

Such functions still define a j-dimensional vector space since the values of $f(x)$ are determined in each coset by its value for one particular element in the coset. With the norm defined again by

$$\|f\|^2 = \sum_{x \in G_H} |f(x)|^2 \tag{79}$$

we obtain a Hilbert space.

An induced representation is now obtained by again setting

$$(U_s f)(x) = f(xs). \tag{80}$$

The next and final generalization is obtained by starting with any unitary representation $h \to L_h$ of H in a representation space $\mathfrak{H}_0$ of dimension n_0. We then define functions $f(x)$ on G with values in $\mathfrak{H}_0$. That is, for each $x \in G$ we associate a vector $f(x) \in \mathfrak{H}_0$. This vector-valued function is assumed to satisfy

$$f(hx) = L_h f(x) \qquad \forall \quad h \in H, x \in G. \tag{81}$$

With the norm defined by

$$\|f\|^2 = \sum_{x \in G_H} \|f(x)\|^2 \tag{82}$$

we obtain a $(j \cdot n_0)$-dimensional vector space and an induced unitary representation

$$(U_s f)(x) = f(xs) \qquad \forall \quad s \in G. \tag{83}$$

This is the induced representation denoted by U^L.

5. *Induced Representations* (*Continuous Case*)

In this subsection we describe the generalization of this method for constructing representations of G to the case of topological groups. In the following we shall apply this only to Lie groups, but many of the definitions and theorems are applicable for locally compact topological groups.

Let us then assume that G is such a group, and $H \subset G$ is a subgroup. The first difference from the finite case already becomes evident: In the finite case we could admit any subgroup; in the case of topological groups, however, we must add the condition that H is *closed* in G ($\bar{H} = H$). We shall see that for the applications we have in mind this is always the case.

We can now define, in complete analogy to the discrete case, the right cosets, but we cannot expect them to form a finite or even a discrete set. Thus instead of a formula such as (73), which would not be correct for the continuous case, we define the space G_H of the right cosets simply as the equivalence classes of the elements $x \in G$ modulo the subgroup H. Two elements x_1, $x_2 \in G$ are said to be equivalent modulo H if there exists an element $y \in H$ such that $x_1 = yx_2$. We shall denote by ξ the class of equivalent elements Hx that contains the element $x \in G$. The correspondence $\xi = \pi(x)$ is called the canonical mapping of G onto the equivalence classes or right cosets G_H.

The cosets G_H inherit a natural topology from the topological space G: A subset $\Delta \subset G_H$ is open if and only if $\pi^{-1}(\Delta)$ is open in the topology of G. Here $\pi^{-1}(\Delta)$ denotes the set

$$\pi^{-1}(\Delta) = \{x | x \in G, \pi(x) \in \Delta\}. \tag{84}$$

With this topology the mapping $\pi(x)$ from G to G_H is continuous.

We also need a measure on the cosets, since we need to replace the sum of the discrete case by an integral. The ideal type of measure would be invariant under right translations, but such a measure is not always possible. Fortunately the weaker requirement of "quasi-invariance" will be sufficient to construct the induced representation.

A measure μ on G_H is said to be quasi-invariant if the translated measure $\mu([\Delta]x) \equiv \mu_x(\Delta)$ has the same null sets as the measure $\mu(\Delta)$. We can prove that such a measure always exists (*43*) on the groups that interest us. The translated measure μ_x is then absolutely continuous with respect to the original one and we can define the Radon-Nikodym derivative (*44*)

$$\frac{d\mu_x}{d\mu}(\xi) = \rho_x(\xi). \tag{85}$$

The function $\rho_x(\xi)$ is positive and essentially bounded and satisfies in addition the identity

$$\rho_{xy}(\xi) = \rho_x(\xi)\,\rho_y(\xi). \tag{86}$$

We now consider the set of all functions from the topological measure space G_H, the vectors $f(\xi)$ of a fixed Hilbert space $\mathfrak{H}_0$, and a unitary representation L of H, which satisfy the following conditions:

(a) $(f(x), g)$ is a Borel function in x for all $g \in \mathfrak{H}_0$.

(b) For all $x \in G$ and all $h \in H$ we have

$$f(hx) = L_h f(x). \tag{87}$$

(c) $\int_{G_H} \|f(x)\|^2 \, d\mu(\xi) < \infty.$

The integration in this last expression makes sense because $\|f(x)\|^2$ is, on account of the unitarity of the representation L, only a function of the cosets.

We can define more generally a scalar product

$$(f, g) = \int_{G_H} (f(x), g(x))\, d\mu(\xi) \tag{88}$$

so that the set of functions $f = \{f(x)\}$ becomes a Hilbert space. We now define the *induced representation* U_x^L in this Hilbert space by setting.

$$(U_x^L f)(y) = f(yx)\,[\rho_x(y)]^{1/2}. \tag{89}$$

It can be verified without difficulty that this is a unitary representation in the (generally) infinite-dimensional Hilbert space $\mathfrak{H}$. In the special case where the subgroup H is the identity element this construction still works. For the measure we can choose the right-invariant Haar measure and the representation that we obtain is again called the regular representation.

The usefulness of the induced representation is that with it we can construct the representation of groups from those of certain subgroups. In order to use this method effectively it is necessary to know something more about the properties of the induced representations when H and L are given. It would be particularly useful to know when the representation U^L is irreducible. A great deal of research has been devoted to this problem with only partial results (*42*).

The Poincaré group belongs to a certain class of groups for which there exists a complete and satisfactory theory of the induced representation. The groups of this class are the so-called *semidirect products*, which we shall discuss in the following subsection.

6. *Semidirect Products*

We consider now a special class of groups, the semidirect products. Let $G_1 \subset G$ be an invariant Abelian subgroup of G and G_2 another subgroup of G such that $G_1 \cap G_2 = e$ and such that every element $z \in G$ can be written as a product

$$z = xy \qquad \text{with} \quad x \in G_1,\ y \in G_2.$$

Because $G_1 \cap G_2 = e$, this product representation is unique.

The semidirect product can also be written as pairs of elements $(x, y) = z$ with the composition law

$$(x_1, y_1)(x_2, y_2) = (x_1 y_1 x_2 y_1^{-1}, y_1 y_2). \tag{90}$$

The transformations $x \to y[x] = yxy^{-1}$ constitute an automorphism of G_1. The semidirect product can thus also be considered as composed of the pairs of which one element is an element from G_1 and the other is an automorphism of G_1.

Examples of semidirect products are many and important. They may occur in discrete or continuous groups. We shall here mention three.

Example 1. Probably the simplest example of a semidirect product, which may serve to illustrate many of the concepts and theorems, is the group S_3, the permutation group of three objects. It is of order 6. The Abelian invariant subgroup G_1 consists of the two cyclic permutations plus the identity and it is of order 3. The group G_2 of automorphisms of G_1 consists of exactly two elements, the identity and the interchange of the two cyclic permutations. Thus the semidirect product $G_1 \wedge G_2$ consists of six elements. Examination of the group table shows that it is isomorphic to the permutation group of three elements.

Example 2. The group of Euclidean motions in the plane consists of translations and rotations around a fixed point in the plane. The translations are an Abelian subgroup G_1 and the rotations G_2 induce an automorphism in G_1. Thus this group, too, is a semidirect product, since every Euclidean motion may be represented as a rotation followed by a translation.

Example 3. The connected component of the Poincaré group G_2 contains as an invariant Abelian subgroup G_1 the translations in Minkowski space. The Lorentz transformations induce an automorphism in G_1 and every element of G can be represented as a product of an element from G_1 with an element from G_2. The composition law (68) is already in the form that shows that G_2 is indeed a semidirect product.

In the following we shall be concerned primarily with the last example. Consequently we shall adopt from now notation conforming to that introduced earlier (in Section IV, C, 1), according to which the invariant Abelian subgroup G_1 will be the translation group T. An element $a \in T$ is represented by the four-vector a. The group G_2 is to be identified with the group L of the Lorentz transformation Λ.

It is also convenient to use the following notation for the characters and the character group of T. Each character will be represented by a function on the group T of modulus one (instead of the exponents mod 2π, as we did in Section IV, B, 6). A general such function will be denoted by $\hat{a}$ and its dependence on a will be written $\langle a, \hat{a} \rangle$. For the translation group T these characters are represented by four-vectors $\hat{a}$ and the foregoing functions take the form (cf. Section IV, B, 6)

$$\langle a, \hat{a} \rangle = \exp(ia \cdot \hat{a}). \tag{91}$$

This notation is convenient since it emphasizes the complete symmetry between the group T and its character group $\hat{T}$ that permits us to identify the characters of the characters with the elements of T by writing $\hat{\hat{a}} = a$.

The automorphisms of the group T induced by Lorentz transformations Λ may be written $a \to \Lambda[a] = \Lambda a$. They induce a dual automorphism in the character group $\hat{a} \to [\hat{a}]\Lambda$ defined by

$$\langle a, [\hat{a}]\Lambda \rangle = \langle \Lambda[a], \hat{a} \rangle. \tag{92}$$

We shall now introduce two concepts that are convenient at this point. Two characters $\hat{a}_1$ and $\hat{a}_2$ that can be transformed into each other by a Lorentz transformation are said to be *equivalent*, and we define the *orbit* of characters by the

Definition. An *orbit* O in the character group is a class of equivalent characters.

We can also introduce the family of all Lorentz transformations that leave a given character $\hat{a}$ invariant. This family is a group attached to the character $\hat{a}$. It is called the little group.

Definition. The *little group* $G_{\hat{a}}$ of the character $\hat{a}$ is the set of all transformations $\Lambda \in L$ that leave $\hat{a}$ invariant: In a formula

$$G_{\hat{a}} = \{\Lambda | \Lambda \in L, [\hat{a}]\Lambda = \hat{a}\}. \tag{93}$$

For the Lorentz group the orbits consist of the family of four-vectors $\hat{a}$ that satisfy a relation $\hat{a} \cdot \hat{a} = m^2 = \text{const}$.

The little group is naturally a subgroup of the Lorentz group L. By combining it with the translation group T we can make it into a subgroup H of the Poincaré group. Thus to every character $\hat{a}$ we associate a subgroup $H = T \wedge G_{\hat{a}}$. This group H is thus the semidirect product of T with the little group $G_{\hat{a}}$. Every irreducible representation L of a group H has the form $L = \hat{a}M$ where $\hat{a}$ is a character and M is an irreducible representation of the little group $G_{\hat{a}}$.

We have now all the concepts needed for the formulation of the fundamental theorem of Mackey and Frobenius

Theorem 17 (Mackey-Frobenius). Let $L = \hat{a}M$ be an irreducible representation of the subgroup $H = T \wedge G_{\hat{a}}$ where $\hat{a}$ is an arbitrary character for T; then the induced representation U^L of G is irreducible. Moreover, every irreducible representation of G can be obtained in this form and two irreducible representations $L = \hat{a}M$ and $L' = \hat{a}'M'$ of G are equivalent if and only if $\hat{a}$ and $\hat{a}'$ are in the same orbit and M is unitarily equivalent to M'.

The proof of this theorem is given by Mackey (*3*, *4*); it is rather long and cannot be reproduced here. Its usefulness for us is that it permits a further reduction of the representation problem of the Poincaré group. In fact the representations of this group can now be completely classified by following these six steps (*45*):

(a) Determine all the characters of T.
(b) Find the orbits O in the charactergroup T.
(c) Select a character $\hat{a}$ in each orbit.
(d) Determine the little group $G_{\hat{a}}$.

(e) Determine all irreducible representations M of the little group $G_{\hat{a}}$ and construct with them the irreducible representations $L = \hat{a}M$ of the subgroup $H = T \wedge G_{\hat{a}}$.

(f) Construct the induced representations U^L.

The most difficult part in this program is usually step (e), as will be seen by examining it for the case of the Poincaré group. For the latter (or rather, its covering group) we have the following situation:

(a) The characters $\hat{a}$ are all of the form

$$\langle a, \hat{a} \rangle = \exp(ia \cdot \hat{a}).$$

(b) Each orbit is determined by the value of the invariant product $m^2 = \hat{a} \cdot \hat{a}$. Here Postulate 1 will restrict the values to $m^2 \geqq 0$, and $\hat{a}^0 \geqq 0$. The orbits are thus hyperboloids in the forward light-cone of the Minkowski space.

(c) For $m^2 \neq 0$ we can select the special character $\hat{a} = (1,0,0,0)$ on the unit hyperboloid. For $m^2 = 0$ there are two possibilities: (i) The character $\hat{a} = (1,0,0,1)$; and (ii) the singular case $\hat{a} = (0,0,0,0)$.

(d) The little group associated with the character $\hat{a} = (1,0,0,0)$ is the group $SU(2, \mathfrak{C})$, that for $\hat{a} = (1,0,0,1)$ is isomorph to the group E_2 of Euclidean motions of a plane, that for $a = (0,0,0,0)$ is the covering group of the Lorentz group, that is, $SL(2, \mathfrak{C})$.

(e) The irreducible representations of $SU(2, \mathfrak{C})$ are the well-known finite-dimensional representations of dimension $2s + 1$ with $s = \frac{1}{2}, 1, \frac{3}{2}, \ldots$, etc. The irreducible representations of E_2 are of two kinds; only one kind seems to be of physical interest, and it corresponds to a finite and discrete value of the spin. The case (c), (ii) does not represent a particle since the momentum and energy are identically zero in this case.

(f) For each of the irreducible representations listed under (e) we construct the induced representation according to formula (89). In all of these cases the measure can be so constructed that $\rho_x(y) = 1$. With this step the problem is solved.

V. Conclusion

We recapitulate the essential steps that led us to the physical representations of the Poincaré group in a quaternionic Hilbert space.

We started with the systems of elementary propositions and we have given some reasons why such a system is always an orthocomplemented, complete, weakly modular, and atomic lattice. Such lattices are thus the basic structures of any physical theory that is concerned with measurable physical quantities. The distributive lattices are characteristic for classical mechanics. In such a lattice every proposition is compatible with every other. At the other extreme we have quantum mechanics, where we find that propositions may form coherent components.

Every coherent component can be represented as the lattice of subspaces in a Hilbert space with coefficients from a field. If this field contains the reals as a subfield (as it must if we have continuous measurable quantities), then there are only three possibilities, since mathematics tells us that there are only three such fields possible: the reals, the complex numbers, and the quaternions.

A lattice has a natural symmetry group, the group of automorphisms. Translated into the language of Hilbert spaces these automorphisms become the ray transformations. A symmetry group of a physical system appears thus as a homomorphism of this group into the group of ray transformations. This is called a ray—or projective—representation of the symmetry group. Relativistic invariance is thus introduced by considering the projective representations of the Poincaré group.

There is a connection between the projective representations and the vector representations that may be rather involved in the complex case. In quaternionic Hilbert spaces $\mathfrak{H}_{\mathfrak{Q}}$ this connection is extremely simple, since we can show that every projective representation of every group can be induced by a unitary representation. This happens to be also true in the complex case for the Poincaré group. But only in the quaternionic space is it true for every group.

The next step is the construction of the *unitary* representation of the Poincaré group in quaternionic space $\mathfrak{H}_{\mathfrak{Q}}$. Here we postulated for physical reasons that the momentum operators must behave under Lorentz transformations like a four-vector. This implies the existence of a unitary and anti-Hermitian linear operator $\mathscr{J}$ that must commute with all the unitary operators of the representation. The existence of the operator $\mathscr{J}$ permits, for every pure imaginary quaternion i, the extraction from $\mathfrak{H}_{\mathfrak{Q}}$ of a complex Hilbert space $\mathfrak{H}_{\mathfrak{C}}^{(i)}$.

The study of these Hilbert spaces shows that there exist simple relations between the unitary representations in $\mathfrak{H}_{\mathfrak{C}}^{(i)}$ and in $\mathfrak{H}_{\mathfrak{Q}}$. These relations were described under the heading of *contractions* and *expansions* of representations.

The final result is that the physical representations in $\mathfrak{H}_{\mathfrak{Q}}$ can always be obtained as expansions of complex representations.

There remains thus the construction of all the complex representations of the Poincaré group. This can be accomplished with the help of the theorem of Mackey-Frobenius for semidirect products. The Poincaré group is such a group and the theorem is directly applicable, giving very quickly all the results obtained by Wigner in 1939.

The theorem of Mackey-Frobenius can also be used for the construction of the nonphysical representations, since the validity of the theorem is independent of the nature of the field. For quaternions, however, the irreducible representations for the subgroup $H = T \wedge G_{\hat{a}}$ [step (*e*)] can in general no longer be constructed in the same way, since the one-dimensional characters need not commute with the representations of the little group $G_{\hat{a}}$. Thus we know nothing about the possible representations that do not satisfy the physically motivated Postulates 1 and 2. Since the latter give essentially the same result as in the complex case, we may look for unexpected possibilities only in the as yet unexplored "unphysical" representations.

REFERENCES

1. E. Wigner, *Ann. of Math.* **40**, 149 (1939).
2. V. Bargmann, *Ann. of Math.* **48**, 568 (1947).
3. G. W. Mackey, *Ann. of Math.* **55**, 101 (1952); **58**, 193 (1953).
4. G. W. Mackey, *Amer. J. Math.* **73**, 576 (1951).
5. V. Bargmann, *Ann. of Math.* **59**, 1 (1954).
6. P. Ehrenfest, *Z. Physik* **78**, 555 (1932).
7. W. Pauli, *Z. Physik* **80**, 573 (1933).
8. G. Birkhoff and J. von Neumann, *Ann. of Math.* **37**, 823 (1936).
9. L. Pontrjagin, "Topological Groups," especially Chapter V, Sect. 37. Princeton Univ. Press, Princeton, New Jersey, 1939.
10. E. C. G. Stueckelberg, *Helv. Phys. Acta* **33**, 727 (1960).
11. E. C. G. Stueckelberg and M. Guenin, *Helv. Phys. Acta* **34**, 621 (1961).
12. D. Finkelstein, J. M. Jauch, and D. Speiser, *J. Mathematical Phys.* **4**, 136 (1963).
13. D. Finkelstein, J. M. Jauch, S. Schiminovich, and D. Speiser, *J. Mathematical Phys.* **3**, 207 (1962); **4**, 788 (1963).
14. C. Piron, *Helv. Phys. Acta* **37**, 439 (1964).
15. G. Emch, *Helv. Phys. Acta* **36**, 739, 770 (1963).
16. P. Jordan, *Arch. Math.* **2**, 166 (1950).
17. S. Maeda, *J. Sci. Hiroshima Univ. Ser. A* **19**, 211 (1955).
18. M. L. Dubreil-Jacotin, L. Lesieur, and R. Croisot, "Leçons sur la théorie des treillis," Cahiers Sci. XXI. Gauthier-Villars, Paris, 1953.
19. G. Birkhoff, Lattices in applied mathematics. *Proc. Symp. Pure Math.*, especially p. 155. Am. Math. Soc., New York, 1961.
20. O. Frink, *Trans. Amer. Math. Soc.* **60**, 452 (1946).
21. P. Destouches-Février, "La Structure des Theories Physiques." Presses Univ. de France, Paris, 1951.
22. G. C. Wick, A. S. Wightman, and E. P. Wigner, *Phys. Rev.* **88**, 101 (1952).
23. G. Emch and C. Piron, *J. Mathematical Phys.* **4**, 469 (1963).
24. E. Artin, "Geometric Algebra." Wiley (Interscience), New York, 1957.
25. M. H. Stone, *Trans. Amer. Math. Soc.* **40**, 37 (1936).
26. L. H. Loomis, *Bull. Amer. Math. Soc.* **53**, 757 (1947).
27. L. P. Horwitz and L. C. Biedenharn, *Helv. Phys. Acta* **38**, 385 (1965).
28. L. P. Horwitz, *Helv. Phys. Acta* **39**, 144 (1966).
29. I. Amemiya and H. Araki, *Publ. Research Inst. Math. Kyoto Univ.* **A2**, 423 (1967).
30. R. Baer, "Linear Algebra and Projective Geometry," Chapter IV. Academic Press, New York, 1952.
31. U. Uhlhorn, *Ark. Fys.* **23**, 307 (1963).
32. E. P. Wigner, "Group Theory," p. 233 ff. Academic Press, New York, 1959.
33. J. S. Lomont and P. Mendelson, *Ann. of Math.* **78**, 548 (1963).

34. V. Bargmann, *J. Mathematical Phys.* **5**, 862 (1964).
35. G. C. Wick, *in* "Preludes in Theoretical Physics" (A. de-Shalit, ed.). North-Holland Publ., Amsterdam, 1966.
36. V. Bargmann, *Ann. of Math.* **59**, 1 (1954).
37. F. Riesz and B. Sz-Nagy, "Functional Analysis," especially Sect. (104). Ungar, New York, 1955. The proof can be transferred almost without change to quaternionic Hilbert space.
38. M. H. Stone, *Ann. of Math.* **33**, 643 (1932).
39. M. Neumark, *Izv. Akad. Nauk. SSSR Ser. Fiz.* **7**, 237 (1943).
40. W. Ambrose, *Duke Math. J.* **11**, 589 (1944).
41. R. Godement, *C. R. Acad. Sci. Paris* **218**, 901 (1944)
42. A survey with reference to literature of this subject is found in G. Mackey, Infinite dimensional group representations. *Colloq. Lecture Am. Math. Soc., 1961.*
43. J. Dieudonné, *Ann. Univ. Grénoble* **23**, 25 (1948).
44. P. R. Halmos, "Measure Theory." Van Nostrand, Princeton, New Jersey, 1950.
45. J. M. Jauch, Lecture notes. *CERN Seminar, Geneva, 1959*, 5425/TH.06, Pt. IV.

Group Theory in Atomic Spectroscopy

B. R. JUDD

THE JOHNS HOPKINS UNIVERSITY, BALTIMORE, MARYLAND

I. Introduction

Group theory plays two roles in atomic spectroscopy. Its most obvious function is to take advantage of the symmetry possessed by the Hamiltonian for the electrons of an atom. If, for example, the atom is free, then the Hamiltonian must be invariant under rotations of the reference frame centered at the nucleus. The rotation group in three dimensions, $O^+(3)$, enters in a direct and physically significant way. It underlies the theory of angular momentum (*1*), and is central to those applications of group theory to atomic spectroscopy that are described by Wigner (*2*).

The second role of group theory dates from the work of Racah (*3*). The fundamental idea is to consider the single-electron eigenfunctions as basis functions for transformations of a much more general character than those of $O^+(3)$. That this is feasible depends on the central-field approximation, on which all of the theory of spectroscopy for heavy atoms is based. In this approximation, each electron is visualized as moving in a smoothed-out electric potential produced by all the other electrons of the atom. The potential is assumed to be spherically symmetric, and this has the consequence that the eigenfunctions for a single electron can be factorized into a radial part, labeled by the principal and azimuthal quantum numbers n and l, and an angular part. The latter is conveniently taken to be a spherical harmonic Y_{lm_l}. A *configuration* specifies the assignment of the quantum numbers n and l to the electrons in an atom: thus the configuration $(nl)^N$ indicates that there are N electrons with quantum numbers n and l. According to the Pauli exclusion principle, N can be at most $4l + 2$, corresponding to the occupation, with both spin orientations, of all m_l values. The collection of configurations $(nl)^N$ $(0 \leqq N \leqq 4l + 2)$ is called a *shell*. Now, under transformations in ordinary three-dimensional space, the $2l + 1$ spherical harmonics Y_{lm_l} $(-l \leqq m_l \leqq l)$ transform among themselves in a well-defined way. But we may, if we wish, consider more general transformations of the $2l + 1$ spherical harmonics with a given l. For example, we may consider all transformations of the Y_{lm_l} that are described by unitary matrices, in which case the harmonics form basis functions for transformations of the unitary group $U(2l + 1)$. The matrices describing a physical rotation form merely a small subset of all possible unitary matrices, so that transformations of the second kind are of a much more general character.

This extension has an important consequence when we examine configurations comprising three or more equivalent electrons (i.e., electrons possessing the same quantum numbers n and l). The Coulomb interaction between the electrons breaks the configuration up into *terms*, that is, energy levels characterized by quantum numbers S and L of the total spin and total orbital angular momentum vectors **S** and **L** of the system. Since the Coulomb interaction is invariant under rotations of the reference frame, the transformations of $O^+(3)$ induce transformations among the $(2S + 1)(2L + 1)$ eigenfunctions that describe a given term; but the terms remain distinct. However, under the more general transformations, such as those of $U(2l + 1)$, collections of terms have to be formed before the ensembles of eigenfunctions transform among themselves. The various groups that can be used in this way provide a means of classifying multielectron eigenfunctions, a property of considerable practical use when the quantum numbers S and L are inadequate to define unambiguously a term of a configuration. A detailed account of this aspect of group theory is given by Hamermesh (*4*). However, the most striking advantage of the formalism—and one recognized from the start by Racah—lies in the calculation of matrix elements. This is an essential step whenever quantities of physical significance are evaluated. Terms in the Hamiltonian are broken up into parts that have well-defined properties with respect to the groups in question. The matrix elements obtained by setting these component parts between the classified eigenfunctions are evaluated by means of the Wigner-Eckart theorem—the theorem being applied not only to $O^+(3)$, but also to the higher groups. Even though eigenfunctions and operators have to be decomposed into parts having well-defined group-theoretical properties before the theorem can be applied, the advantages of doing so are immense. It is no exaggeration to say that the detailed knowledge we now have of the energy-level schemes of many rare-earth and actinide atoms is directly due to the simplifications in the mathematics that this use of group theory has brought about.

The straightforward description of these techniques involves the use of tensor operators (*5*). In recent years, however, it has become increasingly clear that many features of shell theory can be simplified and put in better perspective if the method of second quantization is used (*6*). By forming tensor operators from the creation and annihilation operators, we may enjoy the advantages of the tensor formalism; at the same time, the creation and annihilation operators connect different configurations, so that the basic theoretical unit is the shell rather than the configuration. Properties of different atoms become more intimately related, and the general method seems better suited to the study of many of the problems still outstanding. It was therefore decided to use this method in the present paper. By doing so, it is also possible to avoid some repetition of material already available in the literature.

II. Shell Structure

A. Root Figures

An element of an infinitesimal continuous group possesses the form

$$1 + \sum_{\mu} \epsilon^{\mu} X_{\mu},$$

where the ϵ^{μ} are parameters and the X_{μ} are the so-called *infinitesimal operators*, or *generators*, of the group. The algebraic structure of the group is determined by the *structure constants* $c^{\mu}_{\tau\lambda}$ appearing in the commutation relations

$$[X_{\tau}, X_{\lambda}] = \sum_{\mu} c^{\mu}_{\tau\lambda} X_{\mu}. \tag{1}$$

Indices can be raised and lowered by means of the metric tensor

$$g_{\tau\sigma} = \sum_{\mu,\lambda} c^{\mu}_{\tau\lambda}\, c^{\lambda}_{\sigma\mu}.$$

The commutation relations (1) are too general in form to be useful in identifying groups. For semi-simple groups we take instead the linear combinations $H_1, H_2, \ldots, H_\ell, E_\alpha, E_\beta, \ldots, E_\nu$ of X_μ that satisfy

$$\begin{aligned} [H_i, H_j] &= 0, \\ [H_i, E_\alpha] &= \alpha_i E_\alpha, \\ [E_\alpha, E_\beta] &= c^{\alpha+\beta}_{\alpha\beta} E_{\alpha+\beta}, \qquad (\beta \neq -\alpha), \\ [E_\alpha, E_{-\alpha}] &= \sum_i \alpha^i H_i. \end{aligned} \tag{2}$$

This choice of generators is sometimes called the Cartan-Weyl basis (*7*, *8*). Those components of the metric tensor with Roman subscripts can readily be shown to satisfy

$$g_{ij} = \sum_{\alpha} \alpha_i \alpha_j;$$

the only other nonvanishing components are those of the type $g_{\alpha-\alpha}$. By taking appropriate linear combinations of the operators H_i, we can ensure that g_{ij} is a multiple of the unit matrix. It is often convenient to normalize the operators E_α so that $g_{\alpha-\alpha} = 1$.

The numbers $(\alpha_1 \alpha_2 \cdots \alpha_\ell)$ form the components of a vector $\boldsymbol{\alpha}$ in the space with the metric tensor $g_{ij} = A\delta(i,j)$. This vector is called a *root*; the ℓ-dimensional space is the *weight* space. Groups can be classified by the array of roots, or *root figure*, to which they correspond. The classification is not unique, since it turns out that the precise nature of a group is to some extent determined by the parameters ϵ^μ. All groups considered in this article comprise certain transformations among the 2^{4l+2} multielectron states of the l shell; if we wish to preserve the orthonormality of these states, we are led at once to the unitary group in 2^{4l+2} dimensions and its subgroups. The domain of every parameter ϵ^μ is now bounded (*4*), and the groups are said to be *compact*. By restricting our attention to compact groups, we can identify a group merely by comparing its root figure with the complete listing of root figures for simple groups given by van der Waerden (*9*) or Racah (*10*). If a root figure comprises orthogonal parts, each part must be identified separately; the group being sought is then the direct product of the groups corresponding to the orthogonal parts.

Apart from five exceptional cases, the simple groups fall into four classes, labeled $\mathscr{A}_\ell$, $\mathscr{B}_\ell$, $\mathscr{C}_\ell$, and $\mathscr{D}_\ell$ by Cartan (*7*). These correspond to the special unitary groups, the rotation groups in spaces of odd dimensionality, the symplectic groups, and the rotation groups in spaces of even dimensionality. For describing the root figures, it is convenient to use a set of mutually orthogonal unit vectors $\mathbf{e}_i$. The detailed structures are set out in Table I, together

TABLE I

ROOT FIGURES FOR SIMPLE GROUPS

Group	Alternative designation	Order	Roots
$\mathscr{A}_\ell$	$SU(\ell+1)$	$\ell(\ell+2)$	$\mathbf{e}_i - \mathbf{e}_j$ $(i, j = 1, 2, \ldots, \ell+1;\ i \neq j)$
$\mathscr{B}_\ell$	$O^+(2\ell+1)$	$\ell(2\ell+1)$	$\pm\mathbf{e}_i, \pm\mathbf{e}_i \pm \mathbf{e}_j$ $(i, j = 1, 2, \ldots, \ell;\ i \neq j)$
$\mathscr{C}_\ell$	$Sp(2\ell)$	$\ell(2\ell+1)$	$\pm\mathbf{e}_i \pm \mathbf{e}_j, \pm 2\mathbf{e}_i$ $(i, j = 1, 2, \ldots, \ell;\ i \neq j)$
$\mathscr{D}_\ell$	$O^+(2\ell)$	$\ell(2\ell-1)$	$\pm\mathbf{e}_i \pm \mathbf{e}_j$ $(i, j = 1, 2, \ldots, \ell;\ i \neq j)$
$\mathscr{G}_2$	—	14	$\mathbf{e}_i - \mathbf{e}_j$ $(i, j = 1, 2, 3;\ i \neq j)$ $\pm 2\mathbf{e}_i \mp \mathbf{e}_j \mp \mathbf{e}_k$ $(i, j, k = 1, 2, 3;\ i \neq j \neq k)$

with alternative designations and the total number of generators (or *order*) of the group. Of the five exceptional groups, only one has found a use in atomic spectroscopy. It is called $\mathscr{G}_2$ by Cartan, and its root figure is included in Table I. It is to be noted that the roots for $\mathscr{A}_\ell$ (and for $\mathscr{G}_2$) are all perpendicular to $\sum \mathbf{e}_i$.

B. Annihilation and Creation Operators

In the method of second quantization, a determinantal product state is regarded as a sequence of creation operators acting on the vacuum state $|0\rangle$. We write

$$\{\xi\eta\cdots\omega\} \equiv a_\xi^\dagger a_\eta^\dagger \cdots a_\omega^\dagger |0\rangle, \tag{3}$$

where each Greek symbol represents a quantum-number quartet $(nlm_s m_l)$ defining a single-electron state. As usual, n is the principal quantum number, l the azimuthal quantum number, and the remaining two are the quantum numbers of the projections s_z and l_z of the spin $\mathbf{s}$ and orbital angular momentum $\mathbf{l}$ of a single electron. Since a determinant changes sign if two columns or two rows are interchanged, the creation operators $a_\lambda^\dagger$ must anticommute:

$$a_\xi^\dagger a_\eta^\dagger + a_\eta^\dagger a_\xi^\dagger = 0. \tag{4}$$

The adjoint of Eq. (3) leads to the equation

$$a_\xi a_\eta + a_\eta a_\xi = 0 \tag{5}$$

that the annihilation operators obey. The orthonormality of the determinantal product states yields

$$a_\xi^\dagger a_\eta + a_\eta a_\xi^\dagger = \delta(\eta, \xi). \tag{6}$$

Equations (4), (5), and (6) are the basic equations satisfied by the creation and annihilation operators.

Let us restrict attention to those annihilation and creation operators possessing identical values of n and l. These operators, $8l + 4$ in all, cannot be regarded as the generators of a group, since they are defined with respect to anticommutation, rather than commutation. However, if we add to the creation and annihilation operators the $(4l + 2)(8l + 3)$ distinct nonzero commutators, the set of operators becomes closed with respect to commutation, as can easily be verified by repeated use of Eqs. (4)–(6). The group corresponding to this augmented set of operators can be found by first selecting the operators

$$H_\xi = \tfrac{1}{2}[a_\xi^\dagger, a_\xi], \tag{7}$$

where ξ runs over the $4l + 2$ single-electron states. The H_ξ commute among themselves, and correspond to the operators H_i of Section II, A. For the simple annihilation and creation operators, we find

$$[H_\xi, a_\eta^\dagger] = \delta(\xi, \eta)\, a_\eta^\dagger,$$

$$[H_\xi, a_\eta] = -\delta(\xi, \eta)\, a_\eta,$$

by using Eqs. (4)–(6). The other operators corresponding to the E_α of Eqs. (2) are the commutators $\tfrac{1}{2}[a_\eta^\dagger, a_\zeta^\dagger]$, $\tfrac{1}{2}[a_\eta, a_\zeta]$, and $\tfrac{1}{2}[a_\eta^\dagger, a_\zeta]$ for which $\eta \neq \zeta$. Owing to Eqs. (4)–(6), they can be replaced by $a_\eta^\dagger a_\zeta^\dagger$, $a_\eta a_\zeta$, and $a_\eta^\dagger a_\zeta$. We find

$$[H_\xi, a_\eta^\dagger a_\zeta^\dagger] = \{\delta(\xi, \eta) + \delta(\xi, \zeta)\}\, a_\eta^\dagger a_\zeta^\dagger,$$

$$[H_\xi, a_\eta^\dagger a_\zeta] = \{\delta(\xi, \eta) - \delta(\xi, \zeta)\}\, a_\eta^\dagger a_\zeta,$$

$$[H_\xi, a_\eta a_\zeta] = \{-\delta(\xi, \eta) - \delta(\xi, \zeta)\}\, a_\eta a_\zeta.$$

It is straightforward to show that $g_{ij} = (16l + 6)\,\delta(i,j)$. Comparison with the second of Eqs. (2) shows at once that the operators $a_\eta^\dagger$ correspond to the unit vectors $\mathbf{e}_i$; the operators a_η to $-\mathbf{e}_i$; the operators $a_\eta{}^\dagger a_\zeta{}^\dagger$ to $\mathbf{e}_i + \mathbf{e}_j$; the $a_\eta{}^\dagger a_\zeta$ to $\mathbf{e}_i - \mathbf{e}_j$; and the $a_\eta a_\zeta$ to $-\mathbf{e}_i - \mathbf{e}_j$. To make the correspondence precise, we have only to arrange the $(m_s m_l)$ values in sequence and label them $1, 2, \ldots, 4l+2$. The complete set of roots is thus $\pm\mathbf{e}_i$, $\pm\mathbf{e}_i \pm \mathbf{e}_j$ with all possible combinations of sign. It is unnecessary to check that the third and fourth of Eqs. (2) are satisfied: they follow automatically. From Table I we conclude that the group for which we are searching is $O^+(8l+5)$.

C. Representations

In atomic spectroscopy, the generators of a group G act on the multielectron orthonormal eigenfunctions Ψ_k. If a collection of functions Ψ_k possesses the property that any operator of G acting on any member of the collection produces a linear combination of the Ψ_k, then the functions Ψ_k form a *basis* for a representation R of G. If, further, no functions Φ_j, given by

$$\Phi_j = \sum_k a_{jk} \Psi_k,$$

can be constructed that, for a unitary matrix a_{jk}, break up into two sets of functions, each set separately forming a basis for a representation of G, then the representation R is *irreducible*. Since the H_i are commuting operators, we may evidently form linear combinations Θ_j of the basis functions Ψ_k that are simultaneous eigenfunctions of all the H_i. That is, for each Θ_j we may write

$$H_i \Theta_j = m_i \Theta_j, \qquad (i = 1, 2, \ldots, \ell).$$

The vector $\mathbf{m} \equiv (m_1 m_2 \cdots m_\ell)$ is the *weight* of Θ_j, and defines a point in the weight space. As each Θ_j is considered in turn, an array of points is built up: a feature of this process is that the weights of different Θ_j are sometimes identical, even when R is irreducible. It is traditional to label an irreducible representation by the highest weight of its basis functions, a weight $\mathbf{m}$ being said to be higher than $\mathbf{m}'$ when the first nonvanishing term of the series $m_1 - m_1'$, $m_2 - m_2'$, $\ldots$, $m_\ell - m_\ell'$ is positive.

To illustrate these remarks, we take the group $O^+(8l+5)$ introduced in Section II, B. Since the annihilation and creation operators, acting on any state of the nl shell, produce states that belong to the shell, these states form the basis for a representation of $O^+(8l+5)$. To find the weight of the determinantal product state $\{\lambda\mu\cdots\omega\}$, we operate with the H_ξ of Eq. (7). We first note that

$$H_\xi\{\lambda\mu\cdots\omega\} = (a_\xi{}^\dagger a_\xi - \tfrac{1}{2}) a_\lambda{}^\dagger a_\mu{}^\dagger \cdots a_\omega{}^\dagger |0\rangle,$$

owing to Eq. (6). If $\xi \neq \lambda$, we may write $a_\xi a_\lambda^\dagger = -a_\lambda^\dagger a_\xi$; by continuing this process, a_ξ can be gradually transferred to the right until it acts on $|0\rangle$, with a null result. This is possible only if ξ is not contained in the set $\lambda, \mu, \ldots, \omega$. In this case, the eigenvalue of H_ξ is $-\frac{1}{2}$. If, however, ξ *is* contained in the set $\lambda, \mu, \ldots, \omega$, then the product $a_\xi^\dagger a_\xi$ is transferred to the right until it stands to the immediate left of $a_\xi^\dagger$. Equation (6) gives at once $a_\xi^\dagger a_\xi a_\xi^\dagger = a_\xi^\dagger$, and the eigenvalue of H_ξ is now $1 - \frac{1}{2}$, that is, $+\frac{1}{2}$. Every determinantal product state of the shell therefore possesses a weight of the type $(\pm\frac{1}{2}\pm\frac{1}{2}\cdots\pm\frac{1}{2})$; and it is

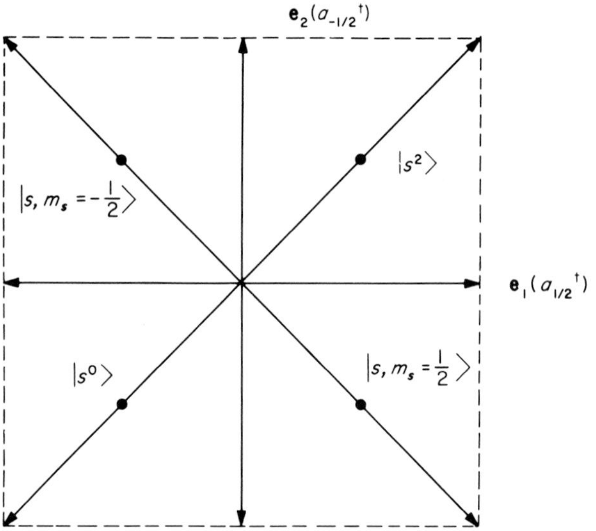

FIG. 1. The representation $(\frac{1}{2}\frac{1}{2})$ of $O^+(5)$ superimposed on the root figure. The subscripts to the annihilation and creation operators specify values of m_s. The diagonal roots correspond to the combinations $a_{\frac{1}{2}}^\dagger a_{-\frac{1}{2}}^\dagger$, $a_{\frac{1}{2}}^\dagger a_{-\frac{1}{2}}$, $a_{-\frac{1}{2}}^\dagger a_{\frac{1}{2}}$, and $a_{-\frac{1}{2}} a_{\frac{1}{2}}$. That it is only possible to take one step in a given direction within the representation $(\frac{1}{2}\frac{1}{2})$ is a direct consequence of the Pauli exclusion principle.

clear that no two determinantal product states share the same weight. Now the array of weights for an irreducible representation must reflect the symmetry of the root figure in the weight space (*10*). This means in our case that the existence of any one of the weights implies the existence of all the others. It follows that the representation we have found is irreducible. It is labeled by its highest weight, namely $(\frac{1}{2}\frac{1}{2}\cdots\frac{1}{2})$. In the language of Murnaghan (*11*), this representation is the simplest *spin* representation of $O^+(8l+5)$; that is, $(\frac{1}{2}\frac{1}{2}\cdots\frac{1}{2})$ has the smallest dimensionality of those representations whose weights are given by half-integral (rather than integral) coordinates.

The special case of an s shell is illustrated in Fig. 1. The weight space for $O^+(5)$ (corresponding to $l = 0$) is two-dimensional; the roots are $\pm\mathbf{e}_1$, $\pm\mathbf{e}_2$, and $\pm\mathbf{e}_1 \pm \mathbf{e}_2$ from Table I. The representation $(\frac{1}{2}\frac{1}{2})$ comprises four weights corresponding to the four eigenstates

$$|s^{0\,1}S\rangle, \qquad |s, m_s = \tfrac{1}{2}\rangle, \qquad |s, m_s = -\tfrac{1}{2}\rangle, \qquad |s^{2\,1}S\rangle,$$

of the s shell. The roots $\pm\mathbf{e}_1$ and $\pm\mathbf{e}_2$ correspond to the annihilation and creation operators for the two states of an s electron. It can be seen that the root vector for a creation operator connects the empty shell state $|s^{0\,1}S\rangle$ with weight $(-\frac{1}{2}\,-\frac{1}{2})$ to either of the two single-electron states with weights $(-\frac{1}{2}\,\frac{1}{2})$ and $(\frac{1}{2}\,-\frac{1}{2})$. This illustrates a quite general feature of operators of the type E_α: they act as shift operators. In fact, if the weight of Θ_j is $\mathbf{m}$, then the weight of $E_\alpha\Theta_j$ is $\mathbf{m} + \boldsymbol{\alpha}$, as can be immediately seen from the equations

$$H_i(E_\alpha \Theta_j) = (E_\alpha H_i + \alpha_i E_\alpha)\Theta_j = (m_i + \alpha_i)(E_\alpha \Theta_j).$$

D. Subgroups

If a subset of the generators of a group can be found that separately satisfies Eq. (1), then the subset forms the generators of a subgroup. The operators of $O^+(8l+5)$ serve as a good example of this. We have only to discard the isolated annihilation and creation operators from the complete set. The remaining operators are $\frac{1}{2}[a_\xi^\dagger, a_\xi]$, $a_\eta^\dagger a_\zeta^\dagger$, $a_\eta a_\zeta$, and $a_\eta^\dagger a_\zeta$ (with $\eta \neq \zeta$). No isolated creation or annihilation operators can arise when the commutators of these operators are considered, so we have found the generators of a subgroup of $O^+(8l+5)$. The operators H_ξ of Eq. (4) again play the role of the H_i of Section II, A, and the roots $\pm\mathbf{e}_i \pm \mathbf{e}_j$ appear as before. The difference with the previous case is simply that there are no roots $\pm\mathbf{e}_i$. From Table I we conclude that the subgroup whose operators are the commutators of the annihilation and creation operators is $O^+(8l+4)$. We write $O^+(8l+5) \supset O^+(8l+4)$.

The complete set of states of the nl shell form the basis for a representation of $O^+(8l+4)$. We note, however, that the operators $a_\eta^\dagger a_\zeta^\dagger$, $a_\eta a_\zeta$, and $a_\eta^\dagger a_\zeta$ connect electronic configurations differing in two electrons or none. The basis functions break up into two sets: those belonging to the configurations $(nl)^N$ with N even, and those belonging to the configurations with N odd. No operator of $O^+(8l+4)$ can connect members of the different sets. It follows that the representation is reducible. The state corresponding to the completely filled shell possesses the weight $(\frac{1}{2}\frac{1}{2}\cdots\frac{1}{2})$, which is thus the representation of $O^+(8l+4)$ for which the states of $(nl)^N$ with N even form the basis. The weights of the states with N odd contain an odd number of minus signs preceding the symbols $\frac{1}{2}$: the highest weight is thus $(\frac{1}{2}\frac{1}{2}\cdots\frac{1}{2}\,-\frac{1}{2})$. To indicate that the representation $(\frac{1}{2}\frac{1}{2}\cdots\frac{1}{2})$ of $O^+(8l+5)$ decomposes into the two representations $(\frac{1}{2}\frac{1}{2}\cdots\frac{1}{2}\,\pm\frac{1}{2})$ of $O^+(8l+4)$ under the reduction $O^+(8l+5) \to O^+(8l+4)$, we write

$$(\tfrac{1}{2}\tfrac{1}{2}\cdots\tfrac{1}{2}) \to (\tfrac{1}{2}\tfrac{1}{2}\cdots\tfrac{1}{2}) \oplus (\tfrac{1}{2}\tfrac{1}{2}\cdots\tfrac{1}{2}\,-\tfrac{1}{2}). \tag{8}$$

This is an example of a *branching rule*. It is understood that the representation on the left belongs to $O^+(8l+5)$ and those on the right to $O^+(8l+4)$.

E. Unitary Groups

A subgroup of $O^+(8l+4)$ can be easily found. We have merely to eliminate the operators $a_\eta^\dagger a_\zeta^\dagger$ and $a_\eta a_\zeta$, leaving those of the type $\frac{1}{2}[a_\xi^\dagger, a_\xi]$ and $a_\eta^\dagger a_\zeta$ $(\eta \neq \zeta)$. It is straightforward to prove that this subset is closed with respect to commutation. The operators $H_\xi = \frac{1}{2}[a_\xi^\dagger, a_\xi]$ commute among themselves as before, and the equation

$$[H_\xi, a_\eta^\dagger a_\zeta] = \{\delta(\xi, \eta) - \delta(\xi, \zeta)\} a_\eta^\dagger a_\zeta$$

indicates that the roots are all of the type $\mathbf{e}_i - \mathbf{e}_j$. It appears from Table I that this subgroup of $O^+(8l+4)$ is $SU(4l+2)$. However, a difficulty presents itself. As has been mentioned in Section II, A, the roots are all perpendicular to $\sum \mathbf{e}_i$, so the weight space really possesses only $4l+1$ dimensions. A weight $(m_1 m_2 \ldots m_{4l+2})$ will only fall in the weight space if $\sum m_i = 0$; to ensure that this happens, we must replace each H_ξ by

$$H'_\xi = H_\xi - (4l+2)^{-1} \sum_\eta H_\eta. \tag{9}$$

The operators H'_ξ and $a_\eta^\dagger a_\zeta$ can properly be taken as the generators of $SU(4l+2)$, though it must be remembered that the H'_ξ are not linearly independent, since $\sum H'_\xi = 0$.

It is clear that the states of each electronic configuration $(nl)^N$ form the basis for a representation of $SU(4l+2)$. Every determinantal product state is an eigenstate of all the H'_ξ; but, owing to Eq. (9), the weights are fractions with denominator $4l+2$. To avoid this awkwardness, it is often convenient to replace each H'_ξ by $a_\xi^\dagger a_\xi$. The group formed by the $(4l+2)^2$ operators $a_\xi^\dagger a_\eta$ is no longer simple, and the weights fall in the full $(4l+2)$-dimensional space. These disadvantages are offset by certain simplifications in the mathematics. To identify the group, we note that any linear transformation of the $4l+2$ single-electron states can be carried out by an operator of the type $\sum \epsilon_{\xi\eta} a_\xi^\dagger a_\eta$, so the operators $a_\xi^\dagger a_\eta$ can be regarded as the generators for the general linear group in $4l+2$ dimensions, $GL(4l+2)$. However, it is convenient to choose parameters $\epsilon_{\xi\eta}$ so that the transformation is unitary, thereby preserving the orthonormality of the states. The group can thus be labeled $U(4l+2)$, the unitary group in $4l+2$ dimensions.

The eigenvalue of $a_\xi^\dagger a_\xi$ for a state $\{\lambda\mu\cdots\omega\}$ of $(nl)^N$ is either 1 or 0 according as ξ is present or not in the sequence $\lambda, \mu, \ldots, \omega$. As ξ runs through the $4l+2$ possible single-electron states, N eigenvalues 1 and $4l+2-N$ eigenvalues 0 are produced. The ${}^{4l+2}C_N$ ways of arranging these symbols in sequence correspond to the number of states of $(nl)^N$. The representation with these states as a basis is irreducible, and is designated by its highest weight, $[11\cdots10\cdots0]$. In keeping with tradition, brackets rather than parentheses are used for denoting representations of unitary groups. Another custom is to omit zeros from the brackets except for the representation $[00\cdots0]$, which is written $[0]$. As an example of the branching rules for the reduction $O^+(8l+4) \to U(4l+2)$, we set $l = 1$, corresponding to p electrons. We obtain

$$\begin{aligned} (\tfrac{1}{2}\tfrac{1}{2}\tfrac{1}{2}\tfrac{1}{2}\tfrac{1}{2}\tfrac{1}{2}) &\to [0] \oplus [11] \oplus [1111] \oplus [111111], \\ (\tfrac{1}{2}\tfrac{1}{2}\tfrac{1}{2}\tfrac{1}{2}\tfrac{1}{2}\,-\tfrac{1}{2}) &\to [1] \oplus [111] \oplus [11111]. \end{aligned} \tag{10}$$

These branching rules, taken with Eq. (8), describe the decomposition of the p shell into separate configurations p^N.

III. Coupled Tensors

A. The Group $O^+(3)$

To study the structure of the configuration $(nl)^N$, the subgroups of $U(4l+2)$ must be examined. In Section II, subgroups of $O^+(8l+5)$ were found simply by rejecting unwanted operators from the initial set. The only way to continue this procedure with the operators $a_\xi^\dagger a_\eta$ is to make selections on the basis of the quantum numbers ξ and η; that is, on m_s and m_l. These quantum numbers are associated with a preferred direction in space—the z axis—and any distribution of the ξ into different sets would impose this preferred direction on the analysis. Since all directions are equivalent for a free atom, such a step is to be postponed for as long as possible. The way to achieve this is to replace the products $a_\xi^\dagger a_\eta$ by linear combinations that have well-defined properties with respect to $O^+(3)$.

Generators for $O^+(3)$ are easy to find. The familiar commutation relations satisfied by the components of any angular momentum vector can be written for $\mathbf{L}$ as

$$[L_z, L_\pm] = \pm L_\pm,$$

where $L_\pm = L_x \pm iL_y$. Thus L_z plays the role of H_i and $L_\pm$ that of E_α in Eqs. (2). The roots are $\pm\mathbf{e}_1$, and the group with generators L_z, $L_\pm$ is identified as $O^+(3)$ from Table I. The equations

$$\begin{aligned} L_z|\gamma LM_L\rangle &= M_L|\gamma LM_L\rangle, \\ L_\pm|\gamma LM_L\rangle &= \{L(L+1) - M_L(M_L \pm 1)\}^{1/2}\,|\gamma LM_L \pm 1\rangle, \end{aligned} \tag{11}$$

which follow from the theory of angular momentum (*1*), show that the kets $|\gamma L M_L\rangle$ (for $M_L = -L, -L+1, \ldots, L$) form the basis for a representation of $O^+(3)$. This representation is irreducible, with highest weight (L). It is denoted by $\mathscr{D}_L$. The symbol γ in Eqs. (11) stands for additional quantum numbers that may be necessary to specify the kets unambiguously. This analysis can be repeated for any other angular-momentum vector, of course.

The vector **L** is not in a form where its properties with respect to $a_\xi^\dagger$ and a_η can be conveniently studied. In general, an operator F comprising a sum of single-electron operators f must be written

$$F = \sum_{\lambda,\nu} a_\lambda^\dagger \langle\lambda| f |\nu\rangle a_\nu \tag{12}$$

in the language of second quantization. This can be readily verified by setting F between two states of the type occurring in Eq. (3). We have only to make the replacements $F \to \mathbf{L}$ and $f \to \mathbf{l}$ to get the appropriate form for **L**.

B. Commutators

As a first step to an analysis of the products $a_\xi^\dagger a_\eta$, each operator separately is examined. This introduces us to a central problem in theoretical spectroscopy: how to attach group-theoretical labels to a set of operators O_j. Characteristic equations for linear transformations of operators O_j and basis functions Θ_j are

$$O_j' = U O_j U^{-1}, \qquad \Theta_j' = U\Theta_j.$$

For an infinitesimal transformation given by $U = 1 + \epsilon^\mu X_\mu$, these equations can be written

$$O_j' - O_j = \epsilon^\mu [X_\mu, O_j], \qquad \Theta_j' - \Theta_j = \epsilon^\mu X_\mu \Theta_j.$$

The study of operators can thus be carried out just as for basis functions: it is only necessary to replace the products $X_\mu \Theta_j$ by the commutators $[X_\mu, O_j]$. In practice, however, the properties of many sets of basis functions are well known, and it is more convenient to establish the one-to-one correspondence $O_j \leftrightarrow \Theta_j$ by verifying $c_{\mu i} \equiv b_{\mu i}$ in the equations

$$[X_\mu, O_j] = \sum_i b_{\mu i} O_i, \qquad X_\mu \Theta_j = \sum_i c_{\mu i} \Theta_i.$$

The present problem is a good example of this method. With the aid of the anticommutation relations (4)–(6), we find

$$\begin{aligned} &[L_z, a_\xi^\dagger] = m_l a_\xi^\dagger, \\ &[L_\pm, a_\xi^\dagger] = \{l(l+1) - m_l(m_l \pm 1)\}^{1/2} a_\eta^\dagger, \end{aligned} \tag{13}$$

where $\xi \equiv (m_s\, m_l)$ and $\eta \equiv (m_s m_l \pm 1)$. The second-quantized form for $\mathbf{L}$ is used to obtain these results. A comparison of Eqs. (11) and (13) shows that the operators $a_\xi^\dagger$ for a given m_s transform under the operators $\mathbf{L}$ according to $\mathscr{D}_l$. They are said to form the components of a tensor of rank l in the orbital space. Repeating this analysis with $\mathbf{S}$ instead of $\mathbf{L}$, we find that the two operators $a_\xi^\dagger$ for a given m_l form the components of a tensor of rank s $(=\frac{1}{2})$ in the spin space. The $4l+2$ components $a_\xi^\dagger$ thus constitute a *double* tensor, which is written $\mathbf{a}^\dagger$.

To form a double tensor from the annihilation operators, we first define

$$\bar{a}_\nu = (-1)^x a_\sigma, \tag{14}$$

where $\nu \equiv (m_s m_l)$, $x = s + l - m_s - m_l$, and $\sigma \equiv (-m_s - m_l)$. The commutation relations of the $\bar{a}_\nu$ with $\mathbf{S}$ and $\mathbf{L}$ show that the $\bar{a}_\nu$ form the components of a double tensor of ranks s and l in the spin and orbital spaces, respectively. It is denoted by $\mathbf{a}$.

C. Subgroups of $U(4l+2)$

Since $\mathbf{a}^\dagger$ and $\mathbf{a}$ are tensor operators, they can be coupled to form $(\mathbf{a}^\dagger\mathbf{a})^{(\kappa k)}$ according to the usual rules of angular momentum theory (*1*). In detail,

$$(\mathbf{a}^\dagger\mathbf{a})^{(\kappa k)}_{\pi q} = \sum_{\xi,\eta} (s m_s s m_s' | s s \kappa \pi)(l m_l l m_l' | l l k q)\, a_\xi^\dagger \bar{a}_\eta, \tag{15}$$

where $\xi \equiv (m_s m_l)$ and $\eta \equiv (m_s' m_l')$. The two coefficients preceding $a_\xi^\dagger \bar{a}_\eta$ are Clebsch-Gordan coefficients for the group $O^+(3)$: they serve to combine the products $a_\xi^\dagger \bar{a}_\eta$ in such a way that a linear combination is produced that transforms according to $\mathscr{D}_\kappa$ in the spin space and to $\mathscr{D}_k$ in the orbital space. The $(4l+2)^2$ operators $a_\xi^\dagger a_\eta$ are now replaced by the tensor components $(\mathbf{a}^\dagger\mathbf{a})^{(\kappa k)}_{\pi q}$, where κ, k, π, and q run over those integers satisfying

$$-\kappa \leqq \pi \leqq \kappa, \qquad -k \leqq q \leqq k, \qquad 0 \leqq \kappa \leqq 1, \qquad 0 \leqq k \leqq 2l.$$

The commutation relations that the operators for $U(4l+2)$ satisfy, namely

$$[a_\xi^\dagger a_\eta, a_\nu^\dagger a_\lambda] = \delta(\eta, \nu)\, a_\xi^\dagger a_\lambda - \delta(\xi, \lambda)\, a_\nu^\dagger a_\eta,$$

are replaced by the equivalent set

$$[(\mathbf{a}^\dagger \mathbf{a})^{(\kappa k)}_{\pi q}, (\mathbf{a}^\dagger \mathbf{a})^{(\kappa' k')}_{\pi' q'}]$$

$$= \sum_{\kappa'', k'', \pi'', q''} \{(2\kappa+1)(2\kappa'+1)(2k+1)(2k'+1)\}^{1/2} \{(-1)^{\kappa+k+\kappa'+k'} - (-1)^{\kappa''+k''}\}$$

$$\times (\kappa\pi\kappa'\pi'|\kappa\kappa'\kappa''\pi'')(kqk'q'|kk'k''q'')$$

$$\times W(\kappa\kappa' ss; \kappa'' s)\, W(kk'll; k''l)\, (\mathbf{a}^\dagger \mathbf{a})^{(\kappa'' k'')}_{\pi'' q''}. \tag{16}$$

The Clebsch-Gordan and W coefficients are related to the 3-j and 6-j symbols, and can be found from the tables of Rotenberg *et al.* (*12*).

Equation (16) is well suited to finding the generators of subgroups of $U(4l+2)$, but it is no longer always a trivial matter to identify the groups themselves. From the complete set of tensors, we first select the two subsets $(\mathbf{a}^\dagger \mathbf{a})^{(10)}$ and $(\mathbf{a}^\dagger \mathbf{a})^{(0k)}$ $(0 \leqq k \leqq 2l)$. It is clear that either subset forms by itself a subgroup of $U(4l+2)$. The vector $(\mathbf{a}^\dagger \mathbf{a})^{(10)}$, having rank 1 with respect to spin and rank zero with respect to orbit, must be proportional to $\mathbf{S}$; the first subset thus corresponds to $O^+(3)$. To remind us that $\mathbf{S}$ forms the generators of this group, it is convenient to write it as $O^+_S(3)$. The tensors $(\mathbf{a}^\dagger \mathbf{a})^{(0k)}$ are scalar in the spin space but admit of all possible components in the orbital space. There are $(2l+1)^2$ of them, and they can be regarded as the generators of $U(2l+1)$. If we put $\kappa = 0$, $\kappa' = 1$, and $k' = 0$ in Eq. (16), we must have $\kappa'' = 1$ and $k'' = k$ to satisfy the triangular conditions for the nonvanishing of the Racah coefficient W. But in this case

$$\{(-1)^{\kappa+k+\kappa'+k'} - (-1)^{\kappa''+k''}\} = 0. \tag{17}$$

Hence operators from different subsets commute, and together form the generators for the direct product $O^+_S(3) \times U(2l+1)$. The decomposition $U(4l+2) \to O^+_S(3) \times U(2l+1)$ separates the spin and orbital spaces.

We note at once that the operators $(\mathbf{a}^\dagger \mathbf{a})^{(0k)}$ for odd k form a subgroup of $U(2l+1)$; since if $\kappa = \kappa' = 0$ in Eq. (16), and if both k and k' are odd, then k'' must be odd too—for otherwise Eq. (17) would be satisfied. It turns out that this subgroup is $O^+(2l+1)$ (*10*). The three components of $(\mathbf{a}^\dagger \mathbf{a})^{(01)}$ form in turn a subgroup of $O^+(2l+1)$, for it is obviously impossible to produce an odd k'' exceeding 1 in Eq. (16) if $k = k' = 1$. This group is $O^+_L(3)$, since $(\mathbf{a}^\dagger \mathbf{a})^{(01)}$ must be proportional to $\mathbf{L}$. To summarize the complete decomposition from shell to term, we write

$$O^+(8l+5) \supset O^+(8l+4) \supset U(4l+2) \supset O^+_S(3) \times U(2l+1)$$
$$\supset O^+_S(3) \times O^+(2l+1) \supset O^+_S(3) \times O^+_L(3). \tag{18}$$

In practice, the spin and orbital spaces are connected by the spin-orbit interaction. It is thus useful to introduce the subgroup $O_J^+(3)$ of $O_S^+(3) \times O_L^+(3)$ whose generators are $\mathbf{J} = \mathbf{S} + \mathbf{L}$. The reduction process need not stop at this point. If the atom is situated in a crystal at a site of definite point symmetry P, then the decomposition $O_J^+(3) \rightarrow P$ should be considered. Alternatively, an atom in a magnetic field would make $O_J^+(3) \rightarrow O^+(2)$ a useful final step in the reduction of $O^+(8l+5)$, the single generator of $O^+(2)$ being J_z.

D. The Configurations f^N

A remarkable simplification takes place for $l = 3$, corresponding to f electrons. The group $O^+(2l+1)$ is $O^+(7)$, and it possesses the tensors $(\mathbf{a}^\dagger \mathbf{a})^{(0k)}$ with $k = 1$, 3, and 5 as generators. From Eq. (16), we would expect the commutator of two components of $(\mathbf{a}^\dagger \mathbf{a})^{(05)}$ to yield the components of tensors $(\mathbf{a}^\dagger \mathbf{a})^{(0k'')}$ for which $k'' = 1$, 3, and 5. Quite fortuitously, however,

$$W(5533; 33) = 0,$$

and all terms for which $k'' = 3$ disappear. Now the commutator of $(\mathbf{a}^\dagger \mathbf{a})^{(05)}_{0q}$ and $(\mathbf{a}^\dagger \mathbf{a})^{(01)}_{0q'}$ does not yield any components of $(\mathbf{a}^\dagger \mathbf{a})^{(03)}$, and neither does the commutator of $(\mathbf{a}^\dagger \mathbf{a})^{(01)}_{0q}$ with $(\mathbf{a}^\dagger \mathbf{a})^{(01)}_{0q'}$. Thus the fourteen components of the tensors $(\mathbf{a}^\dagger \mathbf{a})^{(01)}$ and $(\mathbf{a}^\dagger \mathbf{a})^{(05)}$ form the generators of a subgroup of $O^+(7)$.

To find the group, we select the commuting operators $(\mathbf{a}^\dagger \mathbf{a})^{(01)}_{00}$ and $(\mathbf{a}^\dagger \mathbf{a})^{(05)}_{00}$ to play the roles of the H_i in Eqs. (2). The E_α are very easy to obtain. For $|q| > 1$ they are all of the type $(\mathbf{a}^\dagger \mathbf{a})^{(05)}_{0q}$; when $|q| = 1$, suitable linear combinations of these operators with $(\mathbf{a}^\dagger \mathbf{a})^{(01)}_{0q}$ must be constructed. The root figure can be found with the aid of Eq. (16). For example, the two equations

$$[(\mathbf{a}^\dagger \mathbf{a})^{(01)}_{00}, (\mathbf{a}^\dagger \mathbf{a})^{(05)}_{05}] = -(\tfrac{25}{56})^{1/2} (\mathbf{a}^\dagger \mathbf{a})^{(05)}_{05}$$

$$[(\mathbf{a}^\dagger \mathbf{a})^{(05)}_{00}, (\mathbf{a}^\dagger \mathbf{a})^{(05)}_{05}] = (\tfrac{3}{56})^{1/2} (\mathbf{a}^\dagger \mathbf{a})^{(05)}_{05}$$

give the root running out from the origin to the point $\{-(\frac{25}{56})^{1/2}, (\frac{3}{56})^{1/2}\}$. The entire set of roots is sketched in Fig. 2. Apart from a rotation of axes, the root figure is identical to that of $\mathcal{G}_2$ listed in Table I. Thus for f electrons we can replace $O^+(7) \supset O_L^+(3)$ by the more detailed decomposition

$$O^+(7) \supset \mathcal{G}_2 \supset O_L^+(3).$$

The use of $\mathcal{G}_2$ is an important feature of Racah's analysis (*3*), and is largely responsible for the progress that has been made during the last decade in the analysis of actinide and rare-earth spectra.

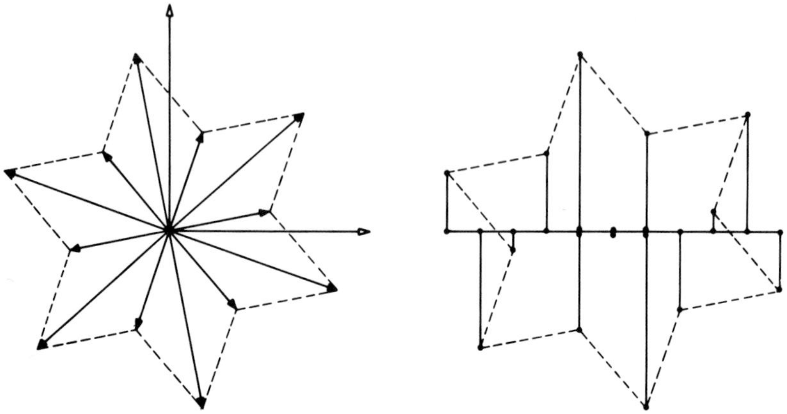

FIG. 2. On the left is shown the root figure for $\mathscr{G}_2$; the horizontal and vertical axes correspond to $(\mathbf{a}^\dagger\mathbf{a})^{(01)}_{00}$ and $(\mathbf{a}^\dagger\mathbf{a})^{(05)}_{00}$, respectively. The reduction $\mathscr{G}_2 \to O_L^+(3)$, for which the generators for $O_L^+(3)$ are the components of $(\mathbf{a}^\dagger\mathbf{a})^{(01)}$, is accomplished by projecting the weights of a representation of $\mathscr{G}_2$ onto the horizontal axis and interpreting the projections as weights of representations of $O^+(3)$. This is illustrated on the right for the representation (11) of $\mathscr{G}_2$, which decomposes into $\mathscr{D}_1$ and $\mathscr{D}_5$ of $O^+(3)$.

IV. Representations

A. Branching Rules

In Section II, E, it was shown that the states of a configuration $(nl)^N$ form the basis for a representation of the type $[11\cdots 1]$ of $U(4l+2)$. Under the decomposition represented by (18), these representations break up first into representations of $O^+(3) \times U(2l+1)$; the representations of $U(2l+1)$ then break up into representations of $O^+(2l+1)$, which in turn yield representations of $O_L^+(3)$. It would be possible to identify these representations by the methods of Section II, using the commuting operators $(\mathbf{a}^\dagger\mathbf{a})^{(\kappa k)}_{00}$ to play the role of the H_i. However, the problem of determining branching rules occurs in many applications of group theory, and is not peculiar to atomic spectroscopy. For this reason, there seems little point in giving a detailed description here. The reader is referred to the book by Hamermesh (*4*), and to the articles by Jahn (*13*) and Flowers (*14*).

Nevertheless, it is probably useful to give an example, and the p shell is taken for that purpose. The reduction $U(4l+2) \to O_S^+(3) \times U(2l+1)$ becomes $U(6) \to O_S^+(3) \times U(3)$. The commuting operators for $U(3)$ are all of the type $(\mathbf{a}^\dagger\mathbf{a})^{(0k)}_{00}$. If we put $\kappa = 0$ in Eq. (15), we obtain, on abbreviating m_l to m,

$$(\mathbf{a}^\dagger\mathbf{a})^{(0k)}_{00} = \sum_m (lml - m|llk0)(2)^{-1/2}(-1)^{l+m+1}(a_{\frac{1}{2}m}{}^\dagger a_{\frac{1}{2}m} + a_{-\frac{1}{2}m}{}^\dagger a_{-\frac{1}{2}m}).$$

For the purpose of plotting out the weights, it is convenient to take the operators

$$H_i = a_{\frac{1}{2}m}{}^{\dagger} a_{\frac{1}{2}m} + a_{-\frac{1}{2}m}{}^{\dagger} a_{-\frac{1}{2}m} \tag{19}$$

rather than their linear combinations. The operators H_1, H_2, and H_3 correspond to $m_l = m = 1$, 0, and -1 respectively. Every determinantal product state of p^N is an eigenstate of H_i; in fact H_i merely counts the number of times

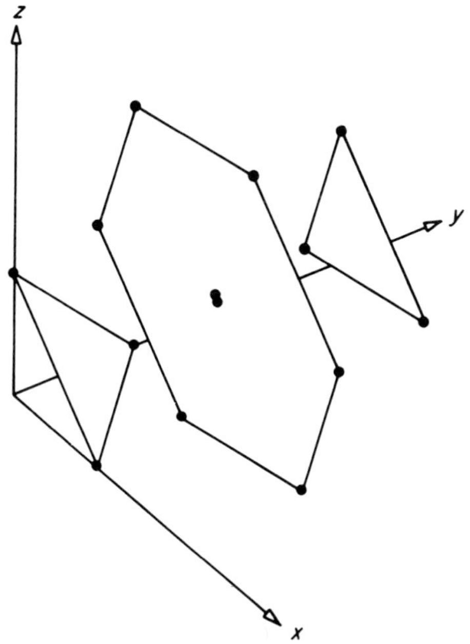

FIG. 3. The arrays of weights for the irreducible representations [1], [21], and [221] of $U(3)$, corresponding to the states of p, p^3, and p^5 for which $S = M_S = \frac{1}{2}$. Projections of the weights onto the plane $x + y + z = 0$ give the weights of the representations **3**, **8**, and $\bar{\mathbf{3}}$ of $SU(3)$.

the corresponding m_l value occurs. For example, take the state ψ of p^4 defined by the $(m_s m_l)$ values $(\frac{1}{2}1)$, $(-\frac{1}{2}1)$, $(\frac{1}{2}0)$, and $(-\frac{1}{2}-1)$. We see

$$H_1\psi = 2\psi, \qquad H_2\psi = \psi, \qquad H_3\psi = \psi.$$

The state thus corresponds to the weight [211]. If we select linear combinations of determinantal product states that belong to a definite S and M_S, then the weights $[\lambda_1\lambda_2\lambda_3]$ define an irreducible representation of $U(3)$. States for which $S = M_S = \frac{1}{2}$ occur in p, p^3, and p^5; they form bases for the irreducible representations [1], [21], and [221] of $U(3)$. The array of weights for these representations are drawn in Fig. 3. It is to be noticed that the weights for a representation of p^N lie in the plane $x + y + z = N$.

Since $L_z = H_1 - H_3$, it is a simple matter to carry out the final reduction $U(3) \rightarrow O_L^+(3)$. All the weights $[\lambda_1 \lambda_2 \lambda_3]$ of a representation of $U(3)$ are considered, and the various eigenvalues $M_L = \lambda_1 - \lambda_3$ written down. A string of M_L values running from L to $-L$ implies the existence of a representation $\mathscr{D}_L$. For example, the representation [21] comprises the weights [210], [201], [111], [102], [012], [120], [111], and [021]. The respective M_L values are 2, 1, 0, −1, −2, 1, 0, − 1. Thus [21] decomposes into $\mathscr{D}_2^+ \oplus \mathscr{D}_1$. It is often convenient to replace $\mathscr{D}_L$ by the capitalized spectroscopic symbol for L. The complete classification of the p shell is given in Table II. Spin assignments are indicated by the prefixed multiplicities $2S + 1$.

TABLE II

CLASSIFICATION OF THE STATES OF p^N

p^N	$U(6)$	$O_S^+(3) \times U(3)$	$O_S^+(3) \times SU(3)$	v	$O_S^+(3) \times O_L^+(3)$
p^0	[0]	$^1[0]$	$^1\mathbf{1}$	0	^1S
p^1	[1]	$^2[1]$	$^2\mathbf{3}$	1	^2P
p^2	[11]	$^1[2]$	$^1\mathbf{6}$	0	^1S
				2	^1D
		$^3[11]$	$^3\overline{\mathbf{3}}$	2	^3P
p^3	[111]	$^2[21]$	$^2\mathbf{8}$	1	^2P
				3	^2D
		$^4[111]$	$^4\mathbf{1}$	3	^4S
p^4	[1111]	$^1[22]$	$^1\overline{\mathbf{6}}$	0	^1S
				2	^1D
		$^3[211]$	$^3\mathbf{3}$	2	^3P
p^5	[11111]	$^2[221]$	$^2\overline{\mathbf{3}}$	1	^2P
p^6	[111111]	$^1[222]$	$^1\mathbf{1}$	0	^1S

Following the arguments of Section II, E, the weights of $SU(3)$ can be found by projecting the weights of $U(3)$ onto the plane $x + y + z = 0$. Thus we see $[1] \rightarrow (\frac{2}{3}\, -\frac{1}{3}\, -\frac{1}{3})$ and $[221] \rightarrow (\frac{1}{3}\, \frac{1}{3}\, -\frac{2}{3})$. Two representations such as these, that can be obtained, one from the other, by a reflection in the origin, are called *adjoint*. In the notation that labels an irreducible representation by its dimension, these two representations may be distinguished by writing **3** and $\overline{\mathbf{3}}$. They are the same representations that label the quark and the anti-quark. The representation [21] yields the self-adjoint representation **8**, and corresponds to the meson and baryon octets. Representations of $SU(3)$ are included in Table II.

For configurations more complex than p^N, special rules have been devised to permit the rapid calculation of the relevant branching rules. Most of the cases can be found in the sources mentioned earlier, or elsewhere (*5*).

B. Seniority

The reduction scheme represented by Eq. (18) is not the only one available. Instead of separating the spin and orbital spaces by the decomposition $U(4l+2) \to O_S^+(3) \times U(2l+1)$, we may select those tensors $(\mathbf{a}^\dagger\mathbf{a})^{(\kappa k)}$ of $U(4l+2)$ for which $\kappa + k$ is odd. If, in Eq. (16), both $\kappa + k$ and $\kappa' + k'$ are odd, it is obvious that the only terms in the summation are those for which $\kappa'' + k''$ is odd—for otherwise Eq. (17) would be satisfied. These tensors therefore form the generators for a subgroup of $U(4l+2)$. It turns out that this group is the symplectic group in $4l+2$ dimensions, $Sp(4l+2)$ (*5*). A representation $[11\cdots1]$ of $U(4l+2)$ comprising N symbols 1 breaks up into a sequence of irreducible representations of $Sp(4l+2)$. They are all of the type $(11\cdots10\cdots0)$. A representation of this kind, in which v symbols 1 appear, is conveniently abbreviated to (v). The decomposition can now be written

$$[11\cdots1] \to \sum_v (v), \qquad v = N, N-2, N-4, \ldots. \tag{20}$$

The last number in the sequence is either 1 or 0 according as N is odd or even. The number v is called the *seniority*.

The tensors $(\mathbf{a}^\dagger\mathbf{a})^{(10)}$ and $(\mathbf{a}^\dagger\mathbf{a})^{(0k)}$ for odd k are contained in the operators of $Sp(4l+2)$, and, as we have already seen in Section III, C, they form the generators for $O_S^+(3) \times O^+(2l+1)$. Thus the introduction of $Sp(4l+2)$ gives the scheme

$$U(4l+2) \supset Sp(4l+2) \supset O_S^+(3) \times O^+(2l+1)$$

as an alternative to

$$U(4l+2) \supset O_S^+(3) \times U(2l+1) \supset O_S^+(3) \times O^+(2l+1).$$

Seniority was first introduced by Racah (*15*) without using group-theoretical methods, though it is clear from a remark in a later paper (*3*) that he realized the connection with symplectic symmetry.

One of the most striking developments of shell theory in recent years has been the discovery that the seniority v can be directly related to certain properties of the group $O^+(3)$. We first define the components $Q_\pm$ and Q_z of a vector $\mathbf{Q}$ as follows:

$$Q_+ = \left\{\frac{(2l+1)}{2}\right\}^{1/2} (\mathbf{a}^\dagger \mathbf{a}^\dagger)^{(00)},$$

$$Q_- = -\left\{\frac{(2l+1)}{2}\right\}^{1/2} (\mathbf{aa})^{(00)},$$

$$Q_z = -\left\{\frac{(2l+1)}{8}\right\}^{1/2} \{(\mathbf{a}^\dagger \mathbf{a})^{(00)} + (\mathbf{a}\,\mathbf{a}^\dagger)^{(00)}\}.$$

It is straightforward to show that the components of $\mathbf{Q}$ satisfy the equations

$$[Q_+, Q_-] = 2Q_z, \qquad [Q_z, Q_\pm] = \pm Q_\pm.$$

These are identical to the commutation relations satisfied by the components of an angular-momentum vector, and $\mathbf{Q}$ is called the *quasispin*. With the aid of Eq. (15), we find

$$Q_z = \tfrac{1}{4} \sum_\xi (a_\xi^\dagger a_\xi - a_\xi a_\xi^\dagger) = \tfrac{1}{2} \sum_\xi a_\xi^\dagger a_\xi - \tfrac{1}{2}(2l+1).$$

The eigenvalue M_Q of Q_z for any state of $(nl)^N$ is thus given by

$$M_Q = -\tfrac{1}{2}(2l+1-N).$$

By expanding the coupled tensor products, it can be shown that Q_+ and Q_- (as well as Q_z) commute with $(\mathbf{a}^\dagger \mathbf{a})^{(\kappa k)}$ when $\kappa + k$ is odd. It follows that Q_+ and Q_-, acting on a basis state for a representation (v) of $Sp(4l+2)$, cannot produce states belonging to a different representation (v'). The operators Q_+ and Q_- are shift operators, inasmuch as they connect states differing by 2 in N, but their field is limited to states of the same seniority. According to the decompositions (10) and (20), the smallest value of N for which $(nl)^N$ contains basis states for (v) is just v. It follows that the minimum value of M_Q is $-\frac{1}{2}(2l+1-v)$. In analogy with the quantum numbers S and L, which represent the extrema of $|M_S|$ and $|M_L|$, we write

$$Q = \tfrac{1}{2}(2l+1-v). \tag{21}$$

Thus the quantum numbers Q and M_Q of quasispin carry the same information as v and N.

The components of $\mathbf{Q}$ are linear combinations of the operators for $O^+(8l+4)$. It has just been mentioned that the operators of $Sp(4l+2)$ commute with $\mathbf{Q}$; hence we can write

$$O^+(8l+4) \supset O_Q^+(3) \times Sp(4l+2),$$

where the subscript Q to $O^+(3)$ indicates that the generators of this group are the components of **Q**. For p electrons, the decompositions of the representations $(\frac{1}{2}\frac{1}{2}\cdots\frac{1}{2}\pm\frac{1}{2})$ of $O^+(8l+4)$ into irreducible representations of $O_Q^+(3) \times Sp(4l+2)$ are given by

$$(\tfrac{1}{2}\tfrac{1}{2}\tfrac{1}{2}\tfrac{1}{2}\tfrac{1}{2}\tfrac{1}{2}) \to {}^4(000) \oplus {}^2(110),$$

$$(\tfrac{1}{2}\tfrac{1}{2}\tfrac{1}{2}\tfrac{1}{2}\tfrac{1}{2}-\tfrac{1}{2}) \to {}^3(100) \oplus {}^1(111),$$

where the representations $\mathscr{D}_Q$ of $O_Q^+(3)$ are indicated by the prefixed multiplicity $2Q+1$. The representations of $Sp(6)$ are written out in full and not contracted to (v). The classification of the states of p^N according to seniority is included in Table II.

C. Alternative Decompositions

As we consider in turn each subgroup of a sequence such as (18), the states of the nl shell are combined and recombined into orthonormal basis functions for the irreducible representations of the groups in question. If, in the branching rules used to study the various decompositions, no irreducible representation occurs more than once, then the irreducible representations completely define a state to within a phase factor. For example, we see from Table II that $|M_Q S M_S L M_L\rangle$ defines a state of the p shell. The five quantum numbers in the ket are not sufficient to specify a state of the d shell: in fact, it was to remedy this defect that Racah introduced the concept of seniority (*15*). In the quasispin notation, a state of the d shell is thus defined by $|QM_Q S M_S L M_L\rangle$. Alternatively, we may use the scheme (18) and write a state of the d shell as $|d^N W S M_S L M_L\rangle$, where W denotes an irreducible representation of $O^+(2l+1)$ (in this case $O^+(5)$).

For the f shell, we find that the branching rules for the reduction $O^+(7) \to O_L^+(3)$ often give duplicated representations $\mathscr{D}_L$ of $O_L^+(3)$. The group $\mathscr{G}_2$ is of immense value here, and effects an almost complete separation of the states. For only two irreducible representations U of $\mathscr{G}_2$ [namely (31) and (40)] that occur in f^N is an additional classificatory symbol τ required. We write $|f^N WU\tau S M_S L M_L\rangle$ for a state of the f shell; it is sometimes convenient to replace $f^N W$ by QM_Q.

It might seem strange that the reduction scheme $O^+(7) \supset \mathscr{G}_2 \supset O_L^+(3)$ is used when another scheme, such as $O^+(7) \supset O^+(6) \supset O^+(5) \supset O^+(4) \supset O^+(3)$, would yield irreducible representations that would completely define a state. The reason is that the final group $O^+(3)$ in the latter sequence does not correspond to rotations in the real three-dimensional space, and hence all the familiar selection rules on L that occur in atomic spectroscopy would be lost if it were used. Of course, the states that occur in nature do not in general correspond to unique representations W and U; but in this case the process of constructing the appropriate linear combinations of pure WU states is trivial compared to the complexities of combining states at the $O^+(3)$ level.

It should also be mentioned at this point that a reduction such as $\mathscr{G}_2 \to O^+(3)$ is ill-defined unless the corresponding generators of group and subgroup are specified. The reduction of Section III, D corresponded to discarding the tensor $(\mathbf{a}^\dagger \mathbf{a})^{(05)}$, leaving $(\mathbf{a}^\dagger \mathbf{a})^{(01)}$. The operator $(\mathbf{a}^\dagger \mathbf{a})^{(01)}_{00}$ has already been used as one of the two commuting operators H_i of $\mathscr{G}_2$, so that reduction of a representation U of $\mathscr{G}_2$ into irreducible representations of $O_L^+(3)$ may be accomplished by projecting the weights of U onto the axis corresponding to $(\mathbf{a}^\dagger \mathbf{a})^{(01)}$. This is illustrated in Fig. 2 for $U \equiv (11)$. (A special system, based on oblique coordinates, is used for labeling irreducible representations of $\mathscr{G}_2$; the details of this need not concern us here.) From the array of projected weights, we at once deduce $(11) \to \mathscr{D}_1 \oplus \mathscr{D}_5$. But if we had performed the reduction $\mathscr{G}_2 \to O^+(3)$ by taking for the operators of $O^+(3)$ the tensor components

$$\mathscr{L}_+ = 2(\mathbf{a}^\dagger \mathbf{a})^{(05)}_{05}, \qquad \mathscr{L}_- = -2(\mathbf{a}^\dagger \mathbf{a})^{(05)}_{0-5},$$

$$\mathscr{L}_z = -2[(\mathbf{a}^\dagger \mathbf{a})^{(05)}_{05}, (\mathbf{a}^\dagger \mathbf{a})^{(05)}_{0-5}],$$

the branching rules would have been quite different. In fact, since $(\mathbf{a}^\dagger \mathbf{a})^{(05)}_{05}$ is an E_α generator of $\mathscr{G}_2$ corresponding to one of the six longer roots $\boldsymbol{\alpha}$, we obtain the reduction of the representation (11) by projecting the weights onto one of these roots. The result now is

$$(11) \to 3\mathscr{D}_0 \oplus 4\mathscr{D}_{\frac{1}{2}} \oplus \mathscr{D}_1.$$

D. Inner Kronecker Products

As far as the orbital space is concerned, Eq. (15) combines pairs of operators, each belonging to the representation $\mathscr{D}_l$ of $O^+(3)$, into operators that transform according to $\mathscr{D}_k$. This is described by writing

$$\mathscr{D}_l \boxtimes \mathscr{D}_l = \sum_{k=0}^{2l} \mathscr{D}_k = \mathscr{D}_0 \oplus \mathscr{D}_1 \oplus \cdots \oplus \mathscr{D}_{2l}. \tag{22}$$

The representation $\mathscr{D}_l \boxtimes \mathscr{D}_l$ is an example of an inner *Kronecker* (direct) *product*, and Eq. (22) gives its decomposition into irreducible representations of $O^+(3)$.

The generalization to any group G is straightforward. The products $\Lambda_h \Omega_i$, constructed from quantities Λ_h and Ω_i that separately transform according to representations R and R' of G, themselves transform according to a representation of G. This representation is denoted by $R \boxtimes R'$ and is in general reducible. The group $O^+(3)$ has a special property: if R and R' are irreducible, then a given irreducible representation R'' occurs not more than once in the reduction of $R \boxtimes R'$. This is not true in general. When the multiplicity $c(RR'R'')$ exceeds unity, an additional symbol β is required to define the Clebsch-Gordan coefficients. The generalization of the coefficients for $O^+(3)$ that appear in Eq. (15) is

$$(RhR'i|RR'R''\beta j).$$

The decomposition of inner Kronecker products into their irreducible parts arises not only in atomic spectroscopy but in all branches of physics where group theory is used. It therefore seems best to treat this topic as we did the question of branching rules, and simply give references and an example. Hamermesh (*4*) gives an elementary discussion; full details can be obtained from Weyl (*16*). A knowledge of inner Kronecker products is often very useful for setting up a chain calculation for finding branching rules (*5*, *13*).

Suppose Λ_h and Ω_i are two operators with weights $\mathbf{m}$ and $\mathbf{m}'$. Following the arguments of Section III, B, this means we can write

$$[H_j, \Lambda_h] = m_j \Lambda_h, \qquad [H_j, \Omega_i] = m_j' \Omega_i,$$

for all j. It is straightforward to deduce from these equations the result

$$[H_j, \Lambda_h \Omega_i] = (m_j + m_j') \Lambda_h \Omega_i.$$

In other words, the weight of $\Lambda_h \Omega_i$ is $\mathbf{m} + \mathbf{m}'$. If we know the arrays of weights for the representations R and R', we can very easily find the array for $R \boxtimes R'$ by merely forming all possible combinations $\mathbf{m} + \mathbf{m}'$. Take, for example, the two arrays of weights (2, 1, 0, −1, −2) and (1, 0, −1) corresponding to $\mathscr{D}_2$ and $\mathscr{D}_1$ of $O^+(3)$. The rule just formulated gives

$$(3, 2, 1, 0, -1; 2, 1, 0, -1, -2; 1, 0, -1, -2, -3),$$

corresponding to $\mathscr{D}_2 \boxtimes \mathscr{D}_1$. This array is identical to

$$(3, 2, 1, 0, -1, -2, -3; 2, 1, 0, -1, -2; 1, 0, -1),$$

from which we deduce

$$\mathscr{D}_2 \boxtimes \mathscr{D}_1 = \mathscr{D}_3 \oplus \mathscr{D}_2 \oplus \mathscr{D}_1.$$

The general result

$$\mathscr{D}_S \boxtimes \mathscr{D}_L = \mathscr{D}_{S+L} \oplus \mathscr{D}_{S+L-1} \oplus \cdots \oplus \mathscr{D}_{|S-L|}$$

follows by an obvious extension of the method.

V. The Wigner-Eckart Theorem

A. Matrix Elements

Analyses of complex atoms rest on the central-field approximation. The total Hamiltonian $\mathscr{H}$ is approximated by a central part $\mathscr{H}'$; this determines the single-electron eigenfunctions but it leaves the states $|\psi\rangle$ of a configuration degenerate. This degeneracy is removed to some extent by the perturbation potential V $(=\mathscr{H} - \mathscr{H}')$, which makes itself felt in the calculations through the matrix elements $\langle\psi'|V|\psi\rangle$. A knowledge of the properties of these matrix elements is therefore of the greatest importance.

As explained in Section IV, C, group theory permits us to define a state $|\psi\rangle$ by a sequence of irreducible representations of certain groups, occasionally augmented by an additional distinguishing symbol (such as τ). The operator V, on the other hand, corresponds to interactions of physical significance, and these do not come with a complete set of group-theoretical labels attached. A preliminary problem—and one that we shall postpone for the moment—is to break V down into operators O that have well-defined properties with respect to the groups in question. Suppose $\langle\psi'|$, O, and $|\psi\rangle$ correspond to irreducible representations R, R', and R'' of a group G. A typical matrix element is defined by writing

$$\langle\gamma Ri|O(\gamma' R' i')|\gamma'' R'' i''\rangle,$$

where i, i', and i'' distinguish the components of the representations (and may, of course, define irreducible representations of subgroups of G). The symbols γ, γ', and γ'' are additional labels that are required if a representation occurs more than once among the states or operators being considered.

To evaluate the matrix element, we note that the combination $O(\gamma' R' i')|\gamma'' R'' i''\rangle$ transforms according to $R' \boxtimes R''$. It can thus be expanded in terms of certain functions $|\gamma''' \beta R''' i'''\rangle$ that form bases for the irreducible representations R''':

$$O(\gamma' R' i')|\gamma'' R'' i''\rangle = \sum_{R''', \beta, i'''} (R' R'' \beta R''' i'''|R' i', R'' i'')|\gamma''' \beta R''' i'''\rangle.$$

To form the entire matrix element, we introduce $\langle\gamma Ri|$ on both sides of this equation. The final step is to prove that $\langle\gamma Ri|\gamma''' \beta R''' i'''\rangle$ vanishes for $R \neq R'''$

or $i \neq i'''$, and that for $R = R'''$ it is independent of i. An explicit demonstration, based on Schur's lemma, can be readily constructed for finite groups (*5*). This method can be generalized to compact continuous groups without difficulty. For $O^+(3)$, we may follow Edmonds' method (*1*) and make use of the properties of the generators $\mathbf{J}$ to obtain the result. For example,

$$\begin{aligned}\langle \gamma JM | \gamma''' J''' M''' \rangle &= M^{-1} \langle \gamma JM | J_z | \gamma''' J''' M''' \rangle \\ &= M^{-1} M''' \langle \gamma JM | \gamma''' J''' M''' \rangle \,;\end{aligned}$$

and if $\langle \gamma JM | \gamma''' J''' M''' \rangle$ is not to vanish, we must have $M = M'''$. The condition $J = J'''$ follows on replacing J_z by the operator $\mathbf{J}^2$, and the invariance with respect to M can be established by using the shift operators $J_\pm$. Stone has stated that these methods can be equally well adapted to any semisimple group (*17*). The final result can thus be put in the form

$$\langle \gamma Ri | O(\gamma' R' i') | \gamma'' R'' i'' \rangle = \sum_\beta A_\beta (R' R'' \beta Ri | R' i', R'' i''), \tag{23}$$

where A_β is independent of i, i', and i''. This result is generally referred to as the Wigner-Eckart theorem (*2*, *18*). It is sometimes useful to describe A_β in detail by writing

$$A_\beta = \langle \gamma R \| O_\beta(\gamma' R') \| \gamma'' R'' \rangle.$$

The quantity on the right-hand side of this equation is called a *reduced* matrix element. The number of terms in the sum over β is $c(R' R'' R)$.

B. Single-Particle Operators

The most familiar application of the Wigner-Eckart theorem is to the group $O^+(3)$. This is because most perturbations V have well-defined properties with respect to rotations in three-dimensional space, and the quantum numbers S, L, and J that are used to describe atomic levels are simply labels for irreducible representations of this group. The fact that a level J breaks up into $2J+1$ equally spaced components when an atom is placed in a magnetic field corresponds to the fact that $(1JJM | 10JM)$ is proportional to M. The selection rule $\Delta J = 0, \pm 1$ (with $J = 0 \to J = 0$ forbidden) for electric-dipole radiation corresponds to the conditions that must be satisfied if $(1JJ'M' | 1qJM)$ is not to vanish. Examples of this kind are well known, and there is little point in taking time to describe them in detail here. We turn instead to the higher groups such as $\mathscr{G}_2$ and $O^+(2l+1)$.

The first problem is to assign representations to our operators. We are not yet in a position to provide a general solution, but we can at any rate begin with those operators of the type F (see Section III, A). It can be seen from Eq. (12) that the coefficients of the operators $a_\lambda{}^\dagger a_\nu$ are simply the matrix elements $\langle\lambda| f |\nu\rangle$ of the single-particle operator f. If the products $a_\lambda{}^\dagger a_\nu$ are considered separately, it is clear that we shall be able to treat an arbitrary operator of type F. The procedure follows the lines laid down in Section III, B, the aim being to establish a one-to-one correspondence between the operators $a_\lambda{}^\dagger a_\nu$ and certain states. As a basis for drawing such a correspondence, we introduce the operators $\bar{a}_\eta$ through Eq. (14) and use the fundamental anti-commutation relations to obtain the equations

$$[a_\xi{}^\dagger \bar{a}_\eta + a_\eta{}^\dagger \bar{a}_\xi, a_\lambda{}^\dagger \bar{a}_\nu] = (-1)^x\,[\delta(\eta,-\lambda)\, a_\xi{}^\dagger \bar{a}_\nu + \delta(\xi,-\lambda)\, a_\eta{}^\dagger \bar{a}_\nu]$$

$$+(-1)^y\,[\delta(\xi,-\nu)\, a_\lambda{}^\dagger \bar{a}_\eta + \delta(\eta,-\nu)\, a_\eta{}^\dagger \bar{a}_\xi],$$

$$(a_\xi{}^\dagger \bar{a}_\eta + a_\eta{}^\dagger \bar{a}_\xi)\, a_\lambda{}^\dagger a_\nu{}^\dagger|0\rangle = (-1)^x\,[\delta(\eta,-\lambda)\, a_\xi{}^\dagger a_\nu{}^\dagger + \delta(\xi,-\lambda)\, a_\eta{}^\dagger a_\nu{}^\dagger]|0\rangle$$

$$+(-1)^y\,[\delta(\xi,-\nu)\, a_\lambda{}^\dagger a_\eta{}^\dagger + \delta(\eta,-\nu)\, a_\eta{}^\dagger a_\xi{}^\dagger]|0\rangle,$$

where $x = s + l + m_{s\lambda} + m_{l\lambda}$ and $y = s + l + m_{s\nu} + m_{l\nu}$. The delta functions of the type $\delta(\eta,-\lambda)$ are abbreviations for the product $\delta(m_{s\eta},-m_{s\lambda})\,\delta(m_{l\eta},-m_{l\lambda})$. It is immediately apparent from the foregoing equations that the correspondence

$$a_\lambda{}^\dagger \bar{a}_\nu \leftrightarrow a_\lambda{}^\dagger a_\nu{}^\dagger|0\rangle \tag{24}$$

can be drawn for all groups whose generators are linear combinations of the operators $(a_\xi{}^\dagger \bar{a}_\eta + a_\eta{}^\dagger \bar{a}_\xi)$. Equation (15) can be used to show that this condition is equivalent to selecting only those tensors $(\mathbf{a}^\dagger \mathbf{a})^{(\kappa k)}$ for which $\kappa + k$ is odd. It follows that the correspondence (24) is valid for the group $O^+(3)$ and $O^+(2l+1)$ that occur in the reduction scheme (18); for $\mathscr{G}_2$; and for $Sp(4l+2)$ of Section IV, B. On coupling the operators on both sides of (24), we obtain the correspondence

$$(\mathbf{a}^\dagger \mathbf{a})^{(SL)}_{M_S M_L} \leftrightarrow (\mathbf{a}^\dagger \mathbf{a}^\dagger)^{(SL)}_{M_S M_L}|0\rangle = |l^2\, SLM_S M_L\rangle.$$

As an example, the classification of the states of f^2 according to the sequence

$$U(14) \supset Sp(14) \supset O_S^+(3) \times O^+(7) \supset O_S^+(3) \times \mathscr{G}_2 \supset O_S^+(3) \times O_L^+(3)$$

is given in Table III. When $S + L$ is odd, the tensor $(\mathbf{a}^\dagger \mathbf{a})^{(SL)}$ corresponds to the forbidden states of f^2. These are also included in the table. As in Table II,

TABLE III

CLASSIFICATION OF THE OPERATORS $(\mathbf{a}^{\dagger}\mathbf{a})^{(SL)}$ FOR f ELECTRONS

$U(14)$	$Sp(14)$	$O_S^+(3) \times O^+(7)$	$O_S^+(3) \times \mathcal{G}_2$	$O_S^+(3) \times O_L^+(3)$
[11]	(0000000)	$^1(000)$	$^1(00)$	^1S
	(1100000)	$^1(200)$	$^1(20)$	^1DGI
		$^3(110)$	$^3(10)$	^3F
			$^3(11)$	^3PH
[2]	(2000000)	$^3(000)$	$^3(00)$	^3S
		$^3(200)$	$^3(20)$	^3DGI
		$^1(110)$	$^1(10)$	^1F
			$^1(11)$	^1PH

the representations $\mathcal{D}_S$ are indicated by prefixed multiplicities $2S+1$, and the $\mathcal{D}_L$ by the corresponding spectroscopic symbol. From this table, we deduce, for example, that the tensor $(\mathbf{a}^{\dagger}\mathbf{a})^{(02)}$ corresponds to the classification (1100000) (200) (20) for the respective groups $Sp(14)$, $O^+(7)$, and $\mathcal{G}_2$.

C. EXAMPLES

The spin-orbit interaction provides us with a good opportunity to display the power of the Wigner-Eckart theorem. We set f equal to $\xi(r)\mathbf{s}\cdot\mathbf{l}$ in Eq. (12); the function ξ depends on the central potential in which the electrons are supposed to move, and is purely radial in character. The Clebsch-Gordan coefficients that arise when $\langle\lambda|f|\nu\rangle$ is evaluated can be used to couple the annihilation and creation operators; the radial integrals are simplified by writing

$$\zeta = \langle nl|\xi(r)|nl\rangle.$$

The result for a shell of equivalent electrons nl is

$$F = \zeta\left[\frac{l(l+1)(2l+1)}{2}\right]^{1/2}(\mathbf{a}^{\dagger}\mathbf{a})^{(11)0},$$

the final zero indicating that the spin and orbital ranks are coupled to rank zero.

The familiar application of the Wigner-Eckart theorem makes use of these ranks alone—the vanishing of $c(\mathcal{D}_S\mathcal{D}_{S'}\mathcal{D}_1)$, $c(\mathcal{D}_L\mathcal{D}_{L'}\mathcal{D}_1)$, and $c(\mathcal{D}_J\mathcal{D}_{J'}\mathcal{D}_0)$ producing the selection rules ΔS, $\Delta L = 0, \pm 1$ and $\Delta J = 0$. However, we see from Table III that for f electrons the tensor $(\mathbf{a}^{\dagger}\mathbf{a})^{(11)}$ corresponds to the sequence of representations (1100000) (110) (11). This classification forms the basis for new selection rules. For example, an analysis of the Kronecker products shows that $c((21)\,(11)\,(11))$ is zero. This implies that every matrix element of the spin-orbit interaction vanishes between a state corresponding to the representation (21) of $\mathscr{G}_2$ and one corresponding to (11).

The scarcity of tables of Clebsch-Gordan coefficients for groups such as $\mathscr{G}_2$, $O^+(7)$, and $Sp(14)$ may make it appear that applications of Eq. (23) to cases where $c(R'\,R''\,R) > 0$ are severely limited. Extremely useful results can nevertheless be obtained by directly relating sets of matrix elements without explicitly using the Clebsch-Gordan coefficients as intermediaries. For example, the terms ^3P, ^3F, and ^3H of f^2 correspond to (110) of $O^+(7)$ (see Table III), and so do the terms ^6P, ^6F, and ^6H of f^5. (A complete classification of terms of f^N is presented in Table 2-1 of Wybourne (*19*).) Furthermore, the operators $(\mathbf{a}^\dagger\mathbf{a})^{(\kappa k)}$ with k even (and greater than zero) correspond to (200) of $O^+(7)$. Now it can be shown that

$$c((200)\,(110)\,(110)) = 1.$$

We deduce that a constant A exists, independent of L, L', M_L, M_L', and k (provided k is even and greater than zero), for which

$$\langle f^{2\,3}LM_S\,M_L|(\mathbf{a}^\dagger\mathbf{a})^{(\kappa k)}_{\pi q}|\,f^{2\,3}L'\,M_S'\,M_L'\rangle = A\langle f^{5\,6}LM_S''\,M_L|(\mathbf{a}^\dagger\mathbf{a})^{(\kappa k)}_{\pi q}|\,f^{5\,6}L'\,M_S'''\,M_L'\rangle. \quad (25)$$

In the analysis of the spectra of rare-earth ions in crystals, the effect of the lattice is taken into account by expanding the electric potential it produces in spherical harmonics Y_{kq}. Owing to conservation of parity, only those harmonics need by considered for which k is even, and the harmonic Y_{00} is usually dropped because it leads to constant displacements of all the levels of the rare-earth ion. The term in the Hamiltonian that depends on Y_{kq} can be directly related to $(\mathbf{a}^\dagger\mathbf{a})^{(0k)}_{0q}$, and Eq. (25) may thus be used to express the matrix elements for f^5 in terms of those for f^2, which are much easier to calculate. This procedure was used by Axe and Dieke (*20*) in their analysis of the spectrum of Sm^{3+} substituted for La^{3+} in $LaCl_3$.

The need for using relations like Eq. (25) was relieved a few years ago by the publication of tables of matrix elements for all configurations p^N, d^N, and f^N by Nielson and Koster (*21*). The matrix elements are reduced with respect to $O^+(3)$; that is, the Wigner-Eckart theorem has been used to separate out the dependence of the matrix elements on M_S and M_L. The fact that the Wigner-Eckart theorem can be applied at any stage of a reduction scheme such as (18) means that the Clebsch-Gordan coefficients must factorize. Let the specification Ri of Eq. (23) be replaced by $R\tau ri$, where r denotes an irreducible representation of a subgroup H of G, and τ is an additional symbol that may be necessary to make the classification unambiguous. When

$c(R'R''R) = 1$, the sum over β in Eq. (23) reduces to a single term, and we see at once that we can write

$$(R'R''\beta R\tau ri|R'\tau'r'i', R''\tau''r''i'')$$
$$= \sum_{\alpha} (r'r''\alpha ri|r'i', r''i'')(\beta R\tau r|R'\tau'r' + R''\tau''r'')_{\alpha}. \qquad (26)$$

It has recently become common to refer to the coefficient on the right as an *isoscalar factor* (*22*). The symbol β is redundant for $c(R'R''R) = 1$, but by preserving it we avoid having to make any change in Eq. (26) for $c(R'R''R) > 1$. The general result was obtained by Racah (*3*). The tables of Nielson and Koster are an extremely rich source for unnormalized values of the isoscalar factors $(\beta U\tau L|U'\tau'L' + U''\tau''L'')$ and $(\beta' WU|W'U' + W''U'')$, where here, as in Section IV, C, the symbols W and U stand for irreducible representations of $O^+(7)$ and $\mathscr{G}_2$.

D. Quasispin

The representations of $Sp(4l + 2)$, as well as those of $O^+(2l + 1)$, can be used to describe the operators $(\mathbf{a}^\dagger\mathbf{a})^{(\kappa k)}$. No example has been given of this because any analysis involving $Sp(4l + 2)$ can usually be more effectively carried out in terms of quasispin. The only problem is to assign quasispin ranks K to our operators; the component ρ (the analog of π and q) is necessarily zero for an operator that leaves the number of electrons invariant. The remark was made in Section IV, B that $\mathbf{Q}$ commutes with $(\mathbf{a}^\dagger\mathbf{a})^{(\kappa k)}$ when $\kappa + k$ is odd: it follows hat for these operators, $K = 0$. To avoid having to examine in detail the commutation of the operators with $\mathbf{Q}$ when $\kappa + k$ is even, we consider in some detail the decomposition $O^+(8l + 4) \to O_Q^+(3) \times Sp(4l + 2)$. The aim is to find the representations of $O^+(8l + 4)$ that can be assigned to operators of physical interest, and then, by decomposing these representations into irreducible representations of $O_Q^+ \times Sp(4l + 2)$, find the association between representations $\mathscr{D}_K$ of $O_Q^+(3)$ and representations of $Sp(4l + 2)$.

To begin, we note that the $4l + 2$ operators $a_\lambda^\dagger$ and a_ν yield members of their own set when their commutators with the operators $\frac{1}{2}[a_\xi^\dagger, a_\eta]$ of $O^+(8l + 4)$ are calculated. They thus transform according to a representation of $O^+(8l + 4)$. To find the representation, we use the relations

$$[H_\xi, a_\lambda^\dagger] = [a_\xi^\dagger a_\xi - \tfrac{1}{2}, a_\lambda^\dagger] = \delta(\xi, \lambda)\, a_\lambda^\dagger,$$

$$[H_\xi, a_\nu] = [a_\xi^\dagger a_\xi - \tfrac{1}{2}, a_\nu] = -\delta(\xi, \nu)\, a_\nu.$$

The weights are all of the type $(00\cdots0\pm10\cdots0)$, and the representation, which is clearly irreducible, is $(10\cdots0)$. An operator comprising $\mathcal{N}$ annihilation and creation operators must therefore correspond to some component of a representation (w) of $O^+(8l+4)$ that occurs in the decomposition of $(10\cdots0)^{\mathcal{N}}$. Not all representations (w) are useful, since the eigenstates are basis functions for $(\frac{1}{2}\frac{1}{2}\cdots\frac{1}{2}\pm\frac{1}{2})$, and we must have

$$c((\tfrac{1}{2}\tfrac{1}{2}\cdots\tfrac{1}{2}\pm\tfrac{1}{2})(\tfrac{1}{2}\tfrac{1}{2}\cdots\tfrac{1}{2}\pm\tfrac{1}{2})(w))>0.$$

This is found to limit (w) to those representations $(11\cdots10\cdots0)$ that contain an even number $\mathcal{N}'$ of symbols 1 such that $\mathcal{N}'\leqq\mathcal{N}$.

The branching rules for the reduction $O^+(8l+4)\rightarrow O_Q^+(3)\times Sp(4l+2)$ are given in Table IV for $\mathcal{N}'=0$, 2, and 4. These are the only ones required

TABLE IV

BRANCHING RULES FOR $O^+(8l+4)\rightarrow O_Q^+(3)\times Sp(4l+2)$

$O^+(8l+4)$	$O_Q^+(3)\times Sp(4l+2)$
$(0\cdots0)$	$^1(0\cdots0)$
$(110\cdots0)$	$^1(20\cdots0)$
	$^3(0\cdots0)(110\cdots0)$
$(11110\cdots0)$	$^1(0\cdots0)(110\cdots0)(220\cdots0)$
	$^3(110\cdots0)(20\cdots0)(2110\cdots0)$
	$^5(0\cdots0)(110\cdots0)(11110\cdots0)$

for single-particle and two-particle operators. The representations $\mathscr{D}_K$ are given as prefixed multiplicities $2K+1$. This table was obtained from the known branching rules for the decomposition of representations $[11\cdots1]$ of $U(8l+4)$ into, on the one hand, a single irreducible representation $(11\cdots10\cdots0)$ of $O^+(8l+4)$ and, on the other, irreducible representations of $O^+(3)\times Sp(4l+2)$ (*14*). To study the tensors $(\mathbf{a}^\dagger\mathbf{a})^{(\kappa k)}$, we limit ourselves to the representations $(0\cdots0)$ and $(110\cdots0)$ of $O^+(8l+4)$. As we expect, the representation $(20\cdots0)$ of $Sp(4l+2)$, to which the tensors belong when $\kappa+k$ is odd, is associated with a quasispin rank K of zero. It can also be seen that $(110\cdots0)$, corresponding to tensors for which $\kappa+k$ is even, is associated with $K=1$. Applying the Wigner-Eckart theorem to the quasispin space, we deduce that, for such operators, matrix elements diagonal in Q show a dependence on M_Q that is given by $(1QQM_Q|10QM_Q)$. This is proportional to M_Q, that is, to $(2l+1-N)$. This simple factor expresses the dependence on N of matrix elements of, for example, the spin-orbit interaction, taken between states of the same seniority.

E. The Coulomb Interaction

Of all the two-particle interactions, the Coulomb interaction between the electrons is the most important. In the actinide and rare earth series, it constitutes the largest part of the perturbation potential V. It is responsible for the breaking up of a configuration into *terms*, that is, energy levels characterized by S and L, each one possessing a degeneracy $(2S+1)(2L+1)$. In what follows, we specialize to the f shell ($l=3$), which shows to advantage the power of the method in which group theory is used. Instead of repeating Racah's analysis (*3*), it seems preferable to adopt an approach that can be more readily extended to cope with other two-particle interactions. This modification is only practicable because of the existence today of the tables of Nielson and Koster (*21*).

The angular dependence of $1/r_{12}$ is separated out by using the addition theorem

$$\frac{e^2}{r_{12}} = \sum_{k,q} \left\{\frac{4\pi}{(2k+1)}\right\} \left(\frac{r_<^k}{r_>^{k+1}}\right) Y_{kq}^*(\theta_1, \phi_1)\, Y_{kq}(\theta_2, \phi_2), \tag{27}$$

where $r_<$ and $r_>$ are the lesser and greater, respectively, of r_1 and r_2. If we restrict our attention to the f shell, parity considerations permit us to drop terms with odd k; and in order to satisfy $c(\mathscr{D}_l \mathscr{D}_l \mathscr{D}_k) > 0$, we need not consider terms in the sum beyond $k = 2l = 6$. The first term ($k = q = 0$) is a constant and can be ignored if relative term energies alone interest us. We are left with $k = 2$, 4, and 6. It is clear that the spherical harmonics Y_{kq} for a fixed k correspond to the operators $(\mathbf{a}^\dagger \mathbf{a})_{0q}^{(0k)}$; and so, from Table III, we deduce that the spherical harmonics with $k = 2$, 4, and 6 transform according to the representation (20) of $\mathscr{G}_2$ and (200) of $O^+(7)$. It must therefore be possible to combine the product functions formed from pairs of spherical harmonics in such a way that the combinations transform according to the irreducible representations in the following inner Kronecker product decompositions:

$$(200) \boxtimes (200) = (000) \oplus (110) \oplus (200) \oplus (220) \oplus (310) \oplus (400),$$

$$(20) \boxtimes (20) = (00) \oplus (10) \oplus (11) \oplus 2(20) \oplus 2(21) \oplus (30) \oplus (22) \oplus (31) \oplus (40).$$

Since the Coulomb interaction is a scalar with respect to $O^+(3)$, our interest lies in those representations on the right of the foregoing equations that contain $\mathscr{D}_0$ when regarded as representations of $O_L^+(3)$. An analysis of the branching rules for $O^+(7) \to \mathscr{G}_2$ and $\mathscr{G}_2 \to O_L^+(3)$ shows that only three representations of $\mathscr{G}_2$ possess this property, namely (00), (22), and (40); and these representations in turn occur only in the decomposition of the respective representations (000), (220), and (400) of $O^+(7)$. It follows that for f electrons, the Coulomb interaction can be represented in terms of three operators e_1, e_2, and e_3, whose symmetry properties are described by (000)(00) $\mathscr{D}_0$, (400) (40) $\mathscr{D}_0$, and (220) (22) $\mathscr{D}_0$, respectively.

We now turn to f^2, the simplest configuration to exhibit two-particle effects. The Wigner-Eckart theorem is used to analyze as far as possible the matrix elements of the e_i. For example, the matrix elements of e_2 for the singlet terms of f^2 [which belong to (200) (20)] are proportional to

$$((400)(200)(200)(20)LM_L|(400)(40)00,(200)(20)LM_L)$$

by Eq. (23), and this coefficient simplifies to

$$((200)(20)|(400)(40)+(200)(20))((20)L|(40)0+(20)L)$$

by using Eq. (26) twice. The dependence on L is contained in the factor on the right. Apart from a trivial change in the ordering of the quantities forming the inner Kronecker product $R' \boxtimes R''$, this factor also occurs in the evaluation of the matrix elements

$$\langle f^6(220)(20)\,{}^1LM|(\mathbf{a}^\dagger\,\mathbf{a})^{(0L)}_{0M}|f^6(222)(40)\,{}^1S0\rangle.$$

The tensors $\mathbf{U}^{(k)}$ of Nielson and Koster (*21*) are related to the operators $(\mathbf{a}^\dagger\,\mathbf{a})^{(0k)}$ by the equation

$$\mathbf{U}^{(k)} = -(2)^{1/2}(2k+1)^{-1/2}(\mathbf{a}^\dagger\,\mathbf{a})^{(0k)}.$$

It is a straightforward matter to remove the dependence on M of the matrix elements and hence show that the coefficients $((20)L|(40)0+(20)L)$ are proportional to the reduced matrix elements

$$(f^6(220)(20)\,{}^1L\|U^{(L)}\|f^6(222)(40)\,{}^1S)$$

of Nielson and Koster. Their definition differs slightly from the reduced matrix elements of Section V, A, a distinction that can be maintained by using parentheses rather than angular brackets. From their tables, we immediately deduce that the matrix elements of e_2 for the terms ${}^1D$, ${}^1G$, and ${}^1I$ of f^2 can be taken to be $286E_2$, $-130E_2$, and $70E_2$, where E_2 is an undetermined proportionality constant.

This kind of analysis is repeated for other operators and other terms. The term energies, expressed as linear combinations of the proportionality constants E_i, are compared with the results of a direct calculation, which involves the Slater integrals

$$F^{(k)} = \langle (nl)^2|(r^k_</r^{k+1}_>)|(nl)^2\rangle.$$

There are more than enough equations to solve for the E_i in terms of the $F^{(k)}$. The results for the term energies are strikingly simple:

$$
\begin{aligned}
&{}^1S:\ \tfrac{54}{7}E_1 \\
&\qquad\qquad\qquad {}^3P:\ -\tfrac{9}{7}E_1 + 33E_3 \\
&{}^1D:\ \tfrac{5}{7}E_1 + 286E_2 - 11E_3 \\
&\qquad\qquad\qquad {}^3F:\ -\tfrac{9}{7}E_1 \\
&{}^1G:\ \tfrac{5}{7}E_1 - 130E_2 - 4E_3 \\
&\qquad\qquad\qquad {}^3H:\ -\tfrac{9}{7}E_1 - 9E_3. \\
&{}^1I:\ \tfrac{5}{7}E_1 + 70E_2 + 7E_3
\end{aligned}
\tag{28}
$$

Owing to our disregarding the $k = 0$ term in the expansion of r_{12}^{-1}, these results differ from those of Racah (*3*) by a constant energy.

The term energies for f^2 form the starting point for a chain calculation in which the energies for f^N are related to those of f^{N-1} by the equation

$$\langle f^N\psi|e_i|f^N\psi'\rangle = \left[\frac{N}{(N-2)}\right]\sum_{\bar\psi,\bar\psi'}(\psi\{|\bar\psi)\langle f^{N-1}\bar\psi|e_i|f^{N-1}\bar\psi'\rangle(\bar\psi'|\}\psi'). \tag{29}$$

The quantities $(\psi\{|\bar\psi)$ and $(\bar\psi'|\}\psi')$ are coefficients of fractional parentage, and are tabulated by Nielson and Koster (*21*); the factor $N/(N-2)$ merely expresses the ratio of all possible electron pairs for f^N compared to f^{N-1}. As can be imagined, it is a tedious procedure to perform the double sum of Eq. (29). It is at this point that the power of the group-theoretical method makes itself felt. For if ψ and ψ' correspond to values of W, U, and L for which the relevant isoscalar factors

$$(U0|U'L + U''L) \quad \text{and} \quad (WU|W'U' + W''U'')$$

are known, then Eq. (29) need only be used to determine the proportionality constants of the type A_β in Eq. (23). Striking as this simplification is, the use of group theory permits us to go even further. It is clear that $\mathbf{Q}^2$, like $\mathbf{S}^2$, is a sum of two-particle and one-particle operators. The latter can only shift each level of a configuration equally. Using Eq. (21), it can easily be shown that the coefficients of E_1 in the term energies (28) can be reproduced, apart from an additive constant, by

$$Q(Q+1) - S(S+1).$$

It follows that this expression must give, to within an additive constant, the coefficient of E_1 for any term of any configuration f^N.

The introduction of quasispin also simplifies the calculation of the coefficients of E_2 and E_3. As can be seen from Table III, the spherical harmonics with even rank belong to the representation (1100000) of $Sp(14)$. It can be shown that

$$(1100000) \boxtimes (1100000) = (0000000) \oplus (1100000) \oplus (2000000) \oplus (1111000) \oplus (2110000) \oplus (2200000),$$

and also that, of all the representations listed here, only (2200000) contains (400) of $O^+(7)$ in its decomposition. We see from Table IV that (2200000) is associated with a quasispin rank K of zero; this means that the matrix elements of e_2—the operator corresponding to (400)—are diagonal with respect to Q and independent of M_Q. In other words, the coefficients of E_2 are diagonal with respect to seniority and independent of N.

The representation (220), corresponding to e_3, occurs in the reduction of both (1111000) and (2200000). These representations are associated with $K = 2$ and $K = 0$. Racah found empirically that an immense simplification in the calculation of the coefficients of E_3 took place if the operator e_3 was calculated as the sum of two parts, $e_3 + \Omega$ and $-\Omega$. On making a detailed analysis, it turns out that this amounts to nothing more than separating the $K = 2$ part of e_3 from the $K = 0$ part.

The calculation of all the matrix elements of the Coulomb interaction for f^N was completed by Racah (*3*); the results are assembled by Nielson and Koster (*21*). The complete matrices for the Coulomb plus spin-orbit interaction for f^N are now available, and their diagonalization is made feasible by computers. It seems appropriate to conclude this section by taking the spectrum of Pu IV (triply ionized plutonium) as an example of the success of the theory. The ground configuration is $5f^5$, which comprises 73 LS terms. Under the action of the spin-orbit coupling, these terms break up into 198 levels. The complete interaction matrix with 198 rows and columns factorizes into smaller matrices, each one characterized by a value of J, ranging from 1/2 to 21/2. The observed energy levels of Pu^{3+} substituted for La^{3+} in $LaCl_3$ are shown in Fig. 4 on the right. The crystal field breaks up each J level into components, and in some cases neighboring levels overlap to such an extent that it is not possible to determine their separate centers of gravity; these regions are shown hatched. The energy levels on the left of Fig. 4 are the lowest 66 roots of the 198 × 198 matrix, calculated for a particular choice of the E_i and the spin-orbit coupling constant ζ. The fit between experiment and theory is good, but is further improved if two more parameters are introduced to allow

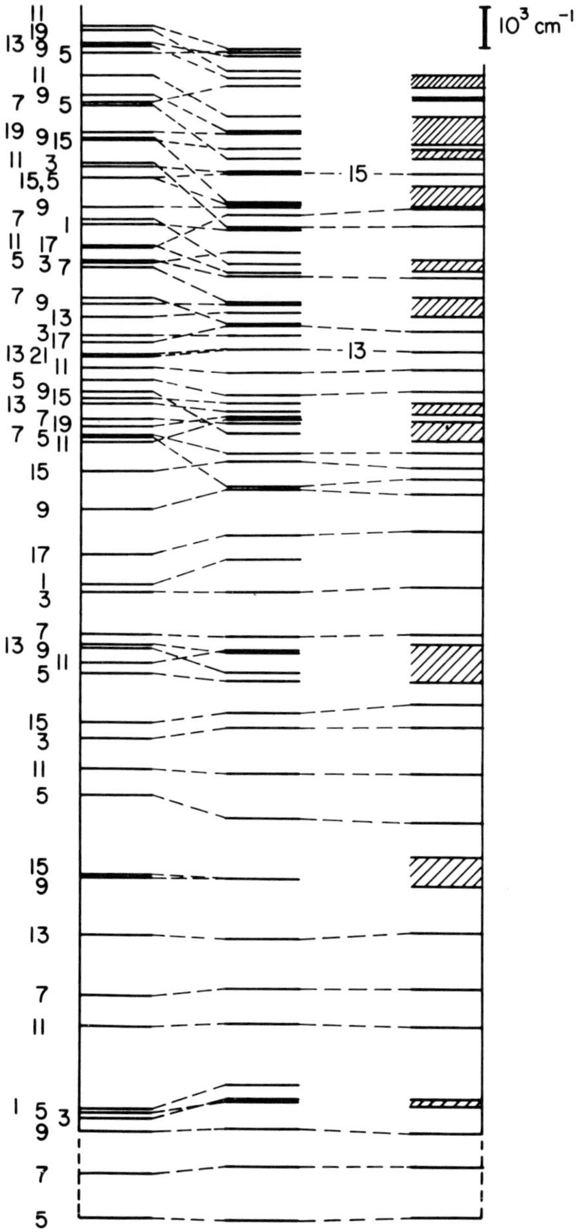

FIG. 4. The levels of Pu IV $5f^5$. The two columns of levels on the left represent the lowest 66 roots of the theoretical matrix, diagonalized under the two conditions described in the text. The observed levels are drawn on the right. The numbers specify values of $2J$.

in some measure for the effect of configuration interaction. This second calculation is shown in the center column of Fig. 4. These results are taken from the work of Lämmermann and Conway (*23*) and that of Conway and Rajnak (*24*).

VI. Conclusion

The complete matrices for the Coulomb and spin-orbit interactions in f^N are now available on magnetic tape (*25*). The basis states are defined by the irreducible representations of various groups, and it is in terms of these states that the eigenstates are expressed. For example, the ground level of Pu IV $5f^5$ is

$$0.812|(110)(11)\,^6H_{5/2}\rangle - 0.378|(211)(30)\,^4G_{5/2}\rangle \\ - 0.310|(111)(20)\,^4G_{5/2}\rangle - 0.128|(211)(21)\,^4F_{5/2}\rangle + \cdots,$$

there being in all 28 distinct states $|W\tau USLJ\rangle$ for $J = 5/2$. Calculations of crystal-field splittings or hyperfine structures must thus be carried out in the framework provided by group theory. The only configurations more complex than f^N that are likely to be encountered comprise inequivalent electrons, though sometimes different configurations overlap to such an extent that they cannot be considered separately. Elliott (*26*) has shown how group theory can be applied to mixed nuclear configurations. His use of the group $SU(3)$ in the harmonic oscillator model of the nucleus has an interesting application to the overlapping atomic configurations d^N, $d^{N-1}s$, and $d^{N-2}s^2$. These three configurations, taken together, are often written as $(d+s)^N$. The six orbital states of an electron that can be in either a d or an s shell may be regarded as forming a basis for the representation [2] of $U(3)$. The states of $(d+s)^N$ can thus be classified by representations of $U(3)$ that appear in the reduction of $[2]^N$, and for certain hypothetical values of the parameters defining the Coulomb interaction, the term energies show the high degeneracies associated with these representations. Racah (*27*) has used this property to check the matrices for $(d+s)^N$.

The group-theoretical methods for $(nl)^N$ have been recently extended by Feneuille (*28*) to mixed configurations of the type $(nl+n'l')^N$. For $(d+s)^N$, this involves using the groups $U(6)$, $O^+(6)$, $O^+(5)$, and $O^+(3)$ to classify the states. The concepts of seniority and quasispin can be carried over to the mixed configurations in a natural way.

Apart from applying group theory to new configurations, there is plenty of scope for consolidation. The analysis of f^N not only works well, it works better than one would expect. Many matrix elements of the type occurring in Eq. (23) vanish even when $c(R'R''R) > 0$; and Racah found that for the operators e_2 and $e_3 + \Omega$, the sum over β in that equation rarely had to extend to as many terms as would be expected from the numbers $c(R'R''R)$. Analogous simplifications occur when group theory is applied to mixed configurations (*28*). The difficulty in understanding these properties lies in the fact that groups such as $Sp(14)$, $O^+(7)$, and $\mathscr{G}_2$ do not lend themselves to a simple algebraic description in the same way that $O^+(3)$ does. Closed expressions are not known for the Clebsch-Gordan coefficients of the higher groups (apart from a few special cases), nor even for the numbers $c(R'R''R)$. The unexpected simplifications suggest the existence of other groups, so far undetected. An approach that makes use of the symmetric groups has yielded a few interesting results (*29*). This method uses the fact that when $R' = R''$, the inner Kronecker product $R' \boxtimes R''$ can be separated into symmetric and antisymmetric parts, thereby leading to a number of selection rules for the isoscalar factors. This has been discussed by de Swart (*30*) for $SU(3)$, and it is clear that a certain fraction of the unexpected zeros can be understood in this way. But to account for them all, it will be necessary to probe deeper into the structure of the configuration.

REFERENCES

1. A. R. Edmonds, "Angular Momentum in Quantum Mechanics." Princeton Univ. Press, Princeton, New Jersey, 1960.
2. E. P. Wigner, "Group Theory." Academic Press, New York, 1959.
3. G. Racah, *Phys. Rev.* **76**, 1352 (1949).
4. M. Hamermesh, "Group Theory and its Application to Physical Problems." Addison-Wesley, Reading, Massachusetts, 1962.
5. B. R. Judd, "Operator Techniques in Atomic Spectroscopy." McGraw-Hill, New York, 1963.
6. B. R. Judd, "Second Quantization and Atomic Spectroscopy." Johns Hopkins Press, Baltimore, Maryland, 1967.
7. E. Cartan, Sur la structure des groupes de transformations finis et continus. Thesis. Nony, Paris, 1894.
8. H. Weyl, *Math. Z.* **23**, 271 (1925); **24**, 328, 377 (1925).
9. B. L. van der Waerden, *Math. Z.* **37**, 446 (1933).
10. G. Racah, Group theory and spectroscopy. *Ergeb. Exakt. Naturw.* **37**, 28 (1965).
11. F. D. Murnaghan, "The Theory of Group Representations," Chapter 10. Johns Hopkins Press, Baltimore, Maryland, 1938.
12. M. Rotenberg, R. Bivins, N. Metropolis, and J. R. Wooten, "The 3-*j* and 6-*j* Symbols." Technology Press, Mass. Inst. of Technol., Cambridge, Massachusetts, 1959.
13. H. A. Jahn, *Proc. Roy. Soc. London Ser. A* **201**, 516 (1950).
14. B. H. Flowers, *Proc. Roy. Soc. London Ser. A* **212**, 248 (1952).
15. G. Racah, *Phys. Rev.* **63**, 367 (1943).
16. H. Weyl, "The Classical Groups," Chapter 7, Sect. 10. Princeton Univ. Press, Princeton, New Jersey, 1946.
17. A. P. Stone, *Proc. Cambridge Philos. Soc.* **57**, 460 (1961).
18. C. Eckart, *Rev. Mod. Phys.* **2**, 305 (1930).
19. B. G. Wybourne, "Spectroscopic Properties of Rare Earths." Wiley, New York, 1965.

20. J. D. Axe and G. H. Dieke, *J. Chem. Phys.* **37**, 2364 (1962).
21. C. W. Nielson and G. F. Koster, "Spectroscopic Coefficients for the p^n, d^n, and f^n Configurations." Technology Press, Mass. Inst. of Technol., Cambridge, Massachusetts, 1963.
22. A. R. Edmonds, *Proc. Roy. Soc. London Ser. A* **268**, 567 (1962).
23. H. Lämmermann and J. G. Conway, *J. Chem. Phys.* **38**, 259 (1963).
24. J. G. Conway and K. Rajnak, *J. Chem. Phys.* **44**, 348 (1966).
25. G. F. Koster and C. W. Nielson, "Energy Matrices for all Configurations of Equivalent *f* Electrons" (Magnetic Tape). Massachusetts Institute of Technology, Cambridge, Massachusetts, 1963.
26. J. P. Elliott, *Proc. Roy. Soc. London Ser. A* **245**, 128 (1958).
27. G. Racah, *Bull. Res. Council Israel Sect. F* **8**, 1 (1959).
28. S. Feneuille, *J. Phys.* **28**, 61, 315, 497, 701 (1967).
29. B. R. Judd and H. Wadzinski, *J. Mathematical Phys.* (in press).
30. J. J. de Swart, *Rev. Mod. Phys.* **35**, 916 (1963).

*Group Lattices and Homomorphisms**

F. A. MATSEN

UNIVERSITY OF TEXAS, AUSTIN, TEXAS

and

O. R. PLUMMER

UNIVERSITY OF ARKANSAS, FAYETTEVILLE, ARKANSAS

I. Introduction

The states of a physical system are characterized by a set of quantum numbers whose values can, in principle, be determined from experiment. The quantum numbers can, also in principle, be obtained from the exact Hamiltonian. Many quantum numbers are supplied by the irreducible representations of the group that commutes with the Hamiltonian. The group

* Supported by the Robert A. Welch Foundation, Houston, Texas.

of the Hamiltonian may have subgroups that also supply quantum numbers. These identify degenerate components of the several states.

The number of exact quantum numbers is often not sufficient to characterize uniquely the several states or to show correlations among states of related systems. For some systems there exist good quantum numbers that supply the necessary additional characterization and that assist in showing correlations among related states.

Good quantum numbers can be introduced by the thought process of turning off small terms in the Hamiltonian. An approximate Hamiltonian obtained in this way may commute with a group to which the group of the exact Hamiltonian is a subgroup and whose irreducible representations may provide good quantum numbers.

It is convenient to treat the groups generated in this way by *lattice theory* (see Section II). Briefly, a lattice of subgroups is a collection of chains of subgroups. At the top of the lattice is the head group to which every group in the lattice is a subgroup. At the bottom of the lattice is the tail group, which is a subgroup to all groups in the lattice.

Associated with each Hamiltonian is a lattice of subgroups, the tail group of which commutes with the Hamiltonian and supplies exact quantum numbers. If in passing down a chain each group commutes with a set of terms in the Hamiltonian of progressively lesser strength, the chain is said to be a physically significant one. The head group is the group of a zero-order Hamiltonian supplying a set of configurations (zero-order states) and the quantum numbers for these configurations. The second group in the chain commutes with a portion of the Hamiltonian that is regarded as a perturbation on the zero-order term. If the perturbation is considerably weaker than the zero-order term, configuration interaction can be neglected and good eigenvalues are obtained by diagonalizing the perturbation Hamiltonian inside each configuration. Under these circumstances the zero-order quantum numbers are good quantum numbers. This process is continued and with each step a good set of quantum numbers is supplied. The process terminates with the tail group. Thus the descent in symmetry down a physically significant chain supplies a set of good quantum numbers that can serve to characterize the states and assist in showing correlation among related states or related systems.

The diagonalization of a Hamiltonian within a configuration is simplified by symmetry adaptation of the basis of the configuration to the group of the Hamiltonian. The size of the secular equation to be solved is reduced and group-theoretical identification of the states of the Hamiltonian is made in advance.

The Hamiltonian for a set of related systems may possess the same lattice but may differ in the relative strengths of the several terms in the Hamiltonian. It is convenient to discuss such a set of systems by means of a model

Hamiltonian in which the relative strengths are treated as variables. The states of the several chains in the lattice are then functions of these parameters. The states of the several chains are correlated by means of a correlation diagram.

In the framework of lattice and perturbation theory we treat the quasi-relativistic $O(1/m^2)$ Dirac equation with varying Euclidean symmetry. The terms in the Dirac Hamiltonian that connect Euclidean (spin-free space) and spin space induce a homomorphism between the group of the full Hamiltonian and the group of the Euclidean Hamiltonian. The group of the Dirac equation for a given point is isomorphic to the double point group. In a magnetic field the appropriate groups are the Zeeman and Paschen-Back groups.

II. Groups

A. Definitions and Notation

We denote a finite group G of order g by

$$G = \{G_k, \quad k = 1 \text{ to } g\} \tag{2.1}$$

where the identity is

$$I = G_1. \tag{2.2}$$

For a continuous group, the group elements are denoted by

$$G_k = G(\mathbf{p}) \tag{2.3}$$

where

$$\mathbf{p} = p_1, \ldots, p_s \tag{2.4}$$

is a finite set of real parameters. We will use finite groups as examples, but much of the material is readily extendable to infinite groups.

Let $\hat{G}$ be a subgroup of G of order $\hat{g}$; $\hat{G}$ is a proper subgroup if $\hat{G} \neq I, G$. Each element of G can be put in the form

$$G_k \equiv G_{ja} \equiv C_j\hat{G}_a, \qquad a = 1 \text{ to } \hat{g}, \quad j = 1 \text{ to } g/\hat{g}, \tag{2.5}$$

where C_j is called a *generator* for the jth coset of $\hat{G}$ in G. The cosets are

$$C_j\hat{G} = \{C_j\hat{G}_1, \cdots, C_j\hat{G}_{\hat{g}}\} = \{G_{j1}, \ldots, G_{j\hat{g}}\}. \tag{2.6}$$

The union of cosets of $\hat{G}$ in G is G.

$$G = C_1\hat{G} \cup C_2\hat{G} \cup \cdots \cup C_{g/\hat{g}}\hat{G}. \tag{2.7}$$

$\hat{G}$ is said to be *normal* if

$$(G_k\hat{G})(G_j\hat{G}) = G_kG_j\hat{G} \tag{2.8}$$

or if

$$G_j^{-1}\hat{G}G_j = \hat{G} \qquad \text{for all} \quad G_j \in G. \tag{2.9}$$

The cosets of a normal subgroup form (under set multiplication) a group called the *factor group* of G by $\hat{G}$, denoted by $G/\hat{G}$.

A group K is said to be a *homomorphic image* of a group G if the rules of multiplication of G are preserved under the replacement of equal-number subsets of G by single elements of K. Let

$$K = \{K_a, \quad a = 1 \text{ to } k\}. \tag{2.10}$$

If the homomorphism exists, we can write

$$G = \{G_{ja}, \quad j = 1 \text{ to } h, a = 1 \text{ to } k\} \tag{2.11}$$

with $hk = g$. The homomorphism can be expressed as

$$G_{ja}G_{kb} = G_{lc} \Rightarrow K_aK_b = K_c \tag{2.12}$$

where

$$\{G_{ja}, \quad j = 1 \text{ to } h\} \to K_a \tag{2.13}$$

or

$$G \overset{h:1}{\to} K. \tag{2.14}$$

If $h = 1$, the homomorphism is an *isomorphism*, denoted

$$G \cong K. \tag{2.15}$$

The factor group $G/\hat{G}$ is a homomorphic image of G

$$G \overset{\hat{g}:1}{\to} G/\hat{G}. \tag{2.16}$$

B. Lattices of Subgroups

A *partially ordered set* is a system consisting of a set $S = \{a, b, c, \ldots\}$ and a relation $\supseteq$ satisfying the following postulates.

(i) $a \supseteq b$, $b \supseteq a$ if and only if $a = b$.

(ii) If $a \supseteq b$ and $b \supseteq c$, then $a \supseteq c$.

A *chain* is a partially ordered set S for which either $a \supseteq b$ or $b \supseteq a$ for every pair $a, b \in S$.

A *lattice* is a partially ordered set in which any two elements have a least upper bound and a greatest lower bound. The *least upper bound* u of two elements a and b is $u \equiv a \cup b$ (a union b). The *greatest lower bound* v of two elements a and b is $v \equiv a \cap b$ (a intersection b). For a finite lattice the least upper bound of the lattice is called the *head* of the lattice and the greatest lower bound is called the *tail* of the lattice. The several chains in a lattice are denoted by C^γ, γ ranging.

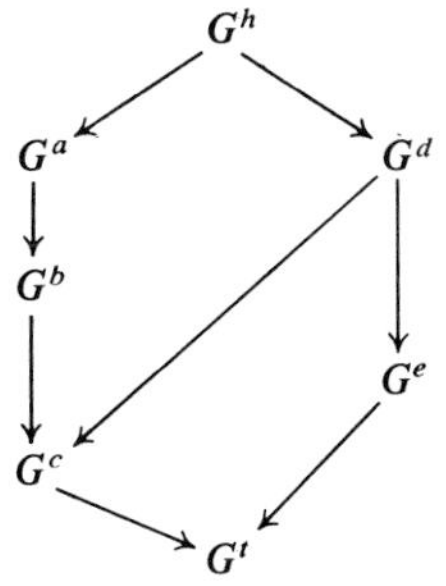

FIG. 1. A sample lattice of subgroups.

A *lattice of subgroups* (*1*) is a partially ordered set of groups in which the group–subgroup relation is the ordering relation. $G^a \supseteq G^b$ means G^b is a subgroup of G^a, $G^a \supset G^b$ means G^b is a proper subgroup of G^a. $G^a \cup G^b$ means the closure of a set union of G^a and G^b, and $G^a \cap G^b$ means their intersection. A chain of subgroups of length p is denoted

$$C^\gamma = \{G^h = G^{\gamma 1} \supset \cdots \supset G^{\gamma j} \supset \cdots \supset G^{\gamma p} = G^t\} \tag{2.17}$$

where

$$G^{\gamma j} = G^{\gamma 1} \cap G^{\gamma 2} \cap \cdots \cap G^{\gamma j} \tag{2.18}$$

is the jth subgroup in the γth chain.

An example of a lattice of subgroups is given in Fig. 1 where $\rightarrow$ replaces $\supset$. The head group is denoted G^h and the tail group G^t. Our example contains three chains. Note that

$$G^h = G^a \cup G^d \quad \text{and} \quad G^t = G^c \cap G^e;$$

$$C^1 = \{G^h \supset G^a \supset G^b \supset G^c \supset G^t\};$$

$$C^2 = \{G^h \supset G^d \supset G^c \supset G^t\};$$

$$C^3 = \{G^h \supset G^d \supset G^e \supset G^t\}.$$

C. Direct Product Groups

The *direct product* of groups G and K is a group denoted by

$$G \times K = \{G_a \times K_b, \quad a = 1 \text{ to } g \text{ and } b = 1 \text{ to } k\}. \tag{2.19}$$

The rule of multiplication is

$$(G_a \times K_b)(G_c \times K_d) = (G_a G_c) \times (K_b K_d). \tag{2.20}$$

The direct product of G with itself is denoted by

$$G \times G = \{G_a \times G_b, \quad a, b = 1 \text{ to } g\}. \tag{2.21}$$

An N-fold direct product of G with itself is denoted by

$$(G)^N \equiv G \times G \times \cdots \times G. \tag{2.22}$$

An *inner direct product* of G with itself is denoted by $G \boxtimes G$ and is defined by

$$G \boxtimes G = \{G_a \times G_a, \quad a = 1 \text{ to } g\}. \tag{2.23}$$

Note that

$$G \times G \supset G \boxtimes G \cong G. \tag{2.24}$$

An N-fold inner direct product of G is denoted by

$$[G]^N = G \boxtimes G \boxtimes \cdots \boxtimes G. \tag{2.25}$$

Note that

$$(G)^N \supset [G]^N \cong G. \tag{2.26}$$

The group $I \times K$ is a normal subgroup of $G \times K$. The cosets

$$\{(G_a \times I)(I \times K), \quad a = 1 \text{ to } g\}$$

form a factor group

$$G \times K \xrightarrow{k:1} \frac{G \times K}{I \times K} \cong G \times I \cong G. \tag{2.27}$$

Let K be a homomorphic image of G (2.11). The direct product

$$G \times K = \left\{G_{ja} \times K_b, \quad j = 1 \text{ to } \frac{g}{k}; \, a, b = 1 \text{ to } k\right\} \tag{2.28}$$

is called a *subdirect product group*. Analogously to (2.22) the group

$$G \boxtimes K = \left\{ G_{ja} \times K_a, \quad j = 1 \text{ to } \frac{g}{k}; a = 1 \text{ to } k \right\} \tag{2.29}$$

is called an *inner subdirect product* group. We note that

$$G \times K \supset G \boxtimes K \cong G. \tag{2.30}$$

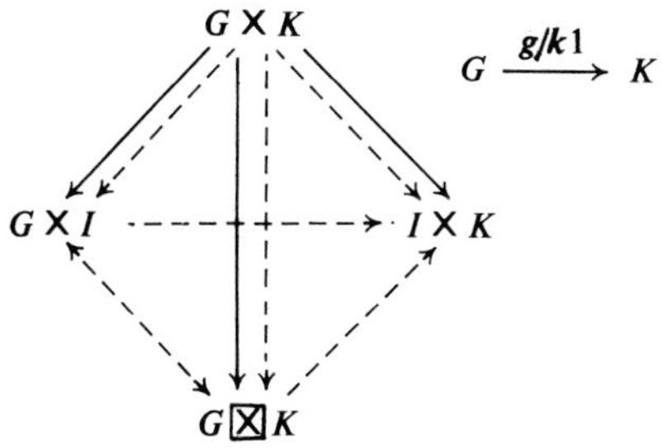

FIG. 2. A lattice of subgroups and homomorphisms.

Because of the homomorphism between G and K and because of the homomorphisms implicit in direct products, the lattice of $G \times K$ exhibits a number of homomorphisms (see Fig. 2). The homomorphisms in Fig. 2 are denoted by dotted arrows that are two headed for isomorphisms.

D. The Lattice of a Hamiltonian

Let

$$\mathscr{H} = \sum_{i=1}^{n} \mathscr{H}(G^i) \tag{2.31}$$

be a Hamiltonian and G^i a group such that

$$[\mathscr{H}(G^i), G^i] = 0. \tag{2.32}$$

The n groups G^i, $i = 1$ to n, generate a lattice with chains

$$C^\gamma = \{G^h = G^{\gamma 1} \cdots G^{\gamma j} \cdots G^{\gamma p}\}. \tag{2.33}$$

We define the (γj)th truncated Hamiltonian by

$$\mathbf{H}(G^{\gamma j}) = \sum_i \delta(\gamma j, i)\mathscr{H}(G^i) \tag{2.34}$$

where

$$\begin{aligned} \delta(\gamma f, i) &= 1 \qquad \text{if} \quad G^i \cap G^{\gamma f} = G^{\gamma f}; \\ \delta(\gamma f, i) &= 0 \qquad \text{otherwise.} \end{aligned} \tag{2.35}$$

If

$$\mathscr{H}(G^{\gamma j}) >> \mathscr{H}(G^{\gamma j+1}), \tag{2.36}$$

where $\mathscr{H}(G^{\gamma j}) = \mathbf{H}(G^{\gamma j}) - \mathbf{H}(G^{\gamma j-1})$, C^γ is said to be the physically significant chain of $\mathscr{H}$. For example, let

$$\mathscr{H} = \mathscr{H}(G^a) + \mathscr{H}(G^b) + \mathscr{H}(G^c)$$

where

$$G^b \cup G^c = G^a \qquad \text{and} \qquad G^b \cap G^c = G^d;$$

then

$$[\mathscr{H}, G^d] = 0.$$

The lattice of $\mathscr{H}$ is

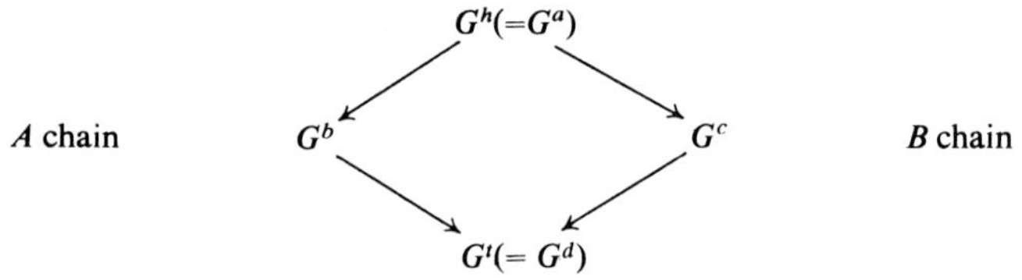

A chain: $\{G^{A1} \supset G^{A2} \supset G^{A3}\} \equiv \{G^a \supset G^b \supset G^d\}$

$\mathbf{H}(G^{A1}) = \mathscr{H}(G^a),$
$\mathbf{H}(G^{A2}) = \mathscr{H}(G^a) + \mathscr{H}(G^b),$
$\mathbf{H}(G^{A3}) = \mathscr{H}(G^a) + \mathscr{H}(G^b) + \mathscr{H}(G^c) = \mathscr{H};$

B chain: $\{G^{B1} \supset G^{B2} \supset G^{B3}\} \equiv \{G^a \supset G^c \supset G^d\}$

$\mathbf{H}(G^{B1}) = \mathscr{H}(G^a),$
$\mathbf{H}(G^{B2}) = \mathscr{H}(G^a) + \mathscr{H}(G^c),$
$\mathbf{H}(G^{B3}) = \mathscr{H}(G^a) + \mathscr{H}(G^c) + \mathscr{H}(G^b) = \mathscr{H}.$

Note that

$\mathscr{H}(G^b) = \mathscr{H}(G^{A2}),$
$\mathscr{H}(G^c) = \mathscr{H}(G^{B2}).$

III. Symmetry Adaptation of Vector Spaces

A: Introduction

We denote a finite vector space by $\mathfrak{B}$ and a general basis of $\mathfrak{B}$ by

$$B^\nu = \{|\nu; i\rangle; \quad i = 1 \text{ to } f^\nu\}. \tag{3.1}$$

Let G be a group of operators on $\mathfrak{B}$. In particular, the group operators transform B^ν according to

$$G_a|\nu; i\rangle = \sum_j^{f^\nu} [G_a]^\nu_{ji}|\nu; j\rangle. \tag{3.2}$$

Here $[G_a]^\nu_{ji}$ is the (j, i)th element in the $f^\nu \times f^\nu$ matrix $[G_a]^\nu$ that represents G_a in the representation $\Gamma^\nu(G)$ of G.

A basis is said to be *symmetry adapted* [this phrase was introduced by Melvin (*3*)] to G if it transforms according to the irreducible representations $\Gamma^\alpha(G)$ of G. We denote a symmetry-adapted basis by

$$B^{\nu S} = \{|\nu; \rho\alpha r\rangle; \quad \rho = 1 \text{ to } f^{\nu\alpha}, r = 1 \text{ to } f^\alpha, \alpha = 1 \text{ to } M\}. \tag{3.3}$$

Then

$$G_a|\nu; \rho\alpha r\rangle = \sum_s^{f^\alpha} [G_a]^\alpha_{sr}|\nu; \rho\alpha s\rangle \tag{3.4}$$

where $[G_a]^\alpha_{sr}$ is the (s, r)th matrix element in the $f^\alpha \times f^\alpha$ matrix $[G_a]^\alpha$ that represents G_a in the αth irreducible representation $\Gamma^\alpha(G)$.

The symmetry adaptation decomposes $\mathfrak{B}$ into subspaces that are invariant under G

$$\mathfrak{B} = \sum_\alpha \sum_\rho \mathfrak{B}(\rho\alpha). \tag{3.5}$$

The basis of $\mathfrak{B}(\rho\alpha)$ is

$$B(\rho\alpha) = \{|\nu; \rho\alpha r\rangle; \quad r = 1 \text{ to } f^\alpha\}. \tag{3.6}$$

The dimension statement is

$$f^\nu = \sum_\alpha f^{\nu\alpha} f^\alpha. \tag{3.7}$$

For a finite group

$$f^{\nu\alpha} = \left(\frac{1}{g}\right) \sum_a^g \chi^\nu(G_a)\chi^\alpha(G_a^{-1}) \tag{3.8}$$

where

$$\chi^{\nu}(G_a) = \sum_{i}^{f^{\nu}} [G_a]^{\nu}_{ii}, \tag{3.9}$$

$$\chi^{\alpha}(G_a) = \sum_{r}^{f^{\alpha}} [G_a]^{\alpha}_{rr}. \tag{3.10}$$

A basis that is symmetry adapted to a finite group can be constructed with the help of the group (Frobenius) algebra $A(G)$ (2). $A(G)$ has a unitary matric basis

$$\eta = \{e^{\alpha}_{rs};\quad \alpha = 1 \text{ to } M;\, r, s = 1 \text{ to } f^{\alpha}\} \tag{3.11}$$

such that

$$e^{\alpha}_{rs} = \left(\frac{f^{\alpha}}{g}\right) \sum_{a}^{g} [G_a^{-1}]^{\alpha}_{sr} G_a \tag{3.12}$$

$$e^{\alpha}_{rs} e^{\beta}_{tu} = \delta(\alpha, \beta)\, \delta(s, t) e^{\alpha}_{ru} \tag{3.13}$$

and

$$G_a e^{\alpha}_{rt} = \sum_{s}^{f^{\alpha}} [G_a]^{\alpha}_{sr} e^{\alpha}_{st}. \tag{3.14}$$

By (3.12) the ket

$$|\nu; i; \alpha rs\rangle \equiv e^{\alpha}_{rs} |\nu; i\rangle \tag{3.15}$$

transforms according to (3.4) so it is symmetry adapted to G. Some of the $|\nu; i; \alpha rs\rangle$ are zero and some may be linearly dependent. We obtain a symmetry-adapted basis by forming f^{ν} linearly independent kets

$$|\nu; \rho\alpha r\rangle = \sum_{i}^{f^{\nu}} \sum_{s}^{f^{\alpha}} |\nu; i; \alpha rs\rangle \langle \nu; i; \alpha rs | \rho\alpha\rangle. \tag{3.16}$$

We note that

$$|\nu; \rho\alpha r\rangle = e^{\alpha}_{rs} |\nu; \rho\alpha s\rangle. \tag{3.17}$$

If $\hat{G}$ is a subgroup of G, the kets can, in addition, be symmetry adapted to $\hat{G}$. These are designated $|\nu; \rho(G)\alpha(G); \rho(\hat{G})\alpha(\hat{G})r(\hat{G})\rangle$ where $\rho(\hat{G}) = 1$ to $f^{\alpha(G)\alpha(\hat{G})}$, $\alpha(\hat{G}) = 1$ to $M(\hat{G})$ and $r(\hat{G}) = 1$ to $f^{\alpha(\hat{G})}$.

The symmetry adaptation to the chain $G \supset \hat{G}$ decomposes $\mathfrak{B}(\rho(G)\alpha(G))$ into spaces that are invariant under $\hat{G}$

$$\mathfrak{B}(\rho(G)\alpha(G)) = \sum_{\rho(\hat{G})} \sum_{\alpha(\hat{G})} \mathfrak{B}(\rho(G)\alpha(G); \rho(\hat{G})\alpha(\hat{G})). \tag{3.18}$$

The basis of $\mathfrak{B}(\rho(G)\alpha(G); \rho(\hat{G})\alpha(\hat{G}))$ is

$$B(\rho(G)\alpha(G); \rho(\hat{G})\alpha(\hat{G})) = \{|\nu; \rho(G)\alpha(G); \rho(\hat{G})\alpha(\hat{G})r(\hat{G})\rangle,\quad r(\hat{G}) = 1 \text{ to } f^{\alpha(\hat{G})}\}. \tag{3.19}$$

The dimension statement is

$$f^{\nu} = \sum_{\alpha(G)} f^{\nu\alpha(G)} f^{\alpha(G)} = \sum_{\alpha(G)} f^{\nu\alpha(G)} \sum_{\alpha(\hat{G})} f^{\alpha(G)\alpha(\hat{G})} f^{\alpha(\hat{G})}. \tag{3.20}$$

The kets transform under $\hat{G}$ according to

$$\hat{G}_a|\nu;\, \rho(G)\alpha(G);\, \rho(\hat{G})\alpha(\hat{G})r(\hat{G})\rangle = \sum_{s(\hat{G})}^{f^{\alpha(\hat{G})}} [\hat{G}_a]^{\alpha(\hat{G})}_{s(\hat{G})r(\hat{G})} \cdot |\nu;\, \rho(G)\alpha(G);\, \rho(\hat{G})\alpha(\hat{G})s(\hat{G})\rangle. \tag{3.21}$$

A ket that is symmetry adapted to the chain

$$C^{\gamma} = \{G^h = G^{\gamma 1} \supset \cdots \supset G^{\gamma j} \supset \cdots \supset G^{\gamma p} = G^t\} \tag{3.22}$$

is written

$$|\nu;\, \rho(G^{\gamma 1})\alpha(G^{\gamma 1});\, \ldots;\, \rho(G^{\gamma j})\alpha(G^{\gamma j});\, \ldots;\, \rho(G^{\gamma p})\alpha(G^{\gamma p})r(G^{\gamma p})\rangle.$$

The range of $\rho(G^{\gamma j+1})$ is 1 to $f^{\alpha(G^{\gamma j})\alpha(G^{\gamma j+1})}$. (3.23)

B. The Eigenvector Problem; Perturbation Theory

We take the vector space $\mathfrak{B}$ as a vector space for a Hamiltonian $\mathscr{H}$. The eigenvalues and eigenvectors of $\mathscr{H}$ in $\mathfrak{B}$ are determined by diagonalizing the representation $[\mathscr{H}]^{\nu}$ of $\mathscr{H}$ in the basis B^{ν} where

$$[\mathscr{H}]^{\nu}_{ij} = \langle\nu;\, i|\mathscr{H}|\nu;\, j\rangle. \tag{3.24}$$

We denote the eigenvalues and eigenvectors by E_K and $|\nu;\, K\rangle$, $K = 1$ to f^{ν}.

If

$$\mathscr{H} = \mathscr{H}(G) \tag{3.25}$$

where

$$[\mathscr{H}(G),\, G] = 0, \tag{3.26}$$

it is convenient to use a basis

$$B^{\nu S} = \{|\nu;\, \rho\alpha r\rangle;\quad \rho = 1 \text{ to } f^{\nu\alpha},\ r = 1 \text{ to } f^{\alpha},\ \alpha = 1 \text{ to } M\}, \tag{3.27}$$

which is symmetry adapted to G. The matrix elements over a symmetry-adapted basis are

$$\langle\nu;\, \rho\alpha r|\mathscr{H}|\nu;\, \rho'\alpha' r'\rangle = \delta(\alpha, \alpha')\,\delta(r, r')\langle\nu;\, \rho\alpha\|\mathscr{H}\|\nu;\, \rho'\alpha\rangle. \tag{3.28}$$

An algebraic derivation for finite groups is as follows. By (3.17) and (3.26)

$$\begin{aligned}\langle \nu;\, \rho\alpha r|\mathscr{H}|\nu;\, \rho'\alpha' r'\rangle &= \langle \nu;\, \rho\alpha s|e^{\alpha}_{sr}\mathscr{H} e^{\alpha'}_{r's'}|\nu;\, \rho'\alpha' s'\rangle \\ &= \delta(\alpha,\, \alpha')\,\delta(r,\, r')\,\langle \nu;\, \rho\alpha s|\mathscr{H} e^{\alpha}_{ss'}|\nu;\, \rho'\alpha s'\rangle. \end{aligned} \tag{3.29}$$

Now for any t and by (3.17)

$$\begin{aligned}\langle \nu;\, \rho\alpha s|\mathscr{H} e^{\alpha}_{ss'}|\nu;\, \rho'\alpha s'\rangle &= \langle \nu;\, \rho\alpha s|e^{\alpha}_{st}\mathscr{H} e^{\alpha}_{ts'}|\nu;\, \rho'\alpha s'\rangle \\ &= \langle \nu;\, \rho\alpha t|\mathscr{H}|\nu; \rho'\alpha t\rangle \\ &\equiv \langle \nu;\, \rho\alpha\|\mathscr{H}\|\nu;\, \rho'\alpha\rangle \qquad \text{(independent of } t). \end{aligned} \tag{3.30}$$

In the symmetry-adapted basis the $f^{\nu} \times f^{\nu}$ dimensional matrix is factored into blocks, each characterized by α. Each of these blocks, in turn, is factored into f^{α} identical blocks of dimension $f^{\nu\alpha} \times f^{\nu\alpha}$. We denote the eigenvalues and eigenkets by E^{α}_{K} and $|\nu;\, K\alpha r\rangle$. The K, αth level is f^{α}-fold degenerate; α is the quantum number supplied by G. If $f^{\nu\alpha} = 1$, the symmetry-adapted kets are eigenkets.

If

$$\mathscr{H} = \mathscr{H}(G) + \mathscr{H}(\hat{G}) \tag{3.31}$$

where

$$G \supset \hat{G}, \tag{3.32}$$

we have, for the lattice,

$$G^{h} = G \cup \hat{G} = G \tag{3.33}$$

and

$$G^{t} = G \cap \hat{G} = \hat{G}. \tag{3.34}$$

Note that

$$[\mathscr{H},\, G^{t}] = 0. \tag{3.35}$$

The matrix elements over a basis that is symmetry adapted to the chain $G \supset \hat{G}$ are given by

$$\begin{aligned}&\langle \nu;\, \rho(G)\alpha(G);\, \rho(\hat{G})\alpha(\hat{G})r(\hat{G})|\mathscr{H}|\nu;\, \rho'(G)\alpha'(G);\, \rho'(\hat{G})\alpha'(\hat{G})r'(\hat{G})\rangle \\ &\quad = \delta(\alpha(\hat{G}),\, \alpha'(\hat{G}))\,\delta(r(\hat{G}),\, r'(\hat{G})) \times \\ &\{\delta(\alpha(G),\, \alpha'(G))\,\langle \nu;\, \rho(G)\alpha(G)\|\mathscr{H}(G)\|\nu;\, \rho'(G)\alpha(G)\rangle \\ &\qquad + \langle \nu;\, \rho(G)\alpha(G);\, \rho(\hat{G})\alpha(\hat{G})\|\mathscr{H}(\hat{G})\|\nu;\, \rho'(G)\alpha'(G);\, \rho'(\hat{G})\alpha(\hat{G})\rangle\}; \end{aligned} \tag{3.36}$$

$\alpha(\hat{G})$ and $r(\hat{G})$ are *exact* quantum numbers.

The eigenkets to $\mathscr{H}(G)$, denoted by $|\nu;\, K\alpha r\rangle$, $K = 1$ to $f^{\nu\alpha}$, are symmetry adapted to G. They can, in addition, be symmetry adapted to $\hat{G}$. These are denoted by

$$|\nu;\, K(G)\alpha(G);\, \rho(\hat{G})\alpha(\hat{G})r(\hat{G})\rangle. \tag{3.37}$$

We call this ket a *symmetry adapted* (eigen)ket, to distinguish it from the general symmetry adapted ket (3.19). The matrix elements over the symmetry-adapted (eigen)ket basis are

$$\begin{aligned}&\langle \nu;\, K(G)\alpha(G);\, \rho(\hat{G})\alpha(\hat{G})r(\hat{G})|\mathscr{H}|\nu;\, K'(G)\alpha'(G);\, \rho'(\hat{G})\alpha'(\hat{G})r'(\hat{G})\rangle\\ &\quad = \delta(\alpha(\hat{G}),\, \alpha'(\hat{G}))\,\delta(r(\hat{G}),\, r'(\hat{G}))\,\{\delta(\alpha(G),\, \alpha'(G))\,\delta(K(G),\, K'(G))\,\delta(\rho(\hat{G}),\, \rho'(\hat{G}))\\ &\qquad \cdot \langle \nu;\, K(G)\alpha(G)\|\mathscr{H}(G)\|\nu;\, K(G)\alpha(G)\rangle\\ &\qquad + \langle \nu;\, K(G)\alpha(G);\, \rho(\hat{G})\alpha(\hat{G})\|\mathscr{H}(\hat{G})\|\nu;\, K'(G)\alpha'(G);\, \rho'(\hat{G})\alpha(\hat{G})\rangle\}. \end{aligned} \tag{3.38}$$

If $\mathscr{H}(\hat{G}) << \mathscr{H}(G)$,

$$\begin{aligned}&\langle \nu;\, K(G)\alpha(G);\, \rho(\hat{G})\alpha(\hat{G})r(\hat{G})|\mathscr{H}|\nu;\, K'(G)\alpha'(G);\, \rho'(\hat{G})\alpha'(\hat{G})r'(\hat{G})\rangle\\ &\quad \approx \delta(\alpha(\hat{G}),\, \alpha'(\hat{G}))\,\delta(r(\hat{G}),\, r'(\hat{G}))\,\delta(\alpha(G),\, \alpha'(G))\,\delta(K(G),\, K'(G))\\ &\qquad \cdot \{\langle \nu;\, K(G)\alpha(G)\|\mathscr{H}(G)\|\nu;\, K(G)\alpha(G)\rangle\,\delta(\rho'(\hat{G}),\, \rho(\hat{G}))\\ &\qquad + \langle \nu;\, K(G)\alpha(G);\, \rho(\hat{G})\alpha(\hat{G})\|\mathscr{H}(\hat{G})\|\nu;\, K(G)\alpha(G);\, \rho'(\hat{G})\alpha(\hat{G})\rangle\}. \end{aligned} \tag{3.39}$$

The approximation in (3.39) is that of first-order perturbation theory. Thus

$$\mathscr{H} = \mathscr{H}^0 + \mathscr{H}', \tag{3.40}$$

$$\mathscr{H}^0 = \mathscr{H}(G), \tag{3.41}$$

$$\mathscr{H}' = \mathscr{H}(\hat{G}). \tag{3.42}$$

The kets $|\nu;\, K(G)\alpha(G);\, \rho(\hat{G})\alpha(\hat{G})r(\hat{G})\rangle$, with $K(G)$ and $\alpha(G)$ fixed, are zero-order kets to the perturbation $\mathscr{H}(\hat{G})$. They span a subspace or a *configuration* of the space $\mathscr{H}(G)$. The approximation (3.39) neglects *configuration interaction* between states of different $K(G)$ and $\alpha(G)$. If this approximation is valid, $K(G)$ and $\alpha(G)$ are *good* quantum numbers. The perturbation $\mathscr{H}(\hat{G})$ splits the f^{α}-fold degeneracy of the zero-order states. This splitting is an example of the removal of degeneracy by a descent in symmetry.

Consider the γth chain of length p (Section II,D)

$$C^{\gamma} = \{G^h \supset \cdots \supset G^{\gamma j} \supset \cdots \supset G^t\} \tag{3.43}$$

in a lattice of subgroups and a Hamiltonian

$$\mathscr{H} = \sum_i^n \mathscr{H}(G^i). \tag{3.44}$$

If

$$\mathscr{H}(G^{\gamma j}) >> \mathscr{H}(G^{\gamma j+1}), \tag{3.45}$$

so that the perturbation theory applies, we can construct a symmetry-adapted (eigen)ket basis to the chain C^{γ} of length p

$$|\nu; K(G^{\gamma 1})\alpha(G^{\gamma 1}); \ldots; K(G^{\gamma j})\alpha(G^{\gamma j}); \ldots; \rho(G^{\gamma p})\alpha(G^{\gamma p})r(G^{\gamma p})\rangle. \quad (3.46)$$

To construct these kets $\mathscr{H}(G^{\gamma 1})$ is diagonalized in the ν basis. Next $\mathscr{H}(G^{\gamma 2})$ is diagonalized in $\mathfrak{B}(K(G^{\gamma 1})\alpha(G^{\gamma 1}))$, and so on. The matrix elements are

$$\begin{aligned}
&\langle \nu; K(G^{\gamma 1})\alpha(G^{\gamma 1}); \ldots; K(G^{\gamma j})\alpha(G^{\gamma j}); \ldots; \rho(G^{\gamma p})\alpha(G^{\gamma p})r(G^{\gamma p})|\mathscr{H}|\nu;\\
&\quad K'(G^{\gamma 1})\alpha'(G^{\gamma 1}); \ldots; K'(G^{\gamma j})\alpha'(G^{\gamma j}); \ldots; \rho'(G^{\gamma p})\alpha'(G^{\gamma p})r'(G^{\gamma p})\rangle\\
&\quad \simeq \delta(\alpha(G^{\gamma p}), \alpha'(G^{\gamma p}))\, \delta(r(G^{\gamma p}), r'(G^{\gamma p}))\, \delta(K(G^{\gamma 1}), K'(G^{\gamma 1}))\\
&\qquad \cdot \delta(\alpha(G^{\gamma 1}), \alpha'(G^{\gamma 1})) \cdots \delta(K(G^{\gamma p-1}), K'(G^{\gamma p-1}))\, \delta(\alpha(G^{\gamma p-1}), \alpha'(G^{\gamma p-1}))\\
&\qquad \Bigg\{ \sum_{i=1}^{p-1} \{\langle \nu; K(G^{\gamma 1})\alpha(G^{\gamma 1}); \ldots; K(G^{\gamma i})\alpha(G^{\gamma i})\|\mathscr{H}(G^{\gamma i})\|\nu; K(G^{\gamma 1})\alpha(G^{\gamma 1});\\
&\qquad \ldots; K(G^{\gamma i})\alpha(G^{\gamma i})\rangle\} + \langle \nu; K(G^{\gamma 1})\alpha(G^{\gamma 1});\\
&\qquad \ldots; \rho(G^{\gamma p})\alpha(G^{\gamma p})\|\mathscr{H}(G^{\gamma p})\|\nu; K(G^{\gamma 1})\alpha(G^{\gamma 1}); \ldots; \rho'(G^{\gamma p})\alpha(G^{\gamma p})\rangle\} \Bigg\}.
\end{aligned} \quad (3.47)$$

The Hamiltonian $\mathbf{H}(G^{\gamma j})$ is the zero-order Hamiltonian for the perturbation $\mathscr{H}(G^{\gamma j+1})$, which splits the degeneracy in the states of $\mathbf{H}(G^{\gamma j})$. The perturbation is always taken in first-order and configuration interaction among the states of $\mathbf{H}(G^{\gamma j})$ is neglected. If (3.45) holds, the neglect of configuration interaction is justified so the $K(G^{\gamma j})$, $\alpha(G^{\gamma j})$ are good quantum numbers and C^{γ} is a physically significant chain. Again $\alpha(G^{\gamma p})$ and $r(G^{\gamma p})$ are exact quantum numbers.

The Hamiltonian for a set of related systems may possess the same lattice but may differ in the relative strengths of the several terms in the Hamiltonian. It is convenient to discuss such a set by means of a model Hamiltonian in which the relative strengths are treated as variables. By appropriate choice of strengths, a particular chain is made physically significant so that the subspaces related to this chain provide good quantum numbers for the system. By a continuous change in strengths, physical significance is transformed from one chain to another. The states of the several chains are correlated by means of a correlation diagram. In a correlation diagram the states of the two chains that possess the same quantum number (or numbers) under the terminal group of the Hamiltonian are linked with the proviso that states with the same terminal group quantum numbers do not cross. Such diagrams contribute to understanding of the infamous "intermediate case" for which only the exact quantum numbers are good quantum numbers. A sample lattice and correlation diagram is given in Fig. 3.

Hamiltonian

$$\mathscr{H} = \mathscr{H}(G^a) + \mathscr{H}(G^b) + \mathscr{H}(G^c)$$

A chain

$\mathbf{H}(G^{A1}) = \mathscr{H}(G^a)$
$\mathbf{H}(G^{A2}) = \mathscr{H}(G^a) + \mathscr{H}(G^b)$
$\mathbf{H}(G^{A3}) = \mathscr{H}$
$G^{A1} \supset G^{A2} \supset G^{A3}$

B chain

$\mathbf{H}(G^{B1}) = \mathscr{H}(G^a)$
$\mathbf{H}(G^{B2}) = \mathscr{H}(G^a) + \mathscr{H}(G^c)$
$\mathbf{H}(G^{B3}) = \mathscr{H}$
$G^{B1} \supset G^{B2} \supset G^{B3}$

Lattice

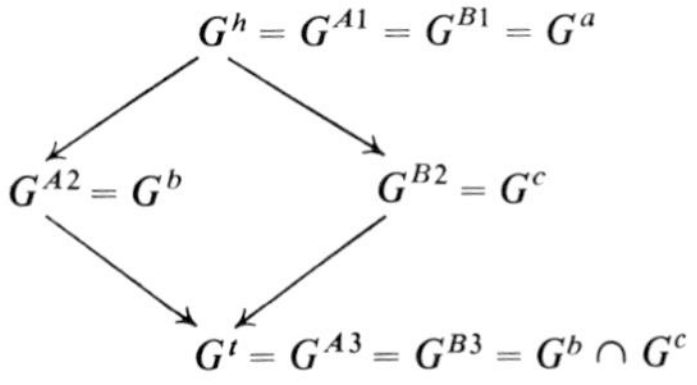

Correlation diagram ($f^{\alpha(G^{\gamma_j})\alpha(G^{\gamma_{j+1}})} = 1$)

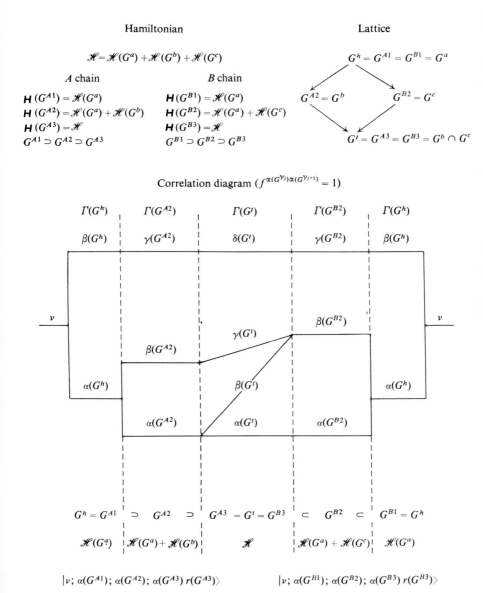

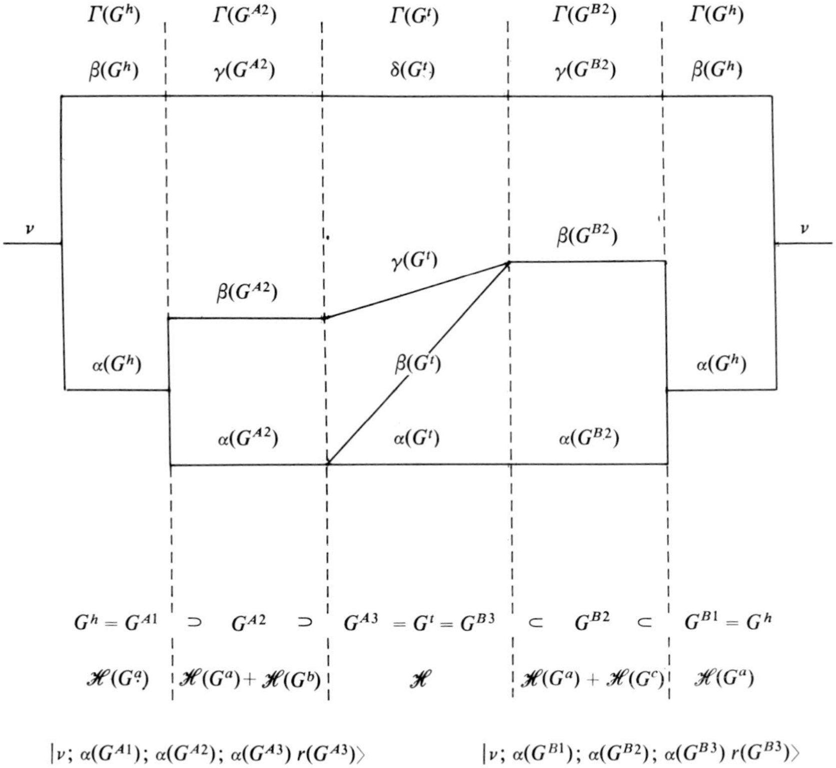

$|\nu;\ \alpha(G^{A1});\ \alpha(G^{A2});\ \alpha(G^{A3})\ r(G^{A3})\rangle$ $\qquad$ $|\nu;\ \alpha(G^{B1});\ \alpha(G^{B2});\ \alpha(G^{B3})\ r(G^{B3})\rangle$

FIG. 3. A sample Hamiltonian, its lattice, and a correlation diagram.

C. Symmetry Adaptation of Product Spaces

The invariant subspaces of a direct product group $G \times K$ is the product $\mathfrak{B}^{\alpha(G)} \times \mathfrak{B}^{\alpha(K)}$ of the invariant subspaces of the separate groups. The dimension of $\mathfrak{B}^{\alpha(G)} \times \mathfrak{B}^{\alpha(K)}$ is $f^{\alpha(G)} \times f^{\alpha(K)}$ with basis elements $|\alpha(G)r(G)\rangle|\alpha(K)r(K)\rangle$ that transform according to

$$G_a \times K_b|\alpha(G)r(G)\rangle\,|\alpha(K)r(K)\rangle$$
$$= \sum_{r'(G)} \sum_{r'(K)} [G_a]^{\alpha(G)}_{r'(G)r(G)} [K_b]^{\alpha(K)}_{r'(K)r(K)} |\alpha(G)r'(G)\rangle\,|\alpha(K)r'(K)\rangle. \tag{3.48}$$

This transformation defines an irreducible representation $\Gamma^{\alpha(G)} \times \Gamma^{\alpha(K)}$ of $G \times K$.

The symmetrical direct product group $G \times G$ (i.e., $G = K$) has a subgroup $G \boxtimes G$ called its inner direct product. It has elements $G_a \times G_a$ isomorphic to G and has the same irreducible representations as G.

We wish to construct from the product space $\mathfrak{B}^{\alpha_1} \times \mathfrak{B}^{\alpha_2}$, kets that transform under $G \boxtimes G$ according to the irreducible representations Γ^{α} of G or $G \boxtimes G$; that is, kets that are *symmetry adapted* to the chain $G \times G \supset G \boxtimes G$. These kets have the form

$$|\alpha_1\alpha_2;\,\rho\alpha r\rangle = \sum_{r_1}^{f^{\alpha_1}} \sum_{r_2}^{f^{\alpha_2}} |\alpha_1 r_1\rangle\,|\alpha_2 r_2\rangle\langle\alpha_1\alpha_2 r_1 r_2|\rho\alpha r\rangle \tag{3.49}$$

and they transform according to

$$G_a \boxtimes G_a|\alpha_1\alpha_2;\,\rho\alpha r\rangle = \sum_{r'}^{f^{\alpha}} [G_a]^{\alpha}_{r'r}|\alpha_1\alpha_2;\,\rho\alpha r'\rangle. \tag{3.50}$$

The brackets $\langle\alpha_1\alpha_2 r_1 r_2|\rho\alpha r\rangle$ are called coupling or Clebsch-Gordan coefficients. The range of ρ is from 1 to $f^{\alpha_1\alpha_2\alpha}$. The dimension statement is

$$f^{\alpha_1} \times f^{\alpha_2} = \sum_{\alpha} f^{\alpha_1\alpha_2\alpha} \times f^{\alpha}. \tag{3.51}$$

For finite groups

$$f^{\alpha_1\alpha_2\alpha} = \frac{1}{g}\sum_a \chi^{\alpha_1}(G_a)\chi^{\alpha_2}(G_a)\chi^{\alpha}(G_a^{-1}). \tag{3.52}$$

Symmetry-adapted bases are conveniently obtained from the matric basis elements of $G \boxtimes G$. These are

$$e^{\alpha}_{rs} = \frac{f^{\alpha}}{g}\sum_a [G_a^{-1}]^{\alpha}_{sr}(G_a \times G_a) \tag{3.53}$$

and they transform according to

$$(G_a \times G_a)e^{\alpha}_{rs} = \sum_{r'} [G_a]^{\alpha}_{r'r} e^{\alpha}_{r's}. \tag{3.54}$$

As in (3.15)

$$|\alpha_1\alpha_2 r_1 r_2;\ \alpha rs\rangle \equiv e^{\alpha}_{rs} |\alpha_1 r_1\rangle\, |\alpha_2 r_2\rangle. \tag{3.55}$$

Some of the kets projected in this way are zero and some are linearly dependent. From the kets of the form (3.55) for a given α and r we select $f^{\alpha_1\alpha_2\alpha}$ linearly independent kets $|\alpha_1\alpha_2;\ \rho\alpha r\rangle$.

From Section II,C

$$G = \{G_{ja};\quad j = 1 \text{ to } g/k,\ a = 1 \text{ to } k\} \tag{3.56}$$

and

$$K = \{K_a;\quad a = 1 \text{ to } k\} \tag{3.57}$$

are two groups such that

$$G_{ja} \to K_a \tag{3.58}$$

is a $g/k:1$ homomorphism. The irreducible representations of K are irreducible representations of G, although the reverse is not true.

An invariant subspace of the subdirect product group $G \times K$ is the space $\mathfrak{B}^{\alpha(G)} \times \mathfrak{B}^{\alpha(K)}$ with basis kets

$$|\alpha(G)r(G)\rangle\, |\alpha(K)r(K)\rangle. \tag{3.59}$$

The product kets are symmetry adapted to the inner subdirect product group $G \boxtimes K$ in the usual manner with kets

$$|\beta(G)\beta(K);\ \rho\alpha(G)r(G)\rangle = \sum_{s(G)}^{f^{\beta(G)}} \sum_{s(K)}^{f^{\beta(K)}} |\beta(G)s(G)\rangle\, |\beta(K)s(K)\rangle \times \langle\beta(G)\beta(K)s(G)s(K)|\rho\alpha(G)r(G)\rangle. \tag{3.60}$$

These kets transform according to

$$(G_{ja} \times K_a)|\beta(G)\beta(K);\ \rho\alpha(G)r(G)\rangle = \sum_{s(G)} [G_{ja}]^{\alpha(G)}_{s(G)r(G)} |\beta(G)\beta(K);\ \rho\alpha(G)s(G)\rangle. \tag{3.61}$$

Since $G \xrightarrow{g/k:1} K$, $G \boxtimes K \cong G$ so the irreducible representations of $G \boxtimes K$ are the irreducible representations of G.

IV. The Lattice of the Quasi-Relativistic Dirac Hamiltonian

A. The Dirac Hamiltonian

The Dirac Hamiltonian

$$\mathscr{H} = \sum_{i=0}^{3} \pi_i \times \alpha_i + \Phi \times I \tag{4.1}$$

operates on a product space $\mathfrak{B}^E \times \mathfrak{B}^D$ where $\mathfrak{B}^E$ is the Euclidean three-space and $\mathfrak{B}^D$ is the Dirac four-space.

The operators on $\mathfrak{B}^E$ are

$$\pi_i = p_i - eA_i, \qquad i = 1 \text{ to } 3, \tag{4.2}$$

$$\pi_0 = m \tag{4.3}$$

and Φ, the potential energy. The Dirac operators,

$$\{\alpha_0, \alpha_1, \alpha_2, \alpha_3\} \tag{4.4}$$

are operators on $\mathfrak{B}^D$.

The operators on the Dirac four-space are elements of the Dirac algebra, a simple matric algebra $M(4) = \{X, Y, Z, \ldots\}$ of order sixteen. We construct the algebra as follows. Let $\{|t\rangle, \quad t = 1 \text{ to } 4\}$ be an orthonormal basis of $\mathfrak{B}^D$. The matric basis of $M(4)$ is $\{e_{rs}; \quad r, s = 1 \text{ to } 4\}$ where

$$e_{rs} = |r\rangle\langle s|. \tag{4.5}$$

Then

$$e_{rs}e_{tu} = \delta(s, t)e_{ru} \tag{4.6}$$

and

$$e_{rs}|t\rangle = \delta(s, t)|r\rangle. \tag{4.7}$$

A general element in $M(4)$ is

$$X = \sum_r \sum_s X_{rs}e_{rs} \tag{4.8}$$

where X_{rs} is in the complex number field. In terms of the matric basis

$$\alpha_0(\equiv \beta) = e_{11} + e_{22} - e_{33} - e_{44}, \tag{4.9}$$

$$\alpha_1 = e_{14} + e_{23} + e_{32} + e_{41}, \tag{4.10}$$

$$\alpha_2 = -ie_{14} + ie_{23} - ie_{32} + ie_{41}, \tag{4.11}$$

$$\alpha_3 = e_{13} - e_{24} + e_{31} - e_{42}. \tag{4.12}$$

Note that

$$[\alpha_i, \alpha_j]_+ = 2\delta(i, j)I. \tag{4.13}$$

For the subsequent development we need the *spin* operators

$$\sigma_1 = -i\alpha_2\alpha_3 = e_{12} + e_{21} + e_{34} + e_{43}; \tag{4.14}$$

$$\sigma_2 = -i\alpha_3\alpha_1 = -ie_{12} + ie_{21} - ie_{34} + ie_{43}; \tag{4.15}$$

$$\sigma_3 = -i\alpha_1\alpha_2 = e_{11} - e_{22} + e_{33} - e_{44}. \tag{4.16}$$

Each element in $M(4)$ can be decomposed into even and odd operators

$$X = X_e + X_o \tag{4.17}$$

where

$$[X_e, \beta] = [X_o, \beta]_+ = 0. \tag{4.18}$$

An even operator can be put in the form

$$X_e = X_e' + X_e'' \tag{4.19}$$

where X_e' and X_e'' are elements in a simple matric algebra,

$$M'(2) = \{X_e', Y_e'; Z_e', \ldots\} \qquad \text{and} \qquad M''(2) = \{X_e'', Y_e'', Z_e'', \ldots\}$$

of order four with basis

$$\eta_e' = \{e_{11}, e_{12}, e_{21}, e_{22}\} \tag{4.20}$$

and

$$\eta_e'' = \{e_{33}, e_{34}, e_{43}, e_{44}\}. \tag{4.21}$$

I, σ_1, σ_2, σ_3, and β are even operators.

Carrying out the decomposition, we have

$$I = I' + I'' \tag{4.22}$$

where

$$I' = e_{11} + e_{22}, \tag{4.23}$$

$$I'' = e_{33} + e_{44}; \tag{4.24}$$

and

$$\sigma_i = \sigma_i' + \sigma_i'' \tag{4.25}$$

where

$$\sigma_1' = e_{12} + e_{21}, \qquad \sigma_1'' = e_{34} + e_{43}, \tag{4.26}$$

$$\sigma_2' = -i(e_{12} - e_{21}), \qquad \sigma_2'' = -i(e_{34} - e_{43}), \tag{4.27}$$

$$\sigma_3' = e_{11} - e_{22}, \qquad \sigma_3'' = e_{33} - e_{44}. \tag{4.28}$$

The space of the algebra $M'(2)$ is labeled $\mathfrak{B}'$, a vector space spanned by $\{|1\rangle, |2\rangle\}$. The space of the algebra $M''(2)$ is labeled $\mathfrak{B}''$, a vector space spanned by $\{|3\rangle, |4\rangle\}$.

$\mathfrak{B}'$ and $\mathfrak{B}''$ are invariant subspaces for the group $G(2) = \{I, \beta\}$. The algebra of $G(2)$ is spanned by the orthogonal idempotents

$$e' = (\tfrac{1}{2})(I + \beta), \tag{4.29}$$

$$e'' = (\tfrac{1}{2})(I - \beta). \tag{4.30}$$

Note that

$$e'\mathfrak{B}' = \mathfrak{B}', \qquad e''\mathfrak{B}'' = \mathfrak{B}'', \tag{4.31}$$

$$e''\mathfrak{B}' = 0, \qquad e'\mathfrak{B}'' = 0. \tag{4.32}$$

Consequently, $\mathfrak{B}'$ and $\mathfrak{B}''$ are invariant subspaces for all even operators for

$$[X_e, G(2)] = 0. \tag{4.33}$$

Thus

$$X_e\mathfrak{B}' \to \mathfrak{B}',$$

$$X_e\mathfrak{B}'' \to \mathfrak{B}''.$$

Since, however,

$$[X_o, G(2)] \neq 0, \tag{4.34}$$

$\mathfrak{B}'$ and $\mathfrak{B}''$ are not invariant subspaces for odd operators.

$\mathfrak{B}'$ and $\mathfrak{B}''$ have an approximate characterization as positive and negative energy states, respectively. At low energies the Dirac Hamiltonian is approximately

$$\mathscr{H} \approx m \times \beta. \tag{4.35}$$

$\mathfrak{B}^E \times \mathfrak{B}'$ and $\mathfrak{B}^E \times \mathfrak{B}''$ are eigenstates to this Hamiltonian with eigenvalues $+m$ and $-m$, respectively.

B. The Foldy-Wouthuysen Transformation

The Foldy-Wouthuysen transformation (*4*) is a procedure for transforming the Dirac Hamiltonian into an even operator to an arbitrary order $O(1/m^p)$ by means of a series of unitary transformations. The gth transformation is

$$\mathscr{H}^{(g)} = U^{(g)}\mathscr{H}^{(g-1)}(U^{(g)})^{-1}. \tag{4.36}$$

The transformation operator is

$$U^{(g)} = e^{iS^{(g)}} \tag{4.37}$$

where

$$S^{(g)} = -i\,\frac{(I \times \beta)\Omega_o^{(g-1)}}{2m}\,. \tag{4.38}$$

Here $\Omega_o^{(g-1)}$ is the odd operator to $O(1/m^p)$ in $\mathscr{H}^{(g-1)}$.

The Dirac Hamiltonian may be written

$$\mathscr{H}^{(0)} = m \times \beta + \Omega_e^{(0)} + \Omega_o^{(0)} \tag{4.39}$$

where

$$\Omega_e^{(0)} = \Phi \times I, \tag{4.40}$$

$$\Omega_o^{(0)} = \boldsymbol{\pi} \cdot \boldsymbol{\alpha}. \tag{4.41}$$

Then to $O(1/m^2)$

$$\Omega_e^{(1)} = m \times \beta + \Omega_e^{(0)} + \left(\frac{\beta}{2m}\right)\Omega_o^{(0)2} - \left(\frac{1}{8m^2}\right)[\Omega_o^{(0)}, [\Omega_o^{(0)}, \Omega_e^{(0)}]], \tag{4.42}$$

$$\Omega_o^{(1)} = \left(\frac{\beta}{2m}\right)[\Omega_o^{(0)}, \Omega_e^{(0)}] - \left(\frac{1}{3m^2}\right)\Omega_o^{(0)3}, \tag{4.43}$$

$$\Omega_e^{(2)} = \Omega_e^{(1)}, \tag{4.44}$$

$$\Omega_o^{(2)} = \left(\frac{1}{4m^2}\right)[[\Omega_o^{(0)}, \Omega_e^{(0)}], \Omega_e^{(0)}], \tag{4.45}$$

$$\Omega_e^{(3)} = \Omega_e^{(1)}, \tag{4.46}$$

$$\Omega_o^{(3)} = 0. \tag{4.47}$$

Consequently, to $O(1/m^2)$, the Hamiltonian is even;

$$\begin{aligned}
\mathscr{H}^{(3)} &= m \times \beta + \Omega_e^{(1)} \\
&= m \times \beta + \Omega_e^{(0)} + \left(\frac{\beta}{2m}\right)\Omega_o^{(0)2} - \left(\frac{1}{8m^2}\right)[\Omega_o^{(0)}, [\Omega_o^{(0)}, \Omega_e^{(0)}]] \\
&= m \times \beta + \left(\frac{1}{2m}\right)\pi^2 \times \beta + \Phi \times I - \left(\frac{e}{4m^2}\right)(\mathbf{E} \times \boldsymbol{\pi}) \cdot \boldsymbol{\sigma} \\
&\quad - \frac{e}{2m}(\mathbf{H} \times \beta) \cdot \boldsymbol{\sigma} - \frac{e}{8m^2}\,\mathrm{div}\,\mathbf{E}
\end{aligned} \tag{4.48}$$

where

$$e\mathbf{E} = -\nabla\Phi; \mathbf{H} = \text{curl } \mathbf{A}.$$

$\mathfrak{B}^E \times \mathfrak{B}'$ and $\mathfrak{B}^E \times \mathfrak{B}''$ are invariant subspaces to $\mathscr{H}^{(3)}$ since it is an even operator. We select the positive energy states $\mathfrak{B}'$ and the X_e' part of the even operator to obtain a two component equation called the quasi-relativistic Dirac equation.

We define the spin operator

$$S = \tfrac{1}{2}\sigma'. \tag{4.49}$$

The basis kets are eigenkets to S_z and S^2

$$\begin{aligned} S_z|1\rangle &= \tfrac{1}{2}|1\rangle, \qquad & S^2|1\rangle &= \tfrac{3}{4}|1\rangle, \\ S_z|2\rangle &= -\tfrac{1}{2}|2\rangle, \qquad & S^2|2\rangle &= \tfrac{3}{4}|2\rangle. \end{aligned} \tag{4.50}$$

Consequently

$$\begin{aligned} |1\rangle &\equiv \alpha \equiv |\tfrac{1}{2}\tfrac{1}{2}\rangle, \\ |2\rangle &\equiv \beta \equiv |\tfrac{1}{2}\bar{\tfrac{1}{2}}\rangle. \end{aligned} \tag{4.51}$$

We set $\mathfrak{B}' = \mathfrak{B}^S$, the spin space of the Hamiltonian.

We retain only those terms in (4.38) that produce major splitting and define the quasi-relativistic Hamiltonian as

$$\mathscr{H}_{qr} \equiv \left(\frac{p^2}{2m}\right) \times I + \Phi \times I + \mathbf{\Omega} \cdot \mathbf{S} + H_z(L_z \times I - 2I \times S_z). \tag{4.52}$$

The constants in the last two terms have been suppressed. Here

$$\mathbf{\Omega} = \nabla\Phi \times \mathbf{p} \tag{4.53}$$

where

$$\Omega_x = \frac{\partial\Phi}{\partial y} p_z - \frac{\partial\Phi}{\partial z} p_y, \tag{4.54}$$

$$\Omega_y = \frac{\partial\Phi}{\partial z} p_x - \frac{\partial\Phi}{\partial x} p_z, \tag{4.55}$$

$$\Omega_z = \frac{\partial\Phi}{\partial x} p_y - \frac{\partial\Phi}{\partial y} p_x. \tag{4.56}$$

For a central field

$$\Phi = \Phi(r), \qquad r = (x^2 + y^2 + z^2)^{1/2}, \tag{4.57}$$

$$\frac{\partial \Phi}{\partial x} = \lambda x, \tag{4.58}$$

$$\frac{\partial \Phi}{\partial y} = \lambda y, \tag{4.59}$$

$$\frac{\partial \Phi}{\partial z} = \lambda z, \tag{4.60}$$

where

$$\lambda = \frac{1}{r}\frac{\partial \Phi}{\partial r}. \tag{4.61}$$

Then

$$\Omega_x = \lambda(yp_z - zp_y) = \lambda L_x, \tag{4.62}$$

$$\Omega_y = \lambda(zp_x - xp_z) = \lambda L_y, \tag{4.63}$$

$$\Omega_z = \lambda(xp_y - yp_x) = \lambda L_z, \tag{4.64}$$

and

$$\mathbf{\Omega} \cdot \mathbf{S} = \lambda \mathbf{L} \cdot \mathbf{S}. \tag{4.65}$$

C. The Lattice of the Quasi-Relativistic Dirac Hamiltonian

It is sufficient for our purpose to consider here only the proper orthogonal group and its subgroups (see Section II,D, following). In the absence of a magnetic field we have, by (4.52),

$$\mathscr{H} = \mathscr{H}^E \times I + \mathbf{\Omega} \cdot \mathbf{S} \tag{4.66}$$

where

$$\mathscr{H}^E = \left(\frac{p^2}{2m}\right) + \Phi \tag{4.67}$$

and

$$\mathbf{\Omega} = \nabla \Phi \times \mathbf{p}. \tag{4.68}$$

$SU(2)$ is the group of all unitary unimodular transformations on the two-dimensional space $\mathfrak{V}^S$. We denote a group element of $SU(2)$ by

$$U = U(p_1, p_2, p_3) \tag{4.69}$$

where p_1, p_2, and p_3 are real parameters. $O^+(3)$ is the group of proper rotations on the three-dimensional Euclidean space $\mathfrak{V}^E$. We denote an element in $O^+(3)$ by

$$O = O(\alpha, \beta, \gamma) \tag{4.70}$$

where α, β, and γ are the Eulerian angles.

We first construct the group of the term $\mathbf{\Omega} \cdot \mathbf{S}$ in (4.61). To do this we relate $U(p_1, p_2, p_3)$ to $O(\alpha, \beta, \gamma)$ by requiring the commutation

$$(O \times U)^{-1}\mathbf{\Omega} \cdot \mathbf{S}(O \times U) = \mathbf{\Omega} \cdot \mathbf{S}. \tag{4.71}$$

Since $\mathbf{\Omega}$ is a Cartesian tensorial operator

$$O^{-1}\Omega_i O = \sum_j [O]_{ji}\Omega_j \tag{4.72}$$

where $[O]$ is the 3×3 matrix representation of the rotation $O(\alpha, \beta, \gamma)$. Since $\mathbf{S}$ is also a Cartesian tensorial operator, we write

$$U^{-1}S_i U = \sum_k [U]_{ki} S_k \tag{4.73}$$

where $[U]$ is a 3×3 representation of $U(p_1, p_2, p_3)$. By (4.71), (4.72), and (4.73)

$$\begin{aligned}(O \times U)^{-1}\mathbf{\Omega} \cdot \mathbf{S}(O \times U) &= \sum_i (O^{-1}\Omega_i O) \times (U^{-1}S_i U) \\ &= \sum_i \sum_j \sum_k [O]_{ji}[U]_{ki}(\Omega_j \times S_k) \\ &= \sum_i \Omega_i \times S_i,\end{aligned} \tag{4.74}$$

so that

$$\sum_i [O(\alpha, \beta, \gamma)]_{ji}[U(p_1, p_2, p_3)]_{ki} = \delta(j, k). \tag{4.75}$$

For each value of α, β, and γ there are two solutions, which we denote $U_a(\alpha, \beta, \gamma)$, $a = 1, 2$ (see Section IV,D).

The set of elements

$$^dO^+(3) \equiv \{U_a(\alpha, \beta, \gamma), \quad a = 1, 2\} \cong SU(2) \tag{4.76}$$

forms a group, called the double group of $O^+(3)$, exhibiting a 2 to 1 homomorphism to $O^+(3)$. [Double groups are usually treated by requiring that a rotation by 4π be the identity rotation; see, e.g., Tinkham (5).] We use $^dO^+(3)$ for this group since it simplifies the identification of groups in the lattice.

The set of elements

$$O^+(3) \boxtimes {}^dO^+(3) \equiv \{O(\alpha, \beta, \gamma) \boxtimes U_a(\alpha, \beta, \gamma), \quad a = 1, 2\} \tag{4.77}$$

is an inner subdirect product group. The symbol $\boxtimes$ indicates that the common parameters α, β, and γ of the two groups are equal. The group

$$O^{+}(3) \boxtimes {}^{d}O^{+}(3) \cong {}^{d}O^{+}(3)$$

is the group of $\mathbf{\Omega} \cdot \mathbf{S}$.

If we restrict the values of α, β, and γ so as to form a finite group G, the double group is denoted by ${}^{d}G$, and $G \boxtimes {}^{d}G \cong {}^{d}G$.

A simple lattice for a Dirac Hamiltonian may be constructed as follows. Let

$$\Phi = \Phi(O^{+}(3)) + \Phi(G) \tag{4.78}$$

where

$$O^{+}(3) \supset G, \qquad \text{not necessarily finite.} \tag{4.79}$$

Where

$$[\Phi(O^{+}(3)), O^{+}(3)] = 0 \tag{4.80}$$

and

$$[\Phi(G), G] = 0, \tag{4.81}$$

we can then write the Hamiltonian as

$$\mathscr{H} = \mathscr{H}(O^{+}(3)) \times I + \Phi(G) \times I + \mathbf{\Omega} \cdot \mathbf{S} \tag{4.82}$$

where

$$\mathscr{H}(O^{+}(3)) = \left(\frac{p^2}{2m}\right) + \Phi(O^{+}(3)). \tag{4.83}$$

The groups of the several terms are

$$[\mathscr{H}(O^{+}(3)) \times I, O^{+}(3) \times {}^{d}O^{+}(3)] = 0, \tag{4.84}$$

$$[\Phi(G) \times I, G \times {}^{d}O^{+}(3)] = 0, \tag{4.85}$$

$$[\mathbf{\Omega} \cdot \mathbf{S}, O^{+}(3) \boxtimes {}^{d}O^{+}(3)] = 0. \tag{4.86}$$

Since

$$O^{+}(3) \times {}^{d}O^{+}(3) \cap G \times {}^{d}O^{+}(3) = G \times {}^{d}O^{+}(3), \tag{4.87}$$

then

$$[\mathscr{H}(O^{+}(3)) \times I + \Phi(G) \times I, G \times {}^{d}O^{+}(3)] = 0. \tag{4.88}$$

Further, since

$$O^{+}(3) \boxtimes {}^{d}O^{+}(3) \cap G \times {}^{d}O^{+}(3) = G \boxtimes {}^{d}G, \tag{4.89}$$

then

$$[\mathscr{H}, G \boxtimes {}^dG] = 0. \tag{4.90}$$

The lattice of (4.82) is shown in Fig. 4.

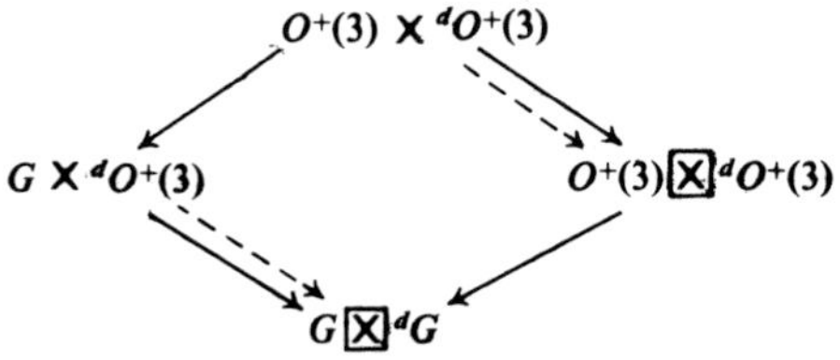

FIG. 4. A lattice for an electron in a field of symmetry G.

In the presence of a magnetic field the Hamiltonian is

$$\mathscr{H} = \mathscr{H}(O^+(3)) \times I + \Phi(G) \times I + \mathbf{\Omega} \cdot \mathbf{S} + H_z(L_z \times I + 2I \times S_z). \tag{4.91}$$

We add the following groups

$$[L_z \times I, O^+(2) \times {}^dO^+(3)] = 0, \tag{4.92}$$

$$[I \times S_z, O^+(3) \times {}^dO^+(2)] = 0. \tag{4.93}$$

Since

$$O^+(2) \times {}^dO^+(3) \cap O^+(3) \times {}^dO^+(2) = O^+(2) \times {}^dO^+(2), \tag{4.94}$$

then

$$[L_z \times I + 2I \times S_z, O^+(2) \times {}^dO^+(2)] = 0; \tag{4.95}$$

$O^+(2) \times {}^dO^+(2)$ is called the Paschen-Back group. Since

$$O^+(3) \boxtimes {}^dO^+(3) \cap O^+(2) \times {}^dO^+(2) = O^+(2) \boxtimes {}^dO^+(2), \tag{4.96}$$

it follows that

$$[\mathscr{H}(O^+(3)) \times I + \mathbf{\Omega} \cdot \mathbf{S} + H_z(L_z \times I + 2I \times S_z), O^+(2) \boxtimes {}^dO^+(2)] = 0. \tag{4.97}$$

The group $O^+(2) \boxtimes {}^dO^+(2)$ is called the Zeeman group. Finally, since

$$G \times {}^dO^+(3) \cap O^+(2) \boxtimes {}^dO^+(2) = G^z \boxtimes {}^dG^z \tag{4.98}$$

where G^z is the subgroup of G that contains rotations about an axis parallel to the magnetic field,

$$[\mathscr{H}, G^z \boxtimes {}^dG^z] = 0. \tag{4.99}$$

The lattice of (4.91) is shown in Fig. 5.

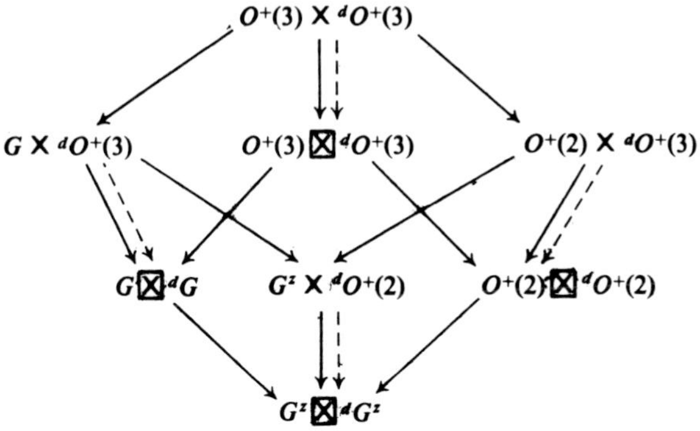

FIG. 5. A lattice for an electron in a field of symmetry G and a magnetic field.

D. APPENDIX: DOUBLE GROUP MATRICES

To find the matrix $[U(p_1p_2p_3)]_{ki}$, we write

$$U(p_1p_2p_3) = \exp\left(i \sum_j p_j S_j\right) \tag{4.100}$$

and compute the quantity $U^{-1}S_kU$ appearing in (4.75). Utilizing the commutation relations among the S_i's, we obtain the result

$$U^{-1}S_kU = \sum_{n=0}^{\infty} \frac{1}{n!} T_n \tag{4.101}$$

where

$$T_0 = S_k \tag{4.102}$$

and

$$T_n = \left[2\, i \sum_j p_j S_j,\, T_{n-1}\right]. \tag{4.103}$$

We find the recursion relation

$$T_{k+2} = -p^2 T_k, \qquad k = 1, 2, \ldots \tag{4.104}$$

where

$$p^2 = \sum_i p_i p_i \tag{4.105}$$

so that

$$T_{2k+2} = (-p^2)^k T_2 \tag{4.106}$$

and

$$T_{2k+1} = (-p^2)^k T_1 \qquad k = 1, 2, \ldots. \tag{4.107}$$

Since

$$T_1 = \sum_{n,m} p_n S_m \epsilon_{nmk}, \qquad T_2 = -p^2 S_k + p_k \mathbf{p} \cdot \boldsymbol{\delta} \tag{4.108}$$

it follows that

$$U^{-1} S_k U = S_k \cos p + \frac{p_k \mathbf{p} \cdot \mathbf{S}(1 - \cos p)}{p^2} + \frac{\sum_{nm} p_n S_m \epsilon_{nmk} \sin p}{p} \tag{4.109}$$

and hence, from (4.73),

$$[U(p_1 p_2 p_3)]_{ki} = \delta_{ki} \cos p + \frac{(1 - \cos p)\, p_k p_i}{p^2} + \frac{\sum_n p_n \epsilon_{nki} \sin p}{p}. \tag{4.110}$$

Equation (4.110) reveals that $[U]$ is orthogonal and hence, with (4.75), that

$$[O]_{ik} = [U^{-1}]_{ki}. \tag{4.111}$$

Thus the parameters p_i are related to a single rotation in Euclidean three-space. We find the rotation in the following way. From (4.110)–(4.111)

$$\sum_j [O]_{ij} p_j = p_i, \tag{4.112}$$

so $\mathbf{p}$ determines the axis of rotation. Moreover, if $\mathbf{N}$ is a unit vector perpendicular to $\mathbf{p}$ and ϕ is the angle of rotation

$$\cos \phi = \sum_{i,j} N_i [O]_{ij} N_j. \tag{4.113}$$

From (4.110)–(4.111) the right-hand side simplifies, yielding

$$\cos \phi = \cos p \tag{4.114}$$

so that $(\sum_i p_i p_i)^{1/2}$ is the angle of rotation. We have thus an expression for U in terms of the Euler homogeneous parameters for O that are equivalent to (α, β, γ). By direct substitution into (4.100) it follows that

$$U\left(\frac{\mathbf{p} + 2\pi n \mathbf{p}}{p}\right) = (-1)^n U(\mathbf{p}) \qquad n = 0, \pm 1, \ldots, \tag{4.115}$$

and hence there are two solutions $U(p_1 p_2 p_3)$ for each operator O.

The inversion operator does not impose a condition on U. We choose to associate the pair i, $-i$ of $U(2)$ with inversion. This preserves the 2:1 homomorphism, and leads naturally to double groups encompassing improper rotations.

V. Applications

A. An Electron in a Central Field

For an electron outside a closed shell we take the Hamiltonian to be, by (4.52) and (4.65),

$$\mathscr{H} = \mathscr{H}^E \times I + \lambda \mathbf{L} \cdot \mathbf{S} \tag{5.1}$$

where

$$\mathscr{H}^E = \left(\frac{p^2}{2m}\right) + \Phi^c(r). \tag{5.2}$$

Here $\Phi^c(r)$ is a spherically symmetric core potential, which we express as

$$\Phi^c(r) = (Z - \delta)\frac{e^2}{r} + v^c(r) \tag{5.3}$$

where δ is a screening parameter and $v^c(r)$ is a non-Coulombic correction term.

For $v^c(r) = 0$, $\mathscr{H}^E$ can be expressed in terms of the Casimir operators of $O^+(4) = SU(2) \times SU(2)$ (6). It follows that

$$[\mathscr{H}^E, O^+(4)] = 0. \tag{5.4}$$

The eigenkets are $|\mu M_\mu\rangle|\nu M_\nu\rangle$, where $\mu = \nu = 0, \frac{1}{2}, 1, \ldots,$ and $M_\mu, M_\nu = \mu, \mu - 1, \ldots, -\mu$. These kets can be symmetry adapted to the chain $O^+(4) \supset O^+(3) \supset O^+(2)$. They are denoted by $|nlm_l\rangle$ where $n = 2\nu + 1 = 1, 2, \ldots$ is supplied by $O^+(4)$, $l = n-1, n-2, \ldots, 0$ is supplied by $O^+(3)$, and $m_l = l, l-1, \ldots, -l$ is supplied by $O^+(2)$. The eigenstates depend only on n and are n^2-fold degenerate.

For $v^c(r) \neq 0$

$$[\mathscr{H}^E, O^+(4)] \neq 0, \tag{5.5}$$

so n is not an exact quantum number. But

$$[\mathscr{H}^E, O^+(3)] = 0, \tag{5.6}$$

so l (and m_l) remains an exact quantum number. However, states of different l are no longer degenerate. On the basis of experiment, n is found to be a good

Hamiltonian

$$\mathscr{H} = \left(\frac{p^2}{2m_i} - (Z-\delta)\frac{e^2}{r} + v^c(r)\right) \times I + \lambda \mathbf{L}\cdot\mathbf{S} + H_z(L_z \times I + 2I \times S_z)$$

Lattice

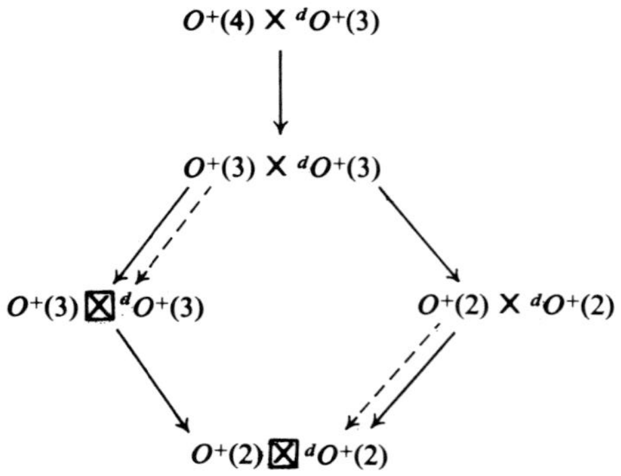

FIG. 6. The Hamiltonian, lattice, and a correlation diagram for an electron in a spherical field.

Correlation diagram

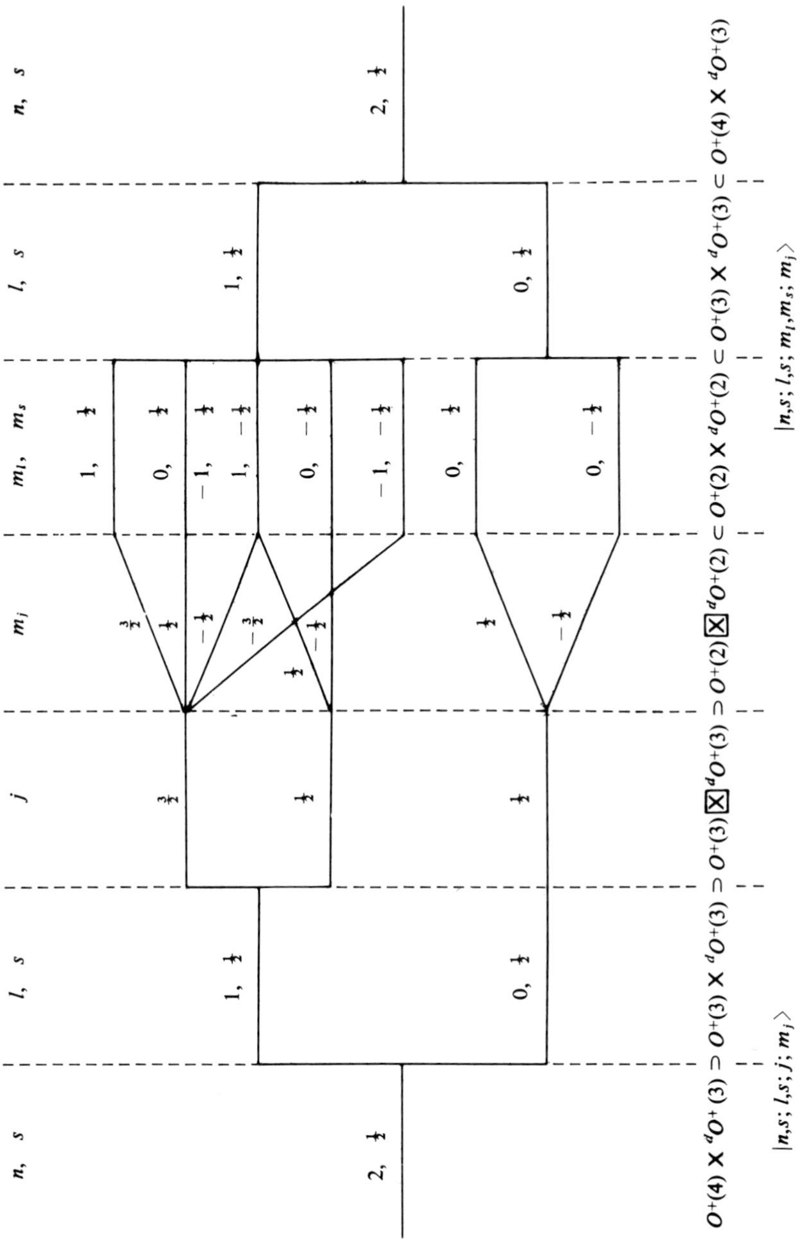

quantum number, so the chain $O^+(4) \supset O^+(3) \supset O^+(2)$ is a physically significant one. We denote the kets by $|n; lm_l\rangle$.

The full Hamiltonian (5.1) acts on a product space $\mathfrak{B}^E \times \mathfrak{B}^S$ spanned by kets $|n; lm_l\rangle|sm_s\rangle$ where $s = \frac{1}{2}$ and $m_s = \pm\frac{1}{2}$. The group of the full Hamiltonian is $O^+(3) \boxtimes {}^dO^+(3) \supset O^+(2) \boxtimes {}^dO^+(2)$. The exact quantum numbers are j and m_j. The chain $O^+(4) \times {}^dO^+(3) \supset O^+(3) \times {}^dO^+(3) \supset O^+(3) \boxtimes {}^dO^+(3) \supset O^+(2) \boxtimes {}^dO^+(2)$ is physically significant. The kets are denoted by $|n, s; l, s; jm_j\rangle$.

In a magnetic field the term

$$H_z(L_z \times I + 2I \times S_z)$$

is added to the Hamiltonian. The group of the Hamiltonian is then $O^+(2) \boxtimes {}^dO^+(2)$ and only m_j is an exact quantum number. The Zeeman chain is

$$O^+(4) \times {}^dO^+(3) \supset O^+(3) \times {}^dO^+(3) \supset O^+(3) \boxtimes {}^dO^+(3) \supset O^+(2) \boxtimes {}^dO^+(2).$$

The kets for this chain are denoted $|n, s; l, s; j; m_j\rangle$. The Paschen-Back chain is

$$O^+(4) \times {}^dO^+(3) \supset O^+(3) \times {}^dO^+(3) \supset O^+(2) \times {}^dO^+(2) \supset O^+(2) \boxtimes {}^dO^+(2).$$

The kets for this chain are denoted $|n; l, s; m_l, m_s; m_j\rangle$. See Fig. 6.

B. N Electrons in a Central Field

The Hamiltonian for N electrons outside a closed shell is taken to be

$$\mathscr{H} = \mathscr{H}^{E0} \times I + \left(\sum_{i<j} \frac{e^2}{r_{ij}}\right) \times I + \sum_i \lambda_i \mathbf{L}_i \cdot \mathbf{S}_i \tag{5.7}$$

where

$$\mathscr{H}^{E0} = \sum_i \left(\frac{p_i^2}{2m} + v^c(r_i)\right). \tag{5.8}$$

We neglect spin-other-orbit, spin-spin, spin-nuclear spin, and other relativistic terms which merely shift energy levels. The lattice of this Hamiltonian is shown in Fig. 5. $\mathscr{H}^{E0} \times I$ is taken as the leading term in the Hamiltonian. Its eigenkets and quantum numbers are

$$|n(N)l(N)m_l(N)\rangle|s(N)m_l(N)\rangle$$
$$= |n_1 l_1 m_{l_1}\rangle|s_1 m_{s_1}\rangle|n_2 l_2 m_{l_2}\rangle|s_2 m_{s_2}\rangle \cdots |n_N l_N m_{l_N}\rangle|s_N m_{s_N}\rangle. \tag{5.9}$$

The group of $\mathscr{H}^{E0} \times I$ and the head group of the lattice is $(O^+(3))^N \times ({}^dO^+(3))^N$.

The group of the full Hamiltonian and the tail group of the lattice is

$$[O^+(3)]^N \boxtimes [{}^dO^+(3)]^N = [O^+(3) \boxtimes {}^dO^+(3)]^N. \tag{5.10}$$

The quantum numbers supplied by the tail group are J and M_J.

In addition

$$[\mathscr{H}, S_N^E \boxtimes S_N^S] = 0 \tag{5.11}$$

where S_N^E and S_N^S are the groups of permutations on the particle indices in $\mathfrak{B}^E$ and $\mathfrak{B}^S$, respectively. Kets that are symmetry adapted to $S_N^E \boxtimes S_N^S \simeq S_N$ are characterized by partitions $[\lambda^{ES}]$ of N, which define *permutation states* (7), and by Yamanouchi symbols y. The Pauli principle requires that only the antisymmetric permutation state

$$[\lambda^{ES}] = [1^N] \tag{5.12}$$

occurs in nature.

The right-hand chain in Fig. 5 is called the *j–j chain* that is related to the truncated Hamiltonian

$$\mathscr{H} = \mathscr{H}^{E0} \times I + \sum_i \lambda_i \mathbf{L}_i \cdot \mathbf{S}_i. \tag{5.13}$$

The group of this Hamiltonian is $(O^+(3) \boxtimes {}^dO^+(3))^N$ and the exact quantum numbers are $j(N)$ and $m_j(N)$. The kets that are symmetry adapted to this Hamiltonian are written

$$|n(N)l(N)s(N); j(N)m_j(N)\rangle = |n_1 l_1 s_1; j_1 m_{j_1}\rangle \cdots |n_N l_N s_N; j_N m_{j_N}\rangle. \tag{5.14}$$

These kets are then symmetry adapted to the group of the full Hamiltonian $[O^+(3) \boxtimes {}^dO^+(3)]^N$ and to $S_N^E \boxtimes S_N^S$. The kets are denoted by

$$|n(N)l(N)s(N); j(N); [1^N]\rho_J J M_J\rangle.$$

The left-hand chain in Fig. 5 is called the *L–S chain* that is related to the truncated Hamiltonian

$$\mathscr{H} = \mathscr{H}^{E0} \times I + \sum_{i<j} \frac{e^2}{r_{ij}} \times I. \tag{5.15}$$

The group of this Hamiltonian is effectively

$$[O^+(3)]^N \times [{}^dO^+(3)]^N.$$

Hamiltonian

$$\mathscr{H} = \mathscr{H}^{E0} \times I + \left(\sum_{i<j} \frac{e^2}{r_{ij}} \right) \times I + \sum_i \lambda_i \, \mathbf{L} \cdot \mathbf{S}_i$$

Lattice

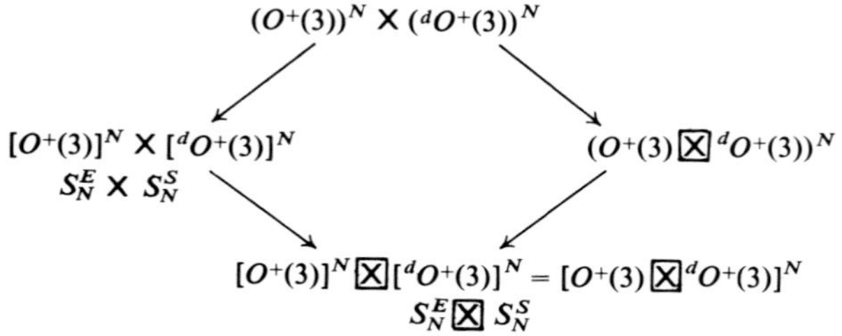

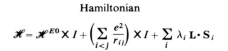

FIG. 7. The Hamiltonian, lattice, and correlation diagram for two electrons in a central field.

Correlation diagram (p^2 configuration)

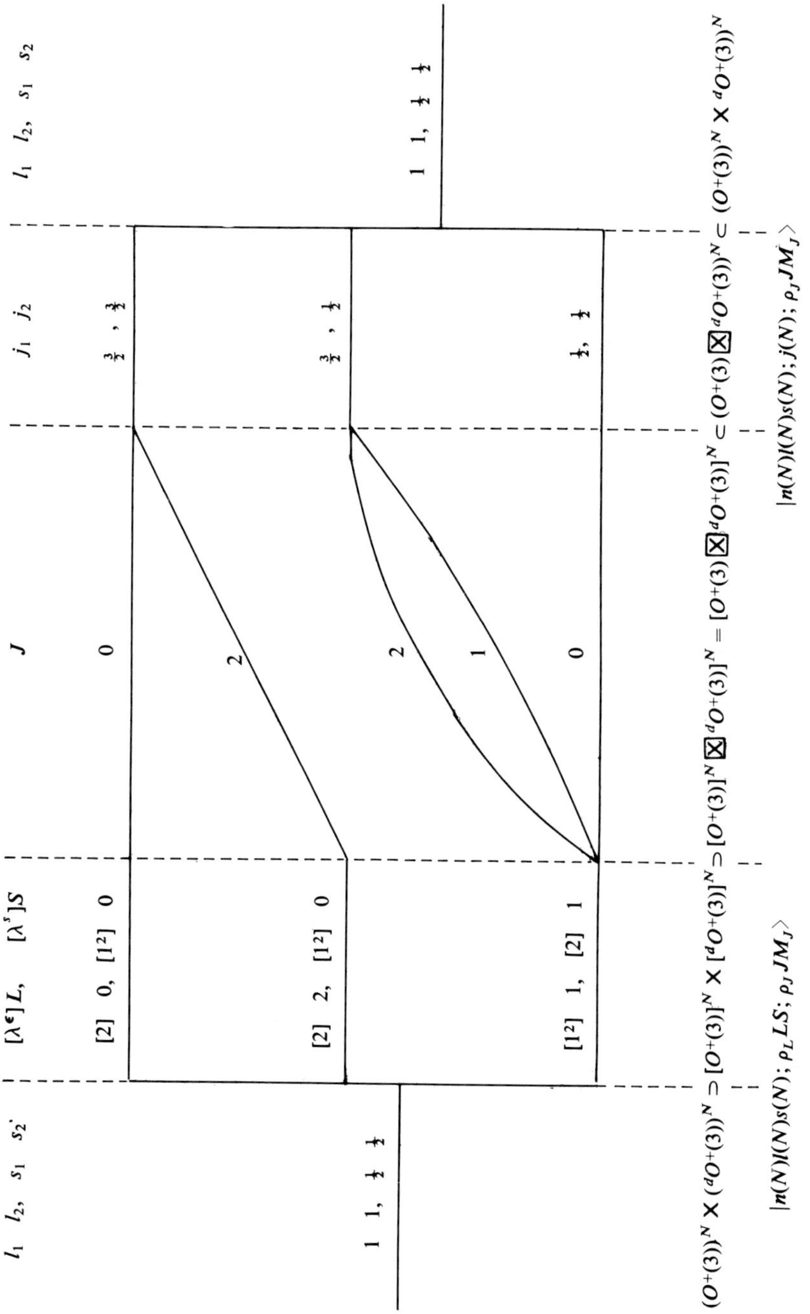

First we adapt the spin kets $|s(N)m_s(N)\rangle$ to S_N^S. We denote the spin permutation state by $[\lambda^S]$ and the symmetry-adapted kets by $|s(N);\,[\lambda^S]y^S M_S\rangle$. Since there are two and only two spin kets for each electron, the permutation states are limited to

$$[\lambda^S] = [N-p, p], \qquad 0 \leqq p \leqq \frac{N}{2}. \tag{5.16}$$

Spin kets that are symmetry adapted to S_N^S are automatically eigenkets to S^2 (and S_z) with

$$S = \frac{N}{2} - p. \tag{5.17}$$

In consequence, the spin quantum number S can replace the permutation quantum number $[\lambda^S]$

$$|s(N);\,[\lambda^S]y^S M_S\rangle \rightarrow |s(N);\,y^S S M_S\rangle. \tag{5.18}$$

We next symmetry adapt the Euclidean (spin-free) kets $|n(N)l(N)m_l(N)\rangle$ to S_N^E and denote the Euclidean (spin-free) permutation states by $[\lambda^E]$. Then the kets are further symmetry adapted to $[O^+(3)]^N$ and are written $|n(N)l(N);\,[\lambda^E]y^E\rho_L LM_L\rangle$. The eigenkets to (5.15) are then $|n(N)l(N);$ $[\lambda^E\rho_L LM_L\rangle\,|s(N);\,y^S SM_S\rangle$. The exact quantum numbers are $[\lambda^E]y^E$, L, M_L, S (or $[\lambda^S]$), y^S, and M_S.

We must now adapt these kets to the group of the full Hamiltonian. The kets adapted to $S_N^E \boxtimes S_N^S$ with $[\lambda^{ES}] = [1^N]$ are

$$\begin{aligned}|n(N)l(N)s(N);\,\rho_L LM_L;\,SM_S[1^N]\rangle \\ = \sum_y |n(N)l(N);\,[\lambda^E]y^E\rho_L LM_L\rangle\,|s(N);\,[\lambda^S]y^S M_S\rangle,\end{aligned} \tag{5.19}$$

where

$$[\lambda^E] = [\tilde{\lambda}^S] = [2^p, 1^{N-2p}]. \tag{5.20}$$

By (5.17) the allowed Euclidean (spin-free) permutation states are specified by the spin quantum number S. Finally, the kets are adapted to $[O^+(3)]^N \boxtimes$ $[{}^dO^+(3)]^N$, and are written $|n(N)l(N)s(N);\,\rho_L LS;\,[1^N]\rho_J JM_J\rangle$. A correlation diagram for the p^2 configuration is given in Fig. 7.

There is for the N-electron system, a lattice that has not yet been discussed. This lattice lies in the Euclidean (spin-free) space $\mathfrak{B}^E$. The one-electron kets $|nlm_l\rangle$, $m_l = l, l-1, \ldots, -l$ span a $(2l+1)$-dimensional space that is invariant under the unitary group $U(2l+1)$. For N electrons in a configuration for which $n_i = n$ and $l_i = l$, the product kets span a $[(2l+1)^N]$-dimensional space that is invariant under $(U(2l+1))^N$ (*8*). The kets can be symmetry adapted to $[U(2l+1)]^N$ with invariant subspaces indexed by the partition

$$[\lambda^E] = [\lambda^1 \cdots \lambda^{2l+1}] \tag{5.21}$$

where

$$\sum_{i=1}^{2l+1} \lambda^i = N. \tag{5.22}$$

The $[U(2l+1)]^N$ group is the head group of a lattice of subgroups. See Fig. 8.

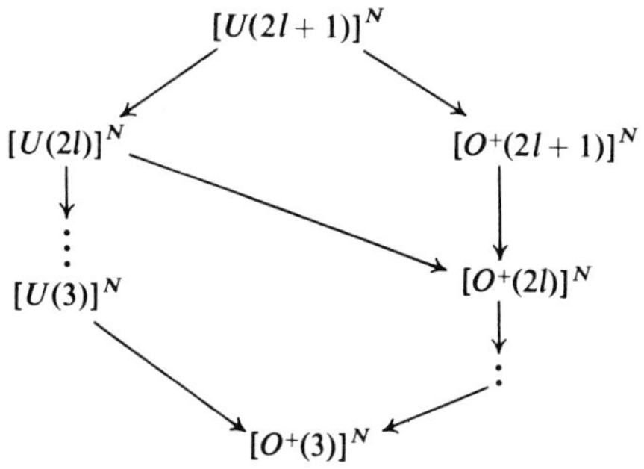

FIG. 8. The lattice of $[U(2l+1)]^N$.

Some of the chains in Fig. 8 have been shown to have physical significance. This subject is treated in detail in the chapter by Judd in this volume.

C. An Electron in a Noncentral Field

Noncentral fields are encountered in crystals and in complex ions. Consider, for example, the complex ion $[Ti(H_2O)_4F_2]^+$. The metal ion Ti^{3+} has one $(3d)$ electron outside the core. A physically significant chain neglecting the inversion is

$$O^+(3) \supset O \supset D_4.$$

The Hamiltonian, the lattice, and a correlation diagram are given in Fig. 9. The symbols for the irreducible representations are the quantum numbers supplied by finite groups.

The hydrogen molecule ion provides a second example of an electron in a noncentral field (*9*). The Euclidean group is $O^+(2)$ (actually $D_{\infty h}$) (see Fig. 10).

Hamiltonian

$$\mathscr{H} = \mathscr{H}(O^+(3)) \times I + \mathscr{H}(O) \times I + \mathscr{H}(D_4) \times I + \mathbf{\Omega} \cdot \mathbf{S}$$

Lattice

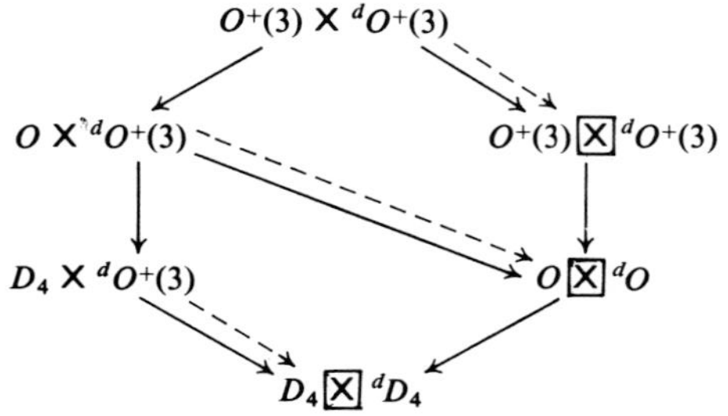

FIG. 9. The Hamiltonian, lattice, and correlation diagram in a tetragonal field.

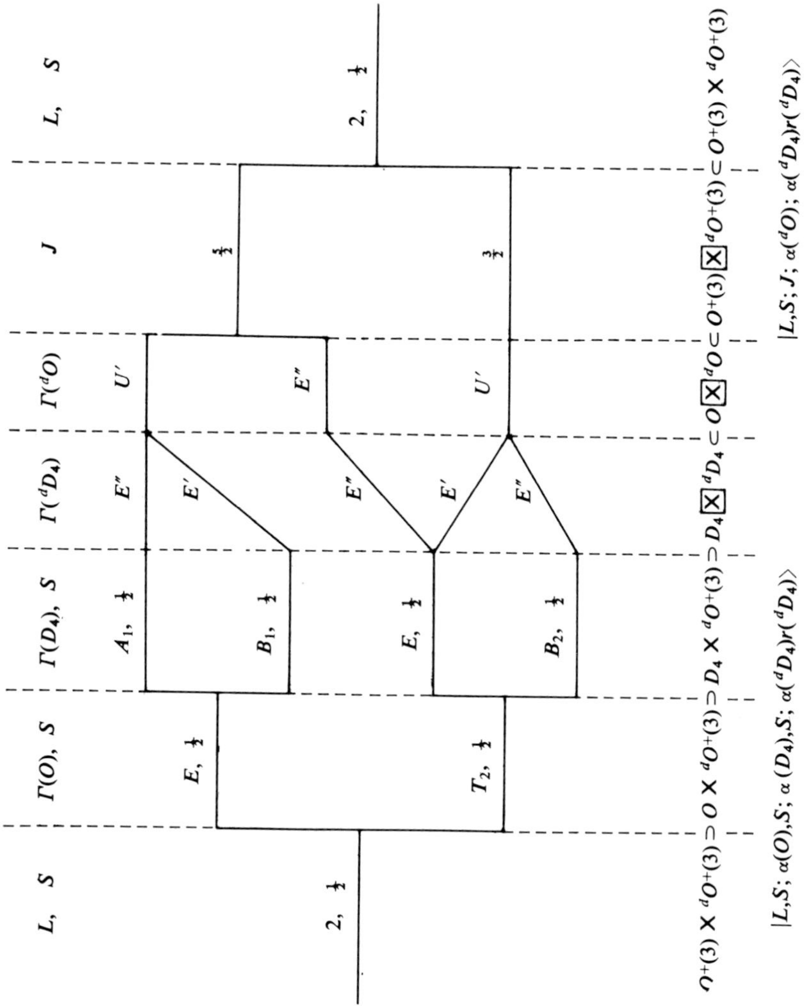
L, S
Γ(O), S
Γ(D4), S
Γ(dD4)
Γ(dO)
J
L, S
2, 1/2
E, 1/2
T2, 1/2
A1, 1/2
B1, 1/2
E, 1/2
B2, 1/2
E″
E′
E″
E′
E″
U′
E″
U′
3/2
3/2
2, 1/2
O+(3) × dO+(3) ⊃ O × dO+(3) ⊃ D4 × dO+(3) ⊃ D4 ⊠ dD4 ⊂ O ⊠ dO ⊂ O+(3) ⊠ dO+(3) ⊂ O+(3) × dO+(3)
|L,S; α(O),S; α(D4),S; α(dD4)r(dD4)⟩
|L,S; J; α(dO); α(dD4)r(dD4)⟩

The order of levels on the left side of the correlation diagram in Fig. 10 are obtained from an exact computation of the Euclidean (spin-free) states (*10*). The exact quantum number is $\Omega = |m_l + m_s| = |m_j|$.

Hamiltonian

$$\mathscr{H} = \left(\frac{p^2}{2m}\right) \times I + \Phi \times I + \lambda L_z S_z$$

where $\Phi = -\left(\frac{e^2}{r_a} + \frac{e^2}{r_b}\right)$ and $\lambda = \left(\frac{e\hbar}{mc}\right)^2 \left\langle \frac{1}{r_a^3} \right\rangle$

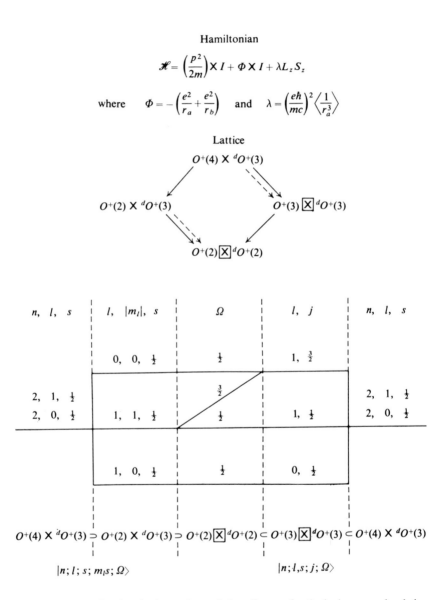

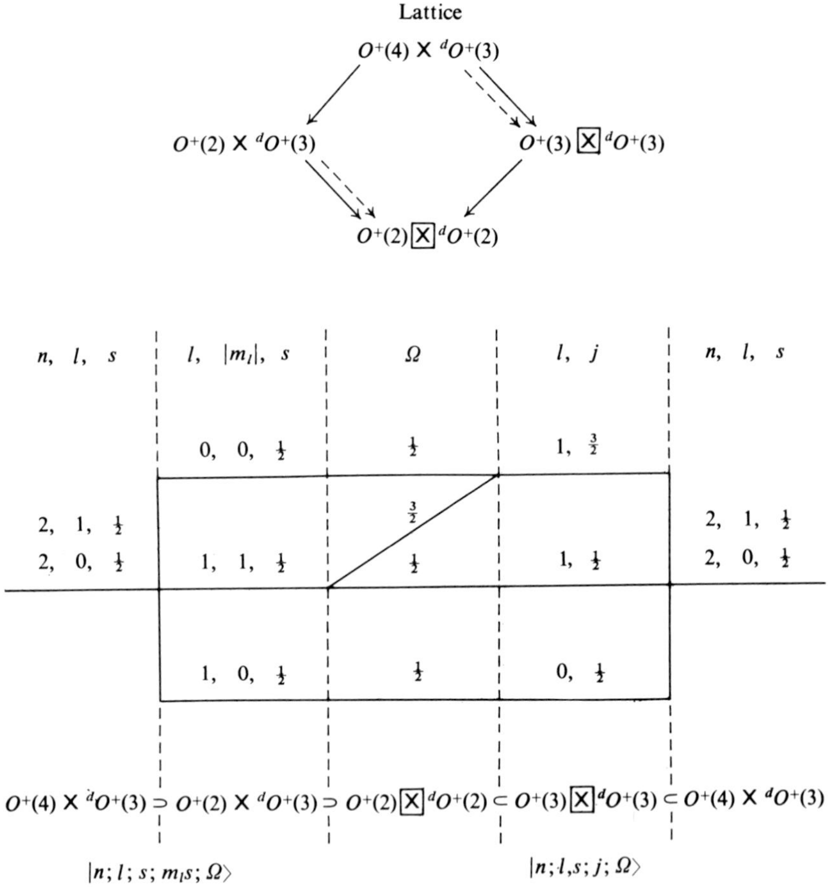

FIG. 10. The Hamiltonian, lattice, and correlation diagram for the hydrogen molecule ion.

D. Nuclear States

In the shell model of the nucleus, the individual nucleons are assumed to move in a spherically symmetrical average Euclidean field described by a three-dimensional harmonic oscillator Hamiltonian

$$\mathscr{H}^E = \frac{p^2}{2M} + \left(\frac{M\omega^2}{2}\right) r^2. \tag{5.23}$$

The equation is separable into three one-dimensional harmonic oscillators with the same force constant. The eigenkets are $|\nu_x\rangle|\nu_y\rangle|\nu_z\rangle$; $\nu_x, \nu_y, \nu_z = 0, 1, 2, \ldots$ with eigenvalues

$$E(\nu) = (\nu + \tfrac{3}{2})\omega \qquad \nu = \nu_x + \nu_y + \nu_z = 0, 1, 2, \ldots. \tag{5.24}$$

The νth state is $[(\nu+1)(\nu+2)/2]$-fold degenerate. The group of $\mathscr{H}^E$ is $U(3)$. Further, since $U(3) \supset O^+(3) \supset O^+(2)$, the eigenkets can be adapted to this chain. An adapted eigenket is written $|\nu l m_l\rangle$ where $\nu = 0, 1, 2 \ldots$ is supplied by $U(3)$, $l = \nu, \nu - 2, \ldots, 1$ or 0 is supplied by $O^+(3)$ and $m_l = l, l-1, \ldots, -l$ is supplied by $O^+(2)$.

A Hamiltonian that includes ordinary spin is, since the field is spherically symmetric,

$$\mathscr{H} = \mathscr{H}^E \times I + \lambda \mathbf{L} \cdot \mathbf{S}. \tag{5.25}$$

For $\lambda = 0$ the group is $U(3) \times {}^dO^+(3)$, the head group. For $\lambda \neq 0$ the group is $O^+(3) \boxtimes {}^dO^+(3)$. The kets are written $|\nu l s; j m_j\rangle$.

For polynucleonic nuclei the procedure is as described in Section V,B for the L–S chain for atoms. Because of the existence of four spin states (spin and isospin) for nucleons, the spin permutation states are characterized by the partition

$$[\lambda^{S_T}] = [\lambda^1, \lambda^2, \lambda^3, \lambda^4] \tag{5.26}$$

where

$$\sum_i \lambda^i = N.$$

For the total ket to be antisymmetrical, that is, $[\lambda^{ES_T}] = [1^N]$, the Euclidean permutation states are restricted to

$$[\lambda^E] = [\lambda^{\tilde{S}_T}] = [4^{\lambda_4}, 4^{\lambda_3}, 2^{\lambda_2}, 1^{\lambda_1}] \tag{5.27}$$

where

$$\sum_{g=1}^{4} g^{\lambda_g} = N.$$

The group of transformations among the degenerate Euclidean orbitals can be taken as the head group of a lattice of groups. For example, $2s$–$1d$ transforms according to $U(6)$.

Certain nuclei possess levels whose separation is given by the rotational formula

$$E = \frac{\hbar^2}{2\mathfrak{J}} \mathsf{I}(\mathsf{I}+1) \tag{5.28}$$

where I is the nuclear spin. The rotational spacing can be obtained from the spherical shell model by making certain assumptions about the form of the nucleon interaction (*11*). The rotational spacing can also be obtained by assuming that the nucleons move in a spheroidal harmonic oscillator field (*12*).

$$\mathscr{H}^E = \frac{p^2}{2M} + \left(\frac{M\omega^2 r^2}{2}\right) + \mathscr{H}_z. \tag{5.29}$$

A simple field suitable for our purpose is

$$\mathscr{H}_z = -\varDelta\left(\frac{M\omega^2}{2}\right) z^2. \tag{5.30}$$

The Hamiltonian is again separable with eigenkets $|\nu_x\rangle|\nu_y\rangle|\nu_\parallel\rangle$ and

$$E(\nu, \nu_\parallel) = [\nu + \tfrac{3}{2} - (\nu_\parallel + \tfrac{1}{2})\varDelta]\omega. \tag{5.31}$$

The group of the Hamiltonian is $U(2)$. For $\varDelta = 0$, the group is $U(3)$. Kets that are symmetry adapted to the chain $U(3) \supset U(2) \supset O^+(2)$ are written $|\nu; \nu_\parallel \nu_\perp \nu_\lambda\rangle$ where $\nu_\parallel = \nu, \nu - 1, \ldots, 0, \nu_\perp = \nu - \nu_\parallel$, and $\pm\nu_\lambda = \nu_\perp, \nu_\perp - 2, \ldots, 1$, or zero.

The Hamiltonian with spin for the spheroidal field is approximated by

$$\mathscr{H} = \mathscr{H}^E \times I + \mathbf{\Omega} \cdot \mathbf{S}. \tag{5.32}$$

For $\varDelta = \mathbf{\Omega} = 0$, the group is $U(3) \times {}^dO^+(3)$. For $\varDelta = 0, \mathbf{\Omega} \neq 0$, the group is $O^+(3) \boxtimes {}^dO^+(3)$. For $\varDelta \neq 0$, $\mathbf{\Omega} = 0$, the group is $U(2) \times {}^dO^+(3)$. For $\varDelta \neq 0$, $\mathbf{\Omega} \neq 0$, the group is $O^+(2) \boxtimes {}^dO^+(2)$. The exact quantum number is

$$\Omega = |\nu_\lambda + m_s| = |m_j|. \tag{5.33}$$

The lattice and a correlation diagram are given in Fig. 11.

Hamiltonian

$$\mathscr{H}=\left(\frac{p^2}{2M}+\frac{M\omega^2}{2}(r^2-\Delta z^2)\right)\times I+\mathbf{\Omega}\cdot\mathbf{S}$$

Lattice

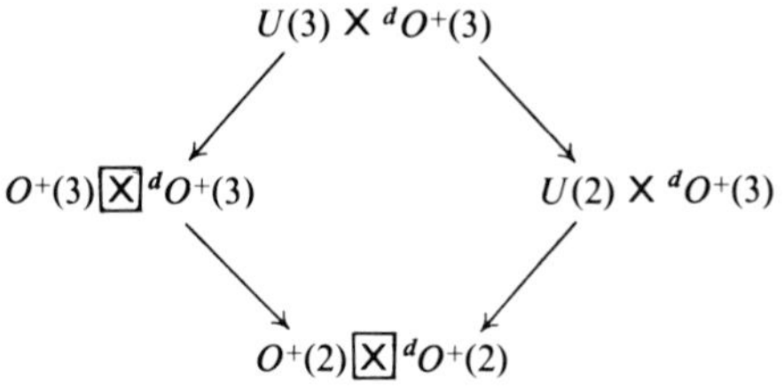

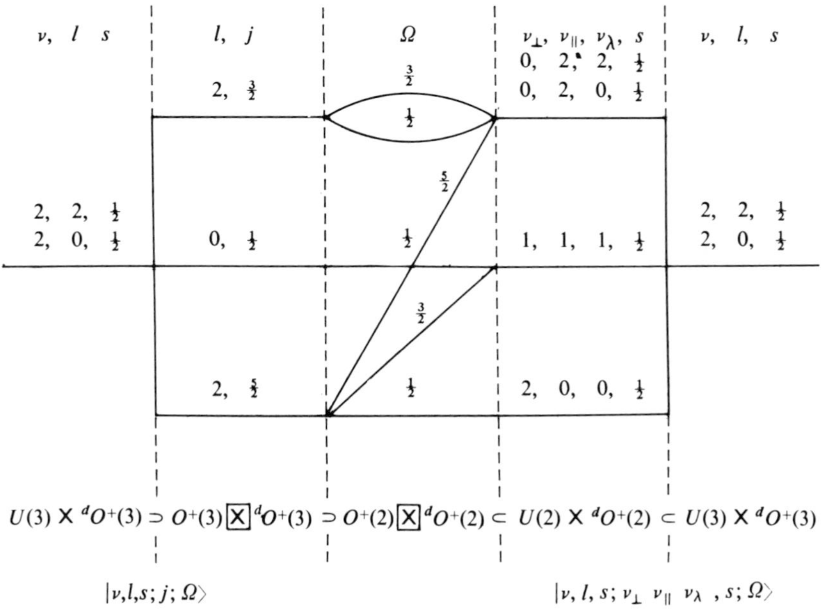

FIG. 11. The Hamiltonian, lattice, and correlation diagram for the Nilsson nuclear orbitals.

Acknowledgments

The authors gratefully acknowledge helpful conversations with Dr. Marcos Moshinsky and Dr. Charles Carlysle.

REFERENCES

1. N. Jacobson, "Lectures in Abstract Algebra," Vol. I. Van Nostrand, Princeton, New Jersey, 1951.
2. D. E. Littlewood, "The Theory of Group Characters." Oxford Univ. Press, London and New York, 1956.
3. M. A. Melvin, *Rev. Mod. Phys.* **28**, 18 (1956).
4. L. Foldy and S. Wouthuysen, *Phys. Rev.* **78**, 29 (1950).
5. M. Tinkham, "Group Theory and Quantum Mechanics." McGraw-Hill, New York, 1964.
6. W. Pauli, *Z. Physik* **36**, 336 (1926); L. Hulthen, *ibid.* **86**, 21 (1933); V. Bargmann, *ibid.* **99**, 376 (1936).
7. F. A. Matsen, *Advan. Quant. Chem.* **1**, 59 (1964).
8. G. Racah, *Group Theory and Spectroscopy*, *Ergeb. Exakt. Naturw.* **37**, 28 (1965).
9. A. Dalgarno, T. N. L. Patterson, and W. B. Somerville, *Proc. Roy. Soc. London Ser. A* **259**, 100 (1960).
10. E. Teller, *Z. Physik* **61**, 458 (1930).
11. J. P. Elliott, *Proc. Roy. Soc. London Ser. A* **245**, 128, 562 (1958).
12. S. G. Nilsson, *Mat.-Fys. Medd. Danske Vid. Selsk.* **16**, 29 (1955).

Group Theory in Solid State Physics

STIG FLODMARK

INSTITUTE OF THEORETICAL PHYSICS
UNIVERSITY OF STOCKHOLM, STOCKHOLM, SWEDEN

I. Introduction

Group theory has become a most useful tool in modern physics for systematizing the description of idealized processes dealing with theoretical concepts such as energy, mass, charge, momentum, and angular momentum; for classifying states in the quantum theory of matter; and, further, for simplifying numerical applications of physical laws. The symmetry of a physical system is due to idealizations, such as closed systems, isotropic spaces, ideal gases, incompressible fluids, and perfect solids. It is a remarkable fundamental property of Nature that idealizations of this kind are really meaningful, that is, conclusions that can be drawn from assumptions of symmetry will become relevant. This may be explained by saying that the configuration of highest possible symmetry usually is the most favorable physical state. On the other hand, physically interesting effects that depend on deviations from idealized models can often be treated as small perturbations, so that lack of symmetry in Nature can also be said to play an important role in the description of many physical phenomena.

Conclusions drawn by merely studying the symmetry of an idealized physical situation are always exact. This may be nice enough, but, furthermore, the results obtained for a specific problem may be used again in other physical situations, since the same symmetry may occur in various different applications.

In this chapter we shall be concerned mainly with the symmetry of solid states. Crystal symmetry is an interesting subject for detailed study because of the variety of lattice structures occurring in Nature. Considerations of symmetry alone may be the most essential part of the work in determining the properties of crystalline solids. It is necessary to make use of the crystal symmetry in order to be able to obtain numerical solutions for the equations of motion of identical particles, such as electrons, phonons, or photons, moving in perfect solids.

Because of the extent of solid state physics, we do not intend to give a complete review here. To do so would just be a rewriting of many excellent books already existing in the field. We shall concentrate on studying some symmetry properties of electrons and phonons in a perfect crystal lattice. For this purpose we start, in Section II, by discussing stationary states in the quantum theory of gases, fluids, and solids, and the role played by symmetry in this theory. In Section III we remind the reader of the fundamental laws of group theory applied to quantum mechanics. In Section IV the properties of certain symmetry groups occurring in solid state physics are briefly reviewed. The subsequent sections of the chapter are devoted to applications to different kinds of particles moving in solids.

II. Stationary States in the Quantum Theory of Matter

The stationary states of quantum mechanics are of fundamental importance for the description of properties of atoms, molecules, and solids. We shall here briefly discuss the well-known theory behind it and the manner in which symmetry can be used for classification and simplification.

A. Gaseous States

Consider a large number of identical molecules, each one described as an isolated quantum-mechanical system by means of a Hamiltonian that does not explicitly depend on time. We then have an idealized gas of molecules, where we do not consider the detailed behavior of the internal molecular states during the time of collision between two molecules because of its shortness in comparison with the mean free time. As a consequence of quantum theory the expectation value of the internal energy for one of the identical systems will be constant in time. Adopting the Born-Oppenheimer approximation (*1*) for separating the nuclear motion of this system from the electronic part, the expectation value of the electronic energy is given by

$$E = \langle \Psi(t) | \mathscr{H} | \Psi(t) \rangle,$$

where $\mathscr{H}$ is the electronic part of the Hamiltonian and $|\Psi(t)\rangle$ is the time-dependent electronic state vector satisfying the quantum-mechanical state equation

$$i\hbar \frac{d}{dt} | \Psi(t) \rangle = \mathscr{H} | \Psi(t) \rangle. \tag{1}$$

Since E is constant in time for states $|\Psi(t)\rangle$ satisfying Eq. (1) with a time-independent Hamiltonian, it depends only on the initial values of the probability amplitudes $\langle \alpha_1 | \Psi(0) \rangle, \langle \alpha_2 | \Psi(0) \rangle, \ldots$, for the electrons at time $t = 0$ to be found in the states $|\alpha_1\rangle, |\alpha_2\rangle, \ldots$, respectively, forming a complete basis set for description of the degrees of freedom of the electrons.

The stationary states of a molecule can be found by looking for the extreme values of E for all the possible initial conditions. A general state $|\Psi(t)\rangle$

satisfying the time-dependent state equation, Eq. (1), may be written as a linear superposition of stationary states, each one of which is multiplied by a time-dependent phase factor depending on the energy of the stationary state. The constant electronic energy for a solution of Eq. (1) is therefore not necessarily limited a priori to the values of stationary states only. As a consequence of Heisenberg's principle of uncertainty, however, molecules cannot exist for a long time in nonstationary states without changing into one of the stationary states. Under normal external pressure there are only small probabilities for transitions between these states, which are accompanied by the emission and absorption of ultraviolet or optical photons. The supposition of a time-independent Hamiltonian can be correct, however, only when the states are considered to be stationary all the time. Explicit consideration of the processes of stationary-state transititions must include the radiation field, which is important when the collisions take place. Neglecting radiation we can thus study only stationary states. Accepting the ideas of quantum statistics, however, some note of the interaction with the radiation field is implicitly taken.

As we have seen, stationary states are of primary importance for determining properties of molecules. In the process of determining these states, the molecular symmetry group is very essential. Molecules that are not found in the electronic ground state may radiate light spontaneously. At low temperatures, when the molecular interaction is negligible, we would therefore expect to find almost all molecules in the ground state, which corresponds to a vanishing angular momentum and the highest possible symmetry. The distribution of molecular states would thus be sharply peaked. For higher temperatures, however, we would expect to find some of the molecules in excited states. The state equation (1) may be used to compute the possible magnitudes of light quanta for molecular absorption and emission spectra. The resulting states may also be used for determining the time-dependent probability amplitudes for transition between any two of these states in the presence of a given external field.

Considering also the nuclear motion, we may have a weak coupling between the rotation-vibration states and the electronic states, depending on temperature. At low temperatures this may yield only a slight displacement of the stationary electronic energy levels. For those vibrational states where the equilibrium molecular symmetry is conserved, the degeneracies of the unperturbed electronic states are not changed; vibrational states violating the molecular equilibrium symmetry, however, will yield a splitting of these degeneracies.

There is another interesting kind of "vibration" that may occur in molecules. This is the so-called resonance between equivalent chemical structures, such as the two equivalent states describing the ammonia molecule with nitrogen on either side of the plane of the hydrogen atoms. Although according to classical physics, the energy is not sufficient for nitrogen to pass through the potential barrier of the hydrogen plane, this is not impossible according to quantum mechanics, since the width of the potential barrier is small enough to give a certain probability for tunneling through. The stationary states describing a molecule of this kind are found as linear combinations of states corresponding to the different equivalent chemical structures of the molecule. Because of the interaction between these structures, the corresponding energy levels are just slightly different, and the splitting is almost exactly the same for all the "ordinary" spectral lines. This fine structure thus yields very sharp transitions in the microwave region with an energy transfer far below those of the ordinary vibrational spectra, which correspond to infrared transitions. This is the reason why ammonia can operate as a maser when it interacts with electromagnetic microwaves of resonance frequency. Very similar situations may occur for molecules, where some of the atomic pieces may take part in so-called hindered rotation.

B. Fluid and Solid States

When the mean free time between two collisions for one of the molecules in a gas becomes shorter, there is a limit where the molecules prefer to keep together with weak intermolecular bonds. Ionic bonds within the free molecules will then be weakened or even broken up, which may make it possible for the ions to move separately. Because of the lack of internal symmetry, the quantum-mechanical treatment of these fluid states is very complicated. We have to rely on very rough and simple models, and group theory does not play an essential role in this connection. We shall therefore not be concerned with this problem here.

Solid as well as fluid states are generally far too complicated to be studied quantitatively by means of quantum theory. This is always true for amorphous solids, where no spatial symmetry exists. Considering the solid as an immense molecule, it is a hopeless problem to solve the Schrödinger equation for all the electrons, even when the nuclear positions are supposed to be known and the Born-Oppenheimer approximation is accepted.

In crystals, however, the spatial symmetry makes it possible to investigate the electronic structure qualitatively and often quantitatively. Several different methods of approach are possible, some of which will be discussed in Section VI.

C. The Role of Symmetry

It is now natural to ask: What is the actual advantage of using symmetry for solving the Schrödinger equation of the stationary states of an atom, a molecule, or a crystal? Neglecting nuclear spin, the external potential field for the electrons of a free atom is spherically symmetric, which corresponds to the conservation of the total angular momentum of the electrons. Consider first the limiting case, when we neglect the part of the electron-electron interaction that is not spherically symmetric, as well as the electronic spin-orbit coupling. Then each electron may be described by means of a spin orbital, where the angular dependence is factored out in the form of a spherical harmonic that transforms irreducibly under the continuous rotation group. It remains to solve for the radial parts of the hydrogenic wave functions, a procedure that cannot be facilitated by means of group theory. Because electrons are identical particles that belong to the antisymmetric irreducible representation of the group of permutations between them, the total electronic wave function will be found as an antisymmetric product sum of the spherically symmetry-adapted spin orbitals.

When the interelectronic Coulomb forces are taken into full account, the spherical symmetry is broken, degeneracies are removed, and mixing between the pure states take place. In the LS coupling scheme used for light atoms, the total orbital angular momentum $\mathbf{L}$ and the total spin angular momentum $\mathbf{S}$ are supposed to be conserved separately, yielding terms of degeneracy $(2S + 1)$, where S is the spin quantum number.

By inclusion of spin-orbit interaction the symmetry is further decreased and the term degeneracies are further split, yielding a fine-structure spectrum. The remaining degeneracies are removed by magnetic-field splitting. Thus, hyperfine structures will be obtained by including the small effects of electronic interaction with the nuclear magnetic moment. Group theory therefore plays an important role in the classification of atomic states and is most valuable for the simplification of their determination.

For molecules the spherical symmetry is broken and the electrons cannot be well described by factoring the angular dependent parts of their spin orbitals in the form of spherical harmonics of one atomic center. Using the method where the molecular orbitals are taken as linear combinations of atomic orbitals (LCAO method), however, the proper combinations to be used in the basis are found by the requirement that they transform irreducibly under the molecular point group. Forming many-electron basis functions as products of these orbitals, it remains again to construct linear combinations of those products that transform irreducibly under the point group. It is an essential simplification of the resulting secular equations for determining the energy eigenvalues to first make full symmetry adaptation with respect to the molecular point group.

The situation is quite similar for an atom in a crystal, when the remaining part of the crystal may be considered as a perturbing ligand field that has point-group symmetry. The point group represents a lower symmetry than the continuous rotation group and will usually cause mixing between those atomic states that are degenerate in the limit when the crystal field vanishes. These degeneracies will thus in general be split by the crystal ligand field.

Considering the whole crystal, the atomic orbitals of the electrons should be symmetry adapted with respect to the total crystallographic space group. Without using the periodicity of the crystal potential, it is not possible in practice to solve the Schrödinger equation for an electron moving in a solid.

It should be noted that the methods of forming symmetry-adapted crystal-orbital states that are introduced in Section VI can be used also for determining lattice vibrations (see Section V), ligand field states, and molecular states, since all these can be treated formally by means of the tight-binding method. A general computer program for symmetry projections of the crystal-orbital states may thus take care of all these different cases.

III. The Group of the Hamiltonian

The symmetry group that can be used for simplifying the calculation of stationary states of a given Hamiltonian in quantum theory is denoted as the group of the Schrödinger equation, or the group of the Hamiltonian. In this section we shall summarize the main steps in the straightforward procedure of utilizing this group in general.

A. Representation Theory

We shall now study the group-theoretical problem of simplifying the procedure for solving the stationary states of the Hamiltonian of a quantum-mechanical system. The stationary states are particular solutions of Eq. (1) written as

$$|\Psi(t)\rangle = |\psi\rangle \exp\left(-\frac{i}{\hbar} Et\right), \tag{2}$$

where $|\psi\rangle$ is a solution of the eigenvector equation

$$\mathscr{H}|\psi\rangle = E|\psi\rangle \tag{3}$$

of the Hamiltonian $\mathscr{H}$. In order to solve Eq. (3), we use a suitable basis set of state vectors $|\alpha_1\rangle, |\alpha_2\rangle, \ldots$. For completeness, this set should generally be of infinite order, but it may be cut off at finite order in approximate treatments of bound states. We write the set of basis vectors in a row matrix according to

$$\boldsymbol{\alpha} = (|\alpha_1\rangle, |\alpha_2\rangle, \ldots). \tag{4}$$

A general state vector $|\psi\rangle$ in the basis spanned by Eq. (4) may be written

$$|\psi\rangle = \sum_i |\alpha_i\rangle \psi_i = \boldsymbol{\alpha\psi}, \tag{5}$$

where $\boldsymbol{\psi}$ is a column matrix formed by the components

$$\psi_i = \langle \alpha_i | \psi \rangle \tag{6}$$

of $|\psi\rangle$ in the basis of Eq. (4), in the case when this is orthogonal.

The group of the Hamiltonian is denoted by

$$G = \{\mathscr{A}, \mathscr{B}, \mathscr{C}, \ldots, \mathscr{P}, \ldots\}. \tag{7}$$

It is supposed to contain only a finite number of symmetry operators, or group elements, $\mathscr{P}$, all of which commute with the Hamiltonian:

$$[\mathscr{P}, \mathscr{H}] = 0; \qquad \text{all} \quad \mathscr{P} \in G. \tag{8}$$

The symmetry operators, as well as $\mathscr{H}$, will act as linear operators in the vector space spanned by Eq. (4). The action of any group element $\mathscr{P}$ contained in G is given by

$$\mathscr{P}|\alpha_k\rangle = \sum_i |\alpha_i\rangle P_{ik}, \tag{9}$$

where P_{ik} is a component of a square matrix $\mathbf{P}$. In particular, if the basis of Eq. (4) is orthogonal, the matrix elements of $\mathbf{P}$ are given by

$$P_{ik} = \langle \alpha_i | \mathscr{P} | \alpha_k \rangle. \tag{10}$$

Generally, however, for a basis that is not necessarily orthogonal, it is seen from Eq. (9) that

$$\langle \alpha_i | \mathscr{P} | \alpha_k \rangle = \sum_j \Delta_{ij} P_{jk}. \tag{11}$$

Here $\Delta_{ij} = \langle \alpha_i | \alpha_j \rangle$ are elements of the overlap, or metric, matrix of the basis in Eq. (4),

$$\boldsymbol{\Delta} = \boldsymbol{\alpha}^{\dagger}\boldsymbol{\alpha}, \tag{12}$$

which is reduced to a unit matrix in the special case of orthogonality.

Using matrix notation, we can rewrite Eq. (9) as

$$\mathscr{P}\boldsymbol{\alpha} = \boldsymbol{\alpha}\mathbf{P}. \tag{13}$$

Multiplying Eq. (13) from the left by $\mathbf{\Delta}^{-1}\boldsymbol{\alpha}^\dagger$ and using Eq. (12), we obtain

$$\mathbf{P} = \mathbf{\Delta}^{-1}\boldsymbol{\alpha}^\dagger \mathscr{P}\boldsymbol{\alpha}, \tag{14a}$$

in accordance with Eq. (11). Multiplying Eq. (13) from the right by $\mathbf{\Delta}^{-1}\boldsymbol{\alpha}^\dagger$, we obtain the reverse relation,

$$\mathscr{P} = \boldsymbol{\alpha}\mathbf{P}\mathbf{\Delta}^{-1}\boldsymbol{\alpha}^\dagger, \tag{14b}$$

since $\boldsymbol{\alpha}\mathbf{\Delta}^{-1}\boldsymbol{\alpha}^\dagger$ is the resolution of the identity operator in terms of dyadic products $|\alpha_i\rangle\langle\alpha_j|$ of the basis vectors.

From Eq. (13) it is obvious that the set of square matrices

$$\Gamma = \{\mathbf{A}, \mathbf{B}, \mathbf{C}, \ldots, \mathbf{P}, \ldots\} \tag{15}$$

forms a matrix representation of G in the basis of Eq. (4). Actually, using Eq. (13), we find

$$\mathscr{A}\mathscr{B}\boldsymbol{\alpha} = \mathscr{A}\boldsymbol{\alpha}\mathbf{B} = \boldsymbol{\alpha}\mathbf{A}\mathbf{B}, \tag{16}$$

which proves the theorem. Operating with $\mathscr{P}$ on a general state vector defined by Eq. (5), we find, by using Eq. (13),

$$\mathscr{P}|\psi\rangle = \mathscr{P}\boldsymbol{\alpha}\boldsymbol{\psi} = \boldsymbol{\alpha}\mathbf{P}\boldsymbol{\psi}, \tag{17}$$

which means that the state vector obtained when $\mathscr{P}$ operates on $|\psi\rangle$ is represented by the column matrix $\mathbf{P}\boldsymbol{\psi}$ in the basis $\boldsymbol{\alpha}$.

B. Irreducible Subspaces

We shall now investigate the change of the group representation given by Eq. (15) under a transformation of the basis system. Suppose the basis $\boldsymbol{\beta}$ be obtained from $\boldsymbol{\alpha}$ by means of the nonsingular matrix $\mathbf{S}^{-1}$, according to

$$\boldsymbol{\beta} = \boldsymbol{\alpha}\mathbf{S}^{-1}; \qquad \boldsymbol{\alpha} = \boldsymbol{\beta}\mathbf{S}. \tag{18}$$

[We want to do it this way only in order that $\boldsymbol{\psi}'$ in Eq. (19) shall represent $|\psi'\rangle = \mathscr{S}|\psi\rangle$.] Inserting Eq. (18) for $\boldsymbol{\alpha}$ into Eq. (5), it is seen that

$$\boldsymbol{\psi}' = \mathbf{S}\boldsymbol{\psi} \tag{19}$$

is the column representing $|\psi\rangle$ in the basis $\boldsymbol{\beta} = \mathscr{S}^{-1}\boldsymbol{\alpha}$. Provided that $\mathscr{S}$ is unitary and $\boldsymbol{\alpha}$ orthogonal, $\boldsymbol{\psi}'$ also represents the state $|\psi'\rangle = \mathscr{S}|\psi\rangle$ in the original basis $\boldsymbol{\alpha}$. The components of $\boldsymbol{\psi}'$ are then given by

$$\psi_i' = \langle \alpha_i | \psi' \rangle = \langle \alpha_i | \mathscr{S} | \psi \rangle = \langle \beta_i | \psi \rangle$$

in this case. Using Eqs. (18) and (13), we find, also when $\mathbf{S}$ is not unitary,

$$\mathscr{P}\boldsymbol{\beta} = \mathscr{P}\boldsymbol{\alpha}\mathbf{S}^{-1} = \boldsymbol{\alpha}\mathbf{P}\mathbf{S}^{-1} = \boldsymbol{\beta}\mathbf{S}\mathbf{P}\mathbf{S}^{-1} = \boldsymbol{\beta}\mathbf{P}', \tag{20}$$

where

$$\mathbf{P}' = \mathbf{S}\mathbf{P}\mathbf{S}^{-1}. \tag{21}$$

Thus $\mathbf{P}'$ is the matrix representing $\mathscr{P}$ in the basis $\boldsymbol{\beta}$, as well as $\mathscr{P}' = \mathscr{S}\mathscr{P}\mathscr{S}^{-1}$ in the basis $\boldsymbol{\alpha}$. Accordingly,

$$\Gamma' = \mathbf{S}\Gamma\mathbf{S}^{-1} \tag{22}$$

is another representation of the group, equivalent to Γ. In particular, choosing $\mathbf{S} = \boldsymbol{\Delta}^{1/2}$, where $\boldsymbol{\Delta}$ is the metric matrix defined by Eq. (12), $\boldsymbol{\beta}$ becomes an orthogonal basis.

In the case when it is possible to find a linear transformation of the basis according to Eq. (18) so that the basis $\boldsymbol{\beta}$ contains a subbasis invariant under the group operators, the vector space is said to be *reducible*; it is *completely reducible* if the remaining part of $\boldsymbol{\beta}$ is also invariant under the group operators. If there is no such linear transformation, the space is said to be *irreducible* under G.

Suppose now that $\boldsymbol{\beta}$ is a reduced basis. In the case of a completely reducible vector space, the matrix $\mathbf{P}'$ in Eqs. (20) and (21), representing a general group element $\mathscr{P}$ in the basis $\boldsymbol{\beta}$, will then be block-diagonalized, that is, it is composed of nonzero submatrices, or blocks, along the main diagonal, and vanishing matrix elements outside these blocks. Each block ${}^{\lambda}\mathbf{P}$ represents $\mathscr{P}$, when operating on the basis ${}^{\lambda}\boldsymbol{\beta}$, spanning the λth unreduced subspace of $\boldsymbol{\beta}$. The set of block matrices ${}^{\lambda}\Gamma = \{{}^{\lambda}\mathbf{A}, {}^{\lambda}\mathbf{B}, \ldots, {}^{\lambda}\mathbf{P}, \ldots\}$ thus forms a representation of the group. This representation is irreducible if all its matrix representatives cannot be further block-diagonalized by a common similarity transformation.

It may occur that ${}^{\lambda}\mathbf{P}$ and ${}^{\lambda'}\mathbf{P}$ are equivalent when $\lambda \neq \lambda'$. Then there is a nonsingular matrix $\mathbf{S}_{\lambda}$ of the same order as ${}^{\lambda}\mathbf{P}$ such that $\mathbf{S}_{\lambda}\,{}^{\lambda}\mathbf{P}\mathbf{S}_{\lambda}^{-1} = {}^{\lambda'}\mathbf{P}$. By a suitable modification of the original matrix $\mathbf{S}$ in Eq. (22), it is always possible, however, to choose $\boldsymbol{\beta}$ in such a way that equivalent representatives are also equal, that is, ${}^{\lambda}\mathbf{P} = {}^{\lambda'}\mathbf{P}$. We suppose that $\boldsymbol{\beta}$ is chosen this way. We may then introduce a double index notation (n, j) for λ, where j symbolizes the irreducible representative ${}^{\lambda}\mathbf{P} = {}^{j}\mathbf{P}$ and n labels different appearances of ${}^{j}\mathbf{P}$ along the main diagonal of $\mathbf{P}'$. Two irreducible subspaces $^{nj}\boldsymbol{\beta}$ and $^{n'j'}\boldsymbol{\beta}$ of $\boldsymbol{\beta}$ are thus symmetry equivalent (i.e., $^{j}\mathbf{P} = {}^{j'}\mathbf{P}$) only when $j = j'$.

In the case when the representation is reducible, but not completely reducible, the matrix elements outside blocks along the main diagonal of each $\mathbf{P}'$ vanish completely at only one side of the diagonal. Such a representation cannot be unitary, since the inverse of any group element also belongs to the group, and therefore is represented by a matrix with vanishing elements at the same side of the blocks as for the representative of the group element itself. For finite groups, however, reducibility always means complete reducibility, since the representations can then always be chosen unitary. In the following we shall consider only completely reducible group representations.

When the irreducible subspaces are obtained, the problem of solving Eq. (3) has been simplified as much as possible by means of symmetry. We shall summarize in the following paragraphs the well-known properties of irreducible representations that are contained in Schur's lemma.

If $^{\lambda}\Gamma$ and $^{\lambda'}\Gamma$ are two irreducible representations and there is a matrix $\mathbf{M}$ satisfying the condition

$$^{\lambda}\mathbf{P}\mathbf{M} = \mathbf{M}\,{}^{\lambda'}\mathbf{P}; \qquad \text{all} \quad \mathscr{P} \in G, \tag{23}$$

where $^{\lambda}\mathbf{P}$ and $^{\lambda'}\mathbf{P}$ are the two irreducible representatives of $\mathscr{P}$ contained in $^{\lambda}\Gamma$ and $^{\lambda'}\Gamma$, respectively, then either $\mathbf{M} = 0$ or $^{\lambda}\Gamma$ and $^{\lambda'}\Gamma$ are equivalent (i.e., $\mathbf{M}$ is nonsingular). For a detailed proof, the reader may consult any book on elementary group theory.

By suitable choices for the matrix $\mathbf{M}$ in Eq. (23), it is not difficult to prove the fundamental orthogonality relations between elements of the irreducible representations:

$$\frac{l_j}{g} \sum_{\mathscr{P} \in G} {}^{j}P^{*}_{\mu\nu}\, {}^{j'}P_{\mu'\nu'} = \delta_{jj'}\, \delta_{\mu\mu'}\, \delta_{\nu\nu'}. \tag{24}$$

Here l_j is the order of the jth irreducible representation, g is the order of the group and $^{j}P_{\mu\nu}$ is a matrix element of the jth nonequivalent irreducible representative $^{j}\mathbf{P}$ of the group element $\mathscr{P}$. It is also supposed that $^{j}\mathbf{P}$ is unitary.

Returning to our original problem, the eigenvalue equation (3) may be written in matrix form,

$$\boldsymbol{\alpha}(\mathbf{H} - E)\boldsymbol{\psi} = 0, \tag{25}$$

by introducing Eq. (5) and using the relation $\mathscr{H}\boldsymbol{\alpha} = \boldsymbol{\alpha}\mathbf{H}$ analogous to Eq. (13). In accordance with Eq. (14a), the Hamiltonian matrix $\mathbf{H}$ representing $\mathscr{H}$ in the basis $\boldsymbol{\alpha}$ is given by

$$\mathbf{H} = \boldsymbol{\Delta}^{-1}\boldsymbol{\alpha}^{\dagger}\mathscr{H}\boldsymbol{\alpha}. \tag{26}$$

Equation (25) then becomes

$$\boldsymbol{\alpha}\boldsymbol{\Delta}^{-1}(\boldsymbol{\alpha}^{\dagger}\mathscr{H}\boldsymbol{\alpha} - E\boldsymbol{\Delta})\boldsymbol{\psi} = 0. \tag{27}$$

The eigenvalues E of Eq. (3) are thus found as roots of the secular equation

$$\det(\boldsymbol{\alpha}^{\dagger}\mathscr{H}\boldsymbol{\alpha} - E\boldsymbol{\Delta}) = 0. \tag{28}$$

We suppose now again that $\boldsymbol{\beta}$ is a reduced basis, divided into parts ${}^{nj}\boldsymbol{\beta}$ spanning different irreducible subspaces:

$$\boldsymbol{\beta} = (\ldots, {}^{nj}\boldsymbol{\beta}, \ldots, {}^{n'j'}\boldsymbol{\beta}, \ldots);$$
$$\mathscr{P}\,{}^{nj}\boldsymbol{\beta} = {}^{nj}\boldsymbol{\beta}\,{}^{j}\mathbf{P}. \tag{29}$$

Then, according to Schur's lemma, nonequivalent irreducible subspaces are orthogonal to each other, and moreover,

$${}^{nj}\boldsymbol{\beta}^{\dagger}\,\mathscr{H}\,{}^{n'j'}\boldsymbol{\beta} = 0, \qquad \text{for} \quad j \neq j'. \tag{30}$$

This equation is obtained by using the left-hand side of Eq. (30) for $\mathbf{M}$ in Eq. (23), which is easily seen to be valid for unitary group elements $\mathscr{P}$ with this choice of $\mathbf{M}$, because of the commutation relations of Eq. (8). After the transformation of the basis $\boldsymbol{\alpha}$ into $\boldsymbol{\beta}$, the secular equation (28) becomes factored with respect to different j values, yielding a separate equation for each nonequivalent irreducible subspace contained in $\boldsymbol{\beta}$. Denoting by $|njm\rangle = |{}^{nj}\boldsymbol{\beta}_m\rangle$ the mth basis vector of ${}^{nj}\boldsymbol{\beta}$, it is further found from Schur's lemma that

$$\langle njm|\mathscr{H}|n'jm'\rangle = \delta_{mm'}\,{}^{j}H_{nn'}, \tag{31}$$

where ${}^{j}H_{nn'}$ is independent of m. Thus the secular equation for the jth irreducible representation is further factored, yielding identical secular equations for each m value, which corresponds to an l_j-fold degeneracy. Solving the factored secular equations, the eigenstates of the jmth symmetry type are thus found as linear combinations of the states $|njm\rangle$ for different values of n.

C. Expectation Values

As we saw in the preceding subsection, the solutions of Eq. (3) will transform irreducibly under the group of the Hamiltonian. Summarizing Eqs. (30) and (31), we may write

$$\langle njm|\mathscr{H}|n'j'm'\rangle = \delta_{jj'}\,\delta_{mm'}\,{}^{j}H_{nn'}, \tag{32}$$

where thus n and n' label the elements of the Hamiltonian submatrix of symmetry type (j, m). Since $\mathscr{H}$ commutes with all the group operators, $\mathscr{H}|njm\rangle$ transforms under G according to the mth column of the jth irreducible representation. Thus $\mathscr{H}$ acts as a scalar when one does not consider the change of label n. Alternatively, we may say that $\mathscr{H}$ transforms according to the identity representation under the group of $\mathscr{H}$. The expectation values of $\mathscr{H}$ are obtained by diagonalizing the matrix defined by the elements ${}^jH_{nn'}$ of Eq. (32). This procedure cannot be facilitated any further using symmetry properties. In the case when the basis contains only one state for each symmetry type, the eigenvalue problem has been completely solved by symmetry alone.

There are also other "scalar" operators that do not change the symmetry-type indices (j, m) of the state, and that commute with $\mathscr{H}$. This is the case for the class operators $\mathscr{M}_i$ defined by using unitary operators $\mathscr{R}^\dagger = \mathscr{R}^{-1}$, as

$$\mathscr{M}_i = \frac{1}{g} \sum_{\mathscr{R} \in G} \mathscr{R}^\dagger \mathscr{P} \mathscr{R} = \frac{1}{g_i} \sum_{\mathscr{P} \in C_i} \mathscr{P}, \tag{33}$$

where g_i is the number of elements of the class C_i. The elements of the class containing a given group element $\mathscr{P}$ are obtained by making all conjugations of the type $\mathscr{R}^\dagger \mathscr{P} \mathscr{R}$, where $\mathscr{R}$ runs through the elements of the group. Together with the Hamiltonian, the class operators form a set of commuting operators that is in general neither complete nor Hermitian. We shall see in subsection E, however, that it is possible to find a complete set of commuting symmetry operators that can be used to classify the symmetry-adapted states.

Since any group element commutes with the class operator of Eq. (33), the matrices $\mathbf{M}_i = {}^{nj}\boldsymbol{\beta}^\dagger \mathscr{M}_i {}^{n'j'}\boldsymbol{\beta}$ fulfill the condition of Schur's lemma. Thus

$$\langle njm|\mathscr{M}_i|n'j'm'\rangle = \langle njm|\mathscr{M}_i|n'jm\rangle \, \delta_{jj'} \, \delta_{mm'} . \tag{34}$$

The only possible nonvanishing matrix elements of any operator $\mathscr{M}$ transforming according to the identity representation ${}^1\Gamma$ (i.e., $\mathscr{P}\mathscr{M}\mathscr{P}^{-1} = \mathscr{M}$), are accordingly those that are diagonal with respect to j and m. On the other hand, operators that belong to irreducible representations other than ${}^1\Gamma$, or that transform according to some mixed representation not containing ${}^1\Gamma$, always have vanishing expectation values.

D. Transition Probabilities and Selection Rules

In addition to the study of expectation values, group theory can be used to investigate the circumstances under which certain quantum-mechanical operators have nonvanishing matrix elements between states of different symmetry types. This is important, since it is possible, by means of pure symmetry arguments, to find out, for example, which of the transition probabilities between pure states are nonvanishing, thus corresponding to permitted transitions, and which are vanishing (forbidden transitions) for a perturbation field of given symmetry.

Dropping the nonsymmetry label n in the notation $|njm\rangle$ of a symmetry-adapted state, we can consider a subspace of symmetry type (j, m) formally as a state vector, $|jm\rangle$. According to Eq. (29), then

$$\mathscr{P}|jm\rangle = \sum_{m'} |jm'\rangle\, {}^{j}P_{m'm}. \tag{35}$$

Similarly, a set of operators ${}^{j}\mathscr{R}_m$ defined for $m = 1, 2, \ldots, l_j$, transforms according to the jth irreducible representation, when

$$\mathscr{P}\, {}^{j}\mathscr{R}_m \mathscr{P}^{-1} = \sum_{m'=1}^{l_j} {}^{j}\mathscr{R}_{m'}\, {}^{j}P_{m'm}; \qquad m = 1, 2, \ldots, l_j. \tag{36}$$

It is seen from Eq. (36) that ${}^{j}\mathscr{R}_m|j''m''\rangle$ transforms under G according to the direct product representation ${}^{j}\Gamma \boxtimes {}^{j''}\Gamma$. Thus the matrix elements $\langle j'm'|{}^{j}\mathscr{R}_m|j''m''\rangle$ differ from zero only when the direct product representation ${}^{j}\Gamma \boxtimes {}^{j''}\Gamma$ contains the irreducible representation ${}^{j'}\Gamma$. This result is directly obtained by means of the orthogonality relations given by Eq. (24), and constitutes a more general rule for finding the vanishing matrix elements of operators with a given symmetry.

E. Projection Operators

We are now looking for a complete set of commuting Hermitian operators that may be used to construct the symmetry-adapted subspaces $|jm\rangle$ from a given basis in Hilbert space. Let us consider the dyadic product operator

$${}^{j}\mathscr{S}_{mm'} = |jm\rangle\langle jm'|. \tag{37}$$

Operating to the right on a state of symmetry type (λ, μ), we find

$${}^{j}\mathscr{S}_{mm'}|\lambda\mu\rangle = |jm\rangle\langle jm'|\lambda\mu\rangle = |jm\rangle\, \delta_{j\lambda}\, \delta_{m'\mu} \tag{38a}$$

on account of the orthogonality between symmetry-adapted subspaces. Operating to the left on the conjugate state, similarly

$$\langle\lambda\mu|\, {}^{j}\mathscr{S}_{mm'} = \langle\lambda\mu|jm\rangle\langle jm'| = \delta_{\lambda j}\, \delta_{\mu m}\langle jm'|. \tag{38b}$$

The product of any two of these operators is given by

$$ {}^{j}\mathscr{S}_{m\mu}\,{}^{j'}\mathscr{S}_{\mu'm'} = |jm\rangle\langle j\mu|j'\mu'\rangle\langle j'm'| = {}^{j}\mathscr{S}_{mm'}\,\delta_{jj'}\,\delta_{\mu\mu'}. \tag{39a} $$

The Hermitian conjugate of the operator in Eq. (37) is given by

$$ {}^{j}\mathscr{S}^{\dagger}_{mm'} = {}^{j}\mathscr{S}_{m'm}. \tag{39b} $$

In particular, those operators of Eq. (37) that have equal lower indices are idempotent and Hermitian:

$$ ({}^{j}\mathscr{S}_{mm})^2 = {}^{j}\mathscr{S}_{mm}; \tag{40a} $$

$$ {}^{j}\mathscr{S}^{\dagger}_{mm} = {}^{j}\mathscr{S}_{mm}. \tag{40b} $$

These are the properties that are characteristic for projection operators. According to Eqs. (38) for the case $m = m'$, the operator ${}^{j}\mathscr{S}_{mm}$ is thus a projection operator onto the subspace of symmetry type (j, m).

Any group element $\mathscr{P}$ of G is block-diagonalized in the symmetry-adapted basis, and its resolution into dyadic-product components thus yields [cf. Eq. (14b)]:

$$ \begin{aligned} \mathscr{P} &= \sum_{\lambda} \sum_{\mu=1}^{l_\lambda} \sum_{\nu=1}^{l_\lambda} |\lambda\mu\rangle\,{}^{\lambda}P_{\mu\nu}\langle\lambda\nu| \\ &= \sum_{\lambda\mu\nu} {}^{\lambda}\mathscr{S}_{\mu\nu}\,{}^{\lambda}P_{\mu\nu}. \end{aligned} \tag{41} $$

Equation (41) yields a linear relationship between the group elements $\mathscr{P}$, the number of which is given by g, and the dyadic-product operators ${}^{\lambda}\mathscr{S}_{\mu\nu}$, the number of which is given by $\sum_\lambda l_\lambda^2 = g$. The inverse transformation is given by

$$ {}^{j}\mathscr{S}_{mm'} = \frac{l_j}{g} \sum_{\mathscr{P}\in G} {}^{j}P^{*}_{mm'}\mathscr{P}, \tag{42} $$

which is seen immediately by using Eq. (41) for $\mathscr{P}$ in Eq. (42) and applying the orthogonality relations of Eq. (24). The projection operator

$$ {}^{j}\mathscr{S}_{mm} = \frac{l_j}{g} \sum_{\mathscr{P}\in G} {}^{j}P^{*}_{mm}\mathscr{P} \tag{43} $$

is known as Wigner's projection operator (*2*) for the symmetry type (j, m), and may be constructed from the knowledge of the diagonal elements of the irreducible representatives. Since there is one such projection operator for each symmetry type, we have thus found a complete set of commuting Hermitian operators that also commute with the Hamiltonian.

Any linear combination of the Wigner projection operators in Eq. (43) defines an operator that cannot change the symmetry type of a given eigenstate of $\mathscr{H}$. Summing over m in Eq. (43) and dividing by the number of terms l_j, we obtain the character operator, or simple characteristic, ${}^j\mathscr{S}$, which still yields projection onto the jth irreducible subspace:

$$ {}^j\mathscr{S} = \frac{1}{g} \sum_{\mathscr{P} \in G} {}^j\chi^*(\mathscr{P})\mathscr{P} = \sum_i \frac{g_i}{g} {}^j\chi_i^* \mathscr{M}_i. \tag{44} $$

Thus ${}^j\mathscr{S}$ is a linear combination of class operators $\mathscr{M}_i$ defined by Eq. (33).

The irreducible character

$$ {}^j\chi(\mathscr{P}) = {}^j\chi_i = \operatorname{tr} {}^j\mathbf{P} \tag{45} $$

is the same for all the elements of the class C_i. Summing over μ and μ' and dividing by l_j in the orthogonality relations of Eq. (24) for $\mu = \nu$, $\mu' = \nu'$, we obtain the orthogonality relations for irreducible characters:

$$ \sum_i \frac{g_i}{g} {}^j\chi_i^* \, {}^{j'}\chi_i = \delta_{jj'}. \tag{46} $$

In order to obtain the inverse of the transformation of Eq. (44), we note that $\mathscr{M}_i$ may be rewritten by using Eqs. (33), (41), (39), and (24):

$$ \begin{aligned} \mathscr{M}_i &= \frac{1}{g} \sum_{\mathscr{R} \in G} \mathscr{R}^\dagger \mathscr{P} \mathscr{R} \\ &= \frac{1}{g} \sum_{\mathscr{R}} \sum_{\lambda\mu\nu} \sum_{\lambda'\mu'\nu'} \sum_{\lambda''\mu''\nu''} {}^\lambda\mathscr{S}^\dagger_{\mu\nu} \, {}^{\lambda'}\mathscr{S}_{\mu'\nu'} \, {}^{\lambda''}\mathscr{S}_{\mu''\nu''} \, {}^\lambda R^*_{\mu\nu} \, {}^{\lambda'}P_{\mu'\nu'} \, {}^{\lambda''}R_{\mu''\nu''} \\ &= \sum_{\lambda\mu\nu} \frac{1}{l_\lambda} {}^\lambda\mathscr{S}_{\nu\nu} \, {}^\lambda P_{\mu\mu} = \sum_\lambda {}^\lambda\mathscr{S} \, {}^\lambda\chi_i. \end{aligned} \tag{47} $$

The class operators may thus be written as linear combinations of the character operators with the irreducible characters as expansion coefficients. According to Eq. (47), a class operator is Hermitian only when the corresponding irreducible characters are all real. Since Eq. (47) is the inverse of Eq. (44), the well-known theorem that the number of irreducible representations is equal to the number of classes is found. Introducing Eq. (44) into Eq. (47), we find

$$\mathscr{M}_i = \sum_j {}^j\mathscr{S}\, {}^j\chi_i = \sum_{i'} \left\{ \frac{g_{i'}}{g} \sum_j {}^j\chi_{i'}^*\, {}^j\chi_i \right\} \mathscr{M}_{i'}. \tag{48}$$

Since the different class operators are linearly independent, we obtain the reverse orthogonality relations for irreducible characters:

$$\frac{g_i}{g} \sum_j {}^j\chi_{i'}^*\, {}^j\chi_i = \delta_{i'i}. \tag{49}$$

Similarly, introducing Eq. (42) into Eq. (41), we find the orthogonality relations between different group elements $\mathscr{P}$ and $\mathscr{R}$:

$$\sum_{\lambda\mu\nu} \frac{l_\lambda}{g}\, {}^\lambda P_{\mu\nu}^*\, {}^\lambda R_{\mu\nu} = \delta_{\mathscr{P}\mathscr{R}}. \tag{50}$$

The group elements may thus be considered as an orthogonal basis spanning a vector space of order g.

F. Reduction of Basis Sets

Knowing the diagonal elements of the irreducible representatives of the elements of the group of the Hamiltonian, the projection operators in Eq. (43) may be constructed for each symmetry type (j, m). For determination of the irreducible subspaces, it suffices to know the irreducible characters. Sometimes it may be useful first to make projections by means of the much more simply applied character operators (44), and apply the symmetry-type projection operators afterwards. For a full symmetry adaptation, it is not sufficient to know the irreducible characters—the whole set of diagonal elements of the irreducible representatives should be known.

Suppose now that we start with a trial basis $\boldsymbol{\alpha}$ as given by Eq. (4). How shall we then proceed to obtain the irreducible subspaces spanned by subsets of the symmetry-adapted basis $\boldsymbol{\beta}$?

Operating with the projection operator of Eq. (43) on the reducible basis $\boldsymbol{\alpha}$, we find by using Eq. (13),

$${}^j\boldsymbol{\alpha}_m = {}^j\mathscr{S}_{mm}\boldsymbol{\alpha} = \boldsymbol{\alpha}\, {}^j\mathbf{S}_{mm}, \tag{51}$$

where

$${}^j\mathbf{S}_{mm} = \frac{l_j}{g} \sum_{\mathscr{P}} {}^jP_{mm}^*\mathbf{P} \tag{52}$$

is the Wigner projection matrix representing ${}^j\mathscr{S}_{mm}$ in the basis $\boldsymbol{\alpha}$. The row matrix ${}^j\boldsymbol{\alpha}_m$ of Eq. (51) contains only state vectors belonging to the irreducible subspace of symmetry type (j, m). Since the order of this row matrix is the same as the order of the original basis $\boldsymbol{\alpha}$, which is supposed to be reducible, it is obvious, however, that the basis ${}^j\boldsymbol{\alpha}_m$ is necessarily linearly dependent. In simple applications, where one can easily calculate the right-hand side of Eq. (51) directly, this may not cause any trouble, since most of the elements of this row matrix may become zero. Redundancies occurring for the non-vanishing elements may be eliminated just by inspection, thus leaving the linearly independent subset wanted. In more complicated applications and in cases when the projections are programmed for electronic computers, however, a more systematic method must be used. We shall here describe a general method for removing these redundancies, which has been proposed by the present author (*3*).

The irreducible subspace of symmetry type (j, m) is spanned by the states $|njm\rangle$ of Eq. (32). We may write the states with different n values in the form of a row matrix ${}^j\boldsymbol{\beta}_m$. This basis must be obtained by a reduction for the symmetry-adapted basis of Eq. (51) according to the relation

$$ {}^j\boldsymbol{\beta}_m = {}^j\boldsymbol{\alpha}_m\, {}^j\mathbf{t}_m, \tag{53} $$

where ${}^j\mathbf{t}_m$ is a rectangular matrix with the same number of columns as the number of states in ${}^j\boldsymbol{\beta}_m$. This rectangular matrix can be found by utilizing the fact that the projection operator is Hermitian and idempotent, as stated in Eqs. (40). The same thing is true for the singular matrix ${}^j\mathbf{S}_{mm}$ defined by Eq. (52):

$$ {}^j\mathbf{S}^{\dagger}_{mm} = {}^j\mathbf{S}_{mm}; \tag{54} $$

$$ {}^j\mathbf{S}^{2}_{mm} = {}^j\mathbf{S}_{mm}. \tag{55} $$

The Hermitian property stated in Eq. (54) implies that there is a unitary transformation diagonalizing the projection matrix ${}^j\mathbf{S}_{mm}$. The idempotency stated in Eq. (55) shows that the eigenvalues s of the projection matrix fulfill the equation $s^2 = s$, the roots of which are given by 1 and 0. If all the eigenvalues vanish, there is obviously no projection, and the original space does not contain any basis vectors of symmetry type (j, m). The only interesting eigencolumns $\mathbf{t}$ of ${}^j\mathbf{S}_{mm}$ are those belonging to the eigenvalue 1, thus satisfying the equation

$$ {}^j\mathbf{S}_{mm}\mathbf{t} = \mathbf{t}. \tag{56} $$

Since the trace does not change under a similarity transformation, the sum of the eigenvalues of the projection matrix, which is obviously equal to the number of normalized $\mathbf{t}$ columns satisfying Eq. (56), is also equal to the trace of ${}^j\mathbf{S}_{mm}$. The order of the basis ${}^j\boldsymbol{\beta}_m$ is thus given by

$$ {}^jN_m = \operatorname{tr} {}^j\mathbf{S}_{mm}. \tag{57}$$

The normalization condition for the eigencolumns yields, according to Eq. (56),

$$\mathbf{t}^\dagger\mathbf{t} = \mathbf{t}^\dagger\, {}^j\mathbf{S}_{mm}\mathbf{t} = 1. \tag{58}$$

Brought together into a rectangular matrix, the eigencolumns in Eq. (56) will thus form part of a unitary square matrix diagonalizing ${}^j\mathbf{S}_{mm}$. This part corresponds to the unit eigenvalues, according to Eq. (58). In accordance with Eqs. (21) and (18), the rectangular matrix thus obtained is therefore a ${}^j\mathbf{t}_m$ matrix, solving Eq. (53). According to Eqs. (51) and (56), Eq. (53) can then be written

$$ {}^j\boldsymbol{\beta}_m = \boldsymbol{\alpha}\, {}^j\mathbf{S}_{mm}\, {}^j\mathbf{t}_m = \boldsymbol{\alpha}\, {}^j\mathbf{t}_m, \tag{59}$$

where ${}^j\mathbf{t}_m$ is thus composed of the nonvanishing eigencolumns of Eq. (56).

Actually, on account of the idempotency stated by Eq. (55), Eq. (56) is fulfilled for $\mathbf{t}$ taken as any one of the columns of the ${}^j\mathbf{S}_{mm}$ matrix itself. The problem of finding ${}^j\mathbf{t}_m$ is therefore equivalent to the problem of orthonormalizing ${}^jN_m$ linearly independent columns of the ${}^j\mathbf{S}_{mm}$ matrix. Because of Eqs. (54) and (55), normalization can be made on dividing each column by the square root of the diagonal element of ${}^j\mathbf{S}_{mm}$ that is contained in this column. The orthogonalization procedure can then be performed according to the ordinary Schmidt method, which can be greatly simplified by using the Hermiticity and idempotency properties again. From Eqs. (54) and (55) we obtain, for a diagonal element of ${}^j\mathbf{S}_{mm}$,

$$({}^j\mathbf{S}_{mm})_{\mu\mu} = ({}^j\mathbf{S}_{mm})^2_{\mu\mu} + \sum_{\nu\neq\mu} |({}^j\mathbf{S}_{mm})_{\mu\nu}|^2, \tag{60}$$

saying that the nondiagonal elements of ${}^j\mathbf{S}_{mm}$ vanish for each row and column containing a diagonal element equal to 1 or 0. The columns with this property are thus immediately orthogonal to all the others. Since the sum of absolute squares in Eq. (60) is positive or zero, a diagonal element of ${}^j\mathbf{S}_{mm}$ can take values lying between 0 and 1, and the absolute value of any nondiagonal element of the projection matrix can never exceed $\frac{1}{2}$. (See Fig. 1.)

The Hermitian conjugate of a column of ${}^j\mathbf{S}_{mm}$ is equal to the corresponding row, as a consequence of Eq. (54). Therefore, using Eq. (55), the μth and νth columns are orthogonal when the element $({}^j\mathbf{S}_{mm})_{\mu\nu} = 0$.

Since the nondiagonal elements $({}^j\mathbf{S}_{mm})_{\mu\nu}$ of the μth column of ${}^j\mathbf{S}_{mm}$ all vanish when the diagonal element $({}^j\mathbf{S}_{mm})_{\mu\mu}$ is equal to 0 or 1, we may first exclude all columns with $({}^j\mathbf{S}_{mm})_{\mu\mu}=0$, which are thus zero columns. Then we select all columns with $({}^j\mathbf{S}_{mm})_{\mu\mu}=1$. Each one of these is already orthogonal to all the others. If the number of these selected columns does not equal ${}^jN_m$, orthogonalization must be performed for the remaining columns. Thus we choose one normalized column $\mathbf{t}_\mu$ with the diagonal element apart from 1 or 0.

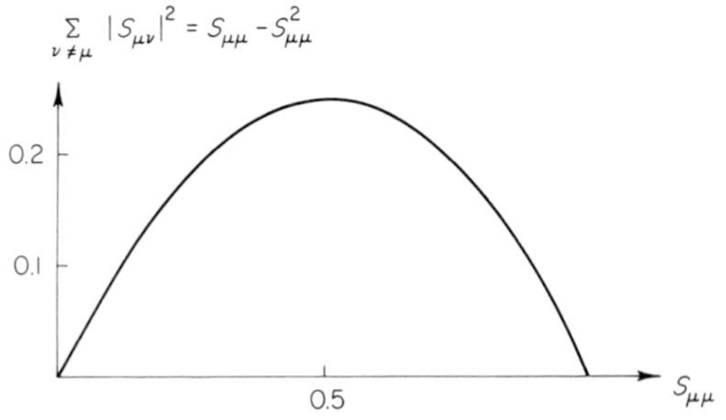

FIG. 1. Sum over absolute squares of the nondiagonal elements of column μ of the projection matrix $\mathbf{S}$ as a function of the corresponding diagonal element $S_{\mu\mu}$. (For convenience the symmetry-type indices (j, m) are omitted here).

If the number of columns is still insufficient, we choose another one of the remaining normalized columns, $\mathbf{t}_\nu$. If then $({}^j\mathbf{S}_{mm})_{\mu\nu}=0$, $\mathbf{t}_\nu$ is already orthogonal to all those columns selected before. If $({}^j\mathbf{S}_{mm})_{\mu\nu}\neq 0$, we may replace $\mathbf{t}_\nu$ by

$$\mathbf{t}_\nu' = \frac{\mathbf{t}_\nu - (\mathbf{t}_\mu^\dagger \mathbf{t}_\nu)\mathbf{t}_\mu}{(1-|\mathbf{t}_\mu^\dagger \mathbf{t}_\nu|^2)^{1/2}}. \tag{61}$$

If the number of selected orthogonal columns is still insufficient, another column has to be orthogonalized to $\mathbf{t}_\mu$ and $\mathbf{t}_\nu'$, and so on.

Apparently, the Schmidt procedure thus described is necessary only for subsets of mutually nonorthogonal columns. When the number of nonvanishing mutually orthogonal columns obtained amounts to ${}^jN_m$, the transformation matrix ${}^j\mathbf{t}_m$ of Eq. (59) can be constructed.

The procedure just described should be repeated for all the symmetry types (j, m) of the group of the Hamiltonian. All the rectangular matrices ${}^j\mathbf{t}_m$ obtained in this way can be composed in the form of a square matrix $\mathbf{S}^{-1}$, which finally yields the wanted transformation of Eq. (18), as is seen from Eq. (59). The sum of all the numbers ${}^jN_m$ defined by Eq. (57) for all the different symmetry types (j, m) is thus equal to the order of the original basis $\boldsymbol{\alpha}$. This may be taken as a criterion for correct calculation.

In most cases of application, the orthogonalization procedure can be further simplified. This is the case when the chosen basis $\boldsymbol{\alpha}$ is separated into subspaces, invariant under G. These subspaces are thus irreducible under a group of higher order containing G as a subgroup. Then all the matrices $\mathbf{P}$ representing $\mathscr{P}$ in the basis $\boldsymbol{\alpha}$, as well as the projection matrix ${}^{j}\mathbf{S}_{mm}$, are block-diagonalized. The symmetry adaptation and reduction procedures may then be performed for each invariant subspace separately. Although the scheme thus becomes more involved, this essential simplification greatly limits the sizes of considered matrices.

IV. Symmetry Groups of Solids

The symmetry groups occurring in solid state theory are essentially of three kinds: crystallographic space groups for static potentials of electrons; dynamic symmetry groups for magnetic crystals; and the group of permutations for identical particles moving in solids. In this section we shall deal with some properties of these groups.

A. The Group of Primitive Translations

In a perfect crystal there is an internal periodic space symmetry due to the lattice structure of the equilibrium atomic arrangement. A translation through a primitive lattice distance will not change the physical environment of a particle moving in the crystal in cases when the surface effects of the finite crystal are not essential. The crystal unit cell is a parallelepiped of least possible volume that can be defined by three displacements in noncoplanar directions, $\mathbf{a}_1$, $\mathbf{a}_2$, and $\mathbf{a}_3$. An arbitrary lattice translation $\mathscr{T}_\mathbf{n}$ is thus determined by the displacement vector

$$\mathbf{n} = \sum_{i=1}^{3} \mathbf{a}_i n^i = \mathbf{an}, \tag{62}$$

where $\mathbf{a}$ is a row matrix the elements of which are the basis vectors $\mathbf{a}_1$, $\mathbf{a}_2$, and $\mathbf{a}_3$ of the crystal lattice, and $\mathbf{n}$ is a column matrix of the contravariant lattice components n^1, n^2, and n^3, which are all integers. In an ordinary crystal the lengths of the unit cell vectors are of the order of angstroms (10^{-7} mm), while the total length in any direction of a single crystal may be of the order of millimeters. Thus, the number of unit cells in a single crystal may be of the order of 10^{21}.

Accordingly, when we are interested only in internal properties of the crystal, it is convenient to consider its dimensions to be infinite. We may thus introduce a macrolattice, the unit cell of which is defined by the three basis vectors

$$\mathbf{A}_s = N^s \mathbf{a}_s, \qquad (s = 1, 2, 3), \tag{63}$$

where N^s may be infinitely large integers. This unit cell is denoted as the *microcrystal*. The volume of the microcrystal is given by

$$V = N^1 N^2 N^3 \mathbf{a}_1 \cdot (\mathbf{a}_2 \times \mathbf{a}_3) = N V_a, \tag{64}$$

where N is the number of primitive unit cells in the microcrystal and V_a is the unit cell volume. For wave functions describing electrons or other particles in crystals, it is customary to introduce periodic boundary conditions over the microcrystal. This is no physical restriction when N^s tends to infinity. We shall therefore consider the microcrystal formally to represent the whole crystal.

The periodicity condition just introduced means that translations through macrolattice vectors must be considered as the identity operator; that is, $\mathscr{T}_{\mathbf{M}} = 1$ for $\mathbf{M} = M^s \mathbf{A}_s$ and M^s an arbitrary integer. The set of primitive translation operators $\mathscr{T}_{\mathbf{n}}$ for $\mathbf{n} = n^s \mathbf{a}_s$ and $n^s = 0, 1, 2, \ldots, N^s - 1$, in one of the three basis directions $\mathbf{a}_s$ thus forms a *cyclic group* C_T^s. The total group G_T of primitive lattice translations is the direct product of these cyclic groups; that is,

$$G_T = C_T^1 \times C_T^2 \times C_T^3. \tag{65}$$

The multiplication rule of primitive translations is given by

$$\mathscr{T}_{\mathbf{m}} \mathscr{T}_{\mathbf{n}} = \mathscr{T}_{\mathbf{m}+\mathbf{n}}, \tag{66}$$

which shows that the group is Abelian (i.e., any two elements of the group commute). Then each element forms a class by itself, and the number of irreducible representations is equal to the number of unit cells N in the microcrystal. Furthermore, all the irreducible representations are one-dimensional and given by all the nonequivalent sets

$$\Gamma(\mathbf{k}) = \{\exp(-i\mathbf{k} \cdot \mathbf{n}), \quad \text{all} \quad \mathscr{T}_{\mathbf{n}} \in G_T\} \tag{67}$$

because the exponential functions occurring in Eq. (67) obey the same multiplication rule as the corresponding translations in Eq. (66). The vector $\mathbf{k}$ labeling the irreducible representations of the group of primitive translations is known as the *reduced wave vector*. In the limiting case, when the dimensions of the unit cell tend toward zero, the group of continuous translations is obtained, and $\mathbf{k}$ equals the ordinary propagation vector of plane waves, representing free particles of momentum $\mathbf{p} = \hbar\mathbf{k}$.

The restriction on **k** due to the periodic boundary condition is given by the requirement that $\mathscr{T}_{\mathbf{A}_s}$ be represented by

$$\exp(-i\mathbf{k} \cdot \mathbf{A}_s) = 1, \qquad (s = 1, 2, 3). \tag{68}$$

The **k** vector is usually represented by its components in the reciprocal lattice, defined by the three basis vectors

$$\mathbf{b}_r = \frac{\mathbf{a}_s \times \mathbf{a}_t}{V_a}, \qquad (r, s, t = 1, 2, 3, \text{ in cyclic order}), \tag{69}$$

each one of which is orthogonal to a crystal lattice plane. Introducing a column matrix **b** for the basis vectors in Eq. (69) and expanding **k** in this basis, we find

$$\mathbf{k} = \sum_{s=1}^{3} k_s \mathbf{b}_s = \mathsf{kb}, \tag{70}$$

where $\mathsf{k} = (k_1, k_2, k_3)$ is a row matrix the elements of which are the covariant, or reciprocal-lattice, components of the reduced wave vector **k**. On account of the orthogonality relations $\mathbf{b}_r \cdot \mathbf{a}_s = \delta_{rs}$ obtained from Eq. (69), the column–row product $\mathsf{b} \cdot \mathsf{a}$ is equal to a unit matrix, and

$$\mathbf{k} \cdot \mathbf{n} = \mathsf{kb} \cdot \mathsf{an} = \mathsf{kn} = \sum_{s=1}^{3} k_s n^s. \tag{71}$$

Using Eq. (71), the condition of Eq. (68) is satisfied when $k_s N^s$ equals 2π times an integer, or

$$k_s = 2\pi \frac{l_s}{N^s}; \qquad l_s = 0, 1, \ldots, N^s - 1; \qquad s = 1, 2, 3. \tag{72}$$

As is seen from Eq. (72), there are exactly N nonequivalent **k** vectors, which is the same as the number of unit cells in the microcrystal. In reciprocal space these **k** vectors form a zone, the volume V_K of which is given by $(2\pi)^3$ times the volume of the reciprocal unit cell:

$$V_K = (2\pi)^3 \mathbf{b}_1 \cdot (\mathbf{b}_2 \times \mathbf{b}_3) = \frac{8\pi^3}{V_a}. \tag{73}$$

Each irreducible representation of the group of primitive translations is labeled by a **k** vector within the zone. A primitive zone vector **K** is defined by the condition

$$\exp(-i\mathbf{K} \cdot \mathbf{n}) = 1 \tag{74}$$

for any primitive lattice vector $\mathbf{n}$, its covariant components K_s thus being 2π times an integer. Any two vectors $\mathbf{k}$ and $\mathbf{k}'$ differing by a nonvanishing zone vector $\mathbf{K}$, that is, fulfilling the condition

$$\mathbf{k}' = \mathbf{k} + \mathbf{K}, \tag{75}$$

are said to be *equivalent* because the corresponding irreducible representations are identical.

The projection operators, defined for arbitrary groups according to Eq. (43), are given by

$$\mathscr{T}(\mathbf{k}) = \frac{1}{N} \sum_{\mathbf{n}} \exp(i\mathbf{k} \cdot \mathbf{n}) \mathscr{T}_{\mathbf{n}} \tag{76}$$

for the group of primitive translations. In accordance with Eq. (39a) these projection operators fulfill the following orthogonality relations:

$$\mathscr{T}(\mathbf{k})\mathscr{T}(\mathbf{k}') = \mathscr{T}(\mathbf{k})\, \delta(\mathbf{k}', \mathbf{k} + \mathbf{K}), \tag{77}$$

where $\delta(\mathbf{k}', \mathbf{k})$ is a Kronecker symbol. Operating on a given trial state $|\varphi_{\mathbf{m}}\rangle$ related spatially to the $\mathbf{m}$th cell according to the relation

$$\mathscr{T}_{\mathbf{n}} |\varphi_{\mathbf{m}}\rangle = |\varphi_{\mathbf{m}+\mathbf{n}}\rangle, \tag{78}$$

the projection operator (76) yields an ordinary Bloch state $|\psi_{\mathbf{k}}\rangle$, in normalized form given by Bloch (*4*)

$$|\psi_{\mathbf{k}}\rangle = (N(\mathbf{k}))^{-1/2} \sum_{\mathbf{n}} \exp(i\mathbf{k} \cdot \mathbf{n}) |\varphi_{\mathbf{n}}\rangle. \tag{79}$$

This is thus a state symmetry adapted with respect to the $\mathbf{k}$th irreducible representation of the group of primitive translations. The normalizing factor in Eq. (79) is determined by

$$N(\mathbf{k}) = N \sum_{\mathbf{n}} \exp(i\mathbf{k} \cdot \mathbf{n}) \langle \varphi_{\mathbf{m}} | \varphi_{\mathbf{m}+\mathbf{n}} \rangle, \tag{80}$$

which is independent of $\mathbf{m}$.

B. Point Groups

In general, molecules and crystals have further spatial symmetry, which is referred to a certain space-point center. The corresponding symmetry operators may be the inversion $\mathscr{I}$ through the central point, or a rotation $\mathscr{C}_n$ through the angle $2\pi/n$ about an n-fold axis containing the central point, or any product combination between these operations yielding reflections and rotary reflections. Here n can take one of the values 1, 2, 3, 4, or 6. For linear molecules like H_2, however, n may take any value, although this cannot be the case for crystals.

The inversion group C_i is given by the elements 1 and $\mathscr{I}$, where the notation 1 is used for the identity operation. Since inversion commutes with all the other point-group operations, this group always occurs as a factor in a direct product describing the point group when proper rotations also occur.

Since $(\mathscr{C}_n)^n = 1$, an n-fold axis defines a cyclic group C_n of order n. In particular, C_1 is the trivial group containing the identity element only.

A reflection σ_h in a plane perpendicular to the rotation axis is found as the combination of $\mathscr{C}_2$ with $\mathscr{I}$. Reflection symmetry σ_h combined with C_n defines the group C_{nh}, which is an Abelian group of order $2n$.

The improper rotation group S_n is the subgroup of C_{nh} containing all integer multiples of the rotary-reflection operator $\mathscr{S}_n = \sigma_h \mathscr{C}_n$. In particular, $S_2 = C_i$ is the inversion group. For odd values of n, it is found that $(\mathscr{S}_n)^n$ is the reflection operator σ_h and, consequently, $S_n = C_{nh}$ in this case.

Reflection symmetry σ_v in a plane containing the axis of C_n defines a group C_{nv} of order $2n$. If a twofold axis perpendicular to the axis of C_n is combined with C_n, the group D_n of order $2n$ appears. This group has thus n twofold axes. Adding further the symmetry plane of σ_h, the group D_{nh} of order $4n$ is obtained, containing C_{1h} and D_n as invariant subgroups. When D_n is combined with reflection symmetry in a plane through the axis of C_n and bisecting any two of the n twofold axes of D_n, the group D_{nd} of order $4n$ is obtained.

The only remaining point groups are now the cubic space groups, which are the tetrahedral group of proper rotations T of order 12, the tetrahedral group T_d of order 24, which includes rotary-reflection operators as well, the direct product group $T_h = T \times C_i$ of order 24, the octahedral group of proper rotations O of order 24, and the full cubic group $O_h = O \times C_i$ of order 48.

The total number of different crystallographic point groups just described is equal to 32. The continuous groups containing $\mathscr{C}_\infty$ are then omitted. since these groups cannot be combined with any crystal lattice symmetry.

The projection operators defined by Eq. (43) are readily found for point groups from their irreducible representations, which can be found in detail as given by Melvin (5). Certain simplifications can be obtained for the direct product groups, since the projection operators of the participating subgroups will then commute with each other. This yields a factoring of the projection operator, which may be an essential simplification. The cubic group O_h, for example, contains 48 elements and 20 symmetry types. Reducing a basis of order 96, say, occurring for an *spdf* orbital approximation for the valence electrons of a cubic arrangement of six atoms, it would be necessary to perform $20 \times 48 \times 96 = 92{,}160$ symmetry operations in order to find the completely symmetry-adapted basis without using factorization. Factoring out the inversion symmetry, however, reduces the algebraic work involved for symmetry adapting by roughly 50%.

It is also possible to obtain some simplification of the projections in the case when there is only one invariant subgroup. This is the case of semidirect product groups, the rather complicated theory of which has been treated by McIntosh (*6*).

C. Symmorphic Crystallographic Groups

A general element of a crystallographic space group may be written

$$\mathscr{F} = \{\mathscr{P}|\mathbf{u}\} = \mathscr{T}_{\mathbf{u}}\mathscr{P} = \mathscr{P}\mathscr{T}_{\mathbf{v}}, \tag{81}$$

where $\mathbf{u} = \mathscr{P}\mathbf{v}$ is a primitive or nonprimitive translation vector and $\mathscr{P}$ is a point-group element. In the special case when the crystallographic space group is given by the product of the group G_T of primitive translations and some point group G_P, it is said to be *symmorphic*. In this case, the translation vectors $\mathbf{u}$ are always primitive lattice vectors, and G_T is an invariant subgroup. A symmorphic space group, denoted by G_S, is thus in general a semidirect product (*6*),

$$G_S = G_T \wedge G_P, \tag{82}$$

since $G_P = G_S/G_T$ is not an invariant subgroup, whereas G_T is. Consequently, the operators $\mathscr{P}$ of G_P do not commute with the projection operators of G_T defined by Eq. (76). It is therefore not possible to find the projections onto irreducible subspaces of G_S by operating with a product of the projection operators of G_T and G_P. However, we may consider the largest subgroup $Q_{\mathbf{k}}$ of G_P, the elements of which commute with the projection operator $\mathscr{T}(\mathbf{k})$ for a certain wave vector $\mathbf{k}$ (*7*). According to Eq. (76), we see that

$$\begin{aligned}\mathscr{P}\mathscr{T}(\mathbf{k}) &= \frac{1}{N}\sum_{\mathbf{m}} \exp(i\mathbf{k}\cdot\mathbf{m})\mathscr{P}\mathscr{T}_{\mathbf{m}} \\ &= \frac{1}{N}\sum_{\mathbf{m}} \exp(i\mathbf{k}\cdot\mathbf{m})\mathscr{T}_{\mathscr{P}\mathbf{m}}\mathscr{P} \\ &= \frac{1}{N}\sum_{\mathbf{n}} \exp(i\mathscr{P}\mathbf{k}\cdot\mathbf{n})\mathscr{T}_{\mathbf{n}}\mathscr{P} = \mathscr{T}(\mathscr{P}\mathbf{k})\mathscr{P},\end{aligned} \tag{83}$$

where we have relabeled the terms in the sum by putting $\mathbf{n} = \mathscr{P}\mathbf{m}$, and used the obvious relation $\mathbf{k}\cdot\mathscr{P}^{-1}\mathbf{n} = \mathscr{P}\mathbf{k}\cdot\mathbf{n}$. The condition $[\mathscr{P}, \mathscr{T}(\mathbf{k})] = 0$ thus means that $\mathbf{k}$ and $\mathscr{P}\mathbf{k}$ must be equivalent wave vectors, or

$$\mathscr{P}\mathbf{k} = \mathbf{k} + \mathbf{K}, \tag{84}$$

since then $\mathscr{T}(\mathbf{k}) = \mathscr{T}(\mathscr{P}\mathbf{k})$. The group $Q_\mathbf{k}$ is thus defined by the elements $\mathscr{P}$ of G_P satisfying Eq. (84), and is denoted as the *little group* connected with $\mathbf{k}$.

Apparently all the projection operators ${}^{jm}\mathscr{P}_\mathbf{k}$ [denoted by ${}^{j}\mathscr{S}_{mm}$ in Eq. (43)] for the different symmetry types (j, m) of $Q_\mathbf{k}$ commute with $\mathscr{T}(\mathbf{k})$. Correctly symmetry-adapted projections will thus result by operating with products of $\mathscr{T}(\mathbf{k})$ and ${}^{jm}\mathscr{P}_\mathbf{k}$, since the second projection operator does not violate the symmetry adaptation obtained by the first one.

Given the vector $\mathbf{k}$, the *star* of $\mathbf{k}$ is obtained as the set of vectors $\mathscr{P}\mathbf{k}$ found by operation on $\mathbf{k}$ with all the elements of G_P. Equivalent $\mathbf{k}$ vectors of the same star are said to belong to the same *prong* of the star. The elements of G_P connected with the prong of $\mathbf{k}$ thus satisfy Eq. (84) and belong to the little group $Q_\mathbf{k}$.

It can be shown that the irreducible representatives of the operators $\mathscr{F}$ in Eq. (81) form supermatrices, the subblocks of which are labeled by the indices μ and ν of two prongs of the star of $\mathbf{k}$ (*8*). Let us here denote by $\mathscr{P}_\mu$ and $\mathscr{P}_\nu$ those elements of G_P yielding wave vectors of the prongs of μ and ν, respectively, when operating on $\mathbf{k}$. The submatrix labeled by μ and ν of the irreducible representative of $\mathscr{F}$ then vanishes, unless the condition

$$\mathscr{P}_\mu^{-1}\mathscr{P}\mathscr{P}_\nu \in Q_\mathbf{k} \tag{85}$$

is fulfilled (*8*).

It is also found that the little groups of different prongs are conjugate to each other. As a matter of fact, any point-group element $\mathscr{P}$ satisfying Eq. (85) will produce $\mathbf{k}$ vectors of the μth prong when operating on $\mathbf{k}$ vectors of prong ν. In particular, for nonvanishing blocks in diagonal position, we put $\mu = \nu$ and Eq. (85) yields

$$\mathscr{P}(\mathscr{P}_\nu\mathbf{k}) \cong \mathscr{P}_\nu Q_\mathbf{k}\mathbf{k}. \tag{86}$$

Thus $\mathscr{P}$ belongs to the little group $Q_{\mathscr{P}_\nu\mathbf{k}}$ of $\mathscr{P}_\nu\mathbf{k}$,

$$Q_{\mathscr{P}_\nu\mathbf{k}} = \mathscr{P}_\nu Q_\mathbf{k}\mathscr{P}_\nu^{-1}, \tag{87}$$

which is conjugate to $Q_\mathbf{k}$. No other nonvanishing submatrices of the irreducible representatives of $\mathscr{F}$ are found in diagonal position. By means of a similarity transformation corresponding to a permutation among the prongs of the star, it is possible to obtain the nonvanishing block for $\mu = \nu$ in the 1, 1 position. This position corresponds to the reference prong of the star, and nonvanishing blocks are found only for $\mathscr{P} \in Q_{\mathbf{k}}$. Since the matrix representative of the projection operator, defined by Eq. (52), takes contribution only from the diagonal elements of the irreducible matrix representatives, it is obvious that the only elements of G_P that contribute to the symmetry adaptation are those of the little group. Consequently, it is impossible to get any further symmetry adaptation by means of the symmetry elements of G_P not contained in the little group. Projection operators yielding the complete spatial symmetry adaptation may therefore be written in product form,

$$^{jm}\mathscr{S}_{\mathbf{k}} = \mathscr{T}(\mathbf{k})\, ^{jm}\mathscr{P}_{\mathbf{k}} = {}^{jm}\mathscr{P}_{\mathbf{k}}\mathscr{T}(\mathbf{k}), \tag{88}$$

as discussed earlier. The explicit form of these operators is obtained from Eqs. (76) and (*43*), where the diagonal elements of the irreducible representatives of the little group of **k** must be inserted in the last equation. This meets with no practical difficulty, since the irreducible representations of all the 32 point groups are well known.

The space group necessary for complete symmetry adaptation of states of a given **k** vector is known as *the group of the* **k** *vector*, $G_{\mathbf{k}}$. For symmorphic space groups, $G_{\mathbf{k}}$ is thus found as a semidirect product, $G_T \wedge Q_{\mathbf{k}}$, between the group of primitive translations and the little group of **k**. Apparently only **k** vectors of some symmetry in the reciprocal space correspond to little groups apart from the trivial point group, C_1. Nontrivial point-group symmetry is found only for certain points, lines, and planes of some symmetry in **k** space. The wave vector $\mathbf{k} = 0$, for example, has the highest possible symmetry, the corresponding little group being G_P. Since the point-group operators do not alter the length **k**, the condition given by Eq. (84) with $\mathbf{K} \neq 0$ may be fulfilled only for those points in **k** space that are equivalent to those lying at Brillouin-zone boundaries (see Section VI,C).

Any prong of the star of **k** may be chosen as a reference prong, since this just corresponds to a similarity transformation of the irreducible representatives of the total space group G_S. Thus all the elements of the point group will transform between **k** vectors of degenerate states. The first Brillouin zone may therefore be divided into parts of equal volume in reciprocal space and the same energy spectrum. The number of these parts is equal to the order of G_P, and they are mapped into each other by point-group operations. Analyzing energy eigenvalues of the crystal Hamiltonian, we see that it is thus necessary to study only one of these regions of the Brillouin zone. The points of nontrivial symmetry in **k** space occur at the boundary surfaces of these regions (see Section VI,D).

D. Nonsymmorphic Crystallographic Groups

In the case when the translation vectors **u** of the crystallographic space-group elements in Eq. (81) are not always primitive lattice vectors, we cannot describe the group as a product group as in Eq. (82). In this case the group is denoted as a *nonsymmorphic* space group G_N. The operators $\mathscr{P}$ occurring for the different elements $\{\mathscr{P}|\mathbf{u}\}$ of G_N still form a point group G_P, the elements of which, however, are generally no longer symmetry operations of the crystal. The symmetry operators containing nonprimitive lattice translations $\mathscr{T}_\mathbf{u}$ cannot be obtained for point-group elements that belong to the crystal symmetry group. These operators are therefore screw-rotations or glide-reflections $\{\mathscr{P}|\mathbf{u}\}$, where neither $\mathscr{P}$ nor $\mathscr{T}_\mathbf{u}$ are elements of the crystal space group separately.

The space-group elements have not been denoted in a unique way in Eq. (81), since the center of the point-group operations is not specified. Suppose that **w** is an arbitrary vector displacing this center, and denote by $\mathscr{P}_\mathbf{w}$ the point-group operator found from $\mathscr{P}$ by translating the point center through the distance **w**. Then $\mathscr{P}$ and $\mathscr{P}_\mathbf{w}$ will be conjugate space group operators:

$$\mathscr{P}_\mathbf{w} = \mathscr{T}_\mathbf{w} \mathscr{P} \mathscr{T}_\mathbf{w}^{-1} = \mathscr{T}_{\mathbf{w}-\mathscr{P}\mathbf{w}} \mathscr{P}. \tag{89}$$

In the special case when $\mathscr{P}\mathbf{w}$ equals **w**, that is, **w** lies in the direction of the axis of rotation or in the plane of reflection defined by $\mathscr{P}$ (which is not true for the inversion operator), it is seen that the position of the point-group center along this axis is immaterial. Choosing **w** arbitrarily and multiplying Eq. (89) from the left by a translation operator through the distance $\mathbf{u}_\mathbf{w}$ defined later, we find, according to Eq. (81),

$$\{\mathscr{P}|\mathbf{u}\} = \{\mathscr{P}_\mathbf{w}|\mathbf{u}_\mathbf{w}\}; \qquad \mathbf{u}_\mathbf{w} = \mathbf{u} + (\mathscr{P} - 1)\mathbf{w}. \tag{90}$$

Since **w** is arbitrary in Eq. (90), there is an infinite number of ways of changing the translational part of the space-group operator without changing this operator itself. For an appropriate choice of **w** it is possible to get all translations occurring for space-group operators isomorphous to the elements of the factor group G_N/G_T as rational fractions of primitive translations, being zero when $\mathscr{P}_\mathbf{w}$ is the identity operator.

The star of the **k** vector is defined, as in the symmorphic case, as the set of vectors obtained from a given **k** vector by operating with the elements $\mathscr{P}$ of G_P on **k**. Equivalent **k** vectors of the star are said to belong to the same prong, and the operators $\mathscr{P}$, transforming within the prong of **k** as defined by Eq. (84), belong to a subgroup of G_P, which we now denote as the *little point group* $P_\mathbf{k}$.

In order to find the symmetry-adapted states for nonsymmorphic groups, we must limit the set of point-group operators for a given **k** vector to those of the little point group. The subset of space-group operators in Eq. (81) containing the elements of $P_{\mathbf{k}}$ combined with those translation vectors **u** that are shorter than the distance between two unit cells in the **u** direction are the space-group operators occurring in the factor group G_N/G_T. Since this set does not form a space group, the group of the **k** vector cannot be obtained in the same way as for symmorphic groups. We shall see, however, that in the nonsymmorphic case, too, we can define a little group, which we shall denote by $Q_{\mathbf{k}}$, as in the symmorphic case.

To obtain $Q_{\mathbf{k}}$ we introduce a positive integer $n(\mathbf{k})$, defined as the lowest common order occurring for the elements of $P_{\mathbf{k}}$ where the order of an element is defined as the lowest power of the element yielding the identity operator. Thus, for any $\mathscr{P}$ in $P_{\mathbf{k}}$

$$\mathscr{P}^{n(\mathbf{k})} = 1. \tag{91}$$

Since all the point groups are finite, $n(\mathbf{k})$ is a finite number. Taking the square of the element in Eq. (81), we obtain

$$\mathscr{F}^2 = \{\mathscr{P}|\mathbf{u}\}^2 = \mathscr{T}_{\mathbf{u}}\mathscr{P}\mathscr{T}_{\mathbf{u}}\mathscr{P} = \mathscr{T}_{\mathbf{u}+\mathscr{P}\mathbf{u}}\mathscr{P}^2 = \{\mathscr{P}^2|\mathbf{u} + \mathscr{P}\mathbf{u}\}. \tag{92}$$

Similarly, for any integer power of $\mathscr{F}$, the following formula is easily proved by induction:

$$\mathscr{F}^s = \{\mathscr{P}^s|\mathscr{R}\mathbf{u}\}, \tag{93}$$

where

$$\mathscr{R} = 1 + \mathscr{P} + \cdots + \mathscr{P}^{s-1} = \frac{1 - \mathscr{P}^s}{1 - \mathscr{P}} \tag{94}$$

is the operator transforming **u**. The expression at the right-hand side of Eq. (94) is just formal, since the operator occurring in the denominator may be shortened with a factor of the numerator. Taking $s = n(\mathbf{k})$ in Eq. (94) for any element $\mathscr{P}$ of the little point group, and using Eq. (91), we obtain $\mathscr{R} = 0$ in cases when $\mathscr{P}\mathbf{u} \neq \mathbf{u}$. In the case $\mathscr{P}\mathbf{u} = \mathbf{u}$, on the other hand, we find that $\mathscr{R}$ in Eq. (93) can be replaced by s times the identity operator. When $\mathscr{P}$ belongs to $P_{\mathbf{k}}$, the operator $\mathscr{P}^s$ of Eq. (93) is also an element of $P_{\mathbf{k}}$. For $s = n(\mathbf{k})$, when $\mathscr{P}^s = 1$ according to Eq. (91), this means in particular that the translation vector $\mathscr{R}\mathbf{u}$ of $\mathscr{F}^{n(\mathbf{k})}$ has to be a primitive lattice vector,

$$\mathscr{R}\mathbf{u} = n(\mathbf{k})\mathbf{u}\delta_{\mathbf{uv}} = \mathbf{m}(\mathbf{k}, \mathbf{u}), \tag{95}$$

where $\mathbf{v} = \mathscr{P}\mathbf{u}$. The primitive translation

$$\mathscr{T}_{\mathbf{m}(\mathbf{k},\mathbf{u})} = \{\mathscr{P}|\mathbf{u}\}^{n(\mathbf{k})} \tag{96}$$

apparently commutes with $\{\mathscr{P}|\mathbf{u}\}$, and may be replaced by its irreducible representative $\exp(-i\mathbf{k} \cdot \mathbf{m}(\mathbf{k}, \mathbf{u}))$ in cases when the operator of Eq. (96) works in a basis of Bloch states, that is, states that are already symmetry adapted with respect to G_T. In the case when this exponential function is equal to unity, the primitive translation of Eq. (96) may be replaced by the identity operator when applied to a Bloch state. Let us then define a number $p(\mathbf{k})$ as the lowest possible integer satisfying the condition

$$\exp(i\mathbf{k} \cdot \mathbf{M}) = 1, \qquad \text{with} \quad \mathbf{M} = p(\mathbf{k})n(\mathbf{k})\mathbf{u} \tag{97}$$

for any $\mathscr{F}$ with $\mathscr{P} \in P_{\mathbf{k}}$. This condition is fulfilled when $p(\mathbf{k})\mathbf{k}$ is a primitive zone vector, since $n(\mathbf{k})\mathbf{u}$ is a primitive lattice vector. Thus $p(\mathbf{k})$ cannot be finite unless the reciprocal-lattice components of $\mathbf{k}$ are rational fractions of 2π. Now we define the set $Q_{\mathbf{k}}$, of operators $\mathscr{F} \in G_N$,

$$\mathscr{F} = \{\mathscr{P}|\mathbf{u}\}^s, \qquad s = 0, 1, \ldots, (p(\mathbf{k})n(\mathbf{k}) - 1) \tag{98}$$

for all distinct combinations where $\mathscr{P} \in P_{\mathbf{k}}$ and the components of $\mathbf{u}$ in the direct lattice may take on only positive values less than unity. The order of this set is thus less than or equal to $p(\mathbf{k})n(\mathbf{k})$ times the order of $P_{\mathbf{k}}$. Considering superlattice translations $\mathscr{T}_{\mathbf{M}}$ for $\mathbf{M}$ given by Eq. (97) as identity operators, the set of Eq. (98) defines a group that is the *little group* $Q_{\mathbf{k}}$ of the wave vector $\mathbf{k}$. The little group is thus limited to operate in a Bloch basis. The group of the $\mathbf{k}$ vector, denoted by $G_{\mathbf{k}}$, is the subgroup of G_N limited by the condition $\mathscr{P} \in P_{\mathbf{k}}$. The little group $Q_{\mathbf{k}}$ is isomorphous with the factor group $F_{\mathbf{k}}$,

$$F_{\mathbf{k}} = \frac{G_{\mathbf{k}}}{G_T(\mathbf{k})}, \tag{99}$$

where $G_T(\mathbf{k})$ is the group of primitive superlattice translations $\mathscr{T}_{\mathbf{M}}$, with $\mathbf{M}$ defined by Eq. (97).

When the components of $\mathbf{k}$ are rational fractions of 2π, the little group has finite order, and its irreducible representatives may be found in the literature (Slater, *9*) for a large number of cases. Tables of irreducible characters occur for all the crystallographic space groups (*10*). In cases when $\mathbf{k}$ lies inside the first Brillouin zone, the irreducible representatives of the elements $\{\mathscr{P}|\mathbf{u}\}$ of the little group are found from those of the little point group simply by multiplying by $\exp(-i\mathbf{k} \cdot \mathbf{u})$ (*8*).

E. Double Space Groups

The space groups hitherto considered are "single groups," which means that they have only single-valued representations. This is the case for operators applied to states in the Schrödinger theory of spin-free electrons only. Including spin states also, according to Pauli's theory (*11*), the representatives of point-group operators will no longer be single valued.

The elements $\mathscr{R}(\phi, \vartheta, \psi)$ of the continuous rotation group in three dimensions are parametrized by the Eulerian angles ϕ, ϑ, and ψ. Thus

$$\mathscr{R}(\phi, \vartheta, \psi) = \mathscr{R}(0, 0, \psi)\mathscr{R}(0, \vartheta, 0)\mathscr{R}(\phi, 0, 0) \tag{100}$$

describes a rotation of a primed coordinate system $x'y'z'$ in relation to an unprimed system xyz that originally coincides with $x'y'z'$. Here ψ and ϕ are angles of right-handed rotations about the z' axis and ϑ about the y' axis, and both coordinate systems are orthogonal and right-handed. The three rotations at the right-hand side of Eq. (100) are taken in sequence from the right to the left. $\mathscr{R}$ can be applied to any vector **B** in three-dimensional space. The rotated vector is denoted by $\mathbf{B}' = \mathscr{R}\mathbf{B}$. The components of $\mathbf{B}'$ in the original system xyz are then obtained according to

$$\begin{pmatrix} B'_x \\ B'_y \\ B'_z \end{pmatrix} = \begin{pmatrix} \cos\phi & -\sin\phi & 0 \\ \sin\phi & \cos\phi & 0 \\ 0 & 0 & 1 \end{pmatrix} \begin{pmatrix} \cos\vartheta & 0 & \sin\vartheta \\ 0 & 1 & 0 \\ -\sin\vartheta & 0 & \cos\vartheta \end{pmatrix} \begin{pmatrix} \cos\psi & -\sin\psi & 0 \\ \sin\psi & \cos\psi & 0 \\ 0 & 0 & 1 \end{pmatrix} \begin{pmatrix} B_x \\ B_y \\ B_z \end{pmatrix} = \mathbf{RB}, \tag{101}$$

where the combined rotation matrix **R** is given by

$$\mathbf{R} = \begin{pmatrix} \cos\phi\cos\vartheta\cos\psi - \sin\phi\sin\psi & -\cos\phi\cos\vartheta\sin\psi - \sin\phi\cos\psi & \cos\phi\sin\vartheta \\ \sin\phi\cos\vartheta\cos\psi + \cos\phi\sin\psi & -\sin\phi\cos\vartheta\sin\psi + \cos\phi\cos\psi & \sin\phi\sin\vartheta \\ -\sin\vartheta\cos\psi & \sin\vartheta\sin\psi & \cos\vartheta \end{pmatrix}. \tag{102}$$

Thus **R** represents the rotation $\mathscr{R}$ of a vector **B** as visualized by an observer in the original coordinate system xyz.

It should be noticed that the sequence of the partial rotation matrices in Eq. (101) is opposite to the sequence of the partial rotations in Eq. (100). This is because the rotation axes are defined in the rotated coordinate system.

The column on the left side of Eq. (101) should be denoted by $\mathbf{B}'$; the notation $\mathbf{B}_{'}$ is used for the components of **B** in the rotated coordinate system $B_{x'}$, $B_{y'}$, $B_{z'}$ found from B_x, B_y, B_z by making the inverse transformation $\mathbf{B}_{'} = \mathbf{R}^{-1}\mathbf{B}$. In particular, the coordinate transformation $\mathbf{r}_{'} = \mathbf{R}^{-1}\mathbf{r}$ is given by the inverse of the matrix of Eq. (102).

Let us now consider the quantum-mechanical spin angular momentum vector $\boldsymbol{\sigma} = \frac{1}{2}\hbar\mathbf{s}$ of an electron, where we take the components of $\mathbf{s}$ to be operators, represented by Pauli's spin matrices

$$\mathbf{s}_x = \begin{pmatrix} 0 & 1 \\ 1 & 0 \end{pmatrix}; \qquad \mathbf{s}_y = \begin{pmatrix} 0 & i \\ -i & 0 \end{pmatrix}; \qquad \mathbf{s}_z = \begin{pmatrix} -1 & 0 \\ 0 & 1 \end{pmatrix}. \tag{103}$$

Rotating the spin vector $\mathbf{s}$ by $\mathscr{R}(\phi, \vartheta, \psi)$, the components of the vector $\mathbf{s}'$ thus obtained are given by Eqs. (101) and (102) for $\mathbf{B} = \mathbf{s}$. It may be readily verified that these components can also be obtained by means of a unitary transformation according to Weyl (*12*):

$$\mathbf{s}_x' = \mathbf{u}\mathbf{s}_x\mathbf{u}^\dagger; \qquad \mathbf{s}_y' = \mathbf{u}\mathbf{s}_y\mathbf{u}^\dagger; \qquad \mathbf{s}_z' = \mathbf{u}\mathbf{s}_z\mathbf{u}^\dagger, \tag{104}$$

where $\mathbf{u}$ is the unitary unimodular matrix

$$\mathbf{u} = \begin{pmatrix} \exp\left(\frac{-i\psi}{2}\right) & 0 \\ 0 & \exp\left(\frac{i\psi}{2}\right) \end{pmatrix} \begin{pmatrix} \cos\frac{\vartheta}{2} & -\sin\frac{\vartheta}{2} \\ \sin\frac{\vartheta}{2} & \cos\frac{\vartheta}{2} \end{pmatrix} \begin{pmatrix} \exp\left(\frac{-i\phi}{2}\right) & 0 \\ 0 & \exp\left(\frac{i\phi}{2}\right) \end{pmatrix} = \begin{pmatrix} a & b \\ -b^* & a^* \end{pmatrix}. \tag{105}$$

The reverse order of angles in Eq. (105) as compared with Eq. (101) should be noted. The Cayley-Klein parameters a and b introduced in Eq. (105) are defined by

$$a = \cos\frac{\vartheta}{2}\exp\left[-\frac{i}{2}(\psi + \phi)\right]; \qquad b = -\sin\frac{\vartheta}{2}\exp\left[-\frac{i}{2}(\psi - \phi)\right]. \tag{106}$$

The explicit values given for a and b are closely connected with the choice of basis for the Pauli matrices as well as other conventions and notations chosen. In the literature all kinds of different conventions occur, including (a) transposition between the basis spin states $|+\rangle$ and $|-\rangle$; (b) multiplication of these states by different phase factors; (c) spinor components taken as basis spin states; (d) matrix notation $\mathbf{u}^\dagger$ used for $\mathbf{u}$; (e) notation B_x' used for $B_{x'}$; (f) change in notation between xyz and $x'y'z'$; (g) rotation of space functions instead of vectors; (h) the opposite sequence used for the Eulerian angles; (i) use of left-handed rotations; (j) use of x' axis instead of y' axis for the rotation angle ϑ; (k) change in notation between ψ and ϕ. In addition, it should be noted that the inverse matrices of Eqs. (105) and (102) are not obtained merely by changing signs of the Eulerian angles, since the order of sequence of the corresponding rotations is also reversed.

It is seen from Eqs. (105) and (106) that a rotation through the angle 2π about any axis yields the result $\mathbf{u} = -\mathbf{1}$. Each rotation $\mathscr{R}$ in a three-dimensional vector space thus corresponds to two distinct matrices, $\mathbf{u}$ and $-\mathbf{u}$, both representing the same operator $\mathscr{R}$. This is why the group of rotations in the two-dimensional spin space is called a double group.

The two-dimensional basis for the spin matrices in Eq. (103) is denoted by $\boldsymbol{\alpha} = (|-\rangle, |+\rangle)$. It corresponds to the symmetry types $|jm\rangle$ for $j = \frac{1}{2}$; $m = -\frac{1}{2}, +\frac{1}{2}$, of the continuous group of all rotations in three-dimensional space. Any state vector $|\xi\rangle = \boldsymbol{\alpha\xi}$ in the space of the two basis states $|-\rangle$ and $|+\rangle$ is represented by the two-component spinor $\boldsymbol{\xi}$ with the components $\xi_1 = \langle -|\xi\rangle$ and $\xi_2 = \langle +|\xi\rangle$. The transformed spin basis is given by $\boldsymbol{\alpha}' = \boldsymbol{\alpha}\mathbf{u}^\dagger$ [cf. Eqs. (18), (21), and (104)]. The transformed spinor is then given by $\boldsymbol{\xi}' = \mathbf{u}\boldsymbol{\xi}$ [cf. Eq. (19)].

Consider now the spin states of $2J$ electrons, for $J = \frac{1}{2}, 1, \frac{3}{2}, \ldots$. According to Weyl, we may then construct a product basis that is irreducible under the continuous group of proper rotations in three dimensions. This basis is given by (*12*)

$$|JM\rangle = \frac{|-\rangle^{J-M}|+\rangle^{J+M}}{((J-M)!\,(J+M)!)^{1/2}} \qquad (M = -J, -J+1, \ldots, J). \tag{107}$$

In the special case of $J = \frac{1}{2}$, we obtain the two-dimensional spin basis of a single electron. We note that the one-electron states with equal spin are indistinguishable, and normalization requires division of the product states by the square root of the number of permutations between these. The representatives of the proper rotations of Eq. (100) in the row basis of Eq. (107) are given by matrices denoted by ${}^J\mathbf{D}^\dagger$. These are the inverse of those matrices that transform the $(2J+1)$-component column spinor representing a general spin state of the $2J$ electrons in the basis of Eq. (107). The spinors are thus transformed by the matrices ${}^J\mathbf{D}$ of order $2J+1$, given by the elements

$$\begin{aligned} {}^J D_{M'M} = &\sum_{K=\max(0,\,M-M')}^{\min(J+M,\,J-M')} \frac{[(J-M)!\,(J+M)!\,(J-M')!\,(J+M')!]^{1/2}}{(J-M'-K)!)\,(J+M-K)!\,K!(K+M'-M)!} \\ &\times a^{J-M'-K} a^{*J+M-K} b^K (-b^*)^{K+M'-M}. \end{aligned} \tag{108}$$

[Wigner has multiplied this result by $(-1)^{M-M'}$ in order to obtain the matrix representing spherical harmonics for integral J values(*2*); Wigner's $\mathscr{R}$ means a positive rotation of the coordinate system, which corresponds to $\mathscr{R}^\dagger$ using our conventions.] In Eq. (108) the sum runs from the larger of the numbers 0 and $M - M'$ to the smaller of the numbers $J + M$ and $J - M'$, and a and b are the Cayley-Klein parameters defined by Eq. (106).

When rotation operations are applied to functions of space and spin coordinates, $F(\mathbf{r}, \mathbf{s})$, the resulting transformation is obtained by letting the inverse operation $\mathscr{R}^{-1}$ act on the vectors $\mathbf{r}$ and $\mathbf{s}$. Denoting the rotation operators in this case by $\mathscr{P}_R$, we thus obtain $\mathscr{P}_R F(\mathbf{r}, \mathbf{s}) = F(\mathscr{R}^{-1}\mathbf{r}, \mathscr{R}^{-1}\mathbf{s})$. The sets of basis space functions transforming irreducibly under the continuous rotation group are given by the spherical harmonics $\langle \vartheta, \phi | Y_{LM} \rangle$ $(M = -L, -L+1, \ldots, L)$. Different irreducible sets are obtained for $L = 0, 1, \ldots$. According to the conventional definition of spherical harmonics (*13*), the transformation matrix representing a rotation in this basis is given by the matrix ${}^L\mathbf{D}^\dagger$ of Eq. (108) for $J = L$, except for a factor $(-1)^{M'-M}$ in each matrix element, just causing a phase factor $(-1)^M$ for each basis function.

Electronic spin-wave functions are usually written as double-valued space functions $\psi(\mathbf{r}, s)$ with $s = -\frac{1}{2}, +\frac{1}{2}$. Using a row basis of these two functions, a spin rotation is represented by the transposed matrix $\tilde{\mathbf{u}}$ of $\mathbf{u} = {}^{1/2}\mathbf{D}$.

Direct product states $|lm\rangle \, |\frac{1}{2}, s\rangle$ transform according to the direct product representation ${}^l\Gamma \boxtimes {}^{1/2}\Gamma$ of the rotation group. This representation may be reduced into its constituents ${}^{l+1/2}\Gamma$ and ${}^{l-1/2}\Gamma$. According to the conventions just discussed, hydrogenlike spin orbitals $\psi_{nlms}(\mathbf{r}) = R_{nl}(r)\, Y_{lm}(\vartheta, \phi)\zeta(s)$ thus transform under proper rotations according to

$$\mathscr{P}_R \psi_{nlms}(\mathbf{r}) = \sum_{m'=-l}^{l} \sum_{s'=-1/2}^{1/2} \psi_{nlm's'}(\mathbf{r})\, (-1)^{m-m'}\, {}^lD^*_{mm'} u_{ss'}, \tag{109}$$

where ${}^lD_{m'm}$ is given by Eq. (108) and $u_{ss'}$ is an element of the matrix $\mathbf{u}$, defined by Eq. (105).

A point-group element $\mathscr{P}$ may be described by three Eulerian angles for the proper rotation part, being rational fractions of 2π, and a fourth label, $\lambda = 0, 1$, according to

$$\mathscr{P}(\phi, \vartheta, \psi, \lambda) = \mathscr{R}(\phi, \vartheta, \psi)\mathscr{I}^\lambda, \tag{110}$$

where $\lambda = 0$ indicates a proper rotation (inversion not included), and $\lambda = 1$ an improper rotation (inversion included). Since the spin vector $\mathbf{s}$, however, is a pseudo-vector, it is left unchanged by space inversion. The representatives of $\mathscr{P}$ in the spin basis $\boldsymbol{\alpha}$ are thus given by Eq. (105) independently of λ. Space functions of odd parity are merely changed in sign by space inversion. Equation (109) may thus be generalized, in order to be valid for point-group operators as well, by simply multiplying by the factor $(-1)^{\lambda l}$.

The Pauli spin theory is, however, not sufficient for describing the influence of space inversion. Although spin should not be affected by inversion, other quantum numbers may change. The helicity, for example, is changed by space inversion for a spinning particle moving in the spin direction. In the four-spinor theory introduced by Eriksson (*14*), the two additional spinor components correspond to the "spin-conjugated spinor." In this theory, each element of the improper rotation group in three dimensions is represented by four-by-four matrices, $\mathbf{P} = \pm\mathbf{U}\mathbf{I}^{\lambda}$ ($\lambda = 0, 1$), where

$$\mathbf{U} = \begin{pmatrix} a & b & 0 & 0 \\ -b^* & a^* & 0 & 0 \\ 0 & 0 & a & -b \\ 0 & 0 & b^* & a^* \end{pmatrix}; \qquad \mathbf{I} = \begin{pmatrix} 0 & 0 & -i & 0 \\ 0 & 0 & 0 & i \\ i & 0 & 0 & 0 \\ 0 & -i & 0 & 0 \end{pmatrix}. \tag{111}$$

Here a and b are again the Cayley-Klein parameters defined by Eq. (106). From Eq. (111) it is seen that $\mathbf{I}^2 = \mathbf{1}$ and $\mathbf{UI} = \mathbf{IU}$. Thus inversion is its own inverse, and commutes with all proper rotations.

According to Eq. (111), inversion actually does change the spin states. Introducing the notation ($|-\rangle$, $|+\rangle$, $|+\rangle'$, $|-\rangle'$) for the four basis states, where the prime indicates "spin conjugation," we may apply the inversion operator $\mathscr{I}$ to a product state $|-\rangle|+\rangle'$ describing an electron pair with opposite spins. By means of Eq. (111) we thus obtain $\mathscr{I}|-\rangle|+\rangle' = |+\rangle'|-\rangle$. Because of the antisymmetry under transposition, the correct spin state of an odd number of electron pairs will thus have odd parity. This will give an explanation to the factor $(-1)^{\lambda l}$ obtained for the integer-valued representations when inversion is included.

For general double space groups, reducible representatives may now be readily found from a subduced reducible double point-group representation, as obtained by generalization of Eq. (109). We shall consider this problem explicitly for the basis used in the tight-binding method in Section VI,H. Some double-valued irreducible representations for crystallographic space groups are given by Elliott (*15*). Once we know the irreducible representations, the reduction of a given basis with respect to the different symmetry types of the double space group is straightforward, using the projection technique described in Section III,F.

In the case when spin-orbit interaction is neglected, the symmetry of the Hamiltonian is further increased. The space group operators may then be applied to space and spin states independently. We are thus dealing with a direct product between two homomorphous groups operating on space and spin states separately. Symmetry adaptation can therefore be done separately for space and spin states in this case.

F. Time-Reversal Symmetry

When dealing with a nonmagnetic solid, time inversion is another symmetry operator that we can use to simplify the problem of solving the Schrödinger equation for the electrons in a solid. Time inversion will change the directions of spin and velocity. For the stationary states in the spinless Schrödinger theory, it is seen from Eq. (2) that time inversion merely corresponds to taking the complex conjugate of the factor $\exp(-iEt/\hbar)$, occurring for the time-dependent state vector. In the Pauli theory of the electron, this may be refined by using the Wigner (*2*) time-inversion operator, given by

$$\Theta = \mathbf{s}_y \mathscr{K} = \begin{pmatrix} 0 & i \\ -i & 0 \end{pmatrix} \mathscr{K}; \qquad \Theta \begin{pmatrix} \xi_1 \\ \xi_2 \end{pmatrix} = \begin{pmatrix} i\xi_2^* \\ -i\xi_1^* \end{pmatrix}. \tag{112}$$

Here $\mathscr{K}$ is the operator of complex conjugation and the action of Θ on the two-component spinor $\boldsymbol{\xi}$ is shown in Eq. (112). Acting on many-electron wave functions, the spatial part is changed by complex conjugation, and each two-component spinor is changed according to Eq. (112). As pointed out by Wigner (*2*), the time-inversion operator is antilinear and antiunitary. His proof has been revised recently by Bargmann (*16*).

In the four-spinor formalism given by Eriksson (*14*), time inversion will be represented by

$$\mathbf{T} = \begin{pmatrix} 0 & 0 & 1 & 0 \\ 0 & 0 & 0 & -1 \\ -1 & 0 & 0 & 0 \\ 0 & 1 & 0 & 0 \end{pmatrix}; \qquad \mathbf{T} \begin{pmatrix} \xi_1 \\ \xi_2 \\ \xi_3 \\ \xi_4 \end{pmatrix} = \begin{pmatrix} \xi_3 \\ -\xi_4 \\ -\xi_1 \\ \xi_2 \end{pmatrix}. \tag{113}$$

(The matrix has been transformed in order to correspond to our conventions for the first two spinor components; the final form, however, is again Eriksson's original matrix in this case.) Operating twice with $\mathscr{T}$, we just obtain a change of sign, i.e., $\mathbf{T}^2 = -\mathbf{1}$. From Eq. (111) we find the important result $\mathbf{TU} = \mathbf{UT}$, according to which time inversion commutes with any space rotation. Taking $\xi_3 = i\xi_2^*$ and $\xi_4 = i\xi_1^*$ in Eq. (113), we obtain Wigner's result, stated in Eq. (112). This is a possible choice, since ξ_2^* and ξ_1^* transform like ξ_1 and ξ_2 under a rotation of the coordinate system, which is seen from the first matrix in Eq. (111). The four-spinor corresponding to this special choice will just change its sign under charge conjugation. It is also seen that the probability $|\xi_1|^2$ of finding an electron with spin $-\frac{1}{2}$ is changed by time inversion into $|\xi_2|^2 = 1 - |\xi_1|^2$. For an adequate description of space inversion, however, it is not sufficient to use only two independent spinor components, as we saw in the previous subsection.

In the Dirac theory of the electron, the four-spinors are not obtained merely by a linear transformation of Eriksson's four-spinors, since the complex conjugate spinor components are also involved. As in the Pauli theory, time inversion is not a linear operator in Dirac's theory; it is antilinear and antiunitary. If we want to include spin conjugation and particle-antiparticle conjugation as well, an eight-component theory should be needed.

G. Magnetic Groups

Investigating the motion of a single particle in a static crystal, we have to consider not only the crystal space symmetry, but the distribution of stationary angular momentum as well. In the case of closed-shell electron structures with perfect electron pairing, the mean spin density vanishes everywhere, and time-inversion symmetry occurs in addition to the spatial symmetry. The symmetry groups are called nonmagnetic in this case. There are 230 nonmagnetic crystallographic space groups altogether.

In a magnetic crystal the time-averaged density of the total angular momentum is different from zero, and may vary from one atom in the crystal to another. We may consider this density as a classical space distribution $\mathbf{s}(\mathbf{r})$, called the spin density for short. It is convenient, however, to consider only localized spin arrangements, normally with a limited number of possibilities for the spin vector located at each atom.

The magnetic space-group elements are those operators that bring the spin density function into itself. Denoting a space-group element by

$$\mathscr{F} = \{\mathscr{P}|\mathbf{u}\} = \mathscr{T}_{\mathbf{u}}\mathscr{P},$$

in accordance with Eq. (81), with $\mathscr{P}$ given by $(-1)^{\lambda}\mathscr{R}(\phi, \vartheta, \psi)$, $\lambda = 0, 1$, in accordance with Eq. (110), a proper magnetic group element may be written simply as $\mathscr{M} = (-1)^{\gamma}\mathscr{F}$ when operating on classical spin distributions. Here $\gamma = 0$ if time inversion is not involved, and $\gamma = 1$ for elements containing time inversion. For a proper magnetic group, time inversion is thus not a symmetry element, but must be combined with certain elements $\mathscr{F}$ of the space group.

Considering now the spin distribution to be described by a discrete set of spin vectors $\mathbf{s}_{\mathbf{m}+\boldsymbol{\mu}}$, located at atomic sites $\boldsymbol{\mu}$ of the unit cell $\mathbf{m}$, we obtain by operating with $\mathscr{M}$

$$\mathscr{M}\mathbf{s}_{\mathbf{m}+\boldsymbol{\mu}} = (-1)^{\gamma}\mathscr{Q}\mathbf{s}_{\mathbf{n}+\boldsymbol{\nu}}, \tag{114}$$

where $\mathscr{Q}$ is the rotation operator $\mathscr{R}$ prescribed to operate on the spin vector alone, and

$$\mathbf{n} + \boldsymbol{\nu} = \mathbf{u} + (-1)^{\lambda}\mathscr{R}(\mathbf{m} + \boldsymbol{\mu}). \tag{115}$$

The vector $\mathbf{n} + \boldsymbol{\nu}$ denotes the transformed site position of the rotated spin vector where $\mathbf{n}$ labels the unit cell and $\boldsymbol{\nu}$ an atomic position in this cell. Since the lattice of all unit-cell vectors has the full point-group symmetry of the crystal, the vector

$$\mathbf{n} - (-1)^{\lambda}\mathscr{R}\mathbf{m} = (-1)^{\lambda}\mathscr{R}\boldsymbol{\mu} + \mathbf{u} - \boldsymbol{\nu} = \mathbf{n}(\mathscr{F}, \boldsymbol{\mu}, \boldsymbol{\nu}) \tag{116}$$

will also be a lattice vector.

There are 1421 different proper magnetic groups. The technique to be used for finding spin waves that are symmetry adapted with respect to the irreducible representatives of these groups is similar to the procedure of finding symmetry-adapted lattice vibrations that is considered in Section V. In Section VI,H, we are going to treat the more general case of symmetry-adapting spin orbitals located at different atomic sites with respect to the irreducible representations of proper magnetic space groups.

It may be convenient also to discuss some other generalized space groups. The Shubnikov groups (*17*) are generalized space groups for crystals where, except for space operations transforming atomic positions into each other, we have the possibility of switching the variables of a two-component quantity, considered as a mark on each atom of black or white color. Apart from the 230 noncolored groups, there are 230 single-colored groups and 1191 two-colored groups that are isomorphic to the 1421 proper magnetic groups.

Using more than two colors, we obtain more generalized groups describing additional possibilities for the spin vectors. The corresponding groups are called colored groups (*17*).

Using more than one independent mark, further generalizations are obtained, as considered by Zamorzaev and Palistrant (*18*). This corresponds to the case of several localized quantum numbers for the crystal structure.

Another generalization approach is considered by Kitz (*19*), who permits additional rotations to be applied to the spin vector alone. This corresponds to the colored groups. The axes of the spin arrangements are then not necessarily invariant under the ordinary space-group operations. The case of linear spin arrangements corresponds to Kitz groups isomorphic to the 1421 proper magnetic groups. For plane and spatial spin arrangements an infinite number of possible groups is obtained.

Another kind of magnetic group is the magnetic translation group introduced by Zak (*20*) in order to simplify the dynamics of a crystal electron moving in a homogeneous external magnetic field. We are going to discuss this group in Section VII,D.

H. Permutation Symmetry for Particles in Solids

In addition to the groups discussed earlier, another kind of symmetry occurs for particles in solids. The concept of a particle in quantum theory is related to the symmetric group the elements of which are defined by all permutations between a set of identical objects. That identical situations appear frequently in Nature may be taken as a consequence of some variation principle. A physical system that contains a set of identical particles should transform under the symmetric group as the basis vectors of one of its symmetry types.

The identical representation is the simplest irreducible representation. Particles transforming according to this representation are bosons, such as photons and phonons. The antisymmetric representation is another one-dimensional representation, where all the even permutations are represented by 1 and all the odd ones by −1. Particles belonging to this representation are fermions, which have half-integral spin, like electrons. Bosons can pile up with an arbitrary number in the same state. This is impossible for fermions, since according to the antisymmetry requirement a transposition should yield a state with the opposite sign. Thus more than one fermion cannot occupy a given state, in accordance with the Pauli principle for electrons.

For more than two identical particles, there are also two-dimensional irreducible representations. The number of representations increases very rapidly with the number of particles. These representations do not seem to play an essential role for characterizing particles in Nature. In the case of weak spin-orbit interaction, however, permutation symmetry occurs for the spatial electron distribution alone, as well as for the spin distribution. The requirement that electronic states be antisymmetric under transpositions thus yield factored states of space and spin, where the space states themselves, as well as the spin states, are symmetry adapted with respect to some irreducible representation of the symmetric group, and the product state shall belong to the antisymmetric representation. This can be obtained by combining the antisymmetric space state with the symmetric spin state, or vice versa. It is also possible, however, that pairs of higher-dimensional irreducible representatives of the symmetric group occur when their product contains the antisymmetric representation.

Taking care of all possible symmetry adaptations that may occur for states of identical particles moving in solids is an extremely complicated problem. We cannot treat the general case, but must consider different specified situations. In the following, we are going to consider some specific examples in which symmetry reduction is most essential.

V. Lattice Vibrations in Solids

We shall now study the theory of lattice vibrations in solids, using the space symmetry of the crystal structure to simplify the determination of principal vibrations in the classical as well as in the quantum-mechanical case.

A. Classical Treatment

1. One Atom per Unit Cell

Consider first a crystal with only one atom of mass M in each unit cell. The position of the atom of the **m**th unit cell is denoted by $\mathbf{R}_\mathbf{m}$. In the equilibrium position, therefore, $\mathbf{R}_\mathbf{m} = \mathbf{m}$. A slightly displaced position will differ from the equilibrium position by a small displacement vector

$$\mathbf{Q}_\mathbf{m} = \mathbf{R}_\mathbf{m} - \mathbf{m} = \sum_{s=1}^{3} \mathbf{a}_s Q^s_\mathbf{m}, \tag{117}$$

where $Q^s_\mathbf{m}$ $(s = 1, 2, 3)$ are the direct-lattice (or contravariant) components of $\mathbf{Q}_\mathbf{m}$. We shall choose the $3N$ quantities $Q^s_\mathbf{m}$ as generalized coordinates, denoted by $\mathbf{Q}$ for short. The corresponding generalized momenta are then given by the reciprocal-lattice (or covariant) components

$$P_{\mathbf{m}s} = M\dot{Q}_{\mathbf{m}s} = M \sum_{l} a_{sl} \dot{Q}^l_\mathbf{m}, \tag{118}$$

where $a_{sl} = \mathbf{a}_s \cdot \mathbf{a}_l$ is an element of the metric tensor for the crystal lattice.

The classical Hamiltonian for the lattice vibrations is supposed to be given by

$$H = \frac{1}{2M} \sum_{\mathbf{m}} \sum_{s=1}^{3} P_{\mathbf{m}s} P^s_\mathbf{m} + \tfrac{1}{2} \sum_{\mathbf{m},\mathbf{n}} \sum_{s,l} Q^s_\mathbf{m} V^{\mathbf{mn}}_{sl} Q^l_\mathbf{n} + \cdots \tag{119}$$

where

$$V^{\mathbf{mn}}_{sl} = \left(\frac{\partial^2 U(\mathbf{Q})}{\partial Q^s_\mathbf{m} \, \partial Q^l_\mathbf{n}} \right)_{\mathbf{Q}=0} \tag{120}$$

are coefficients for the second-order terms in the Taylor expansion of the crystal potential $U(\mathbf{Q})$. These coefficients form a symmetric matrix. Since they also have the translational symmetry of the crystal, we obtain the relations

$$V^{\mathbf{mn}}_{sl} = V^{\mathbf{m}-\mathbf{n},\mathbf{0}}_{sl} = V^{\mathbf{n}-\mathbf{m},\mathbf{0}}_{ls}. \tag{121}$$

Dropping terms of higher order than 2 in the power series for the displacement coordinates $Q^l_\mathbf{m}$ of Eq. (119), we are dealing with the harmonic approximation. Anharmonic terms may change the considered symmetry, and will be disregarded in this connection.

The first set of Hamilton's equations of motion are then given by

$$\dot{P}_{\mathbf{m}s} = -\frac{\partial H(\mathbf{P}, \mathbf{Q})}{\partial Q^s_\mathbf{m}} = -\sum_{\mathbf{n}} \sum_{l} V^{\mathbf{mn}}_{sl} Q^l_\mathbf{n} = M \sum_{l} a_{sl} \ddot{Q}^l_\mathbf{m}. \tag{122}$$

The second set of Hamilton's equations will just correspond to Eq. (118).

Let us now investigate those solutions of Eq. (122) that correspond to principal vibrations obtained when all the atoms vibrate with the same frequency. The general solution may be written as a linear combination between these. The principal vibration with a given angular frequency ω may be obtained by taking the real part of a complex solution, $Q_{\mathbf{m}}^{l} = q_{\mathbf{m}}^{l} \exp(i\omega t)$, where $|q_{\mathbf{m}}^{l}|$ is the vibration amplitude. Inserting this expression into Eq. (122), we find

$$\sum_{\mathbf{n},l} (V_{sl}^{\mathbf{mn}} - M\omega^2 a_{sl}\delta_{\mathbf{mn}})q_{\mathbf{n}}^{l} = 0: \tag{123}$$

Since the crystal has an infinite lattice structure, we would have to solve a secular equation of infinite order in order to find the possible eigenfrequencies ω. We shall see, however, that the translational symmetry will split this equation into (an infinite number of) finite secular equations.

2. Translational Symmetry

We have seen that the harmonic approximation corresponds to an eigenvalue equation for the potential matrix $V_{sl}^{\mathbf{mn}}$ that has the periodicity of the crystal lattice. In order to solve the corresponding secular equation, obtained from Eq. (123), it is necessary to take advantage of this translational symmetry. The spatial part of a principal vibration coordinate at site $\mathbf{m}$ should be symmetry adapted with respect to the $\mathbf{k}$th symmetry type of G_T. Thus these coordinates should be related to each other according to

$$\mathscr{T}_{\mathbf{n}}\, q_{\mathbf{m}}^{l} = q_{\mathbf{m}+\mathbf{n}}^{l} = \exp(-i\mathbf{k}\cdot\mathbf{n})q_{\mathbf{m}}^{l}. \tag{124}$$

In particular, for $\mathbf{m} = \mathbf{0}$ ("central site"), we find the relation

$$q_{\mathbf{n}}^{l} = \exp(-i\mathbf{k}\cdot\mathbf{n})q_{\mathbf{0}}^{l}.$$

Inserting this expression for $q_{\mathbf{n}}^{l}$ into Eq. (123) and using Eq. (121), we obtain

$$\sum_{l=1}^{3} [U_{sl}(\mathbf{k}) - \omega^2 a_{sl}]q_{\mathbf{0}}^{l} = 0, \tag{125}$$

where

$$U_{sl}(\mathbf{k}) = \frac{1}{M}\sum_{\mathbf{n}} \exp(i\mathbf{k}\cdot\mathbf{n})V_{sl}^{\mathbf{n0}} \tag{126}$$

are components of a Hermitian three-by-three matrix. This set of linear equations for $q_{\mathbf{0}}^{l}$ has solutions different from zero only for those values of ω^2 that are roots of a secular equation of third order for each $\mathbf{k}$ vector. These secular equations can be readily solved from the knowledge of $V_{sl}^{\mathbf{n}0}$. The solutions form a continuous spectrum $\pm\omega_l(\mathbf{k})$ with three branches, $l = 1, 2, 3$. Using Eq. (124) for $\mathbf{m} = \mathbf{0}$, we obtain the solutions for arbitrary $\mathbf{n}$. The real vibration coordinates may be obtained by adding solutions for the time-dependent coordinates with opposite phases, $\pm i(\omega t - \mathbf{k}\cdot\mathbf{n})$. For each $\mathbf{k}$ vector, these solutions correspond to one longitudinal and two transverse acoustic vibrations.

3. *The Case of Several Atoms per Unit Cell*

When there is more than one atom in each unit cell, the vector of displacement from equilibrium position for an atom of mass M_μ located at the $\boldsymbol{\mu}$th site of the $\mathbf{m}$th unit cell will be denoted by $Q_{\mathbf{m}+\boldsymbol{\mu}}$. We may then undertake a series of canonical transformations in order to simplify the equations of motion. In the first step we only multiply all the generalized coordinates by $(M_\mu/M)^{1/2}$. This yields new coordinates and momenta, describing the case when all the atomic masses are equal to M. Then it is convenient to introduce Bloch coordinates [see Eq. (130)] and transform them into real form. Arguments of translational symmetry yield, in full analogy to the previous case, the real principal vibrations

$$\mathbf{Q}_{\mathbf{m}+\boldsymbol{\mu}} = \left(\frac{M}{M_\mu}\right)^{1/2} \mathbf{q}_\mu \cos(\mathbf{k}\cdot\mathbf{m} - \omega t), \tag{127}$$

where $\mathbf{q}_\mu$ and ω still have to be solved. The set of linear equations for solving $\mathbf{q}_\mu$ analogous to Eq. (125) now takes indices from two different site positions $\boldsymbol{\mu}$ and $\boldsymbol{\nu}$ of the unit cell. The corresponding secular equation will be

$$\det\{U_{sl}^{\mu\nu}(\mathbf{k}) - \omega^2 a_{sl}\delta_{\mu\nu}\} = 0, \tag{128}$$

where $U_{sl}^{\mu\nu}$ are the components of a Hermitian potential matrix given by

$$U_{sl}^{\mu\nu}(\mathbf{k}) = (M_\mu M_\nu)^{-1/2} \sum_{\mathbf{n}} \exp(i\mathbf{k}\cdot\mathbf{n}) V_{sl}^{\mathbf{n}+\mu,\nu}. \tag{129}$$

The secular equation (128) has the finite order $3N_a$, where N_a is the number of atoms per unit cell. When this is a large number, it may still be troublesome to solve all the secular equations for different $\mathbf{k}$ vectors. Utilizing the full space-group symmetry, however, we are able to obtain further simplification and classification of the solutions with respect to the different symmetry types of the little groups of the different $\mathbf{k}$ vectors.

4. Symmetry Adaptation by Means of the Crystallographic Space Group

We shall now make explicit use of the crystal space symmetry in order to solve Eq. (128). First, we realize that the symmetry adaptation already done corresponds to the construction of Bloch coordinates

$$X_{\mu\mathbf{k}}^{l} = \left(\frac{M_\mu}{M}\right)^{1/2} \frac{1}{N} \sum_{\mathbf{m}} \exp(i\mathbf{k}\cdot\mathbf{m}) Q_{\mathbf{m}+\boldsymbol{\mu}}^{l} \tag{130}$$

obtained by acting with the projection operator $\mathscr{T}(\mathbf{k})$ of Eq. (76) on a general coordinate Q_{μ}^{l} and multiplying the result by a normalizing mass factor $(M_\mu/M)^{1/2}$.

In order to obtain further symmetry adaptation, we have to study the action of a space-group element $\mathscr{F} = \{\mathscr{P}|\mathbf{u}\}$ on a displacement coordinate $Q_{\mathbf{m}+\boldsymbol{\mu}}^{l}$. We then obtain

$$\mathscr{F} Q_{\mathbf{m}+\boldsymbol{\mu}}^{l} = (-1)^{\lambda} \sum_{s=1}^{3} Q_{\mathbf{n}+\boldsymbol{\nu}}^{s} R_{s}^{l}, \tag{131}$$

where $\mathbf{n} + \boldsymbol{\nu}$ is the position vector of the transformed site as given by Eq. (115), and $(-1)^{\lambda} R_{s}^{l}$ is an element of the square matrix representing the point-group element $\mathscr{P}$ in the direct-lattice basis $(\mathbf{a}_1, \mathbf{a}_2, \mathbf{a}_3)$. Operating on a Bloch coordinate, similarly

$$\begin{aligned} \mathscr{F} X_{\mu\mathbf{k}}^{l} &= \left(\frac{M_\mu}{M}\right)^{1/2} \frac{(-1)^{\lambda}}{N} \sum_{\mathbf{n}} \exp\{(-1)^{\lambda} i\mathbf{k}\cdot[\mathscr{R}^{-1}(\mathbf{n}+\boldsymbol{\nu}-\mathbf{u}) - \boldsymbol{\mu}]\} \sum_{s} Q_{\mathbf{n}+\boldsymbol{\nu}}^{s} R_{s}^{l} \\ &= (-1)^{\lambda} \exp[-i\mathscr{P}\mathbf{k}\cdot\mathbf{n}(\mathscr{F}, \boldsymbol{\mu}, \boldsymbol{\nu})] \sum_{s} X_{\nu,\mathscr{P}\mathbf{k}}^{s} R_{s}^{l}, \end{aligned} \tag{132}$$

where $\mathbf{n}(\mathscr{F}, \boldsymbol{\mu}, \boldsymbol{\nu})$ is the unit-cell displacement given by Eq. (116). When $\mathscr{P} = (-1)^{\lambda}\mathscr{R}$ belongs to the little point group $P_{\mathbf{k}}$, Eq. (132) reads

$$\mathscr{F} X_{\mu\mathbf{k}}^{l} = (-1)^{\lambda} \exp[-i\mathbf{k}\cdot\mathbf{n}(\mathscr{F}, \boldsymbol{\mu}, \boldsymbol{\nu})] \sum_{s} X_{\nu\mathbf{k}}^{s} R_{s}^{l}. \tag{133}$$

We are now ready to apply the projection matrix of Eq. (52), the elements of which will take the form [cf. Eq. (88)],

$${}^{jm}P_{\mathbf{k}}(\boldsymbol{\mu}, \boldsymbol{\nu}; s, l) = (-1)^{\lambda} \frac{h_{j\mathbf{k}}}{g_{\mathbf{k}}} \sum_{\mathscr{F}}^{G(\boldsymbol{\mu},\boldsymbol{\nu},\mathbf{k})} {}^{j\mathbf{k}}F_{mm}^{*} \exp[-i\mathbf{k}\cdot\mathbf{n}(\mathscr{F}, \boldsymbol{\mu}, \boldsymbol{\nu})] R_{s}^{l} \tag{134}$$

where $\boldsymbol{\mu}$ and s label the rows and $\boldsymbol{\nu}$ and l the columns, $g_{\mathbf{k}}$ is the order of the little group, and $h_{j\mathbf{k}}$ the order of its jth irreducible representation. The mth diagonal element of $\mathscr{F}$ in this representation is given by ${}^{j\mathbf{k}}F_{mm}$. The sum runs over those elements $\mathscr{F}$ that belong to the "little coset" $G(\boldsymbol{\mu}, \boldsymbol{\nu}, \mathbf{k})$, defined as the subset of elements of the little group transforming the atomic position $\boldsymbol{\mu}$ of a unit cell into the position $\boldsymbol{\nu}$ in another cell, according to Eq. (115) (*21*). Applying this projection matrix to the Bloch coordinates, we obtain the space symmetry-adapted coordinates.

The sum of all traces of the projection matrices for all symmetry types of a given $\mathbf{k}$ vector is equal to the number of independent vibration coordinates $3N_a$ for the atoms in the unit cell. Starting with the $3N_a$ independent coordinates $Q_{\boldsymbol{\mu}}^{l}$ of a unit cell, each one of these gives rise to $h_{j\mathbf{k}}$ projections for each irreducible representation. To avoid all the redundancies thus obtained, the reduction procedure described in Section III must be applied. It is necessary, however, first to transform the projection matrix into Hermitian form, which can be done by means of a similarity transformation. Using an orthogonal coordinate system for the components of $\mathbf{Q}_{\mathbf{m}+\boldsymbol{\mu}}$, the projection matrix becomes Hermitian.

Transforming the reduced symmetry-adapted vibration coordinates finally into real form, the secular equation (128) becomes real and is split with respect to all the symmetry types of the group of $\mathbf{k}$.

B. Quantum-Mechanical Treatment

In a quantum-mechanical treatment of the lattice vibrations, we may proceed in different ways. Starting with a set of orthogonal vibration coordinates $Q_{\mathbf{k}\alpha}$ ($\alpha = 1, 2, \ldots 3N_a$) and the corresponding conjugated momenta $P_{\mathbf{k}\alpha} = -i\hbar\, \partial/\partial Q_{\mathbf{k}\alpha}$, the Schrödinger equation corresponding to the Hamiltonian of Eq. (119) may be solved approximately by introducing a suitable set of basis functions of Bloch function type, which may be further symmetry adapted with respect to the crystallographic space-group symmetry.

It is obvious, however, that the quantum-mechanical problem will become much simpler when the coordinates are transformed into normal coordinates $q_\alpha = {}^{j\mathbf{k}}q_m^{\beta}$, where β labels the different coordinates belonging to the symmetry type (j, m) of the little group of $\mathbf{k}$. These coordinates are found by solving the symmetry-reduced secular equations for all the different symmetry types. In the harmonic approximation, these normal coordinates thus represent independent harmonic oscillators. The product wave function may then be factored according to

$$\Phi(\mathbf{q}) = \prod_{\alpha} \varphi_\alpha(q_\alpha), \tag{135}$$

where $\varphi_\alpha(q_\alpha)$ is an eigenfunction of the single-oscillator Hamiltonian

$$\mathscr{H}_\alpha = \frac{1}{2M} p_\alpha^2 + \tfrac{1}{2} M\omega_\alpha^2 q_\alpha^2. \tag{136}$$

Here p_α is given by $-i\hbar\, \partial/\partial q_\alpha$ and ω_α is the angular frequency of the classical vibration. Except for acceptance of the Born-Oppenheimer approximation yielding separation of the nuclear and electronic motion, the factoring in Eq. (135) is obtained just because of the harmonic approximation, where the Hamiltonian may be written as a sum of contributions $\mathscr{H}_\alpha$. The wave function of Eq. (135) transforms irreducibly under lattice translations, according to the representation labeled by $\sum \mathbf{k}_\alpha$. The direct products of irreducible representations of little groups of $\mathbf{k}$ are, however, not irreducible in general. The symmetry adaptation of product functions necessary in order to find the energy spectrum will thus represent a more complicated problem, which we shall not treat here.

The single-oscillator energies are given by the well-known eigenvalue spectrum of the operator in Eq. (136):

$$E_{\alpha n} = (n + \tfrac{1}{2})\hbar\omega_\alpha; \qquad n = 0, 1, 2, \ldots. \tag{137}$$

The total lattice vibration energy is then given by

$$E = \tfrac{1}{2}\hbar \sum_\alpha \omega_\alpha + \hbar \sum_\alpha n_\alpha \omega_\alpha, \tag{138}$$

where n_α is the value of n for the αth oscillator. The first term in Eq. (138) corresponds to the zero-point energy. A definite state may be described by specifying the $3N_a$ numbers n_α for each $\mathbf{k}$ vector. Transitions into other states can only take place in terms of energy quanta $\hbar\omega_\alpha$, carried by a "particle" called a phonon.

In the harmonic approximation we have thus obtained an independent-particle model describing the lattice oscillations. The propagation vector of a phonon is given by $\mathbf{k}$. There are $3N_a$ branches, three of which correspond to acoustic phonons (one longitudinal and two transverse oscillations). The remaining $(3N_a - 3)$ branches represent optical phonons, the wavelengths of which may be sufficiently short for interaction with infrared photons.

C. Bose Statistics

Since an indefinite number of phonons can occupy the same energy state, phonons are bosons with spin one, and transform according to the identical representation of the symmetric group of permutations between the phonons.

The wave function of Eq. (135) should therefore be replaced by a symmetric product sum, where thus the symmetry-adapted combination is selected out of a set of $(\sum n_\alpha)!$ possible functions, obtained by making all permutations among single-phonon wave functions of a given product function. Because of the degeneracy occurring in the independent-particle model we do not obtain any exchange energy.

Actually, however, phonons do interact, since excitations may occur at the times of phonon collisions in a way similar to that for the atoms of an ideal gas. We may thus consider that the phonons form an ideal Bose gas in thermodynamic equilibrium. The probability of finding a phonon in the state $\varphi_{\alpha n}$ is then given by the canonical distribution

$$\rho(T, \alpha, n) = \frac{1}{Z_1} \exp(-E_{\alpha n}/kT). \tag{139}$$

where $E_{\alpha n}$ is given by Eq. (137), T is the absolute temperature, k is Boltzmann's constant, and Z_1 is the statistical state sum of one-particle states defined by

$$Z_1 = \sum_n \exp\left(\frac{-E_{\alpha n}}{kT}\right). \tag{140}$$

The statistical expectation value for the number of phonons in the vibration mode ω_α (i.e., in any of the states $\varphi_{\alpha n}$ for $n = 0, 1, 2, \ldots$) is then obtained from Eqs. (139)–(140):

$$\langle n \rangle = n(T, \alpha) = \sum_{n=0}^{\infty} n\rho(T, \alpha, n) = (\exp \xi - 1)^{-1}, \tag{141}$$

where $\xi = \hbar\omega_\alpha/kT$. The internal crystal energy due to the lattice vibrations then becomes

$$\langle E \rangle = \sum_\alpha \hbar\omega_\alpha[n(T, \alpha) + \tfrac{1}{2}] \tag{142}$$

with $n(T, \alpha)$ given by Eq. (141). This relation was first derived by Planck (*22*) in the case of photon radiation.

At temperatures close to absolute zero, ξ tends to infinity, and the number of phonons tends toward zero with $\exp(-\xi)$. Most of the phonons are then obtained by contributions to $n(T, \alpha)$ for low ω values, corresponding to long-wave acoustic vibrations.

Particles of low energy passing through the crystal may become absorbed mainly by interaction with the electronic states. Since the energy gaps between the states of low-energy phonons may be of the same order of magnitude as the energy of the incoming particle, the probability for phonon excitations is very small at low temperatures (except for the case of perfect resonance, when the energy of the incoming particle is exactly equal to the energy gap). Thus the entire solid takes on the momentum of the incoming particle when the latter is absorbed (Mössbauer effect).

At high temperatures, we find $\xi \ll 1$, and the classical limit is obtained. The internal crystal energy can then take an almost continuous range of values. Sound waves may thus be easily obtained when incoming particles are absorbed by solids at high temperatures.

Introducing anharmonic effects, we lose the ideal picture of noninteracting particles. Phonons may then be annihilated and created as in a grand canonical ensemble. Second quantization should be introduced for the description of properties where anharmonic effects are essential, such as thermal conduction, diffusion, and surface effects in crystals. We do not intend to treat any of these problems here, however.

In the next section we shall deal with an independent-particle model for the description of the electronic structure in crystals.

VI. Band Theory of Solids

The electronic structure of solids will now be treated by means of quantum theory in the case of perfect crystals. We may then consider a crystal as an infinite molecule, and utilize the crystal symmetry, by means of which it may become possible to solve the Schrödinger equation in a one-electron approximation. This procedure leads to the band theory of solids.

A. Fermi Statistics

As a consequence of the Born-Oppenheimer, or adiabatic, approximation (*1*), we may think of the electrons in a solid as a set of particles moving under the influence of a fixed crystal potential in a way similar to that considered for phonons in the preceding section. There are, however, some fundamental difficulties involved in this picture. First, some electrons are tightly bound to the nuclei. These are the inner-shell electrons, which may be considered separately and treated as an ion core contributing only to the external crystal potential of the valence electrons. The valence electrons may then be considered as almost free, and are allowed to move throughout the whole crystal.

The most serious difficulty with the one-electron picture, however, is that the Coulomb interaction between the electrons cannot be neglected, since it has the same order of magnitude as the attraction of the electrons to the nuclei. This dilemma may be solved by thinking of each electron as moving separately in an effective crystal potential originating from all nuclei and ion cores, together with the mean field of the other valence electrons of the crystal. The electron gas thus defined has properties similar to those of the phonon gas, except for the behavior of the electron wave function under permutations of the electrons.

If we do not consider creation and annihilation processes, we may have a definite number of electrons, which should obey Fermi statistics. Thus, the occupation numbers of the effective one-electron states can be only one or zero. In the crystal ground state at absolute zero temperature, the occupation numbers are equal to one for all the states corresponding to energy levels below a certain limit (Fermi level), and zero for all states with higher energy values. At higher temperatures, when the free electrons are in thermodynamic equilibrium with the phonons, some few electrons occupy excited states with energies slightly above the Fermi level, leaving holes for some states just below this level. These holes will thus behave like positrons. Particles and holes form fundamental concepts for the theoretical description of semiconductor physics where transport phenomena for charged particles in semiconducting crystals are studied. The motion of these particles is closely connected with the electron band structure, which we are going to consider later. For this purpose we shall first derive the Hartree-Fock equations, which are the basic equations for the electronic distribution in atoms, molecules, and crystals.

B. The Hartree-Fock Equations

We start with a Schrödinger Hamiltonian for the nuclei and electrons,

$$H = W + \sum_i u(i) + \sum_{i<j} V(i, j), \tag{143}$$

where W is a pure nuclear and ion-core energy term, and

$$u(i) = (2M)^{-1} p_i^2 + w(\mathbf{r}_i) + \xi_i \mathbf{l}_i \cdot \boldsymbol{\sigma}_i \tag{144}$$

is a one-electron Hamiltonian for the ith electron, with the momentum $\mathbf{p}_i = -i\hbar \operatorname{grad}_i$, the orbital angular momentum $\mathbf{l}_i = \mathbf{r}_i \times \mathbf{p}_i$, and the Pauli spin vector $\boldsymbol{\sigma}_i$. The coupling constant ξ_i for the spin-orbit term may be computed when an approximate solution is known for the electron distribution. The potential energy of the ith valence electron in the field of all the nuclei and ion cores is given by $w(\mathbf{r}_i)$, and $V(i, j)$ is the interaction between the ith and jth electrons consisting of the Coulomb interaction e^2/r_{ij} and possible additional terms due to orbit-orbit, spin-orbit, and spin-spin interactions.

In the ordinary Hartree-Fock approximation used for molecules, the wave function for n electrons is supposed to be described by a single configuration of spin orbitals, $\langle q_i|\chi_i\rangle$, for $i=1, 2, \ldots, n$. Here q_i denotes the space and spin coordinates of the ith electron.

The Hermitian and idempotent Wigner projection operator for antisymmetric states of the symmetric group is given by

$$\mathscr{A} = \frac{1}{n!}\sum_{\mathscr{P}} (-1)^p \mathscr{P}, \tag{145}$$

where $\mathscr{P}$ denotes a permutation between the states $|\chi_i\rangle$, $i = 1, 2, \ldots, n$, and p is the parity, given by the corresponding number of transpositions. Applying the antisymmetry operator to a Hartree product $\langle q|\chi\rangle$ of the n spin orbitals, we obtain a Slater determinant $\langle q|\Phi\rangle$, after normalization written as

$$\langle q|\Phi\rangle = (n!)^{1/2}\langle q|\mathscr{A}|\chi\rangle = (n!)^{-1/2}\det\langle q_i|\chi_j\rangle. \tag{146}$$

Using the wave function of Eq. (146), we find that the expectation value of the Hamiltonian of Eq. (143) becomes

$$\langle\Phi|\mathscr{H}|\Phi\rangle = W + \sum_i \langle\chi_i|u|\chi_i\rangle + \sum_{i<j}\langle\chi_i\chi_j|\mathscr{V}(1-\mathscr{P}_{ij})|\chi_i\chi_j\rangle, \tag{147}$$

where $\mathscr{P}_{ij}$ is the transposition between the states $|\chi_i\rangle$ and $|\chi_j\rangle$, and the expressions within the Dirac brackets at the right-hand side are notations for the ordinary one-electron energy integrals and two-electron Coulomb and exchange energy integrals, respectively.

We introduce the Hermitian Fock operator as an effective one-electron Hamiltonian

$$h = \frac{W}{n} + u + \mathscr{K} - \mathscr{J}, \tag{148}$$

where $\mathscr{K}$ and $\mathscr{J}$ are the Coulomb and exchange operators, defined by

$$\langle\chi_i|\mathscr{K}|\chi_k\rangle = \sum_j \langle\chi_i\chi_j|\mathscr{V}|\chi_k\chi_j\rangle \tag{149}$$

and

$$\langle\chi_i|\mathscr{J}|\chi_k\rangle = \sum_j \langle\chi_i\chi_j|\mathscr{V}|\chi_j\chi_k\rangle, \tag{150}$$

respectively.

The Hartree-Fock equations are now obtained by minimizing the energy expression of Eq. (147) with respect to changes in $|\chi_i\rangle$ under the subsidiary condition of orthonormalized states $\delta\langle\chi_i|\chi_j\rangle = 0$:

$$h|\chi_i\rangle = \sum_j |\chi_j\rangle\langle\chi_j|h|\chi_i\rangle. \tag{151}$$

By diagonalizing the Fock matrix, Eq. (151) becomes an eigenvector equation

$$h|\psi_i\rangle = \epsilon_i|\psi_i\rangle. \tag{152}$$

The states $|\psi_i\rangle$ thus obtained may be used to redefine the Coulomb and exchange operators of Eqs. (149) and (150). The procedure should then be repeated until self-consistency is obtained, when the effective one-electron energy ϵ_i coincides with its value in the next latest step of the procedure, up to a prescribed number of decimal places. The total energy will then be obtained as

$$\langle H\rangle = \tfrac{1}{2}\sum_i [\epsilon_i + \langle\psi_i|u|\psi_i\rangle]. \tag{153}$$

In molecules, it is not necessary to consider the constant contribution of the nuclear energy term W/n to the Fock operator (for fixed nuclear positions). In crystals, however, this is necessary, since in this case the contribution will be infinite, though it has been divided by the infinite number of crystal valence electrons. In order to obtain a convergent series expansion for contributions of increasing distances in the crystal, it will be necessary to divide the crystal Hamiltonian into parts containing interactions between electrically neutral crystal regions (dipole interaction).

In applications to crystals, it is not possible to perform full Hartree-Fock calculations without drastic approximations, even when the biggest modern electronic computers are used and all kinds of symmetry are considered. The Fock operator is usually replaced by an effective one-electron Hamiltonian obtained by specifying a periodic crystal potential.

C. Brillouin Zones

The one-electron orbitals to be used in the simplified Hartree-Fock procedure for determination of the electronic distribution in crystals should be symmetry adapted with respect to the translation group G_T, the irreducible representations of which are labeled by the **k** vector with the components defined by Eq. (72). Starting with a set of orbitals related spatially to a given unit cell, we thus obtain one distinct set of Bloch orbitals for each **k** vector in a unit zone, in accordance with Eq. (79). This unit zone is limited by a parallelepiped spanned by three vectors $\mathbf{K}^i$, $i = 1, 2, 3$, defined as 2π times the basis vectors $\mathbf{b}^i$ of the reciprocal lattice.

Since equivalent $\mathbf{k}$ vectors yield identical Bloch orbital sets, however, the form of the unit zone is not definite. We may transform it in such a way that its geometrical form will become unchanged under the operations of the crystal point group. This can be done by constructing planes in $\mathbf{k}$ space perpendicularly bisecting each one of the vectors $\mathbf{K}^i$. Operation on these planes with the elements of the crystal point group yields a set of planes, the inside region of which defines a polygon called the first Brillouin zone (*23*). This region has the same volume in $\mathbf{k}$ space as the original zone. All its $\mathbf{k}$ vectors are nonequivalent with one another and equivalent with the $\mathbf{k}$ vectors in the original zone. The $\mathbf{k}$ vectors originating from the center of the Brillouin zone and with their end points at the zone boundaries fulfill the relation

$$|\mathbf{k}| = |\mathbf{k} + \mathbf{K}|, \tag{154}$$

where $\mathbf{K}$ is an arbitrary first-order zone vector. Thus there are several equivalent points $\mathbf{k} + \mathbf{K}$ at the Brillouin zone boundaries with the same absolute value for the crystal momentum. Higher-order Brillouin zones are defined by taking higher-order $\mathbf{K}$ vectors in Eq. (154).

D. Degeneracy in k Space

Obviously, the little-group condition $\mathscr{P}\mathbf{k} = \mathbf{k} + \mathbf{K}$ of Eq. (84) is satisfied for nontrivial little groups only for points in $\mathbf{k}$ space satisfying Eq. (154). This means that all points of nontrivial symmetry in $\mathbf{k}$ space are equivalent to points lying at the Brillouin zone surfaces. Thus, certain discrete points, lines, and planes at these boundaries in $\mathbf{k}$ space represent cases when symmetry adaptation can be obtained with respect to little point groups.

In the free-electron limit, when the kinetic energy is proportional to k^2, the energy is continuous and spherically symmetric in $\mathbf{k}$ space. It is seen also from Eq. (154) that the unperturbed states for equivalent points at the Brillouin zone boundaries are degenerate. Taking the crystal potential as a small perturbation, a mixture between these states would occur, giving rise to discontinuities, or energy gaps, at the zone boundaries.

A high order of degeneracy in $\mathbf{k}$ space still occurs in the presence of a crystal potential. As a matter of fact, the energy distribution in $\mathbf{k}$ space $\epsilon(\mathbf{k})$ has the full point-group symmetry of the crystal; that is, $\epsilon(\mathscr{P}\mathbf{k}) = \epsilon(\mathbf{k})$ for any $\mathscr{P} \in G_P$. This is seen from the fact that the space-group element $\mathscr{F} = \{\mathscr{P}|\mathbf{u}\}$, operating on a Bloch orbital of a given $\mathbf{k}$ vector, yields another Bloch orbital, belonging to the symmetry type $\mathscr{P}\mathbf{k}$, as a consequence of Eq. (83). Changing the wave vector of the Fock matrix from $\mathbf{k}$ into $\mathscr{P}\mathbf{k}$ thus means that it just undergoes a similarity transformation according to

$$\langle \psi_{\mathbf{k}}^{\alpha} | h | \psi_{\mathbf{k}}^{\beta} \rangle = \langle \psi_{\mathbf{k}}^{\alpha} | \mathscr{F}^{\dagger} h \mathscr{F} | \psi_{\mathbf{k}}^{\beta} \rangle = \langle \varphi_{\mathscr{P}\mathbf{k}}^{\alpha} | h | \varphi_{\mathscr{P}\mathbf{k}}^{\beta} \rangle. \tag{155}$$

Here the states $\varphi_{\mathbf{k}}^{\alpha}$ for a fixed **k** vector are linear combinations of the $\psi_{\mathbf{k}}^{\mu}$ states, due to the space operations $\mathscr{F}$. A more explicit derivation of this formula is given in Section VI,I for the case of the tight-binding approximation.

In order to investigate the one-electron energy distribution $\epsilon(\mathbf{k})$, it is thus necessary to study only a small region of the first Brillouin zone; this region can be brought over into the remaining part of the Brillouin zone by means of point-group operations. The points, lines, and planes in **k** space corresponding to nontrivial little-group symmetry are always found at the boundaries of these regions.

In the following subsections we shall treat some of the conventional methods used for electron energy band calculations in crystals.

E. The Plane Wave (PW) Method

The simplest method available for energy band calculations is the plane wave (PW) method, which may be used for the almost free electrons of metals. The motion of a perfectly free electron is characterized by its propagation vector **k**, and the wave function describing it is a plane wave,

$$\langle \mathbf{r}|\mathbf{k}\rangle = V^{-1/2}\exp(i\mathbf{k}\cdot\mathbf{r}),$$

where V is the volume chosen for normalization. Introducing a weak periodic crystal potential field $U(\mathbf{r})$ perturbing the free electron, we may use a basis set of free-electron states corresponding to **k** vectors of degenerate crystal states. Such a basis set is already symmetry adapted with respect to G_T. As a matter of fact, using the projection operator of Eq. (76), we obtain

$$\begin{aligned}\mathscr{T}(\mathbf{k})\exp(i\mathbf{k}'\cdot\mathbf{r}) &= \frac{1}{N}\sum_{\mathbf{n}}\exp(i\mathbf{k}\cdot\mathbf{n})\mathscr{T}_{\mathbf{n}}\exp(i\mathbf{k}'\cdot\mathbf{r})\\ &= \exp(i(\mathbf{k}+\mathbf{K})\cdot\mathbf{r})\delta_{\mathbf{k}',\mathbf{k}+\mathbf{K}},\end{aligned}$$

where **K** is an arbitrary unit zone vector.

Let us now consider the special case of a symmorphic space group. It remains then to construct symmetry-adapted wave functions with respect to the symmetry types of the little point groups only. The linear combinations of those different plane waves, the **k** vectors of which belong to the same prong of a star, should be given by symmetry alone. It is not necessary, though, to mix states of all **k** vectors of the star, since different prongs are perfectly non-interacting, as a consequence of symmetry. We should rather consider all different stars of equivalent **k** vectors labeled in sequence of increasing star radii $|\mathbf{k}+\mathbf{K}|$. The plane waves of a **k** vector of the same prong of a star are linearly combined by symmetry adaptations. Choosing one reference **K** for each star of wave vectors equivalent to **k** will thus be sufficient for labeling the basis set of a given symmetry type (j, m) of the little group of **k**. For a given symmetry type, we have to choose only those stars that yield nonvanishing symmetry projections. Denoting the projection operator of an arbitrary symmetry type by $\mathscr{S}$, we have an element of the effective Hamiltonian

$$\mathscr{H} = -\frac{\hbar^2}{2m}\Delta + U(\mathbf{r}), \tag{156}$$

given by

$$\begin{aligned} H_{\mathbf{K}'\mathbf{K}''} &= \frac{g}{h}\langle \mathbf{k} + \mathbf{K}' | \mathscr{S}^{\dagger} \mathscr{H} \mathscr{S} | \mathbf{k} + \mathbf{K}'' \rangle \\ &= \frac{\hbar^2}{2m} |\mathbf{k} + \mathbf{K}'|^2 \delta_{\mathbf{K}'\mathbf{K}''} + U_{\mathbf{K}'\mathbf{K}''}, \end{aligned} \tag{157}$$

where g/h is obtained from the normalizing factor of the symmetry-adapted plane wave (g is the order of the little point group, h the order of its irreducible representation). Note that the Kronecker symbol here is equal to zero only for different stars, since only one **K** vector for each star is used to label the states.

By using the commutation relation $[\mathscr{S}, \mathscr{H}] = 0$, as well as the Hermiticity and idempotency properties of $\mathscr{S}$, we obtain, for the elements of the potential matrix,

$$U_{\mathbf{K}'\mathbf{K}''} = \frac{g}{h}\langle \mathbf{k} + \mathbf{K}' | \mathscr{U} \mathscr{S} | \mathbf{k} + \mathbf{K}'' \rangle = \sum_{\mathscr{P} \in P_{\mathbf{k}}} {}^{j}P^{*}_{mm} U_{\mathbf{K}(\mathscr{P})}. \tag{158}$$

Here $\mathbf{K}(\mathscr{P})$ is given by

$$\mathbf{K}(\mathscr{P}) = \mathscr{P}\mathbf{K}'' - \mathbf{K}' + \mathscr{P}\mathbf{k} - \mathbf{k}, \tag{159}$$

which is a zone vector when $\mathscr{P}$ belongs to the little point group. The quantity $U_{\mathbf{K}(\mathscr{P})}$ is defined by

$$U_{\mathbf{K}} = \langle \mathbf{0} | \mathscr{U} | \mathbf{K} \rangle = \frac{1}{V} \int \exp(i\mathbf{K} \cdot \mathbf{r}) U(\mathbf{r})\, d^3\mathbf{r}, \tag{160}$$

where $V = NV_a$ is the volume of the microcrystal. Introducing the partial contribution $u(\mathbf{r} - \mathbf{n})$ from the **n**th unit cell to the crystal potential

$U(\mathbf{r}) = \sum u(\mathbf{r} - \mathbf{n})$, we further obtain

$$U_{\mathbf{K}} = \frac{1}{V}\sum_{\mathbf{n}} \exp(i\mathbf{K}\cdot\mathbf{n}) \int_{\mathbf{n}\text{th unit cell}} \exp(i\mathbf{K}\cdot(\mathbf{r}-\mathbf{n}))u(\mathbf{r}-\mathbf{n})\, d^3\mathbf{r}$$

$$= \frac{1}{V_a}\int_{\text{unit cell}} \exp(i\mathbf{K}\cdot\mathbf{r})u(\mathbf{r})\, d^3\mathbf{r} = u_{\mathbf{K}}, \tag{161}$$

since the integral over the $\mathbf{n}$th unit cell is independent of $\mathbf{n}$ and the sum of $\exp(i\mathbf{K}\cdot\mathbf{n})$ is equal to N.

From Eqs. (157)–(161) we thus obtain

$$H_{\mathbf{K}'\mathbf{K}''} = \frac{\hbar^2}{2m}|\mathbf{k}+\mathbf{K}'|^2\delta_{\mathbf{K}'\mathbf{K}''} + \sum_{\mathscr{P}\in P_{\mathbf{k}}} {}^{j}P^{*}_{mm}u_{\mathbf{K}(\mathscr{P})}, \tag{162}$$

with $\mathbf{K}(\mathscr{P})$ given by Eq. (159) and $u_{\mathbf{K}}$ by Eq. (161).

The energy elements given by Eq. (162) form a Hermitian matrix of infinite order. For a limited set of stars of a given $\mathbf{k}$ vector, it may be diagonalized by means of standard methods, in order to obtain $\epsilon(\mathbf{k})$.

There is a fundamental reason, however, why this method does not work for other purposes than getting a quick first approach to a more elaborate method, namely, that plane waves are not very suitable to describe the wave function near the atomic nuclei. The convergence is here very slow and a very large number of stars should be considered in the basis. On the other hand, taking sufficiently many stars in the basis, the lowest state should converge toward a Bloch combination of $1s$ atomic orbitals. This would not give a very good description either, since these states will already be occupied by the inner electrons. To obtain agreement with the Pauli exclusion principle, orthogonalization to the ion cores of the inner-shell electrons should thus be required. This is done in the orthogonalized plane wave (OPW) method, which is considered in the next subsection.

F. The Orthogonalized Plane Wave (OPW) Method

The OPW method was introduced by Herring (*24*) in 1940. The core electrons are here described by Bloch states $|\psi^{\mu}_{\mathbf{k}}\rangle$, given by Eq. (79) in terms of atomic states $|\varphi^{\nu}_{\mathbf{n}}\rangle$ suitably modified in order to become approximate eigenstates of $\mathscr{H}$. The different atomic core states are normalized and are supposed to be approximately orthogonal; that is,

$$\langle\varphi^{\mu}_{\mathbf{m}}|\varphi^{\nu}_{\mathbf{n}}\rangle \approx \delta_{\mathbf{mn}}\,\delta_{\mu\nu}, \tag{163}$$

because of the localization of the inner shells.

An OPW state may now be constructed from a free-electron state $|\mathbf{k}\rangle$ by a linear combination with the core states, according to

$$|\mathbf{k}+\mathbf{K}, \mathrm{OPW}\rangle = |\mathbf{k}+\mathbf{K}\rangle - \sum_{\mu}^{\mathrm{core}} |\psi_{\mathbf{k}}^{\mu}\rangle C_{\mathbf{k}+\mathbf{K}}^{\mu}. \tag{164}$$

This is not a normalized state, but we require that it be orthogonal to the core states

$$\langle\psi_{\mathbf{k}}^{\mu}|\mathbf{k}+\mathbf{K}, \mathrm{OPW}\rangle = \langle\psi_{\mathbf{k}}^{\mu}|\mathbf{k}+\mathbf{K}\rangle - C_{\mathbf{k}+\mathbf{K}}^{\mu} = 0. \tag{165}$$

Thus the coefficients $C_{\mathbf{k}+\mathbf{K}}^{\mu}$ are determined according to

$$C_{\mathbf{k}+\mathbf{K}}^{\mu} = \langle\psi_{\mathbf{k}}^{\mu}|\mathbf{k}+\mathbf{K}\rangle = \frac{1}{V_a}\langle\varphi_{\mathbf{0}}^{\mu}|\mathbf{k}+\mathbf{K}\rangle. \tag{166}$$

The little point-group operator $\mathscr{P}$ acting on $|\psi_{\mathbf{k}}^{\nu}\rangle$ yields a linear combination

$$\mathscr{P}|\psi_{\mathbf{k}}^{\nu}\rangle = \sum_{\mu}^{\mathrm{core}} |\psi_{\mathbf{k}}^{\mu}\rangle P_{\mu\nu}, \tag{167}$$

where $P_{\mu\nu}$ are elements of the matrix representing $\mathscr{P}$ in the atomic-orbital basis of the inner shell electrons for a given atom. The $\mathbf{k}$ vector in Eq. (167) is left unchanged when $\mathscr{P}$ belongs to the little point group. All the core states involved in the linear combination of Eq. (167) for nonvanishing $P_{\mu\nu}$ are degenerate in the limit of separated atoms. Thus, the flat-band eigenvalues ϵ_{μ} of the effective Hamiltonian of Eq. (156) are equal for the ion-core states, that is, $\epsilon_{\mu} = \epsilon_{\nu}$ when $P_{\mu\nu} \neq 0$. Taking the symmetry-adapted states with respect to the jmth symmetry type of the little point group of $\mathbf{k}$ and using Eqs. (164)–(167) as well as the degeneracy for ϵ_{μ}, we find that the Hamiltonian matrix in the basis thus obtained becomes

$$H_{\mathbf{K}'\mathbf{K}''}^{\mathrm{OPW}} = \frac{\hbar^2}{2m}|\mathbf{k}+\mathbf{K}'|^2\delta_{\mathbf{K}'\mathbf{K}''} + \sum_{\mathscr{P}\in P_{\mathbf{k}}} {}^{j}P_{mm}^{*}\left\{u_{\mathbf{K}(\mathscr{P})} - \sum_{\mu} \epsilon_{\mu} C_{\mathbf{k}+\mathbf{K}'}^{\mu *} C_{\mathscr{P}(\mathbf{k}+\mathbf{K}'')}^{\mu}\right\}, \tag{168}$$

due to the cancellation of two additional terms obtained. Here the first two terms form the part that corresponds to the matrix element $H_{\mathbf{K}'\mathbf{K}''}$ of the PW method as given by Eq. (162). Since the states of Eq. (164) are not orthonormalized, we also obtain a nonunit overlap matrix, with the elements given by

$$\Delta_{\mathbf{K}'\mathbf{K}''}^{\mathrm{OPW}} = \delta_{\mathbf{K}'\mathbf{K}''} - \sum_{\mu} C_{\mathbf{k}+\mathbf{K}'}^{\mu *} \sum_{\mathscr{P}\in P_{\mathbf{k}}} {}^{j}P_{mm}^{*} C_{\mathscr{P}(\mathbf{k}+\mathbf{K})''}^{\mu}. \tag{169}$$

Using spherical harmonics for the angular dependence of the core states, we can calculate the coefficients $C^{\mu}_{\mathbf{k}+\mathbf{K}}$ defined by Eq. (166) by expanding the plane waves in terms of spherical Bessel functions.

It should be noted that the matrix elements of Eqs. (162) and (168)–(169) can be used for the symmetry-reduced secular equations only when the symmetry projections are linearly independent. Otherwise it would be necessary first to find the rectangular matrices ${}^{j}\mathbf{t}_{m}$ of Section III, F, by means of which the unreduced Hamiltonian matrix $\mathbf{H}$ will be reduced according to ${}^{j}\mathbf{t}^{\dagger}_{m}\mathbf{H}\,{}^{j}\mathbf{t}_{m}$. In this application, however, it will be sufficient to avoid those prongs in the basis that do not belong to the considered symmetry type.

The OPW method has been used frequently by Herman, and has also been programmed by Quelle in a self-consistent form (*25*). It is found that the individual energy bands are very sensitive for the choice of the crystal potential. Also, the convergence for the expansion of the wave functions in terms of the basis functions is slow, particularly for regions near the nuclei. It is essential that the core states be carefully determined, by including corrections from the ligand field, in order not to obtain too much deviation from a correct band structure, because of orthogonalization toward inexact core states.

The simple form of the OPW method described earlier will generally give only a rough picture of the band structure. Actually, it makes no sense to take too many stars in the basis. Essential improvements can be obtained, however, by including the inner-shell states explicitly in the basis, taking care of the so-called quantum defect. This corresponds to a combination between the OPW method and the LCAO (linear combination of atomic orbital) or tight-binding method. The LCAO method will be considered in subsection H.

G. The Augmented Plane Wave (APW) and Related Methods

One difficulty with the OPW method is caused by the supposition of a spherically symmetric potential inside each unit cell in combination with a basis of plane waves. The idea of using short-range spherically symmetric cell potentials was introduced by Wigner and Seitz (*26*). These authors suggested the use of a unit cell with the shape of a polyhedron surrounding each atom. The Wigner-Seitz cell is thus defined in a way similar to the Brillouin zone in reciprocal space. For a point group of high order, such as the full cubic group O_h, the Wigner-Seitz cell has an "almost spherical form." The supposition of a spherical potential may then be natural in a first approach.

This idea was taken up in the *cellular method* introduced by Slater in 1934 (*27*). The cellular wave functions are described by means of a set of spherical harmonics multiplied by a numerically determined solution for the radial function. The main difficulty with the applications of this method is the problem of obtaining sufficiently smooth gradients of the wave function at the boundaries of the Wigner-Seitz cell, particularly near its corners. Successful use of the method has been made by Altmann (*28*), who has also written extensive programs for an electronic computer dealing with the symmetry adaptations necessary in this method.

The augmented plane wave (APW) method proposed by Slater in 1937 (*29*) is an improvement of the cellular method. In the APW method, the crystal potential is supposed to be constant in the region between inscribed spheres in the Wigner-Seitz cells and spherically symmetric inside these spheres. Basis functions containing spherical harmonics are used for description of the wave function inside the spheres, and plane waves for the outside regions. These two kinds of basis functions are thus never mixed, and the requirement of continuity will only concern spherical surfaces. The use of spherical harmonics inside the spheres in the APW method yields a better description of the wave function near the nuclei than in the pure OPW method.

The APW method has been programmed by Wood (*30*), and has been used with great success by the members of Slater's group at the Massachusetts Institute of Technology in Cambridge, Massachusetts. Symmetry adaptations form an essential part in applications of the method and are quite analogous to those of the OPW method. The main features of the technical procedure of finding the secular matrices in the APW method are similar to those for the OPW method. We shall not discuss any details of this problem here.

So far, applications to the APW method have not been made where a perturbation of the supposed properties of the crystal potential has been performed, though this is possible in principle.

The same type of potential as in the APW method is used in the Kohn-Rostocker method, which has also been programmed by these authors (*31*). Here the Schrödinger equation is solved by means of Green functions. Although the technical procedure of calculation thus differs very much from the APW method, these two methods can be used without preference.

In order to obtain an application where full space-group symmetry is considered, we shall study the tight-binding method in the next subsection for the case of several atoms per unit cell. It should also be emphasized that a crystal potential more elaborate than that involved in any of the methods discussed earlier is considered in the extended form of this method, which has been applied by the present author (*32*).

H. The Tight-Binding Method

The tight-binding method was proposed by Bloch in 1928 (*4*). The basis functions used in this method are hydrogenlike atomic orbitals located at each atomic site in the unit cell and linearly combined to form Bloch orbitals. In its original version the interaction between different Bloch orbitals of the same **k** vector was neglected, yielding the concept of an energy band for each atomic orbital. This is a drastic approximation, which may be permissible only for electrons that are tightly bound to the nuclei. For atomic orbitals describing valence electrons, the overlap integrals cannot be neglected. When excited orbitals are included in the basis, difficulties may arise because of the occurrence of approximate linear dependences between the corresponding Bloch orbitals. These difficulties may be eliminated by choosing orbital exponents for the excited orbitals that are much larger than those of the free atoms, thus causing a considerable decrease in size. The excited orbitals will take over the role of the plane waves in the OPW and APW methods. An advantage of the tight-binding method, however, is that continuity of the wave function and its derivatives is always obtained, It is essential, on the other hand, to consider all the inner electrons explicitly in the basis, or at least to use crystal states that have been correctly orthogonalized to the states of the inner-shell core electrons.

The procedure of computing energy bands by means of the tight-binding method has been programmed by the present author in machine language for the Swedish computers BESK-TRASK-FACIT. This program has recently been increased by a separate part for population analysis of the band structure (*33*). It would be desirable, however, to rewrite the program for a modern computer. This has been done for the symmetry-adaptation part in a FORTRAN program (*34*), where arbitrary crystallographic space groups are considered. Another more general symmetry program is now being written, where electron spin is also considered.

The crystal potential considered in the energy band program contains Coulomb interactions from all the nuclei, suitably screened by a supposed electron distribution, at distances arbitrarily far apart. Sufficient convergence is obtained, in the case of a hexagonally close-packed lattice of zirconium-oxygen, for a maximum distance of two unit-cell lengths, corresponding to about 200 considered atomic neighbors. Calculations including about 700 neighbors have also been done, though the computation time then becomes extremely long. All one-electron two-center integrals are computed for s, p, d, and f orbitals in the valence shell; three-center integrals are simplified by means of the Mulliken approximation.

We shall here consider the problem of symmetry adapting the basis to be used in a tight-binding approximation for energy band calculations, generalized by taking electron spin explicitly into account. We will thus consider the crystal point group to be a double group. To be sufficiently general, we shall also consider time inversion. The crystallographic group considered will thus in general be a nonsymmorphic, proper magnetic, double space group.

We denote an atomic state by $|\varphi^{\kappa}_{\mathbf{m}+\boldsymbol{\mu}}\rangle$, where $\kappa = (n, l, m, s)$ represents the ordinary quantum numbers of a hydrogenlike spin orbital, localized to the

$\boldsymbol{\mu}$th atom of the **m**th unit cell. First we investigate the effect of operating on this atomic state with a space-group element $\mathscr{F} = \{\mathscr{P}|\mathbf{u}\}$. In accordance with Eq. (131) we obtain

$$\mathscr{F}|\varphi^{\kappa}_{\mathbf{m}+\boldsymbol{\mu}}\rangle = \sum_{\kappa'} |\varphi^{\kappa'}_{\mathbf{n}+\boldsymbol{\nu}}\rangle P_{\kappa'\kappa}, \tag{170}$$

where $\mathbf{n} + \boldsymbol{\nu}$ is given by Eq. (115), and

$$P_{\kappa'\kappa} = \delta_{l'l}(-1)^{\lambda l+m-m'}\, {}^{l}D^{*}_{mm'}(\phi, \vartheta, \psi)u_{ss'}(\phi, \vartheta, \psi) \tag{171}$$

[cf. Eq. (109)] form elements of the matrix representing $\mathscr{P}$ in the spin-orbital basis of a given atom. We note that these elements are independent of the principal quantum number n. The indices λ, ϕ, ϑ, and ψ are the inversion and Euler rotation labels, respectively, ${}^{l}D_{m'm}$ is given by Eq. (108), and $u_{ss'}$ by Eqs. (105)–(106). The quantum numbers can take the values $n = 1, 2, 3, \ldots$; $l = 0, 1, 2, \ldots, n-1$; $m', m = -l, -l+1, \ldots, l$; $s, s' = -\frac{1}{2}, \frac{1}{2}$.

In the case of a proper magnetic space group, we would have to replace $\mathscr{F}$ by a magnetic space-group element, $\mathscr{M} = \Theta^{\gamma}\mathscr{F}$ ($\gamma = 0, 1$), where Θ is the Wigner time reversal, given by Eq. (112); Θ^{γ} is equal to 1 for $\gamma = 0$, and Θ for $\gamma = 1$. It will then be necessary to include the complex conjugate states $\mathscr{K}|\varphi^{\kappa}_{\mathbf{m}+\boldsymbol{\mu}}\rangle$ in the basis, which may be done by introducing an additional quantum number $t = 1, 2$, to be included in $\kappa = (n, l, m, s, t)$, where $t = 1$ represents the ordinary basis and $t = 2$ the complex conjugate basis. Thus the roots of the secular equations will always appear twice. In doing this, $P_{\kappa'\kappa}$ will be replaced by

$$\begin{aligned} Q_{\kappa'\kappa} &= \delta_{\gamma 0}\,\delta_{l'l}(-1)^{\lambda l+m-m'}({}^{l}D^{*}_{mm'}u_{ss'}\,\delta_{t1} + {}^{l}D_{mm'}u^{*}_{ss'}\,\delta_{t2}) \\ &\quad + \delta_{\gamma 1}\,\delta_{l'l}(-1)^{\lambda l+m-m'}({}^{l}D_{mm'}v^{*}_{ss'}\,\delta_{t1} + {}^{l}D^{*}_{mm'}v_{ss'}\,\delta_{t2}), \end{aligned} \tag{172}$$

with

$$v^{*}_{ss'} = i(-1)^{s+1/2}(\delta_{s,-1/2}u_{1/2,s'} + \delta_{s,1/2}u_{-1/2,s'}). \tag{173}$$

The Bloch states will thus transform according to

$$\mathscr{M}|\psi^{\kappa}_{\boldsymbol{\mu}\mathbf{k}}\rangle = \exp[-i\mathbf{k}\cdot\mathbf{n}(\mathscr{F}, \boldsymbol{\mu}, \boldsymbol{\nu})] \sum_{\kappa'} |\psi^{\kappa'}_{\boldsymbol{\nu}\mathbf{k}}\rangle Q_{\kappa'\kappa}, \tag{174}$$

which is analogous to Eq. (133).

We have now six entities, $\mathbf{u}$, γ, λ, ϕ, ϑ, ψ, labeling the group elements and seven labels, $\mathbf{k}$, $\boldsymbol{\mu}$, n, l, m, s, t, for the description of the basis Bloch states. The elements of the projection matrix for the jdth symmetry type of the little group of **k** become, in analogy to Eq. (134),

$$^{jd}P_{\mathbf{k}}(\boldsymbol{\mu}, \boldsymbol{\nu}; \kappa', \kappa) = \delta_{ab} \frac{h_{j\mathbf{k}}}{g_{\mathbf{k}}} \sum_{\mathscr{F}}^{G(\mu,\nu,\mathbf{k})} {}^{j\mathbf{k}}M_{dd}^{*} \exp[-i\mathbf{k} \cdot \mathbf{n}(\mathscr{F}, \mu, \nu)] Q_{\kappa'\kappa}. \quad (175)$$

The indices $\boldsymbol{\mu}$ and $\boldsymbol{\nu}$ are here considered to be multivalued labels, $\boldsymbol{\mu} = (\mu, a)$ and $\boldsymbol{\nu} = (\nu, b)$, where a, b label different chemical elements and μ, ν label the atoms in the unit cell for one chemical element. Thus a is a block-diagonalizing index for the projection matrix. As is seen from Eq. (172), this is true also for the azimuthal quantum number l. As in Eq. (134), the summation is extended over the elements of the little coset.

The most complicated problem occurring in connection with Eq. (175) is that of finding the diagonal elements of the irreducible matrix representatives of the magnetic little-group elements. In the special case when **k** lies inside the first Brillouin zone, however, these elements are simply given by

$$^{j\mathbf{k}}M_{dd} = (-1)^{\rho\gamma+\sigma\lambda} \exp(-i\mathbf{k} \cdot \mathbf{u})^{\tau\mathbf{k}}R_{dd}, \quad (176)$$

where $j = (\rho, \sigma, \tau)$ for $\rho, \sigma = 0, 1$ is a multilabel for the irreducible representation of a magnetic double group, and $^{\tau\mathbf{k}}R_{dd}$ denotes the dth diagonal element of the τth irreducible representation of the proper subgroup of the double point group connected with the little group of **k**. The label **k** is certainly also a "j label" corresponding to the translation group, but we want to keep this apart from j, since we have to use induced representations labeled by **k**. Although no general formula exists for the quantities $^{\tau\mathbf{k}}R_{dd}$, these values have been completely tabulated for all single point groups (*5*) as well as for a large number of double groups (*9*).

For symmorphic groups, the expression given by Eq. (176) is completely general, since then $\mathbf{u} = 0$. It may therefore be used also for points lying at the boundaries of the first Brillouin zone, in this case. The nonsymmorphic case, however, for points at the Brillouin-zone surface is still an unsolved problem in the sense that no complete tables of irreducible representatives occur in the literature. Extensive tables of irreducible characters, however, have been constructed (*10*), and methods for the construction of the diagonal elements are known, though somewhat troublesome (*35*). It is an important actual problem to find a suitable procedure for programming the quantities $^{j\mathbf{k}}M_{dd}$ for arbitrary cases. (This problem has now been solved in theory (36), and writing of a general program for symmetry adapting electronic states in crystals is proceeding.)

When the projection matrix in Eq. (175) has been computed for all the symmetry types of a given crystallographic group, the procedure of obtaining the rectangular symmetry-reduction matrices according to the technique described in Section III, F is straightforward. These matrices may be directly applied to the secular matrices, yielding block diagonalization of the secular equations.

We should notice that the treatment considered in the foregoing is sufficiently general to be applied for molecular orbitals, too. This problem corresponds to the special case obtained by choosing $\mathbf{k} = 0$. Product states may be treated by a slight generalization of Eq. (172). Thus ligand-field states may also be symmetry adapted by means of the same procedure, choosing $\mathbf{k} = 0$. Symmetry-adapted spin waves will be obtained for the special case when $l = 0$. As we saw in Section V, lattice vibrations may also be treated as a special case obtained for $l = 1$, $\gamma = 0$, $t = 1$, and $\mathbf{u} = \mathbf{1}$.

I. Symmetry Properties of the Irreducible Crystal Hamiltonian

Except for the simplification obtained by symmetry reduction of the secular equations, further simplification can be obtained due to relationships between different elements of the symmetry-reduced secular matrices. We shall here derive these relations for a nonsymmorphic nonmagnetic double group, using an LCAO basis.

We denote the matrix elements of the effective Hamiltonian in the atomic spin-orbital basis by

$$H_{\boldsymbol{\mu\nu}\mathbf{n}}^{\iota\kappa} = \langle \varphi_{\boldsymbol{\mu}}^{\iota} | \mathscr{H} | \varphi_{\mathbf{n}+\boldsymbol{\nu}}^{\kappa} \rangle. \tag{177}$$

We will then obtain the following relationship for the submatrices $\mathbf{H}_{\boldsymbol{\mu\nu}\mathbf{n}}$ defined by the elements in Eq. (177):

$$\mathbf{H}_{\boldsymbol{\mu\nu}\mathbf{n}} = \mathbf{P}^{\dagger} \mathbf{H}_{\boldsymbol{\mu}'\boldsymbol{\nu}'\mathbf{n}'} \mathbf{P}, \tag{178}$$

where

$$\begin{aligned} \boldsymbol{\mu}' &= \mathscr{P}\boldsymbol{\mu} + \mathbf{u} - \mathbf{n}(\mathscr{F}, \boldsymbol{\mu}, \boldsymbol{\mu}'); \\ \boldsymbol{\nu}' &= \mathscr{P}\boldsymbol{\nu} + \mathbf{u} - \mathbf{n}(\mathscr{F}, \boldsymbol{\nu}, \boldsymbol{\nu}'); \\ \mathbf{n}' &= \mathscr{P}\mathbf{n} - \mathbf{n}(\mathscr{F}, \boldsymbol{\mu}, \boldsymbol{\mu}') + \mathbf{n}(\mathscr{F}, \boldsymbol{\nu}, \boldsymbol{\nu}'). \end{aligned} \tag{179}$$

The derivation is just straightforward:

$$\begin{aligned} \langle \varphi_{\boldsymbol{\mu}}^{\iota} | \mathscr{H} | \varphi_{\mathbf{n}+\boldsymbol{\nu}}^{\kappa} \rangle &= \langle \varphi_{\boldsymbol{\mu}}^{\iota} | \mathscr{F}^{\dagger} \mathscr{H} \mathscr{F} | \varphi_{\mathbf{n}+\boldsymbol{\nu}}^{\kappa} \rangle \\ &= \sum_{\iota'\kappa'} P_{\iota'\iota}^{*} \langle \varphi_{\mathscr{P}\boldsymbol{\mu}+\mathbf{u}}^{\iota'} | \mathscr{H} | \varphi_{\mathscr{P}(\mathbf{n}+\boldsymbol{\nu})+\mathbf{u}}^{\kappa'} \rangle P_{\kappa'\kappa} \\ &= \sum_{\iota'\kappa'} P_{\iota\iota'}^{\dagger} \langle \varphi_{\boldsymbol{\mu}'}^{\iota'} | \mathscr{H} | \varphi_{\mathbf{n}'+\boldsymbol{\nu}'}^{\kappa'} \rangle P_{\kappa'\kappa}, \end{aligned}$$

by means of Eq. (179). Thus Eq. (178) is proved.

In a similar way we find the symmetry relations between the corresponding submatrices in the Bloch spinorbital basis, denoted by

$$\mathbf{H}_{\mu\nu\mathbf{k}} = \sum_{\mathbf{n}} \exp(i\mathbf{k}\cdot\mathbf{n})\mathbf{H}_{\mu\nu\mathbf{n}}. \tag{180}$$

For arbitrary operators $\mathscr{P} \in G_P$, these relations are found as

$$\mathbf{H}_{\mu\nu\mathbf{k}} = \exp\{i\mathscr{P}\mathbf{k}\cdot[\mathbf{n}(\mathscr{F}, \boldsymbol{\mu}, \boldsymbol{\mu}') - \mathbf{n}(\mathscr{F}, \boldsymbol{\nu}, \boldsymbol{\nu}')]\}\mathbf{P}^{\dagger}\mathbf{H}_{\mu',\nu',\mathscr{P}\mathbf{k}}\mathbf{P}. \tag{181}$$

The proof goes as follows:

$$\begin{aligned}\mathbf{H}_{\mu\nu\mathbf{k}} &= \sum_{\mathbf{n}} \exp(i\mathbf{k}\cdot\mathbf{n})\mathbf{P}^{\dagger}\mathbf{H}_{\mu'\nu'\mathbf{n}'}\mathbf{P} \\ &= \sum_{\mathbf{n}} \exp\{i\mathscr{P}\mathbf{k}\cdot[\mathbf{n} + \mathbf{n}(\mathscr{F}, \boldsymbol{\mu}, \boldsymbol{\mu}') - \mathbf{n}(\mathscr{F}, \boldsymbol{\nu}, \boldsymbol{\nu}')]\}\mathbf{P}^{\dagger}\mathbf{H}_{\mu'\nu'\mathbf{n}}\mathbf{P} \\ &= \exp\{i\mathscr{P}\mathbf{k}\cdot[\mathbf{n}(\mathscr{F}, \boldsymbol{\mu}, \boldsymbol{\mu}') - \mathbf{n}(\mathscr{F}, \boldsymbol{\nu}, \boldsymbol{\nu}')]\}\mathbf{P}^{\dagger}\mathbf{H}_{\mu',\nu',\mathscr{P}\mathbf{k}}\mathbf{P}.\end{aligned}$$

Now we may consider some important special cases. When $\mathscr{P} \in P_{\mathbf{k}}$, the transformed $\mathbf{k}$ vector $\mathscr{P}\mathbf{k}$ may be put equal to $\mathbf{k}$ in Eq. (181). Another special case is obtained when $\boldsymbol{\mu} = \boldsymbol{\nu}$:

$$\mathbf{H}_{\mu\mu\mathbf{k}} = \mathbf{P}^{\dagger}\mathbf{H}_{\mu',\mu',\mathscr{P}\mathbf{k}}\mathbf{P}. \tag{182}$$

This relation means that for each "star" of atoms obtained from a given site by means of space-group operations, only one reference atom is needed for the construction of the diagonally situated submatrices. All the other blocks along the diagonal may be computed from the knowledge of these reference blocks. Obviously, different chemical elements correspond to different stars of atoms.

We can now also study time inversion, which is an additional symmetry for nonmagnetic groups. Neglecting spin, this symmetry yields the relationship

$$\mathbf{H}_{\mu\nu\mathbf{k}} = \mathbf{H}^{*}_{\mu,\nu,-\mathbf{k}} \tag{183}$$

for arbitrary $\boldsymbol{\mu}$ and $\boldsymbol{\nu}$, since, in addition to taking the complex conjugate, we also have to change the sign of the crystal momentum. For those $\mathbf{k}$ vectors where space inversion belongs to the little group of $\mathbf{k}$, we may replace $\mathscr{I}\mathbf{k} = -\mathbf{k}$ in Eq. (183) by $\mathbf{k}$. Thus the Hamiltonian matrix is real in this case, which is a useful symmetry relation.

By systematically considering all space-group elements, a large number of symmetry relations are obtained. Many of these merely show the cancellation of mixed elements between symmetry-reduced bases, and therefore contribute nothing new. Other cases may simply correspond to relations between degenerate secular matrices for different prongs of the star of **k**. Still, however, there are many useful relations between the elements in the same symmetry-reduced secular matrix.

Let us consider a simple example to see the usefulness of the obtained relations. Suppose that space inversion is a symmetry element of the crystal group. The atoms may then be combined into pairs ($\boldsymbol{\mu}$, $\boldsymbol{\nu}$), of atoms related to each other by inversion, according to $\boldsymbol{\mu} = \mathscr{I}\boldsymbol{\nu}$; $\boldsymbol{\nu} = \mathscr{I}\boldsymbol{\mu}$. Since space inversion will change the sign of **k**, we obtain, by means of Eq. (181) for $\mathbf{P} = \mathbf{I}$ and by using Eq. (183),

$$\mathbf{H}_{\mu\nu k} = \mathbf{I}\mathbf{H}^*_{\nu\mu k}\mathbf{I}; \tag{184}$$

$$\mathbf{H}_{\mu\mu k} = \mathbf{I}\mathbf{H}^*_{\nu\nu k}\mathbf{I}. \tag{185}$$

Furthermore, since $\mathbf{H}_k$ is Hermitian, we obtain, by taking the transpose of the submatrix $\mathbf{H}_{\mu\nu k}$,

$$\tilde{\mathbf{H}}_{\mu\nu k} = \mathbf{H}^*_{\nu\mu k} = \mathbf{I}\mathbf{H}_{\mu\nu k}\mathbf{I}, \tag{186}$$

where the last relation is obtained from Eq. (184). Consequently, all the elements below the main diagonal of this submatrix are determined by the knowledge of those elements lying above this diagonal.

In the energy band program written by the author, all possible symmetry relations are considered and used for numerical checking of the secular matrices.

VII. Electromagnetic Fields in Solids

Energy band calculations form a valuable background for studying transport phenomena in crystals, such as the motion of excited electrons and holes in transistors. We shall here consider the band structure to be known, and shall investigate some properties of band electrons under the influence of an external electromagnetic field treated as a small perturbation. For this purpose, we shall study the Wannier theory of band electrons.

A. Wannier States

Starting with a set of localized atomic states $|\varphi^{\kappa}_{\mathbf{m}+\mu}\rangle$, we may construct the corresponding Bloch states $|\psi^{\kappa}_{\mathbf{k}\mu}\rangle$, according to Eqs. (79) – (80). The inverse transformation may be written as

$$|\varphi^{\kappa}_{\mathbf{m}+\boldsymbol{\mu}}\rangle = \frac{1}{N} \sum_{\mathbf{k}} (N(\mathbf{k}, \kappa))^{1/2} \exp(-i\mathbf{k} \cdot \mathbf{m}) |\psi^{\kappa}_{\mathbf{k}\boldsymbol{\mu}}\rangle, \tag{187}$$

where

$$N(\mathbf{k}, \kappa) = N \sum_{\mathbf{n}} \exp(i\mathbf{k} \cdot \mathbf{n}) \langle \varphi^{\kappa}_{\boldsymbol{\mu}} | \varphi^{\kappa}_{\mathbf{n}+\boldsymbol{\mu}} \rangle. \tag{188}$$

In the case when the atomic overlap vanishes, this transformation is unitary.

Let us now suppose that we have transformed the Bloch basis into symmetry-adapted form and solved all the symmetry-reduced secular equations. The states corresponding to these solutions are still Bloch states. They should also be labeled by the symmetry-type indices j, m of the little group of $\mathbf{k}$ and by a further index β, numbering the roots of the symmetry-adapted equations. The symmetry indices may again be composed of subindices due to factoring of the little group. Here, however, we shall use only one single band index, b, as a short notation for all these quantum numbers. The one-electron crystal states thus obtained are given by

$$|\chi^b_{\mathbf{k}}\rangle = \sum_{\kappa,\boldsymbol{\mu}} |\psi^{\kappa}_{\mathbf{k}\boldsymbol{\mu}}\rangle \langle \psi^{\kappa}_{\mathbf{k}\boldsymbol{\mu}} | \chi^b_{\mathbf{k}} \rangle, \tag{189}$$

where $\langle \psi^{\kappa}_{\mathbf{k}\boldsymbol{\mu}} | \chi^b_{\mathbf{k}} \rangle$ are the coefficients found by solving the factored secular equation for a given $\mathbf{k}$ vector. These states are all orthogonal and noninteracting; that is, the Hamiltonian is diagonal in this basis.

We can now make a unitary transformation yielding localized Wannier states (*37*), according to

$$|\Phi^b_{\mathbf{m}}\rangle = N^{-1/2} \sum_{\mathbf{k}} \exp(-i\mathbf{k} \cdot \mathbf{m}) |\chi^b_{\mathbf{k}}\rangle, \tag{190}$$

which is similar to Eq. (187). For the inner flat-band electrons, these states should be very close to the corresponding atomic states. The valence states, however, may be somewhat delocalized. The states of Eq. (190) are all orthogonal and normalized. They are not uniquely determined, however, since we may multiply each crystal state $|\chi^b_{\mathbf{k}}\rangle$ by an arbitrary phase factor.

The energy bands $\epsilon_b(\mathbf{k})$ are characterized by the band index b. These bands may not always be uniquely defined as functions of $\mathbf{k}$, because of the occurrence of degeneracies and overlapping bands. In the case of considerable mixing between some of the atomic states, it is often impossible to distinguish between overlapping bands, particularly in regions close to the points of intersection. In the following, however, we shall consider an idealized case wherein the different energy bands are regarded as perfectly distinguished.

Introducing Wannier states in the expression of an energy band in **k** space, we obtain a Fourier expansion,

$$\epsilon_b(\mathbf{k}) = \langle \chi_{\mathbf{k}}^b | \mathscr{H} | \chi_{\mathbf{k}}^b \rangle = \sum_{\mathbf{m}} \exp(i\mathbf{k} \cdot \mathbf{m}) \epsilon_b(\mathbf{m}), \tag{191}$$

where

$$\epsilon_b(\mathbf{m}) = \langle \Phi_{\mathbf{0}}^b | \mathscr{H} | \Phi_{\mathbf{m}}^b \rangle \tag{192}$$

may be taken as a kind of localized energy in ordinary space originating from the **m**th unit cell and, in case of band degeneracies, from those other unit cells $\mathscr{P}\mathbf{m}$, which can be obtained from **m** by operation with the point-group elements. The energy expression of Eq. (192) is usually also related to an atomic site $\boldsymbol{\mu}$ and an atomic orbital κ (or a combination between those of the site and orbital quantum numbers that are symmetry related to each other), because a certain atomic state often occurs with an occupation number being close to unity for a given crystal state of band index b.

B. Quasi-Classical Band Mechanics

The localization of the Wannier states will make them suitable for describing particles moving in solids. The macroscopic position of a particle in a crystal need not be specified more accurately than to the region of a unit cell. We shall therefore introduce the Wannier lattice operator **x**, defined by (*38*)

$$\mathbf{x} | \Phi_{\mathbf{n}}^b \rangle = \mathbf{n} | \Phi_{\mathbf{n}}^b \rangle. \tag{193}$$

Operating with **x** on a crystal state, we obtain

$$\mathbf{x} | \chi_{\mathbf{k}}^b \rangle = N^{-1/2} \sum_{\mathbf{n}} \exp(i\mathbf{k} \cdot \mathbf{n}) \mathbf{n} | \Phi_{\mathbf{n}}^b \rangle = -i \nabla_{\mathbf{k}} | \chi_{\mathbf{k}}^b \rangle. \tag{194}$$

Considering the crystal states as states of "free" particles, we may describe a band electron in a weak external field by means of a wave packet

$$| \psi \rangle = \sum_{b,\mathbf{k}} | \chi_{\mathbf{k}}^b \rangle \langle \chi_{\mathbf{k}}^b | \psi \rangle. \tag{195}$$

From Eq. (194) we then obtain

$$\langle \chi_{\mathbf{k}}^b | \mathbf{x} | \psi \rangle = i \nabla_{\mathbf{k}} \langle \chi_{\mathbf{k}}^b | \psi \rangle. \tag{196}$$

Operating on the expansion coefficients $\langle \chi_{\mathbf{k}}^b | \psi \rangle$, considered as wave functions in the **k**-diagonal representation, the lattice operator may thus be replaced by $i\nabla_{\mathbf{k}}$. Because of the commutation relations

$$[x_s, \hbar k_t] = i\hbar\delta_{st}, \qquad (s, t = 1, 2, 3), \tag{197}$$

the canonically conjugate momentum of the lattice operator is given by $\hbar\mathbf{k}$.

In a quasi-classical treatment of the particle, we may thus consider the lattice operator $\mathbf{x}$ as a cell position canonically conjugate to the crystal momentum. For a free band electron, the Hamiltonian is given by $H = \epsilon_b(\mathbf{k})$, and Hamilton's equations of motion become

$$\hbar\dot{\mathbf{x}} = \nabla_{\mathbf{k}}\epsilon_b(\mathbf{k}); \qquad \hbar\dot{\mathbf{k}} = 0, \tag{198}$$

yielding conservation for the crystal momentum.

Adding an external electromagnetic field, the Hamiltonian becomes

$$\mathscr{H}(\hbar\mathbf{k}, \mathbf{x}) = \epsilon_b(\boldsymbol{\varkappa}) + eV(\mathbf{x}), \tag{199}$$

where $V(\mathbf{r})$ is the electric potential field, e the charge of the particle (negative for an electron, positive for a hole), and $\hbar\mathbf{k}$ the generalized crystal momentum defined by the magnetic vector potential $\mathbf{A}(\mathbf{r})$ according to

$$\hbar\mathbf{k} = \hbar\boldsymbol{\varkappa} + \frac{e}{c}\mathbf{A}(\mathbf{x}). \tag{200}$$

Hamilton's equations of motion now become

$$\begin{aligned} \hbar\dot{\mathbf{x}} &= \nabla_{\boldsymbol{\varkappa}}\epsilon_b(\boldsymbol{\varkappa}); \\ \hbar\dot{\mathbf{k}} &= \frac{e}{\hbar c}\nabla_{\mathbf{x}}\nabla_{\boldsymbol{\varkappa}}\epsilon_b(\boldsymbol{\varkappa}) \cdot \mathbf{A}(\mathbf{x}) - e\nabla_{\mathbf{x}}V(\mathbf{x}). \end{aligned} \tag{201}$$

By taking the derivative of Eq. (200) with respect to time and using Eq. (201), we obtain the Lorentz force:

$$\hbar\dot{\boldsymbol{\varkappa}} = \frac{e}{c}\dot{\mathbf{x}} \times \mathbf{B} - e\nabla_{\mathbf{x}}V(\mathbf{x}), \tag{202}$$

where $\mathbf{B}(\mathbf{x}) = \nabla_{\mathbf{x}} \times \mathbf{A}(\mathbf{x})$ is the external magnetic field. The crystal momentum will thus change in accordance with the classical equations of motion.

C. Band Electrons in Electric Fields

We shall now study some quantum-mechanical corrections to the quasi-classical treatment of a particle of charge e moving in the crystal under the influence of a constant homogeneous electric field $\mathbf{E}$.

Suppose that the particle is found in a pure crystal state of the band b for $\mathbf{k} = \mathbf{k}_0$ at the time $t = 0$. Thus

$$|\Psi(t=0)\rangle = |\chi_{\mathbf{k}_0}^b\rangle \tag{203}$$

is a stationary state for the unperturbed Hamiltonian H_0, in the $\mathbf{k}$-diagonal representation replaced by $\epsilon_b(\mathbf{k})$. In the presence of an electric field, the Hamiltonian is given by

$$H_0 - e\mathbf{E}\cdot\mathbf{x} \to \mathscr{H} = \epsilon_b(\mathbf{k}) + ie\mathbf{E}\cdot\nabla_{\mathbf{k}}, \tag{204}$$

where $\mathbf{x}$ is the Wannier lattice operator in the Bloch representation given by $-i\nabla_{\mathbf{k}}$, according to Eq. (194).

Though it would be more adequate to start with a wave packet at time $t = 0$ with its amplitude maximum at $\mathbf{k} = \mathbf{k}_0$, it may still be valuable to investigate the limiting case of a delta function distribution in $\mathbf{k}$ space. The state of the particle at a later time $t > 0$ is then given by

$$|\Psi(t)\rangle = \exp\left(-\frac{i}{\hbar}\mathscr{H}t\right)|\Psi(0)\rangle = |\chi_{\mathbf{k}}^b\rangle \exp[-if(\mathbf{k})], \tag{205}$$

the first relation being true, since $\mathscr{H}$ is explicitly time independent. The $\mathbf{k}$ vector occurring in the last relation of Eq. (205) is the time-dependent $\mathbf{k}$ vector found from Eq. (201) in the quasi-classical treatment,

$$\mathbf{k} = \mathbf{k}(t) = \mathbf{k}_0 + \frac{e\mathbf{E}t}{\hbar}, \tag{206}$$

and the phase $f(\mathbf{k})$ is found as

$$f[\mathbf{k}(t)] = \frac{1}{eE}\int_{k_{0E}}^{k_E(t)} \epsilon_b(\mathbf{k})\, dk_E, \tag{207}$$

where k_E is the component of $\mathbf{k}$ in the $\mathbf{E}$ direction. The proof for these relationships was given by Wannier (*37*), and we shall repeat his arguments here.

The time dependence of the unit-cell translation operator $\mathcal{T}_{\mathbf{n}}$ may be obtained according to

$$i\hbar\dot{\mathcal{T}}_{\mathbf{n}} = [\mathcal{T}_{\mathbf{n}}, \mathcal{H}] = -\mathbf{E}\cdot[\mathcal{T}_{\mathbf{n}}, \mathbf{x}] = e\mathbf{E}\cdot\mathbf{n}\mathcal{T}_{\mathbf{n}}. \tag{208}$$

Since $\mathcal{T}_{\mathbf{n}}$ is diagonal in the Bloch representation, it may be replaced by its eigenvalue $\exp(-i\mathbf{k}\cdot\mathbf{n})$, where $\mathbf{k}$ is taken to be time dependent. Using this expression for $\mathcal{T}_{\mathbf{n}}$ at both sides in Eq. (208), we obtain Eq. (206).

Considering the implicit time dependence of the pure crystal state in Eq. (205),

$$|\chi_{\mathbf{k}}^{b}\rangle = \exp\left[if(\mathbf{k}) - \frac{i}{\hbar}\mathcal{H}t\right]|\Psi(0)\rangle, \tag{209}$$

we find by time derivation of both sides in Eq. (209) and multiplication by $i\hbar$:

$$i\hbar\dot{\mathbf{k}}\cdot\nabla_{\mathbf{k}}|\chi_{\mathbf{k}}^{b}\rangle = [-\hbar\dot{\mathbf{k}}\cdot\nabla_{\mathbf{k}}f(\mathbf{k}) + H_0 + ie\mathbf{E}\cdot\nabla_{\mathbf{k}}]|\chi_{\mathbf{k}}^{b}\rangle, \tag{210}$$

where Eq. (204) has been inserted for $\mathcal{H}$. Because of Eq. (206), the term on the left-hand side in Eq. (210) cancels the last term on the right-hand side, and we obtain the phase relation $H_0 = e\mathbf{E}\cdot\nabla_{\mathbf{k}}f(\mathbf{k})$, yielding Eq. (207). This finally proves Eqs. (205)–(207).

Suppose now that the direction of the homogeneous $\mathbf{E}$ field coincides with a reciprocal-lattice direction $\mathbf{K}$. For a period of time $\tau = \hbar K/eE$, the $\mathbf{k}$ vector has then changed into an equivalent $\mathbf{k}$ vector, $\mathbf{k}+\mathbf{K}$. The unitary operator

$$\mathcal{U}(\tau, \mathbf{x}) = \exp\left(-\frac{i}{\hbar}\mathcal{H}\tau\right) \to \exp\{-if[\mathbf{k}(\tau)]\} \tag{211}$$

yielding the state $|\Psi(\tau)\rangle = \mathcal{U}(\tau, \mathbf{x})|\Psi(0)\rangle$ is thus periodic in the lattice; that is, $\mathcal{U}(\tau, \mathbf{x}) = \mathcal{U}(\tau, \mathbf{x}+\mathbf{n})$; it is diagonal in the Bloch basis and its eigenvalue is given by the phase change during the period τ.

Since all Bloch states are changed by the same phase factor after the period τ, any state formed as a wave packet of pure crystal states will be restored after this time, as far as its amplitude is concerned. This situation is due to the periodic boundary condition, yielding the concept of the microcrystal.

Thus, we can speak of closed orbits for the moving particles, yielding a stationary-state quantization rule of Bohr-Sommerfeld type for the energy states. Stationary states of this kind can occur only for $\mathbf{E}$ fields in directions that have rational components in reciprocal space. The field directions will thus become quantized.

D. Band Electrons in Magnetic Fields

Let us now consider the quantum-mechanical behavior of a crystal particle moving under the influence of a homogeneous magnetic field **B**. We may choose a gauge where the vector potential is given by

$$\mathbf{A}(\mathbf{r}) = \tfrac{1}{2}\mathbf{B} \times \mathbf{r}. \tag{212}$$

In accordance with Eq. (200), we should replace the **k** vector by

$$\boldsymbol{\varkappa} = \mathbf{k} - \frac{e}{\hbar c}\mathbf{A}(\mathbf{r}). \tag{213}$$

In accordance with Wannier (*37*), we may then introduce the generalized Bloch functions

$$\begin{aligned}\langle \mathbf{r} | B_{\mathbf{k}}^{b} \rangle &= \langle \mathbf{r} | \chi_{\boldsymbol{\varkappa}}^{b} \rangle \\ &= N^{-1/2} \sum_{\mathbf{n}} \exp(i\boldsymbol{\varkappa} \cdot \mathbf{n}) \langle \mathbf{r} | \Phi_{\mathbf{n}}^{b} \rangle \\ &= N^{-1/2} \sum_{\mathbf{n}} \exp(i\mathbf{k} \cdot \mathbf{n}) \langle \mathbf{r} | W_{\mathbf{n}}^{b} \rangle,\end{aligned} \tag{214}$$

where $|\Phi_{\mathbf{n}}^{b}\rangle$ are the ordinary Wannier states for the band b of the unperturbed crystal Hamiltonian defined by Eq. (190), and $|W_{\mathbf{n}}^{b}\rangle$ are generalized Wannier states defined by the wave functions

$$\langle \mathbf{r} | W_{\mathbf{n}}^{b} \rangle = \exp\left[-\frac{ie}{\hbar c}\mathbf{A}(\mathbf{r}) \cdot \mathbf{n}\right] \langle \mathbf{r} | \Phi_{\mathbf{n}}^{b} \rangle. \tag{215}$$

The generalized Bloch functions are symmetry adapted with respect to a factor group of the magnetic translation group defined by Zak (*20*). This factor group is isomorphic with the ordinary translation group, though it should be observed that the set of operators $\exp(i\boldsymbol{\varkappa} \cdot \mathbf{n})$ with **k** replaced by $-i$ grad do not even form a group for $\mathbf{B} \neq 0$, since the product of two such operators differs by a phase factor from a member of the set.

The magnetic translation group, which commutes with the homogeneous magnetic-field Hamiltonian, contains elements of the type

$$\exp(i\boldsymbol{\varkappa} \cdot \mathbf{n}) \exp\left[\frac{ie}{\hbar c}\phi(\mathbf{n}_1, \mathbf{n}_2, \ldots, \mathbf{n}_s)\right], \tag{216}$$

where $\phi(\mathbf{n}_1, \mathbf{n}_2, \ldots, \mathbf{n}_s)$ denotes the magnetic flux through a closed polygon given by the lattice vectors $(\mathbf{n}_1, \mathbf{n}_2, \ldots, \mathbf{n}_s, -\mathbf{n})$. The symmetry-adapted functions belonging to the symmetry types of this group have been fully investigated by Zak (*20*) for **B** fields with rational direct-lattice components.

The generalized Bloch states, defined by Eq. (214), will obviously become mixed in the presence of an external magnetic field. Since the classical orbits in the limit of zero crystal field are closed circles, we may expect to find stationary solutions in the quantum-mechanical case. Let us suppose, then, that a stationary state is given by

$$|\psi\rangle = \sum_{\mathbf{k}} |B_{\mathbf{k}}^b\rangle \langle B_{\mathbf{k}}^b|\psi\rangle, \tag{217}$$

where we neglect band mixing [cf. Eq. (195)]. The expansion coefficients $\langle B_{\mathbf{k}}^b|\psi\rangle = \psi(\mathbf{k})$ may thus be considered as the wave function in **k** space corresponding to the band *b*. The Hamiltonian will then become a differential operator in **k** space (*37*):

$$\mathscr{H} = \epsilon_b\left(\mathbf{k} - \frac{ie}{\hbar c}\mathbf{A}(\nabla_{\mathbf{k}})\right). \tag{218}$$

Here we have substituted the Wannier lattice operator $\mathbf{x}^*$ for the argument **r** in $\mathbf{A}(\mathbf{r})$, where $\mathbf{x}^* = i\nabla_{\mathbf{k}}$ when operating on wave functions in **k** space [cf. Eq. (196)].

A detailed knowledge of the crystal band structure $\epsilon_b(\mathbf{k})$ would make it possible to solve the eigenfunctions in **k** space of the operator in Eq. (218) by numerical methods. Suppose that we have a weak magnetic field $\mathbf{B} = \mathbf{e}_z B$ in the *z* direction. Neglecting terms of higher-order powers in *B* in a Taylor series expansion for $\mathscr{H}$, we obtain

$$\epsilon_b\left(\mathbf{k} - \frac{ie}{2\hbar c}\mathbf{B} \times \nabla_{\mathbf{k}}\right) = \epsilon_b(\mathbf{k}) - \frac{ieB}{2\hbar c}[\text{grad}_{\mathbf{k}}\, \epsilon(\mathbf{k})] \cdot (\mathbf{e}_z \times \nabla_{\mathbf{k}}) + \cdots. \tag{219}$$

If we introduce cylindrical coordinates (k, k_ϕ, k_z) for **k**, the stationary wave equation in **k** space may be written

$$\epsilon(\mathbf{k})\psi(\mathbf{k}) - \frac{ieB}{2\hbar c}\frac{1}{k}\left[\frac{\partial\epsilon(\mathbf{k})}{\partial k}\frac{\partial\psi(\mathbf{k})}{\partial k_\phi} - \frac{\partial\epsilon(\mathbf{k})}{\partial k_\phi}\frac{\partial\psi(\mathbf{k})}{\partial k}\right] = \lambda\psi(\mathbf{k}), \tag{220}$$

where the band index *b* has been omitted for convenience.

We have thus found a simplified Schrödinger equation in **k** space for solving the stationary states of the particle. For an actual crystal, however, the band structure may be extremely complicated, and numerical solutions would be difficult to obtain.

Considering the idealized case of a cylindrically symmetrical energy band distribution, we can put $\partial\epsilon(\mathbf{k})/\partial k_\phi = 0$ in Eq. (220). The solutions are then easily found:

$$\psi_m(\mathbf{k}) = \frac{1}{2\pi} f(k, k_z) \exp(im\, k_\phi);$$

$$\lambda_m(k) = \epsilon(k) + m \frac{eB}{2\hbar c} \frac{1}{k} \frac{d\epsilon(k)}{dk}; \qquad (m = 0, \pm 1, \pm 2, \ldots) \qquad (221)$$

Here $\epsilon(k)$ is an energy band in the plane $k_z = 0$ and $f(k, k_z)$ is an arbitrary normalized function of k and k_z. In the limit of zero crystal potential, the Zeeman splitting in Eq. (221) becomes

$$\frac{eB}{2\hbar c} \frac{1}{k} \frac{d\epsilon(k)}{dk} = \frac{eB}{2\hbar c} \frac{\hbar^2}{M} = \tfrac{1}{2}\hbar\omega,$$

where $\omega = eB/Mc$ is equal to the Larmor frequency for the classical motion and M is the effective mass of the particle.

For crystal potentials that are not cylindrically symmetrical, however, k will no longer be a good quantum number, and the form of the solution will change completely. It might be interesting to investigate the possible simplifications for finding the solutions of Eq. (220) by using the crystal space group symmetry.

REFERENCES

1. M. Born and J. R. Oppenheimer, *Ann. Physik* **84**, 457 (1927).
2. E. P. Wigner, "Gruppentheorie und ihre Anwendung auf die Quantenmechanik der Atomspektren." Vieweg and Son, Brunswick, Germany, 1931; "Group Theory and its Application to the Quantum Mechanics of Atomic Spectra." Academic Press, New York, 1959.
3. S. Flodmark, *Phys. Rev.* **132**, 1343 (1963).
4. F. Bloch, *Z. Physik* **52**, 555 (1928).
5. M. A. Melvin, *Rev. Mod. Phys.* **28**, 20 (1956).
6. H. V. McIntosh, *J. Mol. Spectry.* **5**, 269 (1960).
7. L. P. Bouckaert, R. Smoluchowski, and E. Wigner, *Phys. Rev.* **50**, 58 (1936).
8. G. F. Koster, *Solid State Phys.* **5**, 173 (1957).
9. O. V. Kovalev, Irreducible representations of space groups. *Izd. Akad. Nauk Ukr. SSR, Lieu* (1961); J. C. Slater, Quantum theory of molecules and solids. "Symmetry and Energy Bands in Crystals," Vol. 2. McGraw-Hill, New York, 1965.
10. J. Zak, *J. Math. and Phys.* **1**, 165 (1960); A. Casher and M. Gluck, Character tables for the irreducible representations of space groups. Progr. Rept. No. 2. Technion, Haifa, Israel, 1963.
11. W. Pauli, *Z. Physik* **43**, 601 (1927).

12. H. Weyl, "Gruppentheorie und Quantenmechanik." Hirzel, Stuttgart, 1938; "Theory of Groups and Quantum Mechanics." Dover, New York, 1950.
13. E. U. Condon and G. H. Shortley, "The Theory of Atomic Spectra." Cambridge Univ. Press, London and New York, 1953.
14. H. A. S. Eriksson, *Ark. Mat. Astron. Fys.* **29A**, No. 14 (1943); **33B**, No. 6 (1946); *Ark. Fys.* **6**, 349 (1953).
15. R. J. Elliott, *Phys. Rev.* **96**, 280 (1954); O. V. Kovalev, *Ukr. Fiz. Zh.* **6**, 366 (1961).
16. V. Bargmann, *J. Math. and Phys.* **5**, 7 (1964).
17. A. V. Shubnikov and N. V. Belov, *in* "Colored Symmetry" (W. T. Holser, ed.). Macmillan, New York, 1964.
18. A. V. Zamorzaev and A. F. Palistrant, *Soviet Physics Cryst.* **9**, 660 (1965).
19. A. Kitz, *Phys. Status Solidi* **10**, 455 (1965).
20. J. Zak, *Phys. Rev.* **134**, A1602, A1607 (1964); **136**, A776 (1964).
21. S. Flodmark, *Ark. Fys.* **21**, 89 (1962).
22. M. Planck, *Verhandl. Deut. Ges. Phys.* **2**, 237 (1900).
23. L. Brillouin, *J. Phys. Radium* **1**, 377 (1930).
24. C. Herring, *Phys. Rev.* **57**, 1169 (1940).
25. F. Herman, *Phys. Rev.* **93**, 1214 (1954); F. W. Quelle, Jr., Energy bands in semiconductors. *Proc. Intern. Conf. Semicond. Phys., Prague, 1960*, p. 48. Czech. Akad. Sci., Prague, Czech., 1961; *Bull. Amer. Phys. Soc.* **7**, 214 (1962).
26. E. Wigner and F. Seitz, *Phys. Rev.* **43**, 804 (1933); **46**, 509 (1934).
27. J. C. Slater, *Phys. Rev.* **45**, 794 (1934); *Rev. Mod. Phys.* **6**, 209 (1934).
28. S. L. Altmann, *Proc. Roy. Soc. London Ser. A* **244**, 153 (1958); S. L. Altmann and C. J. Bradley, *Phys. Lett.* **1**, 336 (1962).
29. J. C. Slater, *Phys. Rev.* **51**, 846 (1937).
30. V. E. Wood and J. R. Reitz, *Phys. and Chem. Solids* **23**, 229 (1962).
31. W. Kohn and J. Rostocker, *Phys. Rev.* **94**, 1111 (1954).
32. S. Flodmark, *Ark. Fys.* **14**, 513 (1959); **18**, 49 (1960); **26**, 45 (1964).
33. S. Flodmark, *Intern. J. Quantum Chem.*, **I**, 147 (1967).
34. S. Flodmark, Symmetry projection program (Sympro). Quantum Chemistry Program Exchange, Air Force Office of Scientific Research, Indiana University, Bloomington, Indiana, *Q.C.P.E.* No. 46 (1964).
35. I. V. V. Raghavacharyulu, *Canad. J. Phys.* **39**, 830 (1961).
36. S. Flodmark and E. Blokker, *Intern. J. Quantum Chem., Symposium, 1967.* To be published.
37. G. H. Wannier, *Phys. Rev.* **52**, 191 (1937).
38. G. H. Wannier, *Rev. Mod. Phys.* **34**, 645 (1962).

*Group Theory of Harmonic Oscillators and Nuclear Structure**

P. KRAMER† *and M. MOSHINSKY*

INSTITUTO DE FÍSICA, UNIVERSIDAD DE MÉXICO, MÉXICO

* Work supported by the Comisión Nacional de Energía Nuclear, México.

† Present address: Institut für Theoretische Physik, Tübingen, Germany.

I. Introduction and Summary

In its simplest terms, nuclear physics concerns itself with the dynamics of n-nucleon systems, for which it is usually assumed that only two-body forces contribute; that is, the Hamiltonian has the form

$$\mathscr{H} = \sum_{s=1}^{n} \frac{1}{2m} (\mathbf{p}^s)^2 + \sum_{s<t=2}^{n} V^{st}$$

where s, t refer to the particle indices and V^{st} is an interaction derived from the data on the dynamics of the two-nucleon system.

The ideal for a nuclear physicist would be to derive from this Hamiltonian all the experimental information on nuclei, such as the binding energy, energy levels, reaction cross sections, and transition probabilities. The complexities involved in the exact solution of the foregoing Hamiltonian for even small n are such that at present we are still very far from this ideal. Therefore, the problems of nuclear physics and, in particular, of nuclear structure have been analyzed with the help of models.

One of the most fruitful models has been the shell model, the basic idea of which, borrowed from atomic physics, is that in first approximation the shell model states are built from independent single-particle states in some kind of common potential. In practical applications this common potential is usually taken as that of a harmonic oscillator (ho) (*1–5*) and the correlation between the particles in wave functions constructed from these ho single-particle states is established through the action of some type of residual force. The nuclear shell model is now supported by a great deal of experimental evidence.

An extension of this model to the set of shells associated with a single level of an ho potential was given by Elliott (*3*), who was able to make use of the symmetry group of the ho to show that this extension encompasses the collective model, so that within its framework we can discuss, among other things, such phenomena as the appearance of rotational bands.

Another of the important models in nuclear physics is the cluster model of the nucleus (*6*, *7*), in which the particles are grouped into clusters consistent with the requirements of the Pauli principle, each cluster being in a state of minimal internal energy. This model has been very effective in promoting understanding of both the structure and reactions of light nuclei. As for the models mentioned earlier here, the ho states have been very important in the analysis of cluster states, among other reasons because they show in a particularly transparent way how a many-particle state can be expressed in terms of states that are functions of the internal coordinates of each cluster as well as of the intercluster coordinates.

The brief discussion of nuclear models just given clearly shows that the description of the states in terms of single-particle ho states is a useful one. Yet, in most of the applications discussed in the literature, the role of the ho states is a subsidiary one, as these states are grafted on existing formalisms mainly for the computational ease they provide.

In recent years the richness of the theoretical structure of the problem of n nucleons in a harmonic oscillator potential became apparent (*8–13*). Kretzschmar (*8*, *9*) used the symmetry groups of the system to study the building up of shell model states and the elimination of center-of-mass motions Bargmann and Moshinsky (*10*, *11*) found a complete set of integrals of motion for the problem and indicated how the states associated with these integrals of motion could be explicitly constructed. Kramer and Moshinsky (*12*) explicitly classified the previous states from the standpoint of the irreducible representations (IR) of the symmetric group of n particles. These authors and many others have contributed to the development of concepts and techniques, such as the Wigner coefficients of unitary groups, lowering operators, mathematically natural chains of subgroups of the unitary group and the corresponding states that are bases for its IR (Gelfand states), and others, that are basic in the construction of these states (*14–18*).

All of these developments in the problem of n particles in a harmonic oscillator potential suggested the usefulness of inverting the approach by which the ho states were appearing in problems of nuclear structure. Rather than graft these states onto existing models, we shall in this paper turn the problem around and start with a full discussion of the problem of n nucleons in a harmonic oscillator potential or interacting through two-body harmonic oscillator forces. The symmetry group of this problem is the unitary group of $3n$ dimensions $\mathbf{U}(3n)$ (*19*). The states of n particles in the harmonic oscillator will be characterized by the IR of this group and of an appropriate chain of subgroups. These chains of subgroups can be defined in a variety of ways, providing independent procedures for characterizing our n-particle states. We shall show that the characterization of the states by definite chains of subgroups (*20–23*) leads to states either identical or equivalent to those constructed in the shell, collective, or cluster model. In this way the different nuclear models just mentioned will be related to particular ways of characterizing the states of n nucleons in the ho potential.

One of the main purposes of this paper is to extend the concept of fractional parentage coefficients (fpc) to the states of n particles in an ho potential or interacting through two-body ho forces. In this way we will be able to separate from our n-particle state one- or two-particle states, so as to reduce the calculation of one- or two-body operators to the evaluation of one- or two-particle matrix elements. We also indicate how to derive in a systematic way the fpc for the spin-isospin part of the states. We shall then be in a position to discuss the matrix elements of a realistic Hamiltonian with respect to our n-particle state and, thus, to discuss the physical problems mentioned earlier: binding energies; energy levels; transition probabilities; and clustering effects.

A basic limitation in our approach will be that our single-particle states will always be of the ho type (*24*). We feel, though, that the use of these states for n-nucleon systems provides us with techniques of such scope and power that it is worthwhile to explore them fully before turning to the problem of modifying them to represent the physical situation more accurately.

We now outline the plan followed in this chapter. In Section II we show that the Hamiltonian of n particles in a common ho potential has as symmetry group $\mathbf{U}(3n)$. Furthermore, the physics of the problem requires the characterization of the n-particle states by the irreducible representation (IR) of a

$\mathscr{U}(3) \times U(n)$ subgroup (*8–12*) where the $\mathscr{U}(3)$, $U(n)$ unitary groups are associated with the three-dimensional space and the n particle indices, respectively. We further completely classify the states by the mathematically natural (*25*) chain of subgroups

$$\mathscr{U}(3) \supset \mathscr{U}(2) \supset \mathscr{U}(1), \tag{1.1a}$$

$$U(n) \supset U(n-1) \supset \cdots \supset U(1) \tag{1.1b}$$

that leads to the concept of a Gelfand (*26*) state which is fundamental for the following development. We finally show how to pass from the chain Eq. (1.1a) to the more physically significant chain (*14*, *25*)

$$\mathscr{U}(3) \supset \mathscr{O}(3) \supset \mathscr{O}(2), \tag{1.2}$$

where the $\mathscr{O}$ are orthogonal groups of the dimensions indicated.

In Section III we turn to the central problem, which is the construction of n-particle orbital states with permutational symmetry, that is, states characterized by the chain

$$U(n) \supset S(n), \tag{1.3}$$

where $S(n)$ is the symmetric group of n dimensions. We show that it is very convenient to introduce in Eq. (1.3) an intermediate group $K(n)$, which is a semidirect product of the group of diagonal unitary matrices $A(n)$ and of $S(n)$; that is,

$$K(n) = A(n) \wedge S(n). \tag{1.4}$$

This group, besides providing extra quantum numbers for the characterization of the states, allows us to obtain a shell structure from our ho states (*20*). We show explicitly how to obtain the transformation brackets from the Gelfand states to these ho shell model states with permutational symmetry. In this section we also discuss translational-invariant states, that is, states corresponding to a system of n particles interacting through two-body ho forces. We indicate how to eliminate the center-of-mass motion and determine a chain of groups (*12*)

$$U(n) \supset U(n-1) \supset O(n-1) \supset S(n) \tag{1.5}$$

that provides a classification scheme for the states of permutational symmetry in this case. We analyze in full detail the translational-invariant four-particle states.

In Section IV we turn to the problem of how to separate the last particle or last two particles from our n-particle state with permutational symmetry. This leads to the concept of harmonic oscillator fractional parentage coefficients (hfpc), not to be confused with the fpc of standard shell theory. We show that the symmetry groups of the ho n-particle problem allow the factorization of the hfpc into a part related to the Wigner coefficients of $\mathscr{U}(3)$ and a part associated with the $U(n)$ group. We indicate how to calculate both parts and, in particular, give explicit expressions for one- and two-particle hfpc for three-particle shell model states and four-particle translational-invariant states.

In Section V we direct our attention to the spin-isospin part of our n-particle states. Our main purpose is to show how spin-isospin states with permutational symmetry can be derived by using techniques almost identical to those used in the orbital part. Specifically, we note that these states can be obtained in a direct way from special Gelfand states in the chain (*27*)

$$\mathbf{U}(4n) \supset \mathscr{U}(4) \times U(n) \tag{1.6}$$

where 4 has to do with the number of components for a one-particle spin (σ)–isospin (τ) state; that is,

$$|\sigma\tau\rangle, \qquad \sigma = \pm\tfrac{1}{2}, \quad \tau = \pm\tfrac{1}{2}. \tag{1.7}$$

In Section VI we indicate how to separate the last particle or last two particles from an n-particle spin-isospin state with permutational symmetry. This leads to the concept of spin-isospin fpc. We obtain these fpc explicitly, using known results (*26*) of the matrix elements of the generators of the unitary groups with respect to Gelfand states.

In Section VII we apply both the orbital and spin-isospin fpc to determine the matrix elements of one- and two-body operators.

The last three sections deal with applications of our general formalism. In Section VIII we discuss the application of a realistic Hamiltonian to the translational-invariant states associated with few-nucleon problems (*28*). We discuss in detail the effect of a Serber force on a four-nucleon problem, taking states of $N = 0$, 1, 2 quanta. We also analyze the influence of a two-particle spin-orbit coupling interaction on the negative parity states.

In Section IX we indicate the connection between the present developments and the Elliott model in a single shell, illustrating it with an application involving a quadrupole-quadrupole interaction plus a one-body spin orbit coupling force. We indicate also how our formalism allows us to generalize the Elliott model to a many-shell configuration.

Finally, in Section X, we discuss clustering of n-particle states, starting with a general definition of clustering in terms of Gelfand states of a special type. We obtain permutational limits on clustering and discuss some applications to light nuclei. All concepts related to clustering, particularly the limiting case of separated clusters, are discussed in detail for a system of four particles. Finally, we introduce the concept of a two-body clustering interaction, relate it to general types of clustering, and show that this interaction, when complemented by a quadrupole-quadrupole interaction, describes appropriately the binding energy of light nuclei (*23*).

In later publications the authors plan to expand the framework developed in this paper, so as to provide a detailed formalism capable of dealing on a basic level with a wide class of problems of nuclear structure.

II. The Symmetry Group U(3n); the Subgroup $\mathscr{U}(3) \times U(n)$; Gelfand States

In this section, a complete classification scheme for orbital n-particle states in a common ho potential is developed. First, the corresponding Hamiltonian is rewritten in such a way as to exhibit its unitary symmetry group **U**(3n) in 3n dimensions. The n-particle states form bases for irreducible representations (BIR) of this group and can be further characterized as BIR of subgroups of **U**(3n). It is shown that a chain of subgroups exists that leads to a complete classification of n-particle states, and these states are explicitly derived by lowering procedures similar to the familiar ones used to derive the states that are BIR of the rotation group.

A. The Harmonic Oscillator Hamiltonian and Its Unitary Symmetry Groups

Denote by $\mathbf{x}^s$ and $\mathbf{p}^s$ the coordinate and momentum vectors of particle s, $s = 1, 2, \ldots, n$ with vector components

$$\begin{aligned} \mathbf{x}^s &= (x_1^s, x_2^s, x_3^s), \\ \mathbf{p}^s &= (p_1^s, p_2^s, p_3^s), \end{aligned} \tag{2.1}$$

and consider the Hamiltonian $\mathscr{H}_0$ of the n particles in a common ho potential given by

$$\mathscr{H}_0 = \sum_{s=1}^{n} \sum_{j=1}^{3} \left[\frac{1}{2m} (p_j^s)^2 + \frac{1}{2} m\omega^2 (x_j^s)^2 \right]. \tag{2.2}$$

Coordinates and momenta obey the canonical commutation relations. On introducing

$$\boldsymbol{\eta}^s = \left(\frac{m\omega}{2\hbar}\right)^{1/2} \mathbf{x}^s - i\left(\frac{1}{2m\omega\hbar}\right)^{1/2} \mathbf{p}^s,$$
$$\boldsymbol{\xi}^s = \left(\frac{m\omega}{2\hbar}\right)^{1/2} \mathbf{x}^s + i\left(\frac{1}{2m\omega\hbar}\right)^{1/2} \mathbf{p}^s = (\boldsymbol{\eta}^s)^\dagger, \tag{2.3}$$

we obtain the new commutation relations

$$[\eta_j^s, \eta_k^t] = [\xi_j^s, \xi_k^t] = 0, \qquad [\xi_j^s, \eta_k^t] = \delta^{st}\,\delta_{jk}. \tag{2.4}$$

Introduce now the dimensionless Hamiltonian

$$\boldsymbol{H}_0 = (\hbar\omega)^{-1}\mathscr{H}_0 - \tfrac{3}{2}n = \sum_{s=1}^{n}\sum_{j=1}^{3} \eta_j^s \xi_j^s = \sum_{s=1}^{n}\sum_{j=1}^{3} \eta_j^s (\eta_j^s)^\dagger, \tag{2.5}$$

for which we find the commutators

$$[\eta_j^s, \boldsymbol{H}_0] = -\eta_j^s, \qquad [\xi_j^s, \boldsymbol{H}_0] = \xi_j^s. \tag{2.6}$$

Suppose, then, that $\boldsymbol{H}_0$ has an eigenstate $|\lambda\rangle$ with eigenvalue λ; that is

$$\boldsymbol{H}_0|\lambda\rangle = \lambda|\lambda\rangle.$$

Then from the commutator of ξ_j^s and $\boldsymbol{H}_0$ we find that

$$\boldsymbol{H}_0\xi_j^s|\lambda\rangle = (\lambda - 1)\xi_j^s|\lambda\rangle,$$

so that the state $\xi_j^s|\lambda\rangle$ is an eigenstate of $\boldsymbol{H}_0$ with lowered eigenvalue $\lambda - 1$. On the other hand, we must have

$$\langle\lambda|\boldsymbol{H}_0|\lambda\rangle = \sum_{s=1}^{n}\sum_{j=1}^{3} \langle\lambda|\eta_j^s(\eta_j^s)^\dagger|\lambda\rangle \geqq 0, \tag{2.7}$$

since each term $\langle\lambda|\eta_j^s(\eta_j^s)^\dagger|\lambda\rangle$ is the norm of the state $(\eta_j^s)^\dagger|\lambda\rangle$. We cannot lower the eigenvalue λ indefinitely because of Eq. (2.7). This implies that the lowering of the eigenvalues of $\boldsymbol{H}_0$ by the operator ξ_j^s terminates so that there must be a state $|0\rangle$ such that

$$\xi_j^s|0\rangle = 0, \qquad s = 1, 2, \ldots, n, \quad j = 1, 2, 3,$$
$$\boldsymbol{H}_0|0\rangle = 0. \tag{2.8}$$

From the commutator of η_j^s and $\mathbf{H}_0$ we see that η_j^s applied to an eigenstate of $\mathbf{H}_0$ raises the eigenvalue by one. Therefore all eigenstates of $\mathbf{H}_0$ with eigenvalue N can be obtained by applying homogeneous polynomials of degree N, $P(\eta_j^s)$, in the operators η_j^s to the normalized ground state $|0\rangle$, which satisfies Eq. (2.8) and is given explicitly by

$$|0\rangle = \left(\frac{m\omega}{\hbar\pi}\right)^{3n/4} \exp\left[-\frac{m\omega}{2\hbar}\sum_{s=1}^{n}\sum_{j=1}^{3}(x_j^s)^2\right]. \tag{2.9}$$

With respect to such states, ξ_j^s can be interpreted from the commutation relations Eq. (2.4) as

$$\xi_j^s = \frac{\partial}{\partial\eta_j^s}. \tag{2.10}$$

Returning to the form Eq. (2.5) of the Hamiltonian $\mathbf{H}_0$, we see immediately that it is invariant under $3n$-dimensional unitary transformations affecting the $3n$ indices $s = 1, 2, \ldots, n, j = 1, 2, 3$ of η_j^s. The $(3n)^2$ operators

$$\mathbf{C}_{jk}^{st} = \eta_j^s \xi_k^t \tag{2.11}$$

all commute with $\mathbf{H}_0$ and satisfy, from Eqs. (2.3) and (2.4), the relations

$$[\mathbf{C}_{jk}^{st}, \mathbf{C}_{j'k'}^{s't'}] = \delta^{ts'}\,\delta_{kj'}\,\mathbf{C}_{jk'}^{st'} - \delta^{st'}\,\delta_{jk'}\,\mathbf{C}_{j'k}^{s't}, \tag{2.12a}$$

$$(\mathbf{C}_{jk}^{st})^\dagger = \mathbf{C}_{kj}^{ts}. \tag{2.12b}$$

Clearly, the linear combination of these operators form a Lie algebra, and we shall show in the Appendix that real parameters can be chosen in such a way that these operators generate the Lie algebra of $\mathbf{U}(3n)$ and hence can be interpreted as the $(3n)^2$ generators of $\mathbf{U}(3n)$.

The generators of $\mathbf{U}(3n)$ can be contracted with respect to either the upper or the lower indices, giving the operators

$$\mathscr{C}_{jk} = \sum_{s=1}^{n} \mathbf{C}_{jk}^{ss}, \qquad C^{st} = \sum_{j=1}^{3} \mathbf{C}_{jj}^{st}. \tag{2.13a,b}$$

From Eq. (2.12) the nine operators $\mathscr{C}_{jk}$ and the n^2 operators C^{st} satisfy among themselves commutation relations

$$[\mathscr{C}_{jk}, \mathscr{C}_{j'k'}] = \delta_{kj'}\mathscr{C}_{jk'} - \delta_{jk'}\mathscr{C}_{j'k}, \tag{2.14a}$$

$$[C^{st}, C^{s't'}] = \delta^{ts'}C^{st'} - \delta^{st'}C^{s't} \tag{2.14b}$$

similar to those of the $\mathbf{C}_{jk}^{st}$, and so they can be interpreted as the generators of unitary groups $\mathscr{U}(3)$ and $U(n)$, respectively. Besides,

$$[\mathscr{C}_{jk}, C^{st}] = 0, \tag{2.15}$$

and so these generators generate the direct product subgroup $\mathscr{U}(3) \times U(n)$ in the chain

$$\mathbf{U}(3n) \supset \mathscr{U}(3) \times U(n). \tag{2.16a}$$

From the form of the generators $\mathscr{C}_{jk}$ and C^{st} we see that the groups $\mathscr{U}(3)$ and $U(n)$ are connected with unitary transformations affecting, respectively, the indices $j = 1, 2, 3$ and $s = 1, 2, \ldots, n$ of η_j^s. These groups admit the canonical (*15*, *16*) chain of subgroups

$$\mathscr{U}(3) \supset \mathscr{U}(2) \supset \mathscr{U}(1), \tag{2.16b}$$

$$U(n) \supset U(n-1) \supset \cdots \supset U(1), \tag{2.16c}$$

where the group $U(m)$, $m = 1, 2, \ldots, n$ affects only the indices s in η_j^s if $s = 1, 2, \ldots, m$, while $\mathscr{U}(3)$, $\mathscr{U}(2)$, and $\mathscr{U}(1)$ affect only the indices $j = 1, 2, 3$, $j = 1, 2$, $j = 1$, respectively. The generators of $U(m)$, $m = 1, 2, \ldots, n$, and of $\mathscr{U}(k)$, $k = 1, 2, 3$, are C^{st}, $1 \leqq s, t \leqq m$ and $\mathscr{C}_{ij}$, $1 \leqq i, j \leqq k$.

Since $\mathbf{U}(3n)$ is the symmetry group of $\mathbf{H}_0$, the eigenstates of $\mathbf{H}_0$ form bases for irreducible representations (BIR) of $\mathbf{U}(3n)$. For a given eigenvalue of $\mathbf{H}_0$ the states can be further characterized by the requirement that they form a basis of all the subgroups in the chains Eqs. (2.16b,c). We shall prove that this requirement completely specifies the states.

The subgroup $\mathscr{U}(3) \times U(n)$ is physically significant (*8*, *9*, *11*) as it separates the behavior of the states in three-dimensional space from that related to the particle indices. The subgroups in the chain Eqs. (2.16b,c), on the other hand, form a mathematically natural, rather than physically significant, chain of subgroups (*25*). We will show later how to pass from the simple eigenstates that are BIR of all groups in the chain Eqs. (2.16b,c) to eigenstates corresponding to physically more significant groups.

B. n-Particle States as Bases for Irreducible Representations of the Groups $\mathbf{U}(3n) \supset \mathscr{U}(3) \times U(n)$

What are the quantum numbers corresponding to states that are BIR of the groups Eqs. (2.16)? As is well known, an IR of a unitary group in r dimensions is characterized by r integer partition numbers, so that the corresponding bases are characterized by the partitions for all the unitary groups appearing in Eqs. (2.16). Since the BIR of **U**(3n) is formed from one vector η_j^s in 3n dimensions, the IR of **U**(3n) is characterized by one nonvanishing partition number, that is, by a partition $[N0^{3n-1}]$, and its bases are the eigenstates of $\boldsymbol{H}_0$ with eigenvalue N. The IR of the groups $\mathscr{U}(k)$, $k = 1, 2, 3$, and $U(m)$, $m = 1, 2, \ldots, n$, are characterized by partitions $[h_{1k} \cdots h_{kk}]$ and $\{k_{1m} \cdots k_{mm}\}$, respectively, where

$$h_{1k} \geqq h_{2k} \geqq \cdots \geqq h_{kk} \geqq 0, \qquad k_{1m} \geqq k_{2m} \geqq \cdots \geqq k_{mm} \geqq 0. \tag{2.17}$$

The partitions of two groups $U(m)$ and $U(m-1)$ in the canonical chain Eq. (2.16c) are related by the inequalities (*15*)

$$k_{1m} \geqq k_{1m-1} \geqq k_{2m} \geqq k_{2m-1} \geqq \cdots \geqq k_{m-1m-1} \geqq k_{mm}. \tag{2.18}$$

The set of partitions for the chain $U(n) \supset \cdots \supset U(1)$ is most conveniently arranged into a Gelfand (*26*) pattern

$$\{k_{st}\} = \left\{ \begin{array}{ccccccc} k_{1n} & & k_{2n} & \cdots\cdots\cdots & & & k_{nn} \\ & k_{1n-1} & & k_{2n-1} & \cdots & k_{n-1n-1} & \\ & \ddots & & \ddots & ⋰ & & \\ & & k_{12} & & k_{22} & & \\ & & & k_{11} & & & \end{array} \right\}. \tag{2.19}$$

The BIR of the groups Eqs. (2.16) can then be denoted by the two Gelfand patterns (*18, 13, 12*) corresponding to the two chains Eqs. (2.16b,c) as

$$|[h_{ij}], \{k_{st}\}\rangle. \tag{2.20}$$

1. State of Highest Weight

We shall now derive the polynomials $P(\eta_j^s)$ which, when applied to the ground state, give the states Eq. (2.20). We shall also show how the partition numbers in $[h_{ij}]$ and $\{k_{st}\}$ arise in the process of deriving these polynomials.

To obtain these polynomials, recall the procedure by which we obtain the basis for an IR of the $\mathcal{O}^+(3) \supset \mathcal{O}^+(2)$ chain of groups. First we determine the state of highest weight $|ll\rangle$ in the basis, i.e., the one satisfying

$$L_+|ll\rangle = 0, \qquad L_0|ll\rangle = l|ll\rangle;$$

then we apply the lowering operator L_- and normalize to get the state

$$|lm\rangle = \left[\frac{(l+m)!}{(l-m)!(2l)!}\right]^{1/2} (L_-)^{l-m}|ll\rangle.$$

In a similar way we shall use the generators of the unitary groups $\mathscr{U}(3)$ and $U(n)$ to obtain all states from one state of highest weight. From the commutation relations Eqs. (2.14) of the generators $\mathscr{C}_{ij}$ and C^{st} we see that all generators $\mathscr{C}_{jj}$, $j = 1, 2, 3$, and C^{ss}, $s = 1, 2, \ldots, n$, commute among themselves. Therefore we may first of all require that the polynomials $P(\eta_j^s)$ satisfy the differential equations

$$\mathscr{C}_{jj}P(\eta_j^s) = w_j P(\eta_j^s), \qquad C^{ss}P(\eta_j^s) = w^s P(\eta_j^s) \tag{2.21}$$

where the ξ_j^s are interpreted as in Eq. (2.10), and denote by (w_1, w_2, w_3), $(w^1, w^2, \cdots, w^n)$ the weights of the polynomial with respect to $\mathscr{U}(3)$ and $U(n)$, respectively. Then define the weights (w_1, w_2, w_3), $(w^1, w^2, \cdots, w^n)$ to be higher than $(\bar{w}_1, \bar{w}_2, \bar{w}_3)$, $(\bar{w}^1, \bar{w}^2, \cdots, \bar{w}^n)$ if in $(w_1 - \bar{w}_1, w_2 - \bar{w}_2, w_3 - \bar{w}_3)$, $(w^1 - \bar{w}^1, w^2 - \bar{w}^2, \cdots, w^n - \bar{w}^n)$ the first nonvanishing component is positive.

From the commutators

$$[\mathscr{C}_{kk}, \mathscr{C}_{ij}] = (\delta_{ik} - \delta_{jk})\mathscr{C}_{ij}, \qquad [C^{mm}, C^{st}] = (\delta^{sm} - \delta^{tm})C^{st} \tag{2.22}$$

we find that the generators $\mathscr{C}_{ij}$, $i < j$, and C^{st}, $s < t$, raise the weight (w_1, w_2, w_3) and $(w^1, w^2, \ldots, w^n)$, respectively, whereas the generators $\mathscr{C}_{ij}$, $i > j$, and C^{st}, $s > t$, lower the weight. We can then define a polynomial P of highest weight $(h_1, h_2, h_3) \equiv (h_{13}, h_{23}, h_{33})$, $(k_{1n}, k_{2n}, \ldots, k_{nn})$ by the requirements

$$\begin{aligned} &j = 1, 2, 3: \quad \mathscr{C}_{jj}P = h_j P; \qquad s = 1, 2, \ldots, n: \quad C^{ss}P = k_{sn}P; \\ &i < j = 2, 3: \quad \mathscr{C}_{ij}P = 0; \qquad s < t = 2, 3, \ldots, n: \quad C^{st}P = 0; \end{aligned} \tag{2.23}$$

in which, from Eq. (2.10), the generators $\mathscr{C}_{ij}$, C^{st} can be interpreted as first-order differential operators. Then we have a definite system of linear differential equations that can be solved, and the eigenvalues $[h_1h_2h_3]$, $\{k_{1n}, k_{2n}, \ldots, k_{nn}\}$ characterize the irreducible representation of $\mathscr{U}(3)$ and $U(n)$. As shown by Moshinsky (*15*), these equations have a solution if, and only if,

$$h_j = k_{jn}, \quad j = 1, 2, 3; \qquad k_{sn} = 0, \quad 3 < s \leqq n; \qquad h_1 \geqq h_2 \geqq h_3 \geqq 0; \tag{2.24}$$

and in this case

$$P = P^{[h_1h_2h_3]} = \mathrm{N}[h_1h_2h_3](\varDelta_1^1)^{h_1-h_2}(\varDelta_{12}^{12})^{h_2-h_3}(\varDelta_{123}^{123})^{h_3}, \tag{2.25}$$

where

$$\Delta^{s_1 s_2 \cdots s_r}_{j_1 j_2 \cdots j_r} = \sum_{\mathbf{p}} (-1)^{\mathbf{p}} \mathbf{p} \eta^{s_1}_{j_1} \eta^{s_2}_{j_2} \cdots \eta^{s_r}_{j_r} \tag{2.26}$$

with $\mathbf{p}$ a permutation of the indices $(s_1 s_2 \cdots s_r)$. The generators $\mathscr{C}_{ij}$ and C^{st}, when applied to the determinant Eq. (2.26), change the lower index j into i and the upper index t into s, respectively. From these properties it is easy to check that Eq. (2.25) is really a solution of the differential Eqs. (2.23). To evaluate the normalization constant, we take the scalar product

$$\langle 0 | [(\Delta^1_1)^{h_1-h_2} (\Delta^{12}_{12})^{h_2-h_3} (\Delta^{123}_{123})^{h_3}]^\dagger (\Delta^1_1)^{h_1-h_2} (\Delta^{12}_{12})^{h_2-h_3} (\Delta^{123}_{123})^{h_3} | 0 \rangle$$

and use the commutation relations Eq. (2.4) to obtain (*14*)

$$\mathsf{N}[h_1 h_2 h_3] = \left[\frac{(h_1 - h_2 + 1)(h_1 - h_3 + 2)(h_2 - h_3 + 1)}{(h_1 + 2)!(h_2 + 1)!h_3!} \right]^{1/2}. \tag{2.27}$$

2. *Lowering Operators*

From the polynomial Eq. (2.25) of highest weight we would now like to derive the full set of polynomials $P^{[h_{ij}],\{k_{st}\}}$ by the use of lowering operators, which would play, for the groups $\mathscr{U}(3)$ and $U(n)$, the same role as L_- for $\mathcal{O}^+(3)$ and $\mathcal{O}^+(2)$. It is clear that the lowering operators of the groups $\mathscr{U}(k)$ and $U(m)$ will be functions of the generators $\mathscr{C}_{ij}$, $1 \leqq i, j \leqq k$, C^{st}, $1 \leqq s, t \leqq m$, of these groups. These generators all commute with the expressions $\sum_{j=1}^k \mathscr{C}_{jj}$, $\sum_{s=1}^m C^{ss}$, respectively, with eigenvalues given by Eq. (2.21) as

$$\sum_{j=1}^{k} \mathscr{C}_{jj} P^{[h_{ij}],\{k_{st}\}} = \sum_{j=1}^{k} w_j P^{[h_{ij}],\{k_{st}\}}, \qquad \sum_{s=1}^{m} C^{ss} P^{[h_{ij}],\{k_{st}\}} = \sum_{s=1}^{m} w^s P^{[h_{ij}],\{k_{st}\}},$$

and therefore these eigenvalues can be calculated by taking polynomials of highest weight in $\mathscr{U}(k)$ and $U(m)$. As for $\mathscr{U}(3)$ and $U(n)$, the components of the highest weight are the partition numbers of $\mathscr{U}(k)$ and $U(m)$, so that the eigenvalues of $\sum_{j=1}^k \mathscr{C}_{jj}$ and $\sum_{s=1}^m C^{ss}$ are given by $\sum_{j=1}^k h_{jk}$ and $\sum_{s=1}^m k_{sm}$, respectively. But then, by taking differences of these expressions for all groups $\mathscr{U}(k)$, $k = 1, 2, 3$, and $U(m)$, $m = 1, 2, \ldots, n$, we find that

$$\begin{aligned} \mathscr{C}_{kk} P^{[h_{ij}],\{k_{st}\}} &= w_k P^{[h_{ij}],\{k_{st}\}} = \left(\sum_{j=1}^{k} h_{jk} - \sum_{j=1}^{k-1} h_{jk-1} \right) P^{[h_{ij}],\{k_{st}\}}, \\ C^{mm} P^{[h_{ij}],\{k_{st}\}} &= w^m P^{[h_{ij}],\{k_{st}\}} = \left(\sum_{s=1}^{m} k_{sm} - \sum_{s=1}^{m-1} k_{sm-1} \right) P^{[h_{ij}],\{k_{st}\}}. \end{aligned} \tag{2.28}$$

Clearly the state

$$P^{[h_1h_2h_3]}|0\rangle$$

is characterized by Gelfand patterns as

$$P^{[h_1h_2h_3]}|0\rangle = \left|\begin{matrix} h_1 & h_2 & h_3 \\ h_1 & h_2 & \\ h_1 & & \end{matrix}, \quad \begin{matrix} h_1 \; h_2 \; h_3 \; 0 \cdots\cdots 0 \\ h_1 \; h_2 \; h_3 \; 0 \; \cdots \; 0 \\ \ddots \quad \ddots \quad \ddots \quad \ddots \quad \therefore \\ h_1 \; h_2 \; h_3 \; 0 \\ h_1 \; h_2 \; h_3 \\ h_1 \; h_2 \\ h_1 \end{matrix}\right\rangle . \tag{2.29}$$

The degree of the polynomial is given by the eigenvalue of

$$\mathbf{H}_0 = \sum_{j=1}^{3} \mathscr{C}_{jj} = \sum_{s=1}^{n} C^{ss} = \sum_{s=1}^{n}\sum_{j=1}^{3} \mathbf{C}_{jj}^{ss}, \tag{2.30}$$

which is $N = h_1 + h_2 + h_3$.

To define now the lowering operators for the groups $\mathscr{U}(k)$ and $U(m)$, denote for convenience the states of highest weight in all canonical subgroups of $\mathscr{U}(k-1)$ and $U(m-1)$ by

$$\left|\begin{matrix} h_{ik} \\ h_{ik-1} \end{matrix}\right\rangle, \qquad \left|\begin{matrix} k_{sm} \\ k_{sm-1} \end{matrix}\right\rangle, \tag{2.31}$$

respectively. Then the effect of a lowering operator $\mathscr{L}_{kj}$ in $\mathscr{U}(k)$ or L^{mt} in $U(m)$ can be defined by

$$\mathscr{L}_{kj}\left|\begin{matrix} h_{ik} \\ h_{ik-1} \end{matrix}\right\rangle \propto \left|\begin{matrix} h_{ik} \\ h_{ik-1} - \delta_{ij} \end{matrix}\right\rangle, \tag{2.32a}$$

$$L^{mt}\left|\begin{matrix} k_{sm} \\ k_{sm-1} \end{matrix}\right\rangle \propto \left|\begin{matrix} k_{sm} \\ k_{sm-1} - \delta_{st} \end{matrix}\right\rangle. \tag{2.32b}$$

It is clear that states with arbitrary $[h_{ij}]$, $\{k_{st}\}$ could be obtained from the highest weight state in $\mathscr{U}(3)$ and $U(n)$ with the help of the lowering operators $\mathscr{L}_{kj}$, $1 \leqq j < k \leqq 3$, and L^{mt}, $1 \leqq t < m \leqq n$. We shall now derive the explicit expressions for the lowering operators $\mathscr{L}_{21}$ of $\mathscr{U}(2)$ and $\mathscr{L}_{31}$, $\mathscr{L}_{32}$ of $\mathscr{U}(3)$.

Consider first a state

$$\left|\begin{matrix} h_{12} & & h_{22} \\ & h_{11} & \end{matrix}\right\rangle \tag{2.33}$$

in $\mathscr{U}(2)$ with weight $(h_{11}, h_{12}+h_{22}-h_{11})$. Since $[\mathscr{C}_{jj}, \mathscr{C}_{21}] = (\delta_{2j}-\delta_{1j})\mathscr{C}_{21}$, the operator $\mathscr{C}_{21}$ clearly changes this weight to $(h_{11}-1, h_{12}+h_{22}-h_{11}+1)$, so that

$$\mathscr{C}_{21}\left|\begin{matrix} h_{12} & & h_{22} \\ & h_{11} & \end{matrix}\right\rangle \propto \left|\begin{matrix} h_{12} & & h_{22} \\ & h_{11}-1 & \end{matrix}\right\rangle \tag{2.34}$$

and hence $\mathscr{L}_{21} = \mathscr{C}_{21}$. Next consider the state

$$\left|\begin{matrix} h_{13} & & h_{23} & & h_{33} \\ & h_{12} & & h_{22} & \\ & & h_{12} & & \end{matrix}\right\rangle \tag{2.35}$$

of $\mathscr{U}(3)$ of highest weight in $\mathscr{U}(2)$. The generator $\mathscr{C}_{32}$ will lower the weight $(h_{12}, h_{22}, h_{13}+h_{23}+h_{33}-h_{12}-h_{22})$ to $(h_{12}, h_{22}-1, h_{13}+h_{23}+h_{33}-h_{12}-h_{22}+1)$. But since $\mathscr{C}_{32}$ and $\mathscr{C}_{12}$ commute, this state is still of highest weight in $\mathscr{U}(2)$, so that we conclude $\mathscr{L}_{32} = \mathscr{C}_{32}$. The generator $\mathscr{C}_{31}$, when applied to the state Eq. (2.35), changes the weight to $(h_{12}-1, h_{22}, h_{13}+h_{23}+h_{33}-h_{12}-h_{22}+1)$, but since $\mathscr{C}_{31}$ and $\mathscr{C}_{12}$ do not commute, this state will not be of highest weight in $\mathscr{U}(2)$. Looking, then, for higher-order expressions in the nine generators of $\mathscr{U}(3)$, we see that the combination $\mathscr{C}_{21}\mathscr{C}_{32}$ has the same effect on the weight as $\mathscr{C}_{31}$. Therefore, we try the combination

$$\mathscr{L}_{31} = \alpha\mathscr{C}_{31} + \beta\mathscr{C}_{21}\mathscr{C}_{32} \tag{2.36}$$

and demand that the state resulting from the application of this operator be of highest weight in $\mathscr{U}(2)$; that is,

$$\mathscr{C}_{12}(\alpha\mathscr{C}_{31} + \beta\mathscr{C}_{21}\mathscr{C}_{32})\left|\begin{matrix} h_{13} & & h_{23} & & h_{33} \\ & h_{12} & & h_{22} & \\ & & h_{12} & & \end{matrix}\right\rangle$$

$$= [\mathscr{C}_{12}, \alpha\mathscr{C}_{31} + \beta\mathscr{C}_{21}\mathscr{C}_{32}]\left|\begin{matrix} h_{13} & & h_{23} & & h_{33} \\ & h_{12} & & h_{22} & \\ & & h_{12} & & \end{matrix}\right\rangle = 0. \tag{2.37}$$

Now

$$[\mathscr{C}_{12}, \alpha\mathscr{C}_{31} + \beta\mathscr{C}_{21}\mathscr{C}_{32}] = -\alpha\mathscr{C}_{32} + \beta(\mathscr{C}_{11} - \mathscr{C}_{22})\mathscr{C}_{32},$$

and therefore we require that

$$[-\alpha + \beta(\mathscr{C}_{11} - \mathscr{C}_{22})] \left| \begin{matrix} h_{13} & h_{23} & h_{33} \\ h_{12} & h_{22} - 1 & \\ & h_{12} & \end{matrix} \right\rangle = 0. \tag{2.38}$$

or $\alpha = \beta(h_{12} - h_{22} + 1)$. Since h_{12} and h_{22} are the eigenvalues of $\mathscr{C}_{11}$ and $\mathscr{C}_{22}$ when applied to the state Eq. (2.35), we conclude

$$\mathscr{L}_{31} = \mathscr{C}_{31}(\mathscr{C}_{11} - \mathscr{C}_{22} + 1) + \mathscr{C}_{21}\mathscr{C}_{32}. \tag{2.39}$$

We have then obtained all the lowering operators of $\mathscr{U}(3)$ and $\mathscr{U}(2)$. The general derivation of these lowering operators and their normalization has been given by Nagel and Moshinsky (*17*), and we shall now state their result for our states characterized by the chain Eqs. (2.16). Define the operators

$$E^{st} = C^{ss} - C^{tt} + t - s. \tag{2.40}$$

Then the lowering operators in the chain $U(n) \supset U(n-1) \supset \cdots \supset U(1)$ take the form

$$\begin{aligned} L^{21} &= C^{21} \\ L^{31} &= C^{31}E^{12} + C^{21}C^{32} \\ L^{32} &= C^{32} \end{aligned} \tag{2.41a}$$

$$\begin{aligned} n \geqq 4: \quad L^{n1} &= (C^{n1}E^{12}E^{13} + C^{21}C^{n2}E^{13} + C^{31}C^{n3}E^{12} \\ &\quad + C^{21}C^{32}C^{n3}) \prod_{s=4}^{n-1} E^{1s} \\ L^{n2} &= (C^{n2}E^{23} + C^{32}C^{n3}) \prod_{s=4}^{n-1} E^{2s} \\ L^{n3} &= C^{n3} \prod_{s=4}^{n-1} E^{3s} \end{aligned} \tag{2.41b}$$

with the convention

$$\prod_{s=4}^{3} E^{ts} = 1, \tag{2.42}$$

while for $\mathscr{L}_{ik}$, $1 \leqq k < i \leqq 3$, we have already found the expressions Eq. (2.41a) with C^{st} replaced by $\mathscr{C}_{jk}$. The general state $|[h_{ij}], \{k_{st}\}\rangle$ can now be written as

$$|[h_{ij}], \{k_{st}\}\rangle = \mathscr{N}[h_{ij}] \prod_{i=2}^{3} \prod_{k=1}^{i-1} (\mathscr{L}_{ik})^{h_{ki}-h_{ki-1}} \times \mathscr{N}\{k_{st}\} \prod_{s=2}^{n} \prod_{t=1}^{s-1} (L^{st})^{k_{ts}-k_{ts-1}} P^{[h_1h_2h_3]}|0\rangle, \tag{2.43}$$

where $P^{[h_1h_2h_3]}$ is given by Eq. (2.25) and the normalization constants are *(17)*

$$\mathscr{N}\{k_{st}\} = \left[\prod_{s=2}^{n}\left(\prod_{\substack{m \geqslant l=1\\ s-1>m}}^{s-1} \frac{(k_{ls-1}-k_{ms-1}+m-l)!}{(k_{ls}-k_{ms-1}+m-l)!} \times \prod_{\substack{m>l=1\\ s>m}}^{s} \frac{(k_{ls-1}-k_{ms}+m-l-1)!}{(k_{ls}-k_{ms}+m-l-1)!}\right)\right]^{1/2} \tag{2.44}$$

and similarly, for $\mathscr{N}[h_{ij}]$, on replacing in Eq. (2.44) k_{st} by h_{ij} and n by 3.

We have proven that the chain of groups Eqs. (2.16) completely characterizes the states of definite total number of quanta N. Furthermore, we obtained these states explicitly from the highest weight state, using an analytic procedure that employs the lowering operators of the unitary groups in the same way as the lowering operator L_- is used for the $\mathscr{O}^+(3) \supset \mathscr{O}^+(2)$ chain.

3. *The Physical Chain of Groups* $\mathscr{U}(3) \supset \mathscr{O}^+(3) \supset \mathscr{O}^+(2)$

As mentioned earlier, the chain of groups Eqs. (2.16) is not very significant physically. For example, for central interactions, the only symmetries of the problem would be those of the rotation group $\mathscr{O}^+(3)$ and the symmetric group $S(n)$. This classification scheme is still useful for more general interactions. It corresponds to the supermultiplet classification of states together with LS coupling. Therefore, rather than use the chain $\mathscr{U}(3) \supset \mathscr{U}(2) \supset \mathscr{U}(1)$, we should use the chain $\mathscr{U}(3) \supset \mathscr{O}^+(3)$, where the generators of $\mathscr{O}^+(3)$ are the three components of the total orbital angular momentum given by

$$L_j = -i \sum_{k,l=1}^{3} \epsilon_{jkl} \mathscr{C}_{kl}, \qquad j = 1, 2, 3, \tag{2.45}$$

$$\epsilon_{jkl} = -\epsilon_{kjl} = -\epsilon_{jlk}, \qquad \epsilon_{123} = 1.$$

The states in the chain $\mathscr{U}(3) \supset \mathscr{O}^+(3) \supset \mathscr{O}^+(2)$ could be characterized by quantum numbers Ω, L, M as

$$\left\langle \mathbf{x} \middle| \begin{matrix} [h_1 h_2 h_3] \\ \Omega L M \end{matrix}, \{k_{st}\} \right\rangle \tag{2.46}$$

where Ω, L, M are the eigenvalues of the commuting operators

$$\mathbf{\Omega} = \sum_{i,j=1}^{3} (\mathscr{C}_{ij} + \mathscr{C}_{ji}) L_i L_j, \qquad \mathbf{L}^2 = \sum_{j=1}^{3} (L_j)^2, L_3. \tag{2.47}$$

The transformation brackets

$$\left\langle [h_{ij}] \middle| \begin{matrix} [h_1 h_2 h_3] \\ \Omega L M \end{matrix} \right\rangle \tag{2.48}$$

have been discussed by Moshinsky (*14*). They may also be obtained as the eigenvectors of the matrix of $\mathbf{L}^2$ in the chain $\mathscr{U}(3) \supset \mathscr{U}(2) \supset \mathscr{U}(1)$ given by Moshinsky (*22*).

In this way, we can replace the canonical chain of groups

$$\mathscr{U}(3) \supset \mathscr{U}(2) \supset \mathscr{U}(1) \tag{2.16b}$$

by the physical chain of groups

$$\mathscr{U}(3) \supset \mathscr{O}^+(3) \supset \mathscr{O}^+(2). \tag{2.49}$$

The IR L of $\mathscr{O}^+(3)$ contained in a given IR $[h_1 h_2 h_3]$ of $\mathscr{U}(3)$ have been shown by Bargmann and Moshinsky (*11*) to correspond to the solutions of the inequalities

$$\begin{aligned} &h_2 - h_3 - L \leqq 2q \leqq h_1 - h_3 - L - 1 \qquad && h_1 - h_3 - L \quad \text{odd} \\ &h_2 - h_3 - L \leqq 2q \leqq h_1 - h_3 - L && h_1 - h_3 - L \quad \text{even} \end{aligned} \tag{2.50a}$$

with q determined in turn by the nonnegative integer values satisfying

$$\begin{aligned} &0 \leqq 2q \leqq h_2 - h_3 - 1 \qquad && h_1 - h_3 - L \quad \text{odd} \\ &0 \leqq 2q \leqq h_2 - h_3 && h_1 - h_3 - L \quad \text{even} \end{aligned} \tag{2.50b}$$

The possible values of L in the reduction from $\mathscr{U}(3)$, or rather $\mathscr{S}\mathscr{U}(3)$, to $\mathscr{O}^+(3)$ have also been discussed by Elliott (*3*).

C. Appendix: Generators of the Unitary Group in r Dimensions

Write the unitary $r \times r$ matrix U as

$$U = \exp(B). \tag{2.51}$$

Then $U^\dagger = U^{-1}$ requires

$$\exp(B^\dagger) = \exp(-B), \tag{2.52}$$

or $B^\dagger = -B$, so that B must be anti-Hermitian. If A is a real antisymmetric and S a real symmetric matrix, B can be written as

$$\begin{aligned} B &= A + iS, \\ b_{ik} &= a_{ik} + is_{ik}, \end{aligned} \tag{2.53}$$

and hence B and U are given in terms of the $r(r-1)/2$ real parameters a_{ik}, $i > k$, and $r(r+1)/2$ real parameters s_{ik}, $i \geqq k$. Now let U act on the complex vectors $\mathbf{z}^s = (z_1^s, z_2^s, \ldots, z_r^s)$ in an r-dimensional vector space as the transformation

$$z_i^s \to z_i'^s = \sum_k u_{ik} z_k^s, \tag{2.54}$$

and consider analytic functions $f(z_i^s)$ defined on this space. Define $f'(z_i^s)$ by

$$f'(z_i^s) \equiv f(z_i'^s) \tag{2.55}$$

and assume that U is near the identity so that in the expansion

$$U = \exp(B) = e + B + \cdots \tag{2.56}$$

only linear terms need to be kept. Then

$$z_i'^s = z_i^s + \sum_{k=1}^{r} b_{ik} z_k^s + \cdots \tag{2.57}$$

$$f'(z_i^s) = f(z_i^s) + \sum_{t=1}^{r} \sum_{j=1}^{r} \sum_{k=1}^{r} b_{jk} z_k^t \frac{\partial}{\partial z_j^t} f(z_i^s) + \cdots. \tag{2.58}$$

Introducing $b_{jk} = a_{jk} + is_{jk}$, we can write this as

$$f'(z_i^s) = f(z_i^s) + \left[\sum_{j>k} a_{jk} \mathfrak{A}_{kj} + \sum_{j \geqslant k} s_{jk} \mathfrak{S}_{kj}\right] f(z_i^s) + \cdots, \tag{2.59}$$

where

$$
\begin{aligned}
j > k: \qquad & \mathfrak{A}_{kj} = \sum_{t=1}^{r} \left(z_k^t \frac{\partial}{\partial z_j^t} - z_j^t \frac{\partial}{\partial z_k^t} \right), \\
j \geqq k: \qquad & \mathfrak{S}_{kj} = i \sum_{t=1}^{r} \left(z_k^t \frac{\partial}{\partial z_j^t} + z_j^t \frac{\partial}{\partial z_k^t} \right).
\end{aligned}
\tag{2.60}
$$

The commutators of these r^2 operators can be expressed as linear combinations of the same set of operators. From Eq. (2.59) we then conclude that the real linear combinations of these r^2 operators form the Lie algebra of $U(r)$, so that the $\mathfrak{A}_{kj}$, $\mathfrak{S}_{kj}$ are the generators of $U(r)$. This reasoning is familiar from the rotation group in three dimensions, $\mathcal{O}^+(3)$, whose Lie algebra is given by the real linear combinations of the generators iL_1, iL_2, iL_3.

To obtain the bases of IR of $U(r)$, a different choice of the generators of $U(r)$ is more convenient. Recall that in the case of $\mathcal{O}^+(3)$ we can choose one of the three generators, say $L_0 = L_3$, to characterize the bases of IR of $\mathcal{O}^+(3)$ by its eigenvalue. The other two generators can then be chosen so as to lower or raise the eigenvalue of L_0 by putting $L_\pm = L_1 \pm iL_2$ to obtain

$$
[L_0, L_\pm] = \pm L_\pm \tag{2.61}
$$

and, by means of L_0, L_+, L_-, the BIR of the group can be derived as discussed in Section II. The role of the operator L_0 for the unitary group $U(r)$ is played by the r commuting operators

$$
C_{jj} = -i\tfrac{1}{2}\mathfrak{S}_{jj} = \sum_s z_j^s \frac{\partial}{\partial z_j^s} \tag{2.62a}
$$

whose eigenvalues define the weight $(w_1, w_2, \ldots, w_r)$. By introducing the remaining $r(r-1)$ operators in the form

$$
\begin{aligned}
j > k: \qquad & C_{kj} = \tfrac{1}{2}(\mathfrak{A}_{kj} - i\mathfrak{S}_{kj}) = \sum_s z_k^s \frac{\partial}{\partial z_j^s}; \\
j < k: \qquad & C_{kj} = \tfrac{1}{2}(\mathfrak{A}_{jk} - i\mathfrak{S}_{jk}) = \sum_s z_k^s \frac{\partial}{\partial z_j^s};
\end{aligned}
\tag{2.62b}
$$

we obtain the commutation relations

$$
[C_{kj}, C_{k'j'}] = \delta_{jk'} C_{kj'} - \delta_{kj'} C_{k'j}, \tag{2.63}
$$

which give, in particular,

$$
[C_{jj}, C_{kl}] = (\delta_{jk} - \delta_{jl}) C_{kl}. \tag{2.64}
$$

Therefore, the generators C_{kl} are the lowering and raising generators of $U(r)$ analogous to L_- and L_+ of $\mathcal{O}^+(3)$. The linear combinations

$$\sum_{j,k} b_{jk} C_{kj}, \qquad b_{jk}^* = -b_{kj}, \tag{2.65}$$

from Eq. (2.58) are seen to generate the Lie algebra of $U(r)$. It should be noted, though, that the generators C_{kj} belong to the complex extension of the Lie algebra of $U(r)$ just as L_+, L_- belong to the complex extension of the Lie algebra of $\mathcal{O}^+(3)$. Nevertheless, the linear combinations of the C_{kj} generate the proper Lie algebra of $U(r)$, provided their coefficients are restricted as in Eq. (2.65).

The correspondence between the operators Eq. (2.62) and the operators

$$\mathscr{C}_{ik} = \sum_s \eta_i^s \xi_k^s \tag{2.13a}$$

is easily established by noting that ξ_j^s, when acting on a function $f(\eta_j^s)$, can be interpreted as $\partial/\partial\eta_j^s$. Moreover, in this case we obtain the property

$$\mathscr{C}_{ik}^\dagger = \mathscr{C}_{ki} \tag{2.66}$$

under Hermitian conjugation. Then Eq. (2.65) can be seen to be an anti-Hermitian operator, so that an operator

$$\exp\left[\sum_{j,k} b_{jk} \mathscr{C}_{kj}\right] \tag{2.67}$$

is unitary and its matrix elements define a unitary representation of $U(r)$.

The close relationship between the spaces spanned by the complex numbers z_j^s and by the operators η_j^s, respectively, has been analyzed by Bargmann (*29*).

III. The Central Problem: Permutational Symmetry of the Orbital States

In the preceding section we achieved a complete classification of the orbital n-particle states in a common ho potential. We also introduced the total orbital angular momentum L connected with the group $\mathcal{O}^+(3)$ into this scheme. These orbital states must be combined with states in spin-isospin space to give completely antisymmetric n-particle states satisfying the Pauli principle. A systematic procedure for doing this is given by the Wigner supermultiplet classification of states together with LS coupling; that is, by first constructing separately n-particle orbital states with definite permutational symmetry and orbital angular monentum L, as well as n-particle spin-isospin states with permutational symmetry, spin S and isospin T, and then coupling these two sets of states to a totally antisymmetric n-particle state with definite total angular momentum J.

We shall here consider the construction of orbital states with definite permutational symmetry; in Section V the corresponding problem for the spin-isospin part will be discussed. Consider the states

$$\left\langle \mathbf{x}^1\mathbf{x}^2\cdots\mathbf{x}^n \middle| \begin{matrix}[h_1h_2h_3]\\ \Omega LM\end{matrix}, \quad \{k_{st}\}\right\rangle. \tag{3.1}$$

A permutation of particle s and t applied to these states requires the replacement of vector $\boldsymbol{\eta}^s$ by $\boldsymbol{\eta}^t$ and $\boldsymbol{\eta}^t$ by $\boldsymbol{\eta}^s$ in the corresponding polynomial $P(\eta_j^s)$. Clearly, this is an operation within the group $U(n)$, and therefore only affects the Gelfand pattern $\{k_{st}\}$ of the groups $U(n) \supset U(n-1) \supset \cdots \supset U(1)$. To require permutational symmetry then means to require that the states transform irreducibly under the groups $U(n) \supset S(n)$ rather than

$$U(n) \supset U(n-1) \supset \cdots \supset U(1),$$

and the central problem that we shall be concerned with in this section is to find the transformation brackets between the states that are bases of the groups in these two chains.

What characterizes a BIR of the group $S(n)$? We recall that an IR of $S(n)$ is given by a partition

$$f = \{f_1 f_2 \cdots f_n\} \tag{3.2}$$

with $f_1 + f_2 + \cdots + f_n = n$ and $f_1 \geqq f_2 \geqq \cdots \geqq f_n \geqq 0$. This partition can be visualized by drawing a Young pattern (*30*, *31*) containing f_j boxes in the jth row. For example, for $S(3)$, the partitions and corresponding Young patterns are

{3}: 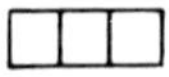

{21}: 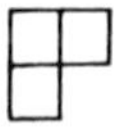

{111}: 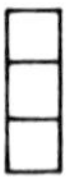

The bases of an IR may be characterized by filling in numbers in the Young patterns in such a way that they increase along each row to the right and downward in each column to obtain the Young tableau for a given partner in the BIR of $S(n)$. In $S(3)$, these Young tableaux are

$$\{3\}: \quad \begin{array}{|c|c|c|}\hline 1 & 2 & 3 \\ \hline \end{array}$$

$$\{21\}: \quad \begin{array}{|c|c|}\hline 1 & 2 \\ \hline 3 & \\ \cline{1-1} \end{array} \qquad \begin{array}{|c|c|}\hline 1 & 3 \\ \hline 2 & \\ \cline{1-1} \end{array}$$

$$\{111\}: \quad \begin{array}{|c|}\hline 1 \\ \hline 2 \\ \hline 3 \\ \hline \end{array}$$

A Young tableau can be denoted by writing the number of the row, $r_1, r_2, \ldots, r_n$ in which the numbers $1, 2, \ldots, n$ are to be found. The set $r = (r_1 r_2 \ldots r_n)$ is the Yamanouchi symbol [(*30*), p. 221] of a row of an IR of $S(n)$. For example, the Yamanouchi symbols for the rows of the IR of $S(3)$ are:

$$\{3\} \quad \begin{array}{|c|c|c|}\hline 1 & 2 & 3 \\ \hline \end{array} \quad : \quad r = (111);$$

$$\{21\} \quad \begin{array}{|c|c|}\hline 1 & 2 \\ \hline 3 & \\ \cline{1-1} \end{array} \quad : \quad r = (112);$$

$$\begin{array}{|c|c|}\hline 1 & 3 \\ \hline 2 & \\ \cline{1-1} \end{array} \quad : \quad r = (121);$$

$$\{111\} \quad \begin{array}{|c|}\hline 1 \\ \hline 2 \\ \hline 3 \\ \hline \end{array} \quad : \quad r = (123).$$

From the rules for the determination of the Young tableau, it is clear that on removing the box containing the number n, a Young tableau of the IR $\{f_j - \delta_{jr_n}\}$ of the group $S(n-1)$ on letters $1, 2, \ldots, n-1$ results. The Yamanouchi or Young orthogonal representation (*30, 31*) results on demanding that the IR f of $S(n)$ remain irreducible under all groups $S(m)$, $1 \leqq m \leqq n-1$, with IR $f^m = \{f_{jm}\} \equiv \{f_{jm+1} - \delta_{jr_m}\}$ in the chain

$$S(n) \supset S(n-1) \supset \cdots \supset S(1). \tag{3.3}$$

Then the matrix elements of the transpositions $(m-1, m)$ $2 \leqq m \leqq n$, are found to be [(*30*), p. 221]

$$\begin{aligned} &\langle f, (r_1 \cdots r_{m-2} \bar{r}_{m-1} \bar{r}_m r_{m+1} \cdots r_n) | (m-1, m) | f, (r_1 \cdots r_{m-2} r_{m-1} r_m r_{m+1} \cdots r_n) \rangle \\ &\qquad = \delta_{\bar{r}_{m-1}, r_{m-1}} \delta_{\bar{r}_m, r_m} \sigma_m + \delta_{\bar{r}_{m-1}, r_m} \delta_{\bar{r}_m, r_{m-1}} (1 - \sigma_m^2)^{1/2}, \\ &\sigma_m^{-1} = f_{r_m, m} - f_{r_{m-1}, m-1} + r_{m-1} - r_m . \end{aligned} \tag{3.4}$$

All other permutations can be written as products of the special transpositions $(m-1, m)$, and their matrix representations can be derived from the matrices given in Eq. (3.4). Note that the application of transpositions allows us to obtain one basis function from another, since for $r_m \neq r_{m-1}$

$$|f,(r_1 \cdots r_m r_{m-1} \cdots r_n)\rangle = (1-\sigma_m^2)^{-1/2}[(m-1, m) - \sigma_m]|f,(r_1 \cdots r_{m-1} r_m \cdots r_n)\rangle. \quad (3.5)$$

In this way, all partner functions of a BIR of $S(n)$ can be derived from a standard one.

To obtain BIR of $S(n)$ from the Gelfand states Eq. (3.1), we could, for example, diagonalize the Wigner projection operator for the symmetric group,

$$c_{rr}^f = \frac{|f|}{n!} \sum_{\mathbf{p} \in S(n)} D_{rr}^{*f}(\mathbf{p})\mathbf{p}, \quad (3.6)$$

(*32*, p. 114) with $|f|$ being the dimension of the IR f of $S(n)$, between Gelfand states $|\{k_{st}\}\rangle$. Each of the mutually orthogonal eigenstates of one Wigner projection operator with eigenvalue 1 would be a member of a BIR of $S(n)$ with partition f and Yamanouchi symbol r. All other partners of the same IR with $r' \neq r$ can be found from Eq. (3.5), and the different BIR of $S(n)$ with the same partition f could be distinguished by a multiplicity index χ. In a manner similar to the passing from the chain of groups $\mathscr{U}(3) \supset \mathscr{U}(2) \supset \mathscr{U}(1)$ to the chain $\mathscr{U}(3) \supset \mathscr{O}^+(3) \supset \mathscr{O}^+(2)$ discussed in Section VII, we then obtain the transformation brackets between states of permutational symmetry corresponding to the chain $U(n) \supset S(n)$ and Gelfand states corresponding to the chain $U(n) \supset U(n-1) \supset \cdots \supset U(1)$. The transformation bracket could be denoted by

$$\left\langle \{k_{st}\} \middle| \begin{matrix} \{h_1 h_2 h_3\} \\ \chi f r \end{matrix} \right\rangle \quad (3.7)$$

where $\{h_1 h_2 h_3\}$ denotes the IR of $U(n)$. In the following subsections we shall show how to determine, in part, the additional index χ by use of groups intermediate between $U(n)$ and $S(n)$.

A. Shell Model States in the $\mathscr{U}(3) \times U(n)$ Scheme

We shall develop here a scheme for the classification of three-particle states based on the concept of shells. Some of the results herein have an immediate generalization to n-particle states (discussed in Section III,A,5); these results are indicated by a superscript n in the number of the corresponding formula.

1. Three-Particle Shell Model States in the $\mathscr{U}(3) \times U(n)$ Scheme

We say that several particles are in the same shell if they have the same energy; that is, using an ho potential, if they have equal numbers of quanta. Since the energy of particle s for a Gelfand state is given by $\hbar\omega w^s$, we see that the shell structure is determined by the weight of the states. The weight is related to the IR of a subgroup $A(3)$ of $U(3)$ formed by the diagonal unitary matrices

$$\mathbf{a} = \begin{pmatrix} \exp(i\alpha^1) & 0 & 0 \\ 0 & \exp(i\alpha^2) & 0 \\ 0 & 0 & \exp(i\alpha^3) \end{pmatrix}, \tag{3.8}$$

as $\mathbf{a}$, applied to a Gelfand state, gives

$$\mathbf{a}\left|\begin{matrix} h_1 & h_2 & h_3 \\ q_1 & q_2 & \\ r_1 & & \end{matrix}\right\rangle = \left|\begin{matrix} h_1 & h_2 & h_3 \\ q_1 & q_2 & \\ r_1 & & \end{matrix}\right\rangle \exp[-i(w^1\alpha^1 + w^2\alpha^2 + w^3\alpha^3)] \tag{3.9}$$

with $w^1 = r_1$, $w^2 = q_1 + q_2 - r_1$, $w^3 = h_1 + h_2 + h_3 - q_1 - q_2$ being the three components of the weight of the state.

So far, we have not considered permutations of particles. Permutations $\mathbf{p}$ on the vectors $\boldsymbol{\eta}^1\boldsymbol{\eta}^2\boldsymbol{\eta}^3$ are represented by 3×3 permutation matrices. It is easy to see that the matrix $\mathbf{pap}^{-1}$ is obtained from $\mathbf{a}$ by applying the permutation $\mathbf{p}$ to the diagonal entries of $\mathbf{a}$. Therefore, any product of two matrices $\mathbf{ap}$, $\mathbf{a}'\mathbf{p}'$ can be written again in the form $\mathbf{a}''\mathbf{p}'' = \mathbf{apa}'\mathbf{p}^{-1}\mathbf{pp}'$, so that the set $\{\mathbf{ap}\}$ is easily seen to form a group $K(3)$ of which $A(3)$ is an invariant subgroup. This group $K(3)$ then comprises all products of elements of the invariant subgroup $A(3)$ and the subgroup $S(3)$ and, since $A(3)$ and $S(3)$ have only the identity in common, $K(3)$ is the semidirect product group $A(3) \wedge S(3)$ of $A(3)$ and $S(3)$ (*33, 34*).

Since the group $K(3)$ contains the group $S(3)$, the chain $U(3) \supset K(3) \supset S(3)$ can be used to construct states with permutational symmetry. We shall see that the IR of $K(3)$ are still characterized by a weight up to permutations of the weight components. Therefore the occupation numbers of the shells are fixed by an IR of $K(3)$ and $K(3)$ may be called the symmetry group of the three-particle shell model.

The class structure of $K(3)$ resembles that of $S(3)$. If we transform an element $\mathbf{ap}$ by an element $\mathbf{bq}$, $\mathbf{a}, \mathbf{b} \in A(3)$, $\mathbf{p}, \mathbf{q} \in S(3)$, we find

$$(\mathbf{bq})\mathbf{ap}(\mathbf{bq})^{-1} = \mathbf{a}'\mathbf{p}' = [\mathbf{b}(\mathbf{qaq}^{-1})(\mathbf{qpq}^{-1}\mathbf{b}^{-1}\mathbf{qp}^{-1}\mathbf{q}^{-1})]\{\mathbf{qpq}^{-1}\}. \tag{3.10^{n}}$$

The expression in square brackets is an element of $A(3)$ and $\mathbf{p}' = \mathbf{qpq}^{-1}$ is a permutation of the same class of $S(3)$ as $\mathbf{p}$. The eigenvalues ϵ_j, $j = 1, 2, 3$, of the matrix $\mathbf{ap} \in K(3)$ for the three cases $\mathbf{p} = (1)(2)(3)$, $\mathbf{p} = (j)(k,l)$, $\mathbf{p} = (j,k,l)$ that [in the notation $(1^{\beta_1}2^{\beta_2}\cdots)$ indicating the numbers β_1 of 1-cycles, β_2 of 2-cycles, etc., for the classes of $S(3)$] correspond to the three classes (1^3), (12), (3), respectively, of $S(3)$, are given by

$$\begin{aligned}
&\mathbf{p} = (1)(2)(3): \quad \epsilon_j = \exp[i\alpha^j], \qquad j = 1, 2, 3;\\
&\mathbf{p} = (j)(k, l): \quad \epsilon_{1,2} = \pm\exp\left[\frac{i}{2}(\alpha^k + \alpha^l)\right], \qquad \epsilon_3 = \exp[i\alpha^j]; \\
&\mathbf{p} = (j, k, l): \quad \epsilon_j = \sigma^{j-1}\exp\left[\frac{i}{3}(\alpha^1 + \alpha^2 + \alpha^3)\right],\\
&\qquad\qquad j = 1, 2, 3, \quad \sigma = \exp\left[\frac{2\pi i}{3}\right].
\end{aligned} \tag{3.11}$$

2. Irreducible Representations of the Groups $K(3)$ and $K(n)$

We consider now the IR of $K(3)$ following the discussion of IR of semidirect product groups given by McIntosh (*33*). First, take the Abelian invariant subgroup $A(3)$ of $K(3)$. Its one-dimensional IR are characterized by the weight $\mathbf{w} = (w^1, w^2, w^3)$ as

$$D^{\mathbf{w}}(\mathbf{a}) = \exp[-i(w^1\alpha^1 + w^2\alpha^2 + w^3\alpha^3)]. \tag{3.12}$$

Then define the group of the weight or little group W as a subgroup of $S(3)$ consisting of all elements $\mathbf{h}$ that fulfill

$$\mathbf{h} \in W: \quad D^{\mathbf{w}}(\mathbf{hah}^{-1}) = D^{\mathbf{w}}(\mathbf{a}), \tag{3.13^{n}}$$

that is, the permutations $\mathbf{h} \in W$ leave the weight $\mathbf{w}$ unchanged. For example, if $\mathbf{w} = (u, u, w)$, the group of the weight is the direct sum $S(2) \oplus S(1)$ with elements $(1)(2)(3) = \mathbf{e}$ and $(1, 2)(3)$. The direct sum appears because we consider $S(3)$ as a matrix group. The IR of the group of the weight are direct product representations of the IR of the groups in the direct sum. We denote these IR by f_w which, in general, is $f_w = f^1 f^2 \cdots$ with $f^1, f^2, \ldots$ denoting the partitions of the groups in the direct sum. Using such an IR of W, we form the direct product matrices

$$D^{\mathbf{w}}(\mathbf{a})\mathbf{D}^{f_w}(\mathbf{h}).$$

These matrices constitute a representation of the subgroup $A(3) \wedge W$ of

$A(3) \wedge S(3)$ since, on defining

$$\mathbf{D}^{(\mathrm{w},\, f_w)}(\mathbf{ah}) \equiv D^{\mathrm{w}}(\mathbf{a})\mathbf{D}^{f_w}(\mathbf{h}), \tag{3.14$^\mathrm{n}$}$$

we find

$$\begin{aligned}\mathbf{D}^{(\mathrm{w},\, f_w)}(\mathbf{aha'h'}) &= \mathbf{D}^{(\mathrm{w},\, f_w)}(\mathbf{aha'h}^{-1}\mathbf{hh'})\\ &= D^{\mathrm{w}}(\mathbf{aha'h}^{-1})\mathbf{D}^{f_w}(\mathbf{hh'})\\ &= D^{\mathrm{w}}(\mathbf{a})\, D^{\mathrm{w}}(\mathbf{ha'h}^{-1})\mathbf{D}^{f_w}(\mathbf{h})\mathbf{D}^{f_w}(\mathbf{h'})\\ &= D^{\mathrm{w}}(\mathbf{a})\mathbf{D}^{f_w}(\mathbf{h})\, D^{\mathrm{w}}(\mathbf{a'})\mathbf{D}^{f_w}(\mathbf{h'})\\ &= \mathbf{D}^{(\mathrm{w},\, f_w)}(\mathbf{ah})\mathbf{D}^{(\mathrm{w},\, f_w)}(\mathbf{a'h'})\end{aligned} \tag{3.15$^\mathrm{n}$}$$

where $D^{\mathrm{w}}(\mathbf{ha'h}^{-1}) = D^{\mathrm{w}}(\mathbf{a'})$ was used since $\mathbf{h} \in W$. This representation is irreducible (*33*), as can be proved, for example, by taking its characters and showing that their scalar product is zero for $(\mathbf{w}', f_{w'}) \neq (\mathbf{w}, f_w)$ and equals the order $(2\pi)^3 n_1!n_2!n_3!$, $n_1 + n_2 + n_3 = 3$ of the group $A(3) \wedge W$ if $(\mathbf{w}', f_{w'}) = (\mathbf{w}, f_w)$, $W = S(n_1) \oplus S(n_2) \cdots$ (*32*, p. 87). We shall denote the order of a group G by $|G|$ and the dimension of an IR κ of G by $|\kappa|$ so that, e.g.,

$$|A(3) \wedge W| = (2\pi)^3 n_1!n_2!n_3!, \qquad n_1 + n_2 + n_3 = n.$$

Next we choose right coset generators $\mathbf{c}_1 = \mathbf{e}, \mathbf{c}_2, \ldots,$ of W in $S(3)$. A systematic choice of coset generators has been discussed by Horie (*35*). With their help we induce a representation of $K(3)$ from the IR Eq. (3.14$^\mathrm{n}$) of $A(3) \wedge W$ by putting

$$\begin{aligned}\mathbf{D}^{(\mathrm{w},\, f_w)}_{\bar{m}m}(\mathbf{ap}) &= \mathbf{D}^{(\mathrm{w},\, f_w)}(\mathbf{c}_{\bar{m}}\mathbf{apc}_m^{-1})\delta(\mathbf{c}_{\bar{m}}\mathbf{pc}_m^{-1}, \mathbf{h} \in W)\\ &= D^{\mathrm{w}}(\mathbf{c}_{\bar{m}}\mathbf{ac}_{\bar{m}}^{-1})\mathbf{D}^{f_w}(\mathbf{c}_{\bar{m}}\mathbf{pc}_m^{-1})\delta(\mathbf{c}_{\bar{m}}\mathbf{pc}_m^{-1}, \mathbf{h} \in W).\end{aligned} \tag{3.16$^\mathrm{n}$}$$

The δ is one if $\mathbf{c}_{\bar{m}}\mathbf{pc}_m^{-1}$ equals some $\mathbf{h} \in W$ and zero otherwise. For given $\mathbf{c}_{\bar{m}}$ and $\mathbf{p} \in S(n)$, there is one and only one $\mathbf{c}_m$ such that $\mathbf{c}_{\bar{m}}\mathbf{pc}_m^{-1} = \mathbf{h} \in W$. This follows from the uniqueness of the coset representative $\mathbf{hc}_m$ of $\mathbf{c}_{\bar{m}}\mathbf{p}$. Moreover, for $\mathbf{c}_{m'} \neq \mathbf{c}_{\bar{m}}$, $\mathbf{c}_{m'}\mathbf{p}$ and $\mathbf{c}_{\bar{m}}\mathbf{p}$ belong to different right cosets. From these properties it is easy to check that Eq. (3.16$^\mathrm{n}$) is a representation of $K(3)$. We have

$$\begin{aligned}\mathbf{D}^{(\mathrm{w},\, f_w)}_{\bar{m}m}(\mathbf{apa'p'}) = {} & D^{\mathrm{w}}(\mathbf{c}_{\bar{m}}\mathbf{ac}_{\bar{m}}^{-1})\, D^{\mathrm{w}}(\mathbf{c}_{\bar{m}}\mathbf{pa'p}^{-1}\mathbf{c}_{\bar{m}}^{-1})\\ & \times \mathbf{D}^{f_w}(\mathbf{c}_{\bar{m}}\mathbf{pp'c}_m^{-1})\delta(\mathbf{c}_{\bar{m}}\mathbf{pp'c}_m^{-1}, \mathbf{h} \in W).\end{aligned} \tag{3.17$^\mathrm{n}$}$$

There is one and only one $\mathbf{c}_{m'}$ such that $\mathbf{c}_{\bar{m}}\mathbf{p}\mathbf{c}_{m'}^{-1} \in W$. Then

$$D^{\mathrm{w}}(\mathbf{c}_{\bar{m}}\mathbf{p}\mathbf{a}'\mathbf{p}^{-1}\mathbf{c}_{\bar{m}}^{-1}) = D^{\mathrm{w}}(\mathbf{c}_{\bar{m}}\mathbf{p}\mathbf{c}_{m'}^{-1}\mathbf{c}_{m'}\mathbf{a}'\mathbf{c}_{m'}^{-1}\mathbf{c}_{m'}\mathbf{p}^{-1}\mathbf{c}_{\bar{m}}^{-1})$$
$$= D^{\mathrm{w}}(\mathbf{c}_{m'}\mathbf{a}'\mathbf{c}_{m'}^{-1}), \tag{3.18^{n}}$$

$$\mathbf{D}^{f_{\mathrm{w}}}(\mathbf{c}_{\bar{m}}\mathbf{p}\mathbf{p}'\mathbf{c}_{m}^{-1})\delta(\mathbf{c}_{\bar{m}}\mathbf{p}\mathbf{p}'\mathbf{c}_{m}^{-1}, \mathbf{h} \in W)$$
$$= \mathbf{D}^{f_{\mathrm{w}}}(\mathbf{c}_{\bar{m}}\mathbf{p}\mathbf{c}_{m'}^{-1}\mathbf{c}_{m'}\mathbf{p}'\mathbf{c}_{m}^{-1})\delta(\mathbf{c}_{\bar{m}}\mathbf{p}\mathbf{p}'\mathbf{c}_{m}^{-1}, \mathbf{h} \in W)$$
$$= \mathbf{D}^{f_{\mathrm{w}}}(\mathbf{c}_{\bar{m}}\mathbf{p}\mathbf{c}_{m'}^{-1})\delta(\mathbf{c}_{\bar{m}}\mathbf{p}\mathbf{c}_{m'}^{-1}, \mathbf{h}' \in W)$$
$$\times \mathbf{D}^{f_{\mathrm{w}}}(\mathbf{c}_{m'}\mathbf{p}'\mathbf{c}_{m}^{-1})\delta(\mathbf{c}_{m'}\mathbf{p}'\mathbf{c}_{m}^{-1}, \mathbf{h}'' \in W), \tag{3.19^{n}}$$

so that

$$\mathbf{D}_{\bar{m}m}^{(\mathrm{w},f_{\mathrm{w}})}(\mathbf{a}\mathbf{p}\mathbf{a}'\mathbf{p}') = \sum_{m'} \mathbf{D}_{\bar{m}m'}^{(\mathrm{w},f_{\mathrm{w}})}(\mathbf{a}\mathbf{p})\mathbf{D}_{m'm}^{(\mathrm{w},f_{\mathrm{w}})}(\mathbf{a}'\mathbf{p}'). \tag{3.20^{n}}$$

To illustrate the appearance of these representations, consider an example. Suppose again $\mathbf{w} = (u, u, w)$ so that the group of the weight is $S(2) \oplus S(1)$ and choose the three coset generators $\mathbf{c}_1 = \mathbf{e}$, $\mathbf{c}_2 = (1, 3)$, $\mathbf{c}_3 = (2, 3)$ where $\mathbf{e}$ denotes the unit element. The IR of $W = S(2) \oplus S(1)$ are one-dimensional, so that the rows of the representation of $K(3)$ are labeled by the index $m = 1, 2, 3$ of the coset generators only. The three cosets are $M_1 = W\mathbf{c}_1 = \{\mathbf{e}, (1, 2)\}$, $M_2 = W\mathbf{c}_2 = \{(1, 3), (1, 2, 3)\}$, $M_3 = W\mathbf{c}_3 = \{(2, 3), (3, 2, 1)\}$. The IR of $S(2) \oplus S(1)$ are given by $D^{\{f_1 f_2\}}(\mathbf{e})D^{\{1\}}(\mathbf{e}) = 1$, $D^{\{f_1 f_2\}}(1, 2)D^{\{1\}}(\mathbf{e}) = (-1)^{f_1}$. From Eq. (3.16^{n}) all representation matrices can be written as

$$\mathbf{D}^{(\mathrm{w},f_{w})}(\mathbf{a}\mathbf{p})$$
$$= \begin{pmatrix} \exp[-i(u\alpha^1 + u\alpha^2 + w\alpha^3)] & 0 & 0 \\ 0 & \exp[-i(w\alpha^1 + u\alpha^2 + u\alpha^3)] & 0 \\ 0 & 0 & \exp[-i(u\alpha^1 + w\alpha^2 + u\alpha^3)] \end{pmatrix}$$
$$\times \mathbf{D}^{(\mathrm{w},f_{w})}(\mathbf{p}). \tag{3.21b}$$

Then from $\mathbf{c}_m\mathbf{e} = \mathbf{e}\mathbf{c}_m$ we have

$$\mathbf{D}^{(\mathrm{w},f_{w})}(\mathbf{e}) = \begin{pmatrix} 1 & 0 & 0 \\ 0 & 1 & 0 \\ 0 & 0 & 1 \end{pmatrix} \tag{3.21b}$$

and, from $\mathbf{c}_1(1, 2) = (1, 2)$, $\mathbf{c}_2(1, 2) = (3, 2, 1)$, $\mathbf{c}_3(1, 2) = (1, 2, 3)$,

$$\mathbf{D}^{(\mathrm{w},f_{w})}(1, 2) = \begin{pmatrix} (-1)^{f_1} & 0 & 0 \\ 0 & 0 & (-1)^{f_1} \\ 0 & (-1)^{f_1} & 0 \end{pmatrix}. \tag{3.21b}$$

In the same way we obtain the other matrices

$$\mathbf{D}^{(\mathbf{w},\,f_w)}(1,3)=\begin{pmatrix}0&1&0\\1&0&0\\0&0&(-1)^{f_1}\end{pmatrix},\qquad \mathbf{D}^{(\mathbf{w},\,f_w)}(2,3)=\begin{pmatrix}0&0&1\\0&(-1)^{f_1}&0\\1&0&0\end{pmatrix},$$

$$\mathbf{D}^{(\mathbf{w},\,f_w)}(1,2,3)=\begin{pmatrix}0&(-1)^{f_1}&0\\0&0&1\\(-1)^{f_1}&0&0\end{pmatrix},\quad \mathbf{D}^{(\mathbf{w},\,f_w)}(3,2,1)=\begin{pmatrix}0&0&(-1)^{f_1}\\(-1)^{f_1}&0&0\\0&1&0\end{pmatrix}. \qquad (3.21\text{b})$$

McIntosh (*33*) proved, in general, that the representations of a semidirect product group, induced in the way we indicated, are irreducible and that all IR can be obtained in this way. In the present case the irreducibility of the representation Eq. (3.16^{n}) of $K(3)$ can easily be checked by taking the characters that we shall derive here and calculating their scalar products. We shall see, moreover, that no other IR of $K(3)$ appear in the reduction of $U(3)$ to $K(3)$.

Turning back to the IR of $A(3)$, we must distinguish three possibilities for the weight:

$$\begin{aligned}&\text{(a)}\quad \mathbf{w}=(u,u,u);\\ &\text{(b)}\quad \mathbf{w}=(u,u,w),\qquad u\neq w;\\ &\text{(c)}\quad \mathbf{w}=(u,v,w),\qquad u\neq v\neq w\neq u;\end{aligned}\qquad (3.22)$$

since they correspond to different groups of the weight.

(a) $\mathbf{w}=(u,u,u)$. There is a single shell containing three particles. The group of the weight is clearly $S(3)$, and the IR of $K(3)$ are simply the direct product representations of $A(3)$ and $S(3)$,

$$\mathbf{D}^{(u,u,u,f)}(\mathbf{ap})=\exp[-iu(\alpha^1+\alpha^2+\alpha^3)]\mathbf{D}^f(\mathbf{p}). \qquad (3.21\text{a})$$

The characters of this IR are clearly

$$\chi^{(u,u,u,f)}(\mathbf{ap})=\exp[-iu(\alpha^1+\alpha^2+\alpha^3)]\chi^f(\mathbf{p}). \qquad (3.23\text{a})$$

(b) $\mathbf{w}=(u,u,w)$. There are two shells, one of them occupied by two particles. The group of the weight $W=S(2)\oplus S(1)$ was already discussed and the IR of $K(3)$ given. The characters are given by the traces of the matrices

Eq. (3.21b)

$$\chi^{(u,u,w,\{f_1 f_2\}\times\{1\})}(\mathbf{a}(1)(2)(3)) = \exp[-i(u\alpha^1 + u\alpha^2 + w\alpha^3)] + \exp[-i(w\alpha^1 + u\alpha^2 + u\alpha^3)] + \exp[-i(u\alpha^1 + w\alpha^2 + u\alpha^3)], \quad (3.23b)$$

$$\chi^{(u,u,w,\{f_1 f_2\}\times\{1\})}(\mathbf{a}(j)(k,l)) = \exp[-i(u\alpha^k + u\alpha^l + w\alpha^j)](-1)^{f_1},$$

$$\chi^{(u,u,w,\{f_1 f_2\}\times\{1\})}(\mathbf{a}(j,k,l)) = 0.$$

(c) $\mathbf{w} = (u, v, w)$. The three particles are in different shells. The group of the weight is $W = S(1) \oplus S(1) \oplus S(1)$; the IR Eq. (3.14^n) of $A(3) \wedge W$ are

$$D^{(u,v,w,\{1\}\times\{1\}\times\{1\})}(\mathbf{ae}) = D^{(u,v,w)}(\mathbf{a}) = \exp[-i(u\alpha^1 + v\alpha^2 + w\alpha^3)].$$

The induced representation of $K(\dot{3})$ is given by

$$\mathbf{D}^{(u,v,w,\{1\}\times\{1\}\times\{1\})}_{\bar{m}m}(\mathbf{ap}) = D^{(u,v,w)}(\mathbf{c}_{\bar{m}}\mathbf{a}\mathbf{c}_{\bar{m}}^{-1})\delta(\mathbf{c}_{\bar{m}}\mathbf{p}\mathbf{c}_m^{-1}, \mathbf{e}) \quad (3.21c)$$

where the coset generators $\mathbf{c}_1 = \mathbf{e}, \mathbf{c}_2, \ldots, \mathbf{c}_6$ are now all six elements of $S(3)$. If we write the multiplication table of $S(3)$ as in Table I, the condition that

TABLE I

MULTIPLICATION TABLE OF THE GROUP $S(3)$

	m	1	2	3	4	5	6
$\bar{m}$	$\mathbf{c}_m$ \ $\mathbf{c}_{\bar{m}}^{-1}$	**e**	(1,2)	(1,3)	(2,3)	(1,2,3)	(3,2,1)
1	**e**	**e**	(1,2)	(1,3)	(2,3)	(1,2,3)	(3,2,1)
2	(1,2)	(1,2)	**e**	(1,2,3)	(3,2,1)	(1,3)	(2,3)
3	(1,3)	(1,3)	(3,2,1)	**e**	(1,2,3)	(2,3)	(1,2)
4	(2,3)	(2,3)	(1,2,3)	(3,2,1)	**e**	(1,2)	(1,3)
5	$(1,2,3)^{-1}$	(3,2,1)	(1,3)	(2,3)	(1,2)	**e**	(1,2,3)
6	$(3,2,1)^{-1}$	(1,2,3)	(2,3)	(1,2)	(1,3)	(3,2,1)	**e**

$\mathbf{c}_{\bar{m}}\mathbf{p}\mathbf{c}_m^{-1} = \mathbf{e}$ means $\mathbf{p} = \mathbf{c}_{\bar{m}}^{-1}\mathbf{c}_m$, so that the 6×6 matrix representative of $\mathbf{p}$ has entries in the places where $\mathbf{p}$ appears in the multiplication table. These entries are determined by the row $\bar{m}$ to be

$$D^{(u,v,w)}(\mathbf{c}_{\bar{m}}\mathbf{a}\mathbf{c}_{\bar{m}}^{-1}).$$

The character of this representation is

$$\begin{aligned}\chi^{(u,v,w,\{1\}\times\{1\}\times\{1\})}(\mathbf{p}) = \delta(\mathbf{p},\mathbf{e})\Big[&\exp[-i(u\alpha^1 + v\alpha^2 + w\alpha^3)] \\ &+ \exp[-i(v\alpha^1 + u\alpha^2 + w\alpha^3)] \\ &+ \exp[-i(w\alpha^1 + v\alpha^2 + u\alpha^3)] \\ &+ \exp[-i(u\alpha^1 + w\alpha^2 + v\alpha^3)] \\ &+ \exp[-i(w\alpha^1 + u\alpha^2 + v\alpha^3)] \\ &+ \exp[-i(v\alpha^1 + w\alpha^2 + u\alpha^3)]\Big]. \end{aligned} \tag{3.23c}$$

From the explicit form of the characters we can easily verify the relations

$$\int_{\mathbf{a} \in A(3)} d\mathbf{a} \sum_{\mathbf{p} \in S(3)} \chi^{\kappa}(\mathbf{ap})\chi^{*\rho}(\mathbf{ap}) = \delta^{\kappa\rho}(2\pi)^3 3! \tag{3.24}$$

for the characters of the induced representations κ, ρ of $K(3)$, which proves the irreducibility of the corresponding representations, since $(2\pi)^3 3!$ is the order of the mixed continuous group $K(3)$ [(*32*), p. 87].

3. *Irreducible Representations of K(3) Contained in an Irreducible Representation of U(3)*

We may use the results of subsection III,A,2 to find the $K(3)$ content of a given IR of $U(3)$ by standard character technique. The multiplicity of the IR μ of a subgroup $F \subset G$ in an IR λ of G is given by the well-known expression

$$m(\lambda, \mu) = |F|^{-1} \sum_{\mathbf{h} \in F} \chi^{\lambda}(\mathbf{h})\chi^{*\mu}(\mathbf{h}), \tag{3.25}$$

where $|F|$ is the order of F and χ^{λ} and χ^{μ} are characters of IR of G and F, respectively. Applying this to the groups $K(3) \subset U(3)$, we need the characters of $U(3)$ for the elements of $K(3)$. Now the character of any element of $U(3)$ is a function of the three eigenvalues of the element [since all elements of $U(3)$ with the same eigenvalues belong to the same class] and, in fact, is a symmetric polynomial in the three eigenvalues ϵ_1, ϵ_2, ϵ_3 given by Weyl's formula (*36*).

We shall use another procedure for deriving this polynomial by calculating directly the trace of the IR

$$\left\langle \begin{matrix} h_1 & & h_2 & & h_3 \\ & q_1' & & q_2' & \\ & & r_1' & & \end{matrix} \middle| U(3) \middle| \begin{matrix} h_1 & & h_2 & & h_3 \\ & q_1 & & q_2 & \\ & & r_1 & & \end{matrix} \right\rangle . \tag{3.26}$$

Since the characters are class functions, it suffices to consider a class representative of $U(3)$ of the form

$$\boldsymbol{\epsilon} = \begin{pmatrix} \epsilon_1 & 0 & 0 \\ 0 & \epsilon_2 & 0 \\ 0 & 0 & \epsilon_3 \end{pmatrix}. \tag{3.27}$$

Now the BIR of $U(3)$ are homogeneous polynomials of degree α, β, γ in the vectors $\boldsymbol{\eta}^1$, $\boldsymbol{\eta}^2$, $\boldsymbol{\eta}^3$ acting on the ground state, with (α, β, γ) being the weight. Therefore,

$$\left\langle \begin{matrix} h_1 & & h_2 & & h_3 \\ & q_1' & & q_2' & \\ & & r_1' & & \end{matrix} \middle| \boldsymbol{\epsilon} \middle| \begin{matrix} h_1 & & h_2 & & h_3 \\ & q_1 & & q_2 & \\ & & r_1 & & \end{matrix} \right\rangle = \epsilon_1^{-\alpha} \epsilon_2^{-\beta} \epsilon_3^{-\gamma} \, \delta_{q_1' q_1} \, \delta_{q_2' q_2} \, \delta_{r_1' r_1} \tag{3.28}$$

where $\alpha = r_1$, $\beta = q_1 + q_2 - r_1$, $\gamma = h_1 + h_2 + h_3 - q_1 - q_2$. The trace of $\boldsymbol{\epsilon}$ in the IR $\{h_1 h_2 h_3\}$ of $U(3)$ is then given by multiplying each term $\epsilon_1^{-\alpha} \epsilon_2^{-\beta} \epsilon_3^{-\gamma}$ by the multiplicity $m(\{h_1 h_2 h_3\}, (\alpha, \beta, \gamma))$ of the weight and summing over all different weights, so that

$$\chi^{\{h_1 h_2 h_3\}}(\epsilon_1 \epsilon_2 \epsilon_3) = \sum_{(\alpha,\beta,\gamma)} m(\{h_1 h_2 h_3\}, (\alpha, \beta, \gamma)) \epsilon_1^{-\alpha} \epsilon_2^{-\beta} \epsilon_3^{-\gamma}. \tag{3.29}$$

Since the numbering of the three vectors $\boldsymbol{\eta}^1$, $\boldsymbol{\eta}^2$, $\boldsymbol{\eta}^3$ in the Gelfand basis is arbitrary, the weight multiplicity is independent of the order of α, β, γ.

To calculate the multiplicity of the weight (α, β, γ), we recall that the values of the numbers q_1, q_2, r_1 are restricted by the inequalities

$$\begin{aligned} h_1 \geqq q_1 \geqq h_2 \geqq q_2 \geqq h_3, \\ q_1 \geqq r_1 \geqq q_2. \end{aligned} \tag{3.30}$$

Introducing the weight (α, β, γ) and the number $f = (q_1 - q_2)/2$, which is integer or half-integer, depending on whether $\alpha + \beta$ is even or odd, these inequalities can be rewritten as

$$f \geqq \frac{\alpha - \beta}{2} \geqq -f,$$

$$h_1 - \frac{\alpha + \beta}{2} \geqq f \geqq h_2 - \frac{\alpha + \beta}{2}, \tag{3.31}$$

$$-h_3 + \frac{\alpha + \beta}{2} \geqq f \geqq -h_2 + \frac{\alpha + \beta}{2},$$

so that, for given $\{h_1 h_2 h_3\}$, (α, β, γ),

$$\max\left(\left|\frac{\alpha - \beta}{2}\right|, \left|h_2 - \frac{\alpha + \beta}{2}\right|\right) \leqq f \leqq \min\left(h_1 - \frac{\alpha + \beta}{2}, \frac{\alpha + \beta}{2} - h_3\right). \tag{3.32}$$

Since for fixed $\{h_1 h_2 h_3\}$, (α, β, γ), any value of f can appear at most once, the number of possible (either integer or half-integer) values of f determines the multiplicity of the weight; that is,

$$m(\{h_1 h_2 h_3\}, (\alpha, \beta, \gamma)) = 1 + \min\left(h_1 - \frac{\alpha + \beta}{2}, \frac{\alpha + \beta}{2} - h_3\right)$$
$$- \max\left(\left|\frac{\alpha - \beta}{2}\right|, \left|h_2 - \frac{\alpha + \beta}{2}\right|\right), \tag{3.33}$$

if

$$\min\left(h_1 - \frac{\alpha + \beta}{2}, \frac{\alpha + \beta}{2} - h_3\right) - \max\left(\left|\frac{\alpha - \beta}{2}\right|, \left|h_2 - \frac{\alpha + \beta}{2}\right|\right) \geqq 0;$$

$$m(\{h_1 h_2 h_3\}, (\alpha, \beta, \gamma)) = 0$$

if

$$\min\left(h_1 - \frac{\alpha + \beta}{2}, \frac{\alpha + \beta}{2} - h_3\right) - \max\left(\left|\frac{\alpha - \beta}{2}\right|, \left|h_2 - \frac{\alpha + \beta}{2}\right|\right) < 0$$

where the second case results because a weight (α, β, γ) can only be realized if the inequality Eq. (3.32) for f admits at least one solution.

To use Eq. (3.25) for the multiplicity of IR of $K(3)$ in IR of $U(3)$ we need the eigenvalues ϵ_1, ϵ_2, ϵ_3 for the matrix **ap** that were calculated in Eq. (3.11). The summation over all elements of $K(3)$ implies an integration over $\alpha^1\alpha^2\alpha^3$ and a sum over $\mathbf{p} \in S(3)$. We shall always use the letter m for the multiplicity of IR of a subgroup F in an IR of a group G. Then, in the case of $U(3) \supset K(3)$,

$$m(\{h_1h_2h_3\}, (\mathbf{w}, f_w)) = (2\pi)^{-3} \int_0^{2\pi} d\alpha^1\, d\alpha^2\, d\alpha^3 \times \left[(3!)^{-1} \sum_{\mathbf{p} \in S(3)} \chi^{\{h_1h_2h_3\}}(\epsilon_1(\mathbf{ap}), \epsilon_2(\mathbf{ap}), \epsilon_3(\mathbf{ap}))\chi^{*(\mathbf{w}, f_w)}(\mathbf{ap}) \right]. \quad (3.34)$$

Using the characters of $K(3)$, we find for the three cases

(a): $m(\{h_1h_2h_3\}, (u, u, u, \{f_1 f_2 f_3\}))$

$$= \tfrac{1}{6}\Big[m(\{h_1h_2h_3\}, (u, u, u))\chi^{*\{f_1 f_2 f_3\}}(1^3) + \sum_{\alpha+\beta=2u} m(\{h_1h_2h_3\}, (\alpha, \beta, u))(-1)^{\beta} 3\chi^{*\{f_1 f_2 f_3\}}(12) + \sum_{\alpha+\beta+\gamma=3u} m(\{h_1h_2h_3\}, (\alpha, \beta, \gamma))\sigma^{-\beta-2\gamma} 2\chi^{*\{f_1 f_2 f_3\}}(3) \Big]; \quad (3.35a)$$

(b): $m(\{h_1h_2h_3\}, (u, u, w, \{f^1 f^2\} \times \{1\}))$

$$= \tfrac{1}{2}\Big[m(\{h_1h_2h_3\}, (u, u, w))\chi^{*\{f_1 f_2\}}(1^2)\chi^{*\{1\}}(1) + \sum_{\alpha+\beta=2u} m(\{h_1h_2h_3\}, (\alpha, \beta, w))(-1)^{\beta}\chi^{*\{f_1 f_2\}}(2)\chi^{*\{1\}}(1) \Big],$$

$$\chi^{*\{f_1 f_2\}}(1^2) = \chi^{*\{1\}}(1) = 1, \qquad \chi^{*\{f_1 f_2\}}(2) = (-1)^{f_1}, \quad (3.35b)$$

(c): $m(\{h_1h_2h_3\}, (u, v, w, \{1\} \times \{1\} \times \{1\})) = m(\{h_1h_2h_3\}, (u, v, w)). \quad (3.35c)$

4. Construction of Three-Particle Shell Model States

To construct explicitly the BIR of $K(3)$ from BIR of $U(3)$ (i.e., from Gelfand states), we can use the Wigner projection operators (*32*, p. 114). We specify the rows of the group of the weight by the symbol r_w, which denotes Yamanouchi symbols of the groups appearing in $W = S(3)$, $W = S(2) \oplus S(1)$, $W = S(1) \oplus S(1) \oplus S(1)$, respectively. Then the Wigner projection operator is given by

$$c^{(\mathbf{w}, f_w)}_{mrwmrw} = \frac{|(\mathbf{w}, f_w)|}{|K(3)|} \int_{\mathbf{a} \in A(3)} d\mathbf{a} \sum_{\mathbf{p} \in S(3)}$$

$$\times\ D^{*\mathbf{w}}(\mathbf{c}_m \mathbf{a} \mathbf{c}_m^{-1}) D^{*\,f_w}_{rwrw}(\mathbf{c}_m \mathbf{p} \mathbf{c}_m^{-1})\ \delta(\mathbf{c}_m \mathbf{p} \mathbf{c}_m^{-1}, \mathbf{h} \in W)\mathbf{a}\mathbf{p}. \qquad (3.36^n)$$

The second sum can be changed to a sum over the group of the weight,

$$c^{(\mathbf{w}, f_w)}_{mrwmrw} = |A(3)|^{-1} \int_{\mathbf{a} \in A(3)} d\mathbf{a}\, D^{*\mathbf{w}}(\mathbf{c}_m \mathbf{a} \mathbf{c}_m^{-1})\mathbf{a}$$

$$\times \frac{|f_w|}{|W|} \sum_{\mathbf{h} \in W} D^{*\,f_w}_{rwrw}(\mathbf{h}) \mathbf{c}_m^{-1} \mathbf{h} \mathbf{c}_m. \qquad (3.37^n)$$

Clearly the Wigner projection operator factorizes into a part connected with $A(3)$ and a part connected with W, a result discussed in general by McIntosh (*34*).

To use this formula, we need the matrices of all elements $\mathbf{p}$ of $S(3)$ between Gelfand states, that is,

$$\left\langle \begin{matrix} h_1 & h_2 & h_3 \\ q_1' & q_2' & \\ r_1' & & \end{matrix} \right| \mathbf{p} \left| \begin{matrix} h_1 & h_2 & h_3 \\ q_1 & q_2 & \\ r_1 & & \end{matrix} \right\rangle. \qquad (3.38)$$

It is easy to show that

$$\left\langle \begin{matrix} h_1 & h_2 & h_3 \\ q_1' & q_2' & \\ r_1' & & \end{matrix} \right| (1, 2) \left| \begin{matrix} h_1 & h_2 & h_3 \\ q_1 & q_2 & \\ r_1 & & \end{matrix} \right\rangle = (-1)^{q_2}\, \delta_{q_1' q_1}\, \delta_{q_2' q_2}\, \delta_{r_1', q_1+q_2-r_1} \qquad (3.39)$$

From the work of Chacón and Moshinsky (*37*, *38*), we furthermore find

$$\left\langle \begin{matrix} h_1 & h_2 & h_3 \\ q_1' & q_2' & \\ r_1' & & \end{matrix} \right| (2, 3) \left| \begin{matrix} h_1 & h_2 & h_3 \\ q_1 & q_2 & \\ r_1 & & \end{matrix} \right\rangle$$

$$= (-1)^{h_3}\, \delta_{r_1 r_1'}\, \delta_{q_1'+q_2'-r_1', h_1+h_2+h_3-q_1-q_2} [(q_1 - q_2 + 1)(q_1' - q_2' + 1)]^{1/2}$$

$$\cdot\, W(abcd; ef) \qquad (3.40)$$

with

$$a = \tfrac{1}{2}(h_1 - q_1' + h_2 - q_2'), \qquad d = \tfrac{1}{2}(q_1' - r_1 + q_2' - h_3),$$

$$b = \tfrac{1}{2}(r_1 - q_2 + h_2 - q_2'), \qquad e = \tfrac{1}{2}(h_1 - q_1' + r_1 - q_2),$$

$$c = \tfrac{1}{2}(q_1' - r_1 + q_1 - h_2), \qquad f = \tfrac{1}{2}(h_1 - q_1 + r_1 - q_2'),$$

and $W(abcd; ef)$ being an ordinary Racah coefficient.

But then, all other matrix elements of $\mathbf{p} \in S(3)$ are given by the relations

$$\begin{aligned}(1, 3) &= (1, 2)(2, 3)(1, 2),\\ (1, 2, 3) &= (2, 3)(1, 2),\\ (3, 2, 1) &= (1, 2)(2, 3).\end{aligned} \tag{3.41}$$

We now return to the different possibilities of weights $\mathbf{w} = (w^1, w^2, w^3)$ for a given IR $\{h_1h_2h_3\}$ of $U(3)$. For the cases (a), (b) and (c) we find explicitly

$$\text{(a)}: \quad c_{rr}^{(u,u,u,\{f_1f_2f_3\})} = (2\pi)^{-3} \int_0^{2\pi} d\alpha^1\, d\alpha^2\, d\alpha^3 \exp[iu(\alpha^1 + \alpha^2 + \alpha^3)]\mathbf{a}$$

$$\times \frac{|\{f_1f_2f_3\}|}{3!} \sum_{\mathbf{p} \in S(3)} D_{rr}^{*\{f_1f_2f_3\}}(\mathbf{p})\mathbf{p}. \tag{3.42a}$$

These operators are idempotent, and by diagonalizing them between Gelfand states, we obtain a set of states with eigenvalue 1 that then correspond to BIR of $\{f_1f_2f_3\}$ of $S(3)$.

$$\text{(b)}: \quad c_{mm}^{(u,u,w,\{f_1f_2\}\times\{1\})} = (2\pi)^{-3} \int_0^{2\pi} d\alpha^1\, d\alpha^2\, d\alpha^3\, D^{*(u,u,w)}(\mathbf{c}_m^{-1}\mathbf{a}\mathbf{c}_m)\mathbf{a}$$

$$\times (2!)^{-1} \sum_{\mathbf{h} \in S(2)} D^{*\{f_1f_2\}}(\mathbf{h})\mathbf{c}_m^{-1}\mathbf{h}\mathbf{c}_m \tag{3.42b}$$

Choosing, for example, $m = 1$ (i.e., $\mathbf{c}_m = \mathbf{c}_1 = e$), the integral over $\alpha^1\alpha^2\alpha^3$ will select states with weight (u, u, w). In general, there are many states of this type distinguished by the value q_2 as $q_1 + q_2 - r_1 = r_1 = u$. The operator

Eq. (3.42b) then gives

$$c_{11}^{(u,u,w,\{f_1f_2\}\times\{1\})}\left|\begin{matrix} h_1 & h_2 & h_3 \\ q_1 & q_2 & \\ & r_1 & \end{matrix}\right\rangle$$

$$= \frac{1}{2}\sum_{\mathbf{h}\in S(2)} D^{*\{f_1f_2\}}(\mathbf{h})\mathbf{h}\left|\begin{matrix} h_1 & h_2 & h_3 \\ q_1 & q_2 & \\ & r_1 & \end{matrix}\right\rangle \delta_{r_1u}\,\delta_{q_1+q_2-r_1,u}\,\delta_{h_1+h_2+h_3-q_1-q_2,w}$$

$$= \tfrac{1}{2}(1+(-1)^{q_2+f_1})\left|\begin{matrix} h_1 & h_2 & h_3 \\ q_1 & q_2 & \\ & r_1 & \end{matrix}\right\rangle \delta_{r_1u}\,\delta_{q_1+q_2-r_1,u}\,\delta_{h_1+h_2+h_3-q_1-q_2,w}. \qquad (3.43)$$

Therefore, a state of weight (u, u, w) will belong to

$$\{f_1f_2\} = \{2\} \qquad \text{if} \quad q_2 = \text{even},$$

and to

$$\{f_1f_2\} = \{11\} \qquad \text{if} \quad q_2 = \text{odd}.$$

Morevoer, the eigenfunctions of Eq. (3.42b) with eigenvalue 1 may clearly be distinguished by q_2. To find the other members of the basis, we apply the method of Wigner (*32*, p. 112) to derive the other partner functions of a BIR from a given one. Then, denoting the bases in general by $|(\mathbf{w}, f_w)mr_w\rangle$, we have

$$\begin{aligned}
&|(\mathbf{w}, f_w)mr'_w\rangle \\
&= (2\pi)^{-3}\int_{\mathbf{a}\in A(3)} d\mathbf{a}\, D^{*\mathbf{w}}(\mathbf{c}_m\mathbf{a}\mathbf{c}_m^{-1})\mathbf{a}\frac{|f_w|}{|W|}\sum_{\mathbf{p}\in S(3)} D^{*f_w}_{r_w'r_w}(\mathbf{c}_m\mathbf{p})\mathbf{p} \\
&\quad\times \delta(\mathbf{c}_m\mathbf{p}, \mathbf{h}\in W)|(\mathbf{w}, f_w)m = 1r_w\rangle \\
&= \mathbf{c}_m^{-1}(2\pi)^{-3}\int_{\mathbf{a}\in A(3)} d\mathbf{a}\, D^{*\mathbf{w}}(\mathbf{c}_m\mathbf{a}\mathbf{c}_m^{-1})\mathbf{c}_m\mathbf{a}\mathbf{c}_m^{-1} \\
&\quad\times \frac{|f_w|}{|W|}\sum_{\mathbf{h}\in W} D^{*f_w}_{r_w',r_w}(\mathbf{h})\mathbf{h}|(\mathbf{w}, f_w)m = 1r_w\rangle \\
&= \mathbf{c}_m^{-1}(2\pi)^{-3}\int_{\mathbf{a}\in A(3)} d\mathbf{a}\, D^{*\mathbf{w}}(\mathbf{a})\mathbf{a}|(\mathbf{w}, f_w)m = 1r'_w\rangle \\
&= \mathbf{c}_m^{-1}|(\mathbf{w}, f_w)m = 1r'_w\rangle. \qquad (3.44^{\mathrm{n}})
\end{aligned}$$

In the particular case (b) the partners of the BIR are then given by

$$\mathbf{c}_m^{-1}\left|\begin{matrix} h_1 & h_2 & h_3 \\ q_1 & q_2 & \\ & r_1 & \end{matrix}\right\rangle \delta_{r_1 u}\,\delta_{q_1+q_2-r_1,u}\,\delta_{h_1+h_2+h_3-q_1-q_2,w}, \qquad (3.45)$$

$$\mathbf{c}_1 = \mathbf{e}, \quad \mathbf{c}_2 = (1,3), \quad \mathbf{c}_3 = (2,3),$$

with $q_2 =$ even corresponding to $\{f_1 f_2\} = \{2\}$ and $q_2 =$ odd corresponding to $\{f_1 f_2\} = \{11\}$. We may convince ourselves that two such bases with $q_2' \neq q_2$ are orthogonal by considering the matrix element

$$\left\langle \begin{matrix} h_1 & h_2 & h_3 \\ q_1' & q_2' & \\ & u & \end{matrix}\right| \mathbf{c}_{\bar{m}}\mathbf{c}_m^{-1} \left|\begin{matrix} h_1 & h_2 & h_3 \\ q_1 & q_2 & \\ & u & \end{matrix}\right\rangle, \qquad \begin{matrix} q_1+q_2 = q_1'+q_2' = 2u, \\ h_1+h_2+h_3-q_1-q_2 = w. \end{matrix} \qquad (3.46)$$

This expression is zero for $\bar{m} = m$, if $q_2' \neq q_2$.

For $\bar{m} \neq m$ we have the possibilities $\mathbf{c}_{\bar{m}}\mathbf{c}_m^{-1} = (1,3), (2,3), (1,2,3), (3,2,1)$, all of which change the weight (u, u, w). Since the weight components are the eigenvalues of the Hermitian operators C^{11}, C^{22}, C^{33}, states belonging to different weights are orthogonal and the matrix elements Eq. (3.46) are zero. Finally, if $q_2' = q_2$ and $\bar{m} \neq m$, again the matrix element Eq. (3.46) is zero, showing that the partner functions of the same BIR of $K(3)$ are orthogonal.

We conclude that q_2 can be used to distinguish the different bases for the weight $\mathbf{w} = (u, u, w)$, although it is not a good quantum number in general.

(c): In this case

$$c_{mm}^{(u,v,w,\{1\}\times\{1\}\times\{1\})} = (2\pi)^{-3}\int_0^{2\pi} d\alpha^1\, d\alpha^2\, d\alpha^3\, D^{*(u,v,w)}(\mathbf{c}_m^{-1}\mathbf{a}\mathbf{c}_m)\mathbf{a}. \qquad (3.42c)$$

Choosing $m = 1$, we find

$$c_{11}^{(u,v,w,\{1\}\times\{1\}\times\{1\})}\left|\begin{matrix} h_1 & h_2 & h_3 \\ q_1 & q_2 & \\ & r_1 & \end{matrix}\right\rangle$$

$$= \left|\begin{matrix} h_1 & h_2 & h_3 \\ q_1 & q_2 & \\ & r_1 & \end{matrix}\right\rangle \delta_{r_1 u}\,\delta_{q_1+q_2-r_1,v}\,\delta_{h_1+h_2+h_3-q_1-q_2,w}. \qquad (3.47)$$

Again, we derive, from one state with fixed q_2 and weight (u, v, w), the basis

$$\mathbf{c}_m^{-1}\left|\begin{matrix} h_1 & h_2 & h_3 \\ & q_1 \quad q_2 & \\ & u & \end{matrix}\right\rangle \tag{3.48}$$

and may prove that for $\bar{m} \neq m$

$$\left\langle\begin{matrix} h_1 & h_2 & h_3 \\ & q_1' \quad q_2' & \\ & u & \end{matrix}\right| \mathbf{c}_{\bar{m}}\mathbf{c}_m^{-1} \left|\begin{matrix} h_1 & h_2 & h_3 \\ & q_1 \quad q_2 & \\ & u & \end{matrix}\right\rangle = 0, \qquad \begin{matrix} q_1 + q_2 = q_1' + q_2' = u + v, \\ h_1 + h_2 + h_3 = u + v + w, \end{matrix} \tag{3.49}$$

so that all bases derived from states with different q_2 are orthogonal to each other. Also, if $q_2' = q_2$ but $\bar{m} \neq m$, these states are orthogonal to each other.

Having discussed all BIR of $K(3)$, we may now reduce them in the $K(3) \supset S(3)$ chain to IR of $S(3)$. Again consider the three cases (a), (b), (c) separately. In case (a) the states transform irreducibly under $S(3)$. In case (b) on restricting $K(3)$ to $S(3)$ the states transform according to a representation of $S(3)$ induced by $S(2) \oplus S(1)$. The reduction of this representation is given by Littlewood's (*39*) rules and gives the possibilities

$$\begin{aligned} \{2\} \times \{1\} &= \{3\} \oplus \{21\}, \\ \{11\} \times \{1\} &= \{21\} \oplus \{111\}. \end{aligned} \tag{3.50}$$

The first possibility applies if q_2 in Eq. (3.45) is even, the second if q_2 is odd. To find the explicit reduction we apply the Wigner projection operators Eq. (3.6) and the ladder procedure Eq. (3.5) to obtain the results given in Table II. In case (c) Littlewood's rules have to be applied to the representation of the group of the weight $S(1) \oplus S(1) \oplus S(1)$ to give

$$\{1\} \times \{1\} \times \{1\} = \{3\} \oplus 2\{21\} \oplus \{111\}, \tag{3.51}$$

that is, the regular representation of $S(3)$. The explicit reduction is given in Table II. We denote the states corresponding to the chain $U(3) \supset K(3) \supset S(3)$ by

$$\left|\begin{matrix} \{h_1 h_2 h_3\} \\ \chi(\mathbf{w}, f_w)\varphi f r \end{matrix}\right\rangle; \tag{3.52}$$

χ distinguishes between equal IR of $K(3)$ in IR of $U(3)$ and φ between equal IR of $S(3)$ in IR of $K(3)$. The states in cases (b) and (c) are expressed as linear

TABLE II

THREE-PARTICLE SHELL MODEL STATES WITH PERMUTATIONAL SYMMETRY IN TERMS OF BIR OF $K(3)$

(w^1, w^2, w^3)	χ	fr	$\left\lvert\begin{array}{c}\{h_1 h_2 h_3\}\\ \chi(\mathbf{w}, f_w)\varphi fr\end{array}\right\rangle$
(u,u,u)		$\{3\}$ $\{21\}$ $\{111\}$	Derived by diagonalizing the operator Eq. (3.6)
(u,u,w)	q_2 even	$\{3\}(111)$ $\{21\}(112)$ $\{21\}(121)$	$\sqrt{\frac{1}{3}}[1 + (1,3) + (2,3)]$ $\sqrt{\frac{2}{3}}[1 - \frac{1}{2}(1,3) - \frac{1}{2}(2,3)]$ $\sqrt{\frac{1}{2}}[(2,3) - (1,3)]$ $\left\rbrace\ \left\lvert\begin{array}{c}\{h_1 h_2 h_3\}\\(u,u,w)q_2\end{array}\right\rangle$
(u,u,w)	q_2 odd	$\{21\}(112)$ $\{21\}(121)$ $\{111\}(123)$	$\sqrt{\frac{1}{2}}[-(2,3) + (1,3)]$ $-\sqrt{\frac{2}{3}}[1 + \frac{1}{2}(1,3) + \frac{1}{2}(2,3)]$ $\sqrt{\frac{1}{3}}[1 - (1,3) - (2,3)]$ $\left\rbrace\ \left\lvert\begin{array}{c}\{h_1 h_2 h_3\}\\(u,u,w)q_2\end{array}\right\rangle$
(u,v,w)	q_2	$\{3\}(111)$ $\{21\}_1(112)$ $\{21\}_1(121)$ $\{21\}_2(112)$ $\{21\}_2(121)$ $\{111\}(123)$	$\sqrt{\frac{1}{6}}[1 + (1,2) + (1,3) + (2,3) + (1,2,3) + (3,2,1)]$ $\sqrt{\frac{1}{3}}[1 + (1,2) - \frac{1}{2}\{(1,3) + (2,3) + (1,2,3) + (3,2,1)\}]$ $\frac{1}{2}[-(1,3) + (2,3) + (1,2,3) - (3,2,1)]$ $\frac{1}{2}[(1,3) - (2,3) + (1,2,3) - (3,2,1)]$ $-\sqrt{\frac{1}{3}}[1 - (1,2) + \frac{1}{2}\{(1,3) + (2,3) - (1,2,3) - (3,2,1)\}]$ $\sqrt{\frac{1}{6}}[1 - (1,2) - (1,3) - (2,3) + (1,2,3) + (3,2,1)]$ $\left\rbrace\ \left\lvert\begin{array}{c}\{h_1 h_2 h_3\}\\(u,v,w)q_2\end{array}\right\rangle$

combinations of the bases

$$\mathbf{c}_m^{-1}\left|\begin{matrix}\{h_1h_2h_3\}\\(\mathbf{w}, f_w)q_2\end{matrix}\right\rangle \tag{3.53}$$

of the IR of $K(3)$.

5. *n-Particle Shell Model States*

Having studied in detail the three-particle shell model states, we can now outline the group theory of the n-particle ho shell model. First, we introduce the group $K(n)$ consisting of all products **ap** of the elements **a** of the group $A(n)$ of unitary diagonal $n \times n$ matrices, and of the permutation matrices **p** of $S(n)$. This group $K(n)$ is the semidirect product of $A(n)$ and $S(n)$, that is, $K(n) = A(n) \wedge S(n)$. The IR of $A(n)$ are characterized by the weight

$$\mathbf{w} = (w^1, w^2, \ldots, w^n) \tag{3.54}$$

as

$$D^{\mathbf{w}}(a) = \exp[-i(w^1\alpha^1 + w^2\alpha^2 + \cdots + w^n\alpha^n)]. \tag{3.55}$$

We define a reference weight by combining equal weight components, that is, by writing

$$\mathbf{w} = (w^1)^{n_1}(w^2)^{n_2}\cdots(w^k)^{n_k}, \tag{3.56}$$

where n_j is the number of times the weight component w^j appears

We choose an IR f_w of the group of the weight W defined by Eq. (3.13^n) and form the product representation of the group $A(n) \wedge W$. From these representations we induce the representation of $K(n)$ as in Eq. (3.16^n). These representations are shown by McIntosh (*33*) to be irreducible. They are characterized by the reference weight (3.56) and by the IR

$$f_w = f^1 f^2 \cdots f^k \tag{3.57}$$

of the group $W = S(n_1) \oplus S(n_2) \oplus \cdots \oplus S(n_k)$ of the weight. The BIR of $K(n)$ correspond to multishell configurations in which $n_1, n_2, \ldots, n_k$ are the occupation numbers of the k shells with number $w^1, w^2, \ldots, w^k$ of quanta per particle. By introducing the subgroup $S(n)$ of $K(n)$ we obtain states of the form

$$\left|\begin{matrix}[h_1h_2h_3]\\ \Omega LM\end{matrix}, \begin{matrix}\{h_1h_2h_3\}\\ \chi(\mathbf{w}, f_w)\varphi f r\end{matrix}\right\rangle. \tag{3.58}$$

Here, χ distinguishes between repeated IR $(\mathbf{w}, f_w)$ of $K(n)$ and φ between repeated IR f of $S(n)$. If we calculate these states from Gelfand states, we obtain the transformation brackets

$$\left\langle \{k_{st}\} \middle| \begin{matrix} \{h_1 h_2 h_3\} \\ \chi(\mathbf{w}, f_w)\varphi f r \end{matrix} \right\rangle \tag{3.59}$$

mentioned earlier. For these calculations, the matrix elements of the permutations $\mathbf{p}$ between Gelfand states are needed in order to apply the Wigner projection operators Eq. (3.6). These matrix elements can be calculated by an extension of the method used by Chacón and Moshinsky (*37*) for the case $n = 3$. This extension was developed in detail in reference (*38*).

The n-particle shell model states Eq. (3.59) are BIR of the groups in the chain

$$U(n) \supset K(n) \supset S(n).$$

General properties of this chain have been discussed by Kramer (*20, 21*).

B. Translational-Invariant States

The Hamiltonian Eq. (2.2) is not translational invariant, so that its eigenstates may contain spurious excitations of the center-of-mass vector. Let us consider, instead of Eq. (2.2), the translational-invariant Hamiltonian

$$\bar{\mathscr{H}}_0 = \sum_{s=1}^{n}\sum_{j=1}^{3} \frac{1}{2m}(p_j^s)^2 + \frac{1}{4n} m\omega^2 \sum_{s,t=1}^{n}\sum_{j=1}^{3} (x_j^s - x_j^t)^2. \tag{3.60}$$

To deal with the Hamiltonian of Eq. (3.60), introduce Jacobi vectors $\dot{\mathbf{x}}^s$ by the orthogonal transformation

$$\begin{aligned} \dot{\mathbf{x}}^s &= \left(\frac{1}{s(s+1)}\right)^{1/2} \sum_{t=1}^{s} \mathbf{x}^t - \left(\frac{s}{s+1}\right)^{1/2} \mathbf{x}^{s+1}, \qquad 1 \leqq s \leqq n-1, \\ \dot{\mathbf{x}}^n &= \left(\frac{1}{n}\right)^{1/2} \sum_{t=1}^{n} \mathbf{x}^t. \end{aligned} \tag{3.61}$$

Then

$$\sum_{s,t=1}^{n} (\mathbf{x}^s - \mathbf{x}^t)^2 = 2n \sum_{s=1}^{n-1} (\dot{\mathbf{x}}^s)^2, \tag{3.62}$$

so that

$$\bar{\mathscr{H}}_0 = \sum_{s=1}^{n-1} \frac{1}{2m} (\dot{\mathbf{p}}^s)^2 + \frac{1}{2} m\omega^2 \sum_{s=1}^{n-1} (\dot{\mathbf{x}}^s)^2 + \frac{1}{2m} (\dot{\mathbf{p}}^n)^2. \tag{3.63}$$

The eigenstates of $\bar{\mathscr{H}}_0$ can clearly be written as a product of a plane wave $\exp[(i/\hbar)(\dot{\mathbf{x}}^n \cdot \dot{\mathbf{p}}^n)]$ for the center-of-mass part and a state

$$\left\langle \dot{\mathbf{x}} \middle| \begin{matrix} [h_1 h_2 h_3] \\ \Omega L M \end{matrix}, \quad \{k_{st}\} \right\rangle \tag{3.64}$$

of the type Eq. (2.46), but referring to the relative vectors $\dot{\mathbf{x}}^s$ given by the Jacobi transformation Eq. (3.61). Since the actual dependency of the n-particle state on the center-of-mass vector is inessential for our purpose, provided this dependency is the same for all states, we may as well use the old Hamiltonian $\mathscr{H}_0$ (which has the same form in the $\dot{\mathbf{x}}^s$ vectors as $\dot{\mathbf{x}}^s$ and $\mathbf{x}^s$ are related by an orthogonal transformation) related to $\bar{\mathscr{H}}_0$ by

$$\mathscr{H}_0 = \bar{\mathscr{H}}_0 + \tfrac{1}{2} m\omega^2 (\dot{\mathbf{x}}^n)^2 \tag{3.65}$$

and give no excitation to the center-of-mass vector by demanding that the operator

$$\dot{C}^{nn} = \sum_{j=1}^{3} \dot{\eta}_j^n \dot{\xi}_j^n = n^{-1} \sum_{s,t=1}^{n} C^{st}, \tag{3.66}$$

when applied to the states, give zero. If we write the states in terms of Jacobi vectors $\dot{\boldsymbol{\eta}}^1 \dot{\boldsymbol{\eta}}^2 \cdots \dot{\boldsymbol{\eta}}^n$ this implies simply that in the chain $U(n) \supset U(n-1)$ the partitions of both groups are the same, so that

$$\{k_{st}\} = \left\{ \begin{matrix} h_1 & h_2 & h_3 & 0 & 0 & \cdots & 0 \\ & h_1 & h_2 & h_3 & 0 \cdots 0 & & \\ & & \cdot & \cdot & \cdot & \cdot & \cdot \\ & & & \cdot & \cdot & \cdot & \\ & & & & \cdot & & \end{matrix} \right\}. \tag{3.67}$$

Therefore, a convenient chain of groups in order to obtain nonspurious states, is given by $U(n) \supset U(n-1)$. In the next sections we shall show how to extend this scheme to obtain states of permutational symmetry.

1. The Chain $U(n) \supset U(n-1) \supset O(n-1) \supset S(n)$

Assume states written in terms of Jacobi vectors $\dot{\eta}^1\dot{\eta}^2\cdots\dot{\eta}^n$ and characterized by the chain $U(n) \supset U(n-1)$. Under the transpositions $(m-1, m)$, the Jacobi vectors $\dot{\eta}^s$, $1 \leqq s \leqq n-1$ transform as

$$\begin{aligned}(m-1, m)\dot{\eta}^{m-2} &= (m-1)^{-1}\dot{\eta}^{m-2} + [1-(m-1)^{-2}]^{1/2}\dot{\eta}^{m-1},\\ (m-1, m)\dot{\eta}^{m-1} &= [1-(m-1)^{-2}]^{1/2}\dot{\eta}^{m-2} - (m-1)^{-1}\dot{\eta}^{m-1},\end{aligned} \tag{3.68}$$

whereas all other vectors are unchanged. Comparing with the transformations Eq. (3.4) of the Yamanouchi bases for the IR $\{n-1, 1\}$ of $S(n)$, we find that the Jacobi vectors span a basis of this IR with the correspondence

$$\dot{\eta}^m, \quad 1 \leqq m \leqq n-1: \qquad r = (1^m 2 1^{n-m-1}), \qquad f = \{n-1, 1\}; \tag{3.69}$$

whereas

$$\dot{\eta}^n: \qquad r = (1^n), \qquad f = \{n\}. \tag{3.70}$$

The $(n-1)\times(n-1)$ matrices $\mathbf{D}^{\{n-1,1\}}(\mathbf{p})$ form a subgroup of $U(n-1)$ isomorphic to $S(n)$ so that we can introduce the chain $U(n) \supset U(n-1) \supset S(n)$. These matrices, moreover, are orthogonal and therefore admit the intermediate orthogonal group $O(n-1)$ to give the chain

$$\mathbf{U}(3n) \supset \mathscr{U}(3) \times U(n), \qquad U(n) \supset U(n-1) \supset O(n-1) \supset S(n). \tag{3.71}$$

Since we allow no excitation $\dot{\eta}^n$, we have to deal essentially with the chain

$$\mathbf{U}(3n-3) \supset \mathscr{U}(3) \times U(n-1), \qquad U(n-1) \supset O(n-1) \supset S(n). \tag{3.72}$$

To construct the states in the $U(n-1) \supset O(n-1)$ chain we can use a technique analogous to the one used in Section II. First, we demand that the polynomials $P(\dot{\eta}_j^s)$ corresponding to the chain Eq. (3.72) be of highest weight in $\mathscr{U}(3)$, that is,

$$i < j, \qquad \mathscr{C}_{ij}P(\dot{\eta}_j^s) = 0; \qquad \mathscr{C}_{ii}P(\dot{\eta}_j^s) = h_i P(\dot{\eta}_j^s), \qquad i = 1, 2, 3. \tag{3.73}$$

Since these polynomials are at the same time bases of $\mathbf{U}(3n-3)$ with IR $[N]$, they must already belong to the IR $\{h_1h_2h_3\}$ of $U(n-1)$, since the IR of

$\mathbf{U}(3n-3)$ in $\mathbf{U}(3n-3) \supset \mathscr{U}(3) \times U(n-1)$ has the decomposition

$$[N] \supset \sum_{\substack{h_1+h_2+h_3=N \\ h_1 \geqslant h_2 \geqslant h_3 \geqslant 0}} [h_1 h_2 h_3] \times \{h_1 h_2 h_3\}.$$

Now we demand that these polynomials be also of highest weight in $O(n-1)$ by imposing conditions analogous to Eq. (3.73) in terms of the generators

$$\dot{A}^{st} = \dot{C}^{st} - \dot{C}^{ts}, \qquad \dot{C}^{st} = \sum_{j=1}^{3} \dot{\eta}_j^s \dot{\xi}_j^t \tag{3.74}$$

of $O(n-1)$ as discussed by Moshinsky (*40*). Since $U(n-1)$ has only three partition numbers, $O(n-1)$ can have, at most, three partition numbers $(\lambda_1 \lambda_2 \lambda_3)$, which form the highest weight and characterize the IR of $O(n-1)$. The polynomials satisfying these equations have been derived explicitly by Chacón (*41*). For their full characterization, three additional operators with eigenvalues $\chi_1 \chi_2 \chi_3$ are needed; they have been discussed by Resnikoff (*42*). These operators are the generalizations of the operator $\mathbf{\Omega}$, which characterizes the $\mathscr{U}(3) \supset \mathscr{O}(3)$ chain. Having obtained the highest weight state, we may pass in $\mathscr{U}(3)$ to the chain $\mathscr{U}(3) \supset \mathscr{O}(3) \supset \mathscr{O}(2)$ by first deriving all states in the chain $\mathscr{U}(3) \supset \mathscr{U}(2) \supset \mathscr{U}(1)$ with the lowering operators Eq. (2.41) and then passing to the physical chain as discussed in Section II. In $O(n-1)$, on the other hand, the full set of states characterized by the chain

$$O(n-1) \supset O(n-2) \supset \cdots \supset O(2)$$

can be obtained by using the lowering operators given by Pang and Hecht (*43*).

The next step is then the construction of states in the chain $O(n-1) \supset S(n)$. To apply projection operators of IR of $S(n)$, we need the matrix elements of the permutations. Besides, additional quantum numbers are needed to distinguish IR of $S(n)$ repeated in a given IR of $O(n-1)$. The latter questions have been discussed in full detail elsewhere for the particular case of four particles (*12*). We will not give these details here, since we shall derive non-spurious four-particle states in the next section by another method. It is clear that the states in the chain Eq. (3.72) are characterized by

$$\left\langle \dot{\mathbf{x}} \middle| \begin{matrix} [h_1 h_2 h_3] \\ \Omega L M \end{matrix}, \begin{matrix} \{h_1 h_2 h_3\} \\ \chi_1 \chi_2 \chi_3 (\lambda_1 \lambda_2 \lambda_3) \varphi f r \end{matrix} \right\rangle, \tag{3.75}$$

the numbers $\chi_1 \chi_2 \chi_3$ and φ again referring to multiplicities of IR in the chain Eq. (3.72) of groups involved.

2. Translational-Invariant Four-Particle States

The four-particle states are BIR of the group $\mathscr{U}(3) \times U(4)$. Following the general procedure outlined in subsection B,1, we first pass to relative coordinates

$$\begin{aligned}\ddot{\boldsymbol{\eta}}^1 &= \tfrac{1}{2}(\boldsymbol{\eta}^1 + \boldsymbol{\eta}^4 - \boldsymbol{\eta}^2 - \boldsymbol{\eta}^3) = \boldsymbol{\eta}^1 + \boldsymbol{\eta}^4 - \ddot{\boldsymbol{\eta}}^4,\\ \ddot{\boldsymbol{\eta}}^2 &= \tfrac{1}{2}(\boldsymbol{\eta}^2 + \boldsymbol{\eta}^4 - \boldsymbol{\eta}^1 - \boldsymbol{\eta}^3) = \boldsymbol{\eta}^2 + \boldsymbol{\eta}^4 - \ddot{\boldsymbol{\eta}}^4,\\ \ddot{\boldsymbol{\eta}}^3 &= \tfrac{1}{2}(\boldsymbol{\eta}^3 + \boldsymbol{\eta}^4 - \boldsymbol{\eta}^1 - \boldsymbol{\eta}^2) = \boldsymbol{\eta}^3 + \boldsymbol{\eta}^4 - \ddot{\boldsymbol{\eta}}^4,\\ \ddot{\boldsymbol{\eta}}^4 &= \tfrac{1}{2}(\boldsymbol{\eta}^1 + \boldsymbol{\eta}^2 + \boldsymbol{\eta}^3 + \boldsymbol{\eta}^4).\end{aligned} \tag{3.76}$$

If now we consider Gelfand states

$$\left\langle \ddot{\mathbf{x}} \left| \begin{matrix}[h_1 h_2 h_3]\\ \Omega L M\end{matrix} ; \begin{matrix} h_1 & h_2 & h_3 & 0\\ h_1' & h_2' & h_3' & \\ q_1 & q_2 & & \\ r_1 & & & \end{matrix} \right. \right\rangle \tag{3.77}$$

with respect to $U(4) \supset U(3) \supset U(2) \supset U(1)$, elimination of center-of-mass motion requires that the weight component $\ddot{w}^4$ be zero and therefore $h_s' = h_s$, $s = 1, 2, 3$. We then have to deal essentially with a BIR of $\mathscr{U}(3) \times U(3)$ where $U(3)$ now refers to relative coordinates $\ddot{\boldsymbol{\eta}}^1\ddot{\boldsymbol{\eta}}^2\ddot{\boldsymbol{\eta}}^3$. Let us examine the transformation properties of the vectors $\ddot{\boldsymbol{\eta}}^1\ddot{\boldsymbol{\eta}}^2\ddot{\boldsymbol{\eta}}^3$ under $S(4)$. First, we observe that under $S(3)$ they transform exactly like $\boldsymbol{\eta}^1\boldsymbol{\eta}^2\boldsymbol{\eta}^3$. Then, applying to the vectors $\ddot{\boldsymbol{\eta}}^1\ddot{\boldsymbol{\eta}}^2\ddot{\boldsymbol{\eta}}^3$ the special elements $\mathbf{e}$, (1, 4)(2, 3), (2, 4)(1, 3), (3, 4)(1, 2) that form an invariant subgroup $D(2)$ (*30*, p. 43) of $S(4)$, we find that these elements are represented by the matrices

$$\begin{aligned}&\mathbf{e} = \begin{pmatrix} 1 & 0 & 0\\ 0 & 1 & 0\\ 0 & 0 & 1\end{pmatrix}, \qquad (1, 4)(2, 3) = \begin{pmatrix} 1 & 0 & 0\\ 0 & -1 & 0\\ 0 & 0 & -1\end{pmatrix},\\ &(2, 4)(1, 3) = \begin{pmatrix} -1 & 0 & 0\\ 0 & 1 & 0\\ 0 & 0 & -1\end{pmatrix}, \qquad (3, 4)(1, 2) = \begin{pmatrix} -1 & 0 & 0\\ 0 & -1 & 0\\ 0 & 0 & 1\end{pmatrix}.\end{aligned} \tag{3.78}$$

It is well known that $S(4)$ can be written as the semidirect product of $D(2)$ and $S(3)$ (*44*); that is, $S(4) = D(2) \wedge S(3)$, so that all elements of $S(4)$ are obtained as products of elements of $D(2)$ and $S(3)$. Comparing this semidirect product with $K(3) = A(3) \wedge S(3)$ considered in the preceding section, and observing that $D(2)$ is a subgroup of $A(3)$, we have that $K(3)$ contains $S(4)$. Since the reduction $U(3) \supset K(3) \supset S(3)$ was obtained in Section III,A, we could take over these states, written now in terms of the vectors $\ddot{\eta}^1\ddot{\eta}^2\ddot{\eta}^3$, and we need only to relate these states to BIR of $S(4)$. Since $S(4) = D(2) \wedge S(3)$, it suffices to operate with elements of $D(2)$ only. Now for a state with weight (w^1, w^2, w^3) we easily find that

$$\begin{aligned}(1,4)(2,3)|(w^1, w^2, w^3)\rangle &= (-1)^{w^2+w^3}|(w^1, w^2, w^3)\rangle,\\ (2,4)(1,3)|(w^1, w^2, w^3)\rangle &= (-1)^{w^1+w^3}|(w^1, w^2, w^3)\rangle,\\ (3,4)(1,2)|(w^1, w^2, w^3)\rangle &= (-1)^{w^1+w^2}|(w^1, w^2, w^3)\rangle.\end{aligned} \tag{3.79}$$

These properties suggest at once the following distinction: If (w^1, w^2, w^3) is odd-odd-even or even-even-odd, we have two elements of $D(2)$ that give a change of sign; if (w^1, w^2, w^3) is even-even-even or odd-odd-odd, we have the identity representation of $D(2)$.

We then examine the BIR of $U(3) \supset K(3) \supset S(3)$ discussed in Section III,A,4. If the weight is even-even-even or odd-odd-odd, all elements of $D(2)$ are represented by the identity element, so that the BIR of $S(3)$ must go into BIR of $S(4)$. By comparing the explicit form of the IR of $S(3)$ and $S(4)$, given for example by Hamermesh (*30*, pp. 225–226), we find in this case the correspondences

$$\mathbf{w} = \begin{cases}(e, e, e)\\(0, 0, 0)\end{cases}: \quad S(3) \to S(4): \quad \begin{array}{c}\{3\} \to \{4\}\\ \{21\} \to \{22\}\\ \{111\} \to \{1111\}.\end{array} \tag{3.80}$$

This applies to case (a) of Section III,A,4 and, in part, to cases (b) and (c), as indicated in Table III.

If the weight is odd-odd-even or even-even-odd, we must examine the correspondence in more detail. In cases (b) and (c) we know that the IR $\{3\}$ of $S(3)$ could correspond to $\{3\} \times \{1\} = \{4\} + \{31\}$ of $S(4)$. However, the possibility $\{4\}$ is ruled out by the transformation properties Eq. (3.79) under the elements of $D(2)$. Therefore the IR $\{3\}$ of $S(3)$ must correspond to the IR $\{31\}$ and to the Yamanouchi symbol $r = (1112)$ in $S(4)$. Then the ladder procedure Eq. (3.5) can be used to derive the next partner with $r = (1121)$ by means of the relation

$$(1121) = \left(\frac{9}{8}\right)^{1/2}[(3, 4) + \tfrac{1}{3}](1112) = \left(\frac{9}{8}\right)^{1/2}[(3, 4)(1, 2) + \tfrac{1}{3}](1112), \tag{3.81}$$

and yields the results given in Table III. Similarly, if the IR of $S(3)$ is $\{111\}$, we find that this corresponds to the Yamanouchi symbol $r = (1231)$ and to

TABLE III

FOUR-PARTICLE TRANSLATIONAL-INVARIANT STATES WITH PERMUTATIONAL SYMMETRY IN TERMS OF BIR OF $K(3)$

(w^1,w^2,w^3)	χ	fr: (e,e,e); $(0,0,0)$	fr: $(e,e,0)$; $(0,0,e)$	$\left\| \begin{matrix} \{h_1h_2h_3\} \\ \chi(\mathbf{w},f_w)\varphi fr \end{matrix} \right\rangle$
(u,u,u)		$\{4\}$	—	Derived by diagonalizing the operator Eq. (3.6)
		$\{22\}$	—	
		$\{1111\}$	—	
(u,u,w)	q_2 even	$\{4\}(1111)$	$\{31\}(1112)$	$\sqrt{\tfrac{1}{3}}[1 + (1,3) + (2,3)]$
		$\{22\}(1122)$	$\{31\}(1121)$	$\sqrt{\tfrac{2}{3}}[1 - \tfrac{1}{2}(1,3) - \tfrac{1}{2}(2,3)]$ $\Big\}\left\| \begin{matrix} \{h_1h_2h_3\} \\ (u,u,w)q_2 \end{matrix} \right\rangle$
		$\{22\}(1212)$	$\{31\}(1211)$	$\sqrt{\tfrac{1}{2}}[(2,3) - (1,3)]$
(u,u,w)	q_2 odd	$\{22\}(1122)$	$\{211\}(1123)$	$\sqrt{\tfrac{1}{2}}[-(2,3) + (1,3)]$
		$\{22\}(1212)$	$\{211\}(1213)$	$-\sqrt{\tfrac{2}{3}}[1 + \tfrac{1}{2}(1,3) + \tfrac{1}{2}(2,3)]$ $\Big\}\left\| \begin{matrix} \{h_1h_2h_3\} \\ (u,u,w)q_2 \end{matrix} \right\rangle$
		$\{1111\}(1234)$	$\{211\}(1231)$	$\sqrt{\tfrac{1}{3}}[1 - (1,3) - (2,3)]$
(u,v,w)	q_2	$\{4\}(1111)$	$\{31\}(1112)$	$\sqrt{\tfrac{1}{6}}[1 + (1,2) + (1,3) + (2,3) + (1,2,3) + (3,2,1)]$
		$\{22\}_1(1122)$	$\{31\}(1121)$	$\sqrt{\tfrac{1}{3}}[1 + (1,2) - \tfrac{1}{2}\{(1,3) + (2,3) + (1,2,3) + (3,2,1)\}]$
		$\{22\}_1(1212)$	$\{31\}(1211)$	$\tfrac{1}{2}[-(1,3) + (2,3) + (1,2,3) - (3,2,1)]$ $\Bigg\}\left\| \begin{matrix} \{h_1h_2h_3\} \\ (u,v,w)q_2 \end{matrix} \right\rangle$
		$\{22\}_2(1122)$	$\{211\}(1123)$	$\tfrac{1}{2}[(1,3) - (2,3) + (1,2,3) - (3,2,1)]$
		$\{22\}_2(1212)$	$\{211\}(1213)$	$-\sqrt{\tfrac{1}{3}}[1 - (1,2) + \tfrac{1}{2}\{(1,3) + (2,3) - (1,2,3) - (3,2,1)\}]$
		$\{1111\}(1234)$	$\{211\}(1231)$	$\sqrt{\tfrac{1}{6}}[1 - (1,2) - (1,3) - (2,3) + (1,2,3) + (3,2,1)]$

the IR {211} of $S(4)$, from which the next partner $r = (1213)$ is obtained as

$$(1213) = \left(\frac{9}{8}\right)^{1/2} [(3, 4) - \tfrac{1}{3}](1231) = -\left(\frac{9}{8}\right)^{1/2} [(3, 4)(1, 2) + \tfrac{1}{3}](1231). \quad (3.82)$$

The linear combination of four-particle Gelfand states given in Table III can be seen to be identical to those of three-particle Gelfand states given in Table II. This is because the phases for the three-particle states were already chosen in such a way as to make the correspondence one-to-one.

IV. Orbital Fractional Parentage Coefficients

In Section III we discussed several methods of constructing orbital n-particle states with permutational symmetry. To apply a given interaction or to evaluate expectation values of operators, it is very convenient to split these states in such a way as to single out the last particle or the last two particles, since in this way the n-particle problem reduces essentially to a one- or two-particle problem. We shall consider here the splitting of the orbital states or, in other words, the concept of fractional parentage coefficients (fpc) (*45*), and shall show that this splitting implies very definite transformations between chains of groups that allow us to handle the problem step by step.

Two types of fpc will be discussed here, one in which the residual $(n-1)$- or $(n-2)$-particle state will still be characterized by the IR of $S(n-1)$ or $S(n-2)$ and one in which the residual state will be characterized by a Gelfand state associated with a $U(n-1)$ or $U(n-2)$ group. For both types, though, full use will be made of the symmetry properties of the ho states and, in particular, of the characterization of the states by the IR of the $\mathscr{U}(3) \times U(n)$ group. Since our fpc differ from the usual ones of shell model theory, we shall abbreviate them in what follows as hfpc where h stands for harmonic oscillator.

A. One-Particle Fractional Parentage Coefficients

To calculate one-particle matrix elements of shell model states, we would like to split the n-particle states into product states of $n-1$ particles and of particle n. The product states span an IR $[N0^{3n-1}]$ of $\mathrm{U}(3n)$ in the chain

$$\begin{gathered} \mathrm{U}(3n) \supset \mathrm{U}(3n-3) \oplus \mathrm{U}(3) \supset (\mathscr{U}'(3) \times U(n-1)) \oplus (\mathscr{U}''(3) \times U(1)) \\ U(n-1) \supset S(n-1), \qquad U(1) \supset S(1), \end{gathered} \quad (4.1)$$

in which the rows of the IR of $U(n-1)$ and $U(1)$ are characterized, in part, by $S(n-1)$ and $S(1)$, respectively, and where the IR of $\mathbf{U}(3n-3)$ is $[N'0^{3n-4}]$ and the IR of $\mathbf{U}(3)$ is $[N-N']$. To split the n-particle states, therefore, means to change the chain

$$\mathbf{U}(3n) \supset \mathscr{U}(3) \times U(n), \qquad U(n) \supset S(n) \supset S(n-1) \supset \cdots \tag{4.2}$$

into the chain Eq. (4.1) by appropriate transformation coefficients. This can be done in two steps. First, we may couple the product states with a Wigner coefficient of $\mathscr{U}(3)$ to states that transform irreducibly under the group $\mathscr{U}'(3) \equiv \mathscr{U}''(3) \equiv \mathscr{U}(3)$, thereby introducing the chain

$$\mathbf{U}(3n) \supset \mathscr{U}(3) \times [U(n-1) \oplus U(1)], \qquad U(n-1) \supset S(n-1).$$

But since in the chain $\mathbf{U}(3n) \supset \mathscr{U}(3) \times U(n)$ the IR of $\mathscr{U}(3)$ determines the IR of $U(n)$, if $\mathbf{U}(3n)$ has IR $[N0^{3n-1}]$, this chain is really already

$$\begin{aligned} &\mathbf{U}(3n) \supset \mathscr{U}(3) \times U(n) \supset \mathscr{U}(3) \times [U(n-1) \oplus U(1)], \\ &U(n-1) \supset S(n-1). \end{aligned} \tag{4.3}$$

The second coefficient, which connects the chains Eqs. (4.3) and (4.2), is then a transformation coefficient for different chains of subgroups of $U(n)$.

Before proceeding to give the explicit expression of the one-particle hfpc, we note the convenience of first vector coupling the states of $n-1$ particles with the state of particle n, that is, having the states

$$\begin{aligned} &\left[\left| \begin{matrix} [h_1'h_2'h_3'] \\ \Omega'L' \end{matrix}, \begin{matrix} \{h_1'h_2'h_3'\} \\ \chi'f'r' \end{matrix} \right\rangle_{1\cdots n-1} \left| \begin{matrix} [h''] \\ l'' \end{matrix} \right\rangle_n \right]_{LM} \\ &\equiv \sum_{M'm''} \left\{ \langle L'l''M'm''|LM\rangle \left| \begin{matrix} [h_1'h_2'h_3'] \\ \Omega'L'M' \end{matrix}, \begin{matrix} \{h_1'h_2'h_3'\} \\ \chi'f'r' \end{matrix} \right\rangle_{1\cdots n-1} \left| \begin{matrix} [h''] \\ l''m'' \end{matrix} \right\rangle_n \right\} \end{aligned} \tag{4.4}$$

where, when necessary, we shall put outside the kets $|\ \rangle$ indices to indicate the set of particle, for example, $1 \cdots n-1$, or the particle, for example, n, to which they belong. These vector-coupled states will be useful, since later they will allow us to use the standard techniques of Racah algebra for the angular momenta involved.

Using Eq. (4.4), we obtain straightforwardly that the n-particle state could be decomposed in the form

$$\left|\begin{matrix}[h_1h_2h_3] \\ \Omega LM\end{matrix}, \begin{matrix}\{h_1h_2h_3\} \\ \chi fr\end{matrix}\right\rangle_{1\cdots n}$$

$$= \sum_{h_1'h_2'h_3'} \sum_{\Omega'L'} \sum_{\chi'f'r'} \sum_{l''} \left\{\left[\left|\begin{matrix}[h_1'h_2'h_3'] \\ \Omega'L'\end{matrix}, \begin{matrix}\{h_1'h_2'h_3'\} \\ \chi'f'r'\end{matrix}\right\rangle_{1\cdots n-1} \left|\begin{matrix}[h''] \\ l''\end{matrix}\right\rangle_n\right]_{LM}\right.$$

$$\times \left.\left\langle\begin{matrix}[h_1'h_2'h_3'] \\ \Omega'L'\end{matrix}, \begin{matrix}\{h_1'h_2'h_3'\} \\ \chi'f'r'\end{matrix}; \begin{matrix}[h''] \\ l''\end{matrix}\right|\left\}\begin{matrix}[h_1h_2h_3] \\ \Omega L\end{matrix}, \begin{matrix}\{h_1h_2h_3\} \\ \chi fr\end{matrix}\right\rangle\right\}, \tag{4.5}$$

where the last term on the right-hand side would be the hfpc. This hfpc is actually the scalar product of the state Eq. (4.4) and the n-particle state on the left-hand side of Eq. (4.5), and so could be represented in the standard Dirac bracket notation. We replace though the line in the bracket by $|\}$ and eliminate the coupling bracket $[\,]_L$ in the bra to make the coefficients agree with the usual notation for fpc.

We shall show in the next paragraph that the hfpc factorizes as follows

$$\left\langle\begin{matrix}[h_1'h_2'h_3'] \\ \Omega'L'\end{matrix}, \begin{matrix}\{h_1'h_2'h_3'\} \\ \chi'f'r'\end{matrix}; \begin{matrix}[h''] \\ l''\end{matrix}\right|\left\}\begin{matrix}[h_1h_2h_3] \\ \Omega L\end{matrix}; \begin{matrix}\{h_1h_2h_3\} \\ \chi fr\end{matrix}\right\rangle$$

$$= \left\langle\begin{matrix}[h_1'h_2'h_3'] \\ \Omega'L'\end{matrix}, \begin{matrix}[h''] \\ l''\end{matrix}\middle|\begin{matrix}[h_1h_2h_3] \\ \Omega L\end{matrix}\right\rangle \left\langle\begin{matrix}\{h_1h_2h_3\} \\ \{h_1'h_2'h_3'\} \\ \chi'f'r'\end{matrix}\middle|\begin{matrix}\{h_1h_2h_3\} \\ \chi fr\end{matrix}\right\rangle. \tag{4.6}$$

The first factor on the right-hand side of Eq. (4.6) is a reduced Wigner coefficient of $\mathscr{U}(3)$, while the second is the transformation bracket between the different chains of subgroups of $U(n)$ in Eqs. (4.2) and (4.3).

We note that the state Eq. (4.4), before being coupled to a definite angular momentum L and projection M, is characterized by IR of the groups in the chain Eq. (4.1) plus the rotation subgroups $\mathcal{O}'^{+}(3) \supset \mathcal{O}'^{+}(2)$, $\mathcal{O}''^{+}(3) \supset \mathcal{O}''^{+}(2)$ of $\mathscr{U}'(3)$, $\mathscr{U}''(3)$ respectively. To get from these states to those characterized by IR of the groups in the chain Eq. (4.3) plus the rotation subgroups $\mathcal{O}^{+}(3) \supset \mathcal{O}^{+}(2)$, we must couple the product of BIR

$$\left|\begin{matrix}[h_1'h_2'h_3'] \\ \Omega'L'M'\end{matrix}\right\rangle, \tag{4.7a}$$

$$\left|\begin{matrix}[h''] \\ l''m''\end{matrix}\right\rangle, \tag{4.7b}$$

in the $\mathscr{U}(3) \supset \mathcal{O}^+(3) \supset \mathcal{O}^+(2)$ chain to a definite BIR

$$\left| \begin{matrix} [h_1h_2h_3] \\ \Omega LM \end{matrix} \right\rangle, \tag{4.7c}$$

with the help of the Wigner coefficients of $\mathscr{U}(3)$ in the latter chain

$$\left\langle \begin{matrix} [h_1'h_2'h_3'] \\ \Omega' L' M' \end{matrix} ; \begin{matrix} [h''] \\ l''m'' \end{matrix} \middle| \begin{matrix} [h_1h_2h_3] \\ \Omega LM \end{matrix} \right\rangle. \tag{4.8}$$

We shall indicate in Section IV,F how to derive these coefficients explicitly. Here we note only that had we coupled the state of particles $1, \ldots, n-1$ with the state of particle n by the coefficients Eq. (4.8), the scalar product of the resulting state with the state of n particles on the left-hand side of Eq. (4.5) would reduce to the transformation bracket appearing in the last term of Eq. (4.6). This bracket is the one connecting the BIR of $U(n)$ characterized by $\{h_1h_2h_3\}$, reduced through the two different chains of subgroups in Eqs. (4.3) and (4.2). Using the orthogonality properties of the Wigner coefficients we could immediately arrive at the factorization given in Eq. (4.6) if we define the reduced Wigner coefficient by

$$\left\langle \begin{matrix} [h_1'h_2'h_3'] \\ \Omega' L' \end{matrix} ; \begin{matrix} [h''] \\ l'' \end{matrix} \middle| \begin{matrix} [h_1h_2h_3] \\ \Omega L \end{matrix} \right\rangle = \sum_{M'm''} \left\{ \langle L'l''M'm'' | LM \rangle \left\langle \begin{matrix} [h_1'h_2'h_3'] \\ \Omega' L' M' \end{matrix} ; \begin{matrix} [h''] \\ l''m'' \end{matrix} \middle| \begin{matrix} [h_1h_2h_3] \\ \Omega LM \end{matrix} \right\rangle \right\}. \tag{4.9}$$

Clearly, the reduced Wigner coefficient is independent of M (*32*, p. 115) and has the selection rule

$$h_1' + h_2' + h_3' + h'' = h_1 + h_2 + h_3 \tag{4.10}$$

The second factor in Eq. (4.6) is clearly the scalar product of states characterized by the chain of groups in Eqs. (4.2) and (4.3), respectively. These two chains of groups agree in all the subgroups $S(n-1) \supset \cdots \supset S(1)$. Therefore, the second factor in Eq. (4.6) depends only on the IR f', and not on r', of $S(n-1)$. Furthermore, r' must be a part of r; that is, $r = r'r_n$, and so r_n is fully determined once f and f' are given. The second factor in Eq. (4.6) is, therefore, independent of r, r' and so these indices will be suppressed in what follows.

The second factor in Eq. (4.6) can, for example, be evaluated if the transformation brackets between the states Eq. (4.5) and the Gelfand states are known. Then we obtain

$$\left\langle \begin{matrix} \{h_1h_2h_3\} \\ \{h_1'h_2'h_3'\} \\ \chi' f' \end{matrix} \middle| \begin{matrix} \{h_1h_2h_3\} \\ \chi f \end{matrix} \right\rangle$$

$$= \delta(f' \times \{1\}, f)$$

$$\times |f'|^{-1} \sum_{r'} \sum_{\{k_{st}\}_{n-2}} \left\{ \left\langle \begin{matrix} h_1h_2h_3 0 \cdots\cdots 0 \\ h_1'h_2'h_3' 0 \cdots 0 \\ \chi' f' r' \end{matrix} \middle| \begin{matrix} h_1 \quad h_2 \quad h_3 \quad 0 \cdots\cdots 0 \\ h_1' \quad h_2' \quad h_3' \quad 0 \cdots 0 \\ \{k_{st}\}_{n-2} \end{matrix} \right\rangle \right.$$

$$\left. \times \left\langle \begin{matrix} h_1 \quad h_2 \quad h_3 \quad 0 \cdots\cdots 0 \\ h_1' \quad h_2' \quad h_3' \quad 0 \cdots 0 \\ \{k_{st}\}_{n-2} \end{matrix} \middle| \begin{matrix} \{h_1h_2h_3\} \\ \chi f r' r_n \end{matrix} \right\rangle \right\}, \tag{4.11}$$

where, for short, we denoted the lower part of a Gelfand pattern by

$$\{k_{st}\}_m = \left\{ \begin{matrix} k_{1m} \quad k_{2m} \quad k_{3m} \quad 0 \cdots\cdots 0 \\ k_{1m-1} \quad k_{2m-1} \quad k_{3m-1} \cdots 0 \\ \cdots\cdots\cdots\cdots \\ k_{11} \end{matrix} \right\}. \tag{4.12}$$

B. Two-Particle Fractional Parentage Coefficients

The calculation of two-particle matrix elements implies the use of two-particle fpc. These may be obtained, for example, by repeating the procedure of Section IV,A, that is, by splitting off particle $n-1$ and then recoupling to get an expansion of n-particle states in terms of the product states

$$\left[\left[\left| \begin{matrix} [h_1'h_2'h_3'] \\ \Omega' L' \end{matrix}, \begin{matrix} \{h_1'h_2'h_3'\} \\ \chi' f' r' \end{matrix} \right\rangle_{1\cdots n-2} \left[\left| \begin{matrix} [h'''] \\ l''' \end{matrix} \right\rangle_{n-1} \left| \begin{matrix} [h''] \\ l'' \end{matrix} \right\rangle_n \right]_{L''} \right]_{LM}. \tag{4.13}$$

Again we used the shorthand notation of Eq. (4.4) to indicate the couplings. The expansion of the n-particle states of Eq. (4.5) in terms of the foregoing products is then given by the two-particle hfpc

$$\left\langle \begin{matrix}[h_1'h_2'h_3'] \\ \Omega'L'\end{matrix}, \begin{matrix}\{h_1'h_2'h_3'\} \\ \chi'f'r'\end{matrix}; \begin{bmatrix}[h'''] \\ l'''\end{bmatrix}, \begin{matrix}[h''] \\ l''\end{matrix}\Bigg]_{L''} \Bigg| \begin{matrix}[h_1h_2h_3] \\ \Omega L\end{matrix}, \begin{matrix}\{h_1h_2h_3\} \\ \chi fr\end{matrix} \right\rangle$$

$$= \sum_{\bar{h}_1\bar{h}_2\bar{h}_3} \sum_{\bar{\Omega}\bar{L}\bar{\chi}} \Bigg\{ [(2\bar{L}+1)(2L''+1)]^{1/2} W(L'l'''Ll''; \bar{L}L'')$$

$$\times \left\langle \begin{matrix}[h_1'h_2'h_3'] \\ \Omega'L'\end{matrix}; \begin{matrix}[h'''] \\ l'''\end{matrix} \middle| \begin{matrix}[\bar{h}_1\bar{h}_2\bar{h}_3] \\ \bar{\Omega}\bar{L}\end{matrix} \right\rangle \left\langle \begin{matrix}[\bar{h}_1\bar{h}_2\bar{h}_3] \\ \bar{\Omega}\bar{L}\end{matrix}; \begin{matrix}[h''] \\ l''\end{matrix} \middle| \begin{matrix}[h_1h_2h_3] \\ \Omega L\end{matrix} \right\rangle$$

$$\times\, \delta(f' \times \{1\}, \bar{f})\, \delta(\bar{f} \times \{1\}, f)\, \delta_{h_1+h_2+h_3-\bar{h}_1-\bar{h}_2-\bar{h}_3, h''}\, \delta_{\bar{h}_1+\bar{h}_2+\bar{h}_3-h_1'-h_2'-h_3', h'''}$$

$$\times \left\langle \begin{matrix}\{\bar{h}_1\bar{h}_2\bar{h}_3\} \\ \{h_1'h_2'h_3'\} \\ \chi'f'\end{matrix} \middle| \begin{matrix}\{\bar{h}_1\bar{h}_2\bar{h}_3\} \\ \bar{\chi}\bar{f}\end{matrix} \right\rangle \left\langle \begin{matrix}\{h_1h_2h_3\} \\ \{\bar{h}_1\bar{h}_2\bar{h}_3\} \\ \bar{\chi}\bar{f}\end{matrix} \middle| \begin{matrix}\{h_1h_2h_3\} \\ \chi f\end{matrix} \right\rangle \Bigg\} \tag{4.14}$$

where $W(abcd; ef)$ is a Racah coefficient and the other coefficients are as defined earlier. We note that the Yamanouchi symbol $r = r'r_{n-1}r_n$; thus the knowledge of f and $r_{n-1}r_n$ specifies not only f' but also $\bar{f}$. In fact, in the left-hand side of Eq. (4.14) we could have suppressed r and r' if we had introduced the additional partition $\bar{f}$ characterizing the intermediate $(n-1)$-particle state. Some of the δ's in Eq. (4.14) serve to indicate that f' and $\bar{f}$, $\bar{f}$ and f are related by the usual Littlewood rules when we add one block, whereas the others are due to Eq. (4.10).

C. Pair Fractional Parentage Coefficients

In the hfpc obtained previously, the residual $(n-1)$-particle or $(n-2)$-particle states were still characterized by the IR of $S(n-1)$ or $S(n-2)$. In the evaluation of the matrix elements of one-body or two-body operators, we do not really care which way we characterize the $(n-1)$-particle or $(n-2)$-particle states, since we shall see that the operators will affect only the last or last two particles. We have then, for example, the possibility of characterizing the $(n-1)$-particle state as a Gelfand state in $U(n-1)$, in which case, from the analysis of the preceding section, we get

$$\left|\begin{matrix}[h_1h_2h_3] \\ \Omega LM\end{matrix}, \begin{matrix}\{h_1h_2h_3\} \\ \chi fr\end{matrix}\right\rangle_{1\cdots n}$$

$$= \sum_{\{k_{st}\}_{n-1}} \left\{ \left|\begin{matrix}[h_1h_2h_3] \\ \Omega LM\end{matrix}, \begin{matrix}h_1 \quad h_2 \quad h_3 \quad 0\cdots 0 \\ \{k_{st}\}_{n-1}\end{matrix}\right\rangle_{1\cdots n} \right.$$

$$\left. \times \left\langle \begin{matrix}h_1 \quad h_2 \quad h_3 \quad 0\cdots 0 \\ \{k_{st}\}_{n-1}\end{matrix} \middle| \begin{matrix}\{h_1h_2h_3\} \\ \chi fr\end{matrix}\right\rangle \right\}$$

$$= \sum_{\substack{h_1'h_2'h_3' \\ \Omega'L'}} \sum_{l''} \sum_{\{k'_{st}\}_{n-2}} \left\{ \left[\left|\begin{matrix}[h_1'h_2'h_3'] \\ \Omega'L'\end{matrix}, \begin{matrix}h_1' \quad h_2' \quad h_3' \quad 0\cdots 0 \\ \{k'_{st}\}_{n-2}\end{matrix}\right\rangle_{1\cdots n-1} \left|\begin{matrix}[h''] \\ l''\end{matrix}\right\rangle \right]_{LM} \right.$$

$$\left. \times \left\langle \begin{matrix}[h_1'h_2'h_3'] \\ \Omega'L'\end{matrix}; \begin{matrix}[h''] \\ l''\end{matrix} \middle| \begin{matrix}[h_1h_2h_3] \\ \Omega L\end{matrix}\right\rangle \left\langle \begin{matrix}h_1 \quad h_2 \quad h_3 \quad 0\cdots\cdots 0 \\ h_1' \quad h_2' \quad h_3' \quad 0\cdots 0 \\ \{k'_{st}\}_{n-2}\end{matrix} \middle| \begin{matrix}\{h_1h_2h_3\} \\ \chi fr\end{matrix}\right\rangle \right\} \tag{4.15}$$

where $\{k_{st}\}_{n-1}$ in the second line is, of course, identical to

$$\begin{matrix}h_1' \quad h_2' \quad h_3' \quad 0\cdots 0 \\ \{k'_{st}\}_{n-2}\end{matrix}$$

in the last term.

The pair fpc (which we denote this way to distinguish it from the two-particle fpc of the preceding subsection) in which the $(n-2)$-particle state is characterized by a Gelfand state of $U(n-2)$, can be obtained in the following way.

First, we transform the n-particle state into a Gelfand state with respect to $U(n)$, as indicated in the second line of Eq. (4.15). Then we introduce new vectors $\boldsymbol{\eta}'$ by the definition

$$\boldsymbol{\eta}'^{s} = \boldsymbol{\eta}^{s}, \qquad s = 1, 2, \ldots, n-2,$$

$$\boldsymbol{\eta}'^{n-1} = \frac{1}{\sqrt{2}}(\boldsymbol{\eta}^{n-1} + \boldsymbol{\eta}^{n}),$$

$$\boldsymbol{\eta}'^{n} = \frac{1}{\sqrt{2}}(-\boldsymbol{\eta}^{n-1} + \boldsymbol{\eta}^{n}), \tag{4.16}$$

which implies the same relation between $\mathbf{x}'$ and $\mathbf{x}$. This transformation corresponds to a rotation by $\pi/2$ in the two-dimensional space of the vector indices $n-1, n$. The operator corresponding to an infinitesimal rotation of this type is, of course

$$\Lambda^{n-1\,n} = \tfrac{1}{2}(C^{n-1\,n} - C^{n\,n-1}); \tag{4.17a}$$

thus the operator associated with a finite rotation by $\pi/2$ will be

$$\mathcal{O}^{n-1\,n}\left(\frac{\pi}{2}\right) = \exp\left(\frac{\pi}{2}\Lambda^{n-1\,n}\right). \tag{4.17b}$$

As the operator Eq. (4.17a) is an invariant of the subgroup $U(n-2)$ of $U(n)$, this will also hold for the operator Eq. (4.17b), which implies that the application of Eq. (4.17b) to a Gelfand state can only change the second row of the Gelfand pattern, and so the matrix element of Eq. (4.17b) can be written as

$$\left\langle \begin{matrix} h_1 & h_2 & h_3 & 0\cdots\cdots 0 \\ h_1' & h_2' & h_3' & 0\cdots 0 \\ & \{k_{st}'\}_{n-2} & & \end{matrix} \middle| \mathcal{O}^{n-1\,n}\left(\frac{\pi}{2}\right) \middle| \begin{matrix} h_1 & h_2 & h_3 & 0\cdots 0 \\ & \{k_{st}\}_{n-1} & & \end{matrix} \right\rangle \tag{4.18}$$

where the last $n-2$ rows of $\{k_{st}\}_{n-1}$ coincide with $\{k_{st}'\}_{n-2}$. The matrix element Eq. (4.18) will clearly depend only on the first three rows of bra and ket.

We can now use the matrix element Eq. (4.18) to transform the Gelfand state in the second row of Eq. (4.15) into a Gelfand state in the primed coordinates of Eq. (4.16) and then separate the relative coordinate $\mathbf{x}'^n$ from the rest, getting finally

$$\left\langle \mathbf{x}^1 \cdots \mathbf{x}^n \middle| \begin{matrix} [h_1h_2h_3] \\ \Omega LM \end{matrix}, \begin{matrix} \{h_1h_2h_3\} \\ \chi fr \end{matrix} \right\rangle$$

$$= \sum_{\substack{h_1'h_2'h_3' \\ \Omega'L'l''}} \sum_{\{k_{st}'\}_{n-2}} \left\{ \left[\left\langle \mathbf{x}'^1 \cdots \mathbf{x}'^{n-1} \middle| \begin{matrix} [h_1'h_2'h_3'] \\ \Omega'L' \end{matrix}, \begin{matrix} h_1' & h_2' & h_3' & 0\cdots 0 \\ & \{k_{st}'\}_{n-2} & & \end{matrix} \right\rangle \right.\right.$$

$$\times \left.\left\langle \mathbf{x}'^n \middle| \begin{matrix} [h''] \\ l'' \end{matrix} \right\rangle \right]_{LM}$$

$$\times \left\langle \begin{matrix} [h_1'h_2'h_3'] \\ \Omega'L' \end{matrix}, \begin{matrix} h_1' & h_2' & h_3' & 0\cdots 0 \\ & \{k_{st}'\}_{n-2} & & \end{matrix}; \begin{matrix} [h''] \\ l'' \end{matrix} \middle\| \begin{matrix} [h_1h_2h_3] \\ \Omega L \end{matrix}, \begin{matrix} \{h_1h_2h_3\} \\ \chi fr \end{matrix} \right\rangle \Bigg\} \tag{4.19}$$

where the last term in Eq. (4.19) is the pair fractional parentage coefficient for shell model states given explicitly by

$$\left\langle \begin{matrix}[h_1'h_2'h_3'] \\ \Omega'L'\end{matrix}, \begin{matrix} h_1' \;\; h_2' \;\; h_3' \;\; 0\cdots 0 \\ \{k_{st}'\}_{n-2}\end{matrix}; \begin{matrix}[h''] \\ l''\end{matrix} \right\rangle \left. \begin{matrix}[h_1h_2h_3] \\ \Omega L\end{matrix}; \begin{matrix}\{h_1h_2h_3\} \\ \chi fr\end{matrix}\right\rangle$$

$$= \left\langle \begin{matrix}[h_1'h_2'h_3'] \\ \Omega'L'\end{matrix}; \begin{matrix}[h''] \\ l''\end{matrix} \middle| \begin{matrix}[h_1h_2h_3] \\ \Omega L\end{matrix}\right\rangle$$

$$\times \sum_{\{k_{st}\}_{n-1}} \left\{ \left\langle \begin{matrix} h_1 \;\; h_2 \;\; h_3 \;\; 0\cdots\cdots 0 \\ h_1' \;\; h_2' \;\; h_3' \;\; 0\cdots 0 \\ \{k_{st}'\}_{n-2}\end{matrix} \middle| \mathcal{O}^{n-1\,n}\left(\frac{\pi}{2}\right) \middle| \begin{matrix} h_1 \;\; h_2 \;\; h_3 \;\; 0\cdots 0 \\ \{k_{st}\}_{n-1}\end{matrix}\right\rangle \right.$$

$$\left. \times \left\langle \begin{matrix} h_1 \;\; h_2 \;\; h_3 \;\; 0\cdots 0 \\ \{k_{st}\}_{n-1}\end{matrix} \middle| \begin{matrix}\{h_1h_2h_3\} \\ \chi fr\end{matrix}\right\rangle \right\}. \tag{4.20}$$

The summation over $\{k_{st}\}_{n-1}$ in Eq. (4.20) actually reduces to a summation over k_{sn-1}, $s = 1, \ldots, n-1$ only because of the remark after Eq. (4.17b). In Eq. (4.20), the first term of the right-hand side is the reduced Wigner coefficient of $\mathscr{U}(3)$ explicitly determined in Section IV,F. The last term was discussed in detail in Section III,A, where it was explicitly derived for a three-particle system. The middle term, the matrix element of $\mathcal{O}^{n-1\,n}(\pi/2)$, could be obtained from the matrix elements of transpositions with respect to Gelfand states, as clearly

$$\mathcal{O}^{n-1\,n}\left(\frac{\pi}{2}\right) = (1, n-1)(2, n)\mathcal{O}^{12}\left(\frac{\pi}{2}\right)(1, n-1)(2, n) \tag{4.21}$$

where the parentheses stand for the corresponding transpositions. The matrix element of $\mathcal{O}^{12}(\pi/2)$ is trivial, as it corresponds to the effect of a rotation on a BIR of $U(2)$.

With a simple modification, the method just outlined can also be applied to translational-invariant states. Suppose that these states are given in terms of Jacobi vectors $\dot{\boldsymbol{\eta}}^s$ $1 \leqq s \leqq n-1$. Introduce new vectors $\dot{\boldsymbol{\eta}}'^s$ by

$$\begin{aligned}
\dot{\boldsymbol{\eta}}'^s &= \dot{\boldsymbol{\eta}}^s, \qquad s = 1, 2, \ldots, n-3, \\
\dot{\boldsymbol{\eta}}'^{n-2} &= -\left[\frac{n}{2(n-1)}\right]^{1/2} \dot{\boldsymbol{\eta}}^{n-2} - \left[\frac{n-2}{2(n-1)}\right]^{1/2} \dot{\boldsymbol{\eta}}^{n-1} \\
\dot{\boldsymbol{\eta}}'^{n-1} &= \left[\frac{n-2}{2(n-1)}\right]^{1/2} \dot{\boldsymbol{\eta}}^{n-2} - \left[\frac{n}{2(n-1)}\right]^{1/2} \dot{\boldsymbol{\eta}}^{n-1} \\
&= \sqrt{\tfrac{1}{2}}(-\boldsymbol{\eta}^{n-1} + \boldsymbol{\eta}^n),
\end{aligned} \tag{4.22}$$

which implies the same relation between $\dot{\mathbf{x}}'$ and $\dot{\mathbf{x}}$, so that the operator associated with this finite rotation is

$$\mathcal{O}^{n-2\,n-1}(\phi) = \exp[\tfrac{1}{2}\phi(\dot{C}^{n-2\,n-1} - \dot{C}^{n-1\,n-2})] \tag{4.23}$$

with

$$\cos(\tfrac{1}{2}\phi) = -\left[\frac{n}{2(n-1)}\right]^{1/2}, \qquad \sin(\tfrac{1}{2}\phi) = -\left[\frac{n-2}{2(n-1)}\right]^{1/2}.$$

Starting with the states

$$\left\langle \dot{\mathbf{x}} \middle| \begin{matrix}[h_1h_2h_3]\\ \Omega LM\end{matrix}, \begin{matrix}\{h_1h_2h_3\}\\ \chi fr\end{matrix} \right\rangle, \tag{4.24}$$

we first transform to Gelfand states with respect to $U(n-1)$, apply the operator $\mathcal{O}^{n-2\,n-1}(\phi)$, and split off the last vector by a Wigner coefficient of $\mathscr{U}(3)$ to obtain, in complete analogy to Eq. (4.19), that

$$\begin{aligned}
&\left\langle \dot{\mathbf{x}}^1 \cdots \dot{\mathbf{x}}^{n-1} \middle| \begin{matrix}[h_1h_2h_3]\\ \Omega LM\end{matrix}; \begin{matrix}\{h_1h_2h_3\}\\ \chi fr\end{matrix} \right\rangle \\
&= \sum_{\substack{h_1'h_2'h_3'\\ \Omega'L'l''}} \sum_{\{k_{st}'\}_{n-3}} \left\{ \left[\left\langle \mathbf{x}'^1 \cdots \mathbf{x}'^{n-2} \middle| \begin{matrix}[h_1'h_2'h_3']\\ \Omega'L'\end{matrix}, \begin{matrix}\{h_1'h_2'h_3'\}\\ \{k_{st}'\}_{n-3}\end{matrix} \right\rangle \left\langle \mathbf{x}'^{n-1} \middle| \begin{matrix}[h'']\\ l''\end{matrix} \right\rangle \right]_{LM} \right. \\
&\quad \times \left. \left\langle \begin{matrix}[h_1'h_2'h_3']\\ \Omega'L'\end{matrix}, \begin{matrix}\{h_1'h_2'h_3'\}\\ \{k_{st}'\}_{n-3}\end{matrix}; \begin{matrix}[h'']\\ l''\end{matrix} \middle|\middle\} \begin{matrix}[h_1h_2h_3]\\ \Omega L\end{matrix}, \begin{matrix}\{h_1h_2h_3\}\\ \chi fr\end{matrix} \right\rangle \right\},
\end{aligned} \tag{4.25}$$

where the last term is the pair fractional parentage coefficient given by

$$\begin{aligned}
&\left\langle \begin{matrix}[h_1'h_2'h_3']\\ \Omega'L'\end{matrix}, \begin{matrix}\{h_1'h_2'h_3'\}\\ \{k_{st}'\}_{n-3}\end{matrix}; \begin{matrix}[h'']\\ l''\end{matrix} \middle|\middle\} \begin{matrix}[h_1h_2h_3]\\ \Omega L\end{matrix}, \begin{matrix}\{h_1h_2h_3\}\\ \chi fr\end{matrix} \right\rangle \\
&= \left\langle \begin{matrix}[h_1'h_2'h_3']\\ \Omega'L'\end{matrix}, \begin{matrix}[h'']\\ l''\end{matrix} \middle| \begin{matrix}[h_1h_2h_3]\\ \Omega L\end{matrix} \right\rangle \\
&\quad \times \sum_{\{k_{st}\}_{n-2}} \left\{ \left\langle \begin{matrix} h_1 \quad h_2 \quad h_3 \quad 0 \cdots\cdots 0 \\ h_1' \quad h_2' \quad h_3' \quad 0 \cdots 0 \\ \{k_{st}'\}_{n-3} \end{matrix} \middle| \mathcal{O}^{n-2\,n-1}(\phi) \middle| \begin{matrix} h_1 \quad h_2 \quad h_3 \quad 0 \cdots 0 \\ \{k_{st}\}_{n-2} \end{matrix} \right\rangle \right. \\
&\quad \times \left. \left\langle \begin{matrix} h_1 \quad h_2 \quad h_3 \quad 0 \cdots 0 \\ \{k_{st}\}_{n-2} \end{matrix} \middle| \begin{matrix}\{h_1h_2h_3\}\\ \chi fr\end{matrix} \right\rangle \right\},
\end{aligned} \tag{4.26}$$

and all the transformation coefficients now apply to $U(n-1)$ rather than $U(n)$. Similarly to Eq. (4.20) the summation extends only to k_{sn-2}, $s = 1, \ldots, n-2$.

D. Fractional Parentage Coefficients for Three-Particle Shell Model States

To get the single-particle fpc we use Eq. (4.15) but we write the states with respect to particles 1 and 2 as Gelfand states. Then

$$\left|\begin{matrix}[h_1h_2h_3] \\ \Omega LM\end{matrix}, \begin{matrix}\{h_1h_2h_3\} \\ \chi fr\end{matrix}\right\rangle_{123}$$

$$= \sum_{\substack{h_1'h_2' \\ \Omega'L'}} \sum_{\substack{h'' \\ l''}} \left\{ \delta_{h'',h_1+h_2+h_3-h_1'-h_2'} \left[\left|\begin{matrix}[h_1' & h_2' & 0] \\ & \Omega'L' & \end{matrix}, \begin{matrix}h_1' & h_2' \\ k_{11}' & \end{matrix}\right\rangle_{1,2} \left|\begin{matrix}[h''] \\ l''\end{matrix}\right\rangle_3 \right]_{LM} \right.$$

$$\left. \times \left\langle \begin{matrix}[h_1'h_2'0] \\ \Omega'L'\end{matrix}; \begin{matrix}[h''] \\ l''\end{matrix} \middle| \begin{matrix}[h_1h_2h_3] \\ \Omega L\end{matrix} \right\rangle \left\langle \begin{matrix}h_1 \quad h_2 \quad h_3 \\ h_1' \quad h_2' \\ k_{11}'\end{matrix} \middle| \begin{matrix}\{h_1h_2h_3\} \\ \chi fr\end{matrix} \right\rangle \right\}. \tag{4.27}$$

Except for case (a) of Eq. (3.22a) of a single shell, the last coefficient appearing in Eq. (4.27) is given in Table II in terms of matrix elements of permutations. For a single shell, these coefficients are obtained by diagonalizing the Wigner projection operators Eq. (3.42a).

For the pair fractional parentage coefficients, we adopt a procedure differing slightly from that given in the preceding section; we split off the vector $\sqrt{\frac{1}{2}}(\boldsymbol{\eta}^1 - \boldsymbol{\eta}^2)$ rather than $\sqrt{\frac{1}{2}}(\boldsymbol{\eta}^2 - \boldsymbol{\eta}^3)$. This has the advantage that, on splitting the spin-isospin states discussed in Section V into those of particle 1, 2 and of particle 3, the interaction can be applied immediately to particles 1 and 2.

From the vectors $\boldsymbol{\eta}^1$, $\boldsymbol{\eta}^2$ we first pass to

$$\begin{aligned} \boldsymbol{\eta}'^1 &= \sqrt{\tfrac{1}{2}}(\boldsymbol{\eta}^1 - \boldsymbol{\eta}^2), \\ \boldsymbol{\eta}'^2 &= \sqrt{\tfrac{1}{2}}(\boldsymbol{\eta}^1 + \boldsymbol{\eta}^2), \\ \boldsymbol{\eta}'^3 &= \boldsymbol{\eta}^3, \end{aligned} \tag{4.28}$$

by applying the operator

$$\mathcal{O}^{12}\left(-\frac{\pi}{2}\right) = \exp\left[-\frac{\pi}{2}\Lambda^{12}\right]. \tag{4.29}$$

Then

$$\left\langle \begin{matrix} k_{12} & k_{22} \\ \bar{k}_{11} & \end{matrix} \middle| \mathcal{O}^{12}\left(-\frac{\pi}{2}\right) \middle| \begin{matrix} k_{12} & k_{22} \\ k_{11} & \end{matrix} \right\rangle = D^{\frac{1}{2}(k_{12}-k_{22})}_{\bar{k}_{11}-\frac{1}{2}(k_{12}+k_{22}),k_{11}-\frac{1}{2}(k_{12}+k_{22})}\left(0, \frac{\pi}{2}, 0\right) \quad (4.30)$$

is a representation matrix of SU(2) in the notation of Edmonds (*46*, p. 55) Next we exchange the vectors $\boldsymbol{\eta}'^1$ and $\boldsymbol{\eta}'^3$ by applying the permutation (1, 3) to the primed states. Then we find

$$\left\langle \mathbf{x}^1\mathbf{x}^2\mathbf{x}^3 \middle| \begin{matrix} [h_1h_2h_3] \\ \Omega LM \end{matrix}, \begin{matrix} \{h_1h_2h_3\} \\ \chi fr \end{matrix} \right\rangle$$

$$= \sum_{\substack{h_1'h_2'k_{11}' \\ \Omega'L'}} \sum_{h''l''} \left\{ \left[\left\langle \mathbf{x}'^3\mathbf{x}'^2 \middle| \begin{matrix} [h_1'h_2'] \\ \Omega'L' \end{matrix}, \begin{matrix} h_1' & h_2' \\ k_{11}' & \end{matrix} \right\rangle \left\langle \mathbf{x}'^1 \middle| \begin{matrix} [h''] \\ l'' \end{matrix} \right\rangle \right]_{LM} \right.$$

$$\left. \times \left\langle \begin{matrix} [h_1'h_2'] \\ \Omega'L' \end{matrix}, \begin{matrix} h_1' & h_2' \\ k_{11}' & \end{matrix}; \begin{matrix} [h''] \\ l'' \end{matrix} \middle| \right\} \begin{matrix} [h_1h_2h_3] \\ \Omega L \end{matrix}, \begin{matrix} \{h_1h_2h_3\} \\ \chi fr \end{matrix} \right\rangle \right\} \quad (4.31)$$

with the pair fpc given by

$$\left\langle \begin{matrix} [h_1'h_2'] \\ \Omega'L' \end{matrix}, \begin{matrix} h_1' & h_2' \\ k_{11}' & \end{matrix}; \begin{matrix} [h''] \\ l'' \end{matrix} \middle| \right\} \begin{matrix} [h_1h_2h_3] \\ \Omega L \end{matrix}, \begin{matrix} \{h_1h_2h_3\} \\ \chi fr \end{matrix} \right\rangle$$

$$= \delta_{h'',h_1+h_2+h_3-h_1'-h_2'} \left\langle \begin{matrix} [h_1'h_2'] \\ \Omega'L' \end{matrix}; \begin{matrix} [h''] \\ l'' \end{matrix} \middle| \begin{matrix} [h_1h_2h_3] \\ \Omega L \end{matrix} \right\rangle$$

$$\times \sum_{\{k_{st}\}_2} \sum_{\bar{k}_{11}} \left\{ \left\langle \begin{matrix} h_1 & h_2 & h_3 \\ h_1' & h_2' & \\ h_1'+h_2'-k_{11}' & & \end{matrix} \middle| (2,3) \middle| \begin{matrix} h_1 & h_2 & h_3 \\ k_{12} & k_{22} & \\ k_{12}+k_{22}-\bar{k}_{11} & & \end{matrix} \right\rangle \right.$$

$$\times (-1)^{h_2'+k_{22}} D^{\frac{1}{2}(k_{12}-k_{22})}_{\bar{k}_{11}-\frac{1}{2}(k_{12}+k_{22}),k_{11}-\frac{1}{2}(k_{12}+k_{22})}\left(0, \frac{\pi}{2}, 0\right)$$

$$\left. \times \left\langle \begin{matrix} h_1 & h_2 & h_3 \\ k_{12} & k_{22} & \\ k_{11} & & \end{matrix} \middle| \begin{matrix} \{h_1h_2h_3\} \\ \chi fr \end{matrix} \right\rangle \right\} \quad (4.32)$$

where we used the decomposition (1, 3) = (1, 2)(2, 3)(1, 2) as well as the explicit expression for the matrices of (1, 2) with respect to Gelfand states given in Eq. (3.39). The matrix element of (2, 3) is given in Eq. (3.40) while the last coefficient of Eq. (4.32) can be obtained from the Table II.

E. Pair Fractional Parentage Coefficients for Four-Particle Translational-Invariant States

It is advantageous to modify the procedure given in Section IV,C by splitting off the vector $\sqrt{\tfrac{1}{2}}(\boldsymbol{\eta}^1 - \boldsymbol{\eta}^2)$ rather than $\sqrt{\tfrac{1}{2}}(\boldsymbol{\eta}^3 - \boldsymbol{\eta}^4)$. To do this, introduce new relative vectors related to those of Eq. (3.76) by

$$\begin{aligned} \ddot{\boldsymbol{\eta}}'^1 &= \sqrt{\tfrac{1}{2}}(\ddot{\boldsymbol{\eta}}^1 - \ddot{\boldsymbol{\eta}}^2) = \sqrt{\tfrac{1}{2}}(\boldsymbol{\eta}^1 - \boldsymbol{\eta}^2), \\ \ddot{\boldsymbol{\eta}}'^2 &= \sqrt{\tfrac{1}{2}}(\ddot{\boldsymbol{\eta}}^1 + \ddot{\boldsymbol{\eta}}^2) = \sqrt{\tfrac{1}{2}}(\boldsymbol{\eta}^3 - \boldsymbol{\eta}^4), \\ \ddot{\boldsymbol{\eta}}'^3 &= \ddot{\boldsymbol{\eta}}^3, \end{aligned} \tag{4.33}$$

by means of the operator

$$\ddot{\mathcal{O}}^{12}\left(-\frac{\pi}{2}\right) = \exp\left[-\frac{1}{2}\frac{\pi}{2}(\ddot{C}^{12} - \ddot{C}^{21})\right]. \tag{4.34}$$

Then exchange the vectors $\ddot{\boldsymbol{\eta}}'^1$ and $\ddot{\boldsymbol{\eta}}'^3$ by means of the transposition (1, 3). Both transformations are identical to those applied to the three-particle states in Eq. (4.31). Therefore, the decomposition is given by

$$\left\langle \ddot{\mathbf{x}}^1\ddot{\mathbf{x}}^2\ddot{\mathbf{x}}^3 \middle| \begin{matrix}[h_1h_2h_3] \\ \Omega LM\end{matrix}, \begin{matrix}\{h_1h_2h_3\} \\ \chi fr\end{matrix} \right\rangle = \sum_{\substack{h_1'h_2'k_{11}' \\ \Omega' L'}} \sum_{h''l''} \left\{ \left[\left\langle \ddot{\mathbf{x}}'^3\ddot{\mathbf{x}}'^2 \middle| \begin{matrix}[h_1'h_2'] \\ \Omega' L'\end{matrix}, \begin{matrix}h_1' \;\; h_2' \\ k_{11}'\end{matrix} \right\rangle \left\langle \ddot{\mathbf{x}}'^1 \middle| \begin{matrix}[h''] \\ l''\end{matrix} \right\rangle \right]_{LM} \right.$$

$$\left. \times \left\langle \begin{matrix}[h_1'h_2'] \\ \Omega' L'\end{matrix}, \begin{matrix}h_1' \;\; h_2' \\ k_{11}'\end{matrix}; \begin{matrix}[h''] \\ l''\end{matrix} \middle| \right\} \begin{matrix}[h_1h_2h_3] \\ \Omega L\end{matrix}, \begin{matrix}\{h_1h_2h_3\} \\ \chi fr\end{matrix} \right\rangle \right\}. \tag{4.35}$$

The expansion coefficient is given by the expression Eq. (4.32) with the only difference that now χfr refers to four-particle states so that the last coefficient in Eq. (4.32) should now be taken from Table III.

F. One-Row Wigner Coefficents of $\mathscr{U}(3)$

We indicated in Section IV,A that the Wigner coefficients of $\mathscr{U}(3)$ in the $\mathscr{U}(3) \supset \mathcal{O}^+(3)$ chain given by Eq. (4.8) is fundamental for the evaluation of hfpc. How do we determine this one-row Wigner coefficient?

We first give the explicit expression of coefficients of Eq. (4.8) in terms of those in which the states are characterized by the $\mathscr{U}(3) \supset \mathscr{U}(2) \supset \mathscr{U}(1)$ chain, that is,

$$\left| \begin{matrix} h_1' & & h_2' & & h_3' \\ & q_1' & & q_2' & \\ & & r_1' & & \end{matrix} \right\rangle . \tag{4.36}$$

As the transformation brackets between the states of Eq. (4.36) and those of Eq. (4.7c) were determined explicitly in Section II,B,3 in terms of the unitary matrix that diagonalizes the matrix of $\mathbf{L}^2$ with respect to Gelfand states, we can make use of these brackets and write

$$\begin{aligned} &\left\langle \begin{matrix} [h_1'h_2'h_3'] \\ \Omega' L' M' \end{matrix} ; \begin{matrix} [h''] \\ l''m'' \end{matrix} \middle| \begin{matrix} [h_1h_2h_3] \\ \Omega LM \end{matrix} \right\rangle \\ &= \sum_{\substack{q_1'q_2' \\ r_1'}} \sum_{\substack{q'' \\ r''}} \sum_{\substack{q_1q_2 \\ r_1}} \left\{ \left\langle \begin{matrix} [h_1'h_2'h_3'] \\ \Omega' L' M' \end{matrix} \middle| \begin{matrix} h_1' & & h_2' & & h_3' \\ & q_1' & & q_2' & \\ & & r_1' & & \end{matrix} \right\rangle \left\langle \begin{matrix} [h''] \\ l''m'' \end{matrix} \middle| \begin{matrix} h'' & & 0 & & 0 \\ & q'' & & 0 & \\ & & r'' & & \end{matrix} \right\rangle \right. \\ &\times \left\langle \begin{matrix} h_1' & & h_2' & & h_3' \\ & q_1' & & q_2' & \\ & & r_1' & & \end{matrix} ; \begin{matrix} h'' & & 0 & & 0 \\ & q'' & & 0 & \\ & & r'' & & \end{matrix} \middle| \begin{matrix} h_1 & & h_2 & & h_3 \\ & q_1 & & q_2 & \\ & & r_1 & & \end{matrix} \right\rangle \left. \left\langle \begin{matrix} h_1 & & h_2 & & h_3 \\ & q_1 & & q_2 & \\ & & r_1 & & \end{matrix} \middle| \begin{matrix} [h_1h_2h_3] \\ \Omega LM \end{matrix} \right\rangle \right\} . \end{aligned} \tag{4.37}$$

The first two and the last term on the right-hand side of Eq. (4.37) are the brackets referred to earlier, while the third term is the Wigner coefficient of $\mathscr{U}(3)$ in the $\mathscr{U}(3) \supset \mathscr{U}(2) \supset \mathscr{U}(1)$ chain.

To evaluate this Wigner coefficient we note that the states Eq. (4.36) form not only a BIR of the $\mathscr{U}(3)$ group, but also of its unitary unimodular subgroup $\mathscr{S}\mathscr{U}(3)$ (*30*, p. 388). Under $\mathscr{S}\mathscr{U}(3)$, though, the determinant Δ_{123}^{123} defined in Eq. (2.26) is an invariant. Therefore, under $\mathscr{S}\mathscr{U}(3)$ the state (4.36) transforms in the same way as the state

$$\left| \begin{matrix} \bar{h}_1' & & \bar{h}_2' & & 0 \\ & \bar{q}_1' & & \bar{q}_2' & \\ & & \bar{r}_1' & & \end{matrix} \right\rangle \tag{4.38}$$

where all the barred terms are equal to the unbarred ones minus h_3', for example, $\bar{q}_1' = q_1' - h_3'$. The Wigner coefficient in the $\mathscr{U}(3) \supset \mathscr{U}(2) \supset \mathscr{U}(1)$ chain of Eq. (4.37) is then equal to the coefficient

$$\left\langle \begin{matrix} \bar{h}_1' & & \bar{h}_2' & & 0 \\ & \bar{q}_1' & & \bar{q}_2' & \\ & & \bar{r}_1' & & \end{matrix} , \begin{matrix} h'' & & 0 & & 0 \\ & q'' & & 0 & \\ & & r'' & & \end{matrix} \middle| \begin{matrix} \bar{h}_1 & & \bar{h}_2 & & \bar{h}_3 \\ & \bar{q}_1 & & \bar{q}_2 & \\ & & \bar{r}_1 & & \end{matrix} \right\rangle . \tag{4.39}$$

The states

$$\left|\begin{matrix} \bar{h}'_1 & \bar{h}'_2 & 0 \\ & \bar{q}'_1 \;\; \bar{q}'_2 & \\ & \bar{r}'_1 & \end{matrix}\right\rangle, \qquad \left|\begin{matrix} h'' & 0 & 0 \\ & q'' \;\; 0 & \\ & r'' & \end{matrix}\right\rangle \tag{4.40a, b}$$

are now given respectively in terms of polynomials in two vectors, which we could designate as $\boldsymbol{\eta}^1$, $\boldsymbol{\eta}^2$, and an independent third vector, which we could designate by $\boldsymbol{\eta}^3$, acting in both cases on a ground state $|0\rangle$. We could construct these two states explicitly if we considered a system of three particles in an ho potential. This problem would have the symmetry group U(9) and, if we classify the states by the $\mathscr{U}(3) \times U(3)$ subgroup, as well as by the canonical subgroups of $\mathscr{U}(3)$, $U(3)$, we get the state

$$P\begin{pmatrix} h_1 \;\; h_2 \;\; h_3 & h_1 \;\; h_2 \;\; h_3 \\ q_1 \;\; q_2 \quad , & u_1 \;\; u_2 \\ r_1 & v_1 \end{pmatrix}|0\rangle, \tag{4.41}$$

which can be derived from the highest weight state of Eq. (2.25) by applying the lowering operators given in Section II, Eq. (2.41a).

The states Eq. (4.40a,b) are particular cases of Eq. (4.41). For Eq. (4.40a) we consider the state of partition $[\bar{h}'_1\bar{h}'_2]$ of highest weight in $U(3)$, while for Eq. (4.40b) we consider the state of partition $[h'']$, but of lowest weight in $U(3)$, that is,

$$\left|\begin{matrix} \bar{h}'_1 & \bar{h}'_2 & 0 \\ & \bar{q}'_1 \;\; \bar{q}'_2 & \\ & \bar{r}'_1 & \end{matrix}\right\rangle = P\begin{pmatrix} \bar{h}'_1 \;\; \bar{h}'_2 \;\; 0 & \bar{h}'_1 \;\; \bar{h}'_2 \;\; 0 \\ \bar{q}'_1 \;\; \bar{q}'_2 \quad , & \bar{h}'_1 \;\; \bar{h}'_2 \\ \bar{r}'_1 & \bar{h}'_1 \end{pmatrix}|0\rangle \equiv P'\begin{pmatrix} \bar{h}'_1 \;\; \bar{h}'_2 \;\; 0 \\ \bar{q}'_1 \;\; \bar{q}'_2 \\ \bar{r}'_1 \end{pmatrix}|0\rangle, \tag{4.42a}$$

$$\left|\begin{matrix} h'' & 0 & 0 \\ & q'' \;\; 0 & \\ & r'' & \end{matrix}\right\rangle = P\begin{pmatrix} h'' \;\; 0 \;\; 0 & h'' \;\; 0 \;\; 0 \\ q'' \;\; 0 \quad , & 0 \;\; 0 \\ r'' & 0 \end{pmatrix}|0\rangle \equiv P''\begin{pmatrix} h'' \;\; 0 \;\; 0 \\ q'' \;\; 0 \\ r'' \end{pmatrix}|0\rangle. \tag{4.42b}$$

The state Eq. (4.42a) depends only on the vectors $\boldsymbol{\eta}^1$, $\boldsymbol{\eta}^2$, since the application to it of C^{33} gives the same state multiplied by the difference of the sum of the terms in the third and second rows of the $U(3)$ Gelfand pattern, which is zero. The state Eq. (4.42b) depends only on $\boldsymbol{\eta}^3$, since for similar reasons C^{11}, C^{22} applied to it give zero.

The state on the right of Eq. (4.39) could be given by Eq. (4.41) when the partition is $[\bar{h}_1\bar{h}_2\bar{h}_3]$, but now we note that it must correspond to the same IR of $U(2) \supset U(1)$ as the product of the two states of Eq. (4.42a) and Eq. (4.42b), since otherwise the scalar product implied by the coefficient Eq. (4.39) is zero.

Therefore, we have

$$\left|\begin{matrix} \bar{h}_1 & \bar{h}_2 & \bar{h}_3 \\ & \bar{q}_1 \quad \bar{q}_2 & \\ & \bar{r}_1 & \end{matrix}\right\rangle = P\begin{pmatrix} \bar{h}_1 & \bar{h}_2 & \bar{h}_3 \\ & \bar{q}_1 \quad \bar{q}_2 & \\ & \bar{r}_1 & \end{pmatrix}, \begin{matrix} \bar{h}_1 & \bar{h}_2 & \bar{h}_3 \\ & \bar{h}_1' \quad \bar{h}_2' & \\ & \bar{h}_1' & \end{matrix}\Bigg)|0\rangle. \tag{4.42c}$$

The one-row Wigner coefficient of $\mathscr{U}(3)$ is then given by the matrix element

$$\langle 0|P'^{\dagger}\begin{pmatrix} \bar{h}_2' & \bar{h}_1' & 0 \\ & \bar{q}_1' \quad \bar{q}_2' & \\ & \bar{r}_1' & \end{pmatrix}P''^{\dagger}\begin{pmatrix} h'' & 0 & 0 \\ & q'' \quad 0 & \\ & r'' & \end{pmatrix}P\begin{pmatrix} \bar{h}_1 & \bar{h}_2 & \bar{h}_3 & & \bar{h}_1 & \bar{h}_2 & \bar{h}_3 \\ & \bar{q}_1 \quad \bar{q}_2 & & , & & \bar{h}_1' \quad \bar{h}_2' & \\ & \bar{r}_1 & & & & \bar{h}_1' & \end{pmatrix}|0\rangle \tag{4.43}$$

in which $P^{\dagger}$ stands for the Hermitian conjugate of the polynomials. Using the commutation relations of Eq. (2.4), this matrix element was evaluated by Moshinsky giving the explicit algebraic formula of (*14*). This formula has been programmed by T. A. Brody, so that numerical tables of the one-row Wigner coefficients of $\mathscr{U}(3)$ in the $\mathscr{U}(3) \supset \mathscr{U}(2) \supset \mathscr{U}(1)$ chain are available. Since a program for the transformation brackets in Eq. (4.37) is also available, it is only a question of combining these two programs to get the Wigner coefficients Eq. (4.8) and through them, by Eq. (4.9), the reduced Wigner coefficients that appear in the hfpc.

V. Group Theory and *n*-Particle States in Spin-Isospin Space

In the previous sections we dealt with the construction of orbital n-particle states. As out ultimate purpose here is to construct the states for an n-nucleon system satisfying the Pauli principle, it is clear that we must also indicate the procedure for deriving the spin-isospin part of the states. The derivation given here will lead in a natural way to the characterization of spin-isospin states by the IR of the unitary groups of four dimensions $\mathscr{U}(4)$ associated with the supermultiplet classification (*47*).

A. Spin-Isospin States with Permutational Symmetry

Let us denote the spin-isospin states of the sth nucleon by

$$\chi^{s}_{\sigma\tau}, \qquad s = 1, \ldots, n, \ \sigma = \pm\tfrac{1}{2}, \ \tau = \pm\tfrac{1}{2}, \tag{5.1}$$

where σ is the projection of the spin and τ is the projection of the isospin. In this section we will indicate a systematic procedure for deriving n-particle spin-isospin states with definite permutational symmetry, that is, corresponding to a IR of $S(n)$ characterized by

$$f = \{f_1 \cdots f_n\}, \qquad r = (1 r_2 \cdots r_{n-1} r_n), \tag{5.2}$$

where f is a partition of n and r is a Yamanouchi symbol. Furthermore, we would like the states to have definite total spin S and projection M_S, as well as total isospin T and projection M_T.

In what follows we shall denote the pair of indices $\sigma\tau$ by the single index $\mu = 1, 2, 3, 4$ according to the enumeration convention

μ	1	2	3	4
$\sigma\tau$	$\frac{1}{2}\frac{1}{2}$	$\frac{1}{2}-\frac{1}{2}$	$-\frac{1}{2}-\frac{1}{2}$	$-\frac{1}{2}-\frac{1}{2}$

(5.3)

Furthermore, we shall denote by γ the set of two numbers (st) characterizing the spin s and isospin t of the single particle. For a nucleon $\gamma = (\frac{1}{2}\frac{1}{2})$.

The n-particle states in spin-isospin space have then the form

$$|\gamma^n f r \beta S M_S T M_T\rangle = \sum_{\mu_1 \cdots \mu_n} A^{\mu_1 \cdots \mu_n}_{fr\beta S M_S T M_T} \chi^1_{\mu_1} \cdots \chi^n_{\mu_n}, \tag{5.4}$$

where all the parameters in the ket have been explained before, except for β, which represents the extra quantum numbers necessary to distinguish between repeated sets of SM_STM_T associated with a given IR f of $S(n)$. The coefficients A in the summation are precisely the ones we must determine to obtain explicitly the state Eq. (5.4). The main problem is then how to derive in a systematic way the coefficients A. Once we give the procedure for deriving the coefficients A, we shall, in the next section, apply the results of the present one to split the n-particle spin-isospin states into products of a state of $n-1$ particles and the state of particle n, that is, determine the spin-isospin fractional parentage coefficient (fpc) in the expansion

$$\begin{aligned}
|\gamma^n f r \beta S M_S T M_T\rangle = \sum_{\beta' S' T'} \sum_{M_S' \sigma} \sum_{M_T' \tau} \{ &\langle S' \tfrac{1}{2} M_S' \sigma | S M_S\rangle \langle T' \tfrac{1}{2} M_T' \tau | T M_T\rangle \\
&\times |\gamma^{n-1} f' r' \beta' S' M_S' T' M_T'\rangle |\gamma\sigma\tau\rangle \\
&\times \langle \gamma^{n-1} f' \beta' S' T', \gamma \tfrac{1}{2}\tfrac{1}{2} | \} \gamma^n f \beta S T\rangle \}
\end{aligned} \tag{5.5}$$

where the first two terms are Wigner coefficients of $\mathscr{SU}(2)$, the third term is the state for the first $n-1$ particles, the fourth term the state for particle n, and the last term is the fpc. There is no summation over f' as the Yamanouchi symbol r specifies both f' and r' when we eliminate the box containing n in the Young diagram for f, r. The determination of the spin-isospin fpc has been extensively discussed in the literature, particularly by Jahn (*48*). What we shall try here is to present a systematic derivation that uses essentially the same types of ideas as were used in Section IV for the orbital part of the states.

Returning now to the problem of determining the states (5.4), let us introduce the correspondence

$$\chi_\mu^s \leftrightarrow \dot{a}_\mu^s|0\rangle, \qquad \mu = 1, 2, 3, 4, \quad s = 1, \ldots, n, \tag{5.6}$$

where $\dot{a}_\mu^s$ are commuting creation operators and $|0\rangle$ is a vacuum state. Using this correspondence, we see that the n-particle spin-isospin state Eq. (5.4) is equivalent to the one constructed by applying the polynomial of degree n in the creation operators

$$P_{fr\beta SM_STM_T}(\dot{a}_\mu^s) = \sum_\mu A_{fr\beta SM_STM_T}^{\mu_1\cdots\mu_n} \dot{a}_{\mu_1}^1 \cdots \dot{a}_{\mu_n}^n \tag{5.7}$$

to the vacuum state $|0\rangle$.

To establish the complete identity of states of Eqs. (5.4) and (5.7) we must give a procedure for calculating the scalar products of states of the latter type. For this purpose we associate with each creation operator $\dot{a}_\mu^s$ an annihilation operator a_μ^s satisfying the commutation rules

$$[a_{\mu'}^{s'}, \dot{a}_\mu^s] = \delta^{ss'}\delta_{\mu\mu'}, \qquad [\dot{a}_\mu^s, \dot{a}_{\mu'}^{s'}] = [a_\mu^s, a_{\mu'}^{s'}] = 0. \tag{5.8}$$

We then define the scalar product

$$\begin{aligned}(\dot{a}_{\mu_1'}^1 \cdots \dot{a}_{\mu_n'}^n, \dot{a}_{\mu_1}^1 \cdots \dot{a}_{\mu_n}^n) &= \langle 0|a_{\mu_n'}^n \cdots a_{\mu_1'}^1 \dot{a}_{\mu_1}^1 \cdots \dot{a}_{\mu_n}^n|0\rangle \\ &= \delta_{\mu_1'\mu_1} \cdots \delta_{\mu_n'\mu_n}\end{aligned} \tag{5.9}$$

where the explicit expression of the scalar product in Eq. (5.9) is obtained using Eq. (5.8) and the fact that all the n vector creation operators $\dot{a}_{\mu_s}^s$, $s = 1 \cdots n$ are distinct. From Eq. (5.9) we then conclude that the scalar products of states of Eq. (5.7) are identical to those of the states of Eq. (5.4).

We now notice that the polynomials of Eq. (5.7) are given in terms of operators $\dot{a}_\mu^s$, which constitute a $4n$-dimensional vector, as $\mu = 1 \cdots 4$, $s = 1 \cdots n$. Furthermore, this $4n$ vector can be thought of as a set of n vectors in four dimensions, s being the particle index and μ the vector component, or as a set of four vectors in n dimensions where μ now is the particle index and s the vector component. This suggests the possibility of deriving the polynomials of Eq. (5.7) as part of a BIR of a $\mathbf{U}(4n)$ group, with the row of the basis characterized by IR of the $\mathscr{U}(4) \times U(n)$ group. Furthermore, the polynomials of Eq. (5.7) are homogeneous of degree n in the $\dot{a}^s_\mu$, so that the IR of $\mathbf{U}(4n)$, to which they belong, is the symmetric one characterized by the partition $[n]$. Therefore, the IR of the $\mathscr{U}(4)$ and $U(n)$ subgroups must be the same (see Section II), and are characterized by a partition $[f_1 f_2 \cdots]$ of n. We shall show later that this partition can be identified with f, the one that gives the IR of $S(n)$ in Eq. (5.7), and that the $\mathscr{U}(4)$ group is actually the one of supermultiplet theory (*47*). We initiate our discussion of this point by analyzing the IR of the $\mathbf{U}(4n) \supset \mathscr{U}(4) \times U(n)$ chain.

B. Bases for Irreducible Representations of the $\mathbf{U}(4n)$ Group in the $\mathscr{U}(4) \times U(n)$ Chain

The discussion in this section will be very brief, as it will parallel the analysis of the BIR of $\mathbf{U}(3n)$ in the $\mathscr{U}(3) \times U(n)$ chain given in Section II.

Using the $4n$-dimensional vectors $\dot{a}^s_\mu$, $a^{s'}_{\mu'}$ associated with creation and annihilation operators, respectively, we define the operators

$$\hat{\mathbf{C}}^{ss'}_{\mu\mu'} \equiv \dot{a}^s_\mu a^{s'}_{\mu'}, \tag{5.10}$$

which, from Eq. (5.8) and the discussion in Section II, are clearly the generators of a $\mathbf{U}(4n)$ group. (To distinguish the operators associated with the $\mathbf{U}(4n)$ group and its subgroups from the corresponding operators for $\mathbf{U}(3n)$ and its subgroups, we put a circumflex accent above the former operators.) Contracting with respect to the indices s or μ, we get the operators

$$\mathscr{C}_{\mu\mu'} = \sum_s \hat{\mathbf{C}}^{ss}_{\mu\mu'}, \qquad \hat{C}^{ss'} = \sum_\mu \hat{\mathbf{C}}^{ss'}_{\mu\mu}, \tag{5.11a,b}$$

which are the respective generators of the unitary groups $\mathscr{U}(4)$ and $U(n)$ in a $\mathscr{U}(4) \times U(n)$ subgroup of $\mathbf{U}(4n)$.

In a way similar to the analysis in Section II, we could use the canonical chains of subgroups

$$\mathscr{U}(4) \supset \mathscr{U}(3) \supset \mathscr{U}(2) \supset \mathscr{U}(1) \tag{5.12a}$$

$$U(n) \supset U(n-1) \supset \cdots \supset U(1) \tag{5.12b}$$

to characterize the BIR of $\mathscr{U}(4) \times U(n)$ by

$$|[e_{\mu\nu}], \{f_{st}\}\rangle = \hat{P}^{[e_{\mu\nu}]\{f_{st}\}}(\dot{a}^s_\mu)|0\rangle \tag{5.13a}$$

where

$$[e_{1\nu} \cdots e_{\nu\nu}],\ \{f_{1t}, \ldots, f_{tt}\} \tag{5.13b}$$

characterize the respective IR of $\mathscr{U}(\nu)$, $\nu = 1, 2, 3, 4$ and $U(t)$, $t = 1 \cdots n$, and $\hat{P}$ is a polynomial in the creation operators $\dot{a}^s_\mu$. Furthermore,

$$e_{\mu 4} = f_{\mu n} \equiv f_\mu, \qquad \mu = 1, 2, 3, 4, \tag{5.13c}$$

as we shall suppress the index n in $f_{\mu n}$.

The highest weight state of Eq. (5.13), that is, the one with

$$e_{\mu\nu} = e_{\mu 4}, \qquad f_{st} = f_{sn} \equiv f_s, \tag{5.14}$$

is given as in Section II by

$$\hat{P}^{[f_1 f_2 f_3 f_4]} = \mathsf{N}[f_1 f_2 f_3 f_4](\hat{\Delta}^1_1)^{f_1 - f_2}(\hat{\Delta}^{12}_{12})^{f_2 - f_3}(\hat{\Delta}^{123}_{123})^{f_3 - f_4}(\hat{\Delta}^{1234}_{1234})^{f_4} \tag{5.15}$$

where

$$\hat{\Delta}^{s_1 \cdots s_r}_{\mu_1 \cdots \mu_r} = \sum_{\mathbf{p}} (-1)^{\mathbf{p}} \mathbf{p} \dot{a}^{s_1}_{\mu_1} \cdots \dot{a}^{s_r}_{\mu_r} \tag{5.16}$$

with $\mathbf{p}$ being a permutation of $(s_1 \cdots s_r)$, and N being the normalization coefficient

$$\mathsf{N}[f_1 f_2 f_3 f_4] = \left[\frac{(f_1 - f_2 + 1)(f_1 - f_3 + 2)(f_2 - f_3 + 1) \times (f_1 - f_4 + 3)(f_2 - f_4 + 2)(f_3 - f_4 + 1)}{(f_1 + 3)!\,(f_2 + 2)!\,(f_3 + 1)!\,f_4!}\right]^{1/2}. \tag{5.17}$$

All the other states Eq. (5.13) can be obtained from Eq. (5.15) by applying the lowering operators of $U(m)$ (*17*),

$$\hat{L}^{ts} = \prod_{q=s+1}^{t-1} \hat{E}^{sq} \times \sum_{p=0}^{t-s-1} \sum_{q_p > q_{p-1} > \cdots > q_2 > q_1 = s+1}^{t-1} \left\{\prod_{i=1}^{s} (\hat{E}^{sq_i})^{-1} \hat{C}^{tq_p} \hat{C}^{q_p q_{p-1}} \cdots \hat{C}^{q_2 q_1} \hat{C}^{q_1 s}\right\}, \tag{5.18}$$

as well as similar ones of $\mathscr{U}(k)$ given in terms of the generators $\mathscr{C}_{\mu\mu'}$.

In this way we can get the BIR $|[e_{\mu\nu}], \{f_{st}\}\rangle$ of the $\mathscr{U}(4) \times U(n)$ group in the canonical chain Eq. (5.12). We want though to obtain only states of the type Eq. (5.7), which are of the first degree in each one of the operators $\dot{a}^s_{\mu_s}$,

$s = 1, \ldots, n$. We therefore restrict ourselves to states Eq. (5.13) for which

$$\{f_1 f_2 f_3 f_4\} \tag{5.19a}$$

is a partition of n, and furthermore, for which the weight $\hat{\mathbf{w}}$ is

$$\hat{\mathbf{w}} = (11 \cdots 1) \equiv 1^n. \tag{5.19b}$$

These states can be denoted by

$$|[e_{\mu\nu}], \{f_1 f_2 f_3 f_4\}(1 r_2 \cdots r_n)\rangle = \mathcal{N}[e_{\mu\nu}] \prod_{\nu=2}^{4} \prod_{\mu=1}^{\nu-1} (\mathcal{L}_{\nu\mu})^{e_{\mu\nu} - e_{\mu\nu-1}}$$

$$\times \mathcal{N}(f, r) L^{11} L^{2r_2} \cdots L^{nr_n} \hat{P}^{[f_1 f_2 f_3 f_4]} |0\rangle \tag{5.20}$$

where $1 \leqq r_t \leqq t$ indicate the value $f_{r_t t}$ in the IR $[f_{1t} \cdots f_{r_t t} \cdots f_{tt}]$ of $U(t)$ from which we subtract 1 to get the IR of $U(t-1)$. From the inequalities satisfied by the f_{st} (*27*), we see that the set of numbers $r = (1 r_2 \cdots r_n)$ have all the properties of a Yamanouchi symbol (*30*, p. 221). The normalization coefficients $\mathcal{N}(f, r)$, $\mathcal{N}[e_{\mu\nu}]$ are given as particular cases of $\mathcal{N}\{f_{st}\}$,

$$\mathcal{N}\{f_{st}\} = \left\{ \prod_{m=2}^{n} \left[\prod_{t \geqslant s=1}^{m-1} \frac{(f_{sm-1} - f_{tm-1} + t - s)!}{(f_{sm} - f_{tm-1} + t - s)!} \right. \right.$$

$$\left. \left. \times \prod_{t > s=1}^{m} \frac{(f_{sm-1} - f_{tm} + t - s - 1)!}{(f_{sm} - f_{tm} + t - s - 1)!} \right] \right\}^{1/2} \tag{5.21}$$

when f_{st} satisfy the restrictions indicated after Eq. (5.20) or when we replace $\{f_{st}\}$ by $[e_{\mu\nu}]$.

We shall designate the states of the type Eq. (5.20) special Gelfand (SG) states (*27*), since, with respect to $U(n)$, we do not have the most general partitions and weights, but only those corresponding to Eq. (5.19).

The SG states Eq. (5.20) are characterized, insofar as the $\mathcal{U}(4)$ group is concerned, by the canonical chain of subgroups $\mathcal{U}(4) \supset \mathcal{U}(3) \supset \mathcal{U}(2) \supset \mathcal{U}(1)$, that is, by the partitions $[e_{1\nu} \cdots e_{\nu\nu}]$, $\nu = 4, 3, 2, 1$. Comparing the SG states with the states Eq. (5.7) with definite permutational symmetry, we see that the latter are characterized by the total spin S and isospin T, and their projections M_S, M_T, as well as by extra quantum numbers denoted by β. We shall, in the next subsection, indicate how to construct SG states with definite spin and isospin; then, in subsection D, we will prove that these states are BIR of $S(n)$ and are therefore entirely equivalent to the states Eq. (5.7).

C. States with Definite Total Spin and Isospin

To construct states with definite total spin and isospin, we must first show how we can get, within our formalism, the operators associated with these observables. For this purpose we note that the generators of $\mathscr{U}(4)$

$$\mathscr{C}_{\mu\mu'} = \mathscr{C}_{\sigma\tau,\sigma'\tau'}, \tag{5.22}$$

which are sums over products of a creation and an annihilation operator, are not Racah (that is, irreducible) tensors with respect to two-dimensional unitary unimodular transformations either in spin or isospin space. We can, though, have Racah tensors if we construct the linear combinations

$$\Theta^{k\bar{k}}_{q\bar{q}} = \sum_{\tau\tau'} \sum_{\sigma\sigma'} \{\langle \tfrac{1}{2}k\sigma' q | \tfrac{1}{2}\sigma\rangle \langle \tfrac{1}{2}\bar{k}\tau'\bar{q} | \tfrac{1}{2}\tau\rangle \mathscr{C}_{\sigma\tau,\sigma'\tau'}\} \tag{5.23}$$

where $\langle \mid \rangle$ are ordinary Wigner coefficients, and so k, $\bar{k}$ are clearly restricted to the values 0 and 1 only. We note that the operators

$$S_q \equiv \left(\frac{4}{3}\right)^{1/2} \Theta^{10}_{q0}, \qquad T_{\bar{q}} \equiv \left(\frac{4}{3}\right)^{1/2} \Theta^{01}_{0\bar{q}}, \qquad q, \bar{q} = 1, 0, -1, \tag{5.24}$$

when acting on single-particle states

$$|\sigma\tau\rangle = \dot{a}^{1}_{\sigma\tau}|0\rangle, \tag{5.25}$$

have exactly the same effect as the operators of spin and isospin, and so S_q, $T_{\bar{q}}$ are the operators we are looking for. Furthermore, they will also be the generators of the unitary unimodular groups $\mathscr{SU}^{(\sigma)}(2)$, $\mathscr{SU}^{(\tau)}(2)$ associated with transformations in spin and isospin space, respectively.

The states we would like to construct will then be eigenstates of the operators S_0, T_0 as well as of the Casimir operators of $\mathscr{SU}^{(\sigma)}(2)$ and $\mathscr{SU}^{(\tau)}(2)$, that is,

$$\mathbf{S}^2 = \sum (-1)^q S_q S_{-q}, \qquad \mathbf{T}^2 = \sum_{\bar{q}} (-1)^{\bar{q}} T_{\bar{q}} T_{-\bar{q}}. \tag{5.26}$$

This implies that these states are characterized by the chain of groups

$$\mathscr{U}(4) \supset \mathscr{SU}^{(\sigma)}(2) \times \mathscr{SU}^{(\tau)}(2) \tag{5.27}$$

rather than by the canonical chain of the preceding subsection.

To find these eigenstates we would need the matrix elements of the operators $\mathbf{S}^2$, $\mathbf{T}^2$, S_0, T_0 with respect to the Gelfand states of $\mathscr{U}(4)$. As these operators are certain quadratic or linear functions of the generators $\mathscr{C}_{\mu\mu'}$ of $\mathscr{U}(4)$, we need then first, the matrix elements of $\mathscr{C}_{\mu\mu'}$ with respect to the Gelfand states. This is the equivalent problem for $\mathscr{U}(4)$ of the problem of determining the matrix elements of the generators L_q of $\mathscr{O}^+(3)$ with respect to the BIR $|lm\rangle$ of the same group. As Gelfand and Zetlin (*26*) solved this problem in full generality for the $U(n)$ group, we could use their results to determine the matrix elements of $\mathbf{S}^2$, $\mathbf{T}^2$, S_0, T_0 with respect to the Gelfand states of $\mathscr{U}(4)$. Actually, as S_0, T_0 are given by the linear combinations

$$\begin{aligned} S_0 &= \tfrac{1}{2}(\mathscr{C}_{11} + \mathscr{C}_{22} - \mathscr{C}_{33} - \mathscr{C}_{44}), \\ T_0 &= \tfrac{1}{2}(\mathscr{C}_{11} - \mathscr{C}_{22} + \mathscr{C}_{33} - \mathscr{C}_{44}), \end{aligned} \tag{5.28}$$

of weight generators of $\mathscr{U}(4)$, they are diagonal with respect to the Gelfand states and trivial to derive. For $\mathbf{S}^2$, $\mathbf{T}^2$ the matrix elements have been explicitly determined by Kushner and Quintanilla (*49*).

As the operators $\mathbf{S}^2$, $\mathbf{T}^2$, S_0, T_0 commute, we could find the unitary transformations that diagonalize them and so determine the transformation brackets

$$\left\langle \begin{matrix} f_1 & & f_2 & & f_3 & & f_4 \\ & e_{13} & & e_{23} & & e_{33} & \\ & & e_{12} & & e_{22} & & \\ & & & e_{11} & & & \end{matrix} \middle| \begin{matrix} [f_1 f_2 f_3 f_4] \\ \beta S M_S T M_T \end{matrix} \right\rangle \tag{5.29}$$

that take us from the states Eq. (5.20) to the states

$$\left| \begin{matrix} [f_1 f_2 f_3 f_4] \\ \beta S M_S T M_T \end{matrix}, \{f_1 f_2 f_3 f_4\}(1 r_2 \cdots r_n) \right\rangle$$

$$\equiv \left| \begin{matrix} [f_1 f_2 f_3 f_4] \\ \beta S M_S T M_T \end{matrix}, \begin{matrix} f_1 & f_2 & f_3 & f_4 & 0 \cdots\cdots\cdots 0 \\ f_{1n-1} & f_{2n-1} & f_{3n-1} & f_{4n-1} & 0 \cdots 0 \\ & \cdots & \cdots & \cdots & \\ & & 1 & & \end{matrix} \right\rangle, \tag{5.30}$$

where

$$f_{st-1} = f_{st} - \delta_{sr_t} \tag{5.31}$$

and β indicates the numbers necessary (*50*) to distinguish between repeated IR ST of $\mathscr{SU}^{(\sigma)}(2) \times \mathscr{SU}^{(\tau)}(2)$ in a given IR $[f_1 f_2 f_3 f_4]$ of $\mathscr{U}_4$.

In the next subsection we shall show that the states Eqs. (5.30), (5.31), for which we gave an explicit construction procedure, are BIR of the $S(n)$ group, and thus are identical to the states Eq. (5.7) with permutational symmetry.

D. The Special Gelfand States as Bases for Irreducible Representations of the Symmetric Group

The ordinary Gelfand states are BIR of $U(n)$; thus so they will also be a basis, not necessarily irreducible, for the subgroup $S(n)$ of $U(n)$. Furthermore, as the weight operators $(C^{11}, \ldots, C^{nn})$ are interchanged by any permutation of the n indices, it is clear that Gelfand states corresponding to a partition of the type Eq. (5.19a) and weight $\hat{\mathbf{w}} = (1 \cdots 11)$ transform into themselves under permutations. Therefore, the set of states Eq. (5.30) forms a basis for a representation of $S(n)$. The essential point now is to prove that this representation of $S(n)$ is irreducible and, in fact, characterized by the same partition f giving the IR of $U(n)$.

There are several ways of obtaining this proof (*20*, *27*); the one we shall sketch here is based on the possibility of determining the matrix elements of the permutations with respect to the SG states. If these matrix elements turn out to be the same as those that would be obtained from the Yamanouchi analysis (*30*, p. 221) of the IR of the $S(n)$ group, our proof would be complete.

Actually, since all permutations are built up of transpositions, it will be sufficient to find the matrix elements of transpositions with respect to SG states. For this purpose it is first convenient to show that the effect of a transposition (s, t) on an SG state is the same as the effect of the operator

$$C^{st}C^{ts} - 1. \tag{5.32}$$

As the SG states Eq. (5.30) can be put in the form of Eq. (5.7) in which each term of the sum is of first order in the upper index $s = 1, \ldots, n$, we see that the operator C^{st} will change the upper index t into s, and thus it is immediately clear that the operator Eq. (5.32) would have the same effect on the state Eq. (5.7) as the transposition (s, t). We see then that we could determine the matrix elements of the transposition (s, t) if we knew the matrix elements of the generators C^{st} of $U(n)$ with respect to Gelfand states. As mentioned in the previous subsection, these matrix elements have been obtained by Gelfand and Zetlin (*26*). We can then determine the matrix elements of (s, t) with respect to SG states. This was done in another publication (*27*), where it was also shown that the matrix elements are identical to those obtained by the Yamanouchi analysis (*30*, p. 221). Therefore the SG states are BIR of $S(n)$ characterized by the partition f and with the corresponding row given by the Yamanouchi symbol r.

We have then given an explicit procedure for determining the states Eq. (5.7) with permutational symmetry by relating them to particular states in the BIR of U(4n) associated with the partition $[n]$. We shall, in the next section, indicate how this connection can be used to derive the fpc for the spin-isospin states.

VI. Spin-Isospin Fractional Parentage Coefficients

In the following sections we shall use the orbital and spin-isospin fpc to determine the matrix elements of one-body and two-body operators with respect to our n-particle ho states. The orbital fpc were determined in Section IV; in this section we will give a general procedure for obtaining the spin-isospin fpc for any number of particles.

We shall first show that the spin-isospin fpc are related to the Wigner coefficients of $\mathscr{U}(4)$ and then indicate how we can derive the latter.

A. Equivalence of the Fractional Parentage Coefficients and the Wigner Coefficients of $\mathscr{U}(4)$

To determine the fpc in spin-isospin space, let us first consider a state of $n-1$ particles of the type Eq. (5.30); that is,

$$\left|\begin{matrix}[f_1'f_2'f_3'f_4'] \\ \beta'S'M_S'T'M_T'\end{matrix}, \{f_1'f_2'f_3'f_4'\}(1r_2'\cdots r_{n-1}')\right\rangle$$

$$=\left|\begin{matrix}[f_1'f_2'f_3'f_4'] \\ \beta'S'M_S'T'M_T'\end{matrix}, \begin{matrix} f_1' & f_2' & f_3' & f_4' & 0\cdots\cdots\cdots 0 \\ f_{1n-2}' & f_{2n-2}' & f_{3n-2}' & f_{4n-2}' & 0\cdots 0 \\ & \cdots & \cdots & \cdots & \\ & & 1 & & \end{matrix}\right\rangle, \tag{6.1}$$

with

$$f_{st-1}' = f_{st}' - \delta_{sr_t'},$$

as well as the state for particle n in spin-isospin space

$$\left|\begin{matrix}[1] \\ \frac{1}{2}\sigma''\frac{1}{2}\tau''\end{matrix}\right\rangle \equiv \left|\begin{matrix}[1] \\ \mu''\end{matrix}\right\rangle. \tag{6.2}$$

The states Eq. (6.1) are part of a BIR of $\mathscr{U}(4) \times U(n-1)$ characterized by $[f_1'f_2'f_3'f_4']$ for both groups in the direct product, while the states Eq. (6.2) are a basis for the IR [1] of $\mathscr{U}(4)$. In a way similar to the one discussed in Section IV for $\mathscr{U}(3)$, we could construct states of n particles that are BIR of $\mathscr{U}(4)$ by combining products of Eqs. (6.1) and (6.2) with coefficients that are, in turn, products of the Wigner coefficients

$$\langle S'\tfrac{1}{2}M_S'\sigma''|SM_S\rangle\,\langle T'\tfrac{1}{2}M_T'\tau''|TM_T\rangle \tag{6.3}$$

and the reduced Wigner coefficients of $\mathscr{U}(4)$ in the

$$\mathscr{U}(4) \supset \mathscr{S}\mathscr{U}^{(\sigma)}(2) \times \mathscr{S}\mathscr{U}^{(\tau)}(2)$$

chain, that is,

$$\left\langle \begin{matrix} [f_1' f_2' f_3' f_4'] \\ \beta' S' T' \end{matrix} ; \begin{matrix} [1] \\ \frac{1}{2}\frac{1}{2} \end{matrix} \middle| \begin{matrix} [f_1 f_2 f_3 f_4] \\ \beta S T \end{matrix} \right\rangle. \tag{6.4}$$

We shall, in the following subsections, indicate how the coefficients Eq. (6.4) can be explicitly determined; at this point we note only that, since the new n-particle state belongs to the BIR $[n]$ of the group U$(4n)$, it will then also belong to the representation $\{f_1 f_2 f_3 f_4\}$ of $U(n)$. As this new state is of weight $\hat{\mathbf{w}} = (11 \cdots 1)$, it would also correspond to the IR $\{f_1 f_2 f_3 f_4\}$ of $S(n)$. Then, comparing this state with Eq. (5.5), we conclude that the fpc is the same as the reduced Wigner coefficient of $\mathscr{U}(4)$; that is,

$$\langle \gamma^{n-1} f' \beta' S' T', \gamma \tfrac{1}{2}\tfrac{1}{2} | \} \gamma^n f \beta S T \rangle = \left\langle \begin{matrix} [f_1' f_2' f_3' f_4'] \\ \beta' S' T' \end{matrix} ; \begin{matrix} [1] \\ \frac{1}{2}\frac{1}{2} \end{matrix} \middle| \begin{matrix} [f_1 f_2 f_3 f_4] \\ \beta S T \end{matrix} \right\rangle. \tag{6.5}$$

Once we have established this equality, the next point is, is it useful? We will show that with the help of the matrix elements of the generators of the $U(n+1)$ group, we can determine the Wigner coefficients of one block for $U(n)$ in the canonical chain. Combining this result when $n = 4$ with the transformation brackets Eq. (5.29) that take us from the canonical chain Eq. (5.12a) to the physical one, Eq. (5.27), we can determine the reduced Wigner coefficient Eq. (6.4) and thus, from Eq. (6.5), the spin-isospin fpc.

B. One-Block Wigner Coefficients of $U(n)$ in the Canonical Chain

The generators C^{mn+1} with $m = 1, \ldots, n$ of a $U(n+1)$ group have the form

$$C^{mn+1} = \sum_{\mu} \dot{a}_{\mu}^{m} a_{\mu}^{n+1}, \qquad m = 1, \ldots, n \tag{6.6}$$

Now, clearly, with respect to the $U(n)$ subgroup of $U(n+1)$ the set of operators C^{mn+1}, $m = 1, \cdots, n$ form a BIR characterized by $\{1\}$, as this is the IR of $\dot{a}_{\mu}^{m}$,

$m = 1, \ldots, n$, whereas a_μ^{n+1} is obviously an invariant with respect to $U(n)$. We could then use the Wigner-Eckart theorem for the $U(n)$ group to express the matrix elements of C^{mn+1} with respect to the Gelfand states $\{f_{st}\}$ of $U(n+1)$ as

$$\langle\{f_{st}\}|C^{mn+1}|\{f'_{st}\}\rangle = \left\langle \begin{matrix} f'_{1n} \cdots f'_{nn} \\ \cdots\cdots \\ f'_{11} \end{matrix} ; \begin{matrix} 1 \\ m \end{matrix} \middle| \begin{matrix} f_{1n} \cdots f_{nn} \\ \cdots \\ f_{11} \end{matrix} \right\rangle \times \left\langle \begin{matrix} \{f_{sn+1}\} \\ \{f_{sn}\} \end{matrix} \middle\| C^{nn+1} \middle\| \begin{matrix} \{f_{s\,n+1}\} \\ \{f'_{sn}\} \end{matrix} \right\rangle, \tag{6.7}$$

where the first factor on the right-hand side is the Wigner coefficient of $U(n)$ in the canonical chain in which $\begin{pmatrix} 1 \\ m \end{pmatrix}$ stands for

$$\begin{pmatrix} 1 \\ m \end{pmatrix} = \left(\begin{matrix} 1 \quad 0 \cdots\cdots\cdots 0 \\ 1 \quad 0 \cdots\cdots 0 \\ \cdots\cdots\cdots \\ 1 \quad 0 \cdots 0 \\ 0 \cdots 0 \\ \vdots \\ 0 \end{matrix} \right) \begin{matrix} \left.\vphantom{\begin{matrix}1\\1\\1\\1\end{matrix}}\right\} n - m + 1 \\ \left.\vphantom{\begin{matrix}1\\1\\1\end{matrix}}\right\} m - 1 \end{matrix} \tag{6.8}$$

The second factor in Eq. (6.7) is the reduced matrix element that depends on the IR of $U(n)$ and $U(n+1)$ in bra and ket, but not on any of the IR of the subgroups of $U(n)$. We note that only one Wigner coefficient appears in Eq. (6.7), since the product

$$\{f'_{1n} \cdots f'_{nn}\} \boxtimes \{1\} \tag{6.9}$$

is simply reducible.

The matrix element on the left-hand side of Eq. (6.7) was given by Gelfand and Zetlin (*26*); thus, the Wigner coefficient of one block will be determined once we get the explicit value of the reduced matrix element in Eq. (6.7). The latter could be determined by squaring both sides of Eq. (6.7) and summing over all $\{f_{st}\}$, $s \leqq t = 2 \cdots n-1$, remembering that the Wigner coefficients are normalized. More elegant procedures for deriving these reduced matrix elements have been given by several authors (*51*, *52*). Using them, we arrive at the following explicit expression for the one-block Wigner coefficients of $U(n)$

$$\left\langle [f'_{st}], \frac{1}{m} \middle| f_{st} = f'_{st} + \delta_{sl_t} \sum_{t'=m}^{n} \delta_{tt'} \right\rangle$$

$$= \prod_{p=m+1}^{n} S(l_{p-1} - l_p)$$

$$\times [(f'_{l_pp} - f'_{l_{p-1}p-1} + l_{p-1} - l_p)(f'_{l_pp} - f'_{l_{p-1}p-1} + l_{p-1} - l_p + 1)]^{-1/2}$$

$$\times \prod_{q=m}^{n} \left[(-1) \frac{\prod_{k=1}^{q-1} (f'_{l_qq} - f'_{kq-1} + k - l_q + 1)}{\prod_{k=1\, k\neq l_q}^{q} (f'_{l_qq} - f'_{kq} + k - l_q)} \right]^{1/2}$$

$$\times \prod_{q=m}^{n-1} \left[\frac{\prod_{k=1}^{q+1} (f'_{l_qq} - f'_{kq+1} + k - l_q)}{\prod_{k=1}^{q} (f'_{l_qq} - f'_{kq} + k - l_q + 1)} \right]^{1/2}, \tag{6.10}$$

where

$$S(x) = \begin{cases} 1 & \text{for } x \geqq 0 \\ -1 & \text{for } x < 0 \end{cases}.$$

C. The One-Particle Spin-Isospin Fractional Parentage Coefficients

Particularizing Eq. (6.10) to $n = 4$, we have the Wigner coefficients of $\mathscr{U}(4)$ in the canonical chain $\mathscr{U}(4) \supset \mathscr{U}(3) \supset \mathscr{U}(2) \supset \mathscr{U}(1)$. We showed, though, that the spin-isospin fpc are actually the reduced Wigner coefficients in the $\mathscr{U}(4) \supset \mathscr{SU}^{(\sigma)}(2) \times \mathscr{SU}^{(\tau)}(2)$ chain. The passage from one chain to the other is achieved by the same transformation brackets, Eq. (5.29), used for the construction of the spin-isospin states. Using these brackets, we obtain the Wigner coefficients

$$\left\langle \begin{matrix} [f'_1 f'_2 f'_3 f'_4] \\ \beta' S' M'_S T' M'_T \end{matrix} ; \begin{matrix} [1] \\ \tfrac{1}{2}\sigma'' \tfrac{1}{2}\tau'' \end{matrix} \middle| \begin{matrix} [f_1 f_2 f_3 f_4] \\ \beta S M_S T M_T \end{matrix} \right\rangle$$

$$= \sum_{e_{st}', e_{st}} \left\{ \left\langle \begin{matrix} [f'_1 f'_2 f'_3 f'_4] \\ \beta' S' M'_S T' M'_T \end{matrix} \middle| \begin{matrix} f'_1 \; f'_2 \; f'_3 \; f'_4 \\ e'_{13} \; e'_{23} \; e'_{33} \\ e'_{12} \; e'_{22} \\ e'_{11} \end{matrix} \right\rangle \right.$$

$$\times \left\langle \begin{matrix} f'_1 \; f'_2 \; f'_3 \; f'_4 \\ e'_{13} \; e'_{23} \; e'_{33} \\ e'_{12} \; e'_{22} \\ e'_{11} \end{matrix} ; \begin{matrix} 1 \\ \mu'' \end{matrix} \middle| \begin{matrix} f_1 \; f_2 \; f_3 \; f_4 \\ e_{13} \; e_{23} \; e_{33} \\ e_{12} \; e_{22} \\ e_{11} \end{matrix} \right\rangle$$

$$\left. \times \left\langle \begin{matrix} f_1 \; f_2 \; f_3 \; f_4 \\ e_{13} \; e_{23} \; e_{33} \\ e_{12} \; e_{22} \\ e_{11} \end{matrix} \middle| \begin{matrix} [f_1 f_2 f_3 f_4] \\ \beta S M_S T M_T \end{matrix} \right\rangle \right\}, \tag{6.11}$$

where the second term in Eq. (6.11) is given by Eq. (6.10) with $n=4$; the correspondence between the states

$$\left|\begin{matrix}1\\ \mu''\end{matrix}\right\rangle \quad \text{and} \quad \left|\begin{matrix}[1]\\ \frac{1}{2}\sigma''\frac{1}{2}\tau''\end{matrix}\right\rangle$$

is

$$\left|\begin{matrix}1 & 0 & 0 & 0\\ & 1 & 0 & 0\\ & & 1 & 0\\ & & & 1\end{matrix}\right\rangle = \left|\begin{matrix}[1]\\ \frac{1}{2}\frac{1}{2}\frac{1}{2}\frac{1}{2}\end{matrix}\right\rangle, \qquad \left|\begin{matrix}1 & 0 & 0 & 0\\ & 1 & 0 & 0\\ & & 1 & 0\\ & & & 0\end{matrix}\right\rangle = \left|\begin{matrix}[1]\\ \frac{1}{2}\frac{1}{2}\frac{1}{2}-\frac{1}{2}\end{matrix}\right\rangle$$

$$\left|\begin{matrix}1 & 0 & 0 & 0\\ & 1 & 0 & 0\\ & & 0 & 0\\ & & & 0\end{matrix}\right\rangle = \left|\begin{matrix}[1]\\ \frac{1}{2}-\frac{1}{2}\frac{1}{2}\frac{1}{2}\end{matrix}\right\rangle, \qquad \left|\begin{matrix}1 & 0 & 0 & 0\\ & 0 & 0 & 0\\ & & 0 & 0\\ & & & 0\end{matrix}\right\rangle = \left|\begin{matrix}[1]\\ \frac{1}{2}-\frac{1}{2}\frac{1}{2}-\frac{1}{2}\end{matrix}\right\rangle \tag{6.12}$$

due to the enumeration convention Eq. (5.3).

The first and third terms on the right-hand side of Eq. (6.11) are the transformation brackets Eq. (5.29) determined in the process of diagonalizing the matrices (*49*) of $\mathbf{S}^2$, $\mathbf{T}^2$ with respect to Gelfand states.

The reduced Wigner coefficients of $\mathscr{U}(4)$ are then obtained by multiplying Eq. (6.11) by Eq. (6.3) and summing over the indices $M_S'\sigma''M_T'\tau''$. As these coefficients are independent of M_S, M_T, we can choose $M_S=S$, $M_T=T$. From Eq. (6.5) we see then that the one-particle spin-isospin fpc is given explicitly by

$$\langle\gamma^{n-1}f'\beta'S'T', \gamma\tfrac{1}{2}\tfrac{1}{2}|\}\gamma^n f\beta ST\rangle$$

$$= \sum_{M_S'\sigma''}\sum_{M_T'\tau''}\{\langle S'\tfrac{1}{2}M_S'\sigma''|SS\rangle\langle T'\tfrac{1}{2}M_T'\tau''|TT\rangle$$

$$\times\left\langle\begin{matrix}[f_1'f_2'f_3'f_4']\\ \beta'S'M_S'T'M_T'\end{matrix};\begin{matrix}[1]\\ \frac{1}{2}\sigma''\frac{1}{2}\tau''\end{matrix}\middle|\begin{matrix}[f_1f_2f_3f_4]\\ \beta SSTT\end{matrix}\right\rangle. \tag{6.13}$$

We give explicitly, in Tables IV and V, the fpc for states of three and four particles that can be obtained by this procedure. The phase convention was chosen so as to agree with the results obtained previously by Jahn (*48*) for these two cases.

TABLE IV

ONE-PARTICLE SPIN-ISOSPIN fpc FOR THREE-PARTICLE SYSTEMS
$\langle \gamma^2 f' S' T', \gamma \tfrac{1}{2}\tfrac{1}{2} | \} \gamma^3 f S T \rangle$ [a]

f'	$S'T'$	f: {111}, ST: $\frac{1}{2}\frac{1}{2}$	{21}, $\frac{1}{2}\frac{1}{2}$	{21}, $\frac{3}{2}\frac{1}{2}$	{21}, $\frac{1}{2}\frac{3}{2}$	{3}, $\frac{1}{2}\frac{1}{2}$	{3}, $\frac{3}{2}\frac{3}{2}$
{11}	10	$-\frac{1}{\sqrt{2}}$	$\frac{1}{\sqrt{2}}$	1			
{11}	01	$\frac{1}{\sqrt{2}}$	$\frac{1}{\sqrt{2}}$		1		
{2}	00		$\frac{1}{\sqrt{2}}$			$\frac{1}{\sqrt{2}}$	
{2}	11		$-\frac{1}{\sqrt{2}}$	1	1	$\frac{1}{\sqrt{2}}$	1

[a] After Jahn (*48*).

Since all terms in Eqs. (6.11) and (6.13) can be explicitly determined, a group at the University of Mexico is planning a computer program to provide the fpc for spin-isospin states.

The one-particle spin-isospin fpc will be used in the following section to determine the one-body matrix elements. As we shall also be interested in two-body matrix elements, we reproduce in the following subsection the standard procedure for deriving the two-particle spin-isospin fpc from the one-particle fpc.

D. THE TWO-PARTICLE SPIN-ISOSPIN FRACTIONAL PARENTAGE COEFFICIENTS

By definition, the one-particle spin-isospin fpc is obtained when we try to determine the n-particle spin-isospin state of definite permutational symmetry and total spin and isospin from the corresponding state of $n-1$ particles and the state of the nth particle. We could clearly repeat the procedure for the $(n-1)$-particle state and separate from it the $(n-1)$th particle. Carrying out a recoupling procedure so as to get a state in which particles $n-1, n$ are coupled to a definite total spin-isospin, then coupling this state to the residual

TABLE V

ONE-PARTICLE SPIN-ISOSPIN fpc FOR FOUR-PARTICLE SYSTEMS $\langle \gamma^3 f' S'T', \gamma \tfrac{1}{2}\tfrac{1}{2} | \} \gamma^4 ST \rangle$ [a]

f'	$S'T'$	f: {1111}	{211}	{211}	{211}	{22}	{22}	{22}	{22}	{31}	{31}	{31}	{31}	{31}	{4}	{4}	{4}
	ST:	00	10	01	11	00	11	20	02	10	01	11	21	12	00	11	22
{111}	$\frac{1}{2}\frac{1}{2}$	1	1	1	1												
{21}	$\frac{1}{2}\frac{1}{2}$		$-\frac{1}{\sqrt{2}}$	$\frac{1}{\sqrt{2}}$		1	$\frac{1}{\sqrt{3}}$			$-\frac{1}{\sqrt{2}}$	$-\frac{1}{\sqrt{2}}$	$\frac{\sqrt{2}}{\sqrt{3}}$					
{21}	$\frac{3}{2}\frac{1}{2}$		$-\frac{1}{\sqrt{2}}$		$\frac{1}{\sqrt{2}}$		$-\frac{1}{\sqrt{3}}$	1		$\frac{1}{\sqrt{2}}$		$\frac{1}{\sqrt{6}}$	1				
{21}	$\frac{1}{2}\frac{3}{2}$			$\frac{1}{\sqrt{2}}$	$-\frac{1}{\sqrt{2}}$		$-\frac{1}{\sqrt{3}}$		1		$\frac{1}{\sqrt{2}}$	$\frac{1}{\sqrt{6}}$		1			
{3}	$\frac{1}{2}\frac{1}{2}$									1	1	$\frac{1}{\sqrt{3}}$			1	$\frac{\sqrt{2}}{\sqrt{3}}$	
{3}	$\frac{3}{2}\frac{3}{2}$											$-\frac{\sqrt{2}}{\sqrt{3}}$	1	1		$\frac{1}{\sqrt{3}}$	1

[a] After Jahn (*48*).

$(n-2)$-particle state, we get, by using standard Racah algebra, that

$$|\gamma^n f r \beta S M_S T M_T\rangle = \sum_{S'S''} \sum_{T'T''} \{[|\gamma^{n-2} f' r' \beta' S' T'\rangle |\gamma^2 S'' T''\rangle]_{SM_S TM_T}$$
$$\times \langle \gamma^{n-2} f' \beta' S' T', \gamma^2 S'' T'', \dot{f} | \} \gamma^n f \beta S T\rangle\}, \qquad (6.14)$$

where the first term on the right-hand side is the state of $n-2$ particles coupled to a state of definite spin and isospin of the last two particles. The square bracket with the indices $SM_S TM_T$ is a shorthand notation for coupling with ordinary Wigner coefficients of $\mathscr{SU}^{(\sigma),(\tau)}(2)$. The last term of Eq. (6.14) is a two-particle fpc. We note that the n- and $(n-2)$-particle states contain the Yamanouchi symbols r and r', respectively. It is obvious that $r = r' r_{n-1} r_n$; thus the r not only gives the IR f' of $S(n-2)$ for the $(n-2)$-particle state, but also the IR $\dot{f}$ of $S(n-1)$, when we eliminate the block n. The fpc in Eq. (6.14) is clearly independent of the Yamanouchi symbol r' of $S(n-2)$, since both the n- and $(n-2)$-particle states are characterized by the same IR of $S(n-2)$. It depends, though, on r_{n-1}, r_n or, equivalently, on f', $\dot{f}$, and this is explicitly indicated in the fpc.

From the foregoing discussion it is clear that the explicit expression for the two-particle spin-isospin fpc is

$$\langle \gamma^{n-2} f' \beta' S' T', \gamma^2 S'' T'', \dot{f} | \} \gamma^n f \beta S T\rangle$$
$$= \sum_{\bar{\beta}\bar{S}\bar{T}} \{\langle \gamma^{n-2} f' \beta' S' T', \gamma \tfrac{1}{2}\tfrac{1}{2} | \} \gamma^{n-1} \dot{f} \bar{\beta} \bar{S} \bar{T}\rangle$$
$$\times \langle \gamma^{n-1} \dot{f} \bar{\beta} \bar{S} \bar{T}, \gamma \tfrac{1}{2}\tfrac{1}{2} | \} \gamma^n f \beta S T\rangle$$
$$\times [(2\bar{S}+1)(2S''+1)]^{1/2} W(S' \tfrac{1}{2} S \tfrac{1}{2}; \bar{S} S'')$$
$$\times [(2\bar{T}+1)(2T''+1)]^{1/2} W(T' \tfrac{1}{2} T \tfrac{1}{2}; \bar{T} T'')\}. \qquad (6.15)$$

where the first two terms on the right-hand side of Eq. (6.15) are one-particle fpc given by Eqs. (6.11), (6.13), while the last terms are Racah coefficients.

In Table VI (the table is divided into subtables characterized by the partition $f' = \{2\}$ or $\{11\}$ and by $T = 0, 1, 2$) we give the two-particle fpc for the spin-isospin state of four particles obtained from Eq. (6.15) where the one-particle fpc are taken from Tables IV and V. For the system of three particles we do not need a two-particle fpc, as we already have particles 1, 2 coupled together. Two-particle spin-isospin fpc of a similar type have been discussed and tabulated by Elliott, Hope, and Jahn (*53*).

In the next section we will indicate how the spin-isospin fpc and the orbital hfpc obtained earlier can be used to derive the one-body and two-body matrix elements.

TABLE VI

Two-Particle Spin-Isospin fpc for Four-Particle Systems
$\langle \gamma^2 f' S'T', \gamma^2 S''T'', \dot{f} | \} \gamma^4 f ST \rangle$

(a) $f' = \{2\}, \quad T = 0$

$S'T'$	$S''T''$	f: {4} $\dot{f}$: {3} ST: 00	f: {31} $\dot{f}$: {3} ST: 10	f: {31} $\dot{f}$: {21} ST: 10	f: {22} $\dot{f}$: {21} ST: 00	f: {22} $\dot{f}$: {21} ST: 20	f: {211} $\dot{f}$: {21} ST: 10
00	00	$\frac{1}{\sqrt{2}}$			$\frac{1}{\sqrt{2}}$		
00	01						
00	10		$\frac{1}{\sqrt{2}}$	$-\frac{1}{2}$			$-\frac{1}{2}$
00	11						
11	00						
11	01		$-\frac{1}{\sqrt{6}}$	$\frac{1}{2\sqrt{3}}$			$-\frac{\sqrt{3}}{2}$
11	10						
11	11	$\frac{1}{\sqrt{2}}$	$\frac{1}{\sqrt{3}}$	$\frac{\sqrt{2}}{\sqrt{3}}$	$-\frac{1}{\sqrt{2}}$	1	

(b) $f' = \{2\}, \quad T = 1$

$S'T'$	$S''T''$	f: {4} $\dot{f}$: {3} ST: 11	f: {31} $\dot{f}$: {3} ST: 01	f: {31} $\dot{f}$: {3} ST: 11	f: {31} $\dot{f}$: {3} ST: 21	f: {31} $\dot{f}$: {21} ST: 01	f: {31} $\dot{f}$: {21} ST: 11	f: {31} $\dot{f}$: {21} ST: 21	f: {22} $\dot{f}$: {21} ST: 11	f: {211} $\dot{f}$: {21} ST: 01	f: {211} $\dot{f}$: {21} ST: 11
00	00										
00	01		$\frac{1}{\sqrt{2}}$			$-\frac{1}{2}$				$\frac{1}{2}$	
00	10										
00	11	$\frac{1}{\sqrt{3}}$		$\frac{1}{\sqrt{6}}$			$\frac{1}{\sqrt{3}}$		$\frac{1}{\sqrt{6}}$		
11	00	$\frac{1}{\sqrt{3}}$		$-\frac{1}{\sqrt{6}}$			$-\frac{1}{\sqrt{3}}$		$\frac{1}{\sqrt{6}}$		
11	01			$-\frac{1}{\sqrt{3}}$			$\frac{1}{\sqrt{6}}$				$\frac{1}{\sqrt{2}}$
11	10		$-\frac{1}{\sqrt{6}}$	$-\frac{1}{\sqrt{3}}$	$\frac{\sqrt{2}}{\sqrt{3}}$	$\frac{1}{2\sqrt{3}}$	$\frac{1}{\sqrt{6}}$	$-\frac{1}{\sqrt{3}}$		$\frac{\sqrt{3}}{2}$	$-\frac{1}{\sqrt{2}}$
11	11	$\frac{1}{\sqrt{3}}$	$\frac{1}{\sqrt{3}}$		$\frac{1}{\sqrt{3}}$	$\frac{\sqrt{2}}{\sqrt{3}}$		$\frac{\sqrt{2}}{\sqrt{3}}$	$-\frac{\sqrt{2}}{\sqrt{3}}$		

TABLE VI—*continued*

(c) $f' = \{2\}, \quad T = 2$

		f	{4}	{31}	{31}	{22}
		$\dot{f}$	{3}	{3}	{21}	{21}
$S'T'$	$S''T''$	ST	22	12	12	02
00	00					
00	01					
00	10					
00	11					
11	00					
11	01			$\frac{\sqrt{2}}{\sqrt{3}}$	$-\frac{1}{\sqrt{3}}$	
11	10					
11	11		1	$\frac{1}{\sqrt{3}}$	$\frac{\sqrt{2}}{\sqrt{3}}$	1

(d) $f' = \{11\}, \quad T = 0$

		f	{31}	{22}	{22}	{211}	{211}	{1111}
		$\dot{f}$	{21}	{21}	{21}	{21}	{111}	{111}
$S'T'$	$S''T''$	ST	10	00	20	10	10	00
01	00							
01	01			$\frac{1}{\sqrt{2}}$				$\frac{1}{\sqrt{2}}$
01	10							
01	11		$-\frac{1}{2}$			$-\frac{1}{2}$	$-\frac{1}{\sqrt{2}}$	
10	00		$\frac{\sqrt{3}}{2}$			$-\frac{1}{2\sqrt{3}}$	$-\frac{1}{\sqrt{6}}$	
10	01							
10	10			$\frac{1}{\sqrt{2}}$	1	$-\frac{\sqrt{2}}{\sqrt{3}}$	$\frac{1}{\sqrt{3}}$	$-\frac{1}{\sqrt{2}}$
0	11							

TABLE VI—*continued*

(e) $f' = \{11\}$, $T = 1$

$S'T'$	$S''T''$ \ f	$\{31\}$	$\{31\}$	$\{31\}$	$\{22\}$	$\{211\}$	$\{211\}$	$\{211\}$	$\{211\}$
	$\dot{f}$	$\{21\}$	$\{21\}$	$\{21\}$	$\{21\}$	$\{21\}$	$\{21\}$	$\{111\}$	$\{111\}$
	ST	01	11	21	11	01	11	01	11
01	00	$\frac{\sqrt{3}}{2}$				$\frac{1}{2\sqrt{3}}$		$\frac{1}{\sqrt{6}}$	
01	01					$\frac{\sqrt{2}}{\sqrt{3}}$		$-\frac{1}{\sqrt{3}}$	
01	10				$-\frac{1}{\sqrt{2}}$		$-\frac{1}{\sqrt{3}}$		$\frac{1}{\sqrt{6}}$
01	11		$\frac{1}{\sqrt{2}}$				$-\frac{1}{\sqrt{6}}$		$-\frac{1}{\sqrt{3}}$
10	00								
10	01				$-\frac{1}{\sqrt{2}}$		$\frac{1}{\sqrt{3}}$		$-\frac{1}{\sqrt{6}}$
10	10								
11	11	$-\frac{1}{2}$	$\frac{1}{\sqrt{2}}$	1		$\frac{1}{2}$	$\frac{1}{\sqrt{6}}$	$\frac{1}{\sqrt{2}}$	$\frac{1}{\sqrt{3}}$

(f) $f' = \{11\}$, $T = 2$

$S'T'$	$S''T''$ \ f	$\{31\}$	$\{22\}$
	$\dot{f}$	$\{21\}$	$\{21\}$
	ST	12	02
01	00		
01	01		1
01	10		
01	11	1	
10	00		
10	01		
10	10		
10	11		

VII. Evaluation of Matrix Elements of One-Body and Two-Body Operators

In Sections II and III we discussed the construction of orbital n-particle states with permutational symmetry in an ho potential. For both the shell model and the translational-invariant model, these states can be denoted by

$$\left|\begin{matrix}[h_1h_2h_3] \\ \Omega LM\end{matrix}, \quad \begin{matrix}\{h_1h_2h_3\} \\ \chi fr\end{matrix}\right\rangle. \tag{7.1}$$

In Section V we constructed n-particle spin-isospin states with permutational symmetry, which we denoted by

$$\left|\begin{matrix}\tilde{f} \\ \beta SM_S TM_T\end{matrix}, \quad \tilde{f}\tilde{r}\right\rangle \tag{7.2a}$$

where

$$\tilde{f} = [\tilde{f}_1\tilde{f}_2\tilde{f}_3\tilde{f}_4], \qquad \tilde{r} = (1\tilde{r}_2 \cdots \tilde{r}_n). \tag{7.2b}$$

To satisfy the Pauli principle we must construct n-particle states antisymmetric under exchange of both orbital and spin-isospin variables of any two particles. This requires that $\tilde{f}$ be the partition associate to f (*30*, p. 200). Furthermore, we couple the total orbital angular momentum **L** and the total spin **S** to the total angular momentum **J**. The normalized antisymmetric linear combination of the orbital and spin-isospin states are then given by

$$\left|\left[\begin{matrix}[h_1h_2h_3] \\ \Omega L\end{matrix}, \quad \begin{matrix}\{h_1h_2h_3\} \\ \chi f\end{matrix}; \quad \begin{matrix}\tilde{f} \\ \beta STM_T\end{matrix}\right]_{JM}\right\rangle$$
$$= |f|^{-1/2} \sum_r (-1)^r \left[\left|\begin{matrix}[h_1h_2h_3] \\ \Omega L\end{matrix}, \quad \begin{matrix}\{h_1h_2h_3\} \\ \chi fr\end{matrix}\right\rangle \left|\begin{matrix}\tilde{f} \\ \beta STM_T\end{matrix}, \quad \tilde{f}\tilde{r}\right\rangle\right]_{JM} \tag{7.3}$$

where the square bracket with indices JM again indicates vector coupling, in this case of **L** and **S**. In Eq. (7.3), $\tilde{r}$ and r correspond to associate Young tableaux. For example, in $S(3)$ if

$$f = \{3\}, \qquad \boxed{1}\boxed{2}\boxed{3} \qquad r = (111)$$

then

$$\tilde{f} = \{111\}, \qquad \begin{array}{|c|}\hline 1 \\ \hline 2 \\ \hline 3 \\ \hline\end{array} \qquad \tilde{r} = (123)$$

The signature $(-1)^r$ is 1 if the Young tableau corresponding to r is obtained from

$$\begin{array}{|l|}\hline 1\,2 \cdots\cdots\cdots f_1 \\ \hline f_1+1 \cdots f_1+f_2 \\ \hline \end{array}$$
$$\begin{array}{l} \cdots\cdots \\ \cdots \end{array}$$

by an even number of successive interchanges of two numbers and -1 otherwise.

A. One-Body and Two-Body Operators

Let us now consider the form of the one-body and two-body operators that we would like to apply to the states Eq. (7.3). From the way these states are built up, it is clear that it would be convenient to write these operators as sums of products of one operator acting on the orbital state and another operator acting on the spin-isospin state. The latter, in turn, could be decomposed into the product of one operator depending on spins and another depending on isospins, since spin and isospin are related to $\mathscr{SU}(2)$ transformations in independent spaces.

An example of this type of decomposition is given by the one-body spin orbit coupling that can be written as

$$\mathscr{W}^{ls} = \sum_{t=1}^{n} [V(r^t)\mathbf{l}^t]\cdot[\mathbf{s}^t] \tag{7.4a}$$

$$\mathbf{l}^t = \hbar^{-1}\mathbf{x}^t \times \mathbf{p}^t, \qquad r^t = |\mathbf{x}^t| \tag{7.4b}$$

where the first bracket acts only on the orbital part of the state, while the second depends only on the spin of the particle.

We note, incidentally, that a rotation of the coordinate system affects both space and spin (but not isospin) variables, so that Racah (that is, irreducible) tensors can be constructed from space and spin observables. An example is given by Eq. (7.4), where $\mathscr{W}^{ls}$ is clearly a scalar, that is, a Racah tensor of order 0, under rotations of the coordinate system.

To make full use of the techniques of Racah algebra, it is convenient to write the operators acting on orbital states as Racah tensors $T^{k_1}_{q_1}$ and those acting on spin-isospin space as products of Racah tensors, that is, $U^{k_2}_{q_2}V^{\kappa}_{\rho}$, where the first factor depends only on spins and the second only on isospins. A general one-body operator can then be written in terms of coupled tensor operators, that is in terms of the operators

$$\mathscr{W} = \sum_{t=1}^{n} \sum_{q_1 q_2} \langle k_1 k_2 q_1 q_2 | kq \rangle T^{k_1}_{q_1}(t) U^{k_2}_{q_2}(t) V^{\kappa}_{\rho}(t) \tag{7.5}$$

where

$$T^{k_1}_{q_1}(t) \equiv T^{k_1}_{q_1}(\mathbf{x}^t, \mathbf{p}^t) \tag{7.6}$$

and

$$U^{k_2}_{q_2}(t) \equiv U^{k_2}_{q_2}(\mathbf{s}^t), \qquad V^{\kappa}_{\rho}(t) \equiv V^{\kappa}_{\rho}(\mathbf{t}^t) \tag{7.7a,b}$$

act on orbital and spin-isospin states, respectively.

Similarly, all two-body interactions can be written in terms of products of tensor operators coupled to a scalar, that is, as

$$\mathscr{V} = \sum_{1=s<t}^{n} \sum_{q} (-1)^q T^k_q(s, t) U^k_{-q}(s, t) V^{\kappa}_{\rho}(s, t), \tag{7.8}$$

where

$$T^k_q(s, t) \equiv T^k_q(\mathbf{x}^s - \mathbf{x}^t, \mathbf{p}^s - \mathbf{p}^t) \tag{7.9}$$

and

$$U^k_q(s, t) \equiv U^k_q(\mathbf{s}^s, \mathbf{s}^t) \tag{7.10a}$$

$$V^{\kappa}_{\rho}(s, t) \equiv V^{\kappa}_{\rho}(\mathbf{t}^s, \mathbf{t}^t). \tag{7.10b}$$

At the present stage of knowledge of nuclear forces, it is assumed that they are charge independent, which implies independence from isospin, so that V^{κ}_{ρ} in Eq. (7.8) could be taken as unity. The only case of isospin dependence corresponds to the Coulomb interaction to be discussed at the end of this subsection. In this case though, the interaction is independent of spin, and invariance under rotation implies $k = 0$ in Eq. (7.8).

We shall now discuss the possible types of two-body interactions that result from the phenomenological analysis of the nucleon-nucleon interaction.

A central Wigner two-body interaction has $k = 0$,

$$T^0_0(s, t) = V(r^{s,t}), \qquad r^{s,t} = |\mathbf{x}^s - \mathbf{x}^t|, \tag{7.11a}$$

$$U^0_0(s, t) = 1. \tag{7.11b}$$

By introducing the Majorana operator

$$^MP^{s,t},\qquad(7.12)$$

which exchanges particles s and t in the orbital part, we can define central forces of even and odd type

$$V^e(r^{s,t})\,^eP^{s,t},\qquad V^o(r^{s,t})\,^oP^{s,t},\qquad(7.13a,b)$$

$$^eP^{s,t}=\tfrac{1}{2}(1+\,^MP^{s,t}),\qquad ^oP^{s,t}=\tfrac{1}{2}(1-\,^MP^{s,t}).\qquad(7.14a,b)$$

Similarly, we can introduce the Bartlett operator

$$^BP^{s,t}=(\mathbf{s}^s+\mathbf{s}^t)^2-1,\qquad(7.15)$$

which interchanges the spin variables of particles s and t, and define central forces of singlet or triplet type, that is,

$$^1V(r^{s,t})\,^1P^{s,t},\qquad ^3V(r^{s,t})\,^3P^{s,t},\qquad(7.16a,b)$$

$$^1P^{s,t}=\tfrac{1}{2}(1-\,^BP^{s,t}),\qquad ^3P^{s,t}=\tfrac{1}{2}(1+\,^BP^{s,t}).\qquad(7.17a,b)$$

Combining all possibilities, the central forces with $k=0$ could be singlet even, singlet odd or triplet even, triplet odd.

Next we consider the two-body spin orbit force

$$\mathscr{V}^{ls}=\sum_{i=s<t}^{n}[V^{ls}(r^{s,t})\mathbf{l}^{s,t}]\cdot(\mathbf{s}^s+\mathbf{s}^t),\qquad(7.18a)$$

$$\mathbf{l}^{s,t}=\left(\frac{1}{2\hbar}\right)(\mathbf{x}^s-\mathbf{x}^t)\times(\mathbf{p}^s-\mathbf{p}^t),\qquad(7.18b)$$

which can be written in the form of Eq. (7.8) on putting

$$T_q^1(s,t)=V^{ls}(r^{s,t})l_q^{s,t}\qquad(7.19a)$$

$$U_q^1(s,t)=(s^s+s^t)_q\qquad(7.19b)$$

where $q=1,0,-1$ are the spherical components of the vectors indicated. Since this force does not act in the singlet state, it could be triplet even or triplet odd.

The two-body tensor interaction can be written as

$$\mathscr{V}^{\mathrm{T}} = \sum_{1=s<t}^{n} \{V^{\mathrm{T}}(r^{s,t})4[3(\mathbf{s}^s \cdot (\mathbf{x}^s - \mathbf{x}^t))(\mathbf{s}^t \cdot (\mathbf{x}^s - \mathbf{x}^t))(r^{s,t})^{-2} - (\mathbf{s}^s \cdot \mathbf{s}^t)]\}, \quad (7.20)$$

which has the tensor decomposition with $k=2$ for, say, the $q=0$ component

$$\begin{aligned} T_0^2(s,t) &= V^{\mathrm{T}}(r^{s,t})\sqrt{2}(r^{s,t})^{-2}[3(x_0^s - x_0^t)^2 - (r^{s,t})^2] \\ &= V^{\mathrm{T}}(r^{s,t})\left(\frac{32\pi}{5}\right)^{1/2} Y_0^2\left(\frac{\mathbf{x}^s - \mathbf{x}^t}{r^{s,t}}\right), \end{aligned} \quad (7.21a)$$

$$U_0^2(s,t) = \sqrt{\tfrac{1}{2}}[3(s_0^s + s_0^t)^2 - (\mathbf{s}^s + \mathbf{s}^t)^2], \quad (7.21b)$$

where Y_0^2 is a spherical harmonic of the unit vector indicated. The tensor interaction could be triplet even or triplet odd.

We consider now the quadratic spin orbit interaction, which can be defined as

$$\begin{aligned} \mathscr{V}^{Q} &= 2 \sum_{1=s<t}^{n} V^{Q}(r^{s,t})(\mathbf{s}^s \cdot \mathbf{l}^{s,t})(\mathbf{s}^t \cdot \mathbf{l}^{s,t}) \\ &= \sum_{1=s<t}^{n} V^{Q}(r^{s,t})[\tfrac{2}{3}(\mathbf{s}^s + \mathbf{s}^t)^2 - 1](\mathbf{l}^{s,t})^2 \\ &\quad + \tfrac{2}{3} \sum_{1=s<t}^{n} V^{Q}(r^{s,t}) \sum_{q} (-1)^q T_q^2(\mathbf{l}^{s,t}) U_{-q}^2(s,t), \end{aligned} \quad (7.22)$$

where $U_q^2(s,t)$ is the same as appears in the ordinary tensor force Eq. (7.21), while

$$T_0^2(\mathbf{l}^{s,t}) = \sqrt{2}[3(l_0^{s,t})^2 - (\mathbf{l}^{s,t})^2], \quad (7.23)$$

and similarly for the other components $q = 2, \ldots, -2$. This interaction is a mixture of irreducible tensor interactions with $k=0$ and $k=2$.

Finally, we turn to the Coulomb interaction, which depends on isospin, since it can be written as

$$\mathscr{V}^{c} = \sum_{1=s<t}^{n} \frac{e^2}{r^{s,t}}(\tfrac{1}{2} - t_0^s)(\tfrac{1}{2} - t_0^t). \quad (7.24)$$

Although this is a scalar in both orbital and spin space, it can be decomposed in isospin space into $q=0$ components of tensor operators $V_0^{\kappa}(s,t)$ of rank

$\kappa = 0, 1, 2$, since

$$(\tfrac{1}{2} - t_0^s)(\tfrac{1}{2} - t_0^t)$$
$$= \tfrac{1}{6}[3(t_0^s + t_0^t)^2 - (\mathbf{t}^s + \mathbf{t}^t)^2] - \tfrac{1}{2}(t_0^s + t_0^t) + \tfrac{1}{6}(\mathbf{t}^s + \mathbf{t}^t)^2$$
$$\equiv \frac{\sqrt{2}}{6} V_0^2(s, t) - \tfrac{1}{2} V_0^1(s, t) + \tfrac{1}{6} V_0^0(s, t) \equiv \sum_{\kappa=0}^{2} a_\kappa V_0^\kappa(s, t). \tag{7.25}$$

B. General Procedure for Deriving Matrix Elements of One-Body and Two-Body Operators

All the interactions that we have discussed can be written in terms of products of tensor operators $T_{q_1}^{k_1}$ and $U_{q_2}^{k_2} V_\rho^\kappa$ acting on the orbital or spin-isospin states, respectively. Because of the antisymmetry of the states Eq. (7.3), the matrices of $\mathscr{W}$ in Eq. (7.5) and of $\mathscr{V}$ in Eq. (7.8) can be reduced to those for the last particle or the last pair of particles, respectively. Next, by applying standard Racah algebra, we reduce these expressions to those for the orbital and spin-isospin states separately which make up the coupled state Eq. (7.3). Finally, by using fpc, we reduce the matrix elements of $\mathscr{W}$ and $\mathscr{V}$ to those between one- and two-particle states, respectively.

1. One-Body Operators in Shell Model States

Since the states Eq. (7.3) are antisymmetric, the matrices of the operators $\mathscr{W}$ [Eq. (7.5)] can be reduced to the term with $t = n$. We shall adopt the notation of Rose (*54*, p. 85) for the reduced matrix elements and shall then obtain the matrix of $\mathscr{W}$ as (*46*, p. 110)

$$\left\langle \begin{bmatrix} [\bar{h}_1\bar{h}_2\bar{h}_3] \\ \bar{\Omega}\bar{L} \end{bmatrix}, \begin{matrix} \{\bar{h}_1\bar{h}_2\bar{h}_3\} \\ \bar{\chi}\bar{f} \end{matrix}; \begin{matrix} \tilde{\bar{f}} \\ \bar{\beta}\bar{S}\bar{T}\bar{M}_T \end{matrix} \right]_{\bar{J}\bar{M}} \left| \mathscr{W} \right| \left[\begin{matrix} [h_1h_2h_3] \\ \Omega L \end{matrix}, \begin{matrix} \{h_1h_2h_3\} \\ \chi f \end{matrix}; \begin{matrix} \tilde{f} \\ \beta STM_T \end{matrix} \right]_{JM} \right\rangle$$
$$= n\left(\frac{1}{|f||\bar{f}|}\right)^{1/2} \langle JkMq|\bar{J}\bar{M}\rangle\, [(2\bar{L}+1)(2\bar{S}+1)(2J+1)(2k+1)]^{1/2} \begin{Bmatrix} \bar{L} & L & k_1 \\ \bar{S} & S & k_2 \\ \bar{J} & J & k \end{Bmatrix}$$
$$\times \sum_{\bar{r}r} \Bigg\{ (-1)^{\bar{r}}(-1)^{r} \left\langle \begin{matrix} [\bar{h}_1\bar{h}_2\bar{h}_3] \\ \bar{\Omega}\bar{L} \end{matrix}, \begin{matrix} \{\bar{h}_1\bar{h}_2\bar{h}_3\} \\ \bar{\chi}\bar{f}\bar{r} \end{matrix} \right\| T^{k_1}(n) \left\| \begin{matrix} [h_1h_2h_3] \\ \Omega L \end{matrix}, \begin{matrix} \{h_1h_2h_3\} \\ \chi f r \end{matrix} \right\rangle$$
$$\times \langle \tilde{\bar{f}}\bar{\beta}\bar{S}\bar{T}\bar{M}_T \| U^{k_2}(n) V_\rho^\kappa(n) \| \tilde{f}\beta STM_T \rangle \Bigg\} \tag{7.26}$$

where the expression in the curly brace is a $9j$ coefficient (*46*, p. 100).

We have then reduced the calculation of one-body operators to the calculation of the reduced matrix elements for the n-particle orbital and spin-isospin states. The next step is the reduction to single-particle matrix elements by means of fpc for the orbital and the spin-isospin states given in Eqs. (4.5), (4.6) and Eq. (6.5), respectively.

The orbital reduced matrix element becomes, using the decomposition Eq. (4.5) as well as standard Racah algebra,

$$\left\langle \begin{matrix} [\bar{h}_1\bar{h}_2\bar{h}_3] \\ \bar{\Omega}\bar{L} \end{matrix}, \begin{matrix} \{\bar{h}_1\bar{h}_2\bar{h}_3\} \\ \bar{\chi}\bar{f}\bar{r} \end{matrix} \right\| T^{k_1}(n) \left\| \begin{matrix} [h_1h_2h_3] \\ \Omega L \end{matrix}, \begin{matrix} \{h_1h_2h_3\} \\ \chi f r \end{matrix} \right\rangle$$

$$= \sum_{\substack{h_1'h_2'h_3' \\ \chi'f'\Omega'L'}} \sum_{\substack{h''l'' \\ \bar{h}''\bar{l}''}} \left\langle \begin{matrix} \bar{h}'' \\ \bar{l}'' \end{matrix} \right\| T^{k_1}(n) \left\| \begin{matrix} h'' \\ l'' \end{matrix} \right\rangle$$

$$\times (-1)^{L'+k_1-\bar{l}''-L}[(2\bar{l}''+1)(2L+1)]^{1/2} W(\bar{l}''\bar{L}l''L;L'k_1)$$

$$\times \left\langle \begin{matrix} [\bar{h}_1\bar{h}_2\bar{h}_3] \\ \bar{\Omega}\bar{L} \end{matrix}, \begin{matrix} \{\bar{h}_1\bar{h}_2\bar{h}_3\} \\ \bar{\chi}\bar{f} \end{matrix} \right\} \left| \begin{matrix} [h_1'h_2'h_3'] \\ \Omega'L' \end{matrix}, \begin{matrix} \{h_1'h_2'h_3'\} \\ \chi'f' \end{matrix}; \begin{matrix} [\bar{h}''] \\ \bar{l}'' \end{matrix} \right\rangle$$

$$\times \left\langle \begin{matrix} [h_1'h_2'h_3'] \\ \Omega'L' \end{matrix}, \begin{matrix} \{h_1'h_2'h_3'\} \\ \chi'f' \end{matrix}; \begin{matrix} [h''] \\ l'' \end{matrix} \right| \left\} \begin{matrix} [h_1h_2h_3] \\ \Omega L \end{matrix}, \begin{matrix} \{h_1h_2h_3\} \\ \chi f \end{matrix} \right\rangle \tag{7.27}$$

where the last term in Eq. (7.27) is the one-particle hfpc given in Eq. (4.6), while the preceding term is the complex conjugate of the corresponding hfpc as these coefficients form a unitary matrix.

The angular part of the one-body matrix element

$$\left\langle \begin{matrix} \bar{h}'' \\ \bar{l}'' \end{matrix} \right\| T^{k_1}(n) \left\| \begin{matrix} h'' \\ l'' \end{matrix} \right\rangle \tag{7.28a}$$

is easily evaluated by standard procedures (*54*, p. 62); thus we are left with radial integrals of the type

$$\int_0^\infty \mathscr{R}_{\frac{1}{2}(\bar{h}''-\bar{l}''),\bar{l}''}(r^n) V(r^n) \mathscr{R}_{\frac{1}{2}(h''-l''),l''}(r^n)(r^n)^2\,dr^n$$

$$= \sum_p B(\tfrac{1}{2}(\bar{h}''-\bar{l}''), \bar{l}'', \tfrac{1}{2}(h''-l''), l'', p) I_p. \tag{7.28b}$$

In Eq. (7.28b), $\mathscr{R}$ are the radial functions of the ho and the integrals are given in terms of the Talmi integrals of $V(r)$, that is (*1*),

$$I_p = \frac{2}{\Gamma(p+\frac{3}{2})} \int_0^\infty r^{2p+2} e^{-r^2} V\left(\left(\frac{\hbar}{m\omega}\right)^{1/2} r\right) dr, \qquad p = 0, 1, \ldots \tag{7.28c}$$

with $r = (m\omega/\hbar)^{1/2} r^n$, and the numerical coefficients B defined and tabulated by Brody *et al.* (*55, 5*).

The reduction of the spin-isospin matrix element appearing in Eq. (7.26) proceeds in a completely analogous fashion with the help of the spin-isospin one-particle fpc Eq. (6.5). We obtain

$$\langle \bar{f}\bar{\beta}\bar{S}\bar{T}\bar{M}_T, \bar{f}\bar{r} \| U^{k_2}(n) V^{\kappa}_{\rho}(n) \| f\beta S T M_T, fr\rangle$$

$$= \sum_{\beta' S' T'} \{\langle \tfrac{1}{2} \| U^{k_2}(n) \| \tfrac{1}{2}\rangle \langle \tfrac{1}{2} \| V^{\kappa}(n) \| \tfrac{1}{2}\rangle$$

$$\times (-1)^{S'+k_2-\frac{1}{2}-S} [2(2S+1)]^{1/2} W(\tfrac{1}{2}\bar{S}\tfrac{1}{2}S;\, S'k_2)$$

$$\times (-1)^{T'+\kappa-\frac{1}{2}-T} [2(2T+1)]^{1/2} W(\tfrac{1}{2}\bar{T}\tfrac{1}{2}T;\, T'\kappa) \langle T\kappa M_T\rho | \bar{T}\bar{M}_T\rangle$$

$$\times \langle \gamma^n \bar{f}\bar{\beta}\bar{S}\bar{T} \{| \gamma^{n-1} f'\beta' S' T', \gamma\tfrac{1}{2}\tfrac{1}{2}\rangle$$

$$\times \langle \gamma^{n-1} f'\beta' S' T', \gamma\tfrac{1}{2}\tfrac{1}{2} |\} \gamma^n f\beta S T\rangle\} \tag{7.29}$$

where, in a way similar to that indicated after Eq. (7.27), the term before the last is the complex conjugate of the corresponding one-particle spin-isospin fpc of Eq. (6.5). The reduced matrix elements in Eq. (7.29) are trivial to determine, as $U^{k_2}_{q_2}(n)$, $V^{\kappa}_{\rho}(n)$ are functions of the spin or isospin, respectively, of particle n.

2. *Matrix Elements of Two-Body Interactions*

We recall from subsection A that two-body interactions are either charge independent, so that $V^{\kappa}_{\rho}(s, t) = 1$, or Coulomb interactions, for which $k = 0$ and $U^0_0(s, t) = 1$. We shall restrict the discussion in this subsection to charge-independent forces, though at the end of it we shall indicate the modifications we have to make to include the Coulomb interaction.

The matrix elements of $\mathscr{V}$ Eq. (7.8) between the states Eq. (7.3) can be reduced to those of the last pair by using the antisymmetry of the states.

Therefore, these matrix elements are

$$\left\langle \begin{bmatrix} [\bar{h}_1\bar{h}_2\bar{h}_3] , & \{\bar{h}_1\bar{h}_2\bar{h}_3\} ; & \tilde{\bar{f}} \\ \bar{\Omega}\bar{L} & \bar{\chi}\bar{f} & \bar{\beta}\bar{S}TM_T \end{bmatrix}_{JM} \middle| \mathscr{V} \middle| \begin{bmatrix} [h_1h_2h_3] , & \{h_1h_2h_3\} ; & \tilde{f} \\ \Omega L & \chi f & \beta STM_T \end{bmatrix}_{JM} \right\rangle$$

$$= (-1)^{\bar{L}+S-J}[(2\bar{L}+1)(2\bar{S}+1)]^{1/2} W(LS\bar{L}\bar{S}; Jk)$$

$$\times \frac{n(n-1)}{2}\left(\frac{1}{|\bar{f}|\,|f|}\right)^{1/2} \sum_{\bar{r}r} \left\{(-1)^{r}(-1)^{\bar{r}}\right.$$

$$\times \left\langle \begin{matrix} [\bar{h}_1\bar{h}_2\bar{h}_3] , & \{\bar{h}_1\bar{h}_2\bar{h}_3\} \\ \bar{\Omega}\bar{L} & \bar{\chi}\bar{f}\bar{r} \end{matrix} \middle\| T^k(n-1, n) \middle\| \begin{matrix} [h_1h_2h_3] , & \{h_1h_2h_3\} \\ \Omega L & \chi fr \end{matrix} \right\rangle$$

$$\left. \times \langle \tilde{\bar{f}}\bar{\beta}\bar{S}TM_T, \tilde{\bar{f}}\tilde{\bar{r}} \| U^k(n-1, n) \| \tilde{f}\beta STM_T, \tilde{f}\tilde{r} \rangle \right\} \tag{7.30}$$

The orbital part of the matrix element can be reduced by means of the two-particle hfpc Eq. (4.14) or by means of the pair hfpc Eq. (4.20). In the first case we find

$$\left\langle \begin{matrix} [\bar{h}_1\bar{h}_2\bar{h}_3] , & \{\bar{h}_1\bar{h}_2\bar{h}_3\} \\ \bar{\Omega}\bar{L} & \bar{\chi}\bar{f}\bar{r} \end{matrix} \middle\| T^k(n-1, n) \middle\| \begin{matrix} [h_1h_2h_3] , & \{h_1h_2h_3\} \\ \Omega L & \chi fr \end{matrix} \right\rangle$$

$$= \sum_{\substack{h_1'h_2'h_3' \\ \Omega'L'}} \sum_{\substack{h''l''h'''l''' \\ \bar{h}''\bar{l}''\bar{h}'''\bar{l}'''}} \sum_{\bar{L}''L''} \left\{(-1)^{L'+k-\bar{L}''-L}[(2\bar{L}''+1)(2L+1)]^{1/2}\right.$$

$$\times W(\bar{L}''\bar{L}L''L; L'k) \left\langle \begin{bmatrix} [\bar{h}'''] & [\bar{h}''] \\ \bar{l}''' & \bar{l}'' \end{bmatrix}_{\bar{L}''} \middle\| T^k(n-1, n) \middle\| \begin{bmatrix} [h'''] & [h''] \\ l''' & l'' \end{bmatrix}_{L''} \right\rangle$$

$$\times \left\langle \begin{matrix} [\bar{h}_1\bar{h}_2\bar{h}_3] , & \{\bar{h}_1\bar{h}_2\bar{h}_3\} \\ \bar{\Omega}\bar{L} & \bar{\chi}\bar{f}\bar{r} \end{matrix} \middle| \left\{ \begin{matrix} [h_1'h_2'h_3'] , & \{h_1'h_2'h_3'\} ; \\ \Omega'L' & \chi'f'r' \end{matrix} \begin{bmatrix} [\bar{h}'''] & [\bar{h}''] \\ \bar{l}''' & \bar{l}'' \end{bmatrix}_{\bar{L}''} \right\rangle$$

$$\left. \times \left\langle \begin{matrix} [h_1'h_2'h_3'] , & \{h_1'h_2'h_3'\} ; \\ \Omega'L' & \chi'f'r' \end{matrix} \begin{bmatrix} [h'''] & [h''] \\ l''' & l'' \end{bmatrix}_{L''} \right\} \middle| \begin{matrix} [h_1h_2h_3] , & \{h_1h_2h_3\} \\ \Omega L & \chi fr \end{matrix} \right\rangle \right\} \tag{7.31}$$

where we note that $r = r'r_{n-1}r_n$, $\bar{r} = r'\bar{r}_{n-1}\bar{r}_n$, so that the hfpc are actually independent of r', whereas the Yamanouchi symbols r, $\bar{r}$ determine the partitions associated with $n-1$ and $n-2$ particles. Furthermore, the two-particle reduced matrix elements appearing on the right-hand side can be evaluated straightforwardly by means of ho transformation brackets (5).

For the second case, that is, when we use the hfpc of Eq. (4.20), we get

$$\left\langle \begin{matrix}[\bar{h}_1\bar{h}_2\bar{h}_3] \\ \bar{\Omega}\bar{L}\end{matrix}, \begin{matrix}\{\bar{h}_1\bar{h}_2\bar{h}_3\} \\ \bar{\chi}\bar{f}\bar{r}\end{matrix} \right\| T^k(n-1, n) \left\| \begin{matrix}[h_1h_2h_3] \\ \Omega L\end{matrix}, \begin{matrix}\{h_1h_2h_3\} \\ \chi f r\end{matrix} \right\rangle$$

$$= \sum_{\substack{h_1'h_2'h_3' \\ \Omega'L'}} \sum_{\substack{h''l'' \\ \bar{h}''\bar{l}''}} \sum_{\{k_{st}'\}_{n-2}} \left\{ \left\langle \begin{matrix}\bar{h}'' \\ \bar{l}''\end{matrix} \right\| T^k(n-1, n) \left\| \begin{matrix}h'' \\ l''\end{matrix} \right\rangle \right.$$

$$\times (-1)^{L'+k-\bar{l}''-L}[(2\bar{l}''+1)(2L+1)]^{1/2} W(\bar{l}''\bar{L}l''L; L'k)$$

$$\times \left\langle \begin{matrix}[\bar{h}_1\bar{h}_2\bar{h}_3] \\ \bar{\Omega}\bar{L}\end{matrix}, \begin{matrix}\{\bar{h}_1\bar{h}_2\bar{h}_3\} \\ \bar{\chi}\bar{f}\bar{r}\end{matrix} \right| \left\{ \begin{matrix}[h_1'h_2'h_3'] \\ \Omega'L'\end{matrix}, \begin{matrix}\{h_1'h_2'h_3'\} \\ \{k_{st}'\}_{n-2}\end{matrix}; \begin{matrix}[\bar{h}''] \\ \bar{l}''\end{matrix} \right\rangle$$

$$\times \left\langle \begin{matrix}[h_1'h_2'h_3'] \\ \Omega'L'\end{matrix}, \begin{matrix}\{h_1'h_2'h_3'\} \\ \{k_{st}'\}_{n-2}\end{matrix}; \begin{matrix}[h''] \\ l''\end{matrix} \right\} \left| \begin{matrix}[h_1h_2h_3] \\ \Omega L\end{matrix}, \begin{matrix}\{h_1h_2h_3\} \\ \chi f r\end{matrix} \right\rangle \Bigg\}. \tag{7.32}$$

In Eq. (7.32) the reduced matrix element on the right-hand side is already essentially a one-body matrix element with respect to the coordinate $\sqrt{\tfrac{1}{2}}(\mathbf{x}^n - \mathbf{x}^{n-1})$ and can be expressed in terms of Talmi integrals as in Eq. (7.28).

In a similar fashion we can derive the matrix element of two-body operators between translational-invariant states. The only difference in the result is that the pair fpc Eq. (4.26) should be used in Eq. (7.32).

For the evaluation of the reduced matrix elements of the spin-isospin part of the two-body interactions, we use the two-particle fpc Eq. (6.15) to obtain

$$\begin{aligned}
&\langle f\bar{\beta}\bar{S}T, \bar{f}\bar{r} \| U^k(n-1, n) \| f\beta ST, fr\rangle \\
&= \sum_{\beta'S'T'} \sum_{S''\bar{S}''T''} \{\langle \gamma^2\bar{S}''T'' \| U^k(n-1, n) \| \gamma^2 S''T''\rangle \\
&\quad \times (-1)^{S'+k-\bar{S}''-S}[(2\bar{S}''+1)(2S+1)]^{1/2} W(\bar{S}''\bar{S}S''S; S'k) \\
&\quad \times \langle \gamma^n \bar{f}\bar{\beta}\bar{S}\bar{T}\{|\gamma^{n-2}f'\beta'S'T', \gamma^2\bar{S}''T'', \dot{\bar{f}}\rangle \\
&\quad \times \langle \gamma^{n-2}f'\beta'S'T', \gamma^2 S''T'', \dot{f}|\}\gamma^n f\beta ST\rangle\}
\end{aligned} \tag{7.33}$$

where, as before, the Yamanouchi symbols for n particles in bra and ket can be written as $r = r'r_{n-1}r_n$, $\bar{r} = r'\bar{r}_{n-1}\bar{r}_n$, with r' being the same in both cases, since it corresponds to the residual $n-2$ particles. The r determine the partition $\dot{f}$ for $n-1$ particles and f' for $n-2$ particles, and the $\bar{r}$ does the same for $\dot{\bar{f}}, f'$. From Section VII,A we see that, for all forces, $U_q^k(n-1, n)$ depends only on the sum of the spins of particles $n-1$ and n, so that the two-body matrix in Eq. (7.33) is diagonal in S'' and trivial to evaluate.

In the case of the Coulomb interaction, we see from Eq. (7.25) that we have to determine the matrix element of an interaction

$$T_0^0(n-1, n)V_0^{\kappa}(n-1, n), \qquad \kappa = 0, 1, 2, \tag{7.34a}$$

where

$$T_0^0(n-1, n) = \frac{e^2}{r^{n-1\, n}} \tag{7.34b}$$

By a procedure similar to the one that leads to Eq. (7.30) we get, from Eqs. (7.24), (7.25),

$$\left\langle \begin{bmatrix} [\bar{h}_1\bar{h}_2\bar{h}_3] \\ \bar{\Omega}L \end{bmatrix}, \begin{matrix} \{\bar{h}_1\bar{h}_2\bar{h}_3\} \\ \bar{\chi}\bar{f} \end{matrix}; \begin{matrix} \tilde{\bar{f}} \\ \bar{\beta}\bar{S}\bar{T}\bar{M}_T \end{matrix}\right]_{JM} \left| \mathscr{V}^c \right| \left[\begin{matrix} [h_1h_2h_3] \\ \Omega L \end{matrix}, \begin{matrix} \{h_1h_2h_3\} \\ \chi f \end{matrix}; \begin{matrix} \tilde{f} \\ \beta STM_T \end{matrix} \right]_{JM} \right\rangle$$

$$= \frac{n(n-1)}{2}\left(\frac{1}{|\bar{f}|\,|f|}\right)^{1/2} \sum_{\kappa=0}^{2} \sum_{\bar{r}r} \Big\{(-1)^{\bar{r}}(-1)^{r}\langle T\kappa M_T 0|\bar{T}M_T\rangle$$

$$\times \left\langle \begin{matrix} [\bar{h}_1\bar{h}_2\bar{h}_3] \\ \bar{\Omega}L \end{matrix}, \begin{matrix} \{\bar{h}_1\bar{h}_2\bar{h}_3\} \\ \bar{\chi}\bar{f}\bar{r} \end{matrix} \right\| T^0(n-1, n) \left\| \begin{matrix} [h_1h_2h_3] \\ \Omega L \end{matrix}, \begin{matrix} \{h_1h_2h_3\} \\ \chi fr \end{matrix} \right\rangle$$

$$\times \langle \tilde{\bar{f}}\bar{\beta}\bar{S}\bar{T}; \tilde{\bar{f}}\bar{r} \| a_\kappa V^{\kappa}(n-1, n) \| \tilde{f}\beta ST, \tilde{f}r \rangle \Big\}. \tag{7.35}$$

The matrix element of T_0^0 is a particular case of those determined by Eqs. (7.31) and (7.32). The matrix element of $V_\rho^{\kappa}(n-1, n)$ is determined in exactly the same way as $U_q^k(n-1, n)$ in Eq. (7.33) when we interchange the roles of spin S and isospin T. Again, as V_ρ^{κ} depends only on the total isospin of the two particles, the reduced matrix element equivalent to the one that appears in Eq. (7.33) for U_q^k, is diagonal in T$''$ and trivial to evaluate.

C. Matrix Elements for Three-Particle and Four-Particle States

1. *Matrix Elements of One-Body and Two-Body Operators for Three-Particle Shell Model States*

The evaluation of one-body operators for three-particle states follows the general outline of Section VII,B,1. For two-body operators it was mentioned in Section IV,D that a simpler method is obtained by reducing to the pair 1, 2 rather than to the pair 2, 3. The equation corresponding to Eq. (7.30) is, then, with $n = 3$,

$$\langle {}^{-}|\mathscr{V}|\rangle$$

$$= (-1)^{\bar{L}+S-J}[(2\bar{L}+1)(2\bar{S}+1)]^{1/2} W(LS\bar{L}\bar{S}; Jk) 3 \left(\frac{1}{|f||\bar{f}|} \right)^{1/2}$$

$$\times \sum_{\bar{r}r} \left\{ (-1)^{\bar{r}} (-1)^{r} \left\langle \begin{matrix} [\bar{h}_1\bar{h}_2\bar{h}_3] \\ \bar{\Omega}\bar{L} \end{matrix}, \begin{matrix} \{\bar{h}_1\bar{h}_2\bar{h}_3\} \\ \bar{\chi}\bar{f}\bar{r} \end{matrix} \middle\| T^k(1,2) \middle\| \begin{matrix} [h_1h_2h_3] \\ \Omega L \end{matrix}, \begin{matrix} \{h_1h_2h_3\} \\ \chi f r \end{matrix} \right\rangle \right.$$

$$\left. \times \langle \tilde{\bar{f}}\bar{S}TM_T; \bar{f}\tilde{\bar{r}} \| U^k(1,2) \| \tilde{f}STM_T, f\tilde{r} \rangle \right\} \tag{7.36}$$

where bra and ket on the left-hand side are the same as in Eq. (7.30).

The orbital matrix element becomes, on using the pair fpc Eq. (4.32),

$$\left\langle \begin{matrix} [\bar{h}_1\bar{h}_2\bar{h}_3] \\ \bar{\Omega}\bar{L} \end{matrix}, \begin{matrix} \{\bar{h}_1\bar{h}_2\bar{h}_3\} \\ \bar{\chi}\bar{f}\bar{r} \end{matrix} \middle\| T^k(1,2) \middle\| \begin{matrix} [h_1h_2h_3] \\ \Omega L \end{matrix}, \begin{matrix} \{h_1h_2h_3\} \\ \chi f r \end{matrix} \right\rangle$$

$$= \sum_{\substack{h_1'h_2'k_{11}' \\ \Omega'L'}} \sum_{\substack{h''l'' \\ \bar{h}''\bar{l}''}} \left\{ (-1)^{L'+k-\bar{l}''-L} [(2\bar{l}''+1)(2L+1)]^{1/2} W(\bar{l}''\bar{L}l''L; L'k) \right.$$

$$\times \left\langle \begin{matrix} \bar{h}'' \\ \bar{l}'' \end{matrix} \middle\| T^k(1,2) \middle\| \begin{matrix} h'' \\ l'' \end{matrix} \right\rangle$$

$$\times \left\langle \begin{matrix} [\bar{h}_1\bar{h}_2\bar{h}_3] \\ \bar{\Omega}\bar{L} \end{matrix}, \begin{matrix} \{\bar{h}_1\bar{h}_2\bar{h}_3\} \\ \bar{\chi}\bar{f}\bar{r} \end{matrix} \middle\{ \middle| \begin{matrix} [h_1'h_2'] \\ \Omega'L' \end{matrix}, \begin{matrix} h_1' \;\; h_2' \\ k_{11}' \end{matrix}; \begin{matrix} [\bar{h}''] \\ \bar{l}'' \end{matrix} \right\rangle$$

$$\left. \times \left\langle \begin{matrix} [h_1'h_2'] \\ \Omega'L' \end{matrix}, \begin{matrix} h_1' \;\; h_2' \\ k_{11}' \end{matrix}; \begin{matrix} [h''] \\ l'' \end{matrix} \middle| \right\} \begin{matrix} [h_1h_2h_3] \\ \Omega L \end{matrix}, \begin{matrix} \{h_1h_2h_3\} \\ \chi f r \end{matrix} \right\rangle \right\} . \tag{7.37}$$

The spin-isospin matrix element can be evaluated with the help of the one-particle fpc Eq. (6.5) given in Table IV as

$$\langle \tilde{\bar{f}}\bar{S}T, \bar{f}\tilde{\bar{r}} \| U^k(1,2) \| \tilde{f}ST, f\tilde{r} \rangle$$

$$= \sum_{S'\bar{S}'L'} \{ \langle \gamma^2\bar{S}'T' \| U^k(1,2) \| \gamma^2 S'T' \rangle$$

$$\times (-1)^{\frac{1}{2}+k-S'-\bar{S}} [(2\bar{S}'+1)(2S+1)]^{1/2} W(\bar{S}'\bar{S}S'S; \tfrac{1}{2}k)$$

$$\times \langle \gamma^3 \tilde{\bar{f}}\bar{S}T \{ | \gamma^2\bar{S}'T', \gamma\tfrac{1}{2}\tfrac{1}{2} \rangle \langle \gamma^2 S'T', \gamma\tfrac{1}{2}\tfrac{1}{2} | \} \gamma^3 \tilde{f}ST \rangle \}. \tag{7.38}$$

Note that no multiplicity index β is necessary for three-particle spin-isospin states.

2. *Matrix Elements of Two-Body Interactions for Translational-Invariant Four-Particle States*

First we reduce, as in Eq. (7.36), to the first pair 1, 2 of particles, so that

$$\langle^-|\mathscr{V}|\rangle$$

$$= (-1)^{\bar{L}+S-J}[(2\bar{L}+1)(2\bar{S}+1)]^{1/2} W(LS\bar{L}\bar{S}jJk)\, 6 \left(\frac{1}{|f||\bar{f}|}\right)^{1/2}$$

$$\times \sum_{\bar{f}r} \left\{(-1)^r(-1)^{\bar{r}} \left\langle \begin{matrix}[\bar{h}_1\bar{h}_2\bar{h}_3]\\ \bar{\Omega}\bar{L}\end{matrix}, \begin{matrix}\{\bar{h}_1\bar{h}_2\bar{h}_3\}\\ \bar{\chi}\bar{f}\bar{r}\end{matrix} \right\| T^k(1,2) \left\| \begin{matrix}[h_1h_2h_3]\\ \Omega L\end{matrix}, \begin{matrix}\{h_1h_2h_3\}\\ \chi f r\end{matrix} \right\rangle\right.$$

$$\left. \times \langle \bar{f}\bar{S}TM_T, \bar{\bar{f}}\bar{\bar{r}} \| U^k(1,2) \| \bar{f}STM_T, \bar{f}\bar{r}\rangle \right\}. \tag{7.39}$$

The orbital matrix element becomes exactly the expression in Eq. (7.37), but with all symbols now referring to translational-invariant four-particle states, and the pair hfpc now given by Eq. (4.32).

The spin-isospin matrix element is

$$\langle \bar{f}\bar{S}\bar{T}, \bar{f}\bar{r} \| U^k(1,2) \| fST, fr\rangle$$

$$= \sum_{S'T', \bar{S}'\bar{T}'} \sum_{S''T''} \{(-1)^{S''+k-S'-\bar{S}}[(2\bar{S}'+1)(2S+1)]^{1/2}$$

$$\times W(\bar{S}'\bar{S}S'S;\, S''k) \langle \gamma^4\bar{f}\bar{S}\bar{T}\{|\gamma^2\bar{S}'\bar{T}', \gamma^2S''T'', \dot{\bar{f}}\rangle$$

$$\times \langle \gamma^2S'T', \gamma^2S''T'', \dot{f}|\}\gamma^4 fST\rangle \langle \gamma^2\bar{S}'\bar{T}' \| U^k(1,2) \| \gamma^2S'T'\rangle\}. \tag{7.40}$$

VIII. The Few-Nucleon Problem

In the preceding sections we have outlined the general formalism for dealing with n-nucleon problems using states of particles either in a common ho potential or interacting through ho forces. In this and the following sections, we shall apply this formalism to problems of nuclear structure. It is clear, though, that if n is large, we have to restrict our states in some way, for example, by using an ho shell model, in order to reduce the problem to manageable proportions. On the other hand, if n is small, say, between 3 and 6, we can take all states up to a certain number of quanta N and apply to them the physical Hamiltonian. In this way we would obtain information on binding energies, energy levels, eigenstates, transition probabilities between eigenstates, and so on.

We notice also that when n is small, we have to be particularly careful to eliminate spurious states resulting from center-of-mass motion. In this case, therefore, we should use the translational-invariant formalism only.

Herein we shall briefly outline the application of our formalism to the few-nucleon problem (that is, n small), first showing how to determine the matrix elements of the Hamiltonian with respect to translational-invariant states, and then discussing in detail the structure of the four-nucleon problem, taking states up to $N = 2$ quanta.

A. The Intrinsic Hamiltonian

Assuming only two-body interactions, the Hamiltonian could be written

$$\mathscr{H} = \sum_{s=1}^{n} \frac{1}{2m} (\mathbf{p}^s)^2 + \sum_{s<t=2}^{n} V(s, t) \tag{8.1}$$

where $V(s, t)$ depends on the relative coordinates and momenta, as well as on the spins of particles s, t. Making the transformation to Jacobi momenta, as in Eq. (3.61) for the coordinates, we define now the intrinsic Hamiltonian

$$\mathscr{H}_I \equiv \mathscr{H} - \frac{1}{2m} (\dot{\mathbf{p}}^n)^2 = \sum_{s=1}^{n-1} \frac{1}{2m} (\dot{\mathbf{p}}^s)^2 + \sum_{s<t=2}^{n} V(s, t). \tag{8.2}$$

We note that $\dot{\mathbf{x}}^n$, $\dot{\mathbf{p}}^n$ are coordinates and momenta of the center of mass.

We are interested in calculating the matrix elements of $\mathscr{H}_I$ with respect to our translational-invariant states. Since we gave, in the preceding section, a procedure for calculating the matrix elements of two-body interactions, we shall proceed to reduce $\mathscr{H}_I$ to them. We note first, from Eq. (3.65), that our translational-invariant states are eigenstates of the Hamiltonian

$$\mathscr{H}_0 = \sum_{s=1}^{n-1} \frac{1}{2m} (\dot{\mathbf{p}}^s)^2 + \frac{m\omega^2}{2n} \sum_{s<t=2}^{n} (\mathbf{x}^s - \mathbf{x}^t)^2 + \left[\frac{1}{2m} (\dot{\mathbf{p}}^n)^2 + \frac{1}{2} m\omega^2 (\dot{\mathbf{x}}^n)^2\right], \tag{8.3}$$

with eigenvalues

$$\hbar\omega[N + \tfrac{3}{2}n] \tag{8.4}$$

where N is the number of quanta and n the number of particles. Furthermore, these states are also eigenstates of the center-of-mass Hamiltonian in the last bracket of Eq. (8.3) with eigenvalue

$$\tfrac{3}{2}\hbar\omega, \tag{8.5}$$

since there is no excitation in the center-of-mass coordinate.

The matrix elements of $\mathscr{H}_I$ are then given by

$$\begin{aligned}\langle \bar{N}|\mathscr{H}_I|N\rangle &= \hbar\omega[N+\tfrac{3}{2}(n-1)]\,\delta_{\bar{N}N}\\ &\quad + \tfrac{1}{2}n(n-1)\left\langle \bar{N}\left| V(n-1,n) - \frac{m\omega^2}{2n}(\mathbf{x}^{n-1}-\mathbf{x}^{n})^2 \right| N\right\rangle \end{aligned} \tag{8.6}$$

where we use the abbreviated notation $|N\rangle$ to designate a state of the type of Eq. (7.3) and where, of course, $[h_1h_2h_3]$ is a partition of N.

B. The Four-Nucleon Problem

When $n=4$, the IR of $S(4)$ that we may have are $\{4\}$, $\{31\}$, $\{22\}$, $\{211\}$, $\{1111\}$, while the IR of $\mathscr{U}(3)$ are $[h_1h_2h_3]$ with $h_1+h_2+h_3=N$. In Table VII we give the IR of $S(4)$, that is, $\{f_1f_2f_3f_4\}$, as well as the IR of $\mathscr{O}^+(3)$, $\mathscr{S}\mathscr{U}^{(\sigma)}(2)$, $\mathscr{S}\mathscr{U}^{(\tau)}(2)$ (that is, L, S, T), corresponding to each IR of $\mathscr{U}(3)$ for $N=0, 1, 2$.

TABLE VII

IR of $\mathscr{O}^+(3)$, $S(4)$, $\mathscr{S}\mathscr{U}^{(\sigma)}(2) \times \mathscr{S}\mathscr{U}^{(\tau)}(2)$ Corresponding to Each IR of $\mathscr{U}(3)$ for $N=0, 1, 2$ and $n=4$

	IR			
N	$\mathscr{U}(3)$ $[h_1h_2h_3]$	$\mathscr{O}^+(3)$ L	$S(4)$ $\{f_1f_2f_3f_4\}$	$\mathscr{S}\mathscr{U}^{(\sigma)}(2) \times \mathscr{S}\mathscr{U}^{(\tau)}(2)$ (ST)
0	[000]	0	{4}	(00)
1	[100]	1	{31}	$\begin{pmatrix}0\,1\\1\,0\end{pmatrix}$ (11)
2	[200]	0,2	{4}	(00)
			{31}	$\begin{pmatrix}0\,1\\1\,0\end{pmatrix}$ (11)
			{22}	(00) $\begin{pmatrix}0\,2\\2\,0\end{pmatrix}$ (11)
	[110]	1	{211}	$\begin{pmatrix}0\,1\\1\,0\end{pmatrix}$ (11) $\begin{pmatrix}1\,2\\2\,1\end{pmatrix}$

Disregarding the Coulomb interaction, which is plausible for these very light nuclei, we see that the general integrals of motion of the system will be the isotopic spin T, the total angular momentum $J\,(\mathbf{J} = \mathbf{L} + \mathbf{S})$, and the parity π. We give in Table VIII the set of quantum numbers

$$\langle [h_1 h_2 h_3] L, \quad \{f_1 f_2 f_3 f_4\} S \rangle \tag{8.7}$$

of the states associated with given TJ^{π} for $N = 0, 1, 2$.

Calculation of the matrix elements of the different types of forces of Section VII,A can be done as follows. We first note, from Eq. (7.30), that we can reduce these matrix elements to products of others involving either the configuration space part or the spin part. For the latter, the calculation procedure is immediate, using Eq. (7.33) and Table VI of two-particle spin-isospin fpc. For the former we can use Eq. (7.31) or (7.32) and the explicit expression of hfpc of Eqs. (4.32), (4.35). We note that in this hfpc the bracket

$$\left\langle \begin{matrix} h_1 \quad h_2 \quad h_3 \\ k_{12} \quad k_{22} \\ k_{11} \end{matrix} \middle| \begin{matrix} \{h_1 h_2 h_3\} \\ \chi fr \end{matrix} \right\rangle \tag{8.8}$$

is very simple to evaluate, as it is 1 for $N = 0$, and for $N = 1, 2$ the weights are (100), (200), (110), and permutations thereof, so that we can use case (b) of Eq. (3.22) and the corresponding analysis of Table III. Furthermore, for $N = 0, 1, 2$ the reduced Wigner coefficients in Eq. (4.32) are determined very simply. [Using the procedure just detailed, we determined, in another publication (*28*), the matrix elements for the different types of forces of Section VII,A.]

We shall discuss here only two simple cases. One concerns a Serber force, the characteristics of which, along with the corresponding Talmi integrals

$${}^{2S+1}I_p, \qquad S = 0, 1, \quad p = 0, 1, 2, \tag{8.9}$$

are presented in Table IX; in Eq. (8.9) the order p of the Talmi integral is limited to the values indicated as $N \leqq 2$, and $2S + 1$ indicates the triplet or singlet character of the interaction. The other case we shall discuss will be a two-particle spin orbit coupling potential acting on the negative parity states.

For a Serber force we present, in Fig. 1, the energy levels for an ho energy

$$\hbar\omega = 21.8 \text{ MeV}, \tag{8.10}$$

which is the value required to give reasonable agreement with the observed radius of the α particle (*56*). The energy levels are also characterized by LS, since for a Serber force these will be integrals of motions. We also give the partition $\{f_1 f_2 f_3 f_4\}$ for each level. This partition is almost a good quantum

TABLE VIII

IR OF $\mathscr{U}(3)$, $\mathscr{O}^+(3)$, $S(4)$, $\mathscr{S}\mathscr{U}^{(\sigma)}(2)$ FOR GIVEN TJ^{π} [a]

J^π	No. of states	$\langle[h_1h_2h_3]L, \{f_1f_2f_3f_4\}S\rangle$
	(a) $T=0$	
0^+	5	⟨[0]0,{4}0⟩, ⟨[2]0,{4}0⟩, ⟨[2]0,{22}0⟩ ⟨[2]2,{22}2⟩, ⟨[11]1,{211}1⟩
1^+	4	⟨[2]0,{31}1⟩, ⟨[2]2,{31}1⟩ ⟨[2]2,{22}2⟩, ⟨[11]1,{211}1⟩
2^+	6	⟨[2]2,{4}0⟩, ⟨[2]0,{22}2⟩, ⟨[2]2,{31}1⟩ ⟨[2]2,{22}2⟩, ⟨[2]2,{22}0⟩, ⟨[11]1,{211}1⟩
3^+	2	⟨[2]2,{22}2⟩, ⟨[2]2,{31}1⟩
4^+	1	⟨[2]2,{22}2⟩
0^-	1	⟨[1]1,{31}1⟩
1^-	1	⟨[1]1,{31}1⟩
2^-	1	⟨[1]1,{31}1⟩
	(b) $T=1$	
0^+	2	⟨[2]0,{31}0⟩, ⟨[11]1,{211}1⟩
1^+	7	⟨[2]0,{31}1⟩, ⟨[2]2,{31}1⟩, ⟨[2]0,{22}1⟩, ⟨[2]2,{22}1⟩ ⟨[11]1,{211}2⟩, ⟨[11]1,{211}1⟩, ⟨[11]1,{211}0⟩
2^+	5	⟨[2]2,{31}1⟩, ⟨[2]2,{31}0⟩, ⟨[2]2,{22}1⟩ ⟨[11]1,{211}2⟩, ⟨[11]1,{211}1⟩
3^+	3	⟨[2]2,{31}1⟩, ⟨[2]2,{22}1⟩ ⟨[11]1,{211}2⟩
0^-	1	⟨[1]1,{31}1⟩
1^-	2	⟨[1]1,{31}1⟩, ⟨[1]1,{31}0⟩
2^-	1	⟨[1]1,{31}1⟩
	(c) $T=2$	
0^+	2	⟨[2]0,{22}0⟩, ⟨[11]1,{211}1⟩
1^+	1	⟨[11]1,{211}1⟩
2^+	2	⟨[2]2,{22}0⟩, ⟨[11]1,{211}1⟩

[a] Note that ⟨ ⟩ are used as parentheses and not as Dirac brackets.

TABLE IX

PARAMETERS AND TALMI INTEGRALS OF A SERBER FORCE [a]

Serber force[b]:

$$\mathscr{V} = {}^3V^e(r)\left[\frac{1+{}^BP}{2}\right] + {}^1V^e\left[\frac{1-{}^BP}{2}\right]$$

$$V(r) = -V_0\,(\mu r)^{-1}\exp(-\mu r)$$

$${}^3V_0^e = 52.13 \text{ MeV} \qquad {}^3\mu^e = 0.7261\,f^{-1}$$

$${}^1V_0^e = 46.87 \text{ MeV} \qquad {}^1\mu^e = 0.8547\,f^{-1}$$

Talmi integrals:

$$I_p = \frac{2}{\Gamma(p+\frac{3}{2})}\int_0^\infty r^{2p+2}e^{-r^2}V(r)\,dr$$

$${}^3I_0^e = -14.29 \text{ MeV} \qquad {}^3I_1^e = -5.2 \text{ MeV} \qquad {}^3I_2^e = -2.61 \text{ MeV}$$

$${}^1I_0^e = -9.4 \text{ MeV} \qquad {}^1I_1^e = -3.2 \text{ MeV} \qquad {}^1I_2^e = -1.62 \text{ MeV}$$

[a] $\hbar\omega = 21.8$ MeV.
[b] ${}^BP$ is the Bartlett operator equation (7.15).

number, since the Bartlett part of the force, when compared with the Wigner part, is relatively weak.

In Fig. 1 we note that there is only one state of negative energy, that is, actually bound, as is the case for the α particle. The binding energy of $\simeq 24$ MeV is not far removed from the experimental value of 28 MeV. The ground state is a mixture of the states of $N = 2$ and $N = 0$ quanta with $L = S = 0$ and partition $\{4\}$, though the ratio of the squares of the amplitudes of the states 1:10 indicates that the $N = 2$ admixture is still small. The first excited state is a 0^+ state, after which the negative parity states follow as experimentally observed. The position of the levels with $T = 1, 2$ vis-à-vis those of $T = 0$, is also in reasonable agreement with experiment.

Figure 2 illustrates the way the negative parity states of Fig. 1 are decomposed by a two-particle spin orbit force for which there is only one Talmi integral ${}^{ls}I_1$, the value of which was taken as -1.1 MeV. These energy levels (*56, 57*) are compared with experiment, assuming that the lowest negative parity level with $T = 0$ (that is, 2^-) agrees with the experimental one.

The calculations presented here will be continued with a higher upper bound N for the number of quanta, as well as more realistic forces. The only theoretical problem remaining concerns the determination of the Talmi integrals for potentials with repulsive cores, as the different approximation procedures used for this purpose give wildly fluctuating results (*57*).

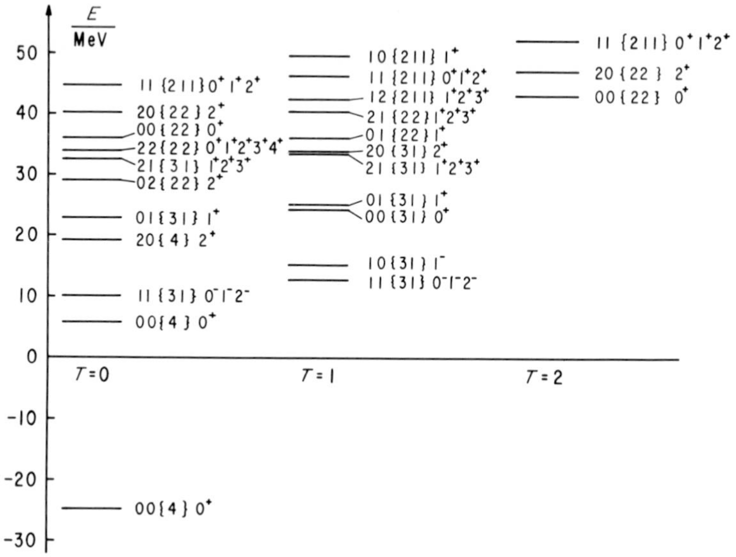

FIG. 1. Energy levels of a Serber force for a four-nucleon system with states up to $N = 2$ quanta. The quantum numbers indicated are $LS\{f_1 f_2 f_3 f_4\}J^{\pi}$.

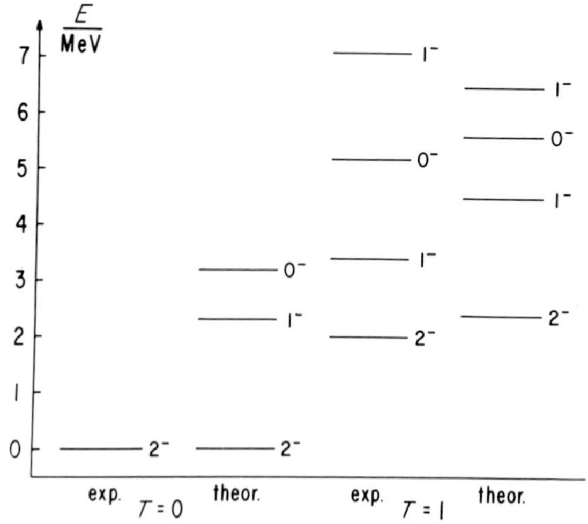

FIG. 2. Effect of a two-body spin orbit interaction on the negative parity states $N = 1$.

IX. The Elliott Model in Nuclear Shell Theory

In this section we shall show how the classification scheme developed by Elliott (3) for a single shell results as a particular case from the classification scheme for orbital n-particle states developed earlier herein. We shall see that the extension of the Elliott classification to general multishell configurations is straightforward. Our classification scheme contains the group $\mathscr{S}\mathscr{U}(3)$ introduced by Elliott from the very beginning. Therefore the quadrupole-quadrupole interaction is diagonal and leads to the appearance of rotational bands.

A. The Elliott Model for a Single Shell

In Section II we discussed a general classification scheme for orbital n-particle states based on the chains of groups

$$\mathrm{U}(3n) \supset \mathscr{U}(3) \times U(n), \tag{9.1}$$

$$\mathscr{U}(3) \supset \mathscr{O}^{+}(3) \supset \mathscr{O}^{+}(2), \tag{9.2}$$

and in Section III,A we introduced the group $K(n)$ as the symmetry group of the ho shell model in the chain of groups

$$U(n) \supset K(n) \supset S(n) \supset S(n-1) \supset \cdots \supset S(1). \tag{9.3}$$

The shell model states are BIR of the groups in the chains Eqs. (9.1)–(9.3). With respect to the IR of $K(n)$, these bases are characterized by the reference weight Eq. (3.56). For a single shell this reference weight is given by

$$\mathbf{w} = (w, w, \ldots, w) \equiv w^{n}. \tag{9.4}$$

The group of the weight in this case is the full group $S(n)$. According to the discussion in Section III,A,5, each BIR of $S(n)$ then corresponds to a BIR of $K(n)$ characterized by $\mathbf{w} = w^n$ and f. To construct these BIR, we have to apply the Wigner projection operators Eq. (3.6) for the IR f of $S(n)$ to the Gelfand states of weight $\mathbf{w} = w^n$. This procedure was discussed explicitly in Section III,A,4 for three-particle states. The n-particle states for a single shell are then characterized according to the IR of the groups in Eqs. (9.1)–(9.3) as

$$\left\langle \mathbf{x}^{1} \cdots \mathbf{x}^{n} \middle| \begin{matrix} [h_1 h_2 h_3] \\ \Omega L M \end{matrix}, \begin{matrix} \{h_1 h_2 h_3\} \\ \chi w^{n} f r \end{matrix} \right\rangle \tag{9.5}$$

with χ taking into account repeated IR of $K(n)$ and hence, in this particular case, of $S(n)$ for a given IR $\{h_1h_2h_3\}$ of $U(n)$.

Elliott (*3*) introduced a group $\mathcal{SU}(3)$ for the classification of n-particle states in a single shell. This group $\mathcal{SU}(3)$ consists of unitary matrices of determinant 1, and appears in our scheme as a subgroup of $\mathcal{U}(3)$. It can be seen (*14*) that all BIR of the IR $[h_1h_2h_3]$ obtained by applying the lowering operators of $\mathcal{U}(3)$ and its subgroups to the state of highest weight Eq. (2.25), depend on the differences $h_1 - h_3$, $h_2 - h_3$, except for a factor $(\Delta_{123}^{123})^{h_3}$. Since Δ_{123}^{123} is an invariant under $\mathcal{SU}(3)$, the IR of $\mathcal{SU}(3)$ contained in an IR of $\mathcal{U}(3)$, must be related to the two numbers $h_1 - h_3$, $h_2 - h_3$. In Elliott's notation the IR of $\mathcal{SU}(3)$ are specified by λ and μ, given by

$$\lambda = h_1 - h_2, \qquad \mu = h_2 - h_3. \tag{9.6}$$

Clearly, we could replace the numbers h_1, h_2, h_3 by $N = h_1 + h_2 + h_3$, λ, μ to relate the states Eq. (9.5) to the states considered by Elliott. The chain of groups Eq. (9.2) is then refined to be

$$\mathcal{U}(3) \supset \mathcal{SU}(3) \supset \mathcal{O}^+(3) \supset \mathcal{O}^+(2) \tag{9.2$'$}$$

and from the Eq. (2.50) it can be seen that the IR L of $\mathcal{O}^+(3)$ are indeed determined by the IR (λ, μ) of $\mathcal{SU}(3)$. The relation of the $\mathcal{SU}(3)$ group to the quadrupole-quadrupole interaction, and hence to the appearance of rotational bands, will be discussed in Section IX,C.

B. Extension of the Elliott Model to Multishell Configurations

In the preceding subsection it was shown that the Elliott classification scheme appears as a particular case of the classification according to the IR of the group Eqs. (9.1)–(9.3). It is clear that by choosing a more general IR of $K(n)$ we could construct more general n-particle states corresponding to a multishell configuration. The reference weight Eq. (3.56) is then given by

$$\mathbf{w} = (w^1)^{n_1}(w^2)^{n_2} \cdots (w^k)^{n_k} \tag{9.7}$$

and the IR of $K(n)$ are further characterized by the IR

$$f_w = f^1 f^2 \cdots f^k \tag{9.8}$$

of the group of the weight $W = S(n_1) \oplus S(n_2) \oplus \cdots \oplus S(n_k)$. Once the BIR of $K(n)$ are constructed by generalizing the methods of subsection A to n-particle states, we can pass over (*20*) to IR of the subgroup $S(n)$ of $K(n)$.

The n-particle states are then given by

$$\left\langle \mathbf{x}^1 \cdots \mathbf{x}^n \middle| \begin{matrix} [h_1h_2h_3] \\ \Omega LM \end{matrix}, \begin{matrix} \{h_1h_2h_3\} \\ \chi((w^1)^{n_1} \cdots (w^k)^{n_k}, f^1 \cdots f^k)\varphi f r \end{matrix} \right\rangle . \tag{9.9}$$

Here, χ distinguishes between repeated IR of $K(n)$ for a given IR of $U(n)$, and φ distinguishes between repeated IR of $S(n)$ for a given IR of $K(n)$. The important point in the present context is that, again, the n-particle states Eq. (9.9) belong to a definite IR (λ, μ) of $\mathscr{S}\mathscr{U}(3)$ with λ and μ given by Eq. (9.6). Therefore, these states correspond to the Elliott model generalized to multi-shell configurations (*20*).

C. The Quadrupole-Quadrupole Interaction

A Gaussian two-body interaction could be expanded in terms of a constant, a dipole-dipole interaction, a quadrupole-quadrupole interaction etc., and similar results hold for an arbitrary two-body interaction. It can be argued that for a sufficiently long range of the interaction, only the first terms of this expansion need be considered (*58*). The first term is constant and therefore irrelevant, and the dipole-dipole interaction can be shown to be related to center-of-mass motion, that is, to be zero between nonspurious states, provided that only states of fixed total number of quanta N are considered (*58*). Therefore, the first term of physical interest is a quadrupole-quadrupole interaction of the type

$$\mathscr{V} = -B \sum_{s,t=1}^{n} \sum_{q=-2}^{+2} (-1)^q (r^s)^2 Y_q^2\left(\frac{\mathbf{x}^s}{r^s}\right)(r^t)^2 Y_{-q}^2\left(\frac{\mathbf{x}^t}{r^t}\right), \tag{9.10}$$

where

$$(r^s)^2 Y_q^2\left(\frac{\mathbf{x}^s}{r^s}\right)$$

is a solid spherical harmonic with respect to particle s. From (2.3) we can introduce the vectors $\boldsymbol{\eta}^s$, $\boldsymbol{\xi}^s$, $\boldsymbol{\eta}^t$, $\boldsymbol{\xi}^t$ in the expression Eq. (9.10), with spherical components defined by

$$\eta_{\pm 1}^s = \mp\sqrt{\tfrac{1}{2}}(\eta_1^s \pm \eta_2^s), \qquad \xi_{\pm 1}^s = \mp\sqrt{\tfrac{1}{2}}(\xi_1^s \pm i\xi_2^s), \tag{9.11}$$
$$\eta_0^s = \eta_3^s, \qquad \xi_0^s = \xi_3^s.$$

Now we determine an approximation of the interaction Eq. (9.10) by keeping only those terms that commute with $\boldsymbol{H}_0$ of Eq. (2.5) and that, besides, leave the shell structure (that is, the occupation numbers of the shells) unchanged. Under these conditions we obtain from Eq. (9.10) the quadrupole-quadrupole interaction proportional to

$$-Q^2 = -\sum_{q=-2}^{+2} (-1)^q Q_q Q_{-q} \tag{9.12}$$

where

$$Q_q = \sum_{s=1}^{n} \sum_{q',q''=-1}^{1} \langle 11q'q''|2q\rangle \eta^s_{q'} \xi^s_{q''}. \tag{9.13}$$

Q_q clearly can be expressed in terms of the generators $\mathscr{C}_{ij}$ of $\mathscr{U}(3)$. We shall now determine the eigenstates and the eigenvalues of $-Q^2$ by showing that it can be expressed in terms of the invariant operators of the groups $\mathscr{U}(3)$ and $\mathscr{O}^+(3)$. An invariant operator of $\mathscr{U}(3)$, by definition, commutes with all generators $\mathscr{C}_{ij}$ of $\mathscr{U}(3)$, as does, for example, the Hamiltonian (2.5). It is easy to verify that the second-order expression

$$\Gamma \equiv \sum_{i,j} \mathscr{C}_{ij}\mathscr{C}_{ji} \tag{9.14}$$

commutes with all $\mathscr{C}_{ij}$ and hence is an invariant operator of $\mathscr{U}(3)$. Consequently, the eigenvalue of Γ can be obtained by applying it to the highest weight state Eq. (2.25) to obtain, with the help of Eqs. (2.23),

$$\begin{aligned}
&\Gamma P^{[h_1h_2h_3]}|0\rangle \\
&= \left[\sum_{j=1}^{3} \mathscr{C}_{jj}\mathscr{C}_{jj} + \sum_{i<j} [\mathscr{C}_{ij}, \mathscr{C}_{ji}] + 2\sum_{i>j} \mathscr{C}_{ij}\mathscr{C}_{ji}\right] P^{[h_1h_2h_3]}|0\rangle \\
&= \left[\sum_j h_j^2 + \sum_{i<j} (h_i - h_j)\right] P^{[h_1h_2h_3]}|0\rangle \\
&= [\tfrac{1}{6}(h_1 + h_2 - 2h_3)(h_1 + h_2 - 2h_3 + 6) + \tfrac{1}{2}(h_1 - h_2)(h_1 - h_2 + 2) \\
&\quad + \tfrac{1}{3}(h_1 + h_2 + h_3)^2] P^{[h_1h_2h_3]}|0\rangle.
\end{aligned} \tag{9.15}$$

We can write Γ in another way by taking as the nine generators of $\mathscr{U}(3)$ the nine linear combinations Q_q, $-2 \leqq q \leqq 2$, defined by Eq. (9.13), L_j, $j = 1, 2, 3$, defined in Eq. (2.45), and $\mathbf{H}_0$. Then Γ can be expressed as

$$\Gamma = Q^2 + \tfrac{1}{2}\mathbf{L}^2 + \tfrac{1}{3}\mathbf{H}_0^2. \tag{9.16}$$

From Eqs. (9.6), (9.15), and (9.16), the eigenvalue of $-Q^2$ with respect to the

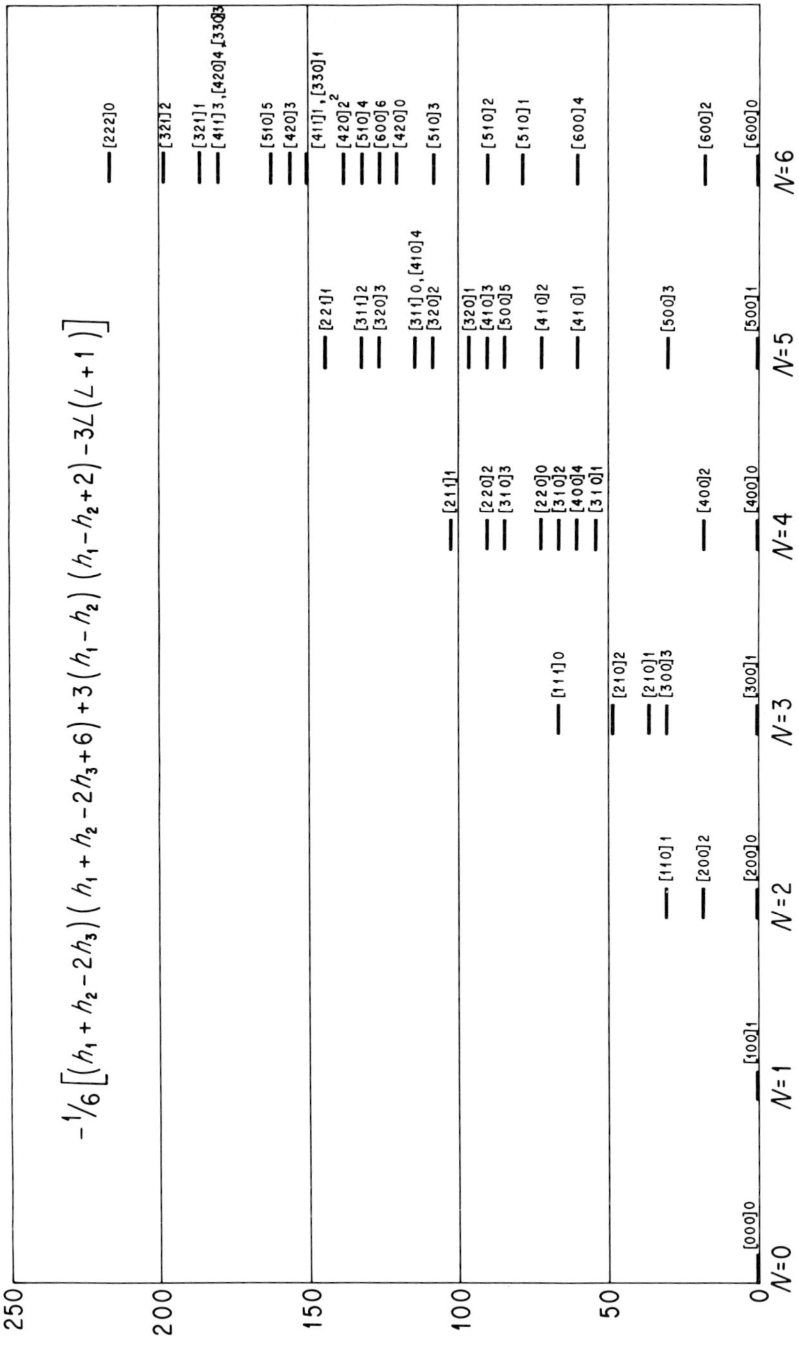

FIG. 3. Eigenvalues of the $-Q^2$ interaction for partitions $[h_1h_2h_3]$ of $\mathscr{U}(3)$ with $N = h_1 + h_2 + h_3 \leqq 6$. The number outside the parentheses is the value of L.

n-particle states Eq. (9.9) of the generalized Elliott model is given by (*10*)

$$-\tfrac{1}{6}[(h_1+h_2-2h_3)(h_1+h_2-2h_3+6)+3(h_1-h_2)(h_1-h_2+2)]+\tfrac{1}{2}L(L+1)$$
$$=-\tfrac{1}{6}[(\lambda+2\mu)(\lambda+2\mu+6)+3\lambda(\lambda+2)]+\tfrac{1}{2}L(L+1). \quad (9.17)$$

We note, first, that this eigenvalue can be expressed in terms of λ, μ, and L, so that it is related to the IR of $\mathscr{SU}(3)$ and $\mathscr{O}^+(3)$ rather than to those of $\mathscr{U}(3)$. Second, the term $\frac{1}{2}L(L+1)$ clearly leads to the appearance of rotational bands for fixed (λ, μ), the possible values of L being given by Eq. (2.50). The eigenvalues Eq. (9.17) of $-Q^2$ are shown in Fig. 3 for the states with $h_1+h_2+h_3 \leqq 6$.

We have seen then that for the states Eq. (9.9) the Q^2 interaction is diagonal and produces rotational bands. However, the translational-invariant states considered in Section III,B also contain the classification according to $\mathscr{SU}(3)$ with subgroups $\mathscr{O}^+(3)$. Therefore, we can consider the Q^2 interaction between translational-invariant n-particle states, as has been emphasized by Kretzschmar (*8*, *9*). We shall study an application along these lines in Section X,E.

D. Single-Shell Applications

Elliott (*3*) not only proposed a classification scheme in a single shell of the ho, but he also gave good physical reasons to consider that, at least in the 2*s*-1*d* shell, we could restrict our states to the highest $\mathscr{SU}(3)$ representations consistent with the number of particles in the shell and with isotopic spin (*59*).

The highest IR of $\mathscr{SU}(3)$ of a given set is determined by the following definition: The IR (λ, μ) of $\mathscr{SU}(3)$ is higher than (λ', μ') if either

$$(\lambda+\mu) > (\lambda'+\mu') \quad (9.18a)$$

or

$$(\lambda+\mu) = (\lambda'+\mu') \qquad \text{but} \qquad \mu > \mu'. \quad (9.18b)$$

In a single shell ν of the ho, a system of n particles has $N = n\nu$ quanta. Among all partitions of N, the one that will be highest in the foregoing sense is obviously $[N]$. It is quite possible, though, that $[N]$ contains IR of $S(n)$, which do not correspond to physical states, that is, fulfill $f_i \leqq 4$, or do not have the isotopic spin of our problem. We would have to choose then the highest IR of $\mathscr{SU}(3)$ that does contain it.

As an example, let us consider the 2*s*-1*d* shell, that is, $\nu = 2$ and the case of F^{20} (*60*), for which the number of particles in this shell is $n = 4$ and the isotopic spin $T = 1$. The number of quanta is $N = 8$; thus, the partitions in decreasing order are [8], [71], [62], ... The IR of $S(n)$ contained in an IR of $\mathscr{U}(3)$ for particles in the $2s$-$1d$ shell can be found from Elliott's table (*3*), using it in the inverse order, since the IR of $\mathscr{U}(6)$ in his analysis are equivalent to the IR of $S(n)$. Applying Elliott's table, we find that [8] contains only the IR {4}, $(ST) = (00)$ of $S(4)$, whereas [71] has the IR {31}, $(ST) = (01), (10), (11)$. We conclude that the states of F^{20} belong to the IR [71] of $\mathscr{U}(3)$, which, from Eq. (2.50), contains IR $L = 1, 2, \ldots, 7$ of $\mathscr{O}^+(3)$.

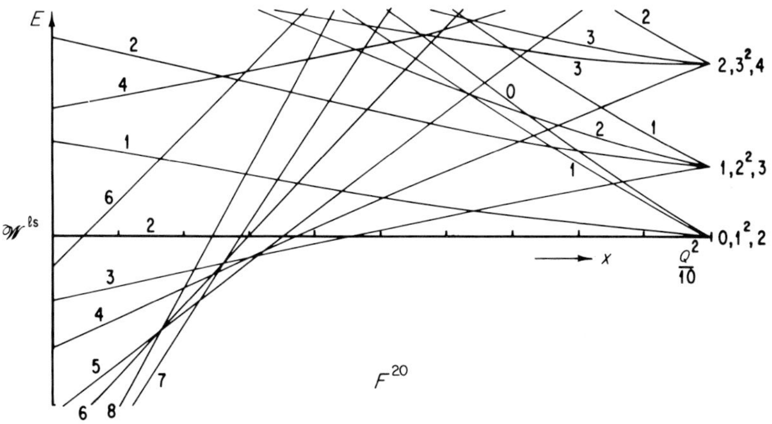

FIG. 4. Energy levels of F^{20} as a function of the parameter x.

Once we have the states associated with an IR of $\mathscr{U}(3)$, we can apply to them a two-body interaction plus a single-particle spin orbit coupling. The first can be evaluated with the help of Eq. (7.30), while for the second we use Eq. (7.26). We have, therefore, a technique for getting the matrices of these interactions that differs from those proposed earlier by Elliott (*3*) or Moshinsky (*22*). This technique has the advantage of starting with states classified from the beginning by IR of $\mathscr{U}(3)$.

If, for the two-body interaction, we take $-Q^2$, which is a good approximation in the long-range limit, we could consider a model interaction (*22*) of the type

$$\mathscr{V} = -V_0[\tfrac{1}{10}xQ^2 + (1-x)\mathscr{W}^{ls}] \tag{9.19}$$

where V_0 is a constant and x a parameter $0 \leqq x \leqq 1$ that measures the ratio of Q^2 to the spin orbit coupling $\mathscr{W}^{ls}$ given by Eq. (7.4). The factor $\frac{1}{10}$ is introduced to reduce the size of Fig. 4, in which the energy levels of F^{20} associated with the states of IR [71] of $\mathscr{U}(3)$ are plotted as functions of x. The matrix elements of Q^2 are diagonal with values given by Eq. (9.17), whereas those of $\mathscr{W}^{ls}$ were calculated as indicated in the preceding paragraph. Reasonable agreement with levels of F^{20} is obtained for $x = 0.64$.

It is planned to use the techniques developed in this article for calculations of few-nucleon problems in the $2p$-$1f$ shell.

X. Clustering Properties and Interactions

In this section we shall consider clustering of nucleons for n-particle states in an ho potential. This requires, first, that we give a precise definition of clustering and, furthermore, that we show this definition to be reasonable.

A. Definition of Clustering; States of Maximum Clustering

By clustering of n-particle states is usually meant a grouping of the n particles into sets of $n_1, n_2, \ldots,$ that have some definite correlation with one another. We shall specify this correlation by following an intuitive approach taken by Wildermuth and Kanellopoulos (*61, 62*), and we shall show that this approach can be extended to a precise and quantitative definition of clustering.

We showed, in Section VIII,B, that the ground state of the α particle can be described to a good approximation by a four-particle ho state with zero total number of quanta. Therefore, an α-particle model of a nucleus would imply the existence of several groups of four particles in zero relative oscillation. Using the n-particle states Eq. (2.46), it is easy to write a state with more general groups of $n_1, n_2, \ldots, n_k$ particles in zero relative oscillation. First, introduce $n-k$ internal relative vectors $\dot{\boldsymbol{\eta}}^1, \ldots, \dot{\boldsymbol{\eta}}^{n-k}$ that describe the relative motion within all groups, then introduce $k-1$ relative vectors $\dot{\boldsymbol{\eta}}^{n-k+1} \cdots \dot{\boldsymbol{\eta}}^{n-1}$ describing the relative motion of the different groups; finally, introduce the center-of-mass vector $\dot{\boldsymbol{\eta}}^n$. By giving no excitation to the first $n-k$ and to the last vector, we obtain a clustered state that is defined as

$$\left\langle \dot{\mathbf{x}} \middle| \begin{matrix} [h_1h_2h_3] \\ \Omega LM \end{matrix}, \begin{matrix} \{h_1h_2h_3\} \\ (n_1)\cdots(n_k)\gamma \end{matrix} \right\rangle \equiv \left\langle \dot{\mathbf{x}} \middle| \begin{matrix} [h_1h_2h_3] \\ \Omega LM \end{matrix}, \{k_{st}\}_{(n_1)\cdots(n_k)} \right\rangle \tag{10.1}$$

with $\{k_{st}\}_{(n_1)\cdots(n_k)}$ being the Gelfand pattern

$$\{k_{st}\}_{(n_1)\cdots(n_k)} = \left\{ \begin{array}{ccccccccccc} h_1 & & h_2 & & h_3 & & 0 & \cdots\cdots & & & 0 \\ & h_1 & & h_2 & & h_3 & & 0 & \cdots\cdots & 0 & \\ & & k_{1n-2} & k_{2n-2} & k_{3n-2} & & 0 & & & 0 & \\ & & \ddots & \ddots & \ddots & & \ddots & & & \cdot^{\cdot^{\cdot}} & \\ & & & k_{1n-k+3} & k_{2n-k+3} & k_{3n-k+3} & 0 & \cdots\cdots & 0 & & \\ & & & k_{1n-k+2} & k_{2n-k+2} & 0 & & 0\cdots 0 & & & \\ & & & & k_{1n-k+1} & 0 & & 0\cdots 0 & & & \\ & & & & 0 & & 0\cdots\cdots 0 & & & & \\ & & & & & \ddots & \cdot^{\cdot^{\cdot}} & & & & \\ & & & & & 0 & & & & & \end{array} \right\}; \tag{10.2}$$

In Eq. (10.1) γ stands for all the nonvanishing k_{st} in the Gelfand pattern Eq. (10.2).

So far, we have defined a clustered state in a simple-minded way. The influence of particle permutations needed for the construction of states with permutational symmetry has been disregarded, and it could be argued that the introduction of permutations completely destroys the clusters. It turns out, however, that the concepts developed thus far are still useful in a more general situation. Using the states Eq. (10.1), we could, first, form the projection operators

$$\left| \begin{matrix}[h_1h_2h_3] \\ \Omega LM\end{matrix}, \begin{matrix}\{h_1h_2h_3\} \\ (n_1)\cdots(n_k)\gamma\end{matrix} \right\rangle \left\langle \begin{matrix}[h_1h_2h_3] \\ \Omega LM\end{matrix}, \begin{matrix}\{h_1h_2h_3\} \\ (n_1)\cdots(n_k)\gamma\end{matrix} \right| .$$

Since by the term clustering we want to refer only to the internal structure of the groups $n_1, n_2, .., n_k$ of particles, we sum these operators over the quantum numbers $h_1h_2h_3$, ΩLM, and γ. The operator resulting from this summation still has the disadvantage that each particle is assumed to be fixed to one cluster, whereas in a more realistic situation, we could only talk about resonating groups in the sense discussed by Wheeler (*63, 64*). To remove this difficulty, we transform by a permutation **p** and sum over all elements of $S(n)$ to obtain a clustering operator

$$\mathfrak{P}^{(n_1)\cdots(n_k)} = \mathcal{N}^{(n_1)\cdots(n_k)} \cdot$$
$$\times \sum_{\substack{\mathbf{p}\in S(n) \\ h_1h_2h_3\Omega LM\gamma}} \mathbf{p}^{-1} \left| \begin{matrix}[h_1h_2h_3] \\ \Omega LM\end{matrix}, \begin{matrix}\{h_1h_2h_3\} \\ (n_1)\cdots(n_k)\gamma\end{matrix} \right\rangle \left\langle \begin{matrix}[h_1h_2h_3] \\ \Omega LM\end{matrix}, \begin{matrix}\{h_1h_2h_3\} \\ (n_1)\cdots(n_k)\gamma\end{matrix} \right| \mathbf{p} \tag{10.3}$$

The factor $\mathcal{N}^{(n_1)\cdots(n_k)}$ in front of Eq. (10.3) takes into account that permutations within a set n_j of particles give no new result and therefore should be counted only once. Similarly, permutations of particles that do not belong to any cluster should not be counted, since the summation over γ is already over all possible states of these particles. Then we get

$$\mathcal{N}^{(n_1)\cdots(n_k)} = [n_1! \cdots n_k!(n - n_1 - \cdots - n_k)!]^{-1}. \tag{10.4}$$

To see what we have gained with this definition, let us calculate the expectation value of the clustering operator Eq. (10.3) between states of permutational symmetry that could be written as

$$\left\langle \dot{\mathbf{x}} \left| \begin{matrix} [h_1h_2h_3] \\ \Omega LM \end{matrix}, \begin{matrix} \{h_1h_2h_3\} \\ \chi fr \end{matrix} \right. \right\rangle. \tag{10.5}$$

Applying the permutations $\mathbf{p}$ to these states and using the orthogonality of the representation matrices of $S(n)$, we find

$$\begin{aligned} &\left\langle \begin{matrix} [h_1h_2h_3] \\ \Omega LM \end{matrix}, \begin{matrix} \{h_1h_2h_3\} \\ \chi fr \end{matrix} \right| \mathfrak{P}^{(n_1)\cdots(n_k)} \left| \begin{matrix} [h_1h_2h_3] \\ \Omega LM \end{matrix}, \begin{matrix} \{h_1h_2h_3\} \\ \chi fr \end{matrix} \right\rangle \\ &= \frac{n!}{n_1!\, n_2! \cdots n_k!\,(n - n_1 - \cdots - n_k)!} \\ &\times |f|^{-1} \sum_{r'\gamma} \left| \left\langle \begin{matrix} [h_1h_2h_3] \\ \Omega LM \end{matrix}, \begin{matrix} \{h_1h_2h_3\} \\ \chi fr' \end{matrix} \right| \begin{matrix} [h_1h_2h_3] \\ \Omega LM \end{matrix}, \begin{matrix} \{h_1h_2h_3\} \\ (n_1)\cdots(n_k)\gamma \end{matrix} \right\rangle \right|^2 . \end{aligned} \tag{10.6}$$

The first factor in this expression is of a statistical nature: it gives the number of possible groupings of n particles into sets of $n_1, n_2, \cdots, n_k$ particles plus $n - n_1 - \cdots - n_k$ residual particles. The second factor is, of course, always smaller than one, as the kets are a subset of the total number of states. Therefore, the statistical factor gives an upper bound for clustering. It is clear that this upper bound could only be approached if all the n particles were in the 1s shell, so that we could take out at random clusters with zero internal excitation. Since the Pauli principle will forbid putting all particles into the 1s shell for $n > 4$, we see that the second factor reflects the limitations imposed by this principle on clustering.

The operator $\mathfrak{P}^{(n_1)\cdots(n_k)}$ allows us to find, for each state, the amount of clustering of type $(n_1)\cdots(n_k)$. Next, we want to know if there is a way of constructing states of maximum clustering in this sense. It turns out that the operator $\mathfrak{P}^{(n_1)\cdots(n_k)}$ can be used for this purpose if its full matrix with elements

$$\left\langle \begin{matrix}[h_1h_2h_3] \\ \Omega LM\end{matrix}, \begin{matrix}\{h_1h_2h_3\} \\ \bar{\chi} fr\end{matrix} \middle| \mathfrak{P}^{(n_1)\cdots(n_k)} \middle| \begin{matrix}[h_1h_2h_3] \\ \Omega LM\end{matrix}, \begin{matrix}\{h_1h_2h_3\} \\ \chi fr\end{matrix} \right\rangle \tag{10.7}$$

is considered. Clearly, $\mathfrak{P}^{(n_1)\cdots(n_k)}$ is Hermitian with real eigenvalues $\mathfrak{p}_q^{(n_1)\cdots(n_k)}$. Since from Eq. (10.6) the diagonal matrix elements of this operator are non-negative for any choice of the additional label χ, this holds also for the eigenvalues of this operator. Now denote for short the matrix with elements Eq. (10.7) by $\langle\bar{\chi}|\mathfrak{P}^{(n_1)\cdots(n_k)}|\chi\rangle$ and the elements of the unitary matrix that diagonalize it by $\langle\chi|q\rangle$. Then we can write the diagonal elements as

$$\langle\chi|\mathfrak{P}^{(n_1)\cdots(n_k)}|\chi\rangle = \sum_q \mathfrak{p}_q^{(n_1)\cdots(n_k)}|\langle\chi|q\rangle|^2, \tag{10.8}$$
$$\sum_q |\langle\chi|q\rangle|^2 = 1.$$

Therefore, the largest eigenvalue of $\mathfrak{P}^{(n_1)\cdots(n_k)}$ determines the largest expectation value of this operator; hence, its eigenstate is the state of maximum clustering.

From Eq. (10.6) we see that clustering is independent of ΩLM. This means that clustered states can appear in rotational bands as discussed in Section IX,C.

What are the values for clustering that we would expect? In the following subsection we shall find upper limits for clustering in terms of permutational symmetry, and we shall see that these limits for the states with lowest excitation are sometimes not far from the expectation value Eq. (10.6) of the clustering operator. For high relative excitation of the clusters it is intuitively clear that we should approximate a model of separated clusters, that is, an α-particle model. This can indeed be proved (*65*) and, for the case of four-particle states, we shall discuss these properties in full detail in Section X,C.

We conclude this general discussion by proving a selection rule for clustering. Assume that we want to arrange a number of $n \leqq 8$ particles into two clusters. In the states Eq. (10.1) this implies that all the energy is carried by only one vector between the two clusters. It is easily seen, from the properties of the Gelfand states, that this is only possible if $h_2 = h_3 = 0$. In general, we find, for the number of clusters k, that if:

$$\begin{aligned} &h_1 \neq 0, \quad h_2 = h_3 = 0, &&\text{then} \quad k \geqq 2; \\ &h_1 \neq 0, \quad h_2 \neq 0, \quad h_3 = 0, &&\text{then} \quad k \geqq 3; \\ &h_1 \neq 0, \quad h_2 \neq 0, \quad h_3 \neq 0, &&\text{then} \quad k \geqq 4. \end{aligned} \tag{10.9}$$

This selection rule for the number of clusters is of particular interest for light nuclei with a small number of clusters.

B. Permutational Limits on Clustering; Wheeler Operators

The evaluation of the matrix elements of the clustering operators is straightforward but, in general, quite laborious. Therefore, we shall try here to get estimates for the amount of clustering from permutational symmetry. A qualitative approach to clustering along similar lines has been followed by Neudachin and co-workers (*66–68*) based on earlier work of Wheeler (*63*); we shall discuss the relations to their work.

Clustering, as defined in the preceding subsection, meant grouping of particles into sets with zero internal excitation. This implies, in particular, that each set n_j, $j = 1, 2, \ldots, k$, has internal symmetry $\{n_j\}$. If, on the other hand, we group the particles into sets of internal symmetry $\{n_j\}$, this does not necessarily imply zero internal excitation. A state with grouping into sets of internal symmetry $\{n_j\}$ can be characterized as follows. Assume states with permutational symmetry, that is, BIR of the groups $U(n) \supset S(n)$. Instead of the chain of subgroups of $S(n)$ used in the Yamanouchi representation, namely, $S(n) \supset S(n-1) \supset \cdots \supset S(1)$, introduce the chain

$$S(n) \supset S(n_1) \oplus S(n_2) \oplus \cdots \oplus S(n_k).$$

Then a state with groups of particles of internal symmetry $\{n_1\}, \{n_2\}, \ldots, \{n_k\}$ can be denoted as

$$\left\langle \dot{\mathbf{x}} \middle| \begin{matrix} [h_1h_2h_3], & \{h_1h_2h_3\} \\ \Omega LM & \chi f \varphi \{n_1\} \cdots \{n_k\} \end{matrix} \right\rangle \tag{10.10}$$

where φ denotes additional quantum numbers in the chain

$$S(n) \supset S(n_1) \oplus \cdots \oplus S(n_k).$$

This state can be used in complete analogy to the clustered states Eq. (10.1) to define an operator

$$\mathfrak{Q}^{(n_1)\cdots(n_k)} = \mathcal{N}^{(n_1)\cdots(n_k)} \sum_{\substack{\mathbf{p} \in S(n) \\ h_1h_2h_3\Omega LM\chi f\varphi}} \mathbf{p}^{-1} \left| \begin{matrix} [h_1h_2h_3], & \{h_1h_2h_3\} \\ \Omega LM & \chi f \varphi \{n_1\} \cdots \{n_k\} \end{matrix} \right\rangle$$
$$\times \left\langle \begin{matrix} [h_1h_2h_3], & \{h_1h_2h_3\} \\ \Omega LM & \chi f \varphi \{n_1\} \cdots \{n_k\} \end{matrix} \right| \mathbf{p} \tag{10.11}$$

with the same factor in front as in Eq. (10.3). Because Wheeler was the first (*63*) to consider groups of particles in an internally symmetric state, we call these operators *Wheeler operators*. Now we evaluate the expectation value of the

Wheeler operators Eq. (10.11) between states Eq. (10.5) of permutational symmetry to obtain

$$\left\langle \begin{matrix}[h_1h_2h_3], & \{h_1h_2h_3\} \\ \Omega LM & \chi fr\end{matrix} \right| \mathfrak{Q}^{(n_1)\cdots(n_k)} \left| \begin{matrix}[h_1h_2h_3], & \{h_1h_2h_3\} \\ \Omega LM & \chi fr\end{matrix} \right\rangle$$

$$= \frac{n!}{n_1!\,n_2!\cdots n_k!\,(n-n_1-\cdots-n_k)!}$$

$$\times\, |f|^{-1} \sum_{r'\varphi} \left| \left\langle \begin{matrix}[h_1h_2h_3], & \{h_1h_2h_3\} \\ \Omega LM & \chi fr'\end{matrix} \right| \begin{matrix}[h_1h_2h_3], & \{h_1h_2h_3\} \\ \Omega LM & \chi f\varphi\{n_1\}\cdots\{n_k\}\end{matrix} \right\rangle \right|^2, \qquad (10.12)$$

in analogy to Eq. (10.6). The sum can be shown to be precisely the multiplicity

$$m(f, \{n_1\} \times \{n_2\} \cdots \{n_k\})$$

$$= \sum_{r'\varphi} \left| \left\langle \begin{matrix}[h_1h_2h_3], & \{h_1h_2h_3\} \\ \Omega LM & \chi fr'\end{matrix} \right| \begin{matrix}[h_1h_2h_3], & \{h_1h_2h_3\} \\ \Omega LM & \chi f\varphi\{n_1\}\cdots\{n_k\}\end{matrix} \right\rangle \right|^2 \qquad (10.13)$$

of the IR $\{n_1\} \times \cdots \times \{n_k\}$ of $S(n_1) \oplus \cdots \oplus S(n_k)$ in the IR f of $S(n)$, as shown in the Appendix (subsection F), which, for example, can be evaluated from the characters of the permutation groups involved, as has been done by Wheeler (*63*). A simpler way of calculating is given by Littlewood's rules (*39*) applied to the product

$$\{n_1\} \times \{n_2\} \times \cdots \times \{n_k\} \times \{1\}^{n-n_1-\cdots-n_k}$$

$$= \sum_f m(f, \{n_1\} \times \{n_2\} \times \cdots \times \{n_k\}) f \qquad (10.14)$$

of partitions.

From the definition of a Wheeler operator it is clear that its expectation values determine upper limits for the expectation values of the analogous clustering operator. In particular, if the Wheeler operator happens to be zero for a given partition f, no clustering of the corresponding type is possible.

In the next subsection we shall illustrate all concepts of this and the preceding subsection on a system of four particles. Here we shall consider the ground state of Li^6 in the shell model and examine its clustering properties. From the work of Kretzschmar (*8*, *9*), the lowest state of six nucleons has $N=2$, $\{h_1h_2h_3\} = \{11\}$, $f = \{411\}$ and $\{h_1h_2h_3\} = \{2\}$, $f = \{42\}$. This latter state can be denoted as

$$\left|\begin{matrix}[2] & \{2\} \\ LM ' & \{42\}r\end{matrix}\right\rangle . \tag{10.15}$$

From the selection rules mentioned in Section X,A we know that clustering into two clusters is possible, and in fact, there are two such types of clustering corresponding to the groupings (4)(2) and (3)(3). Since

$$\begin{aligned}\{4\} \times \{2\} &= \{6\} + \{51\} + \{42\}, \\ \{3\} \times \{3\} &= \{6\} + \{51\} + \{42\} + \{33\},\end{aligned} \tag{10.16}$$

we have

$$\begin{aligned}m(\{42\}, \{4\} \times \{2\}) &= 1, \\ m(\{42\}, \{3\} \times \{3\}) &= 1.\end{aligned} \tag{10.17}$$

Then the expectation value of the Wheeler operator becomes, with $|\{42\}| = 9$

$$\left\langle\begin{matrix}[2] & \{2\} \\ LM ' & \{42\}r\end{matrix}\right|\mathfrak{Q}^{(4)(2)}\left|\begin{matrix}[2] & \{2\} \\ LM ' & \{42\}r\end{matrix}\right\rangle = \frac{6!}{4!\,2!}\,\frac{1}{|\{42\}|}\,m(\{42\}, \{4\} \times \{2\}) = \tfrac{15}{9} = 1.6\dot{6} \tag{10.18}$$

and

$$\left\langle\begin{matrix}[2] & \{2\} \\ LM ' & \{42\}r\end{matrix}\right|\mathfrak{Q}^{(3)(3)}\left|\begin{matrix}[2] & \{2\} \\ LM ' & \{42\}r\end{matrix}\right\rangle = \frac{6!}{3!\,3!}\,\frac{1}{|\{42\}|}\,m(\{42\}, \{3\} \times \{3\}) = \tfrac{20}{9} = 2.2\dot{2}. \tag{10.19}$$

The orbital Young diagram, that is, the partition f, has been used by Neudachin *et al.* (*66–68*) to estimate the cluster structure of light nuclei. The eigenvalues of the Wheeler operators allow us to obtain quantitatively the limitations on clustering implied by the orbital symmetry. They show in particular that the natural grouping [in this case (4)(2)] is not always favored.

By constructing explicitly the ground state Eq. (10.15), we can also calculate the clustering (*65*); we obtain

$$\left\langle\begin{matrix}[2] & \{2\} \\ LM ' & \{42\}r\end{matrix}\right|\mathfrak{P}^{(4)(2)}\left|\begin{matrix}[2] & \{2\} \\ LM ' & \{42\}r\end{matrix}\right\rangle = \tfrac{9}{8} = 1.125, \tag{10.20}$$

$$\left\langle\begin{matrix}[2] & \{2\} \\ LM ' & \{42\}r\end{matrix}\right|\mathfrak{P}^{(3)(3)}\left|\begin{matrix}[2] & \{2\} \\ LM ' & \{42\}r\end{matrix}\right\rangle = \tfrac{29}{15} = 1.93\ldots. \tag{10.21}$$

These values are quite close to the upper limits Eqs. (10.18), (10.19). However, the example of the ground state of Be^8, with $\{h_1h_2h_3\} = \{4\}$ and $f = \{44\}$, gives (*65*)

$$\left\langle \begin{matrix} [4] & \{4\} \\ LM, & \{44\}r \end{matrix} \middle| \mathfrak{Q}^{(4)(4)} \middle| \begin{matrix} [4] & \{4\} \\ LM, & \{44\}r \end{matrix} \right\rangle = 5, \tag{10.22}$$

$$\left\langle \begin{matrix} [4] & \{4\} \\ LM, & \{44\}r \end{matrix} \middle| \mathfrak{P}^{(4)(4)} \middle| \begin{matrix} [4] & \{4\} \\ LM, & \{44\}r \end{matrix} \right\rangle = 1.5. \tag{10.23}$$

In general, we cannot expect the Wheeler operators to give a good estimate for clustering, because essentially they involve infinite-range correlations depending only on permutational symmetry. In contrast to this, clustering as defined in subsection A involves short-range correlations with respect to relative coordinates and momenta. The difference between the two concepts will become apparent as the number of clusters increases: the correlations implied by the Wheeler operators involve all particles, whereas for clustering we expect to find important the effects of the possible spatial arrangements of clusters, a concept recently emphasized by Pauling (*69*). Nevertheless, the Wheeler operators are useful for estimates because they are easy to handle.

C. Clustering of Four-Particle States; Wildermuth States

In this section we shall study the clustering properties of four-particle states as an illustration of the general approach introduced in Section X,A and B. Of particular interest is a clustering corresponding to the operators $\mathfrak{P}^{(3)(1)}$ and $\mathfrak{P}^{(2)(2)}$, since it corresponds to a grouping of all four particles into two clusters. These types of clustering imply the possibility of concentrating the full excitation energy on one vector, and this results in $h_1 = N$, $h_2 = h_3 = 0$ in the IR $\{h_1h_2h_3\}$ of $U(3)$. It is then easy to construct all states with definite permutational symmetry by inspection of Table III. The states are completely characterized by the weight, and application of a permutation gives a state with the permuted weight. In particular, for $\mathbf{w} = (u, u, u)$, there is only one state that has symmetry $f = \{4\}$. Since all states of this type are explicitly given, we are in a position to calculate the matrices of the clustering operators and to diagonalize them.

Let us start with $\mathfrak{P}^{(3)(1)}$. This operator is most conveniently written in terms of Jacobi vectors $\dot{\boldsymbol{\eta}}^s$; therefore, we use the relations of these vectors to the vectors $\ddot{\boldsymbol{\eta}}^s$,

$$\begin{aligned} \dot{\boldsymbol{\eta}}^1 &= \sqrt{\tfrac{1}{2}}(\ddot{\boldsymbol{\eta}}^1 - \ddot{\boldsymbol{\eta}}^2), \\ \dot{\boldsymbol{\eta}}^2 &= \sqrt{\tfrac{1}{6}}(\ddot{\boldsymbol{\eta}}^1 + \ddot{\boldsymbol{\eta}}^2 - 2\ddot{\boldsymbol{\eta}}^3), \\ \dot{\boldsymbol{\eta}}^3 &= -\sqrt{\tfrac{1}{3}}(\ddot{\boldsymbol{\eta}}^1 + \ddot{\boldsymbol{\eta}}^2 + \ddot{\boldsymbol{\eta}}^3). \end{aligned} \tag{10.24}$$

Denoting the states with $h_1 = N$, $h_2 = h_3 = 0$ by their weight (w^1, w^2, w^3), the naively clustered state Eq. (10.1) of type (3)(1) clustering can be denoted by

$$|(0, 0, \dot{N})\rangle \equiv \left\langle \dot{\mathbf{x}} \middle| \begin{matrix} [N], \\ LM \end{matrix} \quad \begin{matrix} N & 0 & 0 \\ & 0 \quad 0 & \\ & 0 & \end{matrix} \right\rangle, \tag{10.25}$$

where the dot above the N indicates that we are referring to the $\dot{\mathbf{x}}$ vectors. The states of permutational symmetry constructed from Table III in terms of the vectors $\ddot{\boldsymbol{\eta}}^1, \ddot{\boldsymbol{\eta}}^2, \ddot{\boldsymbol{\eta}}^3$ we denote by

$$|N\chi fr\rangle \equiv \left\langle \ddot{\mathbf{x}} \middle| \begin{matrix} [N] \\ LM \end{matrix}, \quad \begin{matrix} \{N\} \\ \chi fr \end{matrix} \right\rangle. \tag{10.26}$$

We suppress the quantum numbers LM, since from Eq. (10.6) it is clear that they are fixed throughout the discussion. Now we calculate the matrix of $\mathfrak{P}^{(3)(1)}$ between the states Eq. (10.26),

$$\langle N\bar{\chi} fr|\,\mathfrak{P}^{(3)(1)}|N\chi fr\rangle$$

$$= \binom{4}{3} |f|^{-1} \sum_{r'} \langle N\bar{\chi} fr|(0, 0, \dot{N})\rangle\langle(0, 0, \dot{N})|N\chi fr\rangle. \tag{10.27}$$

This matrix can be diagonalized without using the explicit form of the transformation brackets involved. First, we define a *Wildermuth state* as the projection of the state Eq. (10.25) onto states with permutational symmetry, that is, as

$$|N\varphi_1 fr\rangle = \mathcal{N}_{fr} \frac{|f|}{4!} \sum_{\mathbf{p} \in S(4)} D^{*f}_{rr}(\mathbf{p})\mathbf{p}|(0, 0, \dot{N})\rangle$$

$$= \mathcal{N}_{fr} \frac{|f|}{4!} \sum_{\mathbf{p} \in S(4)} \sum_{\chi \bar{f}\bar{r}} D^{*f}_{rr}(\mathbf{p})\mathbf{p}|N\chi \bar{f}\bar{r}\rangle \langle N\chi \bar{f}\bar{r}|(0, 0, \dot{N})\rangle$$

$$= \mathcal{N}_{fr} \sum_{\chi} |N\chi fr\rangle \langle N\chi fr|(0, 0, \dot{N})\rangle \tag{10.28}$$

with $\mathcal{N}_{fr}$ being a normalization coefficient, where we assume that for at least one r

$$\mathcal{N}_{fr}^{-2} = \sum_{\chi} |\langle N\chi fr|(0, 0, \dot{N})\rangle|^2 \neq 0. \tag{10.29}$$

Next we select, by the Schmidt orthogonalization procedure, states

$$|N\varphi fr\rangle, \qquad \varphi = \varphi_2, \varphi_3, \ldots, \tag{10.30}$$

which complement the state $|N\varphi_1 fr\rangle$ of Eq. (10.28) to a complete set. Orthonormality of these states implies, in particular,

$$j \geqq 2: \quad \langle N\varphi_j fr'|N\varphi_1 fr\rangle = \mathcal{N}_{fr} \sum_{\chi} \langle N\varphi_j fr'|N\chi fr\rangle \langle N\chi fr|(0, 0, \dot{N})\rangle = 0. \tag{10.31}$$

The matrix elements of $\mathfrak{P}^{(3)(1)}$ in the new basis are then given by

$$\begin{aligned}\langle N\varphi_1 fr|\,\mathfrak{P}^{(3)(1)}|N\varphi_1 fr\rangle &= \binom{4}{3} |f|^{-1} \sum_{r'} \mathcal{N}^2_{fr'} \Bigg[\sum_{\bar{\chi}} \langle(0, 0, \dot{N})|N\bar{\chi} fr'\rangle \langle N\bar{\chi} fr'|(0, 0, \dot{N})\rangle \\ &\quad \times \sum_{\chi} \langle(0, 0, \dot{N})|N\chi fr'\rangle \langle N\chi fr'|(0, 0, \dot{N})\rangle\Bigg] \\ &= \binom{4}{3} |f|^{-1} \sum_{\chi r'} |\langle N\chi fr'|(0, 0, \dot{N})\rangle|^2,\end{aligned} \tag{10.32}$$

$$\begin{aligned} i \geqq 2: \quad \langle N\varphi_i fr|\,\mathfrak{P}^{(3)(1)}|N\varphi_j fr\rangle &= \binom{4}{3} |f|^{-1} \sum_{r'} \Bigg[\sum_{\bar{\chi}} \langle N\varphi_i fr'|N\bar{\chi} fr'\rangle \langle N\bar{\chi} fr'|(0, 0, \dot{N})\rangle \\ &\quad \times \sum_{\chi} \langle(0, 0, \dot{N})|N\chi fr'\rangle \langle N\chi fr'|N\varphi_j fr'\rangle\Bigg] = 0. \end{aligned} \tag{10.33}$$

It follows that in the new basis $\mathfrak{P}^{(3)(1)}$ is diagonal with eigenvalues

$$p^{(3)(1)} = \begin{cases} 0 & \text{if} \quad j \geqq 2 \qquad (10.34) \\ \binom{4}{3} |f|^{-1} \sum_{\chi r'} |\langle N\chi fr'|(0, 0, \dot{N})\rangle|^2 & \text{if} \quad j = 1. \qquad (10.35) \end{cases}$$

Before proceeding to the explicit calculation of the eigenvalue of $\mathfrak{P}^{(3)(1)}$, we would like to point out the possible generalization of this type of argument. It is clear that our reasoning is based on the existence of precisely one clustered state Eq. (10.25) for given N. It may therefore be applied to the operator $\mathfrak{P}^{(2)(2)}$ as well and, in general, to any type of clustering that involves grouping of all particles into two clusters similar, for example, to the ground state of Be^8 considered by Wildermuth and Kanellopoulos (*61*, *62*). In all these cases, the projection procedure picks out the maximal clustered state in terms of our general definition.

To evaluate $\mathfrak{p}^{(3)(1)}$ in Eq. (10.35), we first express the state Eq. (10.25) in terms of the states

$$|(u, v, w)\rangle \equiv \left\langle \ddot{\mathbf{x}} \left| \begin{matrix}[N]\\ LM\end{matrix}, \begin{matrix} N & 0 & 0 \\ u+v & \mathbf{0} & \\ & u & \end{matrix} \right.\right\rangle \tag{10.36}$$

with $w = N - u - v$. We find

$$\langle (u, v, w)|(0, 0, \dot{N})\rangle = (-1)^N \left(\frac{1}{3}\right)^{\frac{1}{2}N} \left(\frac{N!}{u!\,v!\,w!}\right)^{1/2} \tag{10.37}$$

Then, from Table III we obtain the coefficients

$$\langle N\chi fr|(u, v, w)\rangle \tag{10.38}$$

so that

$$\langle N\chi fr|(0, 0, \dot{N})\rangle = \sum_{\substack{(u,v,w)\\ u+v+w=N}} \langle N\chi fr|(u, v, w)\rangle(-1)^N \left(\frac{1}{3}\right)^{\frac{1}{2}N} \left(\frac{N!}{u!\,v!\,w!}\right)^{1/2}. \tag{10.39}$$

The possible partitions f are {4} and {31}, and we find

$$f = \{31\}: \quad \mathfrak{p}^{(3)(1)} = \frac{4}{3}\left(\frac{1}{3}\right)^N \sum_{\substack{(u,v,w)=\begin{cases}(0,0,e),\,(0,e,0),\,(e,0,0) & \text{if } N \text{ even}\\ (e,e,0),\,(e,0,e),\,(0,e,e) & \text{if } N \text{ odd}\end{cases}\\ u+v+w=N}} \frac{N!}{u!\,v!\,w!}$$

$$= 1 - \left(-\frac{1}{3}\right)^N, \tag{10.40}$$

$$f = \{4\}: \quad \mathfrak{p}^{(3)(1)} = 4\left(\frac{1}{3}\right)^N \sum_{(u,v,w)=\begin{cases}(e,e,e) & \text{if } N \text{ even}\\ (0,0,0) & \text{if } N \text{ odd}\end{cases}} \frac{N!}{u!\,v!\,w!}$$

$$= 1 + 3\left(-\frac{1}{3}\right)^N. \tag{10.41}$$

Clearly, we have $\mathfrak{p}^{(3)(1)} \to 1$ for $N \to \infty$, which means that for high excitation we obtain the value expected from a model of separated clusters (corresponding to an α-particle model). Then, from the deviation from this value for the first energy levels, we may infer the amount of overlap of the clusters as illustrated in Fig. 5.

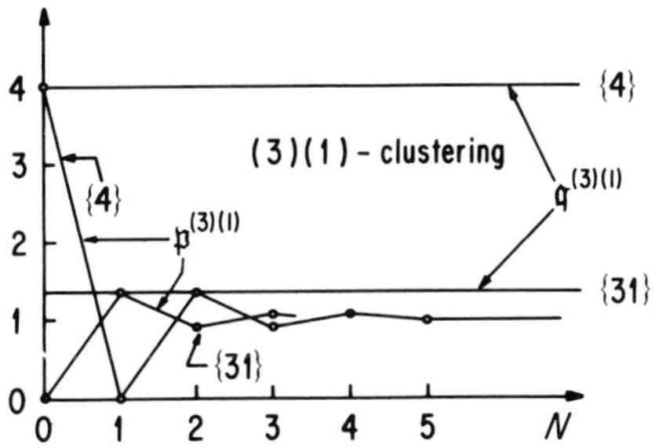

FIG. 5. Eigenvalue $\mathfrak{p}^{(3)(1)}$ of the clustering operator $\mathfrak{P}^{(3)(1)}$ for four-particle Wildermuth states as a function of N. Eigenvalue $\mathfrak{q}^{(3)(1)}$ of corresponding Wheeler operator.

From our general remarks it follows that $\mathfrak{P}^{(2)(2)}$ can be diagonalized in a similar way. The naively clustered state is simply

$$|(0, 0, \ddot{N})\rangle$$

defined similarly to Eq. (10.26) in terms of the $\ddot{\mathbf{x}}$ vectors, and therefore

$$\mathfrak{p}^{(2)(2)} = \binom{4}{2} |f|^{-1} \sum_{\chi, r} |\langle N\chi fr|(0, 0, \ddot{N})\rangle|^2. \tag{10.42}$$

We easily find

$$\begin{aligned}
f = \{4\}: &\quad \mathfrak{p}^{(2)(2)} = 6 \quad \text{if } N = 0, \\
&\quad \mathfrak{p}^{(2)(2)} = 2 \quad \text{if } N \text{ even}, \quad N \neq 0, \\
f = \{31\}: &\quad \mathfrak{p}^{(2)(2)} = 2 \quad \text{if } N \text{ odd}, \\
f = \{22\}: &\quad \mathfrak{p}^{(2)(2)} = 2 \quad \text{if } N \text{ even}, \quad N \neq 0.
\end{aligned} \tag{10.43}$$

This is equal precisely to the value for a model of separated clusters, the number 2 resulting from the presence of two equal clusters. Because almost no energy dependency of $\mathfrak{p}^{(2)(2)}$ exists (see Fig. 6), we see that we should be careful when comparing with the asymptotic value. For low excitation, there will be cluster overlaps not indicated by $\mathfrak{p}^{(2)(2)}$ and we must examine other properties of the states to get information about the overlap.

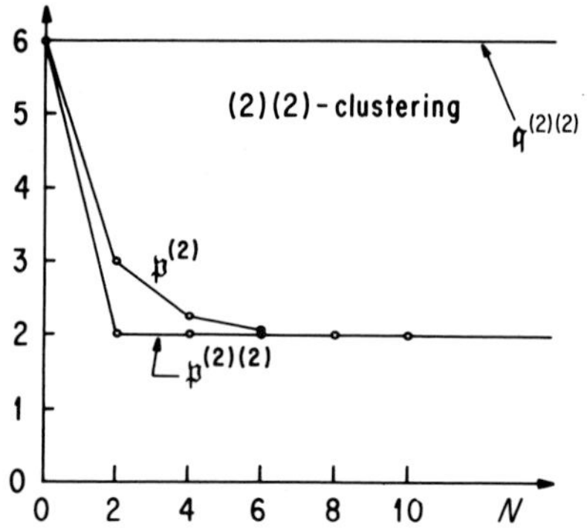

FIG. 6. Eigenvalue $\mathfrak{p}^{(2)(2)}$ of the clustering operator $\mathfrak{P}^{(2)(2)}$ for four-particle Wildermuth states as a function of N. Expectation value $\mathfrak{p}^{(2)}$ of clustering interaction for the same states. Permutational limit $\mathfrak{q}^{(2)(2)}$. In all cases $f = \{4\}$.

Clustering has been discussed by Neudachin *et al.* (*66–68*) in terms of the permutational symmetry. It should be noted that our approach gives different results: at most one of the many states having $\{h_1h_2h_3\} = \{N\}$ and $f = \{31\}$, for example, is characterized by clustering properties of type $\mathfrak{P}^{(3)(1)}$ having $\mathfrak{p}^{(3)(1)} > 0$.

Figure 7 shows the overlap between the Wildermuth states of type (3)(1) and (2)(2) as a function of the total number N of quanta. For the lowest values of N, both types of clustering appear for one and the same state, whereas for higher excitation, the overlap goes to zero.

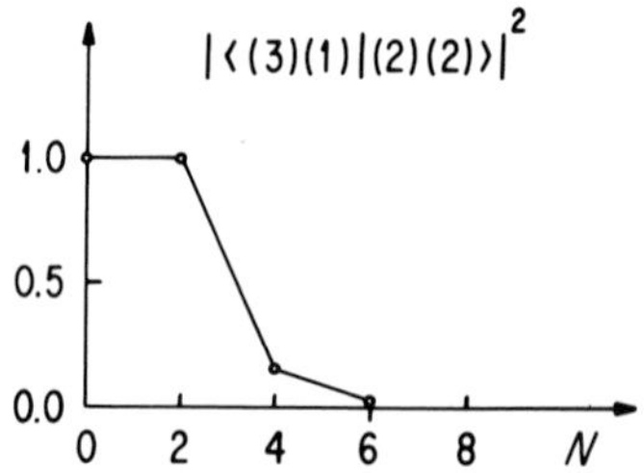

FIG. 7. Overlap of Wildermuth states corresponding to (3)(1) and to (2)(2) clustering of four-particle states as a function of N.

D. Clustering Interaction

In Section IX,C we showed that the quadrupole-quadrupole interaction can account for the appearance of rotational bands in nuclear spectra. In a similar way, we would like to find a model interaction that would favor clustering in the sense discussed in Section X,A. We could, of course, easily introduce, for example, a four-body operator $\mathfrak{P}^{(4)}$ that would favor α-particle clustering. But this would mean introducing clustering by definition, and therefore we would prefer to find a two-body clustering interaction. This clustering interaction should, furthermore, imply a short-range correlation because of the remarks at the end of Section X,B.

A two-body interaction that can be shown to lead to clustering is given by

$$\mathscr{V}^{(2)} = -C \cdot \mathfrak{P}^{(2)} \tag{10.44}$$

where C is a constant and $\mathfrak{P}^{(2)}$ is an operator of the type Eq. (10.3) given by

$$\mathfrak{P}^{(2)} = [2!(n-2)!]^{-1} \sum_{\mathbf{p} \in S(n)\, h_1h_2h_3\, \Omega LM\gamma} \mathbf{p}^{-1} \left| \begin{matrix} [h_1h_2h_3] \\ \Omega LM \end{matrix}, \begin{matrix} \{h_1h_2h_3\} \\ (2)\gamma \end{matrix} \right\rangle$$
$$\times \left\langle \begin{matrix} [h_1h_2h_3] \\ \Omega LM \end{matrix}, \begin{matrix} \{h_1h_2h_3\} \\ (2)\gamma \end{matrix} \right| \mathbf{p} \tag{10.45}$$

Then the two-body matrix elements of $\mathfrak{P}^{(2)}$ between states

$$\langle \sqrt{\tfrac{1}{2}}(\mathbf{x}^1 - \mathbf{x}^2) | \nu l m \rangle \tag{10.46}$$

are given by

$$\langle \nu' l' m' | \mathfrak{P}^{(2)} | \nu l m \rangle = \delta_{\nu' 0}\, \delta_{\nu 0}\, \delta_{l' 0}\, \delta_{l 0}\, \delta_{m' 0}\, \delta_{m 0} \tag{10.47}$$

so that $\mathscr{V}^{(2)}$ acts only between pairs in zero relative oscillation.

It is intuitively clear that this interaction should favor clustering in the sense of Section X,A. Explicit calculations of four-particle states show that states of a high amount of clustering have indeed a high overlap with eigenstates of $\mathscr{V}^{(2)}$. At the same time we observe for the lowest excitations that, in general, the eigenstates of $\mathscr{V}^{(2)}$ correspond to a mixture of different types of clustering. This property is quite natural for a two-body interaction, which cannot distinguish between different, but equally favorable, types of more-particle clustering.

For the asymptotic case of well-separated clusters, it can be shown that the eigenvalue of $\mathfrak{P}^{(2)}$ approaches the number of internal pairs (*65*). Because of cluster overlap, the states of lowest excitation may have higher expectation values of $\mathfrak{P}^{(2)}$, as can be seen in Fig. 6.

From the general relation between clustering and permutational symmetry it follows that the expectation value of $\mathfrak{P}^{(2)}$ must be smaller than the number $\mathfrak{q}^{(2)}$ of symmetric pairs. The eigenvalues of the Wheeler operator

$$\mathfrak{Q}^{(2)} = \tfrac{1}{2} \sum_{s<t} (1 + (s, t)) \tag{10.48}$$

are related to the invariant operators of the symmetric group (*12*), and for bases of the irreducible representation f of $S(n)$ can be shown to be

$$\begin{aligned} \mathfrak{q}^{(2)} &= \frac{1}{2}\frac{n(n-1)}{2}\left[1 + \frac{\chi^f(1^{n-2}2)}{\chi^f(1^n)}\right] \\ &= \frac{1}{2}\frac{n(n-1)}{2} + \frac{1}{4}\sum_s f_s(f_s - 2s + 1). \end{aligned} \tag{10.49}$$

where the χ^f are the characters of the IR of $S(n)$.

Interactions similar to $\mathfrak{P}^{(2)}$, but projecting out pairs with $\rho = 0, 1, 2, \ldots$ quanta of relative motion, have been considered by Brink (*70*), who did not relate them to clustering. The sums of the eigenvalues $\mathfrak{p}_\rho^{(2)}$ of these operators over all even or all odd ρ clearly gives the number of symmetric or antisymmetric pairs respectively, that is,

$$\sum_{\rho \text{ even}} \mathfrak{p}_\rho^{(2)} = \mathfrak{q}^{(2)}, \qquad \sum_{\rho \text{ odd}} \mathfrak{p}_\rho^{(2)} = \frac{n(n-1)}{2} - \mathfrak{q}^{(2)}. \tag{10.50}$$

Besides, we can show (*23*) that for nonspurious states

$$\sum_\rho \rho \mathfrak{p}_\rho^{(2)} = \frac{n}{2} N. \tag{10.51}$$

E. Quadrupole-Quadrupole Interaction and Clustering Interaction in the 1s-1p Shell

We consider here a simple application of model interactions to the lowest states in the 1s-1p shell. Suppose that the 1s shell is filled and that there are $n - 4 \geqq 0$ particles in the 1p shell. The weight of the corresponding Gelfand state is clearly $\mathbf{w} = 0^4 1^{n-4}$ and therefore the group of the weight is $S(4) \oplus S(n-4)$. The only IR of $S(4)$ in the 1s shell is clearly $f = \{4\}$. The Gelfand states for the $n - 4$ particles in the 1p shell, on the other hand, have weight 1, 1, ..., 1; that is, they are SG states in the sense considered in Section

V,D. Therefore, for these states the IR of $U(n-4)$ and of $S(n-4)$ coincide. The n-particle states can have the IR $\{h_1h_2h_3\}$ of $U(n)$ and the IR

$$\{4\} \times \{h_1h_2h_3\} = \sum m(\{f_1f_2f_3f_4\}, \{4\} \times \{h_1h_2h_3\}) \times \{f_1f_2f_3f_4\} \qquad (10.52)$$

of $S(n)$. However, the only states allowed by the Pauli principle are clearly

$$\{f_1f_2f_3f_4\} = \{4h_1h_2h_3\}. \qquad (10.53)$$

Therefore, the IR of $U(n)$ or $\mathscr{U}(3)$ and of $S(n)$ are simply related in this two-shell configuration.

Consider now a model Hamiltonian given by

$$\mathscr{H} = \mathscr{H}_0 - BQ^2 - C\,\mathfrak{P}^{(2)} + D; \qquad (10.54)$$

$-Q^2$ is determined by $h_1h_2h_3$ and by L, according to Eq. (9.17). We choose the states with highest orbital symmetry in Eq. (10.53) and the lowest possible N, L. To calculate the eigenvalue $\mathfrak{p}^{(2)}$ of $\mathfrak{P}^{(2)}$ we use Eqs. (10.50) and (10.51). Since in the chosen configuration the highest excitation of a relative vector $2^{-1/2}(\mathbf{x}^s - \mathbf{x}^t)$ corresponds to two quanta, ρ takes the values $\rho = 0, 1, 2$. Solving Eqs. (10.50) and (10.51) for $\mathfrak{p}^{(2)} \equiv \mathfrak{p}_0^{(2)}$, we find

$$\mathfrak{p}^{(2)} = \tfrac{1}{2}\mathfrak{q}^{(2)} + \tfrac{3}{4}n \qquad (10.55)$$

with $\mathfrak{q}^{(2)}$ given by Eq. (10.49). The parameters in Eq. (10.54) were now chosen so as to fit the experimental values for the ground states of He^4, C^{12}, and O^{16} and to give an overall agreement for the other nuclei, with the result that

$$\hbar\omega = 13.6\ \text{MeV}, \qquad B = 1.0\ \text{MeV}, \qquad C = 7.5\ \text{MeV}. \qquad (10.56)$$

The comparison with experimental values is shown in Fig. 8 where, for each mass number n, the state with highest orbital symmetry was chosen.

If now we compare, for example, the mass eight nuclei Li^8, Be^8, and B^8, we find $\{h_1h_2h_3\} = \{4\}$ for Be^8 and $\{h_1h_2h_3\} = \{31\}$ for Li^8, B^8. In the latter case, the eigenvalue of $\mathfrak{p}^{(2)}$ is reduced by 1 and the eigenvalue of Q^2 by 9. The energy difference when using the Hamiltonian Eq. (10.54) is, therefore, 7.5 MeV from exciting one pair and 9 MeV from changing the Q^2 interaction, giving a total of 16.5 MeV. It thus seems that the Hamiltonian Eq. (10.54) can account for some over-all features of the binding energy in the $1s$-$1p$ shell. Besides, this

Hamiltonian has a very simple structure: $\mathfrak{P}^{(2)}$ could be said to *act within* the clusters, that is, between pairs of zero relative oscillation; Q^2, in contrast, does not act between pairs in zero relative oscillation, since it is given in terms of the generators of $\mathscr{U}(3)$, and therefore the quadrupole-quadrupole interaction could be said to *act between* the clusters.

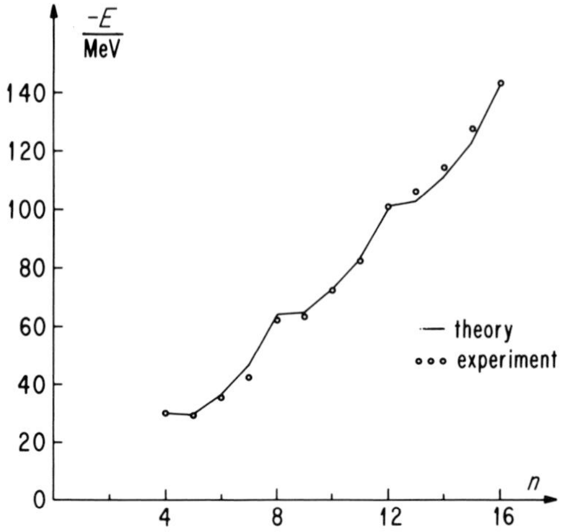

FIG. 8. Comparison of lowest state for nuclei in the $1s$-$1p$ shell (total binding energy after subtraction of Coulomb energy). For each mass number n, only the lowest state of the nucleus with highest orbital symmetry is given.

F. APPENDIX: EIGENVALUES OF WHEELER OPERATORS

To prove Eq. (10.13), we note that the brackets on the right-hand side do not depend on $h_1h_2h_3\Omega LM\chi$, so that the equation could be written as

$$m(f, \{n_1\} \times \{n_2\} \times \cdots \times \{n_k\}) \\ = \sum_{r\varphi} |\langle fr | f\varphi\{n_1\} \times \{n_2\} \times \cdots \times \{n_k\}\rangle|^2. \tag{10.57}$$

For the proof of Eq. (10.57), we consider the subgroup

$$W = S(n_1) \oplus S(n_2) \oplus \cdots \oplus S(n_k)$$

of $S(n)$. Its IR are direct product representations of all the IR $f^1, f^2, \ldots, f^k$

where f^j denotes the IR of $S(n_j)$, and could be written as

$$f_w = f^1 f^2 \cdots f^k. \tag{10.58}$$

Similarly, the rows of this IR could be denoted by the set r_w of all Yamanouchi symbols of the groups $S(n_1)$, $S(n_2)$, ..., $S(n_k)$ as

$$r_w = r^1 r^2 \cdots r^k. \tag{10.59}$$

The Young operator for this IR is given by

$$c^{f_w}_{r_w' r_w} = \frac{|f_w|}{|W|} \sum_{\mathbf{h} \in W} D^{*\, f_w}_{r_w' r_w}(\mathbf{h})\mathbf{h}. \tag{10.60}$$

We evaluate the diagonal element of this operator for $r_w' = r_w$ between the bases of the Yamanouchi IR of $S(n)$ to obtain

$$\langle fr | c^{f_w}_{r_w r_w} | fr \rangle = \frac{|f_w|}{|W|} \sum_{\mathbf{h} \in W} D^{*\, f_w}_{r_w r_w}(\mathbf{h}) \langle fr | \mathbf{h} | fr \rangle. \tag{10.61}$$

Summing over r and r_w, we find

$$\begin{aligned} \sum_{r, r_w} \langle fr | c^{f_w}_{r_w r_w} | fr \rangle &= \frac{|f_w|}{|W|} \sum_{\mathbf{h} \in W} \chi^f(\mathbf{h}) \chi^{*\, f_w}(\mathbf{h}) \\ &= |f_w| m(f, f_w) \end{aligned} \tag{10.62}$$

where $m(f, f_w)$ is the multiplicity of the IR of the subgroup W of $S(n)$ in the IR f of $S(n)$.

On the other hand, we introduce transformation brackets that transform the BIR of $S(n)$ into BIR of W; that is, brackets

$$\langle fr | f\varphi f_w r_w \rangle \tag{10.63}$$

with φ a multiplicity index for repeated IR f_w in a given IR f. Using these transformation brackets, the left-hand side of Eq. (10.61) can be written as

$$\langle fr | c^{f_w}_{r_w r_w} | fr \rangle = \sum_{\varphi} \langle fr | f\varphi f_w r_w \rangle \langle f\varphi f_w r_w | fr \rangle \tag{10.64}$$

so that

$$\sum_{r r_w} \langle fr | c^{f_w}_{r_w r_w} | fr \rangle = \sum_{\varphi r r_w} |\langle fr | f\varphi f_w r_w \rangle|^2. \tag{10.65}$$

Comparing Eqs. (10.62) and (10.65), we find

$$m(f, f_w) = |f_w|^{-1} \sum_{\varphi r r_w} |\langle fr | f\varphi f_w r_w \rangle|^2. \tag{10.66}$$

We particularize this to the case $f_w = \{n_1\} \times \{n_2\} \times \cdots \times \{n_k\}$, in which case $|f_w| = 1$ and r_w is redundant. Then

$$m(f, \{n_1\} \times \{n_2\} \times \cdots \times \{n_k\}) = \sum_{\varphi r} |\langle fr | f\varphi \{n_1\} \times \{n_2\} \times \cdots \times \{n_k\} \rangle|^2,$$

as stated in Eq. (10.57).

Acknowledgments

The authors express their appreciation to Prof. V. Bargmann (who, with M. Moshinsky, developed some of the initial ideas leading to this chapter), as well as to Prof. E. P. Wigner and the late Prof. G. Racah, for many helpful discussions.

Many members of the Instituto de Física, Universidad de México, contributed to the development of the ideas presented here. We are indebted to T. A. Brody for many discussions and suggestions, as well as for programming some of the concepts developed; to J. Nagel for clarification of many concepts and particularly for his contributions to the determination of the lowering operators and their normalization coefficients; and to H. V. McIntosh for very helpful discussions on the IR of semidirect products. We thank E. Chacón, J. Flores, M. de Llano, and P. A. Mello for the contributions mentioned in the text and for discussions. We are indebted to several graduate students for help in preparing the tables and with some calculations. Finally, we thank Mrs. E. Moshinsky for help in the preparation of the manuscript.

Outside our institution we have benefited from discussions with L. C. Biedenharn, K. T. Hecht, J. Louck, F. A. Matsen, and K. Wildermuth.

In addition, P. Kramer expresses his thanks to the Deutscher Akademischer Austauschdienst for a NATO fellowship, to Dr. Fernando Alba for the hospitality extended to him by the Instituto de Física during the two years of his stay, and to Dr. M. S. Vallarta for the support given by the Comisión Nacional de Energía Nuclear during the last part of his stay.

REFERENCES*

1. I. Talmi, *Helv. Phys. Acta* **25**, 185 (1952).
2. S. G. Nilsson, *Kgl. Danske Videnskab. Selskab, Mat.-Fys. Medd.* **29**, No. 16 (1955).
3. J. P. Elliott, *Proc. Roy. Soc. London Ser. A* **245**, 128 (1958).
4. M. Moshinsky, *Nuclear Phys.* **13**, 104 (1959).
5. T. A. Brody and M. Moshinsky, "Tables of Transformation Brackets for Nuclear Shell Model Calculations." Mexico, 1960. Second Edition: Gordon and Breach, New York, 1967.
6. W. Laskar, *Ann. Physics* **17**, 436 (1962); **20**, 175 (1962).

* We do not attempt to give a complete list of references but only those that illustrate the points raised.

7. K. Wildermuth and W. McClure, "Cluster Representation of Nuclei." Springer, Berlin, 1966.
8. M. Kretzschmar, *Z. Physik* **157**, 433 (1960).
9. M. Kretzschmar, *Z. Physik* **158**, 284 (1960).
10. V. Bargmann and M. Moshinsky, *Nuclear Phys.* **18**, 697 (1960).
11. V. Bargmann and M. Moshinsky, *Nuclear Phys.* **23**, 177 (1961).
12. P. Kramer and M. Moshinsky, *Nuclear Phys.* **82**, 241 (1966).
13. J. D. Louck, *J. Mathematical Phys.* **6**, 1786 (1965).
14. M. Moshinsky, *Rev. Mod. Phys.* **34**, 813 (1962).
15. M. Moshinsky, *J. Mathematical Phys.* **4**, 1128 (1963).
16. G. E. Baird and L. C. Biedenharn, *J. Mathematical Phys.* **4**, 1449 (1963).
17. J. G. Nagel and M. Moshinsky, *J. Mathematical Phys.* **6**, 682 (1965).
18. T. A. Brody, M. Moshinsky, and I. Renero, *J. Mathematical Phys.* **6**, 1540 (1965).
19. G. A. Baker, Jr., *Phys. Rev.* **103**, 1119 (1956).
20. P. Kramer, *J. Mathematical Phys.* **9** (1968).
21. P. Kramer, *Z. Physik* **205**, 181 (1967).
22. M. Moshinsky, Group theory and the many body problem. *In* "Physics of Many Particle Systems" (E. Meeron, ed.), p. 407. Gordon and Breach, New York, 1965. Reproduced in pp. 289–439 of Ref. *24*.
23. P. Kramer, *Phys. Lett.* **21**, 182 (1966).
24. B. Bayman, Recent experimental tests of nuclear models. *In* "Many-Body Problems and Other Selected Topics in Theoretical Physics" (M. Moshinsky, T. A. Brody, and G. Jacob, eds.), p. 441. Gordon and Breach, New York, 1966.
25. K. T. Hecht, *Nuclear Phys.* **63**, 177 (1965).
26. I. M. Gelfand and M. L. Zetlin, *Dokl. Akad. Nauk SSSR* **71**, 825 (1950).
27. M. Moshinsky, *J. Mathematical Phys.* **7**, 691 (1966).
28. P. Kramer and M. Moshinsky, *Nuclear Phys.* **A107**, 481 (1968).
29. V. Bargmann, *Rev. Mod. Phys.* **34**, 829 (1962).
30. M. Hamermesh, "Group Theory and its Applications to Physical Problems." Addison Wesley, Reading, Massachusetts, 1962.
31. J. Yamanouchi, *Proc. Phys. Math. Soc. Japan* **19**, 436 (1937).
32. E. P. Wigner, "Group Theory and its Application to the Quantum Mechanics of Atomic Spectra." Academic Press, New York, 1959.
33. H. V. McIntosh, *J. Mol. Spectry.* **10**, 51 (1963).
34. H. V. McIntosh, *J. Mol. Spectry.* **5**, 269 (1960).
35. H. Horie, *J. Phys. Soc. Japan* **19**, 1783 (1964).
36. H. Weyl, *Math. Z.* **23**, 271 (1925).
37. E. Chacón and M. Moshinsky, *Phys. Lett.* **23**, 567 (1966).
38. M. Moshinsky and E. Chacon, Racah coefficients and states with permutational symmetry. *In* "Racah Memorial Volume," in press. North-Holland Publ. Amsterdam.
39. D. E. Littlewood, "The Theory of Group Characters," p. 94. Oxford Univ. Press, London and New York, 1940.
40. M. Moshinsky, *Nuclear Phys.* **31**, 384 (1962).
41. E. Chacón, Ph.D. Thesis, University of Mexico, unpublished.
42. M. Resnikoff, *Nuclear Phys.* **83**, 632 (1966).
43. S. Ch. Pang and K. T. Hecht, *J. Mathematical Phys.* 8, 1233 (1967).
44. S. Altmann, *Rev. Mod. Phys.* **35**, 641 (1963).
45. H. A. Jahn, *Phys. Rev.* **96**, 989 (1954).
46. A. R. Edmonds, "Angular Momentum in Quantum Mechanics." Princeton Univ. Press, Princeton, New Jersey, 1957.

47. E. P. Wigner, *Phys. Rev.* **51**, 106 (1937).
48. H. A. Jahn, *Proc. Roy. Soc. London Ser. A* **205**, 192 (1951).
49. M. Kushner and J. Quintanilla, *Phys. Lett.* **23**, 572 (1965).
50. M. Moshinsky and J. G. Nagel, *Phys. Lett.* **5**, 173 (1963).
51. G. E. Baird and L. C. Biedenharn, *J. Mathematical Phys.* **6**, 1847 (1965).
52. T. A. Brody, M. Moshinsky, and I. Renero, *Rev. Mexicana Fís.* **15**, 145 (1966).
53. J. P. Elliott, J. Hope, and H. A. Jahn, *Phil. Trans. Roy. Soc. London Ser. A* **246**, 241 (1953).
54. M. E. Rose, "Elementary Theory of Angular Momentum." Wiley, New York, 1961.
55. T. A. Brody, G. Jacob, and M. Moshinsky, *Nuclear Phys.* **17**, 16 (1960).
56. A. de Shalit and J. D. Walecka, *Phys. Rev.* **147**, 763 (1966).
57. B. R. Barrett, *Phys. Rev.* **159**, 816 (1967).
58. J. Flores and M. Moshinsky, *Nuclear Phys.* **A93**, 81 (1967).
59. J. Flores, E. Chacón, P. A. Mello, and M. de Llano, *Nuclear Phys.* **72**, 352 (1965).
60. M. de Llano, P. A. Mello, E. Chacón, and J. Flores, *Nuclear Phys.* **72**, 379 (1965).
61. K. Wildermuth and Th. Kanellopoulos, *Nuclear Phys.* **7**, 150 (1958).
62. K. Wildermuth and Th. Kanellopoulos, *Nuclear Phys.* **9**, 449 (1958).
63. J. A. Wheeler, *Phys. Rev.* **52**, 1083 (1937).
64. J. A. Wheeler, *Phys. Rev.* **52**, 1107 (1937).
65. P. Kramer, *Habilitationsschrift*, Tübingen, 1967.
66. V. G. Neudachin, V. G. Shevchenko, and N. P. Yudin, *Phys. Lett.* **10**, 180 (1964).
67. V. G. Neudachin and Yu. F. Smirnov, *Nuclear Phys.* **66**, 25 (1965).
68. V. G. Neudachin and Yu. F. Smirnov, *Atomic Energy Rev.* **3**, 157 (1965).
69. L. Pauling, *Proc. Nat. Acad. Sci. U.S.A.* **54**, 969 (1965).
70. D. M. Brink, *Nuclear Phys.* **40**, 593 (1963).

Broken Symmetry

*L. O'RAIFEARTAIGH**

SYRACUSE UNIVERSITY, SYRACUSE, NEW YORK

I. Introduction

The purpose of this chapter is to consider the broken symmetry groups of elementary particle physics, namely, $SU(3)$ and $SU(6)$, from a rather general and elementary point of view. The aim is to keep the discussion at a level where it can easily be followed by those who are not actively engaged in this field but are peripherally interested in it.

By elementary particles are understood here the hundred or so particles that, with more or less justification, at present go under that name. Clearly, so many particles cannot really be elementary, but for lack of a satisfactory theory we are forced to regard them as elementary for the present. The situation is somewhat similar to the way in which the ninety-two chemical elements were regarded as elementary until the advent of a satisfactory theory of atomic structure. It will be convenient to classify the elementary particles as follows. First, in a class by itself, is the photon γ, which interacts only electromagnetically and has mass zero and spin one. In the next class come the leptons, or particles that interact only electromagnetically or weakly. They are the electron e ($\frac{1}{2}$), μ-meson (106), and the two neutrinos ν_1^0 (0) and ν_2^0 (0) (together with their antiparticles). Here the superscript denotes the electric charge and

* Permanent address: Dublin Institute for Advanced Studies, Dublin, Ireland.

the quantity in parentheses is the mass in millions of electron volts. In the third class come the metastable hadrons; that is, the strongly interacting* particles, which do not decay strongly, and hence have reasonably long lifetimes ($\sim 10^{-10}$ sec). In this class come the strongly interacting metastable mesons [**π**-mesons (140), **K**-mesons (490), and **η**-particle (550)] and the strongly intereacting metastable fermions (baryons) consisting of the nucleons **N** (940), **Λ**-particle (1115), **Σ**'s (1190), **Ξ** (1320), and $\boldsymbol{\Omega}^-$ (1675). Here the boldface letters denote, in general, not single particles but particle multiplets. The particles in each multiplet differ only in their weak and electromagnetic properties. Hence in the limit in which these interactions are neglected, they can be regarded as different (charge) states of a single particle. For example, **N** (940) denotes the multiplet consisting of the proton p and neutron n. In the final class come the particles that interact strongly and decay strongly. The list of such particles is very large and is growing rapidly; see, for example, the "Rosenfeld tables" (*1*). The lifetimes of these last particles are very short ($\sim 10^{-23}$ sec) and, in fact, these particles are observed not directly but as resonances in the scattering and production of the metastable particles. On the other hand, there is ample evidence to support the view that the distinction between metastable particles and resonances is purely a matter of kinematic accidence, so that the division into the last two of the classes just named is a matter of convenience rather than of principle.

The outstanding problem in modern elementary particle physics is to understand the nature of these particles and their interactions. Two main lines of attack on this problem have been developed, namely, the dynamic and group-theoretical approaches. The dynamic approach is probably the more fundamental, but it is also the more difficult, and has not had as much success as one would like. For that reason one has been forced to rely very heavily on the symmetry approach, which, in recent years at any rate, has been more successful.

By far the most successful concept in the symmetry approach is that of isotopic spin invariance. Originally introduced to formulate the charge independence of the nuclear forces in as simple a manner as possible, this concept has been found to be of general validity for strong interactions. Specifically, if an abstract (isotopic spin) group $SU(2)$ is introduced, then all the strongly interacting particles are found to fall into multiplets that can be associated with the various irreducible representations of this group in such a way that the strong interactions of these particles are then invariant under the group transformations. For example, the **π**-, **K**-, and **η**-mesons are associated with the three-, two-, and one-dimensional representations of $SU(2)$, and the **N**, **Λ**, **Σ**, **Ξ**, and $\boldsymbol{\Omega}^-$, with the two-, one-, three-, two-, and one-

* By strong interactions are meant here interactions of the same order of strength as the nuclear interactions. Particles which interact strongly are called hadrons.

dimensional representations, respectively. The effective interactions of these particles are then necessarily restricted to be of the form $\bar{\mathbf{N}}\boldsymbol{\tau}\mathbf{N}\cdot\boldsymbol{\pi}$, $\boldsymbol{\Sigma}\cdot(\boldsymbol{\Sigma}\times\boldsymbol{\pi})$, $\bar{\boldsymbol{\Xi}}\boldsymbol{\Xi}\eta$, etc., where $\boldsymbol{\tau}$ here denotes the three Pauli matrices and $\times$ the vector product.

In addition to being invariant with respect to the isotopic spin group, the strong interactions have been found to be invariant with respect to an independent one-parameter gauge group generated by the hypercharge operator Y, where Y is an additive quantum number somewhat analogous to the charge. Every hadron so far observed is an eigenstate of Y with (low) integer eigenvalues. For example, the hypercharge values of $\mathbf{N}$, $\boldsymbol{\Lambda}$, $\boldsymbol{\Sigma}$, $\boldsymbol{\Xi}$, $\boldsymbol{\Omega}^-$ are 1, 0, 0 – 1, –2, respectively. Thus the full exact invariance group of the strong interactions appears to be* the group consisting of the direct product of the isotopic spin group and the gauge group generated by Y, and which for short we shall call $SU(2) \times Y$. If Q is the charge operator, we also have the following linear relation, due to Gell-Mann and Nishijima,

$$Q = T_3 + \tfrac{1}{2}Y,$$

where T_3 is one of the three generators of $SU(2)$, the index 3 being, of course, conventional.

The group $SU(2) \times Y$ helps enormously in classifying the large number of strongly interacting particles and in understanding their interactions, but there are empirical indications that in these strong interactions a higher symmetry than $SU(2) \times Y$ is involved. This is because of the occurrence of many particles with the same spins and parities, and approximately the same masses and other dynamic properties, in different $SU(2) \times Y$ multiplets. For example, the $\mathbf{N}$, $\boldsymbol{\Lambda}$, $\boldsymbol{\Sigma}$, and $\boldsymbol{\Xi}$ all have the same mass to within about 20% of the mean mass, and all couple to the pion field $\boldsymbol{\pi}$ with approximately the same strength. On the other hand, the dynamic properties of the particles in such multiplets are only approximately the same, so that it is clear that any higher symmetry can be at best an approximate symmetry. In the second half of the fifties much effort was directed toward finding the approximate symmetry group involved. The effort culminated in the discovery of $SU(3)$ by Gell-Mann and Ne'eman in 1961. Later, it was found that a higher, and even less exact, symmetry than $SU(3)$, namely, $SU(6)$ symmetry, was also relevant. It is with a discussion of $SU(3)$ and $SU(6)$ symmetries and their backgrounds that the present chapter is concerned.

The $SU(3)$ and $SU(6)$ symmetries are called *broken* symmetries since, as mentioned in the previous paragraph, they are only approximate symmetries. The name broken symmetry sounds like a contradiction in terms, but

* Here such symmetries as Lorentz invariance and baryon number conservation are not taken into account.

it is not really so. Indeed, in order to be observed, any symmetry must be broken. There are, however, different kinds of breaking and it might be well to distinguish between them. First is the breaking that is at the discretion of the observer. An example is the switching on of an external magnetic field to break the rotational symmetry of the Coulomb potential. Second is breaking that is intrinsic but small. An example is the breaking of isotopic spin invariance by the weak and electromagnetic interactions. Finally comes breaking that is intrinsic and large. This is the case for $SU(3)$ and $SU(6)$. A good question is just how large the breaking can be without destroying the symmetry altogether. Indeed it can be asked whether there is any sense in which we can say that a badly broken symmetry is "valid." It is hoped that during the course of the chapter it will become clear that there is. In particular, $SU(3)$, which is at least approximately independent of space-time, will be seen to be valid to within about 20%, while $SU(6)$, which involves the spin coordinates in an essential way, is valid only in situations in which spin-dependent interactions are negligible. As spin-dependent interactions are usually negligible only in the nonrelativistic limit, the surprising thing is not that $SU(6)$ is badly broken, but that it is relevant at all for high-energy particle physics.

A practical question that presents itself in the case of broken symmetries is how to make predictions. As we shall see, the tool for making predictions is the Wigner-Eckart (W-E) theorem. On account of the central role of this theorem, the whole of this chapter is based on it. The advantage of basing the discussion on the W-E theorem is that it becomes unified, because every prediction that is a consequence of symmetry alone [e.g., of $SU(3)$] is derived by using the W-E theorem in one form or another. The disadvantage is that the dynamic content of the theory tends to become suppressed. That is to say, we tend to concentrate on *using* the way in which various relevant dynamic quantities (e.g., magnetic moments) transform with respect to the group and to ignore the dynamic reasons for assigning the transformation properties. Of course, in the absence of a complete dynamics, the assignment of transformation or tensor properties on dynamic grounds is in the nature of an educated guess anyhow, but on the other hand, most of the physics is contained in that guess. We shall attempt to compensate for the lack of dynamics by discussing the reasons for assigning to each relevant dynamic quantity its particular tensor character. It should be emphasized, however, that the discussion of this article is of a rather general nature. The emphasis is on principles, and particular processes are considered mainly for the purpose of illustration. For a detailed and comprehensive discussion of $SU(3)$ the reader is referred to the accompanying chapter by Behrends and to the three books on the subject listed in (*11*) and (*12*).

In view of the importance of the W-E theorem for the present discussion, it has been thought worthwhile to include a rather detailed proof and discussion of it for the case of the simple compact Lie groups at the outset (Section II), although proofs of the theorem are readily available elsewhere. The elementary particle symmetries $SU(3)$ and $SU(6)$ per se are considered in Sections IV and VIII, respectively. In each case the discussion is along the following general lines. First, the classification of particles according to those groups (compatible with present experimental data) is given. Then comes the question of the behavior with respect to the group of the various physical quantities associated with the particles. The most relevant quantities are the scattering matrix S, the weak and electromagnetic currents, and finally the "mass operator," whose eigenvalues determine the masses of the particles. These quantities are assumed to transform as tensors with respect to $SU(3)$ and $SU(6)$ and the assignment of the correct tensor properties (which, in the absence of a complete dynamics, is in the nature of an educated guess) is discussed. Finally, the comparison of the predictions obtained from these assignments (by means of the W-E theorem) with experiment is sketched.

The intervening sections (V–VII) are devoted to a discussion of some general questions that arise in connection with these symmetries. One question that is discussed is what basis there is for regarding a symmetry that is as badly broken as are $SU(3)$ and $SU(6)$ as valid in any sense. To some extent this question is answered by the evidence in favor of $SU(3)$ and $SU(6)$ presented in Sections IV and VIII. The strength of the evidence in favor of $SU(3)$ is also emphasized by contrasting $SU(3)$ (eightfold-way version) with other schemes, specifically, with global symmetry, $\mathcal{G}_2$ symmetry, and the Sakata model version of $SU(3)$. The latter schemes are discussed in Section V. Another question that might be asked is whether badly broken symmetries occur in more familiar situations, such as atomic and nuclear physics. Examples of such symmetries are given in Section VI, and the analogy (and lack of analogy) between these and $SU(3)$ or $SU(6)$ is briefly discussed.

In Section VII a more general question is discussed, namely, why Lie groups, particularly compact simple Lie groups, play a role in elementary particle physics. A number of plausibility arguments for the appearance of these groups, and for the appearance of $SU(3)$ in particular, are discussed. The arguments are, however, no more than plausible and only touch on the question of the role of Lie groups, which is clearly a very deep one. Indeed, the main purpose of Section VII is to raise the question of the role of Lie groups rather than to answer it.

The final section on $SU(6)$ concludes with a brief discussion of some quasi-relativistic versions of $SU(6)$, specifically $SU(6)_w$ and $U(6, 6)$ symmetries. It stops short of what is probably the most exciting later development of $SU(3)$ and $SU(6)$, namely, the current-algebra approach to particle physics, which opens up the possibility of combining the dynamic and symmetry approaches to the theory of elementary particles. This development is beyond the scope of this chapter, but in view of its importance, we conclude by drawing attention to it and referring the reader to the short list of papers and books on current algebra listed at the end of the chapter.

II. Wigner-Eckart Theorem

In the Introduction the question of deducing the physical consequences of broken symmetry was raised. Since the main tool used in deducing the physical consequences is the Wigner-Eckart (W-E) theorem (*2*), we have thought it worthwhile to devote the present section to a discussion of this theorem.

We begin by considering a particular example from nonrelativistic quantum mechanics. Let

$$E_r = \int d^3x \psi^*_{nlm}(x) x_r \psi_{n''l''m''}(x), \qquad r = 1, 2, 3, \tag{2.1}$$

denote the electric dipole moment (*2*) of a particle in a spherical potential, with wave function $\psi_{nlm}(x)$ in conventional notation. By direct calculation, we easily verify that E_r satisfies the selection rules

$$\Delta m \equiv m - m'' = 0, \pm 1 \qquad \text{and} \qquad \Delta l \equiv l - l'' = \pm 1.$$

Further, we have, for example, using standard notation (*2*) and well-known properties of the spherical harmonics,

$\Delta m = 0, \Delta l = 1$:

$$E_1 = E_2 = 0,$$

$$E_3 = \frac{1}{2\pi} \int r^3\, dr\, R^*_{nl}(r) R_{n''l-1}(r) \int d(\cos\theta)\, d\phi\; Y^*_{lm}(\theta)[\cos\theta\, Y_{l-1m}(\theta)],$$

$$= \frac{1}{2\pi} \int r^3\, dr\, R^*_{nl}(r) R_{n''l-1}(r) \int d(\cos\theta)\, d\phi\; Y^*_{lm}(\theta)$$

$$\times \left\{ \left[\frac{(l+m)\,(l-m)}{(2l+1)(2l-1)}\right]^{1/2} Y_{lm}(\theta) \right\},$$

$$= \left[\frac{(l+m)\,(l-m)}{(2l+1)(2l-1)}\right]^{1/2} \int r^3\, dr\, R^*_{nl}(r) R_{n''l-1}(r); \tag{2.2}$$

while for

$\Delta m = 1, \Delta l = 1$:

$$E_3 = \frac{(E_1 - iE_2)}{\sqrt{2}} = 0,$$

$$\frac{(E_1 + iE_2)}{\sqrt{2}} = \left[\frac{(l+m)(l+m-1)}{(2l+1)(2l-1)\,2}\right]^{1/2} \int r^3\, dr\, R_{nl}^*(r) R_{n''l-1}(r),$$

and so on.

In the same way, the electric quadrupole moment

$$\int d^3x\, \psi_{nlm}^*(x) x_r x_s \psi_{n''l''m''}(x), \tag{2.3}$$

can be shown to satisfy the selection rules $\Delta m = 0, \pm 1, \pm 2$ and $\Delta l = 0, \pm 2$ and to lead to relations similar to (2.2).

The selection rules for Δm and Δl just mentioned, and the relations (2.2), are consequences of the very simple manner in which x_r and $x_r x_s$ transform under rotations, namely, as a vector and a symmetric second-rank tensor, respectively. The selection rules and relations (2.2) should therefore be derivable from group considerations alone. The tool for the derivation is the W-E theorem. However, since it is as easy to prove the general theorem as it is to prove it for this particular case, we proceed now to the general theorem and return to the group-theoretical derivation of (2.2) afterwards.

Attention will be confined to the W-E theorem for compact simple Lie groups (all of whose unitary irreducible representations are finite-dimensional and are labeled discretely). We begin by giving the general definition of a tensor for such a group and by also defining the Clebsch-Gordan coefficients.

Tensors. Let $U(g)$, $g \in G$, denote a unitary (not necessarily irreducible) representation of a simple compact Lie group G on a Hilbert space $\mathfrak{H}$. Let X_α, $\alpha = 1 \cdots n$, be a finite set of self-adjoint operators on H that satisfy the commutation relations

$$U(g) X_\alpha U^\dagger(g) = U_{\alpha\beta}^{\Lambda}(g) X_\beta, \tag{2.4}$$

for all g, where $U_{\alpha\beta}^{\Lambda}(g)$ is an n-dimensional unitary representation of G. Then the X_α form a tensor Λ with respect to $U(g)$. Note that, in general, the representation $U_{\alpha\beta}^{\Lambda}(g)$, which may or may not be irreducible, has nothing to do with the representation $U(g)$. In particular, $U_{\alpha\beta}^{\Lambda}(g)$ may be the trivial representation, in which case the X_α are all scalars. Note also that in terms of the Lie algebra of G with base elements or generators of $U(g)$

$$A_i = \left[\frac{\partial U(g(x))}{\partial x_i}\right]_{x=0}$$

where $x \equiv (x_i, i = 1 \ldots r)$ are the group parameters, Eq. (2.4) may be written

$$[A_i, X_\alpha] = d^\beta_{i\alpha} X_\beta \tag{2.5}$$

where the constants $d^\beta_{i\alpha}$ are derived from $U^\Lambda_{\alpha\beta}(g)$. Since

$$[A_i, A_j] = C^k_{ij} A_k, \tag{2.6}$$

where the C^k_{ij} are the structure constants of the group, it is clear that the base elements A_i themselves (and polynomials in the A_i) form tensors. However, not all tensors are polynomials in the A_i. For example, in the electric dipole moment example mentioned earlier, x_r and $x_r x_s$ are not polynomials in the generators $x_r \dfrac{\partial}{\partial x_s} - x_s \dfrac{\partial}{\partial x_r}$ of the rotation group. The "generator" tensors are simply an important special case.

C-G coefficients. Let $\left|\begin{matrix}\Lambda \\ \lambda\end{matrix}\right\rangle$ denote a complete orthonormal basis in a UIR (unitary irreducible representation) $U^\Lambda(g)$ of G, Λ labeling the representation and λ the state within the representation. Let $U^\Lambda(g) \boxtimes U^{\Lambda'}(g)$ decompose according to

$$U^\Lambda(g) \boxtimes U^{\Lambda'}(g) = \sum_{t=1}^{T} U^{\Lambda_t}(g). \tag{2.7}$$

The C-G coefficients $C^{\Lambda' \Lambda \Lambda_t}_{\lambda' \lambda \lambda_t}$ are then defined as

$$C^{\Lambda' \Lambda \Lambda_t}_{\lambda' \lambda \lambda_t} = \left\langle \begin{matrix}\Lambda_t \\ \lambda_t\end{matrix} \middle| \begin{matrix}\Lambda \; \Lambda' \\ \lambda \; \lambda'\end{matrix} \right\rangle. \tag{2.8}$$

The orthonormality and completeness of the bases $\left|\begin{matrix}\Lambda \\ \lambda\end{matrix}\right\rangle$, $\left|\begin{matrix}\Lambda' \\ \lambda'\end{matrix}\right\rangle$, and $\left|\begin{matrix}\Lambda_t \\ \lambda_t\end{matrix}\right\rangle$ imply, of course, that the transformation (2.8) is unitary, and hence that the C-G coefficients satisfy the orthogonality relations

$$\sum_{\lambda,\lambda'} C^{\Lambda' \Lambda \Lambda_t}_{\lambda' \lambda \lambda_t} C^{\Lambda' \Lambda \Lambda_s}_{\lambda' \lambda \lambda_s} = \delta_{ts} \, \delta_{\lambda_t \lambda_s} \tag{2.9}$$

and the completeness relations

$$\sum_{t,\lambda_t} C^{\Lambda' \Lambda \Lambda_t}_{\lambda' \lambda \lambda_t} C^{\Lambda' \Lambda \Lambda_t}_{\sigma' \sigma \lambda_t} = \delta_{\lambda\sigma} \, \delta_{\lambda'\sigma'}. \tag{2.10}$$

It is assumed that the phases of the states $\left|\begin{matrix}\Lambda\\ \lambda\end{matrix}\right\rangle$ have been chosen so that the C-G coefficients are real (it can easily be proved that this is always possible). It is also assumed that if any multiplicity ($\Lambda_t = \Lambda_s$, $t \neq s$) occurs in the decomposition (2.7), the spaces $\left|\begin{matrix}\Lambda_t\\ \lambda_t\end{matrix}\right\rangle$, $\left|\begin{matrix}\Lambda_s\\ \lambda_s\end{matrix}\right\rangle$ are chosen so that $\left\langle\begin{matrix}\Lambda_t\\ \lambda_t\end{matrix}\middle|\begin{matrix}\Lambda_s\\ \lambda_s\end{matrix}\right\rangle = 0$, all λ_t, λ_s. Note that in general

$$C^{\Lambda'\,\Lambda\,\Lambda_t}_{\lambda'\,\lambda\,\lambda_t} \neq C^{\Lambda'\,\Lambda\,\Lambda_s}_{\lambda'\,\lambda\,\lambda_t} \tag{2.11}$$

for $\Lambda_t = \Lambda_s$, $t \neq s$. Note also that if the matrices $U^{\Lambda}(g)$ have components $U^{\Lambda}_{\lambda\sigma}(g)$ with respect to the (necessarily finite) basis $\left|\begin{matrix}\Lambda\\ \lambda\end{matrix}\right\rangle$, then the relation (2.8) for the bases can be written as the relation

$$U^{\Lambda}_{\lambda\sigma}U^{\Lambda'}_{\lambda'\sigma'} = \sum_{t,\lambda_t,\sigma_t} C^{\Lambda'\,\Lambda\,\Lambda_t}_{\lambda'\,\lambda\,\lambda_t} C^{\Lambda'\,\Lambda\,\Lambda_t}_{\sigma'\,\sigma\,\sigma_t} U^{\Lambda_t}_{\lambda_t\sigma_t} \tag{2.12}$$

for the matrices. This can be seen at once by taking (2.7) between the states $\left\langle\begin{matrix}\Lambda\\ \lambda\end{matrix}\right|\left\langle\begin{matrix}\Lambda'\\ \lambda'\end{matrix}\right|$ and $\left|\begin{matrix}\Lambda\\ \sigma\end{matrix}\right\rangle\left|\begin{matrix}\Lambda'\\ \sigma'\end{matrix}\right\rangle$, using (2.8), and noting that U^{Λ_t} has matrix elements only between $\left|\begin{matrix}\Lambda_t\\ \sigma_t\end{matrix}\right\rangle$ and $\left|\begin{matrix}\Lambda_t\\ \lambda_t\end{matrix}\right\rangle$ in the direct product space.

We turn now to the W-E theorem, and consider for simplicity only the case of a unitary representation $U(g)$ that decomposes into the direct *sum* of unitary irreducible representations. The statement of the theorem in this case is: Let $U(g)$, $g \in G$, be a UIR of a simple compact Lie group G on a Hilbert space $\mathfrak{H}$. Let $\mathfrak{H}_a$ denote the (denumerable) irreducible subspaces of $\mathfrak{H}$ with respect to $U(g)$. Let $\left|\begin{matrix}\Lambda\\ \lambda\end{matrix}\right\rangle$ denote a complete orthonormal basis for $\mathfrak{H}_a$, Λ characterizing the particular irreducible representation carried by $\mathfrak{H}_a$ and λ denoting the state within $\mathfrak{H}_a$. (We may have $\Lambda(\mathfrak{H}_a) = \Lambda(\mathfrak{H}_b)$, $a \neq b$.) Let $T^{\Lambda'}_{\lambda'}$ denote any irreducible tensor of form Λ' and components λ' with respect to $U(g)$. Then

$$\left\langle\begin{matrix}\Lambda\\ \lambda\end{matrix}\middle| T^{\Lambda'}_{\lambda'} \middle|\begin{matrix}\Lambda''\\ \lambda''\end{matrix}\right\rangle = \sum_{\Lambda_t=\Lambda} C^{\Lambda''\,\Lambda'\,\Lambda_t}_{\lambda''\,\lambda'\,\lambda}\langle\Lambda\|T^{\Lambda'}\|\Lambda''\rangle_t, \tag{2.13}$$

where the *reduced* matrix element

$$\langle\Lambda\|T^{\Lambda'}\|\Lambda''\rangle_t = \sum_{\sigma''\sigma'} C^{\Lambda''\,\Lambda'\,\Lambda_t}_{\sigma''\,\sigma'\,\sigma}\left\langle\begin{matrix}\Lambda\\ \sigma\end{matrix}\middle| T^{\Lambda'}_{\sigma'} \middle|\begin{matrix}\Lambda''\\ \sigma''\end{matrix}\right\rangle \tag{2.14}$$

is independent of λ, λ', and λ''.

Here Λ_t denotes the representations in the decomposition of $U^{\Lambda'} \boxtimes U^{\Lambda''}$ that are equivalent to Λ. Note that the t dependence of $\langle \Lambda \| T^{\Lambda'} \| \Lambda'' \rangle_t$ comes from the C-G coefficient [see (2.8)] and not from $\left\langle \begin{matrix} \Lambda \\ \sigma \end{matrix} \middle| T^{\Lambda'}_{\sigma'} \middle| \begin{matrix} \Lambda'' \\ \sigma'' \end{matrix} \right\rangle$, which contains only Λ. In the special case where there is no multiplicity in the reduction of $U^{\Lambda'} \boxtimes U^{\Lambda''}$, Eq. (2.13) reduces to

$$\left\langle \begin{matrix} \Lambda \\ \lambda \end{matrix} \middle| T^{\Lambda'}_{\lambda'} \middle| \begin{matrix} \Lambda'' \\ \lambda'' \end{matrix} \right\rangle = C^{\Lambda'' \, \Lambda' \, \Lambda}_{\lambda'' \, \lambda' \, \lambda} \langle \Lambda \| T^{\Lambda'} \| \Lambda'' \rangle$$

where (2.15)

$$\langle \Lambda \| T^{\Lambda'} \| \Lambda'' \rangle = \sum_{\sigma'' \sigma'} C^{\Lambda'' \, \Lambda' \, \Lambda}_{\sigma'' \, \sigma' \, \sigma} \left\langle \begin{matrix} \Lambda \\ \sigma \end{matrix} \middle| T^{\Lambda'}_{\sigma'} \middle| \begin{matrix} \Lambda'' \\ \sigma'' \end{matrix} \right\rangle .$$

Before going on to the proof of the theorem, it might be well to obtain an intuitive idea of its content. For this purpose consider $\mathfrak{H}$ decomposed into a direct sum of irreducible subspaces $\mathfrak{H}_a$ with respect to $U(g)$. Then $U(g)$ has the block form

$$\begin{bmatrix} U^{(1)}(g) & \cdot & \cdot & \cdot \\ \cdot & U^{(2)}(g) & \cdot & \cdot \\ \cdot & \cdot & U^{(3)}(g) & \cdot \\ \cdot & \cdot & \cdot & \cdot \end{bmatrix}, \tag{2.16}$$

where the matrices $U^{(a)}(g)$ are UIRs of G. Of course, some of the $U^{(a)}(g)$ may be equivalent. In the same basis the tensor $T^{\Lambda'}_{\lambda'}$ will, in general, have the form

$$\begin{bmatrix} T^{\Lambda'}_{(11)\lambda'} & T^{\Lambda'}_{(12)\lambda'} & \text{etc.} \\ T^{\Lambda'}_{(21)\lambda'} & T^{\Lambda'}_{(22)\lambda'} & \text{etc.} \\ \text{etc.} & \text{etc.} & \text{etc.} \end{bmatrix} . \tag{2.17}$$

Thus $T^{\Lambda'}_{\lambda'}$ is not necessarily block-diagonal. To obtain an intuitive idea of the content of the W-E theorem, consider first the case with no multiplicity. In that case the statement is that given the tensor character of $T^{\Lambda'}_{\lambda'}$, the huge matrix (2.17) with block submatrices $T^{\Lambda'}_{(ab)\lambda'}$ can be reduced (modulo the C-G coefficients) to the much smaller matrix

$$\langle a \| T^{\Lambda'} \| b \rangle = \begin{bmatrix} \langle 1 \| T^{\Lambda'} \| 1 \rangle & \langle 1 \| T^{\Lambda'} \| 2 \rangle & \text{etc.} \\ \langle 2 \| T^{\Lambda'} \| 1 \rangle & \langle 2 \| T^{\Lambda'} \| 2 \rangle & \text{etc.} \\ \text{etc.} & \text{etc.} & \text{etc.} \end{bmatrix} \tag{2.18}$$

with *numerical* entries. In the more general case where there is multiplicity, each entry in (2.18) is replaced by a number of entries, the number depending on the multiplicity of U^{Λ} in the reduction of $U^{\Lambda'} \boxtimes U^{\Lambda''}$.

Note that from (2.14) the reduced matrix elements $\langle\Lambda\|T^{\Lambda'}\|\Lambda''\rangle$ are zero unless Λ occurs in the reduction of $\Lambda' \boxtimes \Lambda''$. Thus the reduced matrix (2.18) has in general many zero entries. Note, however, that the nonzero entries are not determined by group-theoretical considerations. They depend in general on the particular tensor chosen, not merely its transformation properties. Thus the role of the group is to reduce the matrix (2.17) to the matrix (2.18) and to determine the entries in (2.18) that are necessarily zero. More information is needed to determine the values of the entries in the reduced matrix that are not necessarily zero. There are two important exceptions to this general rule:

(1) If the tensor $T^{\Lambda'}_{\lambda'}$ is formed from the group generators A_i (i.e., is the important special case mentioned earlier), then it is clear from (2.16) that $T^{\Lambda'}_{\lambda'}$ is block-diagonal. In other words, if $T^{\Lambda'}_{\lambda'}$ is a generator tensor,

$$\langle\Lambda\|T^{\Lambda'}\|\Lambda''\rangle = 0, \qquad a \neq b. \tag{2.19}$$

(2) If the tensor $T^{\Lambda'}_{\lambda'}$ is a scalar (i.e., $T^{\Lambda'}_{\lambda'}$ has one component T) and

$$U(g)TU^{\dagger}(g) = T, \tag{2.20}$$

then (a) T has no matrix elements between *inequivalent* representations,

$$\langle a\|T\|b\rangle = 0, \qquad \Lambda(\mathfrak{H}_a) \neq \Lambda(\mathfrak{H}_b) \tag{2.21}$$

and (b) between equivalent representations, T is a multiple of the unit matrix. Both these statements follow directly from (2.13), since if T is a scalar, $\Lambda' = \lambda' = 0$, and hence

$$\left\langle \begin{matrix}\Lambda \\ \lambda\end{matrix} \middle| T \middle| \begin{matrix}\Lambda'' \\ \lambda''\end{matrix} \right\rangle = C^{\Lambda\ 0\ \Lambda''}_{\lambda\ 0\ \lambda''}\langle\Lambda\|T\|\Lambda''\rangle = \delta_{\Lambda\Lambda''}\delta_{\lambda\lambda''}\langle\Lambda\|T\|\Lambda''\rangle. \tag{2.22}$$

(Actually it is assumed here that the bases λ and λ'' of Λ_s and Λ_t are chosen in the same way. Otherwise T is not a multiple of the unit matrix, but corresponds to a unitary transformation of the basis as one goes from Λ to Λ''.) Note, however, that unlike the generator tensor, T can have nonzero matrix elements between $\mathfrak{H}_a$ and $\mathfrak{H}_b$ for $a \neq b$. It is necessary only that $\Lambda(\mathfrak{H}_a) = \Lambda(\mathfrak{H}_b)$; that is, that U^{Λ} and $U^{\Lambda''}$ be equivalent. We now proceed to the proof of the W-E theorem.

Proof of Wigner-Eckart Theorem. Since $U(g)$ is unitary, we have, from the tensor character of T [Eq. (2.4)],

$$\left\langle \begin{matrix}\Lambda\\ \lambda\end{matrix}\middle| T^{\Lambda'}_{\lambda'} \middle| \begin{matrix}\Lambda''\\ \lambda''\end{matrix}\right\rangle = \sum_{\sigma'} U^{\Lambda'}_{\lambda'\sigma'}(g) \left\langle \begin{matrix}\Lambda\\ \lambda\end{matrix}\middle| U^{\dagger}(g) T^{\Lambda'}_{\sigma'} U(g) \middle| \begin{matrix}\Lambda''\\ \lambda''\end{matrix}\right\rangle. \tag{2.23}$$

On the other hand, the subspace $\mathfrak{H}_{\Lambda}$ is left invariant by $U(g)$. Hence from (2.23)

$$\left\langle \begin{matrix}\Lambda\\ \lambda\end{matrix}\middle| T^{\Lambda'}_{\lambda'} \middle| \begin{matrix}\Lambda''\\ \lambda''\end{matrix}\right\rangle = \sum_{\sigma,\sigma',\sigma''} U^{\dagger\Lambda}_{\lambda\sigma}(g) U^{\Lambda'}_{\lambda'\sigma'}(g) U^{\Lambda''}_{\lambda''\sigma''}(g) \left\langle \begin{matrix}\Lambda\\ \sigma\end{matrix}\middle| T^{\Lambda'}_{\sigma'} \middle| \begin{matrix}\Lambda''\\ \sigma''\end{matrix}\right\rangle. \tag{2.24}$$

Using (2.12) for the $U^{\Lambda'} \boxtimes U^{\Lambda''}$ product in (2.24), we obtain

$$\left\langle \begin{matrix}\Lambda\\ \lambda\end{matrix}\middle| T^{\Lambda'}_{\lambda'} \middle| \begin{matrix}\Lambda''\\ \lambda''\end{matrix}\right\rangle = \sum_{t,\sigma,\sigma',\sigma''} U^{\dagger\Lambda}_{\lambda\sigma}(g) U^{\Lambda_t}_{\lambda_t\sigma_t}(g) C^{\Lambda''\ \Lambda'\ \Lambda_t}_{\lambda''\ \lambda'\ \lambda_t} C^{\Lambda''\ \Lambda'\ \Lambda_t}_{\sigma''\ \sigma'\ \sigma_t} \left\langle \begin{matrix}\Lambda\\ \sigma\end{matrix}\middle| T^{\Lambda'}_{\sigma'} \middle| \begin{matrix}\Lambda''\\ \sigma''\end{matrix}\right\rangle. \tag{2.25}$$

To proceed further we need the concept of orthogonality of inequivalent representations; that is, the relation (*4*)

$$\int d\mu(g)\, U^{\dagger\Lambda}_{\lambda\sigma}(g) U^{\Lambda_t}_{\lambda_t\sigma_t}(g) = \text{const.}\ \delta_{\Lambda\Lambda_t}\delta_{\lambda\lambda_t}\delta_{\sigma\sigma_t} \tag{2.26}$$

where the integration is over the whole group volume and $d\mu(g)$ is the invariant measure. For example, for the rotation group, parametrized by the Euler angles θ, ϕ, χ, $d\mu(g) = \sin\theta\, d\theta\, d\chi\, d\phi$. Using (2.26) in (2.25), we obtain

$$\left\langle \begin{matrix}\Lambda\\ \lambda\end{matrix}\middle| T^{\Lambda'}_{\lambda'} \middle| \begin{matrix}\Lambda''\\ \lambda''\end{matrix}\right\rangle = \text{const.} \sum_{t,\sigma,\sigma'\sigma''} \delta_{\Lambda\Lambda_t} C^{\Lambda''\ \Lambda'\ \Lambda_t}_{\lambda''\ \lambda'\ \lambda} C^{\Lambda''\ \Lambda'\ \Lambda_t}_{\sigma''\ \sigma'\ \sigma} \left\langle \begin{matrix}\Lambda\\ \sigma\end{matrix}\middle| T^{\Lambda'}_{\sigma'} \middle| \begin{matrix}\Lambda''\\ \sigma''\end{matrix}\right\rangle. \tag{2.27}$$

Comparing this expression with (2.13), we see that the theorem is established up to a constant in (2.14). The constant is determined by substituting (2.14) (with the constant) back into (2.13), multiplying both sides by $C^{\Lambda''\ \Lambda'\ \Lambda_s}_{\lambda''\ \lambda'\ \lambda_s}$, summing over $\lambda''\lambda'$, and comparing the result on either side of the resultant equation.

As an application of the W-E theorem, consider again the electric dipole moment (2.1). From the point of view of the connected rotation group $O^{+}(3)$, it is clear that what we are in fact calculating is the matrix element

$$\left\langle \begin{matrix}l\\ m\end{matrix}\middle| T^{1}_{m'} \middle| \begin{matrix}l''\\ m''\end{matrix}\right\rangle, \tag{2.28}$$

in standard angular momentum notation, where

$$T_0^1 = x_3, \qquad T_1^1 = \frac{(x_1 + ix_2)}{\sqrt{2}}, \qquad T_{-1}^1 = \frac{(x_1 - ix_2)}{\sqrt{2}}. \tag{2.29}$$

Clearly, $T_{m'}^1$ is a tensor of rank 1 [i.e., belongs to the $l = 1$ representation of $O^+(3)$]. But by the W-E theorem

$$\left\langle \begin{matrix} l \\ m \end{matrix} \middle| T_{m'}^1 \middle| \begin{matrix} l'' \\ m'' \end{matrix} \right\rangle = C_{m''\ m'\ m}^{l''\ 1\ l} \langle l \| T^1 \| l'' \rangle. \tag{2.30}$$

Hence, from the standard tables for C-G coefficients we obtain at once the selection rules $\Delta m \equiv m'' - m = 0, \pm 1$ and $\Delta l \equiv l'' - l = 0, \pm 1$. These are not quite the selection rules obtained in the earlier direct derivation (there we had also $\Delta l \neq 0$). The reason is that $\Delta l = 0$ is excluded by *parity*, not by the rotation group. [T^1 is odd under parity, while $\|l\rangle$ has parity $(-1)^l$ (independent of m).] Thus in (2.30), the *reduced* matrix element, not the C-G coefficient, vanishes for $\Delta l = 0$. This illustrates the point that to determine the reduced matrix we must go outside the group. [Outside the group in question, that is; in this case we must go outside the connected rotation group $O^+(3)$ and $\Delta l = 0$ is forbidden by the W-E theorem for another group, namely, the two-element space-reflection group.] Note also that the W-E derivation of the selection rules shows at once which selection rules are due to rotational invariance and which to parity conservation.

Inserting the standard C-G coefficients for $\Delta l = \pm 1$, $\Delta m = \pm 1, 0$ in (2.30), we obtain exactly the six formulas (2.2), with

$$\langle l \| T^1 \| l'' - 1 \rangle = \left(\frac{l}{2l + 1} \right)^{1/2} \int_0^\infty r^3\, dr\, R_{nl}^*(r) R_{n''\, l''-1}(r), \qquad \text{etc.} \tag{2.31}$$

Note that the integral on the right-hand side of this equation depends completely on the form of $R_{nl}(r)$, that is, on the particular spherical potential involved. This again emphasizes that the group cannot in general yield any information about the nonzero reduced matrix elements. These are determined by the dynamics. Note, incidentally, that if $T_{m'}^1 \equiv x_r$ were replaced by the tensor $\hat{T}_{m'}^1 = x_r \dfrac{\partial}{\partial x_s} - x_s \dfrac{\partial}{\partial x_r}$, consisting of the three $O^+(3)$ generators, (2.30) would still be valid, as would the selection rules for Δm. But the selection rules for Δl would be $\Delta l = 0$ instead of $\Delta l = \pm 1$. ($\Delta l \neq \pm 1$ because $x_r\, \partial_s - x_s\, \partial_r$ is a generator tensor, $\Delta l = 0$ because it is an axial vector and hence even under parity.)

The foregoing discussion illustrates the use of the W-E theorem in this particular case. The general use is quite analogous. First, we classify the physical states [$\psi_{nlm}(x)$ above] according to a UIR of the group in question. Second, we assign tensor properties to various physical operators [x_r and $x_r x_s$ above]. Third, we use the W-E theorem to relate the matrix elements of these operators.

In the example, the tensor form of x_r and $x_r x_s$ with respect to the rotation group $O^+(3)$ is known in advance. In many cases, however, especially in nuclear and particle physics, we have to guess at the tensor form of an operator. Also, the assignment of a given operator to an *irreducible* tensor representation of a group may be only an approximation. Note that *any* self-adjoint operator is a tensor in the sense that it can be expanded (under suitable convergence conditions) as an infinite sum of components of irreducible tensors. This is because the space of all self-adjoint operators on the representation space $\mathfrak{H}$ defined earlier is itself a vector space, and is left invariant by $U(g)$, since $U(g)$ is unitary. Hence, the space of all self-adjoint operators is itself a representation space for, and carries a unitary representation of, G. If this space is then decomposed into inequivalent (not necessarily irreducible) unitary representations of G, the decomposition is denumerable because the UIRs of the compact simple Lie groups are labeled discretely; hence, the result. Thus the assignment of an operator to an *irreducible* tensor representation of G is essentially the statement that one of the representations in the expansion dominates. For example, for the radiation from an atom, the relevant operator is really* $\exp(ix/2\pi\lambda)$ and it is only when λ, the wavelength of the radiation, is long compared with the dimension of the atom (range of x) that the expansion is dominated by the low moments x_r, $x_r x_s - \frac{1}{3}\delta_{rs} x^2$, etc., which are irreducible tensors.

Finally, it should be mentioned that the general problem of actually determining the C-G coefficients for the compact simple Lie groups has been completely solved only for $SU(2)$. Extensive work has been done on the problem in the case of $SU(3)$. Here the standard tables for the reduction of the physically interesting products $8 \boxtimes 8$, $8 \boxtimes 10$, $8 \boxtimes 27$, $10 \boxtimes 10$, and $10 \boxtimes 10^*$ are those of de Swart and of Chilton and McNamee (*5*). For other $SU(3)$ coefficients, see (*5a*). For $SU(6)$, the coefficients have been obtained for those representations that are of immediate physical interest (*6*).

* This is not Hermitian, of course, but $\sin(x/2\pi\lambda)$ and $\cos(x/2\pi\lambda)$ can be considered instead.

III. Some Relevant Group Theory

This short section will be devoted to a very brief summary of some group theory that will be relevant for the later discussion. In particular, the groups $SU(3)$ and $\mathcal{G}_2$ and their weight diagrams will be discussed.

We restrict our attention to real connected simple compact Lie groups. Real Lie groups are defined in the usual way to be groups whose elements are describable by a finite number of real parameters, each of which can have a continuous range of values. By a connected Lie group is meant a group all of whose elements can be reached by proceeding continuously from the identity, that is, by letting the parameters vary continuously from zero. The compact case is that in which the range of each of the group parameters is closed (and therefore finite). The simple Lie groups are those that contain no invariant Abelian subgroups. An example of a real connected simple compact Lie group is the rotation group in three dimensions. The parameters in this case are the Euler angles, which are real and have ranges $[0, 2\pi]$ and $[0, \pi]$. If the space reflections are included, the group loses its connectivity. An example of a noncompact group is the inhomogeneous Lorentz group, for which the parameters of acceleration range from $-\infty$ to ∞. An example of a nonsimple compact group is the group $U(2)$ of all unitary transformations in two dimensions, which contains the group of all matrices of the form $e^{i\phi}\mathbf{1}$ where $\mathbf{1}$ is the unit 2×2 matrix as an Abelian invariant subgroup. The motivation for restricting oneself to the connected simple compact Lie groups in order to describe the internal symmetry of elementary particles will be discussed in Section VII.

It can be shown that any connected compact simple Lie group G has a corresponding *simply* connected compact simple Lie group $\tilde{G}$ (the *covering* group), in the sense that $\tilde{G} = G \times Z$, $G = \tilde{G}/Z$, where Z is an Abelian group of finite order (*7*). Further, for each $\tilde{G}$ there are only a finite number of G's. A well-known example is the group $SU(2)$ of all unitary unimodular 2×2 matrices, which is the $\tilde{G}$ for itself and for the three-dimensional rotation group $O(3)$ [which is isomorphic to $SU(2)/Z_2$, where Z_2 is the two-element group consisting of 1 and -1 times the unit matrix]. Thus the connected simple compact Lie groups fall into sets, each set being characterized by the simply connected member $\tilde{G}$. Each set can also be characterized by the *Lie algebra* (2.6), which is the same for all elements of the set.

The sets $\tilde{G}$ can in turn be classified (*7*). There are, as is well known, four main classes. These correspond (modulo Z) to the four sets of classical groups:

$SU(l+1)$: the group of all unitary unimodular $(l+1) \times (l+1)$ matrices: $r = (l+1)^2 - 1$;

$O(2l+1)$: the group of all real orthogonal $(2l+1) \times (2l+1)$ matrices: $r = l(2l+1)$;

$USp(2l)$: the group of all unitary symplectic $(2l) \times (2l)$ matrices: $r = l(2l + 1)$;
$O(2l)$: the group of all real orthogonal $(2l) \times (2l)$ matrices: $r = l(2l - 1)$.

Here r is the order of the group (i.e., number of group parameters) or the number of base elements in the Lie algebra, and l is the rank. The rank may be defined as the number of simultaneously commuting elements in the Lie algebra. For all the groups except $O(2l)$, $l = 1, 2, 3, \ldots$. For $O(2l)$, $l = 3, 4, \ldots$, as $O(2)$ is Abelian and $O(4) = O(3) \times O(3)$. There is some overlap for low values of l. The full overlap is

$$\left.\begin{array}{ll} l=1: & SU(2) = O(3) = USp(2) \\ l=2: & \qquad\qquad O(5) = USp(4) \\ l=3: & SU(4) = O(6) \end{array}\right\}, \qquad \text{modulo } Z.$$

Here and henceforth, superscripts such as + in $O^+(3)$ will be suppressed, it being understood that only the connected part of the group is being considered. In addition to the four classes of groups listed earlier there are five exceptional groups, $\mathcal{G}_2, \mathcal{F}_4, \mathcal{E}_6, \mathcal{E}_7, \mathcal{E}_8$, subscripts denoting the rank.

For $l = 1$ there is only one group (modulo Z), namely, the three-dimensional rotation group $O(3)$, whose properties are well known. For $l = 2$ there are three groups (modulo Z):

$SU(3)$: the group of all unimodular (S), unitary (U), 3×3 matrices;
$O(5)$: the group of all real orthogonal 5×5 matrices, $= USp(4)$, the group of all unitary symplectic 4×4 matrices;
$\mathcal{G}_2$: one of the exceptional groups, this is a subgroup of $O(7)$ that leaves one dimension in the eight-dimensional spinor representation of $O(7)$ invariant [in general, $O(2n + 1)$ has a 2^n-dimensional spinor representation]; $\mathcal{G}_2$ is of order 14.

The UIRs of the connected compact simple Lie groups are all classified (*8*), and for future reference [especially for $SU(3)$ and $\mathcal{G}_2$] it is convenient to discuss briefly one of the most important concepts used in the classification, namely, the weight diagrams. Let G be of rank l. Then there are l commuting elements in the Lie algebra of G. In any UIR these become l commuting Hermitian matrices and so can be diagonalized simultaneously. The plot of the sets of l simultaneous eigenvalues (weights) in an l-dimensional Euclidean space is the weight diagram. We illustrate this for $SU(3)$ and $\mathcal{G}_2$. A full description of weight diagrams is given by Racah (*8*).

For $SU(3)$ the lowest-dimensional UIRs are the 3, 3*, 6, 6*, 8, 10, 10*, 15, 15*, 21, 21*, and 27, where d^* denotes the complex conjugate representation to d. [For $SU(3)$, $d^* \neq d$, unless $d = n^3$. There are actually two pairs of UIRs for $d = 15$.] Since $SU(3)$ is of rank 2, there are two commuting elements in the Lie algebra, hence, two simultaneously diagonalizable matrices in any UIR. For definiteness and because they will later be identified with the third component of isotopic spin and hypercharge, respectively, let us call these T_3 and Y. In the three-dimensional representation these matrices are

$$T_3 = \begin{bmatrix} \frac{1}{2} & \cdot & \cdot \\ \cdot & -\frac{1}{2} & \cdot \\ \cdot & \cdot & 0 \end{bmatrix}, \qquad Y = \begin{bmatrix} \frac{1}{3} & \cdot & \cdot \\ \cdot & \frac{1}{3} & \cdot \\ \cdot & \cdot & -\frac{2}{3} \end{bmatrix} \tag{3.1}$$

or, writing the diagonal as a vector,

$$T_3 = (\tfrac{1}{2}, -\tfrac{1}{2}, 0), \qquad Y = (\tfrac{1}{3}, \tfrac{1}{3}, -\tfrac{2}{3}). \tag{3.2}$$

Actually, this is a *definition* of T_3 and Y. The conditions on T_3 and Y are that they be Hermitian [since $SU(3)$ is unitary], traceless [since $SU(3)$ is unimodular], diagonal (by definition), and trace orthogonal. The latter condition is obtained by demanding that Y commute not only with T_3, but with the full $SU(2)$ subgroup of the form

$$\left[\begin{array}{c|c} SU(2) & 0 \\ \hline 0 & 1 \end{array}\right],$$

which will later be identified with the isotopic spin subgroup of $SU(3)$. These conditions are clearly not sufficient to fix the scale of the diagonal elements in (3.1). The point is, however, that once the scale is fixed in one representation, it is fixed for all others. The choice (3.1) leads uniquely to the values (3.5) in the 8, which are the conventional physical values for T_3 and Y for the particles assigned to the 8.

The choice (3.2) yields the three simultaneous pairs of eigenvalues

$$(T_3, Y) = (\tfrac{1}{2}, \tfrac{1}{3}), \qquad (-\tfrac{1}{2}, \tfrac{1}{3}), \qquad (0, -\tfrac{2}{3}). \tag{3.3}$$

If we plot these points in a two-dimensional (T_3, Y) space, we obtain the diagram of Fig. 1. This is the weight diagram of the 3 of $SU(3)$. It has three weights. For the 3* of $SU(3)$ the analogous relation to (3.2) is

$$T_3 = (\tfrac{1}{2}, -\tfrac{1}{2}, 0), \qquad Y = (-\tfrac{1}{3}, -\tfrac{1}{3}, \tfrac{2}{3}); \tag{3.4}$$

Hence the diagram is as in Fig. 2. For the 8 of $SU(3)$ we have

$$T_3 = (\tfrac{1}{2}, -\tfrac{1}{2};\ 1, 0, 0, -1;\ \tfrac{1}{2}, -\tfrac{1}{2}), \qquad Y = (1, 1;\ 0, 0, 0, 0;\ -1, -1), \tag{3.5}$$

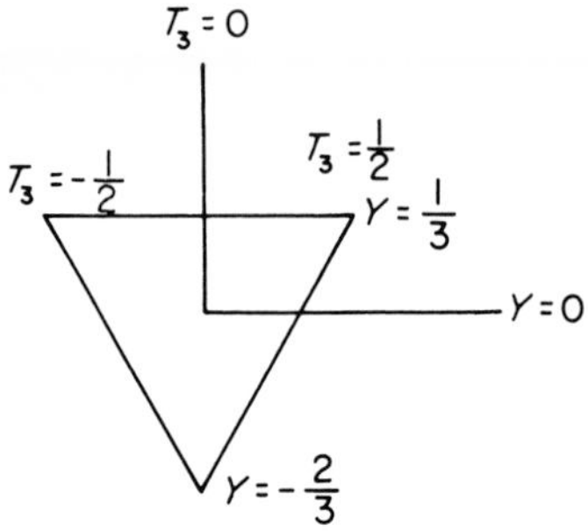

FIG. 1.

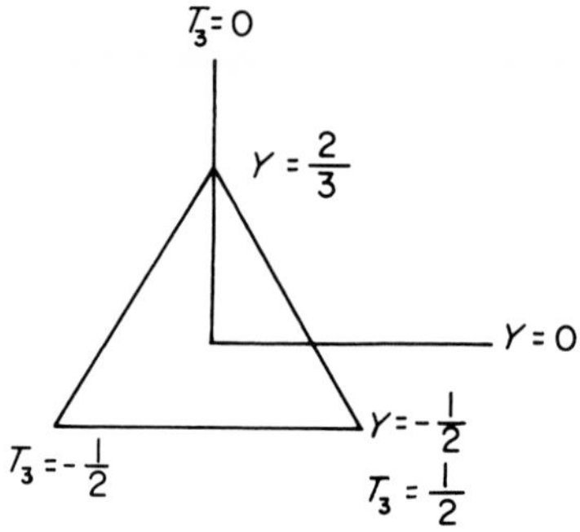

FIG. 2.

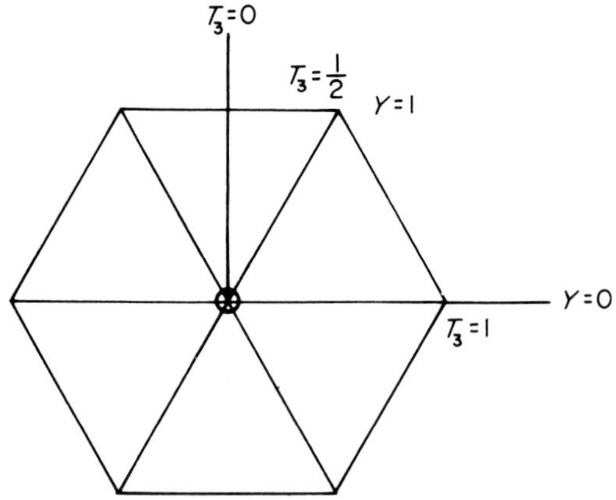

FIG. 3.

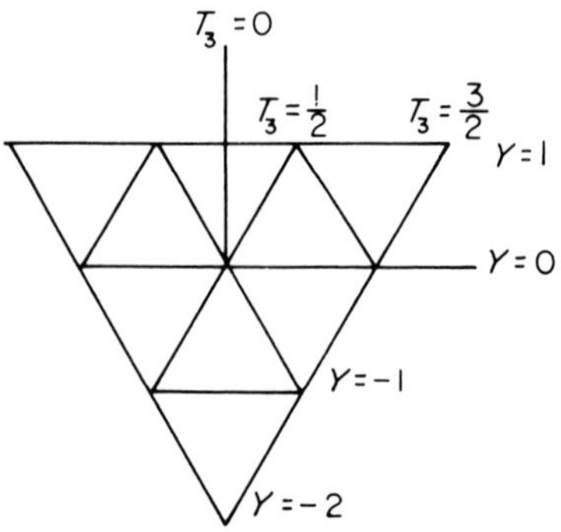

FIG. 4.

and the diagram is as in Fig. 3. The fact that the simultaneous eigenvalue $(T_3, Y) = (0, 0)$ occurs twice is indicated by the circle around the origin on the diagram. Note that, on account of this degeneracy, T_3 and Y alone are not sufficient to label the states of the 8 uniquely. This general feature of higher-dimensional representations of groups of rank $l > 1$ will be discussed later.

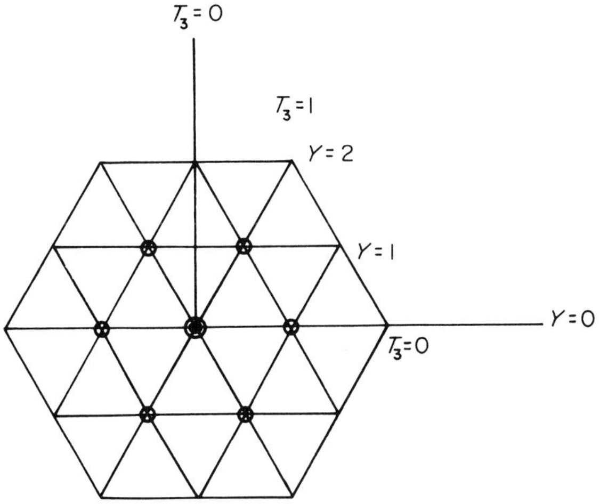

FIG. 5.

For the ten-dimensional representation of $SU(3)$, the analogue of (3.2) is

$$T_3 = (\tfrac{3}{2}, \tfrac{1}{2}, -\tfrac{1}{2}, -\tfrac{3}{2};\ 1, 0, -1;\ \tfrac{1}{2}, -\tfrac{1}{2};\ 0), \quad Y = (1, 1, 1, 1; 0, 0, 0; -1, -1; -2), \quad (3.6)$$

and the corresponding diagram is as in Fig. 4. The diagram of the 10* is the reflection of this in the $Y = 0$ axis. (In general, the d^* diagram is the reflection of the d diagram in this axis.) For the 27 of $SU(3)$ we have the diagram of Fig. 5. Reversing the previous line of reasoning, we can read off the relation analogous to (3.2) from Fig. 5. In fact, the advantage of the diagrams is that they allow us to dispense with the explicit relations of the form (3.2), (3.4), (3.5), and (3.6). Note that the point in the center of the 27 diagram is triply degenerate, while the next ring is doubly degenerate.

The lowest-dimensional representations of $\mathcal{G}_2$ are (*8*) the 7, 14, and 27 (all $\mathcal{G}_2$ representations are self-conjugate). The weight diagram of the 7 is the same as that of the 8 of $SU(3)$ (Fig. 3), but without the multiplicity at the center. The 14 of $\mathcal{G}_2$ is depicted in Fig. 6, and the 27 of $\mathcal{G}_2$ has the same diagram as the 27 of $SU(3)$.

It might not be out of place to discuss some relevant features of the weight diagrams. First, the importance of the particular weight diagram (root diagram) belonging to the *adjoint* representation of the group, that is, the r-dimensional representation generated by the $r \times r$ matrices $M_i = C_{ij}^k$ with rows k and columns j, where the C_{ij}^k are the structure constants of the group, should be mentioned. For $SU(3)$ the adjoint representation is the 8-dimensional one, for $\mathcal{G}_2$ it is the 14. The importance of the root diagram is that

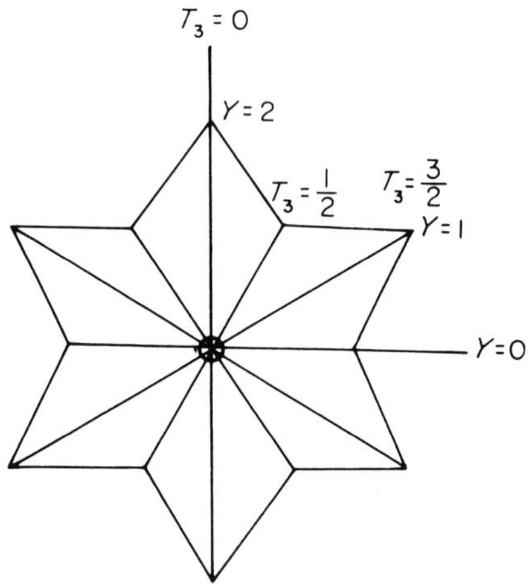

FIG. 6.

the vectors joining the weights in *any* weight diagram of the same group are simply the sums of the roots (vectors from the points on the root diagram to the origin) (*8*). In other words, we can "step" around any weight diagram by using the roots. Another important property of the root diagram is that (for a given group) the weight diagrams are invariant under reflections in the planes (lines for $l = 2$) through the origin perpendicular to the roots (Weyl reflections). This characteristic is the origin of the symmetry of the weight diagrams (Figs. 1–6). Note in particular that the $\mathcal{G}_2$ diagrams are invariant under the reflection R in the $Y = 0$ axis, which is perpendicular to a root of $\mathcal{G}_2$ (Fig. 6). The $SU(3)$ diagrams are not invariant under this (hypercharge) reflection, as there is no root of $SU(3)$ perpendicular to the $Y = 0$ axis (Fig. 3). This is important physically, as it means that $\mathcal{G}_2$ invariance implies hypercharge reflection invariance, but $SU(3)$ invariance does not.

Note that in the diagrams of Figs. 1–6 the degeneracy decreases as one moves away from the center of the diagram. This is a general feature of all UIRs of the simple compact groups. The rate of decrease varies* from group to group and UIR to UIR, but in all cases the outer ring is nondegenerate (*8*). We use the convention that the weight farthest to the right (or, if this is not unique, the weight farthest to the right and the farthest to the top of the diagram) is called the highest weight. It can be shown that there is a one-to-one correspondence between the components of this weight and the UIRs (*8*). Thus the UIRs can be labeled by their highest weights. For example, the 3, 3*, 8, 10, and 27 of $SU(3)$ could be labeled

$$(T_3(\text{highest weight}),\ Y(\text{highest weight})) \equiv (t_3, y)$$
$$= (\tfrac{1}{2}, \tfrac{1}{3}), (\tfrac{1}{2}, -\tfrac{1}{3}), (1, 0), (\tfrac{3}{2}, 1), (2, 0),$$

respectively. There is yet a third convenient way of labeling the UIRs, which can be illustrated for $SU(3)$. Any UIR of $SU(3)$ is the leading UIR in the reduction of the Kronecker product of $\underbrace{3 \boxtimes 3 \cdots \boxtimes 3}_{\lambda} \boxtimes \underbrace{3^* \boxtimes 3^* \boxtimes \cdots \boxtimes 3^*}_{\mu}$, for a given λ and μ (*8*). Hence, we can label the UIRs by the pairs (λ, μ) of nonnegative integers. [Note that (μ, λ) is conjugate to (λ, μ).] The relation between the different labeling schemes is

$$(t_3, y) = \left(\frac{\lambda + \mu}{2}, \frac{\lambda - \mu}{3}\right), \tag{3.7}$$

and the dimension of the UIR (λ, μ) is given by

$$d = \tfrac{1}{2}(\lambda + 1)(\mu + 1)(\lambda + \mu + 2). \tag{3.8}$$

A similar situation holds for the general compact simple group (*8*). We can label the UIRs either by dimension (if there is only one inequivalent representation corresponding to the dimension in question), or by highest weight, or by the number of times certain *fundamental* UIRs must be used in order to obtain the given UIR as the leading UIR in the reduction of the Kronecker product. For a group rank l, there are l fundamental representations. For $SU(3)$ these are the 3 and 3*, as we have seen. For $\mathscr{G}_2$ they are the 7 and 14.

As mentioned earlier, when degeneracy occurs in a weight diagram, the operators T_3 and Y, or more generally $H_1 \cdots H_l$ are not sufficient to label the

* The law of variation is given by Kostants formula; see Jacobson (*9*).

states within a UIR. To complete the labeling in general $(r-3l)/2$ extra operators are needed (*8*). For $SU(3)$, with $r=8$, this means that one extra operator is needed.

It is found as follows: As mentioned earlier, Y commutes with an $SU(2)$ subgroup of $SU(3)$. This subgroup, with generators T_1, T_2, T_3, say, is identified with the physical isotopic spin group, since the latter should commute with Y. The extra operator that labels the states can then be chosen to be the total isotopic spin operator $T(T+1)=T_1^2+T_2^2+T_3^2$. This removes the degeneracy in all representations. For example, the double degeneracy at the center of Fig. 3 contains two states, one with $T=0$ and one with $T=1$. Similarly, at the center of Fig. 5 we have states with $T=0, 1, 2$. For $\mathscr{G}_2$, with $r=14$, four extra operators are needed to label the states in general. However, for the 7, 14, and 27, T is sufficient. In general, the extra $(r-3l)/2$ operators needed to label the states are, like $T(T+1)$, *nonlinear* polynomials in the elements of the Lie algebra of G. This has the consequence that for two combined physical systems they are not *additive* quantum numbers like T_3 and Y. For example, a combination of a $T_3=\frac{1}{2}$, $Y=1$, $T=\frac{1}{2}$ system (e.g., proton) with a $T_3=0$, $Y=0$, $T=1$ system (e.g., neutral pion) has $T_3=\frac{1}{2}$, $Y=1$ but $T=\frac{3}{2}$ or $\frac{1}{2}$.

We conclude this section by noting the following relevant decomposition property of the diagrams in Figs. 1–6. In each case the isotopic spin subgroup of $SU(3)$ or $\mathscr{G}_2$ leaves the horizontal lines in the weight diagrams invariant. (This follows immediately from the fact that the isotopic spin group commutes with Y.) Hence, if we decompose an $SU(3)$ or $\mathscr{G}_2$ representation with respect to the subgroup $SU(2) \times U(1)$ where $U(1)$ is generated by the hypercharge Y, the horizontal lines on the diagrams correspond to invariant subspaces with respect to $SU(2)$. For the 3 and the 10 of $SU(3)$ these subspaces are irreducible. For the 8, the $|Y|=1$ lines of Fig. 3 are $SU(2)$ doublets, but for $Y=0$ we have an $SU(2)$ triplet (with the $T_3=0$ component at the origin) and singlet (at the origin).

In conclusion, it might be worth remarking that $SU(3)$ is simply connected. It is the covering group for itself and for $SU(3)/Z_3$, where Z_3 is the Abelian group with the three elements $j\mathbf{1}$ where $j^3=1$ and $\mathbf{1}$ is the unit 3×3 matrix.

If we define the *triality* t of a representation (λ, μ) of $SU(3)$ to be

$$t=(\lambda-\mu), \qquad \text{modulo } 3, \tag{3.9}$$

then for $SU(3)/Z_3$ the UIR's of triality $t=0$ are true, and those of triality $t=1, 2$ triple valued. The latter are analogous to the double-valued (spinor) representations of $O(3)=SU(2)/Z_2$. So far in elementary particle physics only the $t=0$ representations have appeared.

IV. Particle Physics *SU(3)* from the Point of View of the Wigner-Eckart Theorem

In Section II the use of the Wigner-Eckart (W-E) theorem in deducing the experimental consequences of broken symmetry was described. In this section the application of the theorem to the broken symmetry group $SU(3)$, which is the broken symmetry of greatest interest for particle physics, is described. The procedure consists of three steps. First the states, in this case the elementary particles themselves, are classified according to representations of $SU(3)$. Second, certain physical quantities, specifically the strong S-matrix $S(strong)$, the mass operator M, and the hadron weak and electromagnetic current densities $\mathcal{J}^{w}_{\mu}(x)$ and $\mathcal{J}^{e}_{\mu}(x)$, are given $SU(3)$ tensorial properties. Third, the W-E theorem is used to obtain relations between the matrix elements of these quantities, and finally, the resultant relations are compared with experiment. We shall give a very brief discussion of the first step, the classification. A much more detailed discussion is given by Behrends (this volume) and by Gell-Mann and Ne'eman (*11*), Carruthers (*12*), and Leitner (*13*). Most attention will be paid to the second step. In particular, the motivation behind the assignment of tensorial properties to $S(strong)$, M, $\mathcal{J}^{w}_{\mu}(x)$ and $\mathcal{J}^{e}_{\mu}(x)$ will be discussed. The third step will be illustrated by some explicit examples of the use of the W-E theorem. Finally, the comparison with experiment of the results obtained will be touched on, as it is hoped that the successes of $SU(3)$ that emerge from even this brief discussion will help to answer the question raised in the Introduction concerning the choice of symmetry group. However, for a full and detailed comparison of $SU(3)$ predictions with experiment and for a comprehensive bibliography the reader is referred to Behrends and to the books in references (*11*) and (*12*).

The classification of the particles according to $SU(3)$ will be discussed first. It is assumed, of course, that, as discussed in the previous section, $SU(3)$ contains the isotopic spin group $SU(2)$ as a subgroup [the generators of $SU(3)$ are the generators $T_1 T_2$ and T_3 of the isospin group, the hypercharge Y, which commutes with all of these, and four other generators which, along with T_1 and T_2, do not correspond to quantum numbers of particles]. Hence, the problem is to classify the isotopic multiplets, rather than individual particles, according to $SU(3)$. The process is facilitated by the fact that the $SU(2)$ decomposition of the UIRs of $SU(3)$ can immediately be read off the horizontal lines of an $SU(3)$ weight diagram as described in the previous section. The rules of the game are that we should classify together [in UIRs of $SU(3)$] isotopic spin multiplets with the same J^P values and approximately the same mass.* (The word approximately here is fairly elastic, but more

* This is because $SU(3)$ is assumed to be independent of space-time. This is strictly true, of course, only in the equal mass approximation.

stringent boundary conditions are provided by the mass formula and the decay rates, to be discussed later.) The classifications that are established beyond reasonable doubt to date are as follows [(*12*), (*13*)].

Baryons. $J^P = \frac{1}{2}^+$. The eight $J^P = \frac{1}{2}^+$ metastable baryons **N**, **Λ**, **Σ**, **Ξ** are assigned to the 8 of $SU(3)$ (Fig. 7) (this is called the eightfold way assignment).

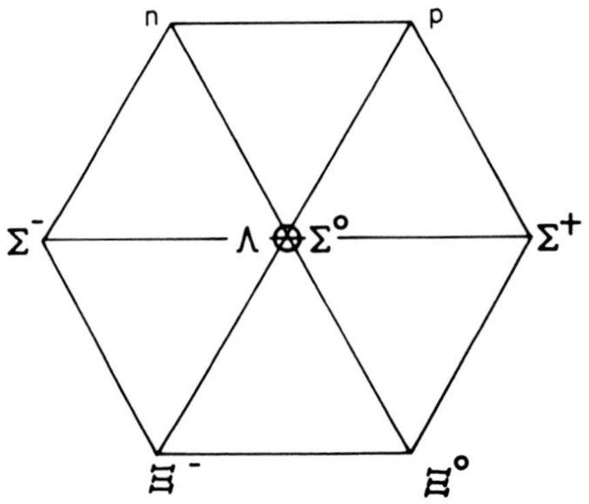

FIG. 7.

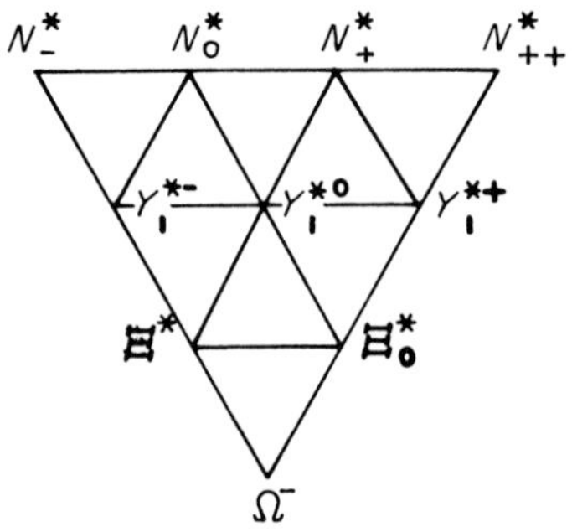

FIG. 8.

$J^P = \frac{3}{2}^+$. The ten $J^P = \frac{3}{2}^+$ baryons **N***(1236), $\mathbf{Y}_1^*$(1385), **Ξ***(1530), and $\mathbf{\Omega}^-$ (1675) are assigned to the 10 of $SU(3)$ (Fig. 8). The figures in parentheses are the masses of the particles in millions of electron volts and serve for identification. Regarding these assignments, some comments may be in order. First, the parities of *two* isotopic multiplets (e.g., **N**, **K** or **N**, **Σ**) are assigned *by convention*. The others are then determined from the parity-conserving weak and electromagnetic interactions, and turn out to be $\frac{1}{2}^+$ and 0^-. [It is, perhaps, interesting to note that had **Λ** come out with the opposite parity experimentally, this would have been a strong argument against $SU(3)$ and, incidentally, an argument in favor of $\mathscr{G}_2$, which, as we shall see, classifies **Λ** as a singlet.] Once P is fixed for the $\frac{1}{2}^+$ members, the relative P values are fixed for the mesons and the higher resonances, all of which connect to the $\frac{1}{2}^+$ by P-conserving processes. The $\frac{3}{2}^+$ J^P is predicted in this way and turns out to be correct for $\mathbf{N}^*$, $\mathbf{Y}_1^*$, and $\mathbf{\Xi}^*$. (For $\mathbf{\Omega}^-$, for which there are only a few events, J^P is not determined.) Note that the $\mathbf{N}^*$ multiplet is the old (3, 3) resonance observed in **π-N** scattering and well described by Chew-Low theory.

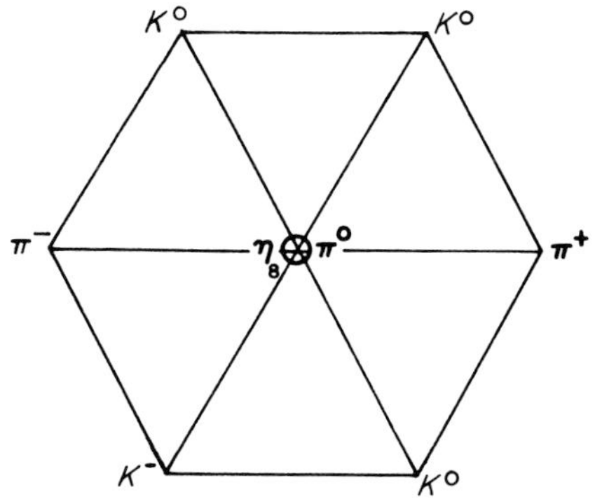

FIG. 9.

It has $T=\frac{3}{2}$ and contains a doubly charged member $\mathbf{N}_{++}^*$. The $\mathbf{\Omega}^-$ particle was *predicted* by $SU(3)$, and its occurrence (at almost exactly the value predicted by the mass formula) is regarded as one of the major triumphs of $SU(3)$. It is interesting to note that the occurrence of the metastable $\mathbf{\Omega}^-$ in the same multiplet with the strongly decaying $\mathbf{N}^*$, $\mathbf{Y}_1^*$, and $\mathbf{\Xi}^*$ indicates that there is no fundamental distinction between metastable particles and resonances. Finally, the foregoing particles exhaust *all* the established $J^P=\frac{1}{2}^+$ and $\frac{3}{2}^+$ particles, except for an **N***(1400), which is another $\frac{1}{2}^+$.

Mesons. There are three multiplets of mesons, which can be classified according to $SU(3)$, namely, the metastable $J^P=0^-$ mesons [**π**(140), **K**(495), **η**(548), and **η***(958)], Fig. 9, and the $J^P=1^-$ and 2^+ mesons [**ρ**(765), **K***(890), **ω**(780), and **φ**(1020)] and [$\mathbf{A}_2$(1320), **K****(1410), **f**(1250), and **f***(1500)], respectively. In each of the last two cases the isospin content of the square bracket is the same as in the case of the 0^-; that is, ($T=1$, $T=\frac{1}{2}$, $T=0$, and $T=0$). If we include the antiparticles for $T=\frac{1}{2}$ and note that antiparticles for $T=0$ and $T=1$ are simply the same particles taken in a different order, we see that we have in each bracket a *nonet* of particles. These nonets are classified according to an *octet + singlet* of $SU(3)$.* We indicate the classification procedure for $J^P = 0^-$: We introduce two linear combinations of $\boldsymbol{\eta}$ and $\boldsymbol{\eta}^*$ defined by

$$\begin{aligned} \boldsymbol{\eta} &= \cos\theta\boldsymbol{\eta}_8 + \sin\theta\boldsymbol{\eta}_0, \\ \boldsymbol{\eta}^* &= -\sin\theta\boldsymbol{\eta}_8 + \cos\theta\boldsymbol{\eta}_0, \end{aligned} \tag{4.1}$$

and assume that $[\boldsymbol{\pi}, \mathbf{K}, \bar{\mathbf{K}}, \boldsymbol{\eta}_8]$ belong to the 8 of $SU(3)$, and $\boldsymbol{\eta}_0$ to the 1 (Fig. 9); similarly for 1^- and 2^+, where $(\boldsymbol{\omega}_8, \boldsymbol{\omega}_0)$ and $(\mathbf{f}_8, \mathbf{f}_0)$, respectively, are introduced. The motivation for the introduction of the angle θ and the corresponding angles θ_1 and θ_2, and the procedures for their determination rest on the mass formula, to be discussed later. A full discussion is given in Behrends (this volume). Note that the procedure just described classifies the mesons according to a *reducible* representation of $SU(3)$. As in the case of the baryons, the multiplets above exhaust the sets of established particles with these J^P values.

The five multiplets above (2 baryon, 3 meson) constitute the established classifications according to $SU(3)$. To put the classification in perspective, it is, perhaps, worth looking at the established particles that have not (yet) been classified according to $SU(3)$.

TABLE I

	$T=\frac{1}{2}, Y=1$	$T=\frac{3}{2}, Y=1$	$T=0, Y=0$	$T=1, Y=0$	$T=\frac{1}{2}, Y=-1$
$\frac{5}{2}^+$	$N(1688)$		$\Lambda(1820)$		$\Xi(1930)$
$\frac{7}{2}^+$		$N(1920)$		$\Sigma(2035)$	
$\frac{1}{2}^-$	N(1570) $N(1700)$	$N(1670)$	$\Lambda(1405)$ $\Lambda(1670)$		
$\frac{3}{2}^-$	$N(1525)$		$\Lambda(1520)$	$\Sigma(1660)$	$\Xi(1815)$
$\frac{5}{2}^-$	$N(1670)$			$\Sigma(1770)$	
$\frac{7}{2}^-$	$N(2190)$		$\Lambda(2100)$		

Baryons. Those whose J^P values are well established are listed in Table I (two Ξ's whose existence is well established but whose J^P values are not, have been included to indicate the way in which some tentative $SU(3)$ octets may be completed). There are about ten other baryon resonances whose existence, masses and isospins are known, but whose J^P values are not yet firmly established.

* Representation mixing in $SU(3)$ was first suggested by Sakurai (*14*).

Mesons. There are no mesons, apart from the 0^-, 1^-, 2^+ and $\eta(1050)$, $J^P = 0^+$, which may not be a genuine resonance, whose J^P values are well established (actually even the J^P values of the 1^- A_1 and the 2^+ K** are not yet quite definite). There are about ten other resonances, notably the $\delta(965)$, $B(1210)$, $D(1285)$, $E(1420)$, K(1800), and $S(1930)$ $T(2200)$ $U(2380)$ whose existence is well established, and about ten more, for example the $\sigma(410)$ and $\kappa(725)$ for whose existence there is some slight evidence.

Having discussed the $SU(3)$ classification, we turn now to the problem of assigning correct $SU(3)$ tensorial properties to $S(strong)$, M, $\mathscr{J}^{w}_{\mu}(x)$ and $\mathscr{J}^{e}_{\mu}(x)$. The mass operator M is first considered. If M is expanded as a sum of inequivalent $SU(3)$ tensors, as discussed in the previous section, then since M is clearly isospin invariant and has hypercharge zero, we know in advance that the tensor *component* of each irreducible part of M will be the $T=0(T_3=0)$ $Y=0$ component. Hence, only those representations with such components will appear; that is,

$$M = M^0 + M^8 + M^{27} + \text{etc.}, \tag{4.2}$$

where the representations not listed are of dimension higher than 27. Since the mass breaking in the physical $SU(3)$ multiplets discussed earlier is of the order of 20%, it is natural to assume that the terms M^8, M^{27}, etc., are about five times as small as M^0. However, we now also make the assumption that the terms M^{27}, etc., are negligible; that is,

$$M = M^0 + M^8. \tag{4.3}$$

Strictly speaking, this is an unwarranted assumption, but it is made because it is the simplest possible assumption and because the terms M^{27}, etc. would allow so many parameters (reduced matrix elements) into the mass formula that there would be effectively no predictions for the physical multiplets mentioned above. If we accept Eq. (4.3)* and proceed to apply it to the well-established multiplets mentioned above, we obtain unbelievably good agreement with experiment for the $\frac{1}{2}^+$ and $\frac{3}{2}^+$ baryons, and no contradiction (see discussion following) for the mesons. In this way the assumption (4.3) is justified a posteriori. For the newer multiplets, however, the assumption may have to be modified (see below). The mass formula for the $\frac{1}{2}^+$ and $\frac{3}{2}^+$ constitutes one of the principal successes of $SU(3)$.

The next tensor to be considered is $S(strong)$. Here we can proceed either by directly assigning tensorial properties to $S(strong)$ or else by considering

* The mass formula for the $\frac{1}{2}^+$ octet is due to Gell-Mann (*10*). The general mass formula is due to Okubo (*15*).

S(*strong*) to be derived from a Hamiltonian

$$\mathscr{H} = \mathscr{H}_0 + \mathscr{H}_1 \tag{4.4}$$

where $\mathscr{H}_0$ is assumed to be $SU(3)$ symmetric, and $\mathscr{H}_1$ is an $SU(3)$-breaking term, to be treated in practice by means of perturbation theory. In the latter case, the tensorial properties of $\mathscr{H}_1$ must be assigned. Because of the success of the mass formula (4.3) and the identification of the mass-breaking operator with the diagonal elements of $\mathscr{H}_1$ in first order of symmetry breaking, it is often assumed that

$$\mathscr{H}_1 = \mathscr{H}_1^8. \tag{4.5}$$

The following two points should, however, be noted. First, the empirical result that the 8 dominates the mass formula implies only that the *diagonal* elements of $\mathscr{H}_1^{27}$, etc., are suppressed. It is an extrapolation of this to suppose that all the matrix elements of $\mathscr{H}_1^{27}$, etc. are suppressed. Second, even for the mass, the use of perturbation theory with $\mathscr{H}_1 = \mathscr{H}_1^8$ is questionable, since the second order of perturbation then contains a 27 and is of order $(1/5)^2 \sim 4\%$, whereas the mass formula (4.3) is correct for the $\frac{1}{2}^+$ and $\frac{3}{2}^+$ to within 1%. Of course, this discrepancy might be explained by the second-order term's coefficient's being small for some dynamic reason.

The alternative procedure to the perturbation approach is to consider the mass formula (4.3) as empirical, and to proceed straight to the *S*-matrix, which we write as

$$S = S^0 + S^8 + S^{27} \text{ etc.} \tag{4.6}$$

for the same reasons as we write the formula (4.2) for *M*. The magnitude of the mass breaking suggests that S^0 dominates this expansion by a factor of about five, and we usually proceed on this assumption. It can also be assumed, if necessary, that S^8 dominates S^{27}, etc.

The next tensor to be considered* is the electromagnetic current $\mathscr{J}_\mu^e(x)$. The electromagnetic charge

$$Q = \int d^3x \, \mathscr{J}_0^e(x) \tag{4.7}$$

is an $SU(3)$ generator, and hence, in particular is a member of an $SU(3)$ 8. Since $SU(3)$ is independent of space-time, it is then natural to assume that $\mathscr{J}_\mu^e(x)$, out of which Q is constructed, is also a member of an 8. To completely

* Although the ideas involved are implicit in the work of Gell-Mann (*10*), the first explicit use of the tensorial properties of the electromagnetic current density in $SU(3)$ is due to Coleman and Glashow (*16*).

justify this assignment, however, one further assumption concerning $\mathcal{J}_{\mu}^{e}(x)$ must be made, namely, that it corresponds to minimal coupling of the electromagnetic field to the hadrons; that is, it corresponds to the coupling obtained by making the substitution $\partial_{\mu} \to \partial_{\mu} \pm ieA_{\mu}(x)$ in the Lagrangian for the charged hadron fields. In this case $\mathcal{J}_{\mu}^{e}(x)$ is of the form

$$\mathcal{J}_{\mu}^{e}(x) = \sum c_{\alpha\beta} e\bar{\psi}_{\alpha}(x)\gamma_{\mu}\psi_{\beta}(x) + d_{\alpha\beta}[e(\partial_{\mu}\varphi_{\alpha}^{*}\varphi_{\beta} - \varphi_{\alpha}^{*}\,\partial_{\mu}\varphi_{\beta}) + e^{2}\varphi_{\alpha}^{*}\varphi_{\beta}A_{\mu}], \quad (4.8)$$

where $\psi_{\alpha}(x)$ and $\varphi_{\alpha}(x)$ are baryon and meson fields corresponding to particles belonging to $SU(3)$ representations $|\Lambda\alpha\rangle$, $|\Lambda'\alpha\rangle$, etc., and $c_{\alpha\beta} = \delta_{\alpha\beta}c_{\alpha}$, etc. are constants that guarantee that the fields have the correct charges. Comparing (4.8) and (4.7), we see that the octet character of Q and $\mathcal{J}_{\mu}^{e}(x)$, respectively, require the same condition on the $c_{\alpha\beta}$, namely,

$$c_{\alpha\beta} = C_{\alpha\ \beta\ Q}^{\bar{\Lambda}\,\Lambda\,8}, \quad (4.9)$$

etc. Hence, the octet character of Q implies that of $\mathcal{J}_{\mu}^{e}(x)$.

Note that the minimality condition on $\mathcal{J}_{\mu}^{e}(x)$ is quite strong, since as well as being an assumption in itself, it requires the use of field theory and of the identification of fields and particles for its implementation. A less restrictive assumption on $\mathcal{J}_{\mu}^{e}(x)$ would be simply locality, but we can see at once that locality alone is not sufficient to guarantee that

$$Q^{8} \to \mathcal{J}_{\mu}^{e}(x)^{8}. \quad (4.10)$$

For example, we could add to the current a term

$$\mathcal{J}_{\mu}^{\Lambda}(x) = \epsilon_{\mu\nu\lambda\sigma}\,\partial_{\nu}\,t_{\sigma\lambda}^{\Lambda}(x), \quad (4.11)$$

where $t_{\sigma\lambda}^{\Lambda}(x)$ is a local antisymmetric pseudo-tensor belonging to any representation Λ of $SU(3)$; $\mathcal{J}_{\mu}^{\Lambda}(x)$ would not contribute to Q, but it would contribute to the magnetic moment operator defined by

$$\mu = \int d^{3}x\,[\mathbf{r} \times \mathcal{J}^{e}(x)]. \quad (4.12)$$

A second point to note is that whereas Q is not only a number of an 8 but an $SU(3)$ generator, $\mathcal{J}_{\mu}^{e}(x)$ is merely a member of an 8. In particular, the magnetic moment operator just defined in (4.12) is a member of an 8, but it is not a generator of $SU(3)$, because if σ is another component of the same 8 as μ, the commutator

$$[\mu, \sigma]$$

does not yield a quantity of the same kind. This is partly because the spatial components of $\mathscr{J}_\mu^e(x)$ occur in μ, and partly because the explicit **r**'s occurring in μ and σ combine to produce a higher moment. It follows that μ can have transition matrix elements between different $SU(3)$ UIRs [it dominates the observed transition $\mathbf{N}^* \to \mathbf{N}\gamma$, where $\mathbf{N}^*$ is the $\frac{3}{2}^+$ N*(1238), for example]. Similarly, within a general UIR of $SU(3)$ μ is not proportional to Q, even in the limit of exact $SU(3)$ symmetry. [In practice it turns out that for the physically relevant $SU(3)$ representations, the 8 and the 10, μ is not proportional to Q for the 8, but is proportional to Q for the 10. This means that μ can allow the observed magnetic moments for uncharged particles in the 8 (e.g., the neutron and $\mathbf{\Lambda}$), even in the limit of exact symmetry.]

Finally, we consider the tensorial character of the weak hadron current $\mathscr{J}_\mu^w(x)$. The tensor character of $\mathscr{J}_\mu^w(x)$ is more complicated and less well grounded than that of $\mathscr{J}_\mu^e(x)$. Partly theoretically and partly phenomologically, one assumes* for $\mathscr{J}_\mu^w(x)$,

$$\mathscr{J}_\mu^w(x) = g \cos \theta[V_\mu^0(x) + A_\mu^0(x)] + g \sin \theta[V_\mu^1(x) + A_\mu^1(x)], \tag{4.13}$$

where $V_\mu^{0,1}(x)$ are the vector currents with $\Delta S = 0, 1$ (S = strangeness = $Y -$ baryon number), respectively, $A_\mu^{0,1}(x)$ are the corresponding axial vector currents, θ is the Cabibbo angle (~ 7.5 deg), and g is the universal weak decay constant, calculated independently from the decay $\mu^+ \to e^+ + \nu + \tilde{\nu}$, which is not influenced by strong interactions. [Note that the same angle θ is used for the V^0/V^1 and A^0/A^1 ratio. Experimentally we know only that $|\theta_V| \simeq |\theta_A|$, so a minus sign in the second bracket of (4.13) is possible (pseudo-Cabibbo theory).] One also assumes for $V_\mu^0(x)$ the conserved vector current (CVC) hypothesis (*18*), which states that

$$\int d^3x\, V_0^0(x) \tag{4.14}$$

is conserved and is simply one of the generators of the total isotopic spin group (partner of T_3). This means that $V_\mu^0(x)$ is simply another component of the *same* isotopic vector as the isotopic vector part of $\mathscr{J}_\mu^e(x)$. The CVC hypothesis is in good agreement with experiment, and the natural extension of it is to assume that $V_\mu(x) = \cos \theta V_\mu^0(x) + \sin \theta V_\mu^1(x)$ is simply another component of the same $SU(3)$ octet as $\mathscr{J}_\mu^e(x)$. Note that the assumption that $V_\mu(x)$ and $\mathscr{J}_\mu^e(x)$ belong to the *same* octet has the important consequence that both currents have the same reduced matrix elements. Finally, that $V_\mu(x)$ is a member of an octet suggests that $A_\mu(x) = \cos \theta V_\mu^0(x) + \sin \theta A_\mu^1(x)$

* The explicit expression (4.13) for the weak current density is due to Cabibbo (*17*). Again, the ideas involved are implicit in the work of Gell-Mann (*10*).

is also a member of an octet. Note, however, that this octet will be different from that of $V_\mu(x)$ and $\mathscr{J}_\mu^e(x)$, and that $A_\mu(x)$, which is axial, is not a conserved current, even in the limit of unbroken $SU(3)$. Of course, all these extrapolations of CVC would be rather academic were they not supported by experimental considerations. These come from the fact that if $\mathscr{J}_\mu^w(x)$ is an octet, then, on scaling down to isospin, $\mathscr{J}_\mu^w(x)$ contains no $T_3=\frac{3}{2}$, no $T=\frac{3}{2}$, and no $S=2$ terms, all of which would be present if $\mathscr{J}_\mu^w(x)$ were partly a member of a 27. The absence of these terms agrees with the observed $\Delta S=\Delta Q$ (for $|\Delta S|=1$) and $\Delta T=\frac{1}{2}$ (at least for V_μ^1) rules in the leptonic decays of the hyperons, which are assumed to proceed through a Hamiltonian of form

$$\mathscr{H}_l=\int d^3x\ \mathscr{J}_\mu^w(x)\mathscr{J}_\mu^{\text{lepton}}(x). \tag{4.15}$$

If octet dominance, i.e., suppression of the 27 in $(8 \boxtimes 8)_{\text{sym}}=1\oplus 8\oplus 27$, is also invoked then the extrapolation of CVC provides an explanation for the observed $\Delta S\neq 2$, $\Delta S=\Delta Q$ (for $|\Delta S|=1$), and $\Delta T=\frac{1}{2}$ rules for the nonleptonic decays. The latter are assumed to proceed through the Hamiltonian

$$\mathscr{H}_{nl}=\int d^3x\ \mathscr{J}_\mu^w(x)\mathscr{J}_\mu^w(x). \tag{4.16}$$

Having classified the particles according to $SU(3)$ and assigned the tensor properties of $S(strong)$, M, $\mathscr{J}_\mu^w(x)$, and $\mathscr{J}_\mu^e(x)$, we come to the third step in the process of bringing $SU(3)$ into contact with physics, which consists in applying the W-E theorem to the matrix elements of these tensors and comparing the result with experiment.

We first consider M. From the assumption (4.2) we can show, using the W-E theorem, that the mass satisfies the formula

$$M=\alpha+\beta Y+\gamma[T(T+1)-\tfrac{1}{4}Y^2] \tag{4.17}$$

where α, β and γ are constants. As mentioned earlier, this formula agrees extraordinarily well with experiment for the baryon multiplets $\frac{1}{2}^+$ and $\frac{3}{2}^+$ (error $<\frac{1}{2}\%$), making one prediction for $\frac{1}{2}^+$ and two for $\frac{3}{2}^+$.

For the three meson multiplets the mass formula makes no prediction (there are four parameters; α, γ, the mixing angle θ, and the mass of the singlet, to be compared with four observed masses). However, the formula is nevertheless not empty. First, the fact that the masses predicted for $\boldsymbol{\eta}_8$, $\boldsymbol{\omega}_8$, and $\mathbf{f}_8$ by the mass formula [i.e., $\boldsymbol{\eta}_8=(4\mathbf{K}-\boldsymbol{\pi})/3$, etc.] lie *between* the observed masses $(\boldsymbol{\eta}, \boldsymbol{\eta}^*)$, $(\boldsymbol{\omega}, \boldsymbol{\varphi})$ and $(\mathbf{f}, \mathbf{f}^*)$, respectively, allows the introduction of the mixing concept (no linear combination of $\boldsymbol{\eta}$ and $\boldsymbol{\eta}^*$, for example, would yield an expectation value for the mass outside the range [η, η^*]). That this happens for all three meson multiplets is in itself nontrivial evidence in favor of $SU(3)$. Second, the mixing angle is predicted by the mass formula and can then be tested in independent processes, notably the decay rates. There the predicted angles θ_1 and θ_2 are in good agreement with experiment (θ_0 is too small to be tested at present).

The mass formula is a vital ingredient in making the $SU(3)$ classification. Thus, for the $\frac{1}{2}^+$ and $\frac{3}{2}^+$ multiplets not only are the J^P values the same and the masses of the particles approximately equal, but in addition the mass differences satisfy the mass formula. For the meson multiplets it is the large violation of the formula that forces (and the form of the violation that allows, see the foregoing) the nontrivial mixing of the octet and singlet. Finally, the fact that the mass formula is not too well satisfied (error $\sim 10\%$) for the possible $\frac{5}{2}^+$ and $\frac{3}{2}^-$ octets of Table I introduces some doubt as to whether these are really $SU(3)$ octets. Another possibility here is that the departure from the mass formula is due to mixing effects with other, as yet unobserved, J^P $\frac{3}{2}^-$ and $\frac{5}{2}^+$ singlets or octets. On the other hand, it might be that for $\frac{3}{2}^-$ and $\frac{5}{2}^+$ the simple formula (4.6) is too restrictive. It is conceivable that, in general, there should be M^{27} terms present, but that these vanish fortuitously for the $\frac{1}{2}^+$ and $\frac{3}{2}^+$.

We next consider $S(strong)$. The invariance of $S(strong)$ to within 20% is tested primarily by the strong decay rates of the resonant particles (e.g., $\mathbf{N}^* \to \mathbf{N}\boldsymbol{\pi}$) and secondarily by the production processes (e.g., $\boldsymbol{\pi}\mathbf{N} \to \mathbf{KY}^*$).

The decay rates are easily calculable, using C-G coefficients and the W-E theorem. For example, for the decuplet decays $\mathbf{N}^* \to \mathbf{N}\boldsymbol{\pi}$ and $\mathbf{Y}_1^* \to \boldsymbol{\Lambda}\boldsymbol{\pi}$ we have

$$\frac{\mathbf{N}^* \to \mathbf{N}\boldsymbol{\pi}}{\mathbf{Y}_1^* \to \boldsymbol{\Lambda}\boldsymbol{\pi}} \simeq \frac{\rho\langle \mathbf{N}^*|S^0|\mathbf{N}\boldsymbol{\pi}\rangle}{\sigma\langle \mathbf{Y}_1^*|S^0|\boldsymbol{\Lambda}\boldsymbol{\pi}\rangle} = \frac{\rho C^{8\;8\;10}_{N\pi N^*}\langle 10\|S^0\|88\rangle}{\sigma C^{8\;8\;10}_{\Lambda\pi Y_1^*}\langle 10\|S^0\|88\rangle} = \left(\frac{\rho}{\sigma}\right)\frac{C^{8\;8\;10}_{N\pi N^*}}{C^{8\;8\;10}_{\Lambda\pi Y_1^*}}, \qquad (4.18)$$

where ρ and σ are phase space factors, and in the C-G coefficients, particle names have been used as shorthand for state labels, e.g., N^*_{++} denotes a state of the 10, with $T=\frac{3}{2}$, $T_3=\frac{3}{2}$, $Y=1$ (see Fig. 8). In the equal mass limit, $\rho=\sigma$, but for the broken mass case ρ may differ from σ by an order of magnitude (for $\boldsymbol{\Omega}^-$ the phase space is even such that $\boldsymbol{\Omega}^-$ cannot decay strongly). See the next paragraph for a typical determination of ρ and σ. The necessity for introducing an ad hoc phase space factor in this way throws considerable doubt on the validity of relations such as (4.25) but no better prescription seems to be available.

It turns out, in point of fact, that for the established resonant multiplets $\frac{3}{2}^+$, 1^-, and 2^+ [which decay practically 100% to $\frac{1}{2}^+ + 0^-$ (e.g., $\boldsymbol{\Xi}^* \to \boldsymbol{\Xi}\boldsymbol{\pi}$), $0^- + 0^-$ (e.g., $\boldsymbol{\rho} \to 2\boldsymbol{\pi}$), and $0^- + 0^-$ or $0^- + 1^-$ (e.g., $\mathbf{A}_2 \to \boldsymbol{\eta}\boldsymbol{\pi}$ or $\boldsymbol{\rho}\boldsymbol{\pi}$), respectively] the decay rates are in reasonable to very good agreement with experiment [see Behrends]. The phase space factors like ρ/σ are, of course, responsible for the coarser part of the agreement, but in general the agreement is significantly better than that to be expected from phase space alone. One of the most remarkable features of the decay rate analyses is that in two cases in which the experimental decay rates are in complete contradiction with phase space and $SU(3)$ without mixing, the use of mixing accounts for the discrepancy. For example, experimentally

$$\frac{\mathbf{f} \to 2\boldsymbol{\pi}}{\mathbf{f} \to \mathbf{K}\bar{\mathbf{K}}} \simeq 50, \qquad \frac{\mathbf{f}^* \to 2\boldsymbol{\pi}}{\mathbf{f}^* \to \mathbf{K}\bar{\mathbf{K}}} \lesssim \tfrac{1}{5}, \tag{4.19}$$

whereas, on account of the much smaller mass of the pion, phase space would predict the ratio $\gg 1$ in both cases. With mixing, $SU(3)$ predicts, using the W-E theorem,

$$\frac{\mathbf{f} \to 2\boldsymbol{\pi}}{\mathbf{f} \to \mathbf{K}\bar{\mathbf{K}}} \simeq \frac{\rho}{\sigma}\left[\frac{\cos\theta_2\left\langle \frac{8}{f_8}\middle| S^0 \middle|\frac{8}{\pi}\right\rangle\left|\frac{8}{\pi}\right\rangle + \sin\theta_2\left\langle \frac{0}{f_0}\middle| S^0 \middle|\frac{8}{\pi}\right\rangle\left|\frac{8}{\pi}\right\rangle}{\cos\theta_2\left\langle \frac{8}{f_8}\middle| S^0 \middle|\frac{8}{K}\right\rangle\left|\frac{8}{\bar{K}}\right\rangle + \sin\theta_2\left\langle \frac{0}{f_0}\middle| S^0 \middle|\frac{8}{K}\right\rangle\left|\frac{8}{\bar{K}}\right\rangle}\right]^2,$$

$$\simeq \frac{\rho}{\sigma}\left[\frac{\cos\theta_2 C^{8\,8\,8_s}_{\pi\,\pi\,8} + \alpha\sin\theta_2 C^{8\,8\,0}_{\pi\,\pi\,0}}{\cos\theta_2 C^{8\,8\,8_s}_{K\,K\,8} + \alpha\sin\theta_2 C^{8\,8\,0}_{K\,\bar{K}\,0}}\right]^2 = \frac{\rho}{\sigma}\,\frac{3(2\sin\theta_2 + \alpha\cos\theta_2)^2}{4(\sin\theta_2 - \alpha\cos\theta_2)^2}, \tag{4.20}$$

where S^0 is the scalar approximation to the S-matrix S,

$$\alpha = \frac{\langle 0\|S^0\|88\rangle}{\langle 8\|S^0\|88\rangle},$$

and the phase space factor ρ/σ is given by

$$\frac{\rho}{\sigma} = \left(\frac{p}{q}\right)^{2l+1} = \left[\frac{m_f(1-4m_\pi^2|m_f^2)^{1/2}}{m_f(1-4m_K^2|m_f^2)^{1/2}}\right]^5 \simeq [(1-4(500)^2|(1250)^2)^{-1/2}]^5$$

$$\simeq \left(\frac{5}{3}\right)^5 \simeq 15, \tag{4.21}$$

where m denotes mass, p and q are the final state $\boldsymbol{\pi}$ and $\mathbf{K}$ three-momenta, respectively, and $l = 2$ is the final state orbital angular momentum. Similarly,

$$\frac{\mathbf{f}^* \to 2\boldsymbol{\pi}}{\mathbf{f}^* \to \mathbf{K}\bar{\mathbf{K}}} = \frac{\rho'}{\sigma'}\cdot\frac{3}{4}\left[\frac{2\cos\theta_2 - \alpha\sin\theta_2}{\cos\theta_2 + \alpha\sin\theta_2}\right]^2, \tag{4.22}$$

where

$$\frac{\rho'}{\sigma'} = \left[\frac{m_{f^*}(1 - 4m_\pi^2|m_{f^*}^2)^{1/2}}{m_{f^*}(1 - 4m_K^2|m_{f^*}^2)^{1/2}}\right]^5 \simeq [(1 - 4(500)^2|(1500)^2)^{-1/2}]^5$$

$$\simeq \left(\frac{3}{\sqrt{5}}\right)^5 \simeq 4.5. \tag{4.23}$$

The values of θ_2 and α can be calculated from the mass formula and from f and A_2 decays, respectively. The values calculated in this way yield

$$\alpha \simeq 2 \cot \theta_2, \tag{4.24}$$

and from (4.22) we see at once that this is exactly what is required to explain (4.19). Note that if there were no mixing ($\sin \theta_2 = 0$), $SU(3)$ would predict

$$\frac{\mathbf{f}^* \to 2\boldsymbol{\pi}}{\mathbf{f}^* \to \mathbf{K}\bar{\mathbf{K}}} = 3\frac{\rho'}{\sigma'},$$

which is even worse than phase space.

We turn now to the production processes. For obvious experimental reasons we are limited to the production from **πN**, **KN**, **NN**, and **N$\bar{\mathbf{N}}$** systems; for example,

$$\boldsymbol{\pi}\mathbf{N} \to \boldsymbol{\pi}\mathbf{N},\ \mathbf{K}\boldsymbol{\Sigma},\ \boldsymbol{\rho}\mathbf{N},\ \mathbf{K}^*\boldsymbol{\Sigma},$$
$$\boldsymbol{\pi}\mathbf{N}^*,\ \mathbf{K}\mathbf{Y}^*,\ \boldsymbol{\rho}\mathbf{N}^*, \qquad \text{etc.} \tag{4.25}$$

Again the theoretical procedure is to use a combination of the W-E theorem and phase-space factors, assuming (except for some special cases) that $S^0 \gg S^8$. However, in the production processes a new problem arises, namely, at what incoming energy the processes should be compared and in what reference frame. The agreement between the $SU(3)$ predictions and experiments is reasonable, though there are serious discrepancies at low energies. These can be removed, but only by assuming that the symmetry-breaking term S^8 is as important as S^0 itself. This disagreement at low energies is one of the most serious difficulties of $SU(3)$.

It is worthwhile to mention that in practice much labor is saved in the calculation of $SU(3)$ production predictions by the use of U-spin invariance, where the U-spin group is an $SU(2)$ subgroup of $SU(3)$ analogous to the isospin group, but directed along the $n - \Xi^0$ axis of Fig. 7 instead of the $\Sigma^- - \Sigma^+$ axis.* The practical advantage of U-spin invariance is that it yields

* U-spin was first introduced by Levinson *et al.* (*19*).

a large number of the $SU(3)$ predictions that are not trivial isospin predictions and at the same time requires only $SU(2)$ C-G coefficients.

There remain the weak and electromagnetic $SU(3)$ predictions. As these are a little complicated and are discussed in detail by Behrends (some of the predictions are also contrasted with $\mathscr{G}_2$ predictions in the next section), we shall not consider their comparison with experiment here. It is worth remarking, however, that the predictions are in good agreement with experiment for both $\mathscr{J}_\mu^e(x)$ and $\mathscr{J}_\mu^w(x)$, and that for $\mathscr{J}_\mu^e(x)$, techniques for exploiting its tensor character have been advanced to the stage where the $SU(3)$ predictions can be practically read off the 8 and 10 weight diagrams (to relevant orders in $e^2/\hbar c$ and in symmetry breaking) (*19a*). The main concept that allows this development is the U-spin just mentioned. The point is that $\mathscr{J}_\mu^e(x)$ is a U-spin scalar.

V. Foils to *SU*(3) and the Eightfold Way

At the outset the question was raised as to how a symmetry that is intrinsically badly broken can make sense. This question is answered to some extent by the brief sketch of the evidence in favor of $SU(3)$ given in the previous section. In this section we attempt to take this discussion a stage further by contrasting $SU(3)$ with some alternative schemes. The schemes considered are global symmetry and $\mathscr{G}_2$ symmetry. Needless to say, other schemes have been attempted, some of which will be mentioned in passing, but for definiteness only the two schemes just specified are considered. An exhaustive survey of all schemes proposed and of all possible connected Lie group schemes is given by Speiser and Tarski (*20*). The question of the assignments of particles within $SU(3)$ will also be discussed by contrasting the accepted eightfold-way assignment of the previous section with the unsuccessful Sakata model assignment.

Global symmetry (to be defined in the following) is first considered. Consider the standard pre-$SU(3)$ strong-interaction Lagrangian (*21*) $\mathscr{L}_\pi + \mathscr{L}_K$, where

$$\mathscr{L}_\pi = g_N \bar{\mathbf{N}}\boldsymbol{\tau}\mathbf{N}\cdot\boldsymbol{\pi} + g_\Xi \bar{\boldsymbol{\Xi}}\boldsymbol{\tau}\boldsymbol{\Xi}\cdot\boldsymbol{\pi} + g_\Sigma(\bar{\boldsymbol{\Sigma}} \times \boldsymbol{\Sigma})\cdot\boldsymbol{\pi} + g_\Lambda \bar{\boldsymbol{\Sigma}}\boldsymbol{\Lambda}\cdot\boldsymbol{\pi} + h.c.,$$

$$\mathscr{L}_K = g_1 \bar{\mathbf{N}}\mathbf{K}\boldsymbol{\Lambda} + g_2 \bar{\mathbf{N}}\boldsymbol{\tau}\mathbf{K}\cdot\boldsymbol{\Sigma} + g_3 \bar{\boldsymbol{\Xi}}\mathbf{K}\boldsymbol{\Lambda} + g_4 \bar{\boldsymbol{\Xi}}\boldsymbol{\tau}\mathbf{K}\cdot\boldsymbol{\Sigma} + h.c., \tag{5.1}$$

and $\mathbf{N}$, $\boldsymbol{\Sigma}$, $\boldsymbol{\Lambda}$, $\boldsymbol{\Xi}$, $\mathbf{K}$, $\boldsymbol{\pi}$ are the nucleon, sigma, lambda, cascade, kaon, and pion fields, respectively. The space-time indices have been suppressed. This interaction Lagrangian is the most general trilinear interaction between the $J^P = \frac{1}{2}^+$ baryons and the $J^P = 0^-$ mesons $\boldsymbol{\pi}$ and $\mathbf{K}$, which is invariant under isospin, hypercharge, and charge conjugation. Global symmetry (*22*) consists in taking for the π-meson couplings

$$g_N^2 = g_\Xi^2 = g_\Sigma^2 = g_\Lambda^2, \tag{5.2}$$

and leaving the **K**-meson couplings $g_1 \cdots g_4$ undetermined. [Proposals for determining the **K** coupling constants relative to each other and relative to the π coupling constants have, of course, also been considered. See, for example, (*22a*).] A theoretical motivation for (5.2) goes back to a speculation of Wigner (*23*) that the conservation of baryon number might be linked to the universality of the strength of pion couplings in much the same way that

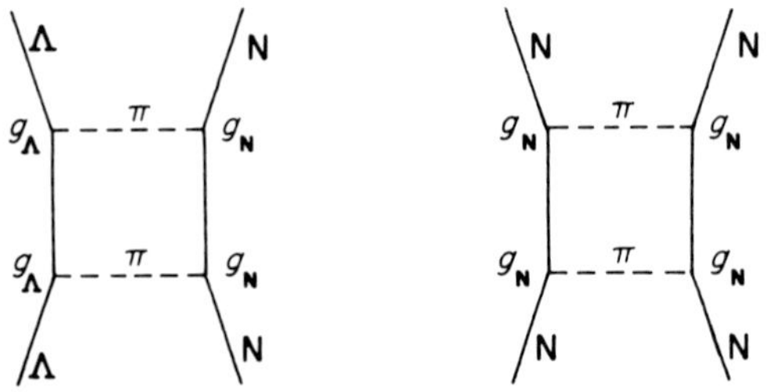

FIG. 10.

the conservation of electric charge is linked to the universality of the electromagnetic charge. It is from this idea of universality that global symmetry derives its name. As pointed out by Sakurai (*24*), however, the analogy is not very close because, whereas the photon field is a vector field that is coupled to a conserved vector current, the pion field is a pseudoscalar and hence is coupled to a pseudoscalar, and therefore nonconserved, current. However, this kind of universality is not the only motivation for (5.2). A strong motivation is the observation that the binding of a **Λ** in a nucleus is of the same order as the binding of a nucleon, an effect that could be explained qualitatively in terms of graphs like that of Fig. 10, with $g_\Lambda^2 \simeq g_N^2$.

Global symmetry requires that the pion coupling be substantially stronger than the **K** coupling, for otherwise the pion-coupling symmetry would be completely masked. This requirement seems to be fulfilled, as the experimental evidence for the cross sections

$$\gamma + p \to n + \pi^+,$$
$$\gamma + p \to \Lambda + K^+,$$

indicates that $g_1^2 \ll g_N^2$. A particularly attractive idea is that the large mass splitting among the baryons **N**, **Σ**, **Λ**, **Ξ** could be explained by the medium-strong **K** interactions breaking the exact, very strong pion symmetry. And in fact, if we calculate the self-energies of the **N**, **Λ**, **Σ**, and **Ξ** to second order in perturbation theory using the Lagrangian (5.1), we can eliminate the coupling constants (*21*) and obtain the relation

$$2(m_{\mathrm{N}} + m_{\Xi}) = 3m_{\Sigma} + m_{\Lambda}, \tag{5.3}$$

between the respective masses. Note the similarity between (5.3) and the $SU(3)$ formula. The difference is that for $SU(3)$ the right-hand side is $3m_{\Lambda} + m_{\Sigma}$. The formula (5.3) agrees with experiment to within 4%. It should be noted, however, that for (5.3) to be nontrivial it is necessary that either $g_1^2 \neq g_3^2$ or $g_2^2 \neq g_4^2$ (otherwise $m_N = m_{\Xi}$) and that either $g_1^2 \neq g_2^2$ or $g_3^2 \neq g_4^2$ (otherwise $m_{\Lambda} = m_{\Sigma}$). Hence the K couplings must be not equal to the $\boldsymbol{\pi}$ coupling constants and also not equal to each other.

The theoretical drawbacks to global symmetry are (a) the lack of any really strong principle to motivate (5.2); (b) the arbitrariness in the **K** coupling constants; (c) the failure to *predict* either the $\frac{1}{2}^+$ or 0^- multiplets just considered [these multiplets appear in (5.1) only because they are observed experimentally] or any higher multiplets. Later experimental evidence has shown that (5.2) is quite badly violated.

It should perhaps be emphasized that the relations (5.2) can be tested experimentally without extrapolation, although the baryon-baryon-meson coupling is clearly off the mass shell. The reason is that, like isospin invariance, global symmetry makes predictions that are independent of the explicit dynamics (provided, of course, that the $\boldsymbol{\pi}$ coupling dominates the **K** coupling so that the latter can be treated perturbatively). The predictions have been analyzed in (*25*). Here we shall just sketch the idea involved. Given global symmetry in the form

$$g_{\mathrm{N}} = g_{\Xi} = g_{\Lambda} = g_{\Sigma} (= g_{\pi}), \qquad g_{\mathrm{K}} \ll g_{\pi}, \tag{5.4}$$

where $g_{\mathrm{K}} = g_1 \cdots g_4$, Eq. (5.1) can be written as

$$\mathscr{L} = g_{\pi}\{\bar{\mathbf{N}}\boldsymbol{\tau}\mathbf{N}\cdot\boldsymbol{\pi} + \bar{\boldsymbol{\Xi}}\boldsymbol{\tau}\boldsymbol{\Xi}\cdot\boldsymbol{\pi} + \bar{\mathbf{Y}}\boldsymbol{\tau}\mathbf{Y}\cdot\boldsymbol{\pi} + \bar{\mathbf{Z}}\boldsymbol{\tau}\mathbf{Z}\cdot\boldsymbol{\pi}\}, \tag{5.5}$$

where

$$\mathbf{Y} = \begin{bmatrix} \Sigma^- \\ \dfrac{\Lambda^0 - \Sigma^0}{\sqrt{2}} \end{bmatrix}, \qquad \mathbf{Z} = \begin{bmatrix} \dfrac{\Lambda^0 + \Sigma^0}{\sqrt{2}} \\ \Sigma^+ \end{bmatrix}.$$

If we now introduce an $SU(2)$ group with respect to which $\mathbf{N}$, $\mathbf{\Xi}$, $\mathbf{Y}$, and $\mathbf{Z}$ are spinors and $\boldsymbol{\pi}$ is a vector (let us call it a K-spin group), then clearly $\mathscr{L}$ is a K-spin invariant. Furthermore, the coupling of $\boldsymbol{\pi}$ to each K-spinor field is the same. Hence (in the approximation in which mass differences are neglected) the amplitudes for $\mathbf{N}\boldsymbol{\pi}$, $\mathbf{\Xi}\boldsymbol{\pi}$, $\mathbf{Y}\boldsymbol{\pi}$, and $\mathbf{Z}\boldsymbol{\pi}$ scattering can all be expressed in terms of two independent amplitudes ($K=\frac{1}{2}$ and $K=\frac{3}{2}$). But for the $\boldsymbol{\pi}\mathbf{N}$ system K-spin coincides with isotopic spin. Hence the $\mathbf{\Xi}\boldsymbol{\pi}$, $\mathbf{Y}\boldsymbol{\pi}$, and $\mathbf{Z}\boldsymbol{\pi}$ and hence, since the $\mathbf{\Sigma}$ and $\mathbf{\Lambda}$ are linear combinations of $\mathbf{Y}$ and $\mathbf{Z}$, the $\mathbf{\Sigma}\boldsymbol{\pi}$ and $\mathbf{\Lambda}\boldsymbol{\pi}$ amplitudes may be expressed in terms of the two $\boldsymbol{\pi}\mathbf{N}$ isotopic amplitudes $T=\frac{1}{2}$ and $\frac{3}{2}$. The $\boldsymbol{\pi}\mathbf{\Lambda}$ and $\boldsymbol{\pi}\mathbf{\Sigma}$ amplitudes cannot be measured directly, of course, due to the lack of $\mathbf{\Lambda}$ and $\mathbf{\Sigma}$ targets, but they can be measured indirectly by means of $\boldsymbol{\pi}\mathbf{\Lambda}$ and $\boldsymbol{\pi}\mathbf{\Sigma}$ production from $\bar{\mathbf{K}}\mathbf{N}$. The point is that the restriction of the S matrix to the $\bar{\mathbf{K}}\mathbf{N}$ and $\boldsymbol{\pi}\mathbf{\Lambda}$, $\boldsymbol{\pi}\mathbf{\Sigma}$ subspaces is, roughly speaking,

$$S=\left[\begin{array}{c|c} \bar{\mathbf{K}}\mathbf{N}\rightarrow\bar{\mathbf{K}}\mathbf{N} & \bar{\mathbf{K}}\mathbf{N}\rightarrow\boldsymbol{\pi}\mathbf{\Lambda},\ \boldsymbol{\pi}\mathbf{\Sigma} \\ \hline \boldsymbol{\pi}\mathbf{\Lambda},\ \boldsymbol{\pi}\mathbf{\Sigma}\rightarrow\bar{\mathbf{K}}\mathbf{N} & \boldsymbol{\pi}\mathbf{\Lambda},\ \boldsymbol{\pi}\mathbf{\Sigma}\rightarrow\boldsymbol{\pi}\mathbf{\Lambda},\ \boldsymbol{\pi}\mathbf{\Sigma} \end{array}\right], \tag{5.6}$$

so the unitarity condition, which is nonlinear, relates the diagonal $\boldsymbol{\pi}\mathbf{\Lambda}$, $\boldsymbol{\pi}\mathbf{\Sigma}\rightarrow\boldsymbol{\pi}\mathbf{\Lambda}$, $\boldsymbol{\pi}\mathbf{\Sigma}$ block to the off-diagonal $\bar{\mathbf{K}}\mathbf{N}\rightarrow\boldsymbol{\pi}\mathbf{\Lambda}$, $\boldsymbol{\pi}\mathbf{\Sigma}$ block. For $g_\pi \gg g_{\mathrm{K}}$ the relationship can be calculated exactly. For details the reader is referred to (*25*): for the comparison with experiment that ultimately decided against global symmetry, see Salam (*26*).

It is worthwhile to write down the ratios for the g's in (5.1) predicted by $SU(3)$ symmetry. Adding an extra term

$$\{g_5\bar{\mathbf{N}}\mathbf{N}+g_6\bar{\mathbf{\Xi}}\mathbf{\Xi}+g_7\bar{\mathbf{\Lambda}}\mathbf{\Lambda}+g_8\bar{\mathbf{\Sigma}}\mathbf{\Sigma}\}\boldsymbol{\eta} \tag{5.7}$$

to the Lagrangian to include the $\boldsymbol{\eta}$ particle and complete the 0^- octet, we find that the relations are

$$\begin{aligned} &g_{\mathrm{N}}=d+f, && g_1=-\frac{1}{\sqrt{3}}d-\sqrt{3}f, && g_5=-\frac{1}{\sqrt{3}}d+\sqrt{3}f,\\ &g_{\Xi}=-d+f, && g_2=d-f, && g_6=-\frac{1}{\sqrt{3}}d-\sqrt{3}f,\\ &g_{\Sigma}=2f, && g_3=-\frac{1}{\sqrt{3}}d+\sqrt{3}f, && g_7=-\frac{2}{\sqrt{3}}g,\\ &g_{\Lambda}=\frac{2}{\sqrt{3}}d, && g_4=-d-f, && g_8=\frac{2}{\sqrt{3}}g. \end{aligned} \tag{5.8}$$

There are two unknown coupling parameters, d and f, in (5.8). This is because the Kronecker product of the eight-dimensional representation of $SU(3)$ with itself contains the 8 twice. ($8 \boxtimes 8 = 27 \oplus 10 \oplus 10^* \oplus 8 \oplus 8 \oplus 1$.) The d in (5.5) comes from the coupling of the 0^--meson octet M_μ, $\mu = 1 \cdots 8$, to the *symmetric* bilinear $\bar{B}_\mu B_\nu + \bar{B}_\nu B_\mu$, where B_μ is the baryon octet. The f comes from the coupling to $\bar{B}_\mu B_\nu - \bar{B}_\nu B_\mu$. Thus, one overall coupling constant and the d/f ratio are left undetermined. Note that the global symmetry relations (5.2) are replaced by the less restrictive relations

$$g_\Sigma = g_N + g_\Xi, \qquad g_\Lambda = \left(\frac{g_N - g_\Xi}{\sqrt{3}}\right), \tag{5.9}$$

which incidentally are incompatible with the global symmetry relations (5.2).

We next consider the group $\mathscr{G}_2$, which is perhaps the most serious rival to $SU(3)$.* We begin by discussing the question of classifying the particles. The lowest-dimensional representations of $\mathscr{G}_2$ are the one-, seven-, fourteen-, and 27-dimensional representations mentioned in Section II, the fourteen-dimensional one being the adjoint or regular representation. We can fit the $J^P = 0^-$ metastable mesons $\boldsymbol{\pi}$ and $\mathbf{K}$ into the 7 very nicely, as it has the correct isotopic spin and hypercharge content. See Fig. 3 (with no multiplicity at the center for $\mathscr{G}_2$). This leaves out the $J^P = 0^-$ $\boldsymbol{\eta}$, which is the remaining member of the $SU(3)$ 0^- octet. The stable $\frac{1}{2}^+$ baryons can also be accommodated in the 7 of $\mathscr{G}_2$, as they have the same isotopic spins as the ($\boldsymbol{\pi}$, $\mathbf{K}$). The $\boldsymbol{\Lambda}$, which is the remaining member of the $SU(3)$ $\frac{1}{2}^+$ octet, is taken to be a $\mathscr{G}_2$ singlet. [It is not possible to accommodate the $\frac{1}{2}^+$ baryons in the 14, or adjoint representation, of $\mathscr{G}_2$, as the 14 has the wrong isospin content, namely, $T = (0, \frac{3}{2}, 1, 0, \frac{3}{2}, 0)$. See Fig. 6.] From the foregoing remarks, it is clear that at least the well-established particles, baryons, and mesons ($\mathbf{N}$, $\boldsymbol{\Xi}$, $\boldsymbol{\Sigma}$, $\boldsymbol{\Lambda}$, $\mathbf{K}$, $\boldsymbol{\pi}$) can be well classified according to $\mathscr{G}_2$, although the isolation of the $\boldsymbol{\Lambda}$ from the other $\frac{1}{2}^+$ particles is a little unsatisfactory.

It is when we try to classify the more recently discovered particles and resonances that $\mathscr{G}_2$ runs into its major difficulties. First, we have to classify the $\boldsymbol{\eta}$. The $\boldsymbol{\eta}$, which has $J^P = 0^-$ and isotopic spin zero, decays into $\gamma\gamma$, 3π, $\pi\gamma\gamma$, and $\gamma\pi\pi$. The rates for these decays, however, are quite the reverse of the rates we would expect from phase-space considerations, for example, $R(3\pi) \simeq R(\gamma\gamma)$, $R(\pi\gamma\gamma) < R(3\pi)$. There are many possible explanations for this, and of course it may be due to some as yet unknown dynamic mechanism. However, a very plausible explanation that fits the observed rates well, is that the decay is invariant under A parity, where $A = CR$, C being the charge

* The case for $\mathscr{G}_2$ has been advocated in particular by Behrends and Sirlin. See, for example, (*27–29*).

conjugation operator and R the hypercharge reflection introduced in Section III. This explanation fits well into the $\mathscr{G}_2$ scheme in which R reflection is implied automatically. If this argument is correct, however, it follows that

$$R|\boldsymbol{\eta}\rangle = -|\boldsymbol{\eta}\rangle. \tag{5.10}$$

(With a plus sign, opposite results for the decay rates would be obtained; that is, the wrong phase-space predictions would actually be reinforced.) From (5.10) it follows at once that $\boldsymbol{\eta}$ cannot be a $\mathscr{G}_2$ singlet. Since the 7 of $\mathscr{G}_2$ has no $T=0$, it follows that the lowest representation of $\mathscr{G}_2$ into which the $\boldsymbol{\eta}$ can be put is the 14. But then from Fig. 7 (and charge conjugation) it is clear that a further three isotopic multiplets, ($T=1$, $Y=0$), ($T=\frac{3}{2}$, $Y=1$), and ($T=0$, $Y=2$), are needed to fill out the 14. These particles have not been observed. Thus $\mathscr{G}_2$ has the option of either not being able to classify the $\boldsymbol{\eta}$ or of predicting the wrong $\boldsymbol{\eta}$-decay rates.

A second difficulty with $\mathscr{G}_2$ is that it fails to classify the well-established $\frac{3}{2}^+$ decuplet satisfactorily. This is an immediate consequence of the fact that $\mathscr{G}_2$ implies R invariance and the existence of a 10 without the corresponding 10* violates it. Specifically, $\mathscr{G}_2$ has only two possibilities. One is to put the whole decuplet in the 27, in which case the extra isotopic multiplets ($T=1$, $Y=2$), ($T=\frac{1}{2}$, $Y=1$), ($T=0, 2$, $Y=0$), ($T=\frac{3}{2}$, $Y=-1$) needed to fill out the 27 multiplet are missing, and an $\boldsymbol{\Omega}^{--}$ and $\boldsymbol{\Omega}^0$ are predicted, along with the $\boldsymbol{\Omega}^-$ in a ($T=1$, $Y=-2$), the $\boldsymbol{\Omega}^{--}$ of which should be observable because of its double charge. The other alternative is to split the multiplet and put the $\mathbf{N}^*$ and $\boldsymbol{\Omega}^-$ in the 14 (the 7 has no $T=\frac{3}{2}$ or $T=0$; see Fig. 6), the $\boldsymbol{\Xi}^*$ in the 7 (the 14 has no $T=\frac{1}{2}$; see Fig. 7), and the $\mathbf{Y}_1^*$ in either set. Then again the other particles needed to complete the multiplet are missing. The inability to accommodate the $\boldsymbol{\eta}$ and $\frac{3}{2}^+$ decuplet constitutes the major argument against $\mathscr{G}_2$. The other more or less well-established multiplets ($1^-, 2^+, \frac{3}{2}^-, \frac{5}{2}^+$) can be classified more or less satisfactorily according to $\mathscr{G}_2$ because they are all octets according to $SU(3)$ and hence can be taken to be either septets + singlets of $\mathscr{G}_2$, or as $\mathscr{G}_2$ 27s, the rest of whose members have not yet been found.

A second argument against $\mathscr{G}_2$, which rests on the mass formula, is less an argument against $\mathscr{G}_2$ than an argument for $SU(3)$. The $SU(3)$ mass formula is, as we saw in the last section, in excellent agreement with experiment for the $\frac{1}{2}^+$ octet and the $\frac{3}{2}^+$ decuplet. To first order in symmetry breaking, the corresponding mass formula for $\mathscr{G}_2$ is

$$M + \alpha Y; \tag{5.11}$$

that is, it is an equal spacing formula. For the $\frac{1}{2}^+$ septet ($\mathbf{N}$, $\boldsymbol{\Sigma}$, $\boldsymbol{\Xi}$) this yields $m_{\mathrm{N}} + m_{\Xi} = 2m_{\Sigma}$, which is in rough agreement with experiment. (For the $\boldsymbol{\Lambda}$, $\mathscr{G}_2$ makes no prediction.) The same formula applies to any $\mathscr{G}_2$ septet. In

TABLE II

	$SU(3)$	$\mathscr{G}_2$
$\frac{1}{2}^+$	(1) $<1\%$ error	(1) 5% error, no Λ prediction
$\frac{3}{2}^+$	(2) $<1\%$ error	(1) $<1\%$ error (many particles unclassified)
$\frac{3}{2}^-$	(1) $\sim 10\%$ error (with present classification)	(1) $<1\%$ error
Mesons	Predicts θ_1, θ_2 in agreement with decays	Equal masses in first-order symmetry breaking; no predictions in second order

fact, as can be seen by inspection, excellent agreement is obtained for the $\mathscr{G}_2$ $\frac{3}{2}^-$ septet [**N***(1512), **Σ***(1660), **Ξ***(1815)]. For the corresponding $SU(3)$ $\frac{3}{2}^-$ octet, the $SU(3)$ formula is off by 10%, if the entries in Table I are the correct ones. For the mesons, $SU(3)$ makes no strong predictions, as discussed earlier; $\mathscr{G}_2$, on the other hand, predicts $m_\pi = m_K$, $m_\rho = m_{K^*}$, and $m_{A_2} = m_{K^{**}}$ to zero order in symmetry breaking [$\alpha = 0$ in (4.8)], and makes no prediction in the next order. For the 14, the first-order mass formula for $\mathscr{G}_2$ is nontrivial, but since the only observed member of the 14 is the **η**, it cannot be applied. For the hypothetical $\frac{3}{2}^+$, it yields the correct relations for **N***, $\mathbf{\Omega}^-$, and $\mathbf{Y}_1^*$, if the latter particle is included. However, it also predicts the masses at which a hypothetical $\frac{3}{2}^+$ $\mathbf{\Xi}_{3/2}^*$, $\bar{\mathbf{Y}}_0^*$, and $\mathbf{Y}_0^*$ (with hypercharge 2) should lie, and at these masses these particles have not been observed.

The $SU(3)$ and $\mathscr{G}_2$ mass predictions may be compared schematically as in Table II. In the table the number in parentheses is the number of predictions. Table II makes clear that it is the classification rather than the mass formula that discriminates against $\mathscr{G}_2$.

As mentioned earlier, the failure of $\mathscr{G}_2$ to classify the $\frac{3}{2}^+$ decuplet is linked to the fact that $\mathscr{G}_2$ automatically implies R invariance. The occurrence of the decuplet without the corresponding 10* represents, of course, a spectacular violation of R invariance [see the ten-dimensional representation of $SU(3)$ in Fig. 4]. There are other violations of R invariance also, and these constitute some evidence against $\mathscr{G}_2$. The most striking violations occur in the electromagnetic interactions. Here, since the hypercharges of the **Ξ**, (**Σ**, **Λ**), and **N** are 1, 0 − 1, respectively, R invariance implies,

$$m_{\Xi^-} - m_{\Xi^0} = m_p - m_n,$$

$$\Gamma_{\Sigma^0} = \Gamma_\Lambda = 0, \qquad \Gamma_p = -\Gamma_{\Xi^-}, \qquad \Gamma_n = \Gamma_{\Xi^0} \tag{5.12}$$

where Γ is the electromagnetic vertex operator, and these results are in clear disagreement with experiment. In fact, $\mathscr{G}_2$ also predicts (*28*), though not via R invariance,

$$\Gamma_{\mathrm{n}} = 0,$$
$$\Gamma_{\mathrm{p}} = \Gamma_{\Sigma^+},$$
$$m_{\Sigma^+} - m_{\Sigma^0} = m_{\mathrm{p}} - m_{\mathrm{n}}, \tag{5.13}$$

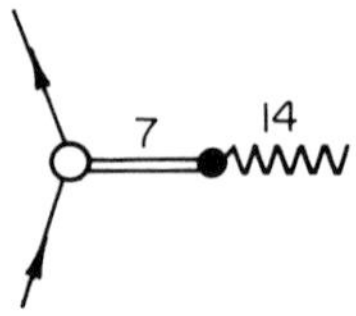

FIG. 11.

the first and third of which are also in clear disagreement with experiment. [The second result is predicted also by $SU(3)$. The corresponding experimental figures are $2.79 = 4.3 \pm 1.5$.] Note that all the foregoing $\mathscr{G}_2$ vertex function predictions can be summed up in the formula

$$\Gamma = \text{const. } Q \tag{5.14}$$

where Q is the charge. The reason is that $\mathscr{J}_Q = \mathscr{J}_Q^{14}$ and hence,

$$\Gamma_7 = \left\langle \begin{matrix} 7 \\ \lambda \end{matrix} \middle| \mathscr{J}_Q^{14} \middle| \begin{matrix} 7 \\ \lambda \end{matrix} \right\rangle = C^{7\,14\,7}_{\lambda\,Q\,\lambda} \langle 7 \| \mathscr{J} \| 7 \rangle,$$
$$\Gamma_\Lambda = \langle 0 | \mathscr{J}_Q^{14} | 0 \rangle = 0. \tag{5.15}$$

Note that there is no multiplicity in the C-G coefficient ($7 \boxtimes 7 = 1 \oplus 7 \oplus 14 \oplus 27$).

$\mathscr{J}_\mu^e(x)$, denoted by $\mathscr{J}$, is a member of the 14 for the same reason as it is a member of the 8 in $SU(3)$ (see Section IV). On account of (5.15) $\mathscr{G}_2$ makes much stronger predictions than $SU(3)$ and they disagree with experiment. Against this, it can be argued that since $\mathscr{G}_2$ [or $SU(3)$] is badly broken anyway, the experimental discrepancy may be due to the symmetry breaking. Of course, at first sight, it does not seem to be very plausible to ascribe *all* of the electromagnetic processes to symmetry breaking, which is implied by this argument, but on the other hand, we can argue that the electromagnetic effects are dominated by the **ω** and **ρ** meson intermediate states (Fig. 11) and in this case $\mathscr{G}_2$ symmetry is certainly broken, since the **ω** and **ρ** belong to a 7 and the electromagnetic field to a 14. If we accept this argument, we can show that already in first order of symmetry breaking, the objectionable Γ predictions are removed and the mass differences are considerably improved. It must be admitted, however, that the improvement occurs mainly because the Γ predictions become so weak even in first order that they cannot be tested at present, while the mass differences (which are not so good in first order) are so weak in second order that only one relation can be tested, and this relation depends also on a dynamic assumption outside the pure symmetry scheme (*29*).

Other violations of R invariance occur in $p\bar{p}$ annihilation and in the strong decays (at least within the $SU(3)$ framework). However, these decays do not constitute conclusive evidence against $\mathscr{G}_2$ for two reasons: (1) the decay data are not completely trustworthy, especially for the $\frac{3}{2}^-$ and $\frac{5}{2}^+$ decays; (2) the violation of R invariance with the $SU(3)$ classification might not necessarily imply the violation with the $\mathscr{G}_2$ classification, although the $\mathscr{G}_2$ classification is somewhat similar for the octets. Strictly speaking, $\mathscr{G}_2$ should be tested systematically for these decays, and this has not been done on account of the other objections to $\mathscr{G}_2$, notably the failure to classify the $\frac{3}{2}^+$ decuplet.

The overall picture for $\mathscr{G}_2$ is therefore the following. The classification is good for the standard 0^- and $\frac{1}{2}^+$ particles (except that **Λ** is a singlet), very bad for the **η** and the decuplet, and no better than $SU(3)$ for the other particles. The respective mass formulas are compared in Table II. The electromagnetic effects and R invariance generally afford strong, but not conclusive evidence against $\mathscr{G}_2$. [Recently some evidence for R invariance in weak interactions has been observed. An analysis of the $\mathscr{G}_2$ predictions (*29*) shows that they are quite definitive and could be tested. An interesting prediction is the allowance of the $\Delta S = -\Delta Q$ process $\Sigma^+ \to \mathrm{n} + e^+ + \nu$ at a rate compatible with present experimental evidence.] Finally, the lack of any substantial evidence in favor of $\mathscr{G}_2$ should be noted.

Having contrasted $\mathscr{G}_2$ and global symmetry with $SU(3)$, we turn now to the question of assignments within $SU(3)$. For purposes of comparison, an alternative assignment to the accepted eightfold-way assignment is considered. This is the Sakata model assignment, which derives its name from a model of the elementary particles proposed by Sakata (*30*) before the advent of $SU(3)$. The essential idea is that all the meson and baryon resonances are bound states of various combinations of three elementary particles, namely, the n, p, and **Λ**. The p provides the unit of electric charge and the **Λ** the unit of strangeness. Within the $SU(3)$ framework, the Sakata model assigns the "sakatons" n, p, **Λ** to the three-dimensional representation of $SU(3)$ (Fig. 12). This allows us to think of the (**π**, **K**, **η**, **η***) nonet as bound states of the sakaton-antisakaton pairs $\bar{\mathbf{N}}\boldsymbol{\tau}\mathbf{N}$, $\bar{\mathbf{\Lambda}}\mathbf{N}$, $\bar{\mathbf{N}}\mathbf{\Lambda}$, $\bar{\mathbf{N}}\mathbf{N} - \bar{\mathbf{\Lambda}}\mathbf{\Lambda}$, $\bar{\mathbf{N}}\mathbf{N} + \bar{\mathbf{\Lambda}}\mathbf{\Lambda}$ and is one of the more plausible features of the model. The serious difficulty of the model is that it does not provide a satisfactory assignment for the remaining **Σ**, **Ξ** particles of the $J^P = \frac{1}{2}^+$ octet. [Note that $SU(3)$ has no five- or two-dimensional representations.]

One consequence of the model is that we lose the very successful $SU(3)$ mass formula for (**N**, **Σ**, **Λ**, **Ξ**). The model also fails to accommodate the well-established $J^P = \frac{3}{2}^+$ decuplet properly because, although the $\frac{3}{2}^+$ particles can be formally assigned to the $SU(3)$ 10 for both the eightfold way and the Sakata model, only the former allows the observed decuplet production $0^- + \frac{1}{2}^+ \rightarrow \frac{3}{2}^+$ and decay $\frac{3}{2}^+ \rightarrow 0^- + \frac{1}{2}^+$. ($8 \boxtimes 8 = 27 \oplus 10 \oplus 10^* \oplus 8 \oplus 8 \oplus 1$ contains the 10, but $3 \boxtimes 8 = 15 \oplus 6 \oplus 3$ does not.)

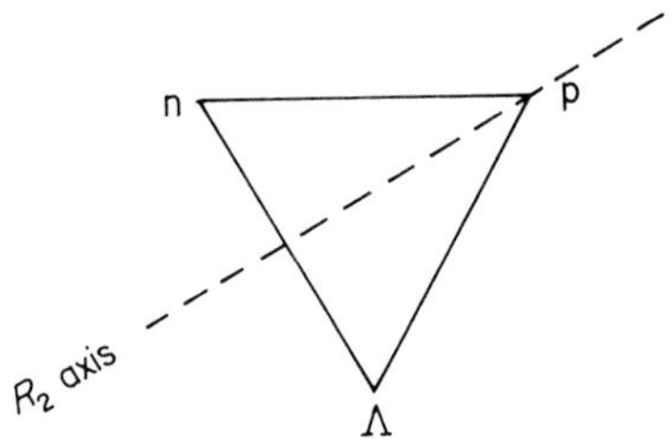

FIG. 12.

Four-particle processes can be compared (*31*) for the Sakata model and the eightfold way (though the comparison is restricted to Sakaton processes). In general, the restrictions implied by the Sakata model are much more severe (the $3 \boxtimes 8$ contains fewer representations than the $8 \boxtimes 8$ and hence allows fewer channels), but are not severe enough to rule it out, except for the $p\bar{p}$ annihilation mentioned below.

Perhaps the most transparent distinction between the predictions of the Sakata and eightfold-way models is the distinction between the R_2 predictions in both cases, where R_2 is the (Weyl) reflection in the $n - \Xi_0$ axis of Fig. 7. In the Sakata model, the sakatons transform under R_2 according to $p \leftrightarrow p$, $\Lambda \leftrightarrow n$ (Fig. 12), whereas in the eightfold-way model, they transform according to $p \leftrightarrow \Sigma^+$, $n \leftrightarrow \Xi^0$, $\Lambda \leftrightarrow (\sqrt{3}\Sigma_0 - \Lambda)/2$ (Fig. 7). Thus, for example, the Sakata model predicts the equality of the reactions,

$$K^- p \rightarrow K^- p \quad \text{and} \quad \pi^- p \rightarrow \pi^- p,$$

whereas the eightfold way does not. More relevant, however, is the reaction (*32*),

$$p\bar{p} \rightarrow K_1^0 K_2^0$$

which is observed to take place at a rate comparable to $p\bar{p} \to K^+K^-$, but is strictly forbidden by the Sakata model. To see that it is forbidden note that under R_2, $p \leftrightarrow p$, $K_0 \leftrightarrow \bar{K}_0$, and that $\sqrt{2}K^0_{1,2} = (K_0 \pm \bar{K}_0)$. For the eightfold way, $\bar{p} \leftrightarrow \Sigma^+$, so that this process is not forbidden. In neither model is the process $\bar{p}p \to K^+K^-$, which is used as a yardstick, forbidden.

Thus the Sakata model fails essentially because of the classification and the process $p\bar{p} = K^0_1 K^0_2$. Note that the Sakata model assigns the p, n, Λ to the 3 of $SU(3)$, which has triality $t = 1$. Its failure means that all the particles observed so far have been assigned to representations with triality zero, that is, the 8 and the 10.

Recently the Sakata idea has emerged in a somewhat different form. It has been proposed (*33*) that all the observed mesons and baryons are bound states of a triplet of much heavier fermions (quarks) than have so far been observed, and that the quarks belong to the 3 of $SU(3)$. Note that since the 3 of $SU(3)$ has triality 1, and the presently observed particles have triality zero, to build the latter out of quarks we must take bound states with number of quarks = number of antiquarks, modulo 3. Thus we assume that the nonets of 0^- and 1^- mesons are quark–antiquark pairs ($3 \boxtimes 3^*$) and the $\frac{1}{2}^+$ and $\frac{3}{2}^+$ baryons are composed of three quarks ($3 \boxtimes 3 \boxtimes 3 = 10 \oplus 8 \oplus 8 \oplus 1$). A particular consequence of this is that for the $3 \boxtimes 3 \boxtimes 3$ to have the additive quantum numbers B (baryon number), Q (charge), and Y (hypercharge) integral, the quarks must have them $\frac{1}{3} \times$ integral [see Eqs. (3.2), (3.5)].

VI. Broken Symmetry in Nuclear and Atomic Physics

In connection with $SU(3)$ symmetry for particle physics, and more especially in connection with $SU(6)$ (to be discussed in Section VII), which mixes $SU(3)$ and ordinary spin, the question naturally arises whether analogous broken symmetries occur in atomic and nuclear physics. It turns out that broken symmetries certainly occur. Whether they are analogous to particle physics $SU(3)$ and $SU(6)$ is, however, another question, and will be very briefly discussed at the end of the section.

Possibly the simplest example of a broken symmetry occurs in the case of the rigid rotator (*34*). As is well known, this is a rotationally invariant system [$O(3)$ is an exact symmetry group] and the energy levels correspond to integral values of the total angular momentum operator, l. The interesting point, however, is that in the energy spectrum each possible value of l, 0, 1, 2, 3, ..., occurs *once and only once*. If we now take a group $O(4)$ containing $O(3)$ as a subgroup [such that the $O(4)$ vector $V_\alpha \to V_i + V_4$ under $O(3)$, $\alpha = 1, \ldots, 4$, $i = 1 \cdots 3$], then it is easy to check that the symmetric tensor representation of $O(4)$ of rank ν (i.e., the UIR carried by the traceless tensor $V_{\alpha_1} V_{\alpha_2} V_{\alpha_3} \ldots V_{\alpha_\nu}$), when decomposed with respect to $O(3)$, contains each representation $l = 0, 1, 2, 3 \ldots$ of $O(3)$ *once and only once*. Thus the symmetric tensor representation of rank ν organizes the lowest ν levels of the rotator into one UIR of $O(4)$. Hence $O(4)$ is a relevant group for classifying the rigid rotator states. But it is by no means an exact symmetry group since its UIRs contain states belonging to completely different energy levels. In fact, it is a very badly broken symmetry. Two interesting points can be mentioned. First, if we take the *noncompact* group $O(3, 1)$ instead of $O(4)$, then for every ν in the foregoing, there exists a UIR of $O(3, 1)$ that contains all the *remaining* levels of the rotator ($l = \nu + 1, \nu + 2, \ldots, \infty$), each one once and only once. Thus $O(4)$ and $O(3, 1)$ classify all the levels of the rotator, the changeover point coming at any arbitrary level ν. Second, $O(4)$ is not unique because there exists an $SU(3)$ group containing $O(3)$ whose symmetric tensor representations classify together the first ν *odd* levels or the first ν *even* levels of the rotator. That is, they classify together the ν lowest levels of the same parity $P = (-1)^l$. Here, however, this kind of process stops. There is no simple group containing $O(3)$ that classifies together the first, fourth, seventh, levels and so on.

A very analogous situation holds for the $3n$-dimensional harmonic oscillator. As this is discussed in detail by Moshinsky and Kramer (this volume) it will be sketched only briefly here. As is well known, the Hamiltonian

$$\mathscr{H} = \sum_{i=1}^{N} \sum_{\alpha=1}^{3} \frac{1}{2m} (p_\alpha^{(i)})^2 + \tfrac{1}{2} m\omega^2 (x_\alpha^{(i)})^2, \tag{6.1}$$

for this system has the $U(3)$ group with generators

$$L_{\alpha\beta} = \frac{1}{\hbar} \sum_{i=1}^{N} [x_\alpha^{(i)} p_\beta^{(i)} - x_\beta^{(i)} p_\alpha^{(i)}],$$

$$Q_{\alpha\beta} = \sum_{i=1}^{N} \left[x_\alpha^{(i)} x_\beta^{(i)} + \frac{1}{\hbar^2} p_\alpha^{(i)} p_\beta^{(i)} \right], \tag{6.2}$$

as an invariance group. In fact, $\mathscr{H} = Q_{\alpha\alpha}$. The $L_{\alpha\beta}$ generate the ordinary rotation group $O(3)$. In the space $L_2^{(N)}$ of the x_α, p_α each symmetric tensor representation of the $SU(3)$ group of $U(3)$ occurs once and only once, and no other UIRs of this $SU(3)$ occur. This regularity can be expressed group theoretically by introducing a group $SU(4)$ containing $SU(3)$. The symmetric tensor representations of rank ν of $SU(4)$ contain the first ν levels of the oscillator once each and the remaining levels can be contained in one UIR of its noncompact form $SU(3, 1)$. As in the case of the rotator, the changeover point ν is arbitrary. Clearly, $SU(4)$ is in this case a broken symmetry group.

Perhaps the most interesting example of both a symmetry and broken symmetry group that occurs in atomic physics is in the case of the hydrogen atom. As is well known (*3*), the energy levels E_n, $n = 0, 1, 2, \ldots$, of the H atom are n^2-fold degenerate, which is a greater degeneracy than the $(2l + 1)$-fold degeneracy that is to be expected from the spherical symmetry of the potential. The degeneracy can be traced (*35*) to the invariance of the Coulomb potential

$$\mathscr{H} = \frac{p^2}{2m} - \frac{ZZ'e^2}{r}, \tag{6.3}$$

under the group $O(4)$, generated by the six operators,

$$\mathbf{L} = \frac{1}{\hbar}[\mathbf{p} \times \mathbf{r}],$$

$$\mathbf{A} = (-2\mathscr{H})^{-1/2}\left[\frac{\mathbf{r}}{r} + \frac{1}{2me^2ZZ'}(\mathbf{L} \times \mathbf{p} - \mathbf{p} \times \mathbf{L})\right], \tag{6.4}$$

the first three of which are the ordinary angular momentum operators and the second three form what is called the *Lenz vector*. The states of each energy level furnish a basis for a UIR (symmetric tensor representation) of $O(4)$, which is an exact symmetry group. However, the H-atom has also a broken symmetry group, for we have the further regularity that each symmetric tensor UIR of $O(4)$ occurs once and only once in the totality of bound-state levels of the H atom. This regularity can be described (*36*) by embedding $O(4)$ in a de Sitter group $O(4, 1)$ (orthogonal group in a space with metric $g_{00} = -1$, $g_{\mu\mu} = 1$, $\mu = 1, 2, 3,$), because $O(4, 1)$ has a UIR (or rather, a class of UIRs) whose decomposition with respect to $O(4)$ yields exactly the symmetric tensor representations of $O(4)$, each one once and only once. The complete set of bound states of the H atom, therefore, furnish a basis for this UIR of $O(4, 1)$. The generators of this $O(4, 1)$ have recently been evaluated explicitly in terms of the operators $\mathbf{r}$ and $\mathbf{p}$ both in the classical (*37*) and quantum-mechanical (*38*) cases.

Perhaps the most celebrated example of a broken symmetry group in nuclear physics is Elliott's $SU(3)$ group (*39*). This broken symmetry group is less academic than those considered above, because the situation it describes is much too complicated in general to be handled by alternative methods. What is observed experimentally is that, to put it very roughly, the energy levels within nuclear shells of nuclei with $16 < A < 40$ correspond to a definite range of total angular momentum values, bounded below by some value K, and presumably bounded above also, though this is not so well established experimentally, and that the corresponding energies are given very approximately by

$$E = E_0 + \epsilon l(l+1), \tag{6.5}$$

where E_0 is the approximate shell energy and $\epsilon \gtrsim E_0$. To explain these results, we suppose that the Hamiltonian for the N particles in the shell is $\mathscr{H} = \mathscr{H}_0 + \mathscr{H}_I$, where $\mathscr{H}_0$ is the basic shell-model potential and $\mathscr{H}_I$ a correction term coming from two-particle short-range interactions. If we now assume that $\mathscr{H}_0$ can be approximated by the three-dimensional harmonic oscillator potential of (6.1), and that $\mathscr{H}_I$ is dominated by a quadrupole-quadrupole force between the particle, that is,

$$\mathscr{H}_I \simeq -\epsilon \sum_{\alpha\beta} Q_{\alpha\beta} Q_{\alpha\beta}, \tag{6.6}$$

where the $Q_{\alpha\beta}$ are as in (6.2), then $\mathscr{H}_0$ is invariant under the $SU(3)$ group of (6.2), while $\mathscr{H}_I$ can be expressed as

$$\mathscr{H}_I \simeq -\epsilon[C_2 - l(l+1)], \tag{6.7}$$

where C_2 is the sum of the squares of the $Q_{\alpha\beta}$ and the $L_{\alpha\beta}$. But C_2 is a Casimir operator of $SU(3)$; that is, it commutes with the $L_{\alpha\beta}$ and $Q_{\alpha\beta}$. Hence, if we regard the levels within a nuclear shell as classified according to a UIR of this $SU(3)$ group, (6.7) leads directly to the observed spectrum (6.5). Furthermore, the UIR of $SU(3)$ determines the values of l that can occur, and these agree, at least in certain cases and for low E values, with the observed ranges. To see how $SU(3)$ determines the l values that can occur, consider the simple case of the eight-dimensional representation of $SU(3)$ with basis $u_\alpha^* v_\beta - \frac{1}{3}\delta_{\alpha\beta}\sum_\gamma u_\gamma^* v_\gamma$, $\alpha, \beta, \gamma = 1, 2, 3$. With respect to the rotation subgroup $O(3)$ generated by $L_{\alpha\beta}$, u_α^* transforms equivalently to u_α. Hence $u_\alpha^* v_\beta - \frac{1}{3}\delta_{\alpha\beta}\sum_\gamma u_\gamma^* v_\gamma$ decomposes with respect to $O(3)$ into $\frac{1}{2}[u_\alpha^* v_\beta + u_\beta^* v_\alpha] - \frac{1}{3}\delta_{\alpha\beta} u_\gamma^* v_\gamma$ and $\frac{1}{2}[u_\alpha^* v_\beta - u_\beta^* v_\alpha]$. Thus the 8 of $SU(3)$ contains $L = 1$ and $L = 2$. It should, perhaps, be emphasized that the UIR of $SU(3)$ that predicts the values of L is determined by other considerations, such as the number of particles in the shell, the lowest energy levels (largest value of C_2) compatible with Fermi statistics, and so on.

Note that Elliott's $SU(3)$ group is not even an approximate symmetry group for the Hamiltonian, since $\mathscr{H}_I$, although somewhat smaller than $\mathscr{H}_0$, is still quite appreciable. Nevertheless, the broken symmetry group is useful because $\mathscr{H}_I$ does not break the symmetry in an arbitrary way, but as a component of a tensor. Actually, it is [in the approximation (6.6)] the component of not only a tensor, but a generator tensor. Hence, as discussed in Section II, it has nonzero matrix elements only within each $SU(3)$ shell, even if two different shells approach each other energetically, or overlap.

Another broken symmetry group in nuclear physics is the $SU(4)$ group introduced by Wigner (*40*). This group combines isotopic spin and ordinary spin in a nontrivial way and is valid in the limit where spin-dependent forces can be neglected. The details of the combination will not be given here, as they are given for the analogous case of particle physics $SU(6)$ in the next section.

We come now to the question of the analogy between the symmetries just mentioned and particle physics $SU(3)$. At the present state of our knowledge, the analogy does not seem to be too good. The basic difference is that whereas the symmetries of this section are all symmetries that can be understood geometrically and, in particular, their groups contain the ordinary rotation group $O^+(3)$ as a subgroup, particle physics $SU(3)$ appears to have no geometrical significance and, far from containing $O^+(3)$ as a subgroup, it commutes with it.

As mentioned earlier, however, there *is* an analogy between Wigner's $SU(4)$ and the $SU(6)$ of particle physics. In both cases the (given) internal group, isospin or $SU(3)$, is combined with the ordinary spin group, and in each case the combination of groups is made in the same way. (Only the classification of the particles is different.) On account of this analogy between $SU(6)$ and Wigner's $SU(4)$, the validity of $SU(6)$ [given $SU(3)$] may actually be easier to understand than the validity of $SU(3)$ itself.

VII. General Questions concerning Broken Symmetry

For the most part the general questions relating to broken symmetry that are dealt with in this section are left unanswered, but as they are generally not discussed at all in the literature, it is perhaps of interest to raise them here.

The first question to be considered is the one raised in the Introduction, namely, whether it is really meaningful to talk of a symmetry when it is so badly broken that it is at best in only qualitative agreement with experiment. In Sections III and IV an attempt was made to answer this question in the case of particle physics $SU(3)$ by sketching the $SU(3)$ successes and contrasting them with the corresponding results for other schemes. The successes are clearly numerous and striking enough to put the relevance of $SU(3)$ beyond doubt. The origin of $SU(3)$ in fundamental interactions remains a mystery, though current-algebra has helped us to understand its role. Note that in each case of broken symmetry discussed, the symmetry is found a posteriori; that is, a regular pattern is first observed either theoretically (as in the case of the rotator, harmonic oscillator, and H atom) or experimentally (as in the case of Elliott's $SU(3)$ and the elementary particle $SU(3)$) and the broken symmetry is introduced afterwards to explain the observed regularity.

A second question that arises concerns the role of the compact simply connected Lie groups. In the case of the geometrical groups such as Elliott's $SU(3)$ or the H atom $O(4)$ (where even the Lenz vector has a geometrical meaning; i.e., it is a vector in the direction of the major axis of the elliptical orbit, with magnitude equal to the eccentricity), the role is understandable. In the case of isospin and $SU(3)$, however, the question arises as to why continuous (Lie) groups should be preferred to other groups, to the permutation groups, for example. In fact, there is a series of questions that might be asked: (i) Why $SU(3)$ among all the connected compact simple Lie groups? (ii) Why connected compact simple Lie groups? (iii) Why Lie groups? Of course, in the background there is always the more fundamental question: Why should higher symmetries exist at all?

With regard to question (i), we can see that, given the existence of isospin and hypercharge, the choice of $SU(3)$ among all other compact simple Lie groups for elementary particles is rather natural. To see this, we note that so far only *two* additive quantum numbers are necessary to label the elementary particles, namely, T_3 (third component of isospin) and Y (hypercharge). This already makes it plausible to consider only the groups of rank 2, since these and only these contain two commuting elements (observables) in their Lie algebra. But, as discussed in Section III, there are only three such groups, namely, $SU(3)$, $\mathscr{G}_2$, and $O(5) \simeq USp(4)$. Of these, $O(5)$ does not get off the ground because it does not yield a reasonable classification even of the metastable $\frac{1}{2}^+$ baryons and 0^- mesons. Its lowest-dimensional representations are of dimension 1, 4, 5, 10, and these do not correspond in any simple way to the eight $\frac{1}{2}^+$ baryons or seven, eight, or nine (depending on whether $\boldsymbol{\eta}$ and $\boldsymbol{\eta}^*$ are counted) 0^- mesons. This question has been analyzed very clearly by Behrends *et al.* (*41*), to which the reader is referred. Possibilities are to put (**N**, **Ξ**) in the 4, and (**Σ**, $\mathbf{X}^{\pm}$) (where $\mathbf{X}^{\pm}$ is a hypothetical $\frac{1}{2}^+$ baryon with $Y = \pm 2$) in the 5, or to put the (**N**, **Ξ**, **Λ**) in the 5. For the 0^- mesons, the most likely possibility would be to put them in the 10, but this requires an extra isoscalar Y-triplet $\mathbf{D}^{+0}$, with Y values ($\pm 2, 0$). The hypothetical $\mathbf{X}^+$ and $\mathbf{D}^{+0}$ needed here have not so far been observed. Also, the scheme requires that the **Σ** be classified separately from **N**, **Λ**, **Ξ**.

A much more serious rival to $SU(3)$ is $\mathscr{G}_2$ since, as discussed in the last section it classifies the eight $\frac{1}{2}^+$ baryons (**Λ** as singlet) and the seven 0^- mesons (**π**, **K**) reasonably well. It is at the next stage of classification, namely, in classifying the $\boldsymbol{\eta}$ and the $\frac{3}{2}^+$ decuplet, that it fails badly in comparison to $SU(3)$, as discussed in Section V. Thus $SU(3)$ remains the only suitable candidate of rank 2.

The next question (ii) is more difficult to answer. First, because unitary (or antiunitary) transformations are the most general linear transformations that preserve the norm of physical states (and hence the probability interpretation of quantum mechanics) and because there are only a finite number of particles observed, it is natural to look for Lie groups with nontrivial finite-dimensional unitary representations, and effectively the only Lie groups of this kind are the simple (and semisimple) compact ones. This argument is, of course, subject to the following two qualifications.

First, in view of our scant knowledge of the real nature of particles, and because most particles are unstable, the restriction to unitary transformations might, in some future theory, be relaxed. For example, we might no longer associate physical states with unit rays, or we might not require all the states in a representation to be physical. On the other hand, a departure from unitarity seems to imply a rather radical departure from the accepted principles of quantum mechanics (in particular, the probability interpretation) and hence, in order to be acceptable, would have to be strongly motivated by physical considerations.

[Of course, a special case of the possibility that we might not require all the states in a representation to be physical already happens in the case of superselection rules (*42*). But in that case the restriction to unitary (or antiunitary) transformations is still retained. For example, to implement isotopic spin symmetry in deducing the equality of the proton–proton and proton–neutron force (in the strong-interaction limit and for antisymmetric space-time wave functions) from the invariance of the strong S matrix under isotopic spin transformations, it is necessary to use norm-preserving transformations of the form

$$\exp\left(i\frac{\pi}{4}\tau_2\right)|\mathrm{p}\rangle = \frac{1}{\sqrt{2}}(|\mathrm{p}\rangle + |\mathrm{n}\rangle)$$

from the physical state $|\mathrm{p}\rangle$ to the unphysical state $(|\mathrm{p}\rangle + |\mathrm{n}\rangle)/\sqrt{2}$. Thus, a more fundamental change than that introduced by superselection rules is understood.]

The second limitation on the argument for connected compact simple Lie groups comes from the observation that whereas, at present, we classify the elementary particle in *finite* multiplets, it is conceivable that we are actually observing only the lower-energy submultiplets of some larger and even infinite-dimensional multiplets (just as one observed first only the lowest atomic and molecular levels). For an infinite-dimensional multiplet we would require a noncompact group to classify the particles. Thus the restriction to compact simple Lie groups follows essentially from the requirements of unitarity and finiteness of the multiplets, either or both of which requirements (and especially the second) might conceivably be relaxed in the future.

The restriction to simple groups rather than direct products of simple groups, which have the same properties, is mainly based on economy, and product groups have, in fact, been used. For example, in the current-algebra theory mentioned at the end of the Introduction it is $SU(3) \times SU(3)$, not $SU(3)$, that plays a role. Similarly, in a theory of the weak interactions that was formulated earlier by Salam and Polkinghorne (*43*), the compact semisimple group $O(4) = O(3) \times O(3)$ of rank 2 played the basic role. [Note that if isospin is regarded as $O(3)$ rather than $SU(2)$, $O(4)$ and not $SU(3)$ would seem to be its natural generalization.] The restriction to connected groups is also by no means compelling. A disconnected part of the isospin group, namely, isospace reflections, played a central role in a theory of elementary particles proposed by d'Espagnat and Prentki (*44*). Finally, with regard to the question of connected versus simply connected groups, at present it is not even clear whether it is $SU(3)$ itself or $SU(3)/Z_3$ that plays the role in particle physics. If only representations of triality zero, such as 8 and 10, continue to appear, then presumably it is $SU(3)/Z_3$. If other trialities, particularly quarks, appear, then it is $SU(3)$.

We come now to the most difficult question (apart from the question why higher symmetries should exist at all), namely, (iii) why Lie groups? We discuss three separate answers to this question, none of which appears to be particularly convincing. The first answer applies primarily to isospin. The argument is that isospin invariance is equivalent to the statement that in the absence of the electromagnetic and weak interactions the particles with the same J^P and mass have the same properties (apart from statistics), and that its existence is therefore very reasonable. However, this is clearly only a plausibility argument, and it does not answer the question why particles with different charges, but the same J^P and mass, should exist. Furthermore, the argument apparently breaks down for $SU(3)$, for there is (so far) no evidence for a medium-strong interaction analogous to the electromagnetic interaction, in the absence of which the hadrons within the same multiplets would all have the same properties.

A second argument is as follows. We note that charge conservation should be a consequence of any reasonable symmetry scheme. But charge conservation, we know, is linked to invariance under a continuous one-parameter Lie group, namely, the group of gauge transformations of the first kind. Hence, the symmetry group in question should contain this continuous group as a subgroup. It is plausible to assume from this that the containing group should also be a continuous group.

This kind of argument has been made more quantitative by various authors. One quantitative version is that suggested by Yamaguchi (*45*) and later generalized and strengthened by Neville and by Okubo *et al.* (*46*). For illustration we produce part of Yamaguchi's argument. Consider three basic baryon fields ψ_1, ψ_2, ψ_3. The linear combinations

$$\psi_\Lambda = \frac{1}{\sqrt{3}}(\psi_1 + \psi_2 + \psi_3), \tag{7.1}$$

and

$$\psi_n = \frac{1}{\sqrt{6}}(2\psi_1 - \psi_2 - \psi_3),$$

$$\psi_p = \frac{1}{\sqrt{2}}(\psi_3 - \psi_2),$$

transform according to the one- and two-dimensional representations of the discrete group S_3 of all permutations of ψ_1, ψ_2, and ψ_3. Assuming the same is true for the corresponding antibaryons, we construct the most general S_3-invariant Fermi-type interaction for these fields. It turns out to be

$$\begin{aligned}\mathscr{H} = {} & a(\bar\psi_\Lambda\psi_\Lambda)^2 + b(\bar\psi_\Lambda\psi_\Lambda)(\bar\psi_p\psi_p + \bar\psi_n\psi_n)\\ & + [b'(\bar\psi_\Lambda\psi_\Lambda)(\bar\psi_p\psi_n - \bar\psi_n\psi_p) + \text{h.c.}]\\ & + c(\bar\psi_p\psi_p + \bar\psi_n\psi_n)^2\\ & + c'(\bar\psi_p\psi_p + \bar\psi_n\psi_n)(\bar\psi_p\psi_n - \bar\psi_n\psi_p)\\ & + d(\bar\psi_p\psi_n - \bar\psi_n\psi_p)^2\\ & + \{f'[(\bar\psi_\Lambda\psi_p)^2 + (\bar\psi_\Lambda\psi_n)^2] + \text{h.c.}\}\\ & + g[(\bar\psi_p\psi_p - \bar\psi_n\psi_n)^2 + (\bar\psi_p\psi_n + \bar\psi_n\psi_p)^2]\\ & + \{h[(\bar\psi_\Lambda\psi_n)(\bar\psi_p\psi_p - \bar\psi_n\psi_n) + (\bar\psi_\Lambda\psi_p)(\bar\psi_p\psi_n + \bar\psi_n\psi_p)] + \text{h.c.}\},\end{aligned} \tag{7.2}$$

where the space-time dependence is suppressed. If we now assume charge conservation invariance with the charge assigned as 1, 0, 0 for p, n, Λ, respectively, then (7.2) reduces to

$$\begin{aligned}\mathscr{H} = {} & a(\bar\psi_\Lambda\psi_\Lambda)^2 + b(\bar\psi_\Lambda\psi_\Lambda)(\bar\psi_p\psi_p + \bar\psi_n\psi_n)\\ & + c(\bar\psi_p\psi_p + \bar\psi_n\psi_n)^2\\ & + f[(\bar\psi_\Lambda\psi_p)(\bar\psi_p\psi_\Lambda) + (\bar\psi_\Lambda\psi_n)(\bar\psi_n\psi_\Lambda)]\\ & + g[(\bar\psi_p\psi_p - \bar\psi_n\psi_n)^2 + 2(\bar\psi_p\psi_n)(\bar\psi_n\psi_p) + 2(\bar\psi_n\psi_p)(\bar\psi_p\psi_n)].\end{aligned} \tag{7.3}$$

We see by inspection that this interaction is isospin invariant and conserves hypercharge. In other words, it is a broken $SU(3)$ interaction. This S_3

invariance + charge conservation forces isospin invariance + hypercharge conservation in this case.

Note that the argument here is not that the Lie groups are distinguished. On the contrary, it is that other groups may be *equivalent* to Lie groups, so that there may, in fact, be no loss in generality by restricting oneself to the Lie groups.

Another quantitative version of the "continuous subgroup → continuous group" type of argument is one due to Feinberg (*47*), who has shown that for

FIG. 13.

a trilinear interaction, hypercharge reflection invariance (invariance under a discrete two-element group) forces hypercharge gauge invariance (invariance under a continuous one-parameter group). This has the consequence that the hypercharge should be an additive, rather than multiplicative, quantum number. (It should be mentioned, however, that this particular result depends on the trilinear nature of the interaction, and follows for the quadrilinear case only on taking other physically relevant conditions into account.)

A third attempt to explain the role of continuous groups is aimed specifically at explaining the origin of isospin and $SU(3)$. This type of attempt is based on the bootstrap approach to particle physics, which supposes that the dynamics of the elementary particles is such that each particle can be regarded as a bound state of the others. A subtheory of this theory supposes that the *symmetries* of the interactions are generated in this self-consistent way. A typical approach of this kind is that due to Cutkosky (*48*). In this work, it is supposed that n vector meson fields interact with themselves by means of a trilinear coupling of the kind

$$C_{\alpha\beta\gamma}\varphi_\alpha\varphi_\beta\varphi_\gamma \tag{7.4}$$

where the space-time indices are suppressed. Lorentz invariance requires a derivative coupling (three vector fields alone cannot produce a scalar) and this requires that the coupling constants $C_{\alpha\underline{\beta\gamma}}$ be such that $C_{\alpha\beta\gamma}$ is antisymmetric in two indices. If we now require that $C_{\alpha\beta\gamma}$ be antisymmetric in all indices, and that the fields correspond to the lowest bound states allowed by the interaction, and if furthermore we require the bootstrap condition

$$C_{\alpha\beta\gamma}C_{\gamma\epsilon\delta}C_{\beta\epsilon\sigma} = \lambda C_{\alpha\delta\sigma} \tag{7.5}$$

(where λ is a constant to be determined), corresponding to the graph of Fig. 13 to be satisfied, then we can show that the $C_{\alpha\beta\gamma}$ must be the structure constants of a compact semisimple Lie group. Thus in this case the bootstrap condition

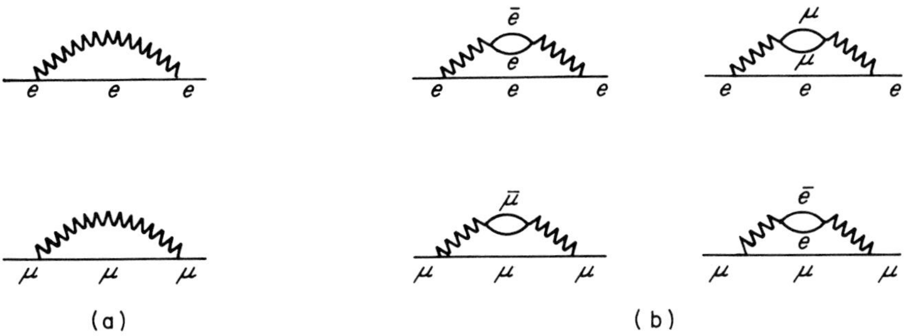

FIG. 14.

(7.5) leads directly to the invariance of the interaction under a continuous group.

The bootstrap approach has also been used to attempt to explain symmetry breaking. To illustrate the idea involved, consider first the following rather trivial example. Consider the Lagrangian

$$\mathscr{L} = i\bar{\psi}_e \partial\!\!\!/ \psi_e + i\bar{\psi}_\mu \partial\!\!\!/ \psi_\mu + e_0\bar{\psi}_e A\!\!\!/ \psi_e + e_0\bar{\psi}_\mu A\!\!\!/ \psi_\mu, \tag{7.6}$$

for the electron and muon fields ψ_e and ψ_μ, respectively, assuming that their bare masses are zero and that both fields interact in the same way with the electromagnetic field A. We then seek solutions to the renormalized Dyson equations (*49*), assuming that the renormalized Green's functions G_R and G_μ for the electron and muon fields, respectively, have poles at masses m_e and m_μ (to be determined). As it is only an example, we make the following approximations. First, we approximate the Feynman-Dyson vertex operators $\Gamma_\alpha(p, k)$ by the Dirac matrices γ_a, and the photon propagator $D(k^2)$ by $1/k^2$. Next, we neglect the contribution to G_R and G_μ from the spectral functions; that is, we take only the pole contribution. (This reduces what is really an integral equation problem to an algebraic one.) Finally, we consider only the contributions of the graphs of Fig. 14 to the self-energies, and for these we use a cutoff energy Λ. A standard self-energy calculation (remembering that the self mass is the total mass) then yields the equations

$$m_e = 2\left(\frac{3\alpha}{4\pi}\right) m_e \log\left(\frac{\Lambda}{m_e}\right) + \alpha^2 m_e F(m_e, m_\mu, \Lambda),$$

$$m_\mu = 2\left(\frac{3\alpha}{4\pi}\right) m_\mu \log\left(\frac{\Lambda}{m_\mu}\right) + \alpha^2 m_\mu F(m_\mu, m_e, \Lambda), \qquad (7.7)$$

where $\alpha = e_0^2/4\pi$ and F is the standard fourth-order self-energy integral coming from the graphs of Fig. 14b. (The fourth order is introduced because in second order the m_e and m_μ do not mix and hence the problem is rather trivial.) These equations are clearly symmetric in m_e and m_μ (and yield the perturbative solution $m_e = m_\mu = 0$). But they have nonsymmetric solutions also; for example,

$$m_e = 0,$$

$$m_\mu = 2\left(\frac{3\alpha}{4\pi}\right) \log\left(\frac{\Lambda}{m_\mu}\right) + \alpha^2 F(m_\mu, 0, \Lambda). \qquad (7.8)$$

To see that the second equation in (7.8) has, in general, nonzero solutions for m_μ, note that when Λ is such that the α^2 term is small compared to the α term, the solution is $m_e \simeq \Lambda e^{-2\pi/3\alpha}$.

Of course, this is a rather trivial example, but it illustrates the way in which symmetric equations may develop nonsymmetric solutions. The generalization of the idea is to suppose that the usual renormalized Dyson equations for the exact fermion and boson Green's functions $G(p)$ and $D(k)$ and the complete vertex operator $\Gamma(p, k)$ are sets of nonlinear equations for these quantities, and although the Lagrangian from which they are derived (and hence the equations themselves) may be invariant with respect to some symmetry, they may admit solutions that are not. This idea is developed in papers by Baker and Glashow (*50*, *51*) (from which the foregoing muon-electron example is taken) and applied specifically to $SU(3)$ by Cutkosky and Tarjanne (*52*) and by later workers.

It is clear that none of the three "explanations" of $SU(3)$ and isospin symmetry just presented is particularly convincing, though all of them serve to make the existence of these symmetries more plausible. The problem of the real origin of isospin, $SU(3)$, and $SU(3)$ breaking is, in fact, one of the outstanding problems in present-day elementary particle physics.

VIII. A Note on *SU(6)*

In this section one of the later developments of $SU(3)$ is discussed, namely, the theory of $SU(6)$, which combines $SU(3)$ and ordinary spin. Since the number of papers on $SU(6)$ is very large, they are not referred to individually here; for details the reader is referred to the review article of Pais (*53*), which contains what is probably the most extensive published list of references.

$SU(6)$ is defined as the group of all unitary unimodular matrices which act on the 6-dimensional space spanned by the wave functions $\psi_A(x)$, $A = (i, r)$ where $i = 1, 2, 3$ is an $SU(3)$ and $r = 1, 2$ a Pauli spin index. The wave functions $\psi_A(x)$ are called *quark* wave functions as they belong to the 3 of $SU(3)$. It should be emphasized that the transformation here is only on the indices A of the wave functions. The arguments x are left unchanged. This observation is of crucial importance for the question of relativistic generalization, discussed later. The procedure just described defines the group, although the observed physical particles are not assigned to the six-dimensional representation just mentioned, any more than they are assigned to the 3 of $SU(3)$. The motivation for the introduction of $SU(6)$ goes back to an $SU(4)$ group, introduced by Wigner in nuclear physics, which combines isospin and spin in the same way (though not with the same classification), and is an approximation in which the spin dependence of the nuclear forces is neglected.

From the point of view of the W-E theorem, we proceed in exactly the same way for $SU(6)$ as for $SU(3)$. First, we classify the particles. Second, we assign tensor properties to the mass, the electromagnetic current, and so on. Then we apply the W-E theorem and compare the results with experiment. The results go beyond $SU(3)$ in two respects. First, $SU(6)$ connects the properties of particles in different $SU(3)$ multiplets. Second, even within an $SU(3)$ multiplet $SU(6)$ supplements the $SU(3)$ predictions by determining the d/f ratios and the mixing angles, which are left undetermined by $SU(3)$. This will be shown in more detail later. As usual, we begin with the classification of the particles.

Classification. It will be remembered from Section IV that the established $SU(3)$ classifications are the baryons $\frac{1}{2}^+$ and $\frac{3}{2}^+$ to an 8 and 10, respectively, and the mesons 0^-, 1^-, and 2^+, each to an $8 \oplus 1$. The $SU(6)$ classification is to put the $\frac{1}{2}^+$ and $\frac{3}{2}^+$ baryons together in the 56-dimensional representation, and the 0^- and 1^- mesons together in the 35, which is the adjoint representation of $SU(6)$. [This leaves the 2^+ mesons unclassified. It is often supposed that they belong to the 189 or 405 of $SU(6)$, but it is not clear that they do as their partners in these multiplets are still missing. There have also been attempts to classify the tentative $\frac{3}{2}^-$ $SU(3)$ octet in the 70 of $SU(6)$.]

Some comments on this classification are in order. First, the assignments chosen can be seen to be very natural ones if we look at them from the point of view of the quarks $\psi_A(x)$ defined above, which, even if they do not exist physically, may be regarded as a convenient way of denoting tensor indices. From $SU(3)$ considerations it is natural to consider the baryons as bound states of three quarks, and the $6 \boxtimes 6 \boxtimes 6$ representation of $SU(6)$ decomposes correspondingly into $56 \oplus 70 \oplus 70 \oplus 20$, the 56 being the completely symmetric part and the 20 the completely antisymmetric part.

Similarly, it is natural to regard the mesons as bound states of quark-antiquark pairs and $6^* \boxtimes 6$ decomposes conveniently into $35 \oplus 1$. Note that when the 56 and 35 are further reduced with respect to $SU(3) \times SU(2)$, we obtain

$$\begin{aligned} 56 &= (8, 2) \oplus (10, 4), \\ 35 &= (9, 3) \oplus (8, 1), \end{aligned} \tag{8.1}$$

where the first figure in the parentheses denotes the $SU(3)$ representation (actually, $9 = 8 \oplus 1$) and the second spin representation (i.e., it is $2j+1$). Note that the foregoing classification implies that particles with different spins appear in the same UIR of $SU(6)$, but this is only to be expected since $SU(6)$ mixes up $SU(3)$ and ordinary spin in a nontrivial way. Note, however, that the particles in each $SU(6)$ multiplet have the same parity. This is because $SU(6)$ commutes with the parity operator. It is worth mentioning that on scaling down to isospin rather than $SU(3)$, the 56 of $SU(6)$ becomes the 20 of $SU(4)$. Wigner's original classification was in the 4 of $SU(4)$.

Note that in the 35, the 0^- mesons occur as a pure $SU(3)$ octet, while the vector mesons occur as an $8 \oplus 1$. This is inevitable, since the 1 that dissociates in $6^* \boxtimes 6 = 35 \oplus 1$ is a scalar with respect to $SU(6)$, hence, with respect to $SU(3) \times SU(2)$, and hence, with respect to $SU(2)$; that is, it has $J = 0$. In $SU(3)$ tensor notation† the 0^- mesons can be written as

$$P^i_j - \tfrac{1}{3}\delta_{ij} \sum_k P^k_k, \qquad i, j, k = 1, 2, 3, \tag{8.2}$$

and the 1^- mesons as

$$V^i_j\,; \tag{8.3}$$

† That is, P^i_j transforms like $\varphi_i^* \varphi_j$ where φ_j belongs to the 3 of $SU(3)$.

that is, the vector mesons are not traceless. Thus the 0^- $SU(3)$ scalar η_0 of Section IV is not included, while the 1^- $SU(3)$ scalar ω_0 is included and is

$$\omega_0 = \frac{1}{\sqrt{3}}(V_1^1 + V_2^2 + V_3^3). \tag{8.4}$$

The $SU(3)$ 1^- octet is then

$$V_j^i - \frac{1}{\sqrt{3}}\delta_{ij}\omega_0. \tag{8.5}$$

In particular, ω_8, which is an isospin scalar, is

$$\begin{aligned} \omega_8 &= \sqrt{\tfrac{3}{2}}\left(V_1^1 + V_2^2 - \frac{2}{\sqrt{3}}\omega_0\right); \\ &= \frac{1}{\sqrt{6}}(V_1^1 + V_2^2 - 2V_3^3). \end{aligned} \tag{8.6}$$

On the other hand, if we scale $SU(6)$ down to $SU(4)$ by including isospin instead of $SU(3)$ (i.e., by suppressing the index 3 throughout), then the large mass of the physical φ compared to the physical ω and ρ suggests that we include in the $SU(4)$ meson multiplet only ω; that is, that we make the identification

$$\begin{aligned} \omega &= \frac{1}{\sqrt{2}}(V_1^1 + V_2^2), \\ \varphi &= V_3^3, \end{aligned} \tag{8.7}$$

for the physical ω and φ. With this identification, we obtain from (8.6) and (8.4)

$$\begin{aligned} \omega &= \sqrt{\tfrac{2}{3}}\omega_0 + \sqrt{\tfrac{1}{3}}\omega_8, \\ \varphi &= \sqrt{\tfrac{1}{3}}\omega_0 - \sqrt{\tfrac{2}{3}}\omega_8, \end{aligned} \tag{8.8}$$

which yields a mixing angle,

$$\theta_1 = \cos^{-1}\sqrt{\tfrac{1}{3}} \simeq 70°,$$

in not too bad agreement with the angle $\theta_1 \simeq 60°$ obtained from the $SU(3)$ mass formula. Some further motivation for the identification (8.7) comes from the $SU(6)$ mass formula, which will now be discussed.

Mass Formula in $SU(6)$. As in $SU(3)$, the problem is to assign correct tensor properties to the mass operator. The simplest assumption would be to generalize the $SU(3)$ formula $M = M^0 + M^8$ to $M = M^0 + M^{35}$, since the 35 is the adjoint represent of $SU(6)$. However, since the $56 \boxtimes 56^*$ of $SU(6)$ contains the 35 only once, we would obtain in this way only two reduced matrix elements, $\langle 56\|0\|56\rangle$ and $\langle 56\|35\|56\rangle$, and hence only two parameters, to describe the 56 mass splitting. This is too stringent. An alternative scheme would be to use the spin independence of the mass and project out from the UIRs occurring in $R \boxtimes R^*$, where $R = 35$ or 56, the parts that transform like (1, 1) and (8, 1) with respect to $SU(3) \times SU(2)$. But this turns out to be too general. Something of a compromise between the foregoing proposals is achieved by assuming that the mass formula is additive with respect to $SU(3)$ and $SU(2)$. Specifically, for the 56 baryons, we assume that it is

$$M = \alpha + \beta Y + \gamma[I(I+1) - \tfrac{1}{4}Y^2] + f[J(J+1)], \tag{8.9}$$

where f is an unspecified function, and α, β, γ are constants *independent of J*. With f unspecified, the *mean* mass difference between the 8 and 10 in the 56, and between the 0^- and 1^- multiplets in the 35, are not predicted. However, f drops out for the mass *differences* within the $SU(3)$ multiplets. Hence (due to the independence of α, β, γ of J) the spacings within the respective pairs of $SU(3)$ multiplets can be related. For the 56, if we use as input the octet $(\Xi - \mathrm{N})$, $(\Xi - \Lambda)$, and $(\Xi - \Sigma)$ mass differences, we predict an equal spacing of approximately 130 MeV for the decuplet. This compares well with the experimentally observed spacing of 145 MeV.

To write down the mass formula for the mesons in the 35, it is convenient to write the 35 in tensor notation as

$$M^{i\alpha}_{j\beta} = \delta_{\alpha\beta}\left(P^i_j - \tfrac{1}{3}\delta_{ij}\sum_k P^k_k\right) + (\boldsymbol{\tau}_2\boldsymbol{\tau})_{\alpha\beta}V^i_j, \tag{8.10}$$

where α, β are spin indices, $\boldsymbol{\tau} = \boldsymbol{\tau}_1, \boldsymbol{\tau}_2, \boldsymbol{\tau}_3$ are the Pauli matrices, and P^i_j and V^i_j are the $SU(3)$ tensors of (8.2) and (8.3). Thus $M^{i\alpha}_{j\beta}$ transforms as the 35 of $SU(6)$. In terms of M, we assume that the mass formula is

$$M^2 = \alpha + \gamma M^{i3}_{jA} M^{jA}_{i3} + f[J(J+1)], \tag{8.11}$$

where α and γ are constants as before, and f is unspecified. The term linear in Y of (8.9) does not appear here due to charge conjugation. $M^{i3}_{jA}\, M^{jA}_{i3}$ is a scalar with respect to spin, and a mixture of a scalar and (33) component of an 8 with respect to $SU(3)$. For an irreducible $SU(3)$ representation $M^{i3}_{jA}\, M^{jA}_{i3}$ would be equivalent to $I(I+1) - \frac{1}{4}Y^2$, but for the vector mesons, which constitute an $SU(3)$ 8 + 1, it is not equivalent. In fact, $M^{i3}_{jA}\, M^{jA}_{i3}$ may be used to derive the mixing angle in (8.8). The point is that the mass as described in (8.11) is diagonal with respect to V^3_3 and $V^1_1 + V^2_2$. Hence these combinations should be regarded as the physical ω and ϕ.

Apart from determining the mixing angle, the formula (8.11) connects the 1^- and 0^- mass differences according to the formula

$$(\mathbf{K}^*)^2 - \boldsymbol{\rho}^2 = \mathbf{K}^2 - \boldsymbol{\pi}^2, \tag{8.12}$$

which can be obtained from (8.11) by inspection, and for the vector mesons alone it yields

$$\begin{aligned} \boldsymbol{\rho}^2 &= \boldsymbol{\omega}^2, \\ 2(\mathbf{K}^*)^2 &= \boldsymbol{\rho}^2 + \boldsymbol{\varphi}^2. \end{aligned} \tag{8.13}$$

The relations (8.13) can be derived by noting that ω and the three ρ's have only the indices 1, 2 with respect to $SU(3)$ and hence are all treated on the same footing by (8.11), while $\mathbf{K}^*$ is of the form $(V^3_1 + V^1_3)/\sqrt{2}$. Each of the relations (8.12) and (8.13) is in very good agreement with experiment ($\sim 2\%$ error).

It might be well to conclude the discussion of the mass formulas in $SU(6)$ by emphasizing that the formulas proposed in (8.9) and (8.11) are not by any means unique, but rather are plausible assumptions that are justified a posteriori by their success.

Following the $SU(3)$ pattern, the next processes to be discussed are the strong decay rates of the resonant particles and the production rates (four-particle processes). The decay rates furnish immediately one of the most serious difficulties of $SU(6)$, namely, in the strict $SU(6)$ limit the decays

$$\tfrac{3}{2}^+ \to \tfrac{1}{2}^+ + 0^- \qquad \text{and} \qquad 1^- \to 0^- + 0^-; \tag{8.14}$$

for example,

$$\mathbf{N}^* \to \mathbf{N}\boldsymbol{\pi} \qquad \text{and} \qquad \boldsymbol{\rho} \to 2\boldsymbol{\pi} \tag{8.15}$$

are forbidden. This can be seen at once by noting that $SU(6)$ conserves ordinary spin independently of orbital angular momentum and in terms of spin the processes (8.15) are $\frac{3}{2} \to \frac{1}{2}$ and $1 \to 0$, respectively. In other words, for these decays the role of orbital angular momentum is vital and orbital angular momentum effects are not taken into account by $SU(6)$. Experimentally, of course, the $\frac{3}{2}^+$ and 1^- decay practically 100% into $\frac{1}{2}^+ + 0^-$ and $0^- + 0^-$, respectively. For much the same reasons $SU(6)$ does not give good predictions for the production rates.

The decay and production rates for $SU(6)$ are not as bad as they look at first sight, however, because there is a modification of $SU(6)$, to be discussed later, which allows the processes (8.14) and yields some good production predictions in the forward direction.

The electromagnetic predictions of $SU(6)$ furnish one of its most striking successes. The charge operator, which is a generator of $SU(3)$ and a three-space $[SU(2)]$ scalar, is assumed to transform with respect to $SU(6)$ as an (8, 1) member of a 35. More interesting is the magnetic moment operator μ which, being a member of an $SU(3)$ 8 and a three-space vector, is assumed to transform like the (8, 3) member of a 35. Because

$$35 \boxtimes 56 = 56 \oplus 70 \oplus 300 \oplus 1134$$

contains the 56 only *once*, the application of the W-E theorem to $\langle 56|\mu|56\rangle$ yields immediately the following results.

(1) The magnetic moments of all the $\frac{1}{2}^+$ and $\frac{3}{2}^+$ baryons are determined in terms of one of them, $\mu(\mathrm{p})$ say, where p = proton. In particular, we obtain the following two predictions that are not given by $SU(3)$:

$$\mu(\mathrm{n}) = -\tfrac{2}{3}\mu(\mathrm{p}), \tag{8.16}$$

$$\mu(10) = q\mu(\mathrm{p}), \tag{8.17}$$

where n denotes neutron and 10 denotes any member of the 10 with charge q, for example, $\mu(\Omega^-) = -\mu(\mathrm{p})$.

The magnetic moments of the 10 are not yet measured, but the agreement of (8.16) with the experimental numbers is the striking success of $SU(6)$ just mentioned. Note that it is the total magnetic moment, not the anomalous part, that is assumed to transform like an (8, 3) member of a 35.

(2) The electromagnetic transition rates $\frac{3}{2}^+ \to \frac{1}{2}^+ + \gamma$ are related to $\mu(\mathrm{p})$. In particular,

$$N^{*+}|\mu|\mathrm{p}\rangle = \frac{2\sqrt{2}}{3}\mu(\mathrm{p}). \tag{8.18}$$

The experimental ratio is $\sim 1.3 \times 2\sqrt{2}/3$, which is not too bad agreement, especially considering that the left-hand and right-hand sides of (8.18) are evaluated at different values of the moment transfer, the left-hand side in particular being nowhere near the static limit. It should also be mentioned that the relativistic generalization $SU(6)$ to be discussed later predicts that there is no *electric or longitudinal* transition $\mathbf{N}^* \to \mathbf{N} + \gamma$ and, in fact, the magnetic transition dominates experimentally.

The electromagnetic mass-difference predictions of $SU(6)$ depend on the assumptions made. The most reasonable assumption is that they come from the second-order contributions of a spin-invariant electromagnetic interaction that transforms like an $SU(3)$ 35. With this assumption, we obtain the following two relations that are not given by $SU(3)$:

$$\begin{aligned} N_0^* - N_+^* &= \mathrm{n} - \mathrm{p}, \\ N_-^* - N_0^* &= \mathrm{n} - \mathrm{p} + (\Sigma^+ + \Sigma^- - 2\Sigma^0). \end{aligned} \tag{8.19}$$

These predictions cannot yet be compared with experiment.

For the weak current $\mathscr{J}_\mu^w(x)$ we proceed in much the same way as for the electromagnetic current, that is, we generalize from $SU(3)$. Specifically, we assume that $\mathscr{J}_\mu^w(x)$ belongs to the 35 of $SU(6)$. There is, however, one important change from the $SU(3)$ case, namely, it is possible to assume that the axial and vector parts of $\mathscr{J}_\mu^w(x)$ belong to the *same* 35. To see why this is possible, we note that in the nonrelativistic limit

$$\begin{aligned} \mathscr{J}_\mu^V(x) &= \bar{\psi}(x)\boldsymbol{\gamma}_\mu\boldsymbol{\lambda}_\alpha\psi(x) + \cdots \to \psi^\dagger(x)\mathbf{1}\boldsymbol{\lambda}_\alpha\psi(x) + \cdots, \\ \mathscr{J}_\mu^A(x) &= \bar{\psi}(x)\boldsymbol{\gamma}_\mu\boldsymbol{\gamma}_5\boldsymbol{\lambda}_\alpha\psi(x) + \cdots \to \psi^\dagger(x)\boldsymbol{\sigma}\boldsymbol{\lambda}_\alpha\psi(x) + \cdots, \end{aligned} \tag{8.20}$$

where $\psi(x)$ denotes the $\frac{1}{2}^+$ fields in the currents, $\cdots$ denotes the other fields, $\boldsymbol{\sigma}$ denotes the three Pauli matrices, and $\boldsymbol{\lambda}_\alpha$, $\alpha = 1 \cdots 9$, the $SU(3)$ generators and unit 3×3 matrix. Since $\boldsymbol{\lambda}_\alpha$ and $\boldsymbol{\sigma}\boldsymbol{\lambda}_\alpha$ are exactly the generators of $SU(6)$ (restricted to $\frac{1}{2}^+$ fields), we can see that $\mathscr{J}_\mu^V(x)$ and $\mathscr{J}_\mu^A(x)$ belong together with respect to $SU(6)$. The most important physical consequence of this is that for β-decay, with a Hamiltonian of the form $\int \mathscr{J}_\mu^w(x)\mathscr{J}_\mu^{\text{lepton}}(x)\,d^3x$, the ratio of the axial vector and vector coupling constants is determined. (There is only one reduced matrix element $\langle 56\|\mathscr{J}_\mu^w(x)\|56\rangle$.) The ratio turns out to be

$$G_A/G_V = 5/3. \tag{8.21}$$

This is not in very good agreement with the experimental value of approximately 1.18. However, it is quite surprising to obtain any prediction at all for G_A/G_V, not to mention finding the right sign and order of magnitude. Further, it should be pointed out that the discrepancy is now well understood in terms of the dynamic calculation of Adler and Weisberger (*62*), based on the current-algebra theory mentioned in the Introduction, and can also be understood in terms of representation mixing in $SU(6)$. These are later developments, however, which will not be discussed here. A second consequence of the 35 character of $\mathscr{J}_\mu^w(x)$ (one reduced matrix element $\langle 56\|\mathscr{J}_\mu^w(x)\|56\rangle$, is that the d/f ratio for all the $\frac{1}{2}^+$ leptonic decays becomes fixed. It turns out to be $\frac{3}{2}$, which compares well with the experimental value of 1.7 ± 0.35.

For nonleptonic decays both S-wave and P-wave (spin-flip) amplitudes must be taken into account. The role of $SU(6)$ in determining the P-wave amplitude, in which orbital angular momentum plays a role, is not clear. For the S-wave amplitude we obtain a little, but not much more, from $SU(6)$ than from $SU(3)$. Specifically, we find:

(a) The S-wave part of the experimentally well-verified (*54*) Lee-Sugawara triangle relation

$$\sqrt{3}(\Sigma_+|\mathrm{p}\pi_0)_S + (\Lambda|\mathrm{p}\pi_-)_S \doteq 2(\Xi_-|\Lambda\pi_-)_S \tag{8.22}$$

follows from 35 dominance in $SU(6)$. In $SU(3)$ we need to assume octet dominance plus a current × current interaction.

(b) The experimentally well-verified (*55*) relation

$$(\Sigma_+|\mathrm{n}\pi_+)_{S\text{-wave}} \simeq 0 \tag{8.22a}$$

follows from 35 dominance and current × current interaction in $SU(6)$. This relation does not follow from $SU(3)$.

This concludes the survey of strict $SU(6)$ theory. The agreement with experiment is reasonably good. However, the nature of the agreement (complete breakdown when orbital angular momentum becomes important) and the nature of the symmetry itself [coupling of only the spin part of the space-time dependence to $SU(3)$] make it clear that the agreement is only a manifestation of some deeper dynamic symmetry. The problem is to find the corresponding dynamics. It is possible, for example, that the analogy with Wigner's nuclear $SU(6)$ theory is closer than we might expect; that in some sense an elementary particle resembles a nucleus; and that for certain processes the spin-independent forces dominate.

A natural question that arises is whether $SU(6)$, which is clearly nonrelativistic, can be regarded as the nonrelativistic limit of some relativistic symmetry. The many difficulties encountered in attempts to construct such a symmetry would seem to indicate that this is probably not the case. It is possible, however, to go a little beyond the strictly nonrelativistic $SU(6)$ mentioned earlier. Two procedures for doing so can be mentioned.

The first is the use of the group $SU(6)_w$ instead of $SU(6)$; $SU(6)_w$ is defined as follows. The basic six-dimensional (quark) representation of $SU(6)$ has generators

$$\boldsymbol{\lambda}_\alpha \times \mathbf{1}, \qquad \boldsymbol{\lambda}_\alpha \times \boldsymbol{\sigma}, \tag{8.23}$$

where $\boldsymbol{\lambda}_\alpha$ are the nine Hermitian 3×3 matrices generating the three-dimensional UIR of $U(3)$, and $\boldsymbol{\sigma}$ are the Pauli matrices generating the two-dimensional UIR of $SU(2)$. If we now use Dirac spinors instead of Pauli spinors, and define

$$\boldsymbol{\tau} = (\boldsymbol{\gamma}_0\boldsymbol{\sigma}_1, \boldsymbol{\gamma}_0\boldsymbol{\sigma}_2, \boldsymbol{\sigma}_3), \tag{8.24}$$

where $\boldsymbol{\gamma}_0$ is the fourth Dirac matrix, $\boldsymbol{\sigma}_i = \epsilon_{ijk}\boldsymbol{\gamma}_j\boldsymbol{\gamma}_k$, $i = 1, 2, 3$, and $\boldsymbol{\gamma}_i$ are the first three Dirac matrices, then $SU(6)_w$ is the group isomorphic to $SU(6)$ whose basic six-dimensional representation is generated by

$$\boldsymbol{\lambda}_\alpha \times \mathbf{1}, \qquad \boldsymbol{\lambda}_\alpha \times \boldsymbol{\tau}. \tag{8.25}$$

Since $\boldsymbol{\gamma}_0^2 = \mathbf{1}$, the $\boldsymbol{\tau}$ generate a (W-spin) group $SU(2)_w$ isomorphic to $SU(2)$.

There are two main advantages to using $SU(6)_w$. First, we obtain invariance under Lorentz transformations *in the z direction.* This is because $\boldsymbol{\gamma}_0\boldsymbol{\sigma}_1$, $\boldsymbol{\gamma}_0\boldsymbol{\sigma}_2$, and $\boldsymbol{\sigma}_3$ (unlike $\boldsymbol{\sigma}_1$ and $\boldsymbol{\sigma}_2$) commute with the generator of these Lorentz transformations, namely, $\boldsymbol{\gamma}_0\boldsymbol{\gamma}_3$. Physically this means that we might expect $SU(6)_w$ to be valid for collinear processes, such as forward scattering or two-body decays. It turns out, in fact, that for forward scattering we can obtain two good $SU(6)_w$ results. The first is the famous Johnson-Treiman (J-T) relation (*56*)

$$\tfrac{1}{2}[\sigma(K^+) - \sigma(K^-)] = [\sigma(K^0) - \sigma(\bar{K}^0)] = [\sigma(\pi^+) - \sigma(\pi^-)] \tag{8.26}$$

for the forward scattering of mesons off protons. For these relations the K part is in good agreement with experiment and the π part is off by about 20%. (It should be remarked, however, that the J-T relation can be derived also in many other ways, e.g., from quark dynamic models.) The second good forward scattering result is the relation (*57*)

$$A_1/A_3 = \sqrt{10} \tag{8.27}$$

for the $T = \frac{1}{2}$ and $T = \frac{3}{2}$ (approximately energy-independent) scattering lengths for the reactions $\pi p \to \pi N^*$ in the S-wave N^* production region. The experimental value is $A_1/A_3 = 3.4 \pm 0.3$. [Note that in this case all the particles involved have strangeness zero, so the result really follows from $SU(4)_w$, i.e., the scaling down of $SU(6)_w$ that results when $SU(3)$ is scaled down to isospin.] There are other $SU(6)_w$ successes, many of them consisting in the removal of the ambiguity in $SU(6)$ when we are no longer in the static limit, as in the case of the $N^* \to N\gamma$ transition mentioned earlier, but it must be admitted that there are also many $SU(6)_w$ forward scattering predictions that have not been verified experimentally. The case against $SU(6)_w$ has been stated by Jackson (*58*).

The second advantage of $SU(6)_w$ is that it allows the $SU(6)$ forbidden reactions $\frac{3}{2}^+ \to \frac{1}{2}^+ + 0^-$ and $1^- \to 0^- + 0^-$ [which, as mentioned earlier, constitute the major objection to $SU(6)$] to proceed. The reason is as follows: For the quarks (in the rest frame) $\boldsymbol{\gamma}_0 = \mathbf{1}$, while for the antiquarks $\boldsymbol{\gamma}_0 = -\mathbf{1}$. Thus $SU(6)$ and $SU(6)_w$ coincide for the baryons (which are, at least formally, bound states of three quarks and no antiquarks). But for the mesons, which are bound states of quark–antiquark pairs, the $SU(6)$ and $SU(6)_w$ assignments are different. For example, the three polarization states ($\boldsymbol{\rho}_\uparrow$, $\boldsymbol{\rho}_0$, and $\boldsymbol{\rho}_\downarrow$) of the $\boldsymbol{\rho}$ and the single polarization state $\boldsymbol{\pi}$ of the pion form representations $J = 1$ and $J = 0$, respectively, of the spin group whereas the corresponding $W = 1$ and $W = 0$ states are ($\boldsymbol{\rho}_\uparrow$, $\boldsymbol{\pi}$, $\boldsymbol{\rho}_\downarrow$) and $\boldsymbol{\rho}_0$. Thus, $\boldsymbol{\rho}_0 \to 2\boldsymbol{\pi}$ is allowed by W-spin because the two W-spin 1 states $\boldsymbol{\pi}$ and $\boldsymbol{\pi}$ can combine to form the $W = 0$ $\boldsymbol{\rho}_0$ state. Similarly, $\mathbf{N}^* \to \mathbf{N}\boldsymbol{\pi}$ is allowed because the $W = \frac{1}{2}$ $\mathbf{N}$ and $W = 1$ $\boldsymbol{\pi}$ can combine to form the $W = \frac{3}{2}$ $\mathbf{N}^*$.

The drawback to $SU(6)_w$ is that it is not completely relativistic, but only "relativistic in the z direction." Note that, like $SU(6)$, $SU(6)_w$ operates only on the tensor indices A of the wave functions $\psi_A(x)$ but not on the arguments x.

The second procedure for making $SU(6)$ relativistic is in a sense a generalization of $SU(6)_w$. In this procedure we replace the W-spin generators $\boldsymbol{\gamma}_0\boldsymbol{\sigma}_1$, $\boldsymbol{\gamma}_0\boldsymbol{\sigma}_2$, and $\boldsymbol{\sigma}_3$ by the complete set of Dirac matrices, namely, $\mathbf{1}$, $\boldsymbol{\gamma}_\mu$, $\boldsymbol{\gamma}_\mu\boldsymbol{\gamma}_5$, $\boldsymbol{\gamma}_\mu\boldsymbol{\gamma}_\nu$, and $\boldsymbol{\gamma}_5$. These matrices generate the basic four-dimensional representation of the pseudounitary group $U(2, 2)$ (i.e., the group of all 4×4 matrices preserving the form $z_1 z_1^* + z_2 z_2^* - z_3 z_3^* - z_4 z_4^*$). This group, of course, contains the homogeneous Lorentz group, generated by $\boldsymbol{\gamma}_\mu\boldsymbol{\gamma}_\nu$ as a subgroup. One combines $U(2,2)$ with $SU(3)$ to form the pseudounitary group $U(6, 6)$ [also called $\tilde{U}(12)$, $U_{\mathscr{L}}(12)$, $M(12)$].

Once again, however, the group operates only on the tensor indices A of the wave functions $\psi_A(x)$, not on the arguments x. Indeed, it could not operate on the x's, since the x's span a four-dimensional (Minkowski) space and $U(6, 6)$ has no four-dimensional representation. This is the crux of the unitarity troubles of $U(6, 6)$, to be described later.

The $U(6, 6)$ quarks are twelve-component quarks, and we proceed to find the quark-antiquark and three-quark representations, as in the case of $SU(6)$. But here we encounter an obvious difficulty; namely, the number of states in each representation of $U(6, 6)$ is much too large to accommodate the corresponding particles [Note that even the basic twelve-dimensional representation has to accommodate the six physical states corresponding to each of the two spin states of each of the three $SU(3)$ quarks]. The most original idea in $U(6, 6)$ theory is the way in which this difficulty is overcome. This is by the use of the field equations and subsidiary conditions [Bargmann-Wigner (*59*) equations] for the various spin fields. To illustrate the idea, consider the simplest $U(6, 6)$ representation, namely, the twelve-dimensional quark representation. To connect the twelve states of this representation to the six physical states, we impose on them the Dirac equation in the rest frame. There we have

$$(\boldsymbol{\gamma}\cdot p - m)\psi^{(i)} = 0 \rightarrow (\boldsymbol{\gamma}_0 m - m)\psi^{(i)} = 0, \tag{8.28}$$

or

$$\begin{bmatrix} 0 & & & \\ & 0 & & \\ & & 2m & \\ & & & 2m \end{bmatrix} \begin{bmatrix} \psi_1^{(i)} \\ \psi_2^{(i)} \\ \psi_3^{(i)} \\ \psi_4^{(i)} \end{bmatrix} = 0, \tag{8.29}$$

[$i = 1, 2, 3$ is the $SU(3)$ index]. Then only six of the ψ's survive, as required. A similar, but less trivial, procedure is used for the higher $U(6, 6)$ representations. For example, the 143-dimensional adjoint representation of $U(6, 6)$ ($12^* \boxtimes 12 = 143 \oplus 1$) corresponds to the 35 of $SU(6)$ and hence to the 0^- and 1^- mesons. But a priori it contains also an antisymmetric second-rank tensor $T_{\mu\nu}$ and a pseudovector P_μ, with $SU(3)$ indices suppressed. The latter become linearly dependent on the 0^- (P) and 1^- (V_μ) when we impose the subsidiary conditions

$$\begin{aligned} T_{\mu\nu} &= \partial_\mu V_\nu - \partial_\nu V_\mu, \\ P_\mu &= \partial_\mu \varphi. \end{aligned} \tag{8.30}$$

Of course, the use of the field equations and subsidiary conditions to obtain relations among the base elements of the $U(6, 6)$ representations immediately breaks $U(6, 6)$ symmetry, since after imposing the conditions we are no longer free to make $U(6, 6)$ transformations. Thus $U(6, 6)$ is intrinsically broken. However, that does not prevent our making predictions based on it. The most striking is a prediction for the absolute value of the magnetic moment of the proton that is in very rough agreement with experiment (3.8 versus 2.8 nucleon magnetons). To illustrate very roughly how such a quantity can be predicted by $U(6, 6)$, consider as a model the case of quarks in $U(2, 2)$ [$U(6, 6)$ with the $SU(3)$ indices suppressed]. The quarks in the 4 of $U(2, 2)$ couple to the mesons in the fifteen-dimensional adjoint representation of $U(2, 2)$ [143 of $U(6, 6)$] by means of a vertex of the form

$$V = g\bar{u}\boldsymbol{\sigma}_A u V_A, \tag{8.31}$$

where the U's are the quark fields, the $\boldsymbol{\sigma}_A$ the fifteen Dirac matrices $\boldsymbol{\gamma}_\mu$, $\boldsymbol{\gamma}_\mu\boldsymbol{\gamma}_5$, $\boldsymbol{\gamma}_\mu\boldsymbol{\gamma}_\nu$, $\boldsymbol{\gamma}_5$, and the V_A the meson fields P, P_μ, V_μ, and $T_{\mu\nu}$ mentioned earlier. Thus, *using the subsidiary conditions* (8.30), we obtain

$$V = g\,[\bar{u}\boldsymbol{\gamma}_5 uP + \bar{u}\boldsymbol{\gamma}_\mu\boldsymbol{\gamma}_5 u\,\partial_\mu P + \bar{u}\boldsymbol{\gamma}_\mu u V_\mu + \bar{u}\boldsymbol{\gamma}_\mu\boldsymbol{\gamma}_\nu u(\partial_\mu V_\nu - \partial_\nu V_\mu)]. \tag{8.32}$$

If we now assume that the electromagnetic interaction of the quarks is dominated by the vector meson intermediate state (Fig. 11), then clearly the term $\bar{u}\gamma_\mu u V_\mu$ in (8.32) produces the electric, and the term $\bar{u}\gamma_\mu\gamma_\nu u(\partial_\mu V_\nu - \partial_\nu V_\mu)$ the magnetic form factor. But the ratio of the coupling constants of these two terms in (8.32) is fixed. Hence, the ratio of the magnetic moment to the charge is fixed.

Not many of the other vertex predictions of $U(6, 6)$ are in even rough agreement with experiment, and in the case of four-particle processes, $U(6, 6)$ runs into an even more serious difficulty than "mere" disagreement with experiment, namely, it violates the unitarity of the S-matrix. It is this difficulty above

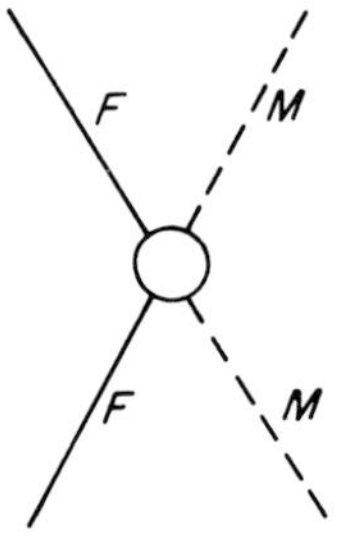

FIG. 15.

all that has led to the abandonment of $U(6, 6)$. To see how the violation of unitarity comes about, consider the fermion-meson scattering graph of Fig. 15 where the fermion is assumed for simplicity to be a $U(6, 6)$ quark and the meson (with field $\varphi(x)$) a $U(6, 6)$ scalar. The $U(6, 6)$-invariant T-matrix is then of the form

$$T_{fi} = f(s, t)\bar{u}_A(p)u^A(q)\varphi(k_1)\varphi(k_2), \tag{8.33}$$

where s and t are the usual invariant variables and $A = 1 \cdots 12$ is a $U(6, 6)$ index. It will be convenient to write A also as αj where $\alpha = 1, \ldots, 4$ is a Dirac spinor index and $j = 1 \cdots 3$ an $SU(3)$ index. The unitarity condition for T is the well-known relation

$$\operatorname{Im} T_{fi} = \sum_n T^*_{nf} T_{ni}\,\delta(E_i - E_n) \tag{8.34}$$

where the sum runs over all possible intermediate states. In the elastic scattering region only the meson-fermion states themselves contribute, and on inserting (8.33) into (8.34) we find that the term on the right-hand side yields a positive energy projection operator

$$\left(\frac{\gamma\cdot p+m}{2m}\right)_{\alpha\alpha'}\delta_{jj'}, \qquad (8.35)$$

sandwiched inside a bilinear term of the form $\bar{u}_A(p)\cdots u^A(q)$ which just matches the bilinear term on the left-hand side. But, under $U(6, 6)$, γ_μ transforms like a generator, while each of the p_μ is a scalar. Therefore the quantity (8.35) is not a $U(6, 6)$ scalar. Hence the unitarity relation (8.34) cannot be $U(6, 6)$ invariant. In the case of Lorentz invariance alone this difficulty is not present because γ_μ and p_μ transform in the same way and so compensate when contracted in the form $\gamma_\mu p_\mu$. No such compensation is possible for $U(6, 6)$ because p_μ has only four components and hence cannot transform contragrediently to γ_μ, which is part of a $U(6, 6)$ 143. [Even for $U(2, 2)$ γ_μ is part of a 15.]

Note that this difficulty with the transformation properties of the p_μ is just the momentum-space analogue of the point, emphasized earlier, that $U(6, 6)$ transforms the indices A but not the arguments x of the wave functions $\psi_A(x)$.

In conclusion it is worth pointing out that invariance under different subgroups of $U(6, 6)$ may be valid and lead to useful results even when $U(6, 6)$ invariance itself is completely violated. Indeed, both $SU(6)$ and $SU(6)_w$ are subgroups of $U(6, 6)$.

Acknowledgments

It is a pleasure to acknowledge my debt to Drs. R. Behrends, M. Goldberg, J. Leitner, H. J. Lipkin, S. Meshkov, N. Mukunda, S. Pakvasa, N. Papastamatiou, and E. C. G. Sudarshan for many invaluable discussions. I am extremely grateful also to Professor M. Peshkin for his kind hospitality at the Argonne National Laboratory, where much of the work for this article was carried out. Finally, I am most grateful to the United States Atomic Energy Commission for partial support.

REFERENCES

1. A. H. Rosenfeld *et al.*, *Rev. Mod. Phys.* **37**, 633 (1965).
2. C. Eckart, *Rev. Mod. Phys.* **2**, 302 (1930); E. P. Wigner, "Group Theory." Academic Press, New York, 1959.
3. L. I. Schiff, "Quantum Mechanics." McGraw-Hill, New York, 1955.
4. F. D. Murnaghan, "The Theory of Group Representations." Johns Hopkins Press, Baltimore, Maryland, 1938.
5. J. J. de Swart, *Rev. Mod. Phys.* **35**, 916 (1963); P. McNamee and F. Chilton, *Rev. Mod. Phys.* **36**, 1005 (1964).

5a. K. T. Hecht, *Nuclear Phys.* **62**, 1 (1965); J. G. Kuriyan, D. Lurie, and A. J. Macfarlane, *J. Mathematical Phys.* **6**, 722 (1965); T. A. Br dy, M. Moshinsky, and I. Renero, *J. Mathematical Phys.* **6**, 1540 (1964); G. E. Baird and L. C. Biedenharn, Duke Univ. preprint (1965); M. Resnikoff, *J. Mathematical Phys.* **8**, 63, 79 (1967); L. Banyai, N. Marinesen, I. Raszillier, and V. Rittenberg, *Phys. Lett.* **14**, 156 (1965); Hov Tei-yu, *Sci. Sinica* **14**, 367 (1965); M. Moshinsky, *Rev. Mod. Phys.* **34**, 813 (1962); *J. Mathematical Phys.* **4**, 1128 (1963); I. S. Gerstein and K. T. Mahanthappa, *Nuovo Cimento* **32**, 239 (1964); N. Mukunda and L. K. Pandit, *J. Mathematical Phys.* **6**, 1547 (1965).
6. C. L. Cook and G. Murtaza, *Nuovo Cimento* **39**, 532 (1965); J. C. Carter, J. J. Coyne, and S. Meshkov, *Phys. Rev. Lett.* **14**, 523 and 1850 (E) (1965).
7. L. S. Pontryagin, "Topological Groups," Chap. IX. Princeton Univ. Press, Princeton, New Jersey, 1958.
8. G. Racah, *Ergeb. exakt. Naturw.* **37**, 28 (1965).
9. N. Jacobson, "Lie Algebras," p. 261. Wiley (Interscience), New York, 1962.
10. M. Gell-Mann, *Phys. Rev.* **125**, 1067 (1962).
11. M. Gell-Mann and Y. Ne'eman, "The Eightfold Way." Benjamin, New York, 1964.
12. P. Carruthers, "Introduction to Unitary Symmetry." Wiley (Interscience), New York, 1966; M. Gourdin, "Unitary Symmetries." North-Holland, Publ., Amsterdam, 1967.
13. J. Leitner, *Proc. Boulder Conf. High Energy Phys., Boulder, 1966.* Gordon and Breach, New York, 1967.
14. J. J. Sakurai, *Phys. Rev. Lett.* **9**, 472 (1962).
15. S. Okubo, *Progr. Theoret. Phys.* **27**, 949 (1962).
16. S. Coleman and S. L. Glashow, *Phys. Rev. Lett.* **6**, 423 (1961).
17. N. Cabibbo, *Phys. Rev. Lett.* **10**, 531 (1963).
18. See, for example, T. D. Lee and C. S. Wu, *Ann. Rev. Nuclear Sci.* **15**, 381 (1965).
19. C. A. Levinson, H. J. Lipkin, and S. Meshkov, *Phys. Rev. Lett.* **10**, 361 (1963).
19a. See, for example, A. J. Macfarlane and E. C. G. Sudarshan, *Nuovo Cimento* **31**, 1176 (1964); S. P. Rosen, *Phys. Rev. Lett.* **11**, 100 (1963).
20. D. R. Speiser and J. Tarski, *J. Mathematical Phys.* **4**, 588 (1963).
21. P. Roman, "Theory of Elementary Particles." North-Holland Publ., Amsterdam, 1960.
22. M. Gell-Mann, *Phys. Rev.* **106**, 1297 (1957); J. Schwinger, *Ann. Physics* **2**, 407 (1957).
22a. A. Pais, *Phys. Rev.* **110**, 574, 1480 (1958); G. Feinberg and F. Gürsey, *ibid.* **114**, 1153 (1959).
23. E. P. Wigner, *Proc. Nat. Acad. Sci. U.S.A.* **38**, 449 (1952).
24. J. J. Sakurai, *Ann. Physics* **11**, 1 (1960).
25. D. Amati and B. Vitale, *Nuovo Cimento* **9**, 895 (1958); M. Ross, *Phys. Rev.* **112**, 986 (1958).
26. A. Salam, *Proc. Kiev Conf. High Energy Phys., Moscow, 1959.*
27. R. E. Behrends and A. Sirlin, *Phys. Rev.* **121**, 324 (1961); *Phys. Rev. Lett.* **5**, 476 (1960); **8**, 221 (1962).
28. R. E. Behrends, *Phys. Rev.* **142**, 1101 (1966).
29. R. E. Behrends and A. Sirlin, *Phys. Rev.* **142**, 1095 (1966).
30. S. Sakata, *Progr. Theoret. Phys.* **16**, 486 (1956).
31. C. A. Levinson, H. J. Lipkin, and S. Meshkov, *Nuovo Cimento* **23**, 236 (1962); *Phys. Lett.* **1**, 44 (1962); C. A. Levinson, H. J. Lipkin, S. Meshkov, A. Salam, and B. Munir, *Phys. Lett.* **1**, 125 (1962).
32. C. A. Levinson, H. J. Lipkin, and S. Meshkov, *Phys. Lett.* **1**, 307 (1962).
33. M. Gell-Mann, *Phys. Lett.* **8**, 214 (1964).
34. A. A. Sokolov, Y. M. Loskutov, and I. M. Ternov, "Quantum Mechanics," Chap. XII. Holt, Rinehart and Winston, New York, 1965.

35. W. Pauli, *Z. Physik* **36**, 336 (1926); V. Fock, *ibid.* **98**, 145 (1935); V. Bargmann, *ibid.* **99**, 576 (1936).
36. See, for example, A. O. Barut and A. Bohm, *Phys. Rev.* **139**, B1107 (1965); Y. Dothan and Y. Ne'eman, *Proc. Second Athens (Ohio) Conf. Resonant Particles, 1965.*
37. H. Bacry, *Nuovo Cimento* **41A**, 221 (1966).
38. R. Musto, *Phys. Rev.* **148**, B1274 (1966).
39. J. P. Elliott, *Proc. Roy. Soc. London Ser. A* **245**, 128 (1958); F. J. Dyson, "Symmetry Groups in Nuclear and Particle Physics." Benjamin, New York, 1966.
40. E. P. Wigner, *Phys. Rev.* **51**, 106 (1937).
41. R. E. Behrends, J. Dreitlein, C. Fronsdal, and B. W. Lee, *Rev. Mod. Phys.* **34**, 1 (1962).
42. See, for example, G. C. Wick, A. S. Wightman, and E. P. Wigner, *Phys. Rev.* **88**, 101 (1952).
43. A. Salam and J. C. Polkinghorne, *Nuovo Cimento* **2**, 685 (1955).
44. B. d'Espagnat and J. Prentki, *Nuclear Phys.* **6**, 596 (1958).
45. Y. Yamaguchi, *in* "Preludes in Theoretical Physics," p. 78. North-Holland Publ., Amsterdam, 1966.
46. D. E. Neville, University of California, Berkeley, preprint (1963); S. Okubo, J. Schechter, and Y. Ueda, *Ann. Physics* **32**, 424 (1965).
47. G. Feinberg, *Phys. Rev.* **125**, 728 (1959).
48. R. E. Cutkosky, *Phys. Rev.* **131**, 1888 (1963).
49. F. J. Dyson, *Phys. Rev.* **75**, 1736 (1949).
50. M. Baker and S. L. Glashow, *Phys. Rev.* **128**, 2462 (1962).
51. S. L. Glashow, *Phys. Rev.* **130**, 2132 (1963).
52. R. E. Cutkosky and P. Tarjanne, *Phys. Rev.* **132**, 1354 (1963).
53. A. Pais, *Rev. Mod. Phys.* **38**, 215 (1966).
54. N. Samios, Argonne Intern. Conf. on Weak Interactions, ANL-7130, 189 (1965).
55. See, for example, R. O. Bangerter *et al.*, *Phys. Rev. Lett.* **17**, 495 (1966).
56. K. Johnson and S. B. Treiman, *Phys. Rev. Lett.* **14**, 189 (1965).
57. M. Olsson, *Phys. Rev. Lett.* **15**, 710 (1965).
58. J. D. Jackson, *Phys. Rev. Lett.* **15**, 990 (1965).
59. V. Bargmann and E. P. Wigner, *Proc. Nat. Acad. Sci. U.S.A.* **34**, 211 (1946).

REFERENCES TO CURRENT ALGEBRA

60. Current algebra was first proposed by M. Gell-Mann, *Physics* **1**, 63 (1964) and (*10*) above.
61. It is now known that most $SU(6)$ results can be derived from current algebra. The first to point this out was B. W. Lee, *Phys. Rev. Lett.* **14**, 676 (1965).
62. The most celebrated calculation based on current algebra is that of the ratio G_A/G_V of the weak axial vector to vector coupling constants by S. Adler and W. Weisberger, *Phys. Rev. Lett.* **14**, 1047 and 1051 (1965), respectively.
63. For a review of the later developments of the current algebra theory and a comprehensive bibliography, see: S. Adler and R. Dashen, "Current Algebras." Benjamin, New York, 1968, and B. Renner, "Current Algebras and their Applications." Pergamon, Oxford, 1968.

*Broken SU(3) as a Particle Symmetry**

R. E. BEHRENDS

BELFER GRADUATE SCHOOL OF SCIENCE
YESHIVA UNIVERSITY, NEW YORK

I. Introduction

Yukawa predicted the existence of the π-meson in 1935, twelve years before it was experimentally discovered. For fourteen years after this experiment, dozens of new elementary particles were discovered whose existence had not been predicted. In 1961, however, Gell-Mann and Ne'eman (*1*) proposed a new theoretical model, based on the group $SU(3)$, which has made it possible

* Supported in part by the National Science Foundation.

to predict the existence of at least a few of the more recently discovered particles, the most notable being the Ω^-, discovered in 1964. In addition to enabling us to predict the existence of new particles, this new model has led to predictions of other properties of the particles. This review is intended to be a relatively self-contained summary of the model of "broken" $SU(3)$ as applied to elementary particles.

From the outset, let us establish what we mean by broken $SU(3)$. As we view the situation, $SU(3)$ is a simple direct generalization of isotopic spin and hence should be treated analogously. Isotopic spin (ι-spin) invariance is analogous to the invariance of a theory under rotations in ordinary space in that it implies that there is no preferred direction in an abstract three-dimensional Euclidean space called *isotopic spin space* or *charge space*. In this charge space, the elementary particles are represented as components of spinors, vectors, and so forth. Of course, we know that isotopic spin invariance holds only in the limit of neglecting the electromagnetic and weak interactions. Thus, since particle interactions stronger than electromagnetism are invariant under isotopic spin transformations, we expect that particle interactions that are stronger (called *strong* interactions) than a new interaction (*moderately strong*) should be invariant under $SU(3)$.

This new moderately strong interaction is not invariant under $SU(3)$, in analogy with the fact that electromagnetism is not invariant under the ι-spin transformations. We view this separation of interactions into $SU(3)$-invariant and $SU(3)$-noninvariant parts as physically significant (and not simply a mathematical device*), just as the separation into ι-spin-invariant and ι-spin-noninvariant parts is physically significant. That is, as we have isotopic spin multiplets of particles, we expect $SU(3)$ supermultiplets of particles.

Since one of the effects of electromagnetism in breaking the symmetry of isotopic spin is to give to particles that are members of the same multiplet different masses (due to self-energy effects, e.g., in the case of the neutron and proton), so we expect the $SU(3)$-symmetry-breaking interaction to give the particles in a supermultiplet different masses. Now, in electromagnetism, we are fortunate in knowing both the dynamical form of the interaction that breaks the ι-spin symmetry and its ι-spin tensor form (it transforms like a linear combination of an isotopic spin scalar and the third component of a vector). In the case of $SU(3)$, however, we do not yet know the dynamical form of the interaction. At most we know that the effective $SU(3)$-symmetry-breaking interaction transforms like one component of one $SU(3)$ tensor.

* By mathematical device, we mean: Given any interaction, by adding and subtracting the same quantity, we can separate this interaction into a part that is invariant under any group and the remainder, which is not invariant. This separation is not physically significant because the particles would not form multiplets of this group (i.e., would not form representations of the group).

As we shall see, however, even this much knowledge is sufficient to make many predictions for physical processes.

To summarize, then, broken $SU(3)$ means here a physically significant separation of all strong interactions into an $SU(3)$-symmetric strong interaction and an effective $SU(3)$-noninvariant moderately strong interaction that transforms in a very specific way under the $SU(3)$ transformations.

As for the apparatus upon which we shall make the mathematical manipulations prescribed by the algebra, we shall draw readily from the usual tools of elementary particle theory. It is, of course, understood that group-theoretical arguments are so general that many of these tools may be unnecessary. On the other hand, our purpose is not to see how little of elementary particle theory is needed in order to obtain all the possible predictions that can be compared with experiment, but rather to find the minimum extensions of the theory that are required. We shall, therefore, leave the question of the minimal assumptions to others to answer.

In order to derive simply the predictions of broken $SU(3)$, we shall, first, briefly motivate and discuss the perturbative approach of dealing with the symmetry-breaking interaction. Then, temporarily ignoring the symmetry-breaking interaction, we shall develop the tools of an $SU(3)$-symmetric theory: the generators of infinitesimal transformations, the finite transformations, the completely labeled state vectors, the properties of tensors, and the generalized Wigner operators (the matrix elements of which are the $SU(3)$ Clebsch-Gordan coefficients). We shall then use the perturbative approach to apply broken $SU(3)$ to the physical particles, relying heavily upon the properties of the Wigner and tensor operators in order to derive simply the many well-known predictions. Specifically, we shall consider the predictions for masses, form factors, decay widths, and weak interactions, introducing quantitative comparisons with present-day experimental results in order to illustrate the degree of agreement that is obtained (since many of the experimental numbers are still tentative at the time of this writing, these numerical comparisons only demonstrate the techniques to be used and the general agreement thus obtained).

II. Perturbative Approach

We describe the state of a physical system by a Heisenberg state vector $|\mathbf{a}\rangle$, characterizing the quantum numbers of the state by a. These physical state vectors, which are constant in time, are chosen to be orthonormal, $\langle\mathbf{b}|\mathbf{a}\rangle = \delta_{ab}$, and are assumed to be complete, $\sum_a |\mathbf{a}\rangle\langle\mathbf{a}| = 1$ (where δ_{ab} is suitably modified for the case of continuous rather than discrete quantum numbers).

We assume the theory to be invariant under proper orthochronous inhomogeneous Lorentz transformations (Poincaré group) and choose the state vectors to be eigenstates of the four-momentum operator $\mathbf{P}_\alpha$ (generators of translations) with eigenvalues p_α (we choose units such that $\hbar = c = 1$); that is, $\mathbf{P}_\alpha|\mathbf{a}, p\rangle = p_\alpha|\mathbf{a}, p\rangle$ (we shall often use the notation of specifying certain quantum numbers in the state vectors, e.g., p in this case, so that a thereby represents the remaining quantum numbers needed to completely specify the state). For $\alpha = 4$ we have $\mathbf{P}_4 = i\mathscr{H}$ where $\mathscr{H}$ is the total Hamiltonian and $p_4 = i\mathscr{E}$ where $\mathscr{E}$ is the total energy. We assume that there exists a unique state of lowest energy, chosen to equal zero, which is the physical vacuum $|\mathbf{0}\rangle$.

Any Heisenberg operator $\mathbf{A}$ that does not depend explicitly on the time satisfies

$$(\mathscr{H}, \mathbf{A}) = -i\frac{\partial \mathbf{A}}{\partial t}\cdot \tag{1}$$

The probability amplitude for a transition from an initial state $|\mathbf{a}\rangle$ to a different final state $|\mathbf{b}\rangle$ is given by the S-matrix element $\langle\mathbf{b}|\mathbf{S}|\mathbf{a}\rangle$ where $\mathbf{S}$ is unitary. It is often convenient to split the total Hamiltonian into two parts $\mathscr{H} = \mathscr{H}_0 + \mathscr{H}_\mathrm{I}$ and to develop $\mathbf{S}$ in a perturbation expansion in powers of $\mathscr{H}_\mathrm{I}$.

Let us now consider a simplified situation. We contemplate a world in which the total Hamiltonian is $\mathscr{H}_0$. Our Heisenberg state vectors for this model are denoted by $|\Psi_a\rangle$ and are assumed to be orthonormal and complete. Operators A not depending explicitly on the time will satisfy

$$(\mathscr{H}_0, A) = -i\frac{\partial A}{\partial t}\cdot \tag{2}$$

In other words, we have the complete formalism of before, except that now it applies to a model world in which $\mathscr{H}_0$ is the total Hamiltonian.

Since the model state vectors $|\Psi_a\rangle$ are complete, we can expand our physical state vectors $|\mathbf{a}\rangle$ in terms of them; that is,

$$|\mathbf{a}\rangle = V|\Psi_a\rangle = \sum_b V_{ba}|\Psi_b\rangle. \tag{3}$$

At time t_0, say, $\mathscr{H} = \mathscr{H}_0 + \mathscr{H}_\mathrm{I}(t_0)$ and we can determine V by use of the equations

$$\begin{aligned} \mathscr{H}|\mathbf{a}\rangle &= \mathscr{E}_a|\mathbf{a}\rangle, \\ \mathscr{H}_0|\Psi_a\rangle &= \mathscr{E}_{0a}|\Psi_a\rangle. \end{aligned} \tag{4}$$

In the Rayleigh-Schrödinger perturbation approach, V_{ba} is expressed as an expansion in powers of $\mathscr{H}_{\mathrm{I}}$ with coefficients that depend on the unperturbed energies $\mathscr{E}_{0c}$. We may then also express the operator V in terms of such an expansion in powers of $\mathscr{H}_{\mathrm{I}}$. The unitary transformation V simply brings $\mathscr{H} = \mathscr{H}_0 + \mathscr{H}_{\mathrm{I}}$ to a "diagonal" form, $\mathscr{H}^d = V^\dagger \mathscr{H} V$.

Here and in what follows we denote the physical Heisenberg operators and state vectors by boldface symbols and our "model world" operators and state vectors by lightface symbols.

Since in our model world we have neglected certain interactions, then, hopefully, we should find more symmetry than in the physical world. That is, there might exist linear unitary transformations W,

$$W|\Psi_a\rangle = |\Psi_a'\rangle = \sum_b w_{ba}|\Psi_b\rangle \tag{5}$$

such that the entire theory is left invariant.

A specific example of such a situation is provided by the well-known isotopic spin transformations. When the electromagnetic and weak interactions are neglected ($\mathscr{H}_{\mathrm{em}}$ and $\mathscr{H}_{\mathrm{W}}$) and certain mass differences are set equal to zero (e.g., the neutron-proton mass difference, $m_{\mathrm{n}} - m_{\mathrm{p}}$ and $m_{\pi^+} - m_{\pi^0}$) we are left with an $\mathscr{H}_0$ (for a pion-nucleon theory) that is invariant under a three-parameter set of continuous transformations among the neutrons and protons and, simultaneously, among the π^+, π^0, and π^-. If we denote the three generators of these isotopic rotations by I_1, I_2, and I_3, then the finite transformation can be written $W = \exp(i\epsilon_1 I_1 + i\epsilon_2 I_2 + i\epsilon_3 I_3)$ where the ϵ_k are three arbitrary real parameters (real since we choose the I_k to be Hermitian). These transformations form a group [see, e.g., Behrends *et al.* (*2*) and references therein] since the result of performing two successive transformations is a transformation of the set and the transformations possess a unique inverse. Moreover, they form a Lie group, since the three generators satisfy the commutation relations $(I_i, I_j) = i\epsilon_{ijk} I_k$.

We note that for the ι-spin group, W not only commutes with $\mathscr{H}_0$ but also with the momentum operator P_i (i.e., as it makes a transformation among neutrons and protons, W does not change the momentum of these states). Moreover, W commutes with the three space rotations (e.g., does not change the angular momentum), with baryon number B, charge conjugation $\mathscr{C}$, parity $\mathscr{P}$, and time reversal $\mathscr{T}$.

If now the physical neutron state vector, say, is expressed in terms of the model neutron state vector (i.e., $|\mathbf{n}\rangle = V|\Psi_n\rangle$), then V can be written in terms of a power series expansion in $\mathscr{H}_{\mathrm{I}} = \mathscr{H}_{\mathrm{em}} + \mathscr{H}_{\mathrm{W}}$. The physically observed neutron-proton mass difference can then be attributed to the self-energy effects arising from the isotopic spin symmetry-breaking interaction $\mathscr{H}_{\mathrm{I}}$.

If we specialize to infinitesimal isotopic spin transformations, we find, from Eq. (5)

$$I_k|\Psi_a\rangle = \sum_b (\iota_k)_{ba}|\Psi_b\rangle \tag{6}$$

where the $(\iota_k)_{ba}$ are constants independent of ϵ_k; that is,

$$\langle\Psi_b|I_k|\Psi_a\rangle = (\iota_k)_{ba}\,\delta^3(\mathbf{p}_a - \mathbf{p}_b). \tag{7}$$

At the time t_0, the time that we expand $|\mathbf{a}\rangle$ in terms of $|\Psi_a\rangle$, we have

$$\begin{aligned} \mathbf{I}_k(t_0) &= I_k \\ (\mathscr{H}, I_k) &= -i\left.\frac{\partial \mathbf{I}_k}{\partial t}\right|_{t=t_0} \end{aligned} \tag{8}$$

Since I_k does not commute with $\mathscr{H}_{\mathrm{I}}$, then $\mathbf{I}_k$ will have a time dependence, given by a unitary transformation on $\mathbf{I}_k(t_0)$. Since this transformation is unitary, $\mathbf{I}_k(t)$ will satisfy the same commutation relations as $\mathbf{I}_k(t_0) = I_k$ except that they must be *equal-time* commutation relations; that is,

$$(\mathbf{I}_i(t), \mathbf{I}_j(t)) = i\epsilon_{ijk}\,\mathbf{I}_k(t). \tag{9}$$

The matrix element of $\mathbf{I}_k$ taken between Heisenberg states could be written (*3*)

$$\langle\mathbf{b}|\mathbf{I}_k(t_0)|\mathbf{a}\rangle = (\iota_k)_{ba}\,F^k_{ba}(\mathbf{p}_a)\,\delta^3(\mathbf{p}_a - \mathbf{p}_b) \tag{10}$$

where in the limit of $V \to 1$, that is, the model world, $F^k_{ba}(\mathbf{p}_a) \to 1$. Thus the deviation of $F^k_{ba}(\mathbf{p}_a)$ from 1 is a measure of the breakdown of isotopic spin symmetry.

Let us now consider the possibility of generalizing these results on isotopic spin. We return to our unitary transformation W. We assume that the set of these transformations forms a compact Lie group that commutes with $\mathscr{H}_0$ and the three-momentum operator P_i, as well as with the three space rotations and B, $\mathscr{C}$, $\mathscr{P}$, and $\mathscr{T}$. These transformations will depend in an essential way on a number of parameters (such as the ϵ_1, ϵ_2, ϵ_3 seen earlier). Some or all of these parameters can be varied continuously in such a way as to connect the transformations to the identity transformation. We shall consider later the remaining finite transformations R, which cannot be connected to the identity (these are similar to the reflection through the origin in a three-dimensional Euclidean space that cannot be connected continuously to the identity rotation).

Consider only those transformations that can be connected to the identity. Since W is unitary, it can be written

$$W = \exp(i\epsilon^A L_A + i\epsilon^0 B) \tag{11}$$

where the ϵ^A $(A = 1, 2, \ldots, r)$ are r arbitrary complex parameters and $(\epsilon^A L_A)^\dagger = \epsilon^A L_A$. The L_A are r generators that satisfy the commutation relations

$$(L_A, L_B) = C_{AB}^D L_D \tag{12}$$

where the C_{AB}^D are the structure constants of a Lie group. We have explicitly separated out an Abelian subgroup of W (its generator commutes with all the other generators) that corresponds to the baryon gauge group, B being the generator of this gauge transformation (ϵ^0 is a real parameter); that is, B commutes with all the L_A,

$$(B, L_A) = 0. \tag{13}$$

(Actually, when we include leptons, we can also separate out of W two more Abelian subgroups, which correspond to muonic and electronic lepton numbers.)

Since, in our generalization, we want to retain the good approximation of isotopic spin invariance, three of the generators L_A will be proportional to I_1, I_2, and I_3 with the commutation relations of the three-dimensional rotation group. That is, the isotopic spin group will be a subgroup of our group of r transformations. And, of course, we will want to pick our states so that I_3 is "diagonal," that is, so that our states are eigenstates of I_3 with eigenvalue ι_3. Now the maximum number of generators L_A that can simultaneously be "diagonalized," and hence lead to additive quantum numbers like ι_3, is called the *rank* of the group. For the isotopic spin group, the rank is one.

From experiment, we know of another additive quantum number, which might be identified with another generator L_A: the electric charge Q. Through the Gell-Mann–Nishijima relation, Q and I_3 are related to what is called the *hypercharge* generator $Y = 2(Q - I_3)$, so that Y also gives rise to an additive quantum number. The advantage of using Y rather than Q is that Y commutes with I_1 and I_2, so that each member of an isotopic spin multiplet will have the same value of the hypercharge y, while these members will not, of course, have the same charge q.

Since from the present experimental situation we know of no other additive quantum numbers besides I_3 and Y that might be identified with a generator L_A, the most natural way to proceed is to examine the second-rank groups in terms of their applicability to the hadrons (strongly interacting particles).

The most obvious group, then, is composed of just the generators I_1, I_2, I_3, and Y. Since Y commutes with each I_k, this group decomposes into an Abelian subgroup (the hypercharge gauge group) and the isotopic spin group. In this case, we have introduced no new generators L_A and there exists no relationship between the generators I_k and Y. Of course, this group applies to the physical situation, since it introduces nothing more than what we already know.

In order to introduce something new, we must introduce some new generators L_A. One way is to introduce new generators that commute with each of the I_k but not with Y. This group is semisimple and would decompose into the isotopic spin group and an independent three-parameter group that has been called the *hypercharge rotation* group. Again there exists no relationship between the I_k and the other generators. Actually, the predictions of this group have been examined and appear to disagree with the experimental situation.

Finally, we might consider the simple Lie groups, those that do not decompose into invariant subgroups. For rank two, there are only three possibilities (*2*); in the notation of Cartan, these are $\mathscr{A}_2$, $\mathscr{B}_2$, and $\mathscr{G}_2$ (the subscript is the rank). The group $\mathscr{A}_2$ is the unitary unimodular group in three dimensions that has eight parameters and is often called $SU(3)$. The group $\mathscr{B}_2$ has ten parameters and is the rotation group in five dimensions. Finally, $\mathscr{G}_2$ has fourteen parameters and is one of the five so-called exceptional groups. The predictions of each of these groups have been compared with experiment and it appears at the present time that $SU(3)$ is the group that applies to the hadrons. For an excellent review of the physical reasons for rejecting all the second-rank Lie groups except $SU(3)$, the reader is referred to the article by O'Raifeartaigh, p. 469 in this volume.

III. Algebra of *SU*(3)

Let us now proceed with an analysis* [see, e.g., Racah (*4*)] of the algebra of $SU(3)$. The number of independent elements L_A of the algebra, the order r, is eight; that is, $SU(3)$ is an eight-parameter group. Since the rank of this group is two, there are two L_A that mutually commute, H_i $(i = 1, 2)$, and that can be taken to be Hermitian, $H_i^\dagger = H_i$,

$$(H_1, H_2) = 0. \tag{14}$$

The six other L_A can be chosen to satisfy

$$(H_i, E_\alpha) = r_i(\alpha)\, E_\alpha \qquad (\alpha = \pm 1, \pm 2, \pm 3) \tag{15}$$

* We follow the method and notation of Behrends *et al.* (*2*).

where $r_i(\alpha)$ is the ith component ($i = 1, 2$) of the root vector $\mathbf{r}(\alpha)$ in a two-dimensional *root* space. When $\mathbf{r}(\alpha)$ is a root, $\mathbf{r}(-\alpha) \equiv -\mathbf{r}(\alpha)$ is also a root and the corresponding operator is $E_{-\alpha}$, the Hermitian conjugate of E_α, that is, $E_\alpha^\dagger = E_{-\alpha}$.

It is possible to normalize the H_i such that the metric tensor g_{ij} in this root space is

$$g_{ij} = \sum_\alpha r_i(\alpha)\, r_j(\alpha) = \delta_{ij} \tag{16}$$

and hence there is no distinction between covariant and contravariant indices. It then follows that the remaining commutation relations can be written

$$\begin{aligned} (E_\alpha, E_{-\alpha}) &= r_i(\alpha)\, H_i \\ (E_\alpha, E_\beta) &= N_{\alpha\beta}\, E_\gamma \end{aligned} \tag{17}$$

where $N_{\alpha\beta}$ is zero if $\mathbf{r}(\alpha) + \mathbf{r}(\beta)$ is not a nonvanishing root and is $C_{\alpha\beta}^{\gamma}$ if $\mathbf{r}(\alpha) + \mathbf{r}(\beta)$ is equal to the nonvanishing root $\mathbf{r}(\gamma)$. It can be shown (*2*) that the $N_{\alpha\beta}$ have the following properties.

$$\begin{aligned} &N_{\alpha\beta} = -N_{\beta\alpha} = -N_{-\alpha,-\beta} = N_{\beta,-\gamma} = N_{-\gamma\alpha}, \\ &N_{\alpha\beta}\, N_{\alpha+\beta,\,\rho} + N_{\rho\alpha}\, N_{\alpha+\rho,\,\beta} + N_{\beta\rho}\, N_{\beta+\rho,\,\alpha} = 0. \end{aligned} \tag{18}$$

[The subscript $\alpha + \beta$ means the labeling of the root that is equal to $\mathbf{r}(\alpha) + \mathbf{r}(\beta)$.] Equations (14)–(18) now constitute what is called the standard form for the commutation relations.

For $SU(3)$, there are six nonvanishing root vectors, the angle between any two adjacent roots is 60°, and the length of each root vector is $1/\sqrt{3}$ by Eq. (16). It then can be shown that the magnitude of each $N_{\alpha\beta}$ is $|N_{\alpha\beta}| = 1/\sqrt{6}$. We make the following choice of signs, consistent with Eq. (18).

$$N_{13} = N_{3\,-2} = N_{-1\,2} = \frac{1}{\sqrt{6}}$$

and choose the root vectors as

$$\mathbf{r}(1) = \tfrac{1}{3}\sqrt{3}(1, 0), \qquad \mathbf{r}(2) = \tfrac{1}{6}\sqrt{3}(1, \sqrt{3}), \qquad \mathbf{r}(3) = \tfrac{1}{6}\sqrt{3}(-1, \sqrt{3}), \tag{19}$$

which is represented by the root diagram of Fig. 1. For convenience, we explicitly list these commutation relations for $SU(3)$:

$$(H_1, H_2) = 0,$$

$$(H_1, E_1) = \frac{1}{\sqrt{3}} E_1, \qquad (E_1, E_{-1}) = \frac{1}{\sqrt{3}} H_1, \qquad (H_2, E_1) = 0,$$

$$(H_1, E_2) = \frac{1}{2\sqrt{3}} E_2, \qquad (E_2, E_{-2}) = \frac{1}{2\sqrt{3}} (H_1 + \sqrt{3} H_2), \qquad (H_2, E_2) = \tfrac{1}{2} E_2,$$

$$(H_1, E_3) = -\frac{1}{2\sqrt{3}} E_3, \qquad (E_3, E_{-3}) = \frac{1}{2\sqrt{3}} (-H_1 + \sqrt{3} H_2), \qquad (H_2, E_3) = \tfrac{1}{2} E_3,$$

$$(E_1, E_3) = \frac{1}{\sqrt{6}} E_2, \qquad (E_2, E_{-3}) = \frac{1}{\sqrt{6}} E_1, \qquad (E_{-1}, E_2) = \frac{1}{\sqrt{6}} E_3,$$

$$E_\alpha^\dagger = E_{-\alpha}, \qquad H_i^\dagger = H_i. \tag{20}$$

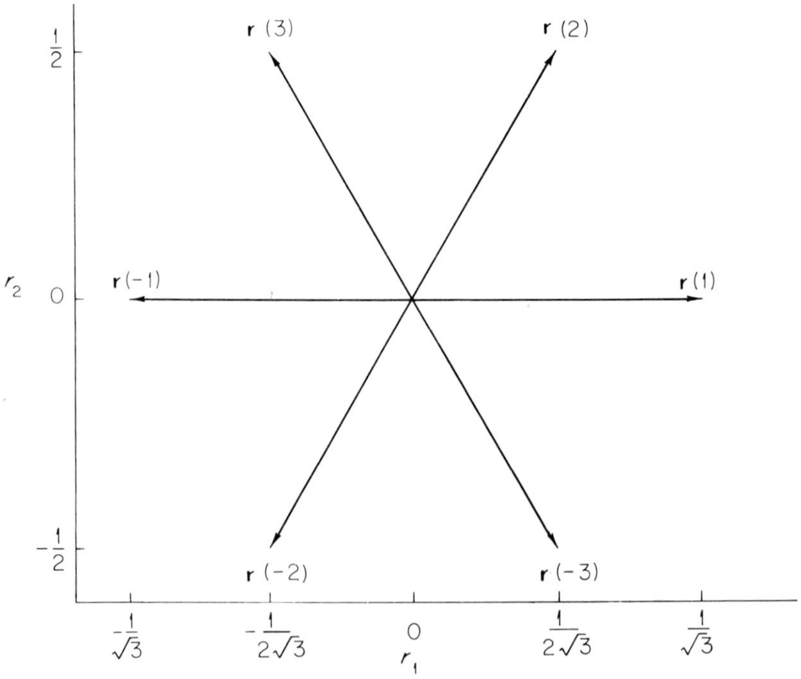

FIG. 1. Root diagram for $SU(3)$.

It might be instructive at this point to make some physical identification. Note that if we identified $I_+ \equiv \sqrt{6}E_1$, $I_- \equiv \sqrt{6}E_{-1}$, $I_3 \equiv \sqrt{3}H_1$, $Y \equiv 2H_2$, the commutation relations on the first two lines would read

$$(I_3, I_+) = I_+, \qquad (I_+, I_-) = 2I_3, \qquad (I_3, Y) = 0, \qquad (I_+, Y) = 0, \qquad I_+^\dagger = I_-, \tag{21}$$

which are the commutation relations for isotopic spin and, if we identify Y with the hypercharge, the commutation of hypercharge with ι-spin. With this identification, $SU(3)$ has the isotopic spin rotation group [an $SU(2)$] as a subgroup.

Now recall that for the ι-spin group we often write the commutation relations not in the standard form, but in terms of the Hermitian operators I_1, I_2, and I_3 where

$$I_1 = \tfrac{1}{2}(I_+ + I_-), \qquad I_2 = \frac{1}{2i}(I_+ - I_-)$$

[for $SU(3)$, this corresponds to writing the commutation relations in terms of the Hermitian L_A]. Now we know that a finite rotation around, say, the second axis in ι-spin space will be generated by the operator

$$S(\theta) = e^{i\theta I_2} = 1 + i\theta I_2 - \tfrac{1}{2}\theta^2 I_2^2 + \cdots.$$

Under such a transformation, the I_k ($k = 1, 2, 3$) will transform according to $I_k' = SI_kS^\dagger$. But since S is unitary, such a transformation will leave the ι-spin commutation relations unchanged in form. A specific rotation, that through 180°, is often very useful. It is called the *charge symmetry operation* in physics and a *Weyl reflection* in mathematics. Specifically, for ι-spin

$$\begin{aligned} I_\pm' &= e^{i\pi I_2} I_\pm e^{-i\pi I_2} = -I_\mp, \\ I_3' &= -I_3. \end{aligned} \tag{22}$$

Let us now translate the isotopic spin notation back to the $SU(3)$ notation. Let $S_1 \equiv \exp(i\pi I_2) = \exp[(\tfrac{3}{2})^{1/2}\pi(E_1 - E_{-1})]$; then

$$\begin{aligned} E_{\pm 1}' &= S_1 E_{\pm 1} S_1^\dagger = -E_{\mp 1}, \\ H_1' &= S_1 H_1 S_1^\dagger = -H_1. \end{aligned} \tag{23}$$

But what does this operation do to the other operators of $SU(3)$? Clearly, since H_2 commutes with $E_{\pm 1}$, we have

$$H_2' = H_2. \tag{24}$$

Moreover, for an arbitrary angle θ, we have, by use of the commutation relations,

$$\begin{aligned} E_2' &= \exp\left[(\tfrac{3}{2})^{1/2}\,\theta(E_1 - E_{-1})\right] E_2 \exp\left[-(\tfrac{3}{2})^{1/2}\,\theta(E_1 - E_{-1})\right] \\ &= E_2 + (\tfrac{3}{2})^{1/2}\,\theta(E_1 - E_{-1}, E_2) + \tfrac{1}{2}[(\tfrac{3}{2})^{1/2}\,\theta]^2 (E_1 - E_{-1}, (E_1 - E_{-1}, E_2)) + \cdots \\ &= E_2 - \tfrac{1}{2}\theta E_3 - \tfrac{1}{2}(\tfrac{1}{2}\theta)^2 E_2 + \frac{1}{3!}(\tfrac{1}{2}\theta)^3 E_3 + \cdots \\ &= E_2 \cos\tfrac{1}{2}\theta - E_3 \sin\tfrac{1}{2}\theta, \end{aligned} \tag{25}$$

so that specifically for $\theta = \pi$, that is, for S_1,

$$E_2' = -E_3. \tag{26}$$

Similarly, we find

$$E_3' = E_2. \tag{27}$$

We have thus explicitly shown a Weyl reflection, which in terms of the root diagram is a reflection through a line perpendicular to root $\mathbf{r}(1)$, and which leaves the commutation relations of $SU(3)$ invariant in form. In terms of physics, this reflection is still the charge symmetry transformation, but now it is part of the whole group $SU(3)$.

Another Weyl reflection that will be useful is that perpendicular to the root $\mathbf{r}(3)$. In order to find an explicit form for this reflection, note that if we define $U_+ \equiv \sqrt{6}E_3$, $U_- \equiv \sqrt{6}E_{-3}, U_3 = \frac{1}{2}\sqrt{3}(-H_1 + \sqrt{3}H_2)$, $Q \equiv \sqrt{3}H_1 + H_2$, then the $SU(3)$ commutation relations on the first and fourth lines of Eq. (20) become

$$\begin{aligned} &(U_+, U_-) = 2U_3, \qquad (U_3, U_+) = U_+, \qquad (Q, U_3) = 0, \\ &(Q, U_+) = 0, \qquad U_+^\dagger = U_-. \end{aligned} \tag{28}$$

These are formally like the ι-spin relations of before. We thus have another $SU(2)$ subgroup of $SU(3)$, which has been dubbed U-spin (5). It is now an easy matter to construct $S_{-3} = \exp(-i\pi U_2) = \exp[(\frac{3}{2})^{1/2}\pi(E_{-3} - E_3)]$ and find how the operators transform under this unitary transformation. Again, for example, consider a rotation through θ

$$
\begin{aligned}
E_1' &= \exp[(\tfrac{3}{2})^{1/2}\theta(E_{-3}-E_3)]\,E_1\exp[-(\tfrac{3}{2})^{1/2}\theta(E_{-3}-E_3)] \\
&= E_1\cos\tfrac{1}{2}\theta + E_2\sin\tfrac{1}{2}\theta
\end{aligned}
\tag{29}
$$

obtained by means of the commutation relations just as in Eq. (25). For $\theta=\pi$, that is, for S_{-3}, we have

$$E_1' = E_2. \tag{30}$$

Similarly, we find

$$
\begin{aligned}
H_1' &= \tfrac{1}{2}H_1 + \tfrac{1}{2}\sqrt{3}H_2, \qquad & E_2' &= -E_1, \\
H_2' &= \tfrac{1}{2}\sqrt{3}H_1 - \tfrac{1}{2}H_2, \qquad & E_3' &= -E_{-3}.
\end{aligned}
\tag{31}
$$

We thus have explicitly constructed two Weyl reflections. From these, we may then form all the Weyl reflections. For example, defining the Weyl reflection perpendicular to $\mathbf{r}(\alpha)$ as $S_\alpha = \exp[(\frac{3}{2})^{1/2}\pi(E_\alpha - E_{-\alpha})]\,[S_\alpha^\dagger = S_{-\alpha}]$, we see

$$
\begin{aligned}
S_1S_{-3}S_1^\dagger &= S_1\exp[(\tfrac{3}{2})^{1/2}\pi(E_{-3}-E_3)]\,S_1^\dagger = \exp[(\tfrac{3}{2})^{1/2}\pi S_1(E_{-3}-E_3)\,S_1^\dagger] \\
&= \exp[(\tfrac{3}{2})^{1/2}\pi(E_{-2}-E_2)] = S_{-2}
\end{aligned}
\tag{32}
$$

since S_1 is unitary and by Eq. (27). In Table I we have listed the action of S_α on each generator.

In a plane, the product of two reflections through a line is a rotation. Thus, S_1S_{-3} generates a counterclockwise rotation through $\frac{2}{3}\pi$ and $S_{-3}S_1$ generates a rotation through $-\frac{2}{3}\pi$. As we can easily check, S_1^4, S_{-3}^4, $(S_1S_{-3})^3$, $(S_{-3}S_1)^3$, $(S_1S_{-3}^2)^2$ commute with all the generators, and hence, by Schur's lemma, must be multiples of the identity operator. In terms of the root diagram, the operations 1, S_1, S_{-3}, S_1S_{-3}, $(S_1S_{-3})^2$, and $S_1S_3S_{-1}$ transform any root vector into the set of all root vectors. The group generated by these reflections and products of reflections is of order 6 and we shall denote this group by S.

In the same manner, we may derive straightforwardly a general relation that will be useful later

$$H_i' \equiv S_\alpha H_i S_\alpha^\dagger = \left(\delta_{ij} - \frac{2r_i(\alpha)\,r_j(\alpha)}{|\mathbf{r}(\alpha)|^2}\right)H_j. \tag{33}$$

Let us also note that

$$e^{i\theta_2H_2}E_\alpha e^{-i\theta_2H_2} = E_\alpha e^{i\theta_2 r_2(\alpha)}, \tag{34}$$

which for $\theta_2 = 4\pi$ commutes with all the generators and hence must be a multiple of the unit operator, that is, an invariant discrete subgroup. We may

TABLE I

ACTION OF WEYL REFLECTIONS ON GENERATORS

Generator	S_1	$S_1^+ = S_{-1}$	S_2	S_{-2}	S_3	S_{-3}
$E_{\pm 1}$	$-E_{\mp 1}$	$-E_{\mp 1}$	$-E_{\mp 3}$	$E_{\mp 3}$	$-E_{\pm 2}$	$E_{\pm 2}$
$E_{\pm 2}$	$-E_{\pm 3}$	$E_{\pm 3}$	$-E_{\mp 2}$	$-E_{\mp 2}$	$E_{\pm 1}$	$-E_{\pm 1}$
$E_{\pm 3}$	$E_{\pm 2}$	$-E_{\pm 2}$	$E_{\mp 1}$	$-E_{\mp 1}$	$-E_{\mp 3}$	$-E_{\mp 3}$
H_1	$-H_1$	$-H_1$	$\frac{1}{2}(H_1 - \sqrt{3}H_2)$	$\frac{1}{2}(H_1 - \sqrt{3}H_2)$	$\frac{1}{2}(H_1 + \sqrt{3}H_2)$	$\frac{1}{2}(H_1 + \sqrt{3}H_2)$
H_2	H_2	H_2	$-\frac{1}{2}(\sqrt{3}H_1 + H_2)$	$-\frac{1}{2}(\sqrt{3}H_1 + H_2)$	$\frac{1}{2}(\sqrt{3}H_1 - H_2)$	$\frac{1}{2}(\sqrt{3}H_1 - H_2)$

make a similar statement for $\theta_1 = 4\sqrt{3}\pi$ for the transformation

$$e^{i\theta_1 H_1} E_\alpha e^{-i\theta_1 H_1} = E_\alpha e^{i\theta_1 r_1(\alpha)}. \tag{35}$$

Now for every semisimple group there exists a set of ℓ independent polynomial functions of the operators, each of which commutes with every operator of the group, the so-called invariants, or Casimir operators, of the group (*4*). Moreover, the product of the degrees of these polynomials equals the order of the group of Weyl reflections. For $SU(3)$, this implies the existence of two Casimir operators, G_2 and G_3, of degrees two and three, respectively (*6*). The simplest of these, G_2, is the analog of the invariant $I^2 = \frac{1}{2}(I_+ I_- + I_- I_+) + I_3^2$ of the isotopic spin rotation group and hence can immediately be written down

$$G_2 = H_1^2 + H_2^2 + \sum_\alpha E_\alpha E_{-\alpha}. \tag{36}$$

The Casimir invariant G_3 is almost as simple to determine. Because $(H_i, G_3) = 0$, it is at most a completely symmetric arbitrary linear combination of terms $H_i H_j H_k$, $H_i E_\alpha E_{-\alpha}$, $E_1 E_3 E_{-2}$, and $E_{-1} E_2 E_{-3}$. Since G_3 must commute with the operators, it must also commute with the Weyl reflections $(G_3, S_\alpha) = 0$, which conditions easily determine the linear combination up to two arbitrary constants. Finally, the condition $(E_1, G_3) = 0$, for example, fixes G_3 completely. The result is

$$\begin{aligned} G_3 = \{&-\tfrac{1}{3}H_2^3 + H_2(H_1^2 + 2E_1 E_{-1} - E_2 E_{-2} - E_3 E_{-3}) \\ &+\sqrt{3}H_1(E_2 E_{-2} - E_3 E_{-3}) + \sqrt{6}(E_1 E_3 E_{-2} + E_{-1} E_2 E_{-3})\}_S \end{aligned} \tag{37}$$

where $\{\}_S$ signifies a completely symmetrized combination of the operators. The symmetrized form can, by the commutation relations, be reordered into the form

$$\begin{aligned} G_3 = &\tfrac{1}{6}H_2^3 + \tfrac{1}{2}H_2[3H_1^2 + 3(E_1, E_{-1})_+ - G_2] - \tfrac{1}{6}(\sqrt{3}H_1 + H_2) \\ &+\tfrac{1}{2}\sqrt{3}H_1[(E_2, E_{-2})_+ - (E_3, E_{-3})_+] + \sqrt{6}(E_2 E_{-3} E_{-1} + E_{-2} E_3 E_1). \end{aligned} \tag{38}$$

For later purposes, it is convenient to reorder both G_2 and G_3 such that the operators E_1, E_2, and E_{-3} are brought to the right. The result is

$$G_2 = H_1^2 + H_2^2 + \tfrac{2}{3}\sqrt{3}H_1 + 2 \sum_{\alpha=1,2,-3} E_{-\alpha} E_\alpha$$

$$\begin{aligned} G_3 = &\tfrac{1}{3}H_2(1 + H_2 + \sqrt{3}H_1)(1 - H_2 + \sqrt{3}H_1) + (1 - H_2 + \sqrt{3}H_1) E_{-2} E_2 \\ &+(1 + 2H_2) E_{-1} E_1 - (1 + H_2 + \sqrt{3}H_1) E_3 E_{-3} \\ &+\sqrt{6}(E_{-1} E_{-3} E_2 + E_{-2} E_3 E_1). \end{aligned} \tag{39}$$

An automorphism is a one-to-one mapping of a group into itself (*6, 7*). An example of an automorphism is provided by the transformation by Weyl reflection that we have explicitly exhibited: $L'_A = S_\alpha L_A S_\alpha^{-1}$. Since S_α is a transformation of the group, this automorphism is called an *inner* automorphism. A transformation $L'_A = RL_A R^{-1}$ where R is not a transformation of the group produces an *outer* automorphism. An example of an outer automorphism for $SU(3)$ is the transformation that takes the two commuting generators H_1 and H_2 into their negatives; that is,

$$H_i' = RH_i R^{-1} = -H_i. \tag{40}$$

Since R is a similarity transformation, it leaves the commutation relations invariant. From $(H_i, E_\alpha) = r_i(\alpha) E_\alpha$, we see that

$$E_\alpha' = RE_\alpha R^{-1} = \eta_\alpha E_{-\alpha}$$

where $\eta_\alpha = \eta_{-\alpha}$ is either ± 1 for each α. In addition, from $(E_\alpha, E_\beta) = N_{\alpha\beta} E_\gamma$ we find $\eta_1 \eta_2 = -\eta_3$, that is, of the three arbitrary η_α, an odd number must be negative. But from the transformations (34) and (35), we can transform any two of the generators E_1, E_2, and E_3 into the negatives of themselves. Thus, the most general form of this outer automorphism can be taken such that $\eta_1 = \eta_2 = \eta_3 = -1$, that is,

$$E_\alpha' = RE_\alpha R^{-1} = -E_{-\alpha}. \tag{41}$$

From Eqs. (36) and (38) we see easily that

$$\begin{aligned} G_2' &= RG_2 R^{-1} = G_2, \\ G_3' &= RG_3 R^{-1} = -G_3. \end{aligned} \tag{42}$$

Clearly, since R does not commute with G_3, which is an invariant of the group, R cannot be one of the transformations of $SU(3)$; that is, R provides a mapping that is an outer automorphism.

Let us turn for a moment to the operation of charge conjugation. We define charge conjugation, $\mathscr{C}$, as the operation that takes each particle into a particle with the opposite charges but with the same momentum, spin, mass, and at the same space-time point x_μ. Thus, $\mathscr{C}$ is a unitary transformation that transforms the H_i to $-H_i$; that is,

$$\mathscr{C} H_i \mathscr{C}^\dagger = -H_i. \tag{43a}$$

From the foregoing discussion about R, we again see that the most general way that $\mathscr{C}$ transforms the E_α can be chosen such that

$$\mathscr{C} E_\alpha \mathscr{C}^\dagger = -E_{-\alpha} \tag{43b}$$

and that $\mathscr{C}$ anticommutes with G_3 and thus is an outer automorphism of $SU(3)$.

But what is the difference between these two outer automorphisms R and $\mathscr{C}$? From the definition of $\mathscr{C}$ the latter also reverses the baryon charge, that is,

$$\mathscr{C} B \mathscr{C}^\dagger = -B. \tag{44}$$

Thus, another outer automorphism can be chosen such that it commutes with the baryon number operator:

$$RBR^\dagger = B. \tag{45}$$

As we shall discuss later, although $\mathscr{C}$ commutes with the $SU(3)$-symmetric Hamiltonian $\mathscr{H}_0$, R will be found not to commute; that is, the $SU(3)$-symmetric theory is not R invariant.

IV. Representations

A. Weights and Labeling of Bases

It is now appropriate to discuss the bases for the algebra, that is, the state vectors $|\Psi_a\rangle$, and the action that the operators have on these bases. Since only two of the operators L_A (namely, H_1 and H_2) commute for $SU(3)$, the state vectors can be chosen such that they are simultaneous eigenstates of these two operators with eigenvalues m_1 and m_2; that is,

$$H_i |\Psi_{a,\mathbf{m}}\rangle = m_i |\Psi_{a,\mathbf{m}}\rangle. \tag{46}$$

The two-component vector $\mathbf{m} = (m_1, m_2)$ is called the *weight* and the two-dimensional vector space spanned by the set of weights is the *weight space*. (Of course, physically, m_1 and m_2 are simply the eigenvalues of $I_3/\sqrt{3}$ and $\frac{1}{2}Y$, namely, $\iota_3/\sqrt{3}$ and $\frac{1}{2}y$.) Bases with different weights are linearly independent. If a weight belongs to only one basis $|\Psi_{a,\mathbf{m}}\rangle$, it is called *simple* (or its multiplicity is one).

Let us multiply this equation by E_α; we obtain

$$E_\alpha H_i |\Psi_{a,\mathbf{m}}\rangle = [H_i E_\alpha - r_i(\alpha) E_\alpha] |\Psi_{a,\mathbf{m}}\rangle = m_i E_\alpha |\Psi_{a,\mathbf{m}}\rangle.$$

Or

$$H_i E_\alpha |\Psi_{a,\mathbf{m}}\rangle = [m_i + r_i(\alpha)]\, E_\alpha |\Psi_{a,\mathbf{m}}\rangle.$$

Thus $E_\alpha|\Psi_{a,\mathbf{m}}\rangle$ is either zero or it is proportional to a linear combination of bases having the weight $\mathbf{m} + \mathbf{r}(\alpha)$. That is,

$$E_\alpha|\Psi_{a,\mathbf{m}}\rangle = \sum_{a'} A_{\alpha a' a}|\Psi_{a',\mathbf{m}+\mathbf{r}(\alpha)}\rangle \tag{47}$$

where the $A_{\alpha a' a}$ are either zero or constants that we shall determine later.

By starting from one basis $|\Psi_{a,\mathbf{m}}\rangle$, we can construct a finite set of N related bases by repeated applications of the operators E_α, E_β, ..., etc. These N bases then constitute the basis for an N-dimensional representation of operators H_i and E_α. If we can find a similarity transformation that separates the bases into two or more sets of bases where members of one set cannot be obtained from members of another set by repeated use of the E_α, then the representation is said to be reducible. When this separation is not possible by a similarity transformation, the representation is said to be irreducible.

Let us make a Weyl reflection S_α

$$S_\alpha H_i S_\alpha^\dagger S_\alpha|\Psi_{a,\mathbf{m}}\rangle = m_i S_\alpha|\Psi_{a,\mathbf{m}}\rangle.$$

By using Eq. (33)

$$\left(\delta_{ij} - \frac{2r_i(\alpha)\,r_j(\alpha)}{|\mathbf{r}(\alpha)|^2}\right) H_j S_\alpha|\Psi_{a,\mathbf{m}}\rangle = m_i S_\alpha|\Psi_{a,\mathbf{m}}\rangle$$

or

$$\begin{aligned} H_i S_\alpha|\Psi_{a,\mathbf{m}}\rangle &= \left[m_i - \frac{2\mathbf{m}\cdot\mathbf{r}(\alpha)\,r_i(\alpha)}{|\mathbf{r}(\alpha)|^2}\right] S_\alpha|\Psi_{a,\mathbf{m}}\rangle \\ &\equiv m_i' S_\alpha|\Psi_{a,\mathbf{m}}\rangle. \end{aligned} \tag{48}$$

Thus $S_\alpha|\Psi_{a,\mathbf{m}}\rangle$ is a basis with the weight $\mathbf{m}'$. Geometrically in the weight space, S_α makes a reflection of $\mathbf{m}$ through a line intersecting the origin and perpendicular to the root $\mathbf{r}(\alpha)$. Weights that are related by a reflection or products of reflections are said to be equivalent. The following theorem will be useful (*4*).

Theorem. For any weight $\mathbf{m}$ and root $\mathbf{r}(\alpha)$, the quantity $2\mathbf{m}\cdot\mathbf{r}(\alpha)/|\mathbf{r}(\alpha)|^2$ is an integer and $m_i' = m_i - 2\mathbf{m}\cdot\mathbf{r}(\alpha) r_i(\alpha)/|\mathbf{r}(\alpha)|^2$ is also a weight and has the same multiplicity as $\mathbf{m}$.

We say that a weight $\mathbf{m}$ is *higher* than a weight $\mathbf{m}'$ if $\mathbf{m} - \mathbf{m}'$ has a positive number for its first nonvanishing component. A *dominant* weight is the highest member of a set of equivalent weights, and the *highest* weight is the highest dominant weight in a representation. Two equivalent irreducible representations (i.e., related by a similarity transformation) have the same highest weight, and two irreducible representations are equivalent if they have the same highest weight.

Cartan has proved that for every simple group of rank ℓ there are ℓ *fundamental* dominant weights $\mathbf{M}^{(i)} \cdots \mathbf{M}^{(\ell)}$ such that any other dominant weight $\mathbf{M}$ is a linear combination

$$\mathbf{M} = \sum_{i=1}^{\ell} \lambda_i \mathbf{M}^{(i)} \tag{49}$$

with λ_i as nonnegative integral coefficients and that there exist ℓ *fundamental* irreducible representations that have the fundamental weights as their highest weight.

For $SU(3)$, we have $\ell = 2$ and therefore two fundamental dominant weights $\mathbf{M}^{(1)}$ and $\mathbf{M}^{(2)}$. In order to find these weights explicitly, we proceed as follows. From the theorem just given, $2\mathbf{m}\cdot\mathbf{r}(\alpha)/|\mathbf{r}(\alpha)|^2$ must be an integer for an arbitrary weight $\mathbf{m} = (m_1, m_2)$ and any root $\mathbf{r}(\alpha)$. To satisfy this, we find $m_1 = (a+b)/2\sqrt{3}$ and $m_2 = (a-b)/6$, where a and b are integers. Thus $\mathbf{m} = \frac{1}{6}a(\sqrt{3}, 1) + \frac{1}{6}b(\sqrt{3}, -1)$. We note that $\frac{1}{6}(\sqrt{3}, 1)$ and $\frac{1}{6}(\sqrt{3}, -1)$ are each dominant in a different set of three equivalent weights and are the fundamental dominant weights. Thus

$$\mathbf{M}(\lambda_1, \lambda_2) = \tfrac{1}{6}\lambda_1(\sqrt{3}, 1) + \tfrac{1}{6}\lambda_2(\sqrt{3}, -1). \tag{50}$$

Let us form the vector $\mathbf{R}$, which is one half the sum of the positive roots (a root with a positive number for its first nonvanishing component). For $SU(3)$,

$$\mathbf{R} = \tfrac{1}{2} \sum_{\alpha+} \mathbf{r}(\alpha) = \frac{1}{\sqrt{3}}(1, 0). \tag{51}$$

By adding this to the highest weight of an irreducible representation characterized by λ_1, and λ_2 [i.e., $\mathbf{M}(\lambda_1, \lambda_2)$], we form the vector

$$\mathbf{K} = \mathbf{R} + \mathbf{M} = \tfrac{1}{6}(\sqrt{3}\lambda_1 + \sqrt{3}\lambda_2 + 2\sqrt{3}, \lambda_1 - \lambda_2). \tag{52}$$

Weyl has shown that the dimension N of any irreducible representation is given by the product (*4*)

$$N = \prod_{\alpha+} \frac{\mathbf{K}\cdot\mathbf{r}(\alpha)}{\mathbf{R}\cdot\mathbf{r}(\alpha)}, \tag{53}$$

which we can calculate easily for $SU(3)$ to be

$$N = (1 + \lambda_1)(1 + \lambda_2)[1 + \tfrac{1}{2}(\lambda_1 + \lambda_2)]. \tag{54}$$

Before, we noted that two inequivalent irreducible representations can be distinguished by their highest weights. Now we see that the highest weights are given in terms of two nonnegative integers λ_1 and λ_2. Thus, inequivalent irreducible representations can be uniquely distinguished by means of λ_1 and λ_2, that is, $|\Psi^{\lambda_1 \lambda_2}_{a,\mathbf{m}}\rangle$.

Let us take the basis associated with the highest weight $\mathbf{M}$ in an irreducible representation. Then, if $\mathbf{r}(\alpha)$ is a positive root, $E_\alpha|\Psi^{\lambda_1\lambda_2}_{a,\mathbf{M}}\rangle$ must be zero since it cannot be the basis having a weight that is higher (or equivalent to a weight that is higher) than the highest weight. If we act on this basis $|\Psi^{\lambda_1\lambda_2}_{a,\mathbf{M}}\rangle$ with the Casimir operators G_2 and G_3 in the form of Eq. (39) (where all the operators with positive roots are to the right), we find

$$\begin{aligned} G_2|\Psi^{\lambda_1\lambda_2}_{a,\mathbf{M}}\rangle &= (H_1^2 + H_2^2 + \tfrac{2}{3}\sqrt{3}H_1 + \sum_{\alpha+} E_{-\alpha}E_\alpha)|\Psi^{\lambda_1\lambda_2}_{a,\mathbf{M}}\rangle, \\ &= (M_1^2 + M_2^2 + \tfrac{2}{3}\sqrt{3}M_1)|\Psi^{\lambda_1\lambda_2}_{a,\mathbf{M}}\rangle, \\ &= \tfrac{1}{9}[\lambda_1^2 + \lambda_2^2 + \lambda_1\lambda_2 + 3(\lambda_1 + \lambda_2)]|\Psi^{\lambda_1\lambda_2}_{a,\mathbf{M}}\rangle, \\ &\equiv g_2|\Psi^{\lambda_1\lambda_2}_{a,\mathbf{M}}\rangle, \end{aligned} \tag{55}$$

where we have used Eq. (50) for $\mathbf{M}$ in terms of λ_1 and λ_2. Similarly *(6, 7)*

$$\begin{aligned} G_3|\Psi^{\lambda_1\lambda_2}_{a,\mathbf{M}}\rangle &= \tfrac{1}{3}H_2(1 + H_2 + \sqrt{3}H_1)(1 - H_2 + \sqrt{3}H_1)|\Psi^{\lambda_1\lambda_2}_{a,\mathbf{M}}\rangle, \\ &= \tfrac{1}{18}(\lambda_1 - \lambda_2)[1 + \tfrac{1}{3}(2\lambda_1 + \lambda_2)][1 + \tfrac{1}{3}(\lambda_1 + 2\lambda_2)]|\Psi^{\lambda_1\lambda_2}_{a,\mathbf{M}}\rangle, \\ &\equiv g_3|\Psi^{\lambda_1\lambda_2}_{a,\mathbf{M}}\rangle. \end{aligned} \tag{56}$$

We thus have the eigenvalues g_2 and g_3 of the Casimir operators G_2 and G_3 for one of the bases of an irreducible representation.

By repeated use of E_α, E_β, etc., we can construct all the bases of this irreducible representation. But both G_2 and G_3 commute with all the E_α. Thus all the bases of an irreducible representation have the same g_2 and g_3 and, since they are independent, g_2 and g_3 constitute another way (instead of λ_1 and λ_2) of uniquely distinguishing inequivalent irreducible representations, that is, $|\Psi^{g_2 g_3}_{a,\mathbf{m}}\rangle$.

So far we have four commuting operators, H_1, H_2, G_2, and G_3, whose eigenvalues we can use to specify a basis. A complete set of commuting operators whose eigenvalues can be used to completely specify a basis consists, in general, of the ℓ H_i, the ℓ G's and $\frac{1}{2}(r - 3\ell)$ other operators (*4*). For $SU(3)$, this means we need $\frac{1}{2}(8 - 6) = 1$ more operator. Since in elementary particle physics we normally label particles by their total isotopic spin, it is convenient to choose this last operator as I^2, which clearly commutes with the previous four operators. Thus we completely characterize a basis in $SU(3)$ by $|\Psi^{g_2 g_3\, \iota_3}_{ay\iota}\rangle$. [The term a represents the remaining space-time quantum numbers needed to completely specify the state. The eigenvalues of I_3, Y, and I^2 are taken as ι_3, y, and $\iota(\iota + 1)$.]

B. Action of Generators on Bases

Now, what we still need are the normalization constants $A_{\alpha a' a}$ for the action of E_α on a basis, that is, $E_\alpha|\Psi^{g_2 g_3\, \iota_3}_{ay\iota}\rangle = \sum A^{\iota_3'\, \iota_3}_{\alpha y' y \iota' \iota}|\Psi^{g_2 g_3\, \iota_3'}_{a y' \iota'}\rangle$. For $\alpha = \pm 1$, we shall determine the constants by a well-known $SU(2)$ technique. For $\alpha = \pm 2, \pm 3$, we shall then follow the rather pedestrian approach of simply generalizing this technique to our situation. Although algebraically rather long, the method has the advantage that it is straightforward. To this end, let us proceed in the following way. We know $I_\pm = \sqrt{6} E_{\pm 1}$. In the usual way, we form

$$I^2 = \tfrac{1}{2}(I_+ I_- + I_- I_+) + I_3^2 = I_- I_+ + I_3^2 + I_3 \tag{57}$$

or

$$E_{-1} E_1 = \tfrac{1}{6} I_- I_+ = \tfrac{1}{6}(I^2 - I_3^2 - I_3).$$

Thus

$$\begin{aligned}\langle \Psi^{g_2 g_3\, \iota_3}_{ay\iota}|I_- I_+|\Psi^{g_2 g_3\, \iota_3}_{ay\iota}\rangle &= 6 \sum_{\iota_3', \iota', y'} |\langle \Psi^{g_2 g_3\, \iota_3'}_{a y' \iota'}|E_1|\Psi^{g_2 g_3\, \iota_3}_{ay\iota}\rangle|^2 \\ &= \langle \Psi^{g_2 g_3\, \iota_3}_{ay\iota}|(I^2 - I_3^2 - I_3)\,|\Psi^{g_2 g_3\, \iota_3}_{ay\iota}\rangle \\ &= \iota(\iota + 1) - \iota_3(\iota_3 + 1).\end{aligned}$$

Note that in order to show that $\iota' = \iota$, we use $(I^2, E_1) = 0$; to show that $y' = y$, we use $(Y, E_1) = 0$; and to show that $\iota_3' = \iota_3 + 1$, we use $(I_3, E_1) = E_1$. Choosing the phase convention of Condon and Shortley (*8*), we have then

$$E_1|\Psi^{g_2 g_3\, \iota_3}_{ay\iota}\rangle = \frac{1}{\sqrt{6}}[\iota(\iota + 1) - \iota_3(\iota_3 + 1)]^{1/2}|\Psi^{g_2 g_3\, \iota_3+1}_{ay\iota}\rangle. \tag{58}$$

To find E_{-1}, we multiply this equation by E_{-1} and use Eq. (57). That is,

$$E_{-1}E_1|\Psi_{ay\iota}^{g_2g_3\,\iota_3}\rangle = \tfrac{1}{6}[\iota(\iota+1)-\iota_3(\iota_3+1)]\,|\Psi_{ay\iota}^{g_2g_3\,\iota_3}\rangle$$

$$= \frac{1}{\sqrt{6}}[\iota(\iota+1)-\iota_3(\iota_3+1)]^{1/2}\,E_{-1}|\Psi_{ay\iota}^{g_2g_3\,\iota_3+1}\rangle$$

or

$$E_{-1}|\Psi_{ay\iota}^{g_2g_3\,\iota_3}\rangle = \frac{1}{\sqrt{6}}[\iota(\iota+1)-\iota_3(\iota_3-1)]^{1/2}\,|\Psi_{ay\iota}^{g_2g_3\,\iota_3-1}\rangle. \tag{59}$$

Let us now use this method for E_2. Consider

$$E_2|\Psi_{ay\iota}^{g_2g_3\,\iota_3}\rangle = \sum_{\iota_3',\,\iota',\,y'} A_{2y'y\iota'\iota}^{\iota_3'\,\iota_3}|\Psi_{ay'\iota'}^{g_2g_3\,\iota_3'}\rangle, \tag{60}$$

where, of course, A_2 is a function of g_2 and g_3. If we multiply this equation by Y and use $(Y, E_2) = E_2$ (remember $Y = 2H_2$),

$$YE_2|\Psi_{ay\iota}^{g_2g_3\,\iota_3}\rangle = (y+1)\,E_2|\Psi_{ay\iota}^{g_2g_3\,\iota_3}\rangle = \sum y'\,A_{2y'y\iota'\iota}^{\iota_3'\,\iota_3}|\Psi_{ay'\iota'}^{g_2g_3\,\iota_3'}\rangle \tag{61}$$

or $y' = y+1$, since the bases are linearly independent. Similarly, by multiplying by I_3 and using $(I_3, E_2) = \frac{1}{2}E_2$ (remember $I_3 = \sqrt{3}H_1$), we find

$$I_3\,E_2|\Psi_{ay\iota}^{g_2g_3\,\iota_3}\rangle = (\iota_3+\tfrac{1}{2})\,E_2|\Psi_{ay\iota}^{g_2g_3\,\iota_3}\rangle = \sum \iota_3'\,A_{2\iota'\iota}^{\iota_3'\,\iota_3}|\Psi_{ay+1,\iota'}^{g_2g_3\,\iota_3'}\rangle \tag{62}$$

or again $\iota_3' = \iota_3 + \frac{1}{2}$, since the various primed bases are linearly independent. Thus the sum over ι_3', y', and ι' is reduced to a sum over ι' and we have

$$E_2|\Psi_{ay\iota}^{g_2g_3\,\iota_3}\rangle = \sum_{\iota'} A_{2\iota'\iota}|\Psi_{ay+1,\iota'}^{g_2g_3\,\iota_3+1/2}\rangle. \tag{63}$$

At this point, let us digress for a moment to show that if we know $A_{2\iota'\iota}$ we also know the action of E_3 on a basis. By multiplying Eq. (63) by $E_{-1}E_1$ and using $(E_{-1}, E_2) = \dfrac{1}{\sqrt{6}}E_3$, $(E_1, E_2) = 0$, $(E_1, E_3) = \dfrac{1}{\sqrt{6}}E_2$, we find

$$E_{-1}\,E_2\,E_1|\Psi_{ay\iota}^{g_2g_3\,\iota_3}\rangle = \left(E_2\,E_{-1} + \frac{1}{\sqrt{6}}E_3\right)E_1|\Psi_{ay\iota}^{g_2g_3\,\iota_3}\rangle$$

$$= \sum_{\iota'} A_{2\iota'\iota}\,E_{-1}\,E_1|\Psi_{ay+1,\iota'}^{g_2g_3\,\iota_3+1/2}\rangle.$$

Now use Eq. (57) to find

$$\frac{1}{\sqrt{6}} E_3 E_1 |\Psi_{ay\iota}^{g_2 g_3 \iota_3}\rangle = \tfrac{1}{6}[\iota(\iota+1) - \iota_3(\iota_3+1)]^{1/2} E_3 |\Psi_{ay\iota}^{g_2 g_3 \iota_3+1}\rangle$$

$$= \sum_{\iota'} \tfrac{1}{6}[\iota'(\iota'+1) - \iota(\iota+1) - \iota_3 - \tfrac{3}{4}] A_{2\iota'\iota} |\Psi_{ay+1,\iota'}^{g_2 g_3 \iota_3+1/2}\rangle$$

or

$$E_3 |\Psi_{ay\iota}^{g_2 g_3 \iota_3+1}\rangle = \sum_{\iota'} \left[\frac{\iota'(\iota'+1) - \iota(\iota+1) - \iota_3 - \frac{3}{4}}{[\iota(\iota+1) - \iota_3(\iota_3+1)]^{1/2}}\right] A_{2\iota'\iota} |\Psi_{ay+1,\iota'}^{g_2 g_3 \iota_3+1/2}\rangle. \quad (64)$$

Thus, when we find $A_{2\iota'\iota}$, we automatically will know the action of E_3 on a basis.

In order to find the relation between ι' and ι, we first form the commutator of I^2 with E_2, which, by the commutation relations, gives

$$(I^2, E_2) = \tfrac{1}{2}\sqrt{3}(H_1 E_2 + E_2 H_1) + (\tfrac{3}{2})^{1/2}(E_1 E_3 + E_3 E_1). \quad (65)$$

We then form the double commutator and, after repeated use of the commutation relations, we obtain

$$(I^2, (I^2, E_2)) = \tfrac{1}{2}(I^2, E_2)_+ + \tfrac{3}{16} E_2. \quad (66)$$

Now if we multiply Eq. (63) by I^4, we find

$$I^4 E_2 |\Psi_{ay\iota}^{g_2 g_3 \iota_3}\rangle = I^2[(I^2, E_2) + E_2 I^2] |\Psi_{ay\iota}^{g_2 g_3 \iota_3}\rangle$$

$$= [(I^2, (I^2, E_2)) + 2I^2 E_2 I^2 - E_2 I^4] |\Psi_{ay\iota}^{g_2 g_3 \iota_3}\rangle$$

$$= [I^2 E_2(2I^2 + \tfrac{1}{2}) - E_2(I^4 - \tfrac{1}{2}I^2 - \tfrac{3}{16})] |\Psi_{ay\iota}^{g_2 g_3 \iota_3}\rangle$$

$$= (\iota + \tfrac{1}{2})^2 [2I^2 E_2 - E_2(\iota + \tfrac{3}{2})(\iota - \tfrac{1}{2})] |\Psi_{ay\iota}^{g_2 g_3 \iota_3}\rangle$$

$$= \sum_{\iota'} \iota'^2(\iota'+1)^2 A_{2\iota'\iota} |\Psi_{ay+1,\iota'}^{g_2 g_3 \iota_3+1/2}\rangle. \quad (67)$$

But also by multiplying Eq. (63) by I^2, we find

$$I^2 E_2 |\Psi_{ay\iota}^{g_2 g_3 \iota_3}\rangle = \sum_{\iota'} \iota'(\iota'+1) A_{2\iota'\iota} |\Psi_{ay+1,\iota'}^{g_2 g_3 \iota_3+1/2}\rangle. \quad (68)$$

Substituting this in the next to last line of Eq. (67), we can write the following relation

$$(\iota - \tfrac{1}{2}) E_2 |\Psi^{g_2 g_3 \iota_3}_{ay\iota}\rangle = -\frac{1}{\iota + \frac{3}{2}} \sum_{\iota'} \left[\frac{\iota'^2(\iota'+1)^2}{(\iota + \frac{1}{2})^2} - 2\iota'(\iota'+1) \right] A_{2\iota'\iota} |\Psi^{g_2 g_3 \iota_3 + 1/2}_{ay+1,\iota'}\rangle. \tag{69}$$

If $\iota \neq \frac{1}{2}$, we must have

$$\iota'^2(\iota'+1)^2 - 2\iota'(\iota'+1)(\iota+\tfrac{1}{2})^2 + (\iota+\tfrac{3}{2})(\iota+\tfrac{1}{2})^2(\iota-\tfrac{1}{2}) = 0.$$

There are two solutions of this equation for $\iota' > 0$. They are $\iota' = \iota \pm \frac{1}{2}$. If $\iota = \frac{1}{2}$, then we must satisfy $\iota'^2(\iota'+1)^2 - 2\iota'(\iota'+1) = 0$ and these solutions are $\iota' = 0$ or 1. Thus, in general, $\iota' = \iota \pm \frac{1}{2}$, and

$$E_2 |\Psi^{g_2 g_3 \iota_3}_{ay\iota}\rangle = A_2^+ |\Psi^{g_2 g_3 \iota_3+1/2}_{ay+1,\iota+1/2}\rangle + A_2^- |\Psi^{g_2 g_3 \iota_3+1/2}_{ay+1,\iota-1/2}\rangle. \tag{70}$$

It then follows that for E_3 acting on a basis

$$E_3 |\Psi^{g_2 g_3 \iota_3+1}_{ay\iota}\rangle = \left[\frac{\iota - \iota_3}{\iota + \iota_3 + 1}\right]^{1/2} A_2^+ |\Psi^{g_2 g_3 \iota_3+1/2}_{ay+1,\iota+1/2}\rangle - \left[\frac{\iota + \iota_3 + 1}{\iota - \iota_3}\right]^{1/2} A_2^- |\Psi^{g_2 g_3 \iota_3+1/2}_{ay+1,\iota-1/2}\rangle.$$

If we multiply this equation by I_- and note that $(I_-, E_3) = 0$, we find

$$E_3 |\Psi^{g_2 g_3 \iota_3}_{ay\iota}\rangle = \left[\frac{\iota - \iota_3 + 1}{\iota + \iota_3 + 1}\right]^{1/2} A_2^+ |\Psi^{g_2 g_3 \iota_3-1/2}_{ay+1,\iota+1/2}\rangle - \left[\frac{\iota + \iota_3}{\iota - \iota_3}\right]^{1/2} A_2^- |\Psi^{g_2 g_3 \iota_3-1/2}_{ay+1,\iota-1/2}\rangle. \tag{71}$$

Let us turn our attention specifically to finding $A_2^\pm$. By use of the Casimir invariant G_2 we can write

$$\langle\Psi^{g_2 g_3 \iota_3}_{ay\iota}|(E_2, E_{-2})_+ + (E_3, E_{-3})_+|\Psi^{g_2 g_3 \iota_3}_{ay\iota}\rangle = g_2 - \tfrac{1}{3}\iota(\iota+1) - \tfrac{1}{4}y^2. \tag{72}$$

On the other hand, the third-order Casimir invariant, after a bit of algebra and use of the commutation relations, can be put in the form

$$\begin{aligned} G_3 = {} & \tfrac{1}{48}Y^3 + \tfrac{1}{4}Y(I^2 - G_2) - \tfrac{1}{12}Y + \tfrac{3}{2}I_3[(E_2, E_{-2})_+ - (E_3, E_{-3})_+] \\ & - \tfrac{1}{4}(I_-, (I_+, I_3[(E_2, E_{-2})_+ - (E_3, E_{-3})_+])). \end{aligned} \tag{73}$$

We thus find

$$g_3 - \tfrac{1}{48}y^3 - \tfrac{1}{4}y[\iota(\iota+1) - g_2] + \tfrac{1}{12}y$$
$$= \iota_3[\tfrac{3}{2} - \tfrac{1}{2}\iota(\iota+1) + \tfrac{1}{2}\iota_3^2]\langle\Psi_{ay\iota}^{g_2 g_3 \iota_3}|\,(E_2, E_{-2})_+$$
$$-(E_3, E_{-3})_+\,|\Psi_{ay\iota}^{g_2 g_3 \iota_3}\rangle$$
$$+\tfrac{1}{4}(\iota_3+1)\,[\iota(\iota+1) - \iota_3(\iota_3+1)]\langle\Psi_{ay\iota}^{g_2 g_3 \iota_3+1}|\,(E_2, E_{-2})_+$$
$$-(E_3, E_{-3})_+\,|\Psi_{ay\iota}^{g_2 g_3 \iota_3+1}\rangle$$
$$+\tfrac{1}{4}(\iota_3-1)\,[\iota(\iota+1) - \iota_3(\iota_3-1)]\langle\Psi_{ay\iota}^{g_2 g_3 \iota_3-1}|\,(E_2, E_{-2})_+$$
$$-(E_3, E_{-3})_+\,|\Psi_{ay\iota}^{g_2 g_3 \iota_3-1}\rangle. \tag{74}$$

To digress for a moment, let us call $D \equiv (E_2, E_{-2})_+ - (E_3, E_{-3})_+$, and note that

$$(I_+, (I_+, D)) = 0.$$

Taken between the states with $\iota_3 + 1$ and $\iota_3 - 1$, we find

$$0 = \{[\iota(\iota+1) - \iota_3(\iota_3-1)]\,[\iota(\iota+1) - \iota_3(\iota_3+1)]\}^{1/2}\,[\langle\Psi^{\iota_3+1}|D|\Psi^{\iota_3+1}\rangle$$
$$+\langle\Psi^{\iota_3-1}|D|\Psi^{\iota_3-1}\rangle - 2\langle\Psi^{\iota_3}|D|\Psi^{\iota_3}\rangle].$$

Similarly, we can show

$$(I_+, (I_-, D)) = 2D.$$

Taken between states of ι_3, we obtain

$$2[\iota(\iota+1) - \iota_3^2 - 1]\langle\Psi^{\iota_3}|D|\Psi^{\iota_3}\rangle = [\iota(\iota+1) - \iota_3(\iota_3+1)]\,\langle\Psi^{\iota_3+1}|D|\Psi^{\iota_3+1}\rangle$$
$$+[\iota(\iota+1) - \iota_3(\iota_3-1)]\,\langle\Psi^{\iota_3-1}|D|\Psi^{\iota_3-1}\rangle.$$

These equations give

$$(\iota_3+1)\,\langle\Psi^{\iota_3}|D|\Psi^{\iota_3}\rangle = \iota_3\langle\Psi^{\iota_3+1}|D|\Psi^{\iota_3+1}\rangle,$$
$$(\iota_3-1)\,\langle\Psi^{\iota_3}|D|\Psi^{\iota_3}\rangle = \iota_3\langle\Psi^{\iota_3-1}|D|\Psi^{\iota_3-1}\rangle. \tag{75}$$

By using these relations in Eq. (74), we find

$$\langle\Psi_{ay\iota}^{g_2 g_3 \iota_3}|\,(E_2, E_{-2})_+ - (E_3, E_{-3})_+\,|\Psi_{ay\iota}^{g_2 g_3 \iota_3}\rangle$$
$$= \frac{2\iota_3}{\iota(\iota+1)}\{g_3 - \tfrac{1}{48}y^3 - \tfrac{1}{4}y[\iota(\iota+1) - g_2] + \tfrac{1}{12}y\} \tag{76}$$

(for $\iota = 0$, the matrix element is zero). By use of the commutation relations for (E_2, E_{-2}) and inserting a complete set of states, the left-hand side of this equation may be written

$$2 \sum' |\langle \Psi_{ay'\iota'}^{g_2 g_3 \iota_3'} | E_2 | \Psi_{ay\iota}^{g_2 g_3 \iota_3} \rangle|^2 - 2 \sum' |\langle \Psi_{ay'\iota'}^{g_2 g_3 \iota_3'} | E_3 | \Psi_{ay\iota}^{g_2 g_3 \iota_3} \rangle|^2 + \tfrac{1}{3}\iota_3.$$

Then by means of Eqs. (70) and (71), Eq. (76) may be rewritten

$$|A_2^+|^2 \frac{4\iota_3}{\iota + \iota_3 + 1} - |A_2^-|^2 \frac{4\iota_3}{\iota - \iota_3} + \tfrac{1}{3}\iota_3$$
$$= \frac{2\iota_3}{\iota(\iota + 1)} \{g_3 - \tfrac{1}{48}y^3 - \tfrac{1}{4}y[\iota(\iota + 1) - g_2] + \tfrac{1}{12}y\}. \quad (77)$$

The second-degree Casimir invariant can be treated similarly, with the result

$$|A_2^+|^2 \frac{4(\iota + 1)}{\iota + \iota_3 + 1} + |A_2^-|^2 \frac{4\iota}{\iota - \iota_3} + \tfrac{1}{2}y = g_2 - \tfrac{1}{3}\iota(\iota + 1) - \tfrac{1}{4}y^2. \quad (78)$$

These two equations may be solved to give

$$|A_2^+|^2 = \frac{\iota + \iota_3 + 1}{(2\iota + 1)} \frac{1}{12(\iota + 1)} \{6g_3 + (\tfrac{1}{2}y + \iota + 1)[3g_2 + 1 - (\tfrac{1}{2}y + \iota + 1)^2]\}$$

and

$$|A_2^-|^2 = \frac{\iota - \iota_3}{(2\iota + 1)} \frac{1}{12\iota} \{-6g_3 + (\iota - \tfrac{1}{2}y)[3g_2 + 1 - (\iota - \tfrac{1}{2}y)^2]\}.$$

By calling

$$A_{y\iota}^{g_2 g_3} = \tfrac{1}{2}(3\iota)^{-1/2}\{[3g_2 + 1 - (\iota - \tfrac{1}{2}y)^2](\iota - \tfrac{1}{2}y) - 6g_3\}^{1/2} \quad (79)$$

we see that

$$|A_2^-| = \left[\frac{\iota - \iota_3}{2\iota + 1}\right]^{1/2} A_{y\iota}^{g_2 g_3}; \qquad |A_2^+| = \left[\frac{\iota + \iota_3 + 1}{2\iota + 1}\right]^{1/2} A_{-y\iota+1}^{g_2 - g_3}. \quad (80)$$

Now to find the action of E_{-2} on a basis, we note that the outer automorphism R operates in the following manner (by noting that R commutes with G_2

and I^2, but anticommutes with I_3, Y, and G_3, we find, up to a phase factor η, how R transforms a basis).

$$RE_2 R^{-1} R|\Psi^{g_2 g_3 \iota_3}_{ay\iota}\rangle = -\eta E_{-2}|\Psi^{g_2 - g_3 - \iota_3}_{a - y\iota}\rangle$$

$$= \eta' \left[\frac{\iota + \iota_3 + 1}{2\iota + 1}\right]^{1/2} A^{g_2 - g_3}_{-y\iota+1}|\Psi^{g_2 - g_3 - \iota_3 - 1/2}_{a, -y-1, \iota+1/2}\rangle$$

$$+ \eta'' \left[\frac{\iota - \iota_3}{2\iota + 1}\right]^{1/2} A^{g_2 g_3}_{y\iota}|\Psi^{g_2 - g_3 - \iota_3 - 1/2}_{a - y - 1, \iota - 1/2}\rangle,$$

which gives

$$E_{-2}|\Psi^{g_2 g_3 \iota_3}_{ay\iota}\rangle = \eta''' \left[\frac{\iota - \iota_3 + 1}{2\iota + 1}\right]^{1/2} A^{g_2 g_3}_{y\iota+1}|\Psi^{g_2 g_3 \iota_3 - 1/2}_{ay-1, \iota+1/2}\rangle$$

$$+ \eta'''' \left[\frac{\iota + \iota_3}{2\iota + 1}\right]^{1/2} A^{g_2 - g_3}_{-y\iota}|\Psi^{g_2 g_3 \iota_3 - 1/2}_{ay-1, \iota-1/2}\rangle \tag{81}$$

where the η's are either ± 1. We may find E_{-3} from E_{-2} in the same manner as we found E_3 from E_2 in Eqs. (63)–(64). Namely, we multiply this equation for E_{-2} by $E_1 E_{-1}$ and use the commutation relations. We find

$$E_{-3}|\Psi^{g_2 g_3 \iota_3}_{ay\iota}\rangle = -\eta''' \left[\frac{\iota + \iota_3 + 1}{2\iota + 1}\right]^{1/2} A^{g_2 g_3}_{y\iota+1}|\Psi^{g_2 g_3 \iota_3 - 1/2}_{ay-1, \iota+1/2}\rangle$$

$$+ \eta'''' \left[\frac{\iota - \iota_3}{2\iota + 1}\right]^{1/2} A^{g_2 - g_3}_{-y\iota}|\Psi^{g_2 g_3 \iota_3 - 1/2}_{ay-1, \iota-1/2}\rangle. \tag{82}$$

In order to find the relations among the various phases, we can use the commutation relation $(E_2, E_{-3}) = \dfrac{1}{\sqrt{6}} E_1$.

Let us now summarize our results.

$$H_1|\Psi^{g_2 g_3 \iota_3}_{ay\iota}\rangle = \frac{1}{\sqrt{3}} \iota_3 |\Psi^{g_2 g_3 \iota_3}_{ay\iota}\rangle, \qquad H_2|\Psi^{g_2 g_3 \iota_3}_{ay\iota}\rangle = \tfrac{1}{2} y |\Psi^{g_2 g_3 \iota_3}_{ay\iota}\rangle,$$

$$E_1|\Psi^{g_2 g_3 \iota_3}_{ay\iota}\rangle = \frac{1}{\sqrt{6}} [\iota(\iota + 1) - \iota_3(\iota_3 + 1)]^{1/2} |\Psi^{g_2 g_3 \iota_3 + 1}_{ay\iota}\rangle,$$

$$E_{-1}|\Psi^{g_2 g_3 \iota_3}_{ay\iota}\rangle = \frac{1}{\sqrt{6}} [\iota(\iota + 1) - \iota_3(\iota_3 - 1)]^{1/2} |\Psi^{g_2 g_3 \iota_3 - 1}_{ay\iota}\rangle,$$

$$E_2|\Psi^{g_2g_3\iota_3}_{ay\iota}\rangle = \eta^+\left[\frac{\iota+\iota_3+1}{2\iota+1}\right]^{1/2} A^{g_2-g_3}_{-y\iota+1}|\Psi^{g_2g_3\iota_3+1/2}_{ay+1,\iota+1/2}\rangle$$

$$+\eta^-\left[\frac{\iota-\iota_3}{2\iota+1}\right]^{1/2} A^{g_2g_3}_{y\iota}|\Psi^{g_2g_3\iota_3+1/2}_{ay+1,\iota-1/2}\rangle,$$

$$E_{-2}|\Psi^{g_2g_3\iota_3}_{ay\iota}\rangle = \eta^-\left[\frac{\iota-\iota_3+1}{2\iota+1}\right]^{1/2} A^{g_2g_3}_{y\iota+1}|\Psi^{g_2g_3\iota_3-1/2}_{ay-1,\iota+1/2}\rangle$$

$$+\eta^+\left[\frac{\iota+\iota_3}{2\iota+1}\right]^{1/2} A^{g_2-g_3}_{-y\iota}|\Psi^{g_2g_3\iota_3-1/2}_{ay-1,\iota-1/2}\rangle,$$

$$E_3|\Psi^{g_2g_3\iota_3}_{ay\iota}\rangle = \eta^+\left[\frac{\iota-\iota_3+1}{2\iota+1}\right]^{1/2} A^{g_2-g_3}_{-y\iota+1}|\Psi^{g_2g_3\iota_3-1/2}_{ay+1,\iota+1/2}\rangle$$

$$-\eta^-\left[\frac{\iota+\iota_3}{2\iota+1}\right]^{1/2} A^{g_2g_3}_{y\iota}|\Psi^{g_2g_3\iota_3-1/2}_{ay+1,\iota-1/2}\rangle,$$

$$E_{-3}|\Psi^{g_2g_3\iota_3}_{ay\iota}\rangle = -\eta^-\left[\frac{\iota+\iota_3+1}{2\iota+1}\right]^{1/2} A^{g_2g_3}_{y\iota+1}|\Psi^{g_2g_3\iota_3+1/2}_{ay-1,\iota+1/2}\rangle$$

$$+\eta^+\left[\frac{\iota-\iota_3}{2\iota+1}\right]^{1/2} A^{g_2-g_3}_{-y\iota}|\Psi^{g_2g_3\iota_3+1/2}_{ay-1,\iota-1/2}\rangle, \tag{83}$$

where

$$A^{g_2g_3}_{y\iota} \equiv \tfrac{1}{2}(3\iota)^{-1/2}\{[3g_2+1-(\iota-\tfrac{1}{2}y)^2](\iota-\tfrac{1}{2}y)-6g_3\}^{1/2}; \qquad A^{g_2g_3}_{y0}=0 \tag{84}$$

and the phases $\eta^+=\pm1$, $\eta^-=\pm1$ have been chosen to satisfy $(E_2, E_{-3}) = \dfrac{1}{\sqrt{6}}E_1$. The phase convention of de Swart (*9*) is $\eta^+=\eta^-=1$.

By using the labeling λ_1 and λ_2 rather than g_2 and g_3, this may be written (*6*, *7*) in a factored form $[A^{\lambda_1\lambda_2}_{y\iota} = A^{g_2g_3}_{y\iota};\ A^{\lambda_2\lambda_1}_{y\iota} = A^{g_2-g_3}_{y\iota}]$

$$A^{\lambda_1\lambda_2}_{y\iota} \equiv \tfrac{1}{2}(3\iota)^{-1/2}\{[\tfrac{1}{3}(\lambda_2-\lambda_1)+\iota-\tfrac{1}{2}y]\,[1+\tfrac{1}{3}(\lambda_1+2\lambda_2)-(\iota-\tfrac{1}{2}y)]$$
$$\times[1+\tfrac{1}{3}(2\lambda_1+\lambda_2)+\iota-\tfrac{1}{2}y]\}^{1/2}. \tag{85}$$

C. Multiplicities and Direct Product Decomposition

From the foregoing, we now can explicitly construct, for any irreducible representation, the weight diagram and the bases associated with each weight in this diagram. We start with a basis that has the highest weight in the irreducible representation and then act on this basis with $E_{-\alpha}$, where $\mathbf{r}(\alpha)$ is a positive root, to generate new bases of the representation. By repeating this procedure with the new bases, we ultimately find all the bases and weights in this irreducible representation. It turns out, in many irreducible representations of $SU(3)$, that some of the weights have more than one basis associated with them; that is, some of the weights have a multiplicity greater than one in the weight diagram. (This is to be contrasted with the irreducible representations of the isotopic spin group, where each weight has only one basis associated with it.) Of course, our states are now completely labeled, so that we distinguish these bases with the same weight by the eigenvalues of the operator I^2. Some weight diagrams are given in Fig. 2.

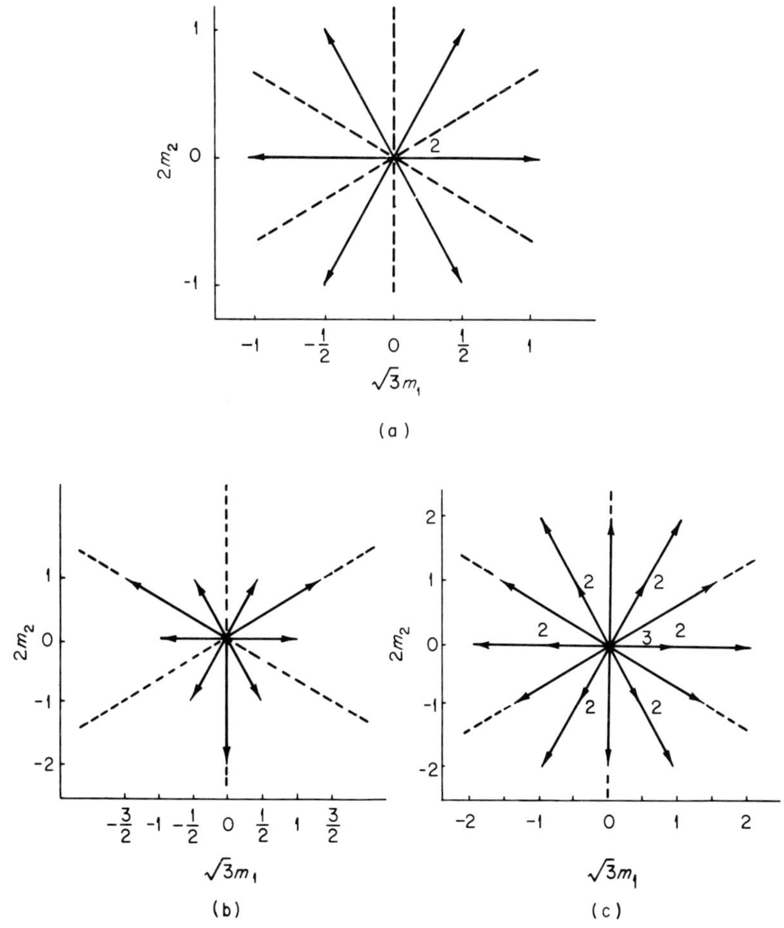

FIG. 2. Weight diagrams for $N = 8$-, 10-, and 27-dimensional representations. The diagram is invariant under reflections through the dashed lines.

It is often of physical interest to know the "content" of an irreducible representation (i.e., the isotopic spin multiplets and the associated hypercharges in an irreducible representation) without actually knowing all the bases. This information could be shown on a weight diagram if we knew the multiplicity of each weight. We will now turn our attention to finding these multiplicities without resorting to the laborious procedure outlined in the previous paragraph.

It will turn out that a problem associated with finding the multiplicities of the weights is that of reducing a product of two irreducible representations into a sum of irreducible representations. (For example, in the isotopic spin case, if we combine an $\iota = 1$ state with an $\iota = 2$ state, we know that the product transforms like a combination of $\iota = 3$, 2, and 1 states). In order to simplify the notation, let us follow De Swart (*9*) and characterize the quantum numbers g_2 and g_3 by μ and the quantum numbers ι, ι_3, and y by ν. We thus write a one-particle state as $|\Psi_\nu^\mu\rangle$. The product representation of two irreducible representations is then, in general, reducible into a sum of irreducible representations; that is,

$$|\Psi_{\nu_1}^{\mu_1}\rangle|\Psi_{\nu_2}^{\mu_2}\rangle = \sum_{\mu\nu\gamma}\begin{pmatrix}\mu_1 & \mu_2 & \mu\gamma \\ \nu_1 & \nu_2 & \nu\end{pmatrix}|\Psi_\nu^{\mu_1\mu_2\mu\gamma}\rangle \tag{86}$$

where the $|\Psi_\nu^{\mu_1\mu_2\mu\gamma}\rangle$ are the irreducible representations contained in the product representation and the

$$\begin{pmatrix}\mu_1 & \mu_2 & \mu\gamma \\ \nu_1 & \nu_2 & \nu\end{pmatrix}$$

are the Clebsch-Gordan cœfficients for $SU(3)$. The index γ distinguishes between two or more of the same irreducible representations when they are contained in a product representation. De Swart (*9*) has written these $SU(3)$ Clebsch-Gordan coefficients in a factored form

$$\begin{pmatrix}\mu_1 & \mu_2 & \mu\gamma \\ \nu_1 & \nu_2 & \nu\end{pmatrix} = C_{\iota_{1z}\,\iota_{2z}\,\iota_z}^{\iota_1\,\iota_2\,\iota}\left(\begin{matrix}\mu_1 & \mu_2 \\ \iota_1 y_1 & \iota_2 y_2\end{matrix}\middle|\begin{matrix}\mu\gamma \\ \iota y\end{matrix}\right) \tag{87}$$

where the $C_{\iota_{1z}\,\iota_{2z}\,\iota_z}^{\iota_1\,\iota_2\,\iota}$ are the usual $SU(2)$ Clebsch-Gordan coefficients. The other factor, called the *isoscalar factor*, has been tabularized for some cases (*9*).

Let us form the matrix element of the operator $e^{i\theta_i H_i}$ by use of Eq. (86). We find

$$\langle \Psi_{\nu_1}^{\mu_1} | e^{i\theta_i H_i} | \Psi_{\nu_1}^{\mu_1} \rangle \langle \Psi_{\nu_2}^{\mu_2} | e^{i\theta_i H_i} | \Psi_{\nu_2}^{\mu_2} \rangle$$
$$= \sum_{\substack{\mu\nu\gamma \\ \mu'\nu'\gamma'}} \langle \Psi_{\nu'}^{\mu_1\mu_2\mu'\gamma'} | \begin{pmatrix} \mu_1 & \mu_2 & \mu'\gamma' \\ \nu_1 & \nu_2 & \nu' \end{pmatrix} \begin{pmatrix} \mu_1 & \mu_2 & \mu\gamma \\ \nu_1 & \nu_2 & \nu \end{pmatrix} e^{i\theta_i H_i} | \Psi_{\nu}^{\mu_1\mu_2\mu\gamma} \rangle.$$

The character χ of an irreducible representation is defined as the sum over all weights of the matrix elements of $e^{i\theta_i H_i}$; that is,

$$\chi(\mu, \theta) \equiv \sum_{\nu} \langle \Psi_{\nu}^{\mu} | e^{i\theta_i H_i} | \Psi_{\nu}^{\mu} \rangle. \tag{88}$$

Thus, if we sum over ν_1 and ν_2 in the previous equation, we obtain

$$\chi(\mu_1, \theta)\, \chi(\mu_2, \theta) = \sum_{\mu\gamma} \chi(\mu\gamma, \theta) \tag{89}$$

by virtue of the orthogonality relation

$$\sum_{\nu_1\nu_2} \begin{pmatrix} \mu_1 & \mu_2 & \mu\gamma \\ \nu_1 & \nu_2 & \nu \end{pmatrix} \begin{pmatrix} \mu_1 & \mu_2 & \mu'\gamma' \\ \nu_1 & \nu_2 & \nu' \end{pmatrix} = \delta_{\mu\mu'}\, \delta_{\nu\nu'}\, \delta_{\gamma\gamma'}. \tag{90}$$

But the characters of the irreducible representations of $SU(3)$ are independent of γ [within $SU(3)$ we cannot distinguish between the same irreducible representations]; that is,

$$\chi(\mu\gamma, \theta) = \chi(\mu\gamma', \theta). \tag{91}$$

Thus, we may write

$$\chi(\mu_1, \theta)\, \chi(\mu_2, \theta) = \sum_{\mu} C(\mu_1, \mu_2, \mu)\, \chi(\mu, \theta) \tag{92}$$

where $C(\mu_1, \mu_2, \mu)$ is an integer and is the multiplicity of an irreducible representation in the product representation.

Weyl has shown that the character can be written (*4*)

$$\chi(\mu, \theta) = \frac{\xi(\mathbf{K}, \theta)}{\xi(\mathbf{R}, \theta)} = \sum_{\mathbf{m}} \omega(\mathbf{m}) \exp(i\mathbf{m} \cdot \boldsymbol{\theta}) \tag{93}$$

where **K** and **R** were introduced before, the sum is over all weights in an irreducible representation, and $\omega(\mathbf{m})$ is the multiplicity (an integer) of the weight $\mathbf{m}$. The $\xi(\mathbf{K}, \theta)$ has the form

$$\xi(\mathbf{K}, \theta) = \sum_S \delta_S \exp[i(S\mathbf{K}) \cdot \boldsymbol{\theta}] = \delta_S \xi(S\mathbf{K}, \theta) \tag{94}$$

where S is the group of Weyl reflections and δ_S is +1 or −1, depending on whether S is an even or an odd number of *reflections*. By remembering that equivalent weights have the same multiplicity, we see that (*10*)

$$\chi(\mu, \theta) = \sum_{\mathbf{m}} \omega(S\mathbf{m}) \exp[i(S\mathbf{m}) \cdot \boldsymbol{\theta}] = \sum_{\mathbf{m}} \omega(\mathbf{m}) \exp[i(S\mathbf{m}) \cdot \boldsymbol{\theta}]. \tag{95}$$

Let us rewrite Eq. (92) in the following ways:

$$\begin{aligned} \sum_{\mu} C(\mu_1, \mu_2, \mu)\, \xi(\mathbf{K}, \theta) &= \xi(\mathbf{K}_1, \theta)\, \chi(\mu_2, \theta) \\ &= \sum_S \delta_S \exp[i(S\mathbf{K}_1) \cdot \boldsymbol{\theta}] \sum_{\mathbf{m}_2} \omega_2(\mathbf{m}_2) \exp[i(S\mathbf{m}_2) \cdot \boldsymbol{\theta}] \\ &= \sum_{\mathbf{m}_2} \omega_2(\mathbf{m}_2) \sum_S \delta_S \exp\{i[S(\mathbf{K}_1 + \mathbf{m}_2)] \cdot \boldsymbol{\theta}\} \\ &= \sum_{\mathbf{m}_2} \omega_2(\mathbf{m}_2)\, \xi(\mathbf{K}_1 + \mathbf{m}_2, \theta). \end{aligned} \tag{96}$$

For the quantity $\mathbf{K}_1 + \mathbf{m}_2$, there are three possibilities: Either $\mathbf{K}_1 + \mathbf{m}_2$ is (i) equal to a $\mathbf{K}$ vector or (ii) a Weyl reflection of a $\mathbf{K}$ vector for a highest weight of some irreducible representation, or (iii) $\mathbf{K}_1 + \mathbf{m}_2$ lies on a symmetry line, that is, $S(\mathbf{K}_1 + \mathbf{m}_2) = \mathbf{K}_1 + \mathbf{m}_2$, in which case ξ is zero. Since one of the elements of the group S is the identity we have $[S\mathbf{K} = \mathbf{K}_1 + \mathbf{m}_2]$

$$\begin{aligned} \sum_{\mu} C(\mu_1, \mu_2, \mu)\, \xi(\mathbf{K}, \theta) &= \sum_{\mathbf{K}} \sum_S \omega_2(S\mathbf{K} - \mathbf{K}_1)\, \xi(S\mathbf{K}, \theta) \\ &= \sum_{\mathbf{K}} \sum_S \delta_S \omega_2(S\mathbf{K} - \mathbf{K}_1)\, \xi(\mathbf{K}, \theta). \end{aligned} \tag{97}$$

The geometrical method of now determining the multiplicities is straightforward (*10*). Let $\mathbf{K}_1 = \mathbf{R}$. Then $\chi(\mu_1, \theta)$ will be the character for the one-dimensional representation. We then must have

$$\sum_S \delta_S \omega_2(S\mathbf{K} - \mathbf{R}) = \delta_{\mathbf{K}\mathbf{K}_2}. \tag{98}$$

We illustrate the method of determining the ω in the case of the 27-dimensional representation. In Fig. 3a we have drawn the weight diagram with the lines through which we can reflect. Next to each weight is the multiplicity of that weight: 1, v, w, y, and z. (We have used the properties that the highest weight

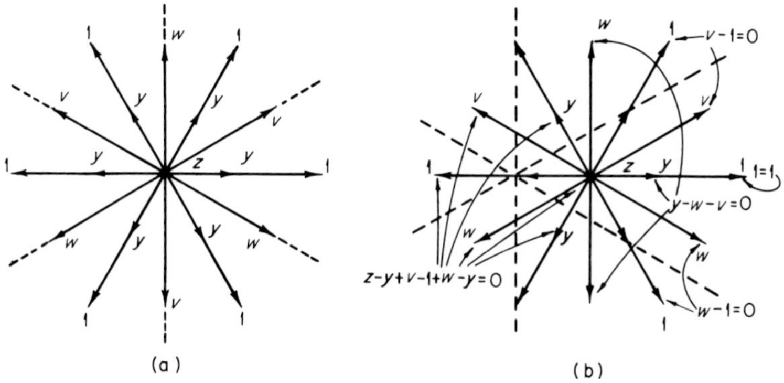

FIG. 3. Weight diagram for $N = 27$ showing graphical technique of determining multiplicities of weights.

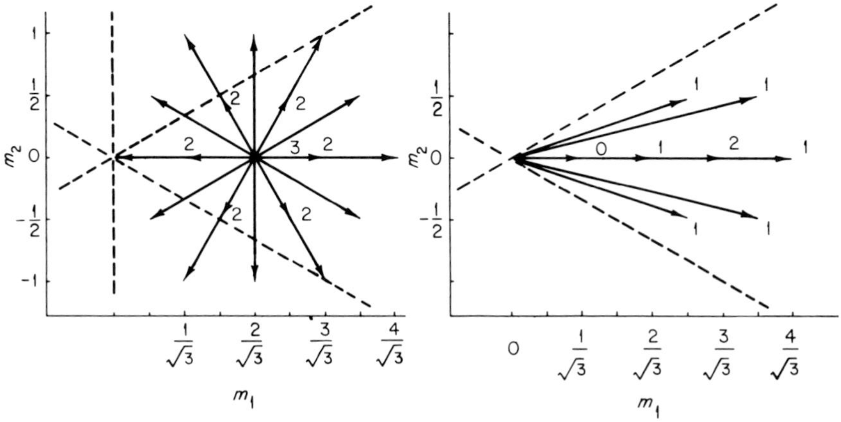

FIG. 4. Weight diagram for $N = 27$ displaced by **K** vector for $N = 8$ showing graphical technique of determining multiplicities of representations contained in the product $8 \boxtimes 27$.

is simple and that equivalent weights have the same multiplicity.) In Fig. 3b we have shifted the symmetry lines to the left by **R**. Then by Eq. (98) we find the set of equations (*9*)

$$1 = 1, \qquad v - 1 = 0, \qquad w - 1 = 0, \qquad y - w - v = 0,$$
$$z - y + v - 1 + w - y = 0.$$

The solution for the multiplicities is thus

$$v = w = \tfrac{1}{2}y = \tfrac{1}{3}z = 1,$$

as illustrated in Fig. 4a (we omit the ones).

Now that we easily can find the multiplicity of the weights within an irreducible representation, let us find the irreducible representations contained within a product representation (*11*). We have

$$C(\mu_1, \mu_2, \mu) = \sum_S \delta_S \omega_2(S\mathbf{K} - \mathbf{K}_1). \tag{99}$$

We again draw the weight diagram of one of the product representations *with* multiplicities attached to each weight. For convenience, we illustrate $8 \boxtimes 27$ with representations 1 and 2 being 8 and 27, respectively, and use the weight diagram for $N = 27$. In Fig. 4a we have shifted the symmetry lines to the point $-\mathbf{K}_1$ [in this case for $N = 8$ this point is $-(2/\sqrt{3})(1, 0)$]. We now reflect all the weights into the region of the $\mathbf{K}$ vectors, remembering the change of sign for odd numbers of reflections, and then list the algebraic sum of the multiplicities at a point. (Again, those vectors on a symmetry line cannot be reflected into this region and count for naught since their ξ vanish.) We have illustrated this procedure in Fig. 4b, with attached multiplicities at each point. Each of these points now represents a $\mathbf{K}$ vector for an irreducible representation. They are easily found to lead to the decomposition

$$8 \boxtimes 27 = 8 \oplus 10 \oplus \overline{10} \oplus 27 \oplus 27 \oplus 35 \oplus \overline{35} \oplus 64.$$

It is sometimes helpful, in considering an unfamiliar irreducible representation, to note that the hypercharge extends from $-\frac{1}{3}(2\lambda_1 + \lambda_2) \leqq y \leqq \frac{1}{3}(\lambda_1 + 2\lambda_2)$ and that the maximum ι-spin in a representation is $\frac{1}{2}(\lambda_1 + \lambda_2)$. These results follow from the highest weight and its Weyl reflections.

V. Tensor and Wigner Operators

We have found how the bases transform under the action of the generators H_i and E_α. But the bases for an irreducible representation can be considered to be the components of an irreducible tensor. We thus know how an irreducible tensor transforms. If these tensors themselves are operators, then instead of multiplication we must use commutation (*4*); that is, if $T_{y\iota}^{g_2 g_3 \iota_3}$ is an irreducible tensor operator, then we have the relations

$$(H_1, T_{y\iota}^{g_2 g_3 \iota_3}) = \frac{1}{\sqrt{3}} \iota_3 T_{y\iota}^{g_2 g_3 \iota_3}, \qquad (H_2, T_{y\iota}^{g_2 g_3 \iota_3}) = \tfrac{1}{2} y T_{y\iota}^{g_2 g_3 \iota_3},$$

$$(E_{\pm 1}, T_{y\iota}^{g_2 g_3 \iota_3}) = \frac{1}{\sqrt{6}} [\iota(\iota + 1) - \iota_3(\iota_3 \pm 1)]^{1/2} T_{y\iota}^{g_2 g_3 \iota_3 \pm 1}, \tag{100}$$

$$(E_{\pm 2}, T_{y\iota}^{g_2 g_3 \iota_3}) = \eta^{\pm}\left[\frac{\iota \pm \iota_3 + 1}{2\iota + 1}\right]^{1/2} A_{\mp y,\, \iota+1}^{g_2 \mp g_3}\, T_{y\pm 1,\, \iota+1/2}^{g_2 g_3\, \iota_3 \pm 1/2}$$

$$+\eta^{\mp}\left[\frac{\iota \mp \iota_3}{2\iota + 1}\right]^{1/2} A_{\pm y\iota}^{g_2 \pm g_3} \cdot T_{y\pm 1,\, \iota-1/2}^{g_2 g_3\, \iota_3 \pm 1/2},$$

$$(E_{\pm 3}, T_{y\iota}^{g_2 g_3 \iota_3}) = \pm\eta^{\pm}\left[\frac{\iota \mp \iota_3 + 1}{2\iota + 1}\right]^{1/2} A_{\mp y \iota+1}^{g_2 \mp g_3}\, T_{y\pm 1,\, \iota+1/2}^{g_2 g_3\, \iota_3 \mp 1/2}$$

$$\mp\eta^{\mp}\left[\frac{\iota \pm \iota_3}{2\iota + 1}\right]^{1/2} A_{\pm y\iota}^{g_2 \pm g_3}\, T_{y\pm 1,\, \iota-1/2}^{g_2 g_3\, \iota_3 \mp 1/2}.$$

[In fact, these transformation properties may be taken as the definition of the tensor operators (*6*).]

Again, by using the shorthand notation $\mu = \{g_2, g_3\}$ and $\nu = \{\iota, \iota_3, y\}$ the irreducible tensor operator may be written T_ν^μ. If we form the matrix element of this operator, that is, $\langle \Psi_{\nu_3}^{\mu_3} | T_{\nu_2}^{\mu_2} | \Psi_{\nu_1}^{\mu_1} \rangle$, then it can be shown (*9*) that

$$\langle \Psi_{\nu_3}^{\mu_3} | T_{\nu_2}^{\mu_2} | \Psi_{\nu_1}^{\mu_1} \rangle = \sum_\gamma \begin{pmatrix} \mu_1 & \mu_2 & \mu_3 \gamma \\ \nu_1 & \nu_2 & \nu_3 \end{pmatrix} \langle \Psi^{\mu_3} \| T^{\mu_2} \| \Psi^{\mu_1} \rangle_\gamma \tag{101}$$

where $\langle \Psi^{\mu_3} \| T^{\mu_2} \| \Psi^{\mu_1} \rangle_\gamma$ is the reduced matrix element and is independent of ν_1, ν_2, and ν_3. This equation is the statement of the Wigner-Eckart theorem for $SU(3)$.

It is convenient at this point to consider the generalized (*12*) "Wigner operator," the operator whose matrix elements are the Clebsch-Gordan coefficients for $SU(3)$. As an example, the matrix elements of the generators H_i and E_α are specific Clebsch-Gordan coefficients. If we designate the H_i and E_α by $\mathscr{T}_\nu^{8_1}$ (i.e., the label $\nu = \{\iota, \iota_3, y\}$ replaces i and α), then

$$\langle \Psi_{\nu_3}^{\mu} | \mathscr{T}_{\nu_2}^{8_1} | \Psi_{\nu_1}^{\mu} \rangle = \begin{pmatrix} \mu & 8_1 & \mu \\ \nu_1 & \nu_2 & \nu_3 \end{pmatrix}. \tag{102}$$

Note that $\mathscr{T}_{\nu_2}^{8_1}$, since it is a generator, cannot connect two different irreducible representations (thus we have just μ and not μ_1 and μ_3). Specifically, we see from Eq. (83) that the matrix elements of H_2 (with $\mathscr{T}_\nu^{8_1} \equiv \mathscr{T}_{\iota\iota_3 y}^{8_1}$, $H_2 \equiv \mathscr{T}_{000}^{8_1}$), and H_1 (i.e., $\mathscr{T}_{100}^{8_1}$) give

$$\begin{pmatrix} \mu & 8_1 & \mu \\ \nu & 000 & \nu \end{pmatrix} = \tfrac{1}{2} y; \qquad \begin{pmatrix} \mu & 8_1 & \mu \\ \nu & 100 & \nu \end{pmatrix} = \frac{1}{\sqrt{3}} \iota_3. \tag{103}$$

The Wigner operators that do not change μ (i.e., cannot connect two different irreducible representations) are often called "multipole" operators and can be completely expressed as polynomials of the generators. Two further examples of such operators are the Casimir invariant operators G_2 and G_3 (up to a normalization factor a_2 and a_3); that is,

$$\begin{pmatrix} \mu & 1_2 & \mu \\ \nu & 000 & \nu \end{pmatrix} = a_2 g_2; \qquad \begin{pmatrix} \mu & 1_3 & \mu \\ \nu & 000 & \nu \end{pmatrix} = a_3 g_3. \tag{104}$$

When these coefficients are nonzero (i.e., when $g_2 \neq 0$ or $g_3 \neq 0$, then the normalization convention is such that they should equal one (i.e., $a_2 = g_2^{-1}$ or $a_3 = g_3^{-1}$). Of course, the identity operator 1 is another trivial example:

$$\begin{pmatrix} \mu & 1_0 & \mu \\ \nu & 000 & \nu \end{pmatrix} = 1. \tag{105}$$

Note that the subscript on 1 (0, 2, or 3) denotes the degree of the polynomial in the generators that forms the multipole operator.

Other multipole operators can be formed in a manner analogous to the way the Casimir invariants are formed. For example, let us consider a second-degree polynomial in the generators. The terms that are antisymmetric in two generators will, by virtue of the commutation relations, reduce to terms linear in the generators. Thus, in order to consider a homogeneous expression of degree two, we must restrict ourselves to bilinear terms that are symmetric in the generators, that is, expressions of the form

$$a_{\alpha\beta}(E_\alpha, E_\beta)_+ + b_{ij} H_i H_j.$$

But each generator transforms as an eight-dimensional representation, so that this symmetric bilinear expression must transform as a linear combination of the symmetric representations in $8 \boxtimes 8$, that is, $1 \oplus 8 \oplus 27$. The bilinear expression that transforms as a one-dimensional representation is none other than the Casimir invariant.

To find the bilinear expression that transforms as an eight-dimensional representation, we proceed as follows. Call $\mathscr{T}^{8_2}_{000}$ that combination which under the commutation relations transforms as H_2. Then $\mathscr{T}^{8_2}_{000}$ must commute with $I_\pm$ and I_3 (i.e., $E_{\pm 1}$ and H_1) so that it must be of the form

$$\mathscr{T}^{8_2}_{000} = a[H_1^2 + (E_1, E_{-1})_+] + bH_2^2 + c[(E_2, E_{-2})_+ + (E_3, E_{-3})_+].$$

Similarly, call $\mathscr{T}^{8_2}_{100}$ the combination that transforms as H_1. Thus, $\mathscr{T}^{8_2}_{100}$ must transform as the third component of an isotopic spin vector; that is, it must have the form

$$\mathscr{T}^{8_2}_{100} = dH_1 H_2 + e[(E_2, E_{-2})_+ - (E_3, E_{-3})_+].$$

But under the Weyl reflection S_{-3}, we have

$$S_{-3}\mathscr{T}^{8_2}_{100} S^{\dagger}_{-3} = \tfrac{1}{2}\mathscr{T}^{8_2}_{100} + \tfrac{1}{2}\sqrt{3}\mathscr{T}^{8_2}_{000}.$$

By carrying out the left-hand side of this equation in terms of the bilinear expression for $\mathscr{T}^{8_2}_{100}$ and equating coefficients, we find

$$\mathscr{T}^{8_2}_{000} = a[H_1^2 + (E_1, E_{-1})_+ - H_2^2 - \tfrac{1}{2}(E_2, E_{-2})_+ - \tfrac{1}{2}(E_3, E_{-3})_+], \tag{106}$$

$$\mathscr{T}^{8_2}_{100} = a[2H_1 H_2 + \tfrac{1}{2}\sqrt{3}(E_2, E_{-2})_+ - \tfrac{1}{2}\sqrt{3}(E_3, E_{-3})_+].$$

If we now take the matrix element of each of these operators, we find two more Clebsch-Gordan coefficients [the matrix elements of $(E_2, E_{-2})_+ \pm (E_3, E_{-3})_+$ have already been given in Eqs. (72) and (76)]. The result is

$$\begin{pmatrix} \mu & 8_2 & \mu \\ \nu & 000 & \nu \end{pmatrix} = \tfrac{1}{2}a[\iota(\iota+1) - \tfrac{1}{4}y^2 - g_2], \tag{107}$$

$$\begin{pmatrix} \mu & 8_2 & \mu \\ \nu & 100 & \nu \end{pmatrix} = \frac{a\iota_3}{\sqrt{3\iota(\iota+1)}}\{3g_3 + \tfrac{1}{4}y[\iota(\iota+1) - \tfrac{1}{4}y^2 + 3g_2 + 1]\}. \tag{108}$$

The last coefficient is zero for $\iota = 0$. The a is a normalization constant that we shall leave undetermined.

The bilinear expression that transforms as a 27-dimensional representation can be obtained as follows. The single term $bE_1 E_1$ is the $\iota = 2$, $\iota_3 = 2$, $y = 0$ member of the 27-dimensional representation. Lowering this twice by means of the isotopic spin lowering operator gives the $\iota = 2$, $\iota_3 = 0$, $y = 0$ member; call it $\mathscr{T}^{27_2}_{200}$.

$$\mathscr{T}^{27_2}_{200} = b\left[(\tfrac{2}{3})^{1/2} H_1^2 - \frac{1}{\sqrt{6}}(E_1, E_{-1})_+\right] = \frac{b}{3\sqrt{6}}[3I_3^2 - I^2]. \tag{109}$$

Its matrix element gives the Clebsch-Gordan coefficient

$$\begin{pmatrix} \mu & 27_2 & \mu \\ \nu & 200 & \nu \end{pmatrix} = \frac{b}{3\sqrt{6}}[3\iota_3^2 - \iota(\iota+1)]. \tag{110}$$

By use of the operators E_3, E_{-2}, and E_{-1} we can find $\mathscr{T}^{27_2}_{100}$:

$$\mathscr{T}^{27_2}_{100} = \eta^- \eta^+ b[(\tfrac{6}{5})^{1/2} H_1 H_2 - (10)^{-1/2}(E_2, E_{-2})_+ + (10)^{-1/2}(E_3, E_{-3})_+], \quad (111)$$

which gives

$$\begin{pmatrix} \mu & 27_2 & \mu \\ \nu & 100 & \nu \end{pmatrix} = \eta^- \eta^+ \frac{b}{(10)^{1/2}} \frac{\iota_3}{\iota(\iota+1)} \{-2g_3 + \tfrac{1}{2}y[\tfrac{1}{12}y^2 + 3\iota(\iota+1) - g_2 - \tfrac{1}{3}]\}. \quad (112)$$

Repeating the procedure, we find

$$\mathscr{T}^{27_2}_{000} = \frac{b}{2(30)^{1/2}}[H_1^2 + (E_1, E_{-1})_+ + 9H_2^2 - 3(E_2, E_{-2})_+ - 3(E_3, E_{-3})_+], \quad (113)$$

which gives

$$\begin{pmatrix} \mu & 27_2 & \mu \\ \nu & 000 & \nu \end{pmatrix} = \frac{b}{2(30)^{1/2}}[\tfrac{4}{3}\iota(\iota+1) + 3y^2 - 3g_2]. \quad (114)$$

If we proceed to examine expressions that are symmetric and homogeneous of degree three in the generators, we can find linear combinations that transform as 1, 8, 10, 10, 27, and 64 (the symmetric parts of $8 \boxtimes 8 \boxtimes 8$). The one-dimensional operator here is simply the Casimir invariant G_3, while the eight-dimensional operator is $G_2 \mathscr{T}^{8_1}_{\nu}$, which gives the same Clebsch-Gordan coefficients as $\mathscr{T}^{8_1}_{\nu}$ (when normalized).

VI. Particle Classification, Masses, and Form Factors

We are now at a point where we can begin to think about assigning the observed particle states to the representations that we have constructed for $SU(3)$. Let us first focus our attention on particle states with baryon number equal to one. From the experimental data on the elastic and inelastic scattering of π-mesons ($\iota = 1$, $y = 0$) by nucleons ($\iota = \tfrac{1}{2}$, $y = 1$), we can make an analysis, as a function of energy, of the $y = 1$ scattering cross section. We discover that at certain energies the cross section for specific final states (having unique angular momentum, parity, and isotopic spin) goes through a maximum value. This resonant behavior of the cross section could be interpreted as the creation of a one-particle state that is extremely short-lived ($\tau \sim 10^{-23}$ sec) and hence has a very large uncertainty in its mass (equal to the width of the resonance at half-maximum).

The best known example of such an elastic scattering resonance is the $\iota = \frac{3}{2}$, $J^P = \frac{3}{2}^+$ resonance in πN scattering at a center-of-mass energy of 1236 MeV with a width of 120 MeV (*11*). This resonance can be interpreted as the sequence

$$\pi^+ + \mathrm{p} \rightarrow N^{*++} \rightarrow \pi^+ + \mathrm{p}.$$

At higher-incident pion energies, other final states become energetically possible. For example, at a center-of-mass energy of 1924 MeV, an $\iota = \frac{3}{2}$, $J^P = \frac{7}{2}^+$ resonance exists in both elastic and inelastic scattering (*13*).* It could be interpreted as the sequence

$$\begin{aligned} \pi^+ + \mathrm{p} \rightarrow N^{*++}(1924) &\rightarrow \pi^+ + \mathrm{p} \\ &\rightarrow K^+ + \Sigma^+ \\ &\rightarrow N^{*++}(1236) + \pi^0 \\ &\rightarrow N^{*+}(1236) + \pi^+. \end{aligned}$$

It will, of course, be our purpose later to try to predict the branching ratios of these various final states by the use of symmetry arguments.

In some cases, we can only make an analysis of the scattering in specific states by observing as a function of energy the correlations that exist between the particles that appear in the final states. Again, these resonances can be interpreted as short-lived particles. An example of such a sequence is

$$\pi^- + \mathrm{p} \rightarrow Y_0^* + K^0$$
$$\quad\quad\quad\quad \lfloor\!\rightarrow \Sigma^+ + \pi^-$$

where the peak of the $\Sigma^+\pi^-$ resonance occurs at a center-of-mass energy of 1405 MeV.

In Fig. 5 we have plotted, for each of the hypercharge channels, the center-of-mass energies of the peaks of those resonances that are considered better established (*13*) at the present time, as well as the masses of those baryons that are either stable or that can decay only via the weak or electromagnetic interactions. Given the rapidly changing experimental situation, such compilations have lifetimes only slightly longer than the particles listed in them. Our compilation is not to be taken as authoritative, but is to be used only as an illustration of the techniques that are being used at the time of the writing of this chapter, in order that the reader may better understand the present

* Unless otherwise specified the compilation of experimental data given by Rosenfeld *et al.* (*13*) has been used.

experimental situation. We hope that the techniques will outlive at least some of the present data.

As to the meson states (baryon number zero), we also find experimentally a spectrum of resonances. In Fig. 6 we have plotted, for each of the hypercharge channels, the center-of-mass energies of the peaks of the experimentally better-established resonances, as well as the masses of those mesons that decay only via the weak or electromagnetic interactions.

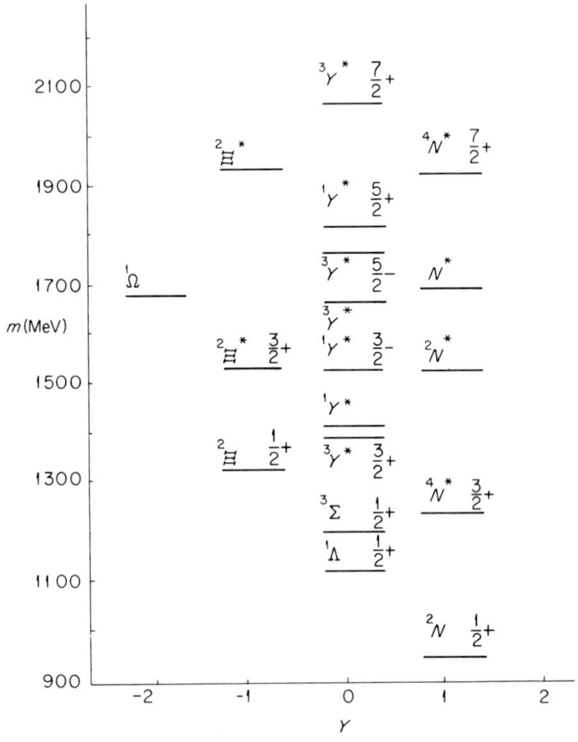

FIG. 5. Peaks of the better-established baryon resonances. The superscript to the left of a symbol is the isotopic spin multiplicity $2\iota + 1$ of the level. On the right side of the level is the J^P value. Only well-established ι and J^P values are given.

In assigning a set of particles to an N-dimensional representation of $SU(3)$, we must choose a set of N states, all of which have the same space-time quantum numbers, for example, total angular momentum J, parity P, and baryon number. And, of course, these N states must have just the proper hypercharges and isotopic spins to fit into the N-dimensional representation. We shall denote baryon supermultiplets by B_{JP}^{N} and meson supermultiplets by M_{JP}^{N}.

As was emphasized in the initial sections, these N states need not have the same observed mass. What is required is that only in some degree of approximation should they have the same mass; namely, in the limit of neglecting the self-energies due to an interaction that violates the $SU(3)$ symmetry. If the

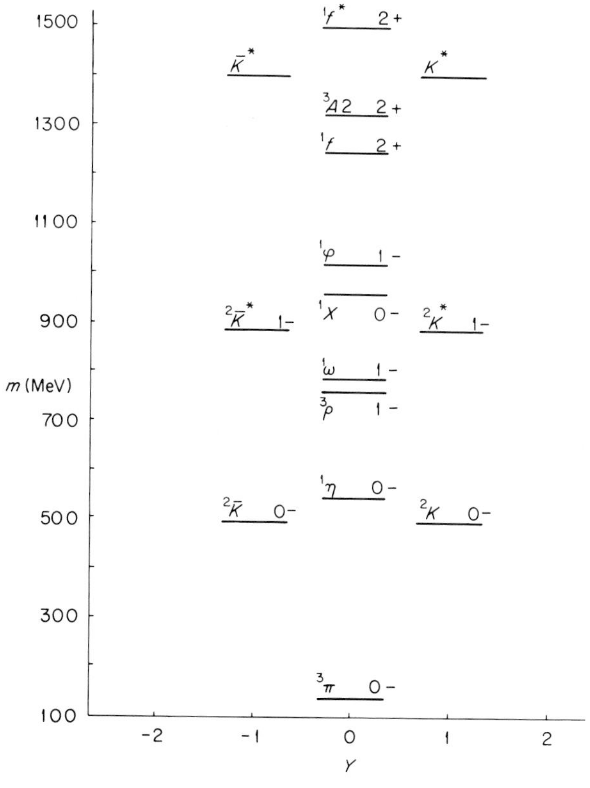

FIG. 6. Peaks of the better-established meson resonances. The superscript to the left of a symbol is the isotopic spin multiplicity $2\iota+1$ of the level. On the right side of the level is the J^P value. Only well-established ι and J^P values are given.

approximation is to be useful, of course, it is necessary that this symmetry-breaking interaction be "relatively small." Or, conversely, if the approximation proves useful, then we may conclude that the symmetry-breaking interaction is weaker than the $SU(3)$-symmetric interaction (to distinguish between the strengths, they are often classified as moderately strong and strong interactions, respectively). It then might be expected that the mass splittings within the $SU(3)$ multiplets should be "relatively small" compared with the symmetric mass.*

In order to be more quantitative with regard to the masses, we have to know the transformation properties [under $SU(3)$] of the moderately strong symmetry-breaking interaction. Gell-Mann (*1*) has suggested that it transforms like the hypercharge generator Y; that is, that it should be a tensor operator T^8_{000}. We therefore can proceed as follows to calculate the observed masses. Let the one-particle physical state vector (Heisenberg) be $|\boldsymbol{\mu\nu}\rangle$ so that the physical masses (the energies in the center-of-mass system), are

$$m(\mu\nu) = \langle\boldsymbol{\mu\nu}|\mathscr{H}|\boldsymbol{\mu\nu}\rangle. \tag{115}$$

As discussed before, we make a perturbation expansion of the Heisenberg state vectors in terms of the $SU(3)$-symmetric state vectors, the expansion being in powers of the $SU(3)$-nonsymmetric part of the Hamiltonian, $\mathscr{H}_{\mathrm{I}}$. We put the expansion in operator form so that it acts on only one $SU(3)$-symmetric state, $|\Psi^\mu_\nu\rangle$, and then write the result in a symbolic form

$$\begin{aligned} m(\mu\nu) &= \langle\boldsymbol{\mu\nu}|\mathscr{H}|\boldsymbol{\mu\nu}\rangle = \langle\Psi^\mu_\nu|V^\dagger\mathscr{H}V|\Psi^\mu_\nu\rangle, \\ &= \langle\Psi^\mu_\nu|\mathscr{H}_0|\Psi^\mu_\nu\rangle + \langle\Psi^\mu_\nu|\sum_{n=1}^{\infty} a_n \mathscr{H}'^n_{\mathrm{I}}|\Psi^\mu_\nu\rangle, \end{aligned} \tag{116}$$

where the a_n (which are operators) are $SU(3)$-symmetric and the $\mathscr{H}'_{\mathrm{I}}$ transforms under the $SU(3)$ transformation like $\mathscr{H}_{\mathrm{I}}$. The $SU(3)$-symmetric mass $m_0(\mu)$ (independent of ν) is $\langle\Psi^\mu_\nu|\mathscr{H}_0|\Psi^\mu_\nu\rangle$.

To first order in the moderately strong symmetry-breaking interaction and by use of the Wigner-Eckart theorem, we find

$$\begin{aligned} m(\mu\nu) &\simeq m_0(\mu) + a(\mu)\begin{pmatrix}\mu & 8_1 & \mu \\ \nu & 000 & \nu\end{pmatrix} + b(\mu)\begin{pmatrix}\mu & 8_2 & \mu \\ \nu & 000 & \nu\end{pmatrix} \\ &= m_0(\mu) + \tfrac{1}{2}a(\mu)\,y + b(\mu)\,[\iota(\iota+1) - \tfrac{1}{4}y^2 - g_2]. \end{aligned} \tag{117}$$

The last step by Eqs. (103) and (107). This is the Gell-Mann–Okubo mass formula (*1, 14*).

* If we take as a measure of relatively small a parameter that is the ratio of the largest difference between an observed mass and the average mass of the eight states with $J^P = \frac{1}{2}^+$ divided by the average mass, we find the number 1/5.4. The corresponding parameters for the case of mass splittings within the isotopic spin multiplets of these eight baryons is $\lesssim 1/284$. Of course, in most of elementary particle physics, isotopic spin invariance is a very good approximation. On the other hand, the number 1/5.4 might still be considered "relatively" small and $SU(3)$ a fair approximation.

Since $\mathscr{H}_0$ is invariant under $SU(3)$, the interaction Hamiltonian $\mathscr{H}_{\mathrm{I}}$ consists of the electromagnetic interaction $\mathscr{H}_{\mathrm{em}}$ and the weak interaction $\mathscr{H}_{\mathrm{W}}$ in addition to the moderately strong symmetry-breaking interaction $\mathscr{H}_{\mathrm{SB}}$; that is, $\mathscr{H}_{\mathrm{I}} = \mathscr{H}_{\mathrm{SB}} + \mathscr{H}_{\mathrm{em}} + \mathscr{H}_{\mathrm{W}}$. So far, we have only considered the mass splitting due to $\mathscr{H}_{\mathrm{SB}}$. Now the electromagnetic interaction is of the form of the electromagnetic current times the electromagnetic four-vector potential. Under the transformations of $SU(3)$, the em current transforms like the electric charge Q (we shall denote such a tensor operator as Q'; similarly, we can denote the tensor operator that transforms like hypercharge Y as Y'). The contribution of the em interaction to the self-energies of the particles will occur only in even orders of $\mathscr{H}_{\mathrm{em}}$, since the photon must be emitted and absorbed. It therefore follows that, including the effects of $\mathscr{H}_{\mathrm{SB}}$ to first order and $\mathscr{H}_{\mathrm{em}}$ to second order with *no* cross terms, Eq. (116) can be written

$$m(\mu\nu) \simeq m_0(\mu) + \tfrac{1}{2}a(\mu)\,y + b(\mu)\,[\iota(\iota+1) - \tfrac{1}{4}y^2 - g_2] + \langle \Psi_\nu^\mu | Q'^2 | \Psi_\nu^\mu \rangle. \qquad (118)$$

We note that since Q'^2 transforms as $8 \boxtimes 8$, it must be a linear combination of the Wigner operators $\mathscr{T}^{\mu}_{\iota 00}$ for 1, 8, 10, $\overline{10}$, and 27 that satisfy $S_{-3}\,Q'^2 S_{-3}^{\dagger} = Q'^2$ and $(E_3,\, Q'^2) = 0$. This implies

$$Q'^2 = c\mathscr{T}^{1}_{000} + \sum_{\gamma} d_\gamma(\mathscr{T}^{8\gamma}_{000} + \sqrt{3}\mathscr{T}^{8\gamma}_{100}) + \sum_{\gamma} e_\gamma(\mathscr{T}^{27\gamma}_{000} + \sqrt{3}\,\mathscr{T}^{27\gamma}_{100} + \sqrt{5}\mathscr{T}^{27\gamma}_{200}). \qquad (119)$$

The matrix element of the em current $\mathbf{j}_\alpha(0)$ [recall $Q = \int d^3x\, j_0(x)$] gives us the electric charge and magnetic moment form factors for the single-particle states. By making our perturbation expansion in operator form, the matrix element of $\mathbf{j}$ has the form (we suppress the space-time properties)

$$\langle \boldsymbol{\mu\nu} | \mathbf{j} | \boldsymbol{\mu\nu} \rangle = \langle \Psi_\nu^\mu | \sum_{n,l} a_{nl}\; Y'^n\; Q'^{2l+1} | \Psi_\nu^\mu \rangle, \qquad (120)$$

since under the $SU(3)$ transformation, j transforms like Q; that is, it is a tensor operator Q'.

To first order in $\mathscr{H}_{\mathrm{em}}$ and zeroth order in $\mathscr{H}_{\mathrm{SB}}$ we find, upon using the properties $Q' = -S_2\,Y'S_2^{\dagger}$ and $U^2 = S_2 I^2 S_2^{\dagger}$ on the Wigner operators in Y' $[= a\mathscr{T}^{8_1}_{000} + b\mathscr{T}^{8_2}_{000}]$, that

$$\langle \boldsymbol{\mu\nu} | \mathbf{j} | \boldsymbol{\mu\nu} \rangle \simeq \tfrac{1}{2}a(\mu)\,q + b(\mu)\,[u(u+1) - \tfrac{1}{4}q^2 - g_2] \qquad (121)$$

where q and u are the charge and U-spin of the state.

A. The Baryon States $B^8_{1/2^+}$

Let us now explicitly assign the states to representations of $SU(3)$. The first obvious set for the baryons is formed by the eight states $N(y=1,\ \iota=\frac{1}{2}$, n, and p), $\Xi(y=-1,\ \iota=\frac{1}{2},\ \Xi^0$, and $\Xi^-)$, $\Sigma(y=0,\ \iota=1,\ \Sigma^+,\ \Sigma^0$, and $\Sigma^-)$, and $\Lambda(y=0,\ \iota=0)$. They all have the same $J^P=\frac{1}{2}^+$ and just the correct hypercharges and isotopic spins to fit into an eight-dimensional representation. Thus, these states are assigned (*1*) to $B^8_{1/2^+}$. For convenience, in Table II we have listed the action of the generators, as well as the results of the three Weyl reflections, on these eight bases (*2*).

According to the mass formula of Eq. (117), which neglects em mass differences, we find one relation (*1*, *14*) among the masses of the four ι-spin multiplets

$$\tfrac{3}{4}m_\Lambda+\tfrac{1}{4}m_\Sigma=\tfrac{1}{2}m_N+\tfrac{1}{2}m_\Xi. \tag{122}$$

If we take the average mass within the isotopic multiplets, the two sides of the equation are presently 1128 and 1135 MeV. In going to second order in the moderately strong symmetry-breaking interaction, we have four unknown parameters (reduced matrix elements) and four unknown masses, so that no predictions are possible for B^8.

If we include the self-energy effects of electromagnetism to second order in $\mathscr{H}_{\rm em}$ but with no cross term with $\mathscr{H}_{\rm SB}$, we find, from Eqs. (118) and (119), the two mass relations (*15*, *16*)

$$\begin{aligned} m_{\Xi^-}-m_{\Xi^0}+m_{\rm n}-m_{\rm p}&=m_{\Sigma^-}-m_{\Sigma^+},\\ m_{\Xi^-}+m_{\Xi^0}+m_{\rm n}+m_{\rm p}&=3m_\Lambda+m_{\Sigma^+}+m_{\Sigma^-}-m_{\Sigma^0}. \end{aligned} \tag{123}$$

At present, the two sides of the first equation are experimentally 7.8 and 7.9 MeV and of the second 4513 and 4541 MeV.

For the electromagnetic form factors to zeroth order in $\mathscr{H}_{\rm SB}$, we find the following relations (*15*) from Eq. (121) (we define $\Gamma_{\rm p}\equiv\langle\mathbf{p}|\mathbf{j}|\mathbf{p}\rangle$, and so forth)

$$\begin{aligned} \Gamma_{\rm p}&=\Gamma_{\Sigma^+}=-(\Gamma_{\Xi^-}+\Gamma_{\rm n})=-(\Gamma_{\Sigma^-}+\Gamma_{\rm n}),\\ \Gamma_{\rm n}&=-2\Gamma_{\Sigma^0}=2\Gamma_\Lambda=\Gamma_{\Xi^0}=-\frac{2}{\sqrt{3}}\Gamma_T \end{aligned} \tag{124}$$

where $\Gamma_T=\langle\mathbf{\Lambda}|\mathbf{j}|\mathbf{\Xi}^0\rangle$ is the transition moment for the decay $\Sigma^0\to\Lambda+\gamma$.

In order to look, in general, at the higher-order corrections to the form factors in the case of B^8 or the higher-order corrections to the mass in the

TABLE II

ACTION OF GENERATORS AND WEYL REFLECTIONS ON BASES OF B^{8a}

	p	n	Ξ^0	Ξ^-	Σ^+	Σ^0	Σ^-	Λ
$\sqrt{6}E_1$		p		Ξ^0		$-\sqrt{2}\Sigma^+$	$\sqrt{2}\Sigma^0$	
$\sqrt{6}E_{-1}$	n		Ξ^-		$-\sqrt{2}\Sigma^0$	$\sqrt{2}\Sigma^-$		
$2\sqrt{3}E_2$			$-\sqrt{2}\Sigma^+$	$\Sigma^0 + \sqrt{3}\Lambda$		p	$\sqrt{2}$n	$\sqrt{3}$p
$2\sqrt{3}E_{-2}$	$\Sigma^0 + \sqrt{3}\Lambda$	$\sqrt{2}\Sigma^-$			$-\sqrt{2}\Xi^0$	Ξ^-		$\sqrt{3}\Xi^-$
$2\sqrt{3}E_3$			$\Sigma^0 - \sqrt{3}\Lambda$	$\sqrt{2}\Sigma^-$	$\sqrt{2}$p	$-$n		$\sqrt{3}$n
$2\sqrt{3}E_{-3}$	$\sqrt{2}\Sigma^+$	$-\Sigma^0 + \sqrt{3}\Lambda$				Ξ^0	$\sqrt{2}\Xi^-$	$-\sqrt{3}\Xi^0$
$\sqrt{3}H_1$	$\frac{1}{2}$p	$-\frac{1}{2}$n	$\frac{1}{2}\Xi^0$	$-\frac{1}{2}\Xi^-$	Σ^+		$-\Sigma^-$	
$2H_2$	p	n	$-\Xi^0$	$-\Xi^-$				
$S_{\pm 1}$	$\mp$n	$\pm$p	$\mp\Xi^-$	$\pm\Xi^0$	$-\Sigma^-$	$-\Sigma^0$	$-\Sigma^+$	Λ
$S_{\pm 2}$	Ξ^-	$\mp\Sigma^-$	$\mp\Sigma^+$	p	$\pm\Xi^0$	$\frac{1}{2}(\Sigma^0 - \sqrt{3}\Lambda)$	$\pm$n	$-\frac{1}{2}(\sqrt{3}\Sigma^0 + \Lambda)$
$S_{\pm 3}$	$\mp\Sigma^+$	$-\Xi^0$	$-$n	$\pm\Sigma^-$	$\pm$p	$\frac{1}{2}(\Sigma^0 + \sqrt{3}\Lambda)$	$\mp\Xi^-$	$\frac{1}{2}(\sqrt{3}\Sigma^0 - \Lambda)$

[a] For the meson bases M^8, substitute (p, n, Ξ^0, Ξ^-, Σ^+, Σ^0, Σ^-, Λ) $\rightarrow$ (K^+, K^0, $\bar{K}^0$, $-\bar{K}^+$, π^+, π^0, π^-, η).

case of higher-dimensional representations, we could proceed, in a straightforward manner, to determine the appropriate linear combination of multipole operators. Namely, we could generalize Eqs. (117), (118), and (121). It is often simpler, however, to use the commutation properties of the tensor operators Eq. (100) and their Weyl reflection properties than it is to find and use these general formulas. Let us demonstrate the procedure.

Consider the matrix element of the current to all orders in $\mathscr{H}_{\text{em}}$ and zeroth order in $\mathscr{H}_{\text{SB}}$ [a slightly better approximation than that leading to Eq. (124)]. The tensor operator in this case is of the form $\sum_{n=0}^{\infty} a_n(Q')^{2n+1}$. But since $(E_3, Q') = 0$, we have

$$\left(E_3, \sum_{n=0}^{\infty} a_n(Q')^{2n+1}\right) = 0. \tag{125}$$

By taking the matrix element of this equation between the states $\langle \mathrm{p}|$ and $|\Sigma^+\rangle$ we find, from Table II,

$$\begin{aligned} 0 &= \langle \mathrm{p}|(E_3, \sum a_n(Q')^{2n+1})|\Sigma^+\rangle \\ &= \frac{1}{\sqrt{6}}\langle \Sigma^+|\sum a_n(Q')^{2n+1}|\Sigma^+\rangle - \frac{1}{\sqrt{6}}\langle \mathrm{p}|\sum a_n(Q')^{2n+1}|\mathrm{p}\rangle \\ &= \frac{1}{\sqrt{6}}(\Gamma_{\Sigma^+} - \Gamma_{\mathrm{p}}). \end{aligned} \tag{126}$$

Similarly, from the matrix element between the states $\langle \Sigma^-|$ and $|\Xi^-\rangle$ we find $\Gamma_{\Sigma^-} = \Gamma_{\Xi^-}$. By proceeding this way for the other matrix elements we find the following set of predictions (*14*) holding to all orders in $\mathscr{H}_{\text{em}}$ and zero order in $\mathscr{H}_{\text{SB}}$.

$$\Gamma_{\mathrm{p}} = \Gamma_{\Sigma^+}, \qquad \Gamma_{\Sigma^-} = \Gamma_{\Xi^-}, \qquad \Gamma_{\mathrm{n}} = \Gamma_{\Xi^0} = \tfrac{3}{2}\Gamma_\Lambda - \tfrac{1}{2}\Gamma_{\Sigma^0} = \Gamma_\Lambda - \frac{1}{\sqrt{3}}\Gamma_T. \tag{127}$$

We can immediately generalize this method to consider the approximation of all orders in $\mathscr{H}_{\text{em}}$ and up to first order in $\mathscr{H}_{\text{SB}}$. The tensor operator in this case is $\sum_n (a_{0n} + a_{1n} Y')(Q')^{2n+1}$. But by the commutation relations, we have

$$\left(E_3, \left(E_3, \sum_{n=0}^{\infty} (a_{0n} + a_{1n} Y')(Q')^{2n+1}\right)\right) = 0. \tag{128}$$

By taking the matrix element of this equation between the states $\langle n|$ and $|\Xi^0\rangle$, we find the one existing relationship that holds to this order. The result (*17*) is

$$-2\sqrt{3}\Gamma_T = 2(\Gamma_{\Xi^0} + \Gamma_n) - \Gamma_{\Sigma^0} - 3\Gamma_\Lambda. \tag{129}$$

Finally, because $(E_1, (E_1, Q' Y'^n)) = 0$, the well-known relationship (*18*)

$$\Gamma_{\Sigma^-} + \Gamma_{\Sigma^+} = 2\Gamma_{\Sigma^0} \tag{130}$$

may easily be shown to hold to first order in $\mathscr{H}_{em}$ and all orders in $\mathscr{H}_{SB}$.

B. The Baryon States $B^{10}_{3/2^+}$

We see from Fig. 5 that the first set of resonant states lying above $B^8_{1/2^+}$ in mass have spin-parity $J^P = \frac{3}{2}^+$. There are ten such states, the $N^*(1236)$ ($y = 1$, $\iota = \frac{3}{2}$, N^{*++}, N^{*+}, N^{*0}, and N^{*-}), the $Y_1^*(1382)$ ($y = 0$, $\iota = 1$, Y_1^{*+}, Y_1^{*0}, Y_1^{*-}), the $\Xi^*(1530)$ ($y = -1$, $\iota = \frac{1}{2}$, Ξ^{*0}, and Ξ^{*-}), and the $\Omega(1676)$ ($y = -2$, $\iota = 0$, Ω^-). The isotopic spin and hypercharge content of $D^{10}(3, 0)$ just fit these ten observed states, so that we characterize (*2*) these states as $B^{10}_{3/2^+}$. For convenience, in Table III we have listed the action of the generators, as well as the action of the three Weyl reflections, on each of the ten bases.

Having already introduced the $SU(3)$-symmetry-breaking interaction, we are now prepared to calculate the mass relations that should hold for $B^{10}_{3/2^+}$. In Eq. (116), let us include terms to second order in $\mathscr{H}_{SB}$ and, at first, to zeroth order in $\mathscr{H}_{em}$ (i.e., we will initially ignore the mass splittings within an isotopic spin multiplet). We obtain

$$m(\mu\nu) \simeq m_0(\mu) + \tfrac{1}{2}a(\mu)\,y + b(\mu)\,[\iota(\iota+1) - \tfrac{1}{4}y^2 - g_2] + \langle \Psi^\mu_\nu |\, Y'^2 | \Psi^\mu_\nu \rangle. \tag{131}$$

As we did earlier, we note that Y'^2 can be written as a linear combination of Wigner operators $\mathscr{T}^\mu_{000}$ for $N = 1$, 8, and 27 (10 and $\overline{10}$ contain no $\iota = 0$, $y = 0$ member). Thus

$$Y'^2 = c\mathscr{T}^1_{000} + \sum_\gamma d_\gamma \mathscr{T}^{8\gamma}_{000} + \sum_\gamma e_\gamma \mathscr{T}^{27\gamma}_{000}. \tag{132}$$

But since $10 \boxtimes 10 = 1 \oplus 8 \oplus 27 \oplus 64$ contains 8 only once, there must exist a relationship between the Clebsch-Gordan coefficients for 8_1 and 8_2. It is easily seen that for $D^{10}(3, 0)$, the relationship $\iota = 1 + \frac{1}{2}y$ holds (*19*). Substituting this into the expression for the 8_2 Clebsch-Gordan coefficient, we find

$$\iota(\iota+1) - \tfrac{1}{4}y^2 - g_2 = 2 + \tfrac{3}{2}y - g_2 = \tfrac{3}{2}y$$

TABLE III

ACTION OF GENERATORS AND WEYL REFLECTIONS ON BASES OF B^{10}

	N^{++}	N^{+}	N^{0}	N^{-}	Y^{+}	Y^{0}	Y^{-}	Ξ^{0}	Ξ^{-}	Ω^{-}
$\sqrt{6}E_1$		$\sqrt{3}N^{++}$	$2N^{+}$	$\sqrt{3}N^{0}$		$-\sqrt{2}Y^{+}$	$\sqrt{2}Y^{0}$		Ξ^{0}	
$\sqrt{6}E_{-1}$	$\sqrt{3}N^{+}$	$2N^{0}$	$\sqrt{3}N^{-}$		$-\sqrt{2}Y^{0}$	$\sqrt{2}Y^{-}$		Ξ^{-}		
$\sqrt{6}E_2$					$-\sqrt{3}N^{++}$	$\sqrt{2}N^{+}$	N^{0}	$-2Y^{+}$	$\sqrt{2}Y^{0}$	$\sqrt{3}\Xi^{0}$
$\sqrt{6}E_{-2}$	$-\sqrt{3}Y^{+}$	$\sqrt{2}Y^{0}$	Y^{-}		$-2\Xi^{0}$	$\sqrt{2}\Xi^{-}$		$\sqrt{3}\Omega^{-}$		
$\sqrt{6}E_3$					$-N^{+}$	$\sqrt{2}N^{0}$	$\sqrt{3}N^{-}$	$\sqrt{2}Y^{0}$	$2Y^{-}$	$\sqrt{3}\Xi^{-}$
$\sqrt{6}E_{-3}$		$-Y^{+}$	$\sqrt{2}Y^{0}$	$\sqrt{3}Y^{-}$		$\sqrt{2}\Xi^{0}$	$2\Xi^{-}$		$\sqrt{3}\Omega^{-}$	
$S_{\pm 1}$	$\mp N^{-}$	$\pm N^{0}$	$\mp N^{+}$	$\pm N^{++}$	$-Y^{-}$	$-Y^{0}$	$-Y^{+}$	$\mp\Xi^{-}$	$\pm\Xi^{0}$	Ω^{-}
$S_{\pm 2}$	$\mp\Omega^{-}$	Ξ^{-}	$\mp Y^{-}$	N^{-}	$\mp\Xi^{0}$	$-Y^{0}$	$\pm N^{0}$	$\pm Y^{+}$	N^{+}	$\pm N^{++}$
$S_{\pm 3}$	N^{++}	$\pm Y^{+}$	Ξ^{0}	$\mp\Omega^{-}$	$\mp N^{+}$	$-Y^{0}$	$\pm\Xi^{-}$	N^{0}	$\mp Y^{-}$	$\pm N^{-}$

when we note that $g_2 = 2$; that is, the Clebsch-Gordan coefficients for 8_1 and 8_2 are proportional in D^{10}. The same must be true for the 27_γ. In fact, substituting $\iota = 1 + \frac{1}{2}y$ in the Clebsch-Gordan coefficient for 27_2, we see that we can write the mass formula as (*17*)

$$m(10, \nu) \simeq m_0(10) + a(10)\,y + b(10)\,y^2, \tag{133}$$

which leads to one relation among the four isotopic multiplets

$$3m_{\Xi*} + m_{N*} = 3m_{Y*} + m_{\Omega}. \tag{134}$$

Experimentally, the two sides of this equation are 5825 and 5823 MeV. In fact, b is within experimental error of being zero, so that the equal mass spacing (*19*) rule $m(10, \nu) \simeq m_0(10) + a(10)y$ holds with a great deal of accuracy.

Let us now include the effects of electromagnetism. Our equation can now be written

$$m(\mu\nu) = \langle \Psi^{\mu}_{\nu} | \sum_{n,l} a_{nl}\, Y'^{n} Q'^{2l} | \Psi^{\mu}_{\nu} \rangle. \tag{135}$$

It will be much simpler at this point to use the direct procedure of finding relations between the masses without resorting to first finding the Wigner operators or the Clebsch-Gordan coefficients. This technique, which was introduced in the cases of B^8, is especially useful when considering terms of the form $Y' Q'^{2n}$ or $Y'^2 Q'^{2n}$. We proceed as follows.

Consider the expression $\langle \Psi^{\mu}_{\nu} | \sum b_l Q'^{2l} | \Psi^{\mu}_{\nu} \rangle$. By means of the relation $S_{-3}\, Q'\, S^{\dagger}_{-3} = Q'$, we find

$$\langle N^+ | \sum_{l=1}^{\infty} b_l\, Q'^{2l} | N^+ \rangle = \langle Y^+ | S_{-3} \sum_{l=1}^{\infty} b_l\, Q'^{2l}\, S^{\dagger}_{-3} | Y^+ \rangle = \langle Y^+ | \sum_{l=1}^{\infty} b_l\, Q'^{2l} | Y^+ \rangle, \tag{136}$$

which may be written $\delta m_{N^+} = \delta m_{Y^+}$. Similarly, we find $\delta m_{\Xi^0} = \delta m_{N^0}$, $\delta m_{\Omega^-} = \delta m_{N^-}$ and $\delta m_{\Xi^-} = \delta m_{Y^-}$. We now also use the relations $(E_3, Q'^{2l}) = 0$ in the following way

$$0 = \langle Y^0 | (E_3, \sum_{l=1} b_l\, Q'^{2l}) | \Xi^0 \rangle = \frac{1}{\sqrt{3}} \langle \Xi^0 | \sum_{l=1} b_l\, Q'^{2l} | \Xi^0 \rangle - \frac{1}{\sqrt{3}} \langle Y^0 | \sum_{l=1} b_l\, Q'^{2l} | Y^0 \rangle,$$

which is written $\delta m_{\Xi^0} = \delta m_{Y^0}$. Similarly, we find $\delta m_{N^-} = \delta m_{Y^-}$. Approximating Eq. (135) by

$$m(\mu\nu) \simeq m_0(\mu) + \langle \Psi_\nu^\mu | \sum_{n=1} a_{n0}\, Y'^n + \sum_{l=1} a_{0l}\, Q'^{2l} | \Psi_\nu^\mu \rangle, \tag{137}$$

that is, to all orders, separately, in $\mathscr{H}_{\text{SB}}$ and $\mathscr{H}_{\text{em}}$, with no cross terms, we find from these relations among the matrix elements of Q'^{2l} the following relationships (*20, 21*) among the observed masses.

$$\begin{aligned} m_{N^+} - m_{N^0} &= m_{Y^+} - m_{Y^0}, \\ m_{\Xi^-} - m_{\Xi^0} &= m_{Y^-} - m_{Y^0} = m_{N^-} - m_{N^0}. \end{aligned} \tag{138}$$

If further we restrict ourselves to second order in Q', then by use of the expression $(E_1, (E_1, (E_1, Q'^2))) = 0$, we find the additional relation (*20–22*)

$$3m_{N^+} + m_{N^-} = 3m_{N^0} + m_{N^{++}}. \tag{139}$$

Let us now consider the approximation

$$m(\mu\nu) \simeq \langle \Psi_\nu^\mu | \sum_{l=0}^{\infty} (a_{0l} + a_{1l}\, Y') Q'^{2l} | \Psi_\nu^\mu \rangle. \tag{140}$$

That is, we are including a cross term in $\mathscr{H}_{\text{SB}}$ and $\mathscr{H}_{\text{em}}$. By use of the expression

$$(E_3, (E_3, (a_0 + a_1\, Y')\, Q'^{2l})) = 0 \tag{141}$$

we find the relations (*23, 25*)

$$\begin{aligned} 2m_{\Xi^-} &= m_{Y^-} + m_{\Omega^-} \\ 2m_{Y^-} &= m_{N^-} + m_{\Xi^-} \\ 2m_{Y^0} &= m_{N^0} + m_{\Xi^0}. \end{aligned} \tag{142}$$

Again restricting the expansion to second order in Q', we obtain Eq. (139).

Let us now consider an even higher approximation, namely,

$$m(\mu\nu) \simeq \langle \Psi_\nu^\mu | \sum_{l=0} (a_{0l} + a_{1l}\, Y' + a_{2l}\, Y'^2) Q'^{2l} | \Psi_\nu^\mu \rangle, \tag{143}$$

that is, to second order in $\mathscr{H}_{\text{SB}}$ and to all orders in $\mathscr{H}_{\text{em}}$. With the aid of the expression $(E_3, (E_3, (E_3, (a_0 + a_1 Y' + a_2 Y'^2) Q'^{2l}))) = 0$ we find the one relation (*21*, *23*) that is valid to this order

$$3m_{\Xi^-} + m_{N^-} = 3m_{Y^-} + m_{\Omega^-}. \tag{144}$$

Again, by restricting the expansion to second order in Q', Eq. (139) is also valid.

C. THE BARYON STATES $B_?^1(1405)$ AND $B_{3/2^-}^8$

The next resonance as we go up the mass scale occurs at 1405 MeV. It consists of one state $Y_0^*(y = 0, \iota = 0)$ and is customarily assigned to the one-dimensional representation. The spin and parity of the state have not yet been established experimentally, so that we denote it as $B_?^1(1405)$.

It might be appropriate to note at this point that in this part of the mass spectrum we are already in a region that is still experimentally rather hazy. We are not referring solely to the statistical fluctuations that occasionally lead to "resonances" that are seen in only one experiment, but also to the possible existence of resonances whose modes of production or decay, or both, make them difficult to detect. We cite two possible examples. One is the case where the cross section for the production of an unobserved resonance along with one or two other particles is so low that the resonance is masked by the statistical fluctuations in the background. The other members of the multiplets associated with this unobserved resonance, on the other hand, may have enhanced cross sections due to dynamical effects such as, for example, the one-meson or one-baryon exchange mechanisms. Of course, such resonances eventually will be observed. As the bombarding energies are raised, the dynamical effects will change and the cross section for the unobserved resonance will become comparable to that for the other members of the multiplet, for example, when produced along with three or four other particles or when the entire multiplet is dominantly produced as the decay product of an even higher resonance. The second example of a state that could have gone undetected up to the present involves a mode of decay that is difficult to detect. For example, if the mass of an undetected particle is such that energy conservation forbids its decay via the strong interactions, its most likely mode of decay is to a lower-mass baryon state by the emission of a photon (if allowed). For such short-lived states (10^{-15}–10^{-20} sec) produced in many-particle final states, detection is difficult unless the photon converts to an electron-positron pair. The essence of these remarks is that only with complete experimental information can we be completely sure of our assignments of resonances to the $SU(3)$ representations.

For the next set of confirmed resonances, only two have well-established spin-parity assignments. They are $Y_0^*(1520)$ ($y=0$, $\iota=0$) and $N_{1/2}^*(1518)$ ($y=1$, $\iota=\frac{1}{2}$, N^{*+}, and N^{*0}) with $J^P=\frac{3}{2}^-$. For two other near-lying confirmed levels, the $Y_1^*(1660)$ ($y=0$, $\iota=1$, Y_1^{*+}, Y_1^{*0}, Y_1^{*-}) and the $\Xi^*(1816)$ ($y=-1$, $\iota=\frac{1}{2}$, Ξ^{*0}, and Ξ^{*-}), the J^P values have not been established. If we assigned those eight states to an eight-dimensional representation, assuming they all had $J^P=\frac{3}{2}^-$, we would immediately find that the mass formula Eq. (117) is not reasonably satisfied. The most likely explanation for this discrepancy is that not all these resonances belong to the same $SU(3)$ multiplet.

As of this writing, the only completed baryon $SU(3)$ multiplets are the $B_{1/2^+}^8$ and the $B_{3/2^+}^{10}$. As the experimental situation is clarified, however, other completed multiplets will emerge and hopefully will reasonably satisfy the mass formula. Ultimately, we should discover that every state belongs to some $SU(3)$ multiplet and that each multiplet is complete.

D. The Meson States $M_{0^-}^8$

From Fig. 6, we see that there are nine states with $J^P=0^-$. These are π ($y=0$, $\iota=1$, π^+, π^0, and π^-), $\eta(549)$ ($y=0$, $\iota=0$), $X(959)$ ($y=0$, $\iota=0$), K ($y=1$, $\iota=\frac{1}{2}$, K^+, and K^0), and $\bar{K}$ ($y=-1$, $\iota=\frac{1}{2}$, $\bar{K}^0$, and $\bar{K}^+$). Clearly, these nine states have the proper isotopic spins and hypercharges to fit into an eight-dimensional and a one-dimensional representation of $SU(3)$; denoting meson states by M_{JP}^N, these states will be labeled $M_{0^-}^1$ and $M_{0^-}^8$. Of course, there exists an ambiguity between the η and the X as to which belongs to which representation, although we might guess that the η belongs to $M_{0^-}^8$, since it is closest in mass to the other members of M^8.

We have already introduced the $SU(3)$ symmetry-breaking interaction in a previous section, so that now we should be able to calculate the mass relations for M^8. We write down our formula for the masses, to zeroth order in $\mathscr{H}_{\text{em}}$ (ignoring for the present the mass splitting within the isotopic spin multiplets) and all orders in $\mathscr{H}_{\text{SB}}$

$$m(\mu\nu) \simeq m_0(\mu) + \langle \Psi_\nu^\mu | \sum_{n=1}^{\infty} a_n \, Y'^n | \Psi_\nu^\mu \rangle. \tag{145}$$

This formula will lead to relations among the masses of the mesons that are *linear* in the masses.

At this point, we must digress for a moment. It has been suggested that for mesons we should use relations that involve the square of masses rather than simply the masses. In the preceding formula, considered a relation for the energy as a function of momentum, $\mathscr{E}_\nu(\mathbf{p})$, such a squared-mass relation would follow from considering the limit as $|\mathbf{p}| \to \infty$ rather than as $|\mathbf{p}| \to 0$ as we have done. On the other hand, because of mixing effects (to be discussed shortly), we see no compelling reason for the use of a squared-mass formula and therefore will only consider linear relations (*24*).

Let us now return to Eq. (145). First of all, we note that due to invariance under the combined transformation of time reversal, charge conjugation, and parity, that is, $\mathscr{T}\mathscr{C}\mathscr{P}$, the mass of a particle and its conjugate are the same; for example, the masses of the π^+ and π^- are equal, as are those of the K^0 and $\bar{K}^0$ and those of the K^+ and $\bar{K}^+$. In fact, when considering only interactions that are invariant under $\mathscr{C}$, the mass of a particle and its charge conjugate are the same. If we consider only the mass arising from $\mathscr{H}_0$ and $\mathscr{H}_{\text{SB}}$, that is, if we neglect the effects of the em and weak interactions, then we may write the δm part of Eq. (145) in terms of multipole operators as

$$\begin{aligned}\delta m(\mu\nu) &\equiv \langle \Psi_\nu^\mu | a_0\, Y' | \Psi_\nu^\mu \rangle + \cdots \\ &= a_0' \sum_\gamma \langle \Psi^\mu \| T^{8\gamma} \| \Psi^\mu \rangle \langle \Psi_\nu^\mu | \mathscr{T}_{000}^{8\gamma} | \Psi_\nu^\mu \rangle + \cdots \end{aligned} \tag{146}$$

explicitly only to lowest order in $\mathscr{H}_{\text{SB}}$. We have explicitly included the reduced matrix element (which is independent of $\nu = \{\iota, \iota_3, y\}$) so that a_0' is a constant representing the remaining factors that a complete calculation would provide. We now use the property that $\mathscr{H}_{\text{SB}}$ is invariant under charge conjugation, thus

$$\begin{aligned}\delta m(\mu\nu) &= \langle \Psi_\nu^{\mu c} | a_0\, Y' | \Psi_\nu^{\mu c} \rangle \\ &= a_0' \sum_\gamma \langle \Psi^{\mu c} \| T^{8\gamma} \| \Psi^{\mu c} \rangle \langle \Psi_\nu^{\mu c} | \mathscr{T}_{000}^{8\gamma} | \Psi_\nu^{\mu c} \rangle + \cdots. \end{aligned} \tag{147}$$

But from Eqs. (43), (103), and (106)

$$\mathscr{C}^\dagger \mathscr{T}_{000}^{8_1} \mathscr{C} = -\mathscr{T}_{000}^{8_1}, \qquad \mathscr{C}^\dagger \mathscr{T}_{000}^{8_2} \mathscr{C} = \mathscr{T}_{000}^{8_2},$$

so that

$$\langle \Psi_\nu^{\mu c} | \mathscr{T}_{000}^{8\gamma} | \Psi_\nu^{\mu c} \rangle = \mp \langle \Psi_\nu^\mu | \mathscr{T}_{000}^{8\gamma} | \Psi_\nu^\mu \rangle. \tag{148}$$

The $-$ and $+$ for $\gamma = 1$ and 2, respectively. We thus have

$$\langle \Psi^{\mu c} \| T^{8\gamma} \| \Psi^{\mu c} \rangle = \mp \langle \Psi^\mu \| T^{8\gamma} \| \Psi^\mu \rangle \tag{149}$$

again for $\gamma = 1$ and 2. Now for the mesons in representations that are self-conjugate (i.e., $g_3 = 0$, such as $N = 1$, 8, 27, etc.) the charge conjugate to a meson is also in the same representation. In this special case we can make an

$SU(3)$ transformation within the representation such that the previous equation becomes

$$\langle \Psi^{\mu} \| T^{8\gamma} \| \Psi^{\mu} \rangle = \mp \langle \Psi^{\mu} \| T^{8\gamma} \| \Psi^{\mu} \rangle \tag{150}$$

or $\langle \Psi^{\mu} \| T^{8_1} \| \Psi^{\mu} \rangle = 0$. Thus for these meson representations

$$\delta m(\mu\nu) = a[\iota(\iota + 1) - \tfrac{1}{4}y^2 - g_2] + \cdots. \tag{151}$$

For M^8 to first order in $\mathscr{H}_{\mathrm{SB}}$, therefore, we find the mass relation $3m_{\eta^8} + m_\pi = 4m_K$, where m_{η^8} denotes the mass of the particle η^8, which belongs to the eight-dimensional representation. Using the observed masses of the π and the K, we find $m_{\eta^8} = 615$ MeV. The observed η is at 548 MeV. This discrepancy could be the result of neglecting second-order effects in $\mathscr{H}_{\mathrm{SB}}$. On the other hand, if two particles have all their usual quantum numbers the same except that they belong to different irreducible representations of $SU(3)$ (e.g., just as the η^8 belongs to $N = 8$, the η^1 belongs to $N = 1$) and if these two states are connected by $\mathscr{H}_{\mathrm{SB}}$, then the observed particles (eigenstates of the total $\mathscr{H}$) will contain a mixture of two irreducible representations (*25*).

In the manner of the usual degenerate perturbation theory, we can formulate the problem in the following way. Call the state vector for the pure $N = 1$, η^1 particle $|1\rangle$ and for the η^8 call it $|8\rangle$. Then the observed η and X state vectors can be written (neglecting multiparticle states)

$$\begin{aligned} |\boldsymbol{\eta}\rangle &= \cos\theta_0 |8\rangle + \sin\theta_0 |1\rangle, \\ |\mathbf{X}\rangle &= -\sin\theta_0 |8\rangle + \cos\theta_0 |1\rangle. \end{aligned} \tag{152}$$

For the physically observed X and η, the total Hamiltonian must be diagonal. Thus,

$$\begin{aligned} \langle \boldsymbol{\eta} | \mathscr{H} | \mathbf{X} \rangle &\equiv \mathscr{H}_{\eta X} = 0 \\ &= (\cos^2\theta_0 - \sin^2\theta_0)\mathscr{H}_{18} + \cos\theta_0 \sin\theta_0 (\mathscr{H}_{11} - \mathscr{H}_{88}) \end{aligned} \tag{153}$$

where we have chosen $\mathscr{H}_{18}$ to be real. But

$$\begin{aligned} \mathscr{H}_{\eta\eta} &= m_\eta = \cos^2\theta_0 \mathscr{H}_{88} + \sin^2\theta_0 \mathscr{H}_{11} + 2\cos\theta_0 \sin\theta_0 \mathscr{H}_{18}, \\ \mathscr{H}_{XX} &= m_X = \sin^2\theta_0 \mathscr{H}_{88} + \cos^2\theta_0 \mathscr{H}_{11} - 2\cos\theta_0 \sin\theta_0 \mathscr{H}_{18}. \end{aligned} \tag{154}$$

From these three equations it follows that

$$\sin^2\theta_0 = \frac{\mathscr{H}_{88} - m_\eta}{m_X - m_\eta}. \tag{155}$$

By identifying $\mathscr{H}_{88} = m_{\eta^8}$, we find $\sin^2\theta_0 = 67/411$ or $\theta_0 \simeq 24°$. We emphasize that by considering mixing to occur, we have introduced another parameter, θ_0, and hence have made no mass predictions. Moreover, by calculating this angle from the physically observed masses, we are assuming the absence of any second-order symmetry-breaking effect, a highly dubious assumption. However, since the first-order mass formula seems to fit fairly well in the case of the baryons, we may hope that the same is true for the mesons, in which case such a calculation for θ_0 is a fairly good approximation, and one that we shall make.

E. The Meson States $M^8_{1^-}$

From Fig. 6, there are nine states with $J^P = 1^-$. These are the $\rho(765)$ ($y = 0$, $\iota = 1$, ρ^+, ρ^0, ρ^-), $K^*(891)$ ($y = 1$, $\iota = \frac{1}{2}$, K^{*0}, K^{*+}), $\bar{K}^*(891)$ ($y = -1$, $\iota = \frac{1}{2}$, $\bar{K}^{*0}$, $\bar{K}^{*+}$), $\omega(783)$ ($y = 0$, $\iota = 0$), and $\varphi(1019)$ ($y = 0$, $\iota = 0$). The situation here is identical to the case of the $M^8_{0^-}$. To first order, the mass formula gives $3m_{\omega^8} = 4m_{K^*} - m_\rho$ where ω^8 signifies the $y = 0$, $\iota = 0$ member of $M^8_{1^-}$. With the observed masses of the K^* and ρ, we find $m_{\omega^8} = 933$ MeV, which agrees with neither the ω nor φ mass. Again, since $\mathscr{H}_{\text{SB}}$ can cause transitions between an $N = 1$ and $N = 8$ representation, we find a mixing angle θ_1 for the physical states

$$
\begin{aligned}
|\boldsymbol{\omega}\rangle &= \cos\theta_1|8\rangle + \sin\theta_1|1\rangle \\
|\boldsymbol{\varphi}\rangle &= -\sin\theta_1|8\rangle + \cos\theta_1|1\rangle
\end{aligned}
\tag{156}
$$

of $\sin^2\theta_1 = 150/236$ or $\theta_1 \simeq 53°$.

F. The Meson States $M^8_{2^+}$

From Fig. 6, the states with verified $J^P = 2^+$ are $A2(1324)$ ($y = 0$, $\iota = 1$), $f(1253)$ ($y = 0$, $\iota = 0$), $f^*(1500)$ ($y = 0$, $\iota = 0$). The states $K^*(1405)$ ($y = 1$, $\iota = \frac{1}{2}$) and $\bar{K}^*(1405)$ are also possible candidates for $J^P = 2^+$. These nine states again present the same situation as for $M^8_{0^-}$ and $M^8_{1^-}$. We find, from $3m_{f^8} = 4m_{K^*} - m_{A2}$, that $m_{f^8} = 1432$. With a mixing between an $N = 1$ and $N = 8$, the physical states would be

$$
\begin{aligned}
|\mathbf{f}\rangle &= \cos\theta_2|8\rangle + \sin\theta_2|1\rangle, \\
|\mathbf{f}^*\rangle &= -\sin\theta_2|8\rangle + \cos\theta_2|1\rangle.
\end{aligned}
\tag{157}
$$

Thus $\sin^2\theta_2 = 179/247$ or $\theta_2 \simeq 58°$.

VII. Some Remarks on R and $SU(3)/Z_3$

Now that we have assigned the particles for five supermultiplets and can see that ultimately all the resonances that have not yet been assigned to a particular multiplet will be so assigned in the future, let us stop for a moment to make a few observations.

First, let us consider the finite transformation R, which we discussed before and which is not one of the transformations of $SU(3)$ (outer automorphism). Is the model theory (of Section II) invariant under R as well as under $SU(3)$? We noted before that $RG_3R^{-1} = -G_3$ [Eq. (42)]. Therefore, if the model theory were invariant under R, representations with $g_3 = 0$ would be allowed, whereas representations with $g_3 \neq 0$ would have to appear in degenerate contragredient pairs, that is, in two representations having the same J^P, baryon number, and g_2, but with opposite g_3 (i.e., contragredient representations) that are degenerate in mass. Since we have assigned $B^{10}_{3/2^+}$ (with $g_3 = 1$) and there are no likely candidates for $B^{\overline{10}}_{3/2^+}$ (i.e., $g_3 = -1$), we can already reasonably conclude that the model theory is not invariant under R.

The next observation is that all of the particle states that have been seen experimentally so far have integer values of the hypercharge. From Eq. (34) we saw that $e^{i4\pi H_2}$ commuted with all the generators of the $SU(3)$ transformations so that it is a discrete subgroup that is a multiple of the identity operator. Let us apply this transformation to a state vector $|\Psi^{\mu}_{\iota,\mathbf{M}}\rangle$ belonging to the highest weight in an irreducible representation.

$$\begin{aligned} \exp(i4\pi H_2)\,|\Psi^{\mu}_{\iota,\mathbf{M}}\rangle &= \exp(i2\pi y)\,|\Psi^{\mu}_{\iota,\mathbf{M}}\rangle, \\ &= \exp[i(2/3)\,\pi(\lambda_1 - \lambda_2)]\,|\Psi^{\mu}_{\iota,\mathbf{M}}\rangle. \end{aligned} \tag{158}$$

[The first line follows from Eq. (46), the second from Eq. (50).] From our observation that y is integer, we conclude that $\frac{1}{3}(\lambda_1 - \lambda_2)$ must be integer. Or, since λ_1 and λ_2 are integers, $\lambda_1 + 2\lambda_2$ must be three times an integer. Thus the only product representations that can be built up from representations that have integral values of y are representations whose λ_1 and λ_2 satisfy this relation. This group, with integer y, is often called $SU(3)/Z_3$ (*26*).

VIII. Couplings and Decay Widths

From analyses of experimental results, there seems to exist a three-field coupling of baryons and mesons—the "Yukawa-type couplings." For the baryons $B^8_{1/2^+}$ coupled to the mesons $M^8_{0^-}$ this coupling, in terms of field operators, is

$$
\begin{aligned}
& ig_{NN\pi}\bar{N}\gamma_5\tau_k N\pi_k + ig_{\Xi\Xi\pi}\bar{\Xi}\gamma_5\tau_k\Xi\pi_k + ig_{\Sigma\Lambda\pi}(\bar{\Lambda}\gamma_5\Sigma_k + \bar{\Sigma}_k\gamma_5\Lambda)\pi_k \\
& + g_{\Sigma\Sigma\pi}\epsilon_{ijk}\bar{\Sigma}_i\gamma_5\Sigma_j\pi_k + ig_{NN\eta}\bar{N}\gamma_5 N\eta + ig_{\Xi\Xi\eta}\bar{\Xi}\gamma_5\Xi\eta \\
& + ig_{\Sigma\Sigma\eta}\bar{\Sigma}_k\gamma_5\Sigma_k\eta + ig_{\Lambda\Lambda\eta}\bar{\Lambda}\gamma_5\Lambda\eta + ig_{N\Lambda K}(\bar{N}\gamma_5\Lambda K + \bar{\Lambda}\gamma_5\bar{K}N) \\
& + ig_{\Xi\Lambda K}(\bar{\Xi}\gamma_5\Lambda K_c + \bar{\Lambda}\gamma_5\bar{K}_c\Xi) + ig_{N\Sigma K}(\bar{N}\gamma_5\tau_k\Sigma_k K + \bar{\Sigma}_k\gamma_5\bar{K}\tau_k N) \\
& + ig_{\Xi\Sigma K}(\bar{\Xi}\gamma_5\tau_k\Sigma_k K_c + \bar{\Sigma}_k\gamma_5\tau_k\bar{K}_c\Xi)
\end{aligned}
\tag{159}
$$

where

$$
N = \begin{pmatrix} \mathrm{p} \\ \mathrm{n} \end{pmatrix}, \quad \Xi = \begin{pmatrix} \Xi^0 \\ \Xi^- \end{pmatrix}, \quad K = \begin{pmatrix} K^+ \\ K^0 \end{pmatrix}, \quad K_c = \begin{pmatrix} \bar{K}^0 \\ -\bar{K}^+ \end{pmatrix}.
$$

Considered as a symmetric strong-interaction Lagrangian density, this coupling is to be invariant under the $SU(3)$ transformations. By use of the $SU(3)$ Clebsch-Gordan coefficients, we could find the ten relations that exist among these twelve coupling parameters g_a. Another simple straightforward approach is to use the reflections.* For example, under S_{-2}, the term $ig_{NN\pi}\sqrt{2}\bar{\mathrm{p}}\gamma_5 n\pi^+ \to -ig_{NN\pi}\bar{\Xi}^-\gamma_5\Sigma^-\bar{K}^0$, which for invariance demands $g_{NN\pi} = -g_{\Xi\Sigma K}$. By either method we find (*27*)

$$
\begin{aligned}
& g_{NN\pi} = -g_{\Xi\Sigma K} = g(\cos\theta + \sin\theta); \qquad g_{\Sigma\Sigma\eta} = g_{\Sigma\Lambda\pi} = -g_{\Lambda\Lambda\eta} = \frac{2}{\sqrt{3}} g\sin\theta; \\
& g_{\Xi\Xi\pi} = -g_{N\Sigma K} = g(\cos\theta - \sin\theta); \qquad g_{\Sigma\Sigma\pi} = 2g\cos\theta; \\
& g_{NN\eta} = g_{\Xi\Lambda K} = \frac{1}{\sqrt{3}} g(3\cos\theta - \sin\theta); \quad g_{\Xi\Xi\eta} = g_{N\Lambda K} = -\frac{1}{\sqrt{3}} g(3\cos\theta + \sin\theta);
\end{aligned}
\tag{160}
$$

where we have expressed all the coupling parameters in terms of the two quantities g and θ. The couplings that have the coefficient $\cos\theta$ are scalars under R, while those having $\sin\theta$ are pseudoscalars, the so-called f and d couplings, respectively. [The relationship between θ and the parameter α employed in (*1*) is $\tan\theta = \alpha/(1-\alpha)$.]

* Extensive use has been made of this technique. See, e.g., (*5*, *20*, *21*) and references therein.

Similarly, for the baryon resonances $B^{10}_{3/2^+}$ coupled to the baryons $B^8_{1/2^+}$ by the mesons $M^8_{0^-}$, we can write an interaction in terms of the field operators

$$\begin{aligned}
&g_{NN^*\pi}\bar{N}N_i^\alpha\partial_\alpha\pi_i - ig_{\Sigma Y^*\pi}\epsilon_{ijk}\bar{\Sigma}_i Y_j^\alpha\partial_\alpha\pi_k + g_{\Lambda Y^*\pi}\bar{\Lambda}Y_j^\alpha\partial_\alpha\pi_j\\
&+g_{\Sigma Y^*\eta}\bar{\Sigma}_i Y_i^\alpha\partial_\alpha\eta + g_{\Xi\Xi^*\pi}\bar{\Xi}\tau_i\Xi^\alpha\partial_\alpha\pi_i + g_{\Xi\Xi^*\eta}\bar{\Xi}\Xi^\alpha\partial_\alpha\eta\\
&+g_{\Sigma N^*K}\bar{\Sigma}_i(\partial_\alpha\bar{K})N_i^\alpha + g_{\Sigma\Xi^*K}\bar{\Sigma}_i(\partial_\alpha\bar{K}_c)\tau_i\Xi^\alpha\\
&+g_{\Lambda\Xi^*K}\bar{\Lambda}(\partial_\alpha\bar{K}_c)\Xi^\alpha + g_{NY^*K}\bar{N}\tau_i Y_i^\alpha\partial_\alpha K\\
&+g_{\Xi Y^*K}\bar{\Xi}\tau_i Y_i^\alpha\partial_\alpha K_c + g_{\Xi\Omega K}\bar{\Xi}\Omega^\alpha\partial_\alpha K + \text{h.c.}
\end{aligned}\tag{161}$$

where $N_i^\alpha = (\delta_{ij} - \frac{1}{3}\tau_i\tau_j)N_j^\alpha$ satisfies $\tau_i N_i^\alpha = 0$ and so is pure $\iota = \frac{3}{2}$. We use

$$\frac{1}{\sqrt{2}}(N_1 + iN_2) = \begin{pmatrix} -\frac{1}{\sqrt{3}}N^0 \\ -N^- \end{pmatrix}; \qquad \frac{1}{\sqrt{2}}(N_1 - iN_2) = \begin{pmatrix} N^{++} \\ \frac{1}{\sqrt{3}}N^+ \end{pmatrix};$$

$$N_3 = i\tau_1 N_2 - i\tau_2 N_1.$$

Moreover, each of the free field operators satisfies, e.g., $\gamma_\alpha\Xi^\alpha = 0$, $p_\alpha\Xi^\alpha = 0$ in order that the observed particles be pure spin $J = \frac{3}{2}$. These conditions can be satisfied by use (*28*) of a spin-projection operator Θ_α^β such that $\Xi^\alpha = \Theta_\beta^\alpha\Xi^\beta$.

Considered as an $SU(3)$-symmetric interaction, the coupling parameters satisfy

$$\begin{aligned}
g_{NN^*\pi} &= \sqrt{6}g_{\Sigma Y^*\pi} = -\sqrt{2}g_{\Lambda Y^*\pi} = \sqrt{2}g_{\Sigma Y^*\eta} = \sqrt{6}g_{\Xi\Xi^*\pi} = \sqrt{2}g_{\Xi\Xi^*\eta}\\
&= -\sqrt{6}g_{\Sigma\Xi^*K} = -g_{\Sigma N^*K} = -\sqrt{2}g_{\Lambda\Xi^*K} = \sqrt{6}g_{NY^*K}\\
&= \sqrt{6}g_{\Xi Y^*K} = -g_{\Xi\Omega K}.
\end{aligned}\tag{162}$$

It should be noted that these three-field couplings might or might not be considered bare interactions (i.e., appearing in the original Lagrangian). What we do know experimentally, however, is that "effective" three-field couplings do exist. What we mean by this might best be illustrated by the example of Σ^0 decay. First, we experimentally observe the decay $\Sigma^0 \to \Lambda + \gamma$, which means that there exists for these three fields an effective coupling whose matrix element (interaction representation) is the matrix element for the decay. On the other hand, we usually assume that there exists no bare coupling of these three fields (i.e., no term of the form $\bar{\Lambda}\sigma_{\alpha\beta}\Sigma^0 F_{\alpha\beta}$ in the original Lagrangian). Since the Λ and Σ^0 are both coupled to charged particles by the strong interactions (e.g., π and K), however, the effective coupling is induced by virtual transitions. In our case, then, we might consider Eqs. (159) and (161) to give the $SU(3)$ form of the effective interactions arising, for example, from a pure quark theory [see, e.g., Gell-Mann (*29*)] or possibly from a theory in which all the bare interactions involve vector and axial vector intermediate mesons (*30*).

A. Baryon Decays

Since we now have noted the effective couplings that exist between the various states, let us consider the decays that can occur and try to find relations among them. For the baryon state $B_{JP}^{N}(\nu_1)$ (remember $\nu = \{\iota, \iota_3, y\}$) to decay into the baryon octet $B_{1/2^+}^{8}(\nu_2)$ and a pseudoscalar meson $M_{0^-}^{8}(\nu_3)$, i.e., $B_{JP}^{N} \to B_{1/2^+}^{8} + M_{0^-}^{8}$, we have as the most general matrix element (*31*)

$$\mathscr{M} = M^{-J+1/2}\,\bar{u}(\nu_2)\,a_{\nu_1\nu_2\nu_3}\,\mathcal{O}u^{\alpha_1\cdots\alpha_{J-1/2}}(\nu_1)\,q_{\alpha_1}\cdots q_{\alpha_{J-1/2}} \tag{163}$$

where q_α, $p_{1\alpha}$, $p_{2\alpha}$ are the four-momenta of the $M_{0^-}^{8}$, B_{JP}^{N}, and $B_{1/2^+}^{8}$, respectively, and $q = p_1 - p_2$. The $u^{\alpha_1\cdots\alpha_{J-1/2}}$ satisfies as subsidiary conditions $p_{1\alpha_1}u^{\alpha_1\cdots\alpha_{J-1/2}} = 0$ and $\gamma_{\alpha_1}u^{\alpha_1\cdots\alpha_{J-1/2}} = 0$ and is symmetric under the interchange of any two indices so that it is a spinor corresponding to pure spin J. These subsidiary conditions can be unified (*28*) into a projection operator $\Theta^{\alpha_1\cdots\alpha_{J-1/2}}_{\beta_1\cdots\beta_{J-1/2}}$ such that $u^{\alpha_1\cdots\alpha_{J-1/2}} = \Theta^{\alpha_1\cdots\alpha_{J-1/2}}_{\beta_1\cdots\beta_{J-1/2}}u^{\beta_1\cdots\beta_{J-1/2}}$. The symbol $\mathcal{O}$ represents 1 or γ_5 when $(-)^{J-1/2}P = -1$ or $+1$, respectively. The $a_{\nu_1\nu_2\nu_3}$ are Lorentz invariant functions of p_1 and p_2 and the factor $M^{J-1/2}$, with M an arbitrary mass, is only included to make the $a_{\nu_1\nu_2\nu_3}$ dimensionless.

From this matrix element we can find the decay rate (*31*) (this calculation is shown in Section X).

$$\Gamma = |a_{\nu_1\nu_2\nu_3}|^2\frac{1}{4\pi}\,[\mathscr{E}_2 - P(-)^{J-1/2}m_2]\,\frac{M}{m_1}\left|\frac{\mathbf{p}}{M}\right|^{2J}\frac{(J-\frac{1}{2})!}{(2J)!!} \tag{164}$$

where $\mathbf{p}$ is the momentum of a final particle in the center-of-mass system.

If we expand the foregoing transition matrix element in terms of the symmetry-breaking interaction representation, then to zero order in $\mathscr{H}_{\mathrm{SB}}$, we find that the $a_{\nu_1\nu_2\nu_3}$ are simply proportional to the $SU(3)$ Clebsch-Gordan coefficients

$$a^{0}_{\nu_1\nu_2\nu_3} = g\sum_{\gamma}\begin{pmatrix} 8 & 8 & \mu_1\gamma \\ \nu_2 & \nu_3 & \nu_1 \end{pmatrix}. \tag{165}$$

If we assume that the $a_{\nu_1 \nu_2 \nu_3}$ are relatively insensitive to the symmetry-breaking interaction (that is, if we assume $a_{\nu_1 \nu_2 \nu_3} \simeq a^0_{\nu_1 \nu_2 \nu_3}$), then the remaining effect of $\mathscr{H}_{\mathrm{SB}}$ to all orders is to change the kinematic factors (e.g., in the spinors u) to their physical values. Thus, by using the $SU(3)$ Clebsch-Gordan coefficients for $a_{\nu_1 \nu_2 \nu_3}$, we include the symmetry-breaking effects on kinematic factors but not on the coupling constants. Later, we shall also include changes in the constants due to symmetry-breaking.

As an illustrative example, we consider the decays $B^{10}_{3/2^+} \to B^8_{1/2^+} + M^8_{0^-}$. The rate is then (*32*)

$$\Gamma = \left[\begin{pmatrix} 8 & 8 & 10 \\ \nu_2 & \nu_3 & \nu_1 \end{pmatrix} \right]^2 \frac{g^2}{12\pi} (\mathscr{E}_2 + m_2) \frac{|\mathbf{p}|^3}{M^2 m_1}$$

$$\simeq \left[\begin{pmatrix} 8 & 8 & 10 \\ \nu_2 & \nu_3 & \nu_1 \end{pmatrix} \right]^2 \frac{g^2}{6\pi} \frac{m_2}{m_1} \frac{|\mathbf{p}|^3}{M^2}, \tag{166}$$

neglecting $|\mathbf{p}|^2/2m_2$ ($\leqq \frac{1}{32}$ for these decays) compared with one. The second and third columns in Table IV show the comparison of predicted (for $a^0_{\nu_1 \nu_2 \nu_3}$) and experimental values of Γ.

In order to include the effects of the symmetry-breaking interaction to first order on $a_{\nu_1 \nu_2 \nu_3}$ we consider the matrix element

$$\langle \mathbf{B}^8_{1/2^+}(\nu_2)\, \mathbf{M}^8_{0^-}(\nu_3) | \mathbf{B}^{10}_{3/2^+}(\nu_1) \rangle = \langle B^8_{1/2^+}(\nu_2)\, M^8_{0^-}(\nu_3) | V^\dagger \mathbf{S} V | B^{10}_{3/2^+}(\nu_1) \rangle \tag{167}$$

where the italic states are $SU(3)$ symmetric. We again note that the operator can be expanded in a power series in $\mathscr{H}_{\mathrm{I}}$, that is,

$$V^\dagger \mathbf{S} V = \sum_{n=0}^{\infty} a_n \mathscr{H}'^{n}_{\mathrm{I}} \tag{168}$$

where again the a_n are $SU(3)$ symmetric and $\mathscr{H}'_{\mathrm{I}}$ transforms under $SU(3)$ as $\mathscr{H}_{\mathrm{I}}$. Since $8 \boxtimes 10 = 8 \oplus 10 \oplus 27 \oplus 35$ and $8 \boxtimes 8 = 1 \oplus 8 \oplus 8 \oplus 10 \oplus \overline{10} \oplus 27$, these symmetry-breaking terms to first order in $\mathscr{H}_{\mathrm{SB}}$ will involve four parameters. This means that five parameters (including g) are needed to describe twelve coupling constants, giving us seven linear relations among the twelve constants. Fortunately, there exists one relation involving only the four observable decay constants of Table IV. This relation may be found by taking the matrix element of $(E_{-3}, (E_{-3}, a_0 + a_1 Y')) = 0$ between the states $\langle \Xi^0 \pi^- |$ and $| N^{*-} \rangle$. The result is

$$-\tfrac{1}{3} \langle \mathbf{n}\boldsymbol{\pi}^- | \mathbf{N}^{*-} \rangle - \frac{1}{\sqrt{6}} \langle (\boldsymbol{\Sigma}^0 - \sqrt{3}\boldsymbol{\Lambda})\, \boldsymbol{\pi}^- | \mathbf{Y}^- \rangle + \frac{1}{\sqrt{3}} \langle \boldsymbol{\Xi}^0 \boldsymbol{\pi}^- | \boldsymbol{\Xi}^{*-} \rangle = 0. \tag{169}$$

TABLE IV

DECAY WIDTHS FOR $B^{10}_{3/2^+}$

Decay	Γ_{exp}	$\Gamma_{\text{th}}(a^0)$	$a^0_{\nu_1\nu_2\nu_3}$	$a_{\nu_1\nu_2\nu_3}/g$	$\Gamma_{\text{th}}(a^1)$
$N^* \to N\pi$	120 ± 1.5	120^a	$a^0_{N^*-n\pi^-} = -\dfrac{g}{\sqrt{2}}$	$-\dfrac{1}{\sqrt{2}}{}^a$	120^a
$Y_1^* \to \Lambda\pi$	40 ± 2	43	$a^0_{Y^-\Lambda\pi^-} = -\frac{1}{2}g$	-0.477	40^a
$Y_1^* \to \Sigma\pi$	4.4 ± 1.0	6.9	$a^0_{Y^-\Sigma^0\pi^-} = \dfrac{g}{2\sqrt{3}} \simeq 0.288g$	0.229	$1.5^{+1.2}$
$\Xi^* \to \Xi\pi$	7.5 ± 1.7	17.3	$a^0_{\Xi^*-\Xi^0\pi^-} = \dfrac{g}{\sqrt{6}} = 0.408g$	0.268	7.5^a

[a] Input is meant here.

In terms of the coupling constants *(33)* $a_{\nu_1\nu_2\nu_3} \propto \langle \boldsymbol{\nu}_2\boldsymbol{\nu}_3 | \boldsymbol{\nu}_1\rangle$

$$-\sqrt{2}a_{N^*-n\pi^-} + \sqrt{6}a_{\Xi^*-\Xi^0\pi^-} = \sqrt{3}a_{Y^-\Sigma^0\pi^-} - 3a_{Y^-\Lambda\pi^-}, \tag{170}$$

which holds up to first order in symmetry breaking. From column 5 we see that the two sides of this equation are 1.66 and 1.83, only about a 7% discrepancy on the present central experimental values. By using three experimental results as inputs, we can make one prediction from this equation. The result is in the last column.

Experimentally, the electromagnetic form factors for B^{10} are almost inaccessible, so that we did not discuss them. On the other hand, the photon modes of decay $B^{10}_{3/2^+} \to B^8_{1/2^+} + \gamma$ may soon be experimentally determined. The matrix element for this type decay can be written

$$\mathscr{M} = ie\langle \mathbf{B}^8_{1/2^+}(\nu_2)|\mathbf{J}_\alpha(0)|\mathbf{B}^N_{JP}(\nu_1)\rangle\, \mathbf{e}_\alpha \left(\frac{p_{10}\,p_{20}}{m_1 m_2}\right)^{1/2} \tag{171}$$

where $\mathbf{e}_\alpha$ is the polarization vector of the photon. By gauge invariance and Lorentz invariance we can show that the most general form of the matrix element of the current is

$$\left(\frac{p_{10}\,p_{20}}{m_1 m_2}\right)^{1/2} \langle \mathbf{B}^8_{1/2^+}(\nu_2)|\mathbf{J}_\alpha(0)|\mathbf{B}^N_{JP}(\nu_1)\rangle =$$

$$\frac{1}{M^{J+1/2}}\bar{u}_2(p_2)\, a_{\nu_2\nu_1}\, [\sigma_{\alpha\epsilon}k_{\alpha_1} + b(\gamma_\epsilon\delta_{\alpha\alpha_1} - \gamma_\alpha\delta_{\epsilon\alpha_1})]\,\mathscr{O}u_1^{\alpha_1\cdots\alpha_{J-1/2}}(p_1)\,k_\epsilon k_{\alpha_2}\cdots k_{\alpha_{J-1/2}} \tag{172}$$

where $a_{\nu_2 \nu_1}$ is an invariant function of the four-momentum $k = p_1 - p_2$, $u^{\alpha_1 \cdots \alpha_{J-1/2}}$ satisfies the subsidiary conditions to be pure spin J, the arbitrary mass M is introduced in the factor $M^{J+1/2}$ in order to make $a_{\nu_2 \nu_1}$ dimensionless, and $\mathcal{O}$ is either 1 or γ_5 depending on whether $P(-)^{J+1/2}$ is -1 or $+1$, respectively.

By the method of spin-projection operators (*28*), we can calculate the rate arising from this matrix element. The result is (e.g., for $b = 0$)

$$\Gamma = \frac{2}{\pi} e^2 |a_{\nu_2 \nu_1}|^2 M \left| \frac{\mathbf{k}}{M} \right|^{2J+2} \frac{(J + \frac{1}{2})!}{(2J+1)(2J)!!}. \tag{173}$$

From Eq. (172), we see that in the limit of $SU(3)$ symmetry, the $a_{\nu_2 \nu_1}$ are just the Clebsch-Gordan coefficients

$$a^0_{\nu_2 \nu_1} = f \sum_\gamma \left[\sqrt{3} \begin{pmatrix} \mu_1 & 8_\gamma & 8 \\ \nu_1 & 000 & \nu_2 \end{pmatrix} + \begin{pmatrix} \mu_1 & 8_\gamma & 8 \\ \nu_1 & 000 & \nu_2 \end{pmatrix} \right], \tag{174}$$

that is, the matrix elements of an operator Q' that transforms like the charge Q. By writing

$$a_{\nu_2 \nu_1} \propto \langle \mathbf{B}^8(\nu_2) | \mathbf{Q}' | \mathbf{B}^N(\nu_1) \rangle = \langle B^8(\nu_2) | V^\dagger Q' V | B^N(\nu_1) \rangle \tag{175}$$

and expanding in a power series in $\mathscr{H}_\text{I}$ we can find relations among the $a_{\nu_2 \nu_1}$ in various approximations.

Let us consider specifically $B^{10} \to B^8 + \gamma$. By use of $(E_3, Q') = 0$, for example,

$$0 = \langle \text{p} | (E_3, Q') | Y^+ \rangle = \frac{1}{\sqrt{6}} \langle \Sigma^+ | Q' | Y^+ \rangle + \frac{1}{\sqrt{6}} \langle \text{p} | Q' | N^{*+} \rangle$$

$$\propto \frac{1}{\sqrt{6}} (a^0_{\Sigma^+ Y^+} + a^0_{\text{p}N^+}).$$

Thus, to zero order in $\mathscr{H}_\text{SB}$ and all orders in $\mathscr{H}_\text{em}$, we find (*21, 34, 35*)

$$a^0_{\Sigma^+ Y^+} = -a^0_{\text{p}N^+}; \qquad a^0_{\Xi^- \Xi^{*-}} = a^0_{\Sigma^- Y^-} = 0;$$

$$a^0_{\Xi^0 \Xi^{*0}} = 2a^0_{\Sigma^0 Y^0} = -\frac{2}{\sqrt{3}} a^0_{\Lambda Y^0} = -a^0_{nN^0}. \tag{176}$$

If we restrict ourselves further to only first order in $\mathscr{H}_\text{em}$, we obtain, by virtue of $(E_1, (E_1, Q')) = 0$, the additional relation (*21, 34, 35*)

$$a^0_{pN^+} = a^0_{nN^0}. \tag{177}$$

By using $(E_1, (E_1, Y'^n Q')) = 0$, we can show, to all orders in $\mathscr{H}_{SB}$ and first order in $\mathscr{H}_{em}$ (*35*),

$$a_{nN^0} = a_{pN^+}; \qquad a_{\Sigma^- Y^-} + a_{\Sigma^+ Y^+} = 2a_{\Sigma^0 Y^0}. \tag{178}$$

Up to first order in $\mathscr{H}_{SB}$ and all orders in $\mathscr{H}_{em}$, we may use

$$(E_3, (E_3, Y'(Q')^{2l+1})) = 0$$

to show (*35*)

$$a_{\Xi^- \Xi^{*-}} = a_{\Sigma^- Y^-}; \qquad a_{\Xi^0 \Xi^{*0}} + \sqrt{3}\, a_{\Lambda Y^0} = a_{\Sigma^0 Y^0} + a_{nN^0}. \tag{179}$$

By use of $(E_3, Q') = 0$ we can show that the photon decay modes $Y_0^*(1405) \to \Sigma^0 + \gamma$ and $\Lambda + \gamma$ are related to all orders in $\mathscr{H}_{em}$ and zero order in $\mathscr{H}_{SB}$. The relation is

$$a_{\Sigma^0 Y^0} = \sqrt{3} a_{\Lambda Y^0}. \tag{180}$$

B. Boson Decays

In considering the classification of meson resonances, we made several assignments: $M^8_{0^-}$; $M^1_{0^-}$; $M^8_{1^-}$; $M^1_{1^-}$; $M^8_{2^+}$; $M^1_{2^+}$. A common decay mode of the higher resonances is $M^8_{0^-} + M^8_{0^-}$. Calling the four-momenta of the two particles in the final state q_1 and q_2, the most general matrix element for such a decay of a state $M^N_{J^P}(\nu_1)$ (where $J^P = 0^+, 1^-, 2^+, 3^-, \ldots$) is

$$\mathscr{M} = (2M)^{-J+1} a_{\nu_1 \nu_2 \nu_3} q_{\alpha_1} \cdots q_{\alpha_J} \varphi^{\alpha_1 \cdots \alpha_J} \tag{181}$$

where $q = q_1 - q_2$, the arbitrary mass M is included to make $a_{\nu_1 \nu_2 \nu_3}$ dimensionless. The completely symmetric tensor $\varphi^{\alpha_1 \cdots \alpha_J}$ satisfies

$$(q_{1\alpha_1} + q_{2\alpha_1}) \varphi^{\alpha_1 \cdots \alpha_J} = 0$$

so that it is pure spin J. By using the method of spin-projection operators (*28*), we can easily calculate the rate in the center-of-mass system (*32*)

$$\Gamma = |a_{\nu_1 \nu_2 \nu_3}|^2 \frac{1}{2\pi} \frac{M^3}{m_0^2} \left| \frac{\mathbf{q}}{M} \right|^{2J+1} \frac{J!}{(2J+1)!!} \tag{182}$$

where m_0 is the mass of M_{JP}^N and $\mathbf{q}$ is the momentum of one of the final particles in the center-of-mass system.

As for the baryons, if we expand the matrix element in terms of the symmetry-breaking interaction, then to zeroth order in $\mathcal{H}_{SB}$ for $a_{\nu_1\nu_2\nu_3}$ and all orders for the kinematic factors, we find

$$a^0_{\nu_1\nu_2\nu_3} = g\sum_{\gamma}\begin{pmatrix} 8 & 8 & \mu_1\gamma \\ \nu_2 & \nu_3 & \nu_1 \end{pmatrix}. \tag{183}$$

As an example, consider the decays $\rho \to 2\pi$, $K^* \to K\pi$, and $\varphi \to K\bar{K}$. Note that $M^1_{1^-}$ cannot decay into $K\bar{K}$ so that only the $M^8_{1^-}$ component of φ contributes to this decay (we use the mixing angle $\theta_1 \simeq 53°$). Also, there is only one $\mathscr{C}$-invariant three-field coupling (i.e., f coupling; the d coupling constant multiplies a term $\rho^0\pi^0\eta^8$ that is not $\mathscr{C}$-invariant). The symmetric predictions and the experimental results (normalized to the $K^* \to K\pi$ width) are listed in the second and third columns of Table V. We should note that the discrepancy between 169 and 125 MeV for the $\rho \to 2\pi$ width is entirely within the range of a reasonable symmetry-breaking effect; that is, the discrepancy between the observed and symmetric coupling constants of the fourth and fifth columns is only about 15%. Unfortunately, when including symmetry breaking to first order, no predictions involving only these three modes can be made without additional assumptions.

Let us now consider (*32*, *36*) the decays of $M^8_{2^+}$ and $M^1_{2^+}$. As we noted before in dealing with the mass relation, the isosinglet member of $M^8_{2^+}$ is mixed with $M^1_{2^+}$, the mixing angle being $\theta_2 \simeq 58°$. As a result, the decays of the $f(1253)$ and the $f^*(1500)$ will involve the mixing angle θ_2 as well as the coupling constants of $M^1_{2^+}$ (call it g_1) and $M^8_{2^+}$ (call it g_8) coupled to $M^8_{0^-} \boxtimes M^8_{0^-}$. We call the ratio $g_1/g_8 = \alpha$. Moreover, for final states involving the η, the mixing angle

TABLE V

DECAY WIDTHS FOR $M^8_{1^-}$ AND $M^1_{1^-}$

Decay	Γ_{exp}	$\Gamma_{(a^0)}$	$a^0_{\nu_1\nu_2\nu_3}$	$a_{\nu_1\nu_2\nu_3}/g$
$\rho \to 2\pi$	125 ± 4	169	$a^0_{\rho^+\pi^+\pi^0} = \dfrac{g}{\sqrt{3}} \simeq 0.576\ g$	0.497
$K^* \to K\pi$	49 ± 2	36.2	$a^0_{K^{*+}K^+\pi^0} = \dfrac{1}{2\sqrt{3}} \simeq 0.288$	0.288 [a]
$\varphi \to K\bar{K}$	2.2 ± 0.7	2.4	$a^0_{\omega^8K^0K^0} = -\frac{1}{2}$	−0.410

[a] Input is meant here.

θ_0 enters, as well as the couplings of $M^8_{2^+}$ to $M^1_{0^-} \boxtimes M^8_{0^-}$ (call the ratio of this coupling to the g_8 coupling α') and of $M^1_{2^+}$ to $M^1_{0^-} \boxtimes M^1_{0^-}$ (call this ratio α''). Further, we note that since $\langle\pi^+\pi^-|A^0\rangle = 0$ by G-invariance, only the d-type coupling enters in this case. In Table VI we list an example of the predictions as well as the experimental results of the various decay modes.

In order to bring in the effect of symmetry breaking on the coupling constants, we use Eq. (168) and the relation

$$(E_{-2}, (E_{-2}, a_0 + a_1 Y')) = 0 \tag{184}$$

taken between the states $\langle\bar{K}^0\pi^-|$ and $|K^{**+}\rangle$ to obtain, up to first order in $\mathscr{H}_{SB}$, the relation

$$0 = -4\langle\boldsymbol{\pi}^+ \mathbf{K}^0|\mathbf{K}^{**+}\rangle - \sqrt{2}\langle\bar{\mathbf{K}}^0 \mathbf{K}^0|\mathbf{A}^0\rangle + \sqrt{6}\langle\boldsymbol{\pi}^+\boldsymbol{\pi}^-|\mathbf{f}^8\rangle - \sqrt{6}\langle\bar{\mathbf{K}}^0\mathbf{K}^0|\mathbf{f}^8\rangle$$

or in terms of couplings

$$4a_{K^{**+}\pi^0 K^+} + a_{A^0 K^0 K^0} + \sqrt{3}a_{f^8 K^0 K^0} - \sqrt{3}a_{f^8\pi^+\pi^-} = 0. \tag{185}$$

In order to test this relation, we must express f^8 in terms of the physical states f and f^*; that is, $|f^8\rangle = \cos\theta_2|\mathbf{f}\rangle - \sin\theta_2|\mathbf{f}^*\rangle$ from Eq. (157). The result is

$$\begin{aligned} 4a_{K^{**+}\pi^0 K^+} &+ \sqrt{3}a_{fK^0K^0}\cos\theta_2 + \sqrt{3}a_{f^*\pi^+\pi^-}\sin\theta_2 \\ &= -a_{A^0K^0K^0} + \sqrt{3}a_{f\pi^+\pi^-}\cos\theta_2 + \sqrt{3}a_{f^*K^0K^0}\sin\theta_2. \end{aligned} \tag{186}$$

The central experimental values, listed in the last column, show that the two sides of this equation are 3.5 and 4.2, about 18% discrepancy on the present central values.

Other relations that can be tested as the data improve are found by taking the matrix element of $(E_3, (E_3, a_0 + a_1 Y')) = 0$ between $\langle K^+K^0|$ and $|A^+\rangle$, leading to

$$\sqrt{3}a_{A^+\pi^+\eta^8} + 2a_{A^0K^0K^0} - a_{K^{**+}K^+\pi^0} - \sqrt{3}a_{K^{**+}K^+\eta^8} = 0; \tag{187}$$

between $\langle K^0K^0|$ and $|\sqrt{3}A^0 + f^8\rangle$, leading to

$$4\sqrt{3}a_{A^0K^0K^0} + 6a_{A^0\pi^0\eta^8} + 4a_{f^8K^0K^0} - a_{f^8\pi^+\pi^-} - 3a_{f^8\eta^8\eta^8} = 0; \tag{188}$$

between $\langle\eta^1K^0|$ and $|\bar{K}^{**0}\rangle$, leading to

$$-4a_{K^{**0}K^0\eta^1} + a_{A^0\pi^0\eta^1} + 3a_{f^8\eta^8\eta^1} = 0; \tag{189}$$

TABLE VI. DECAY WIDTHS FOR $M_{2^+} \to M_{0^-} + M_{0^-}$

Decay	$\lvert\mathbf{q}\rvert^5/m_{\pi^0}^2 m_0^2$	Mult.	$a^0_{\nu_1\nu_2\nu_3}/g$	$\Gamma(a^0)$	Γ_{exp}	$a_{\nu_1\nu_2\nu_3}$
$A2(1320) \to K\bar{K}$	507	2	$-\frac{1}{\sqrt{10}}$	5.6	5.0 ± 1.7	$a_{A^0K^0K^0} = -0.700g$
$A2(1320) \to \eta\pi$	1397	1	$\frac{2}{\sqrt{30}}(\cos\theta_0 + \frac{1}{2}\alpha'\sin\theta_0)$	$\theta_0 = 0$: 10.2 $\neq 0$: 5.1	3 ± 3	$a_{A^0\eta^0\pi^0} = 0.463g$
$K^{**}(1405) \to K\pi$	2340	3	$\frac{1}{\sqrt{10}}$	38.5	39 ± 20	$a_{K^{**+}K^+\pi^0} = 0.747g$
$K^{**}(1405) \to K\eta$	627	1	$-\frac{1}{\sqrt{30}}(\cos\theta_0 - \alpha'\sin\theta_0)$	$\theta_0 = 0$: 1.2 $\neq 0$: 2^a	2 ± 2	$a_{K^{**+}K^+\eta} = -0.565g$
$f(1253) \to \pi\pi$	2970	$\frac{3}{2}$	$\frac{2}{\sqrt{30}}(\cos\theta_2 + \frac{1}{2}\alpha\sin\theta_2)$	118^a	118 ± 16	$a_{f\pi^+\pi^-} = 1.62g$
$f(1253) \to K\bar{K}$	300	2	$-\frac{1}{\sqrt{30}}(\cos\theta_2 - \alpha\sin\theta_2)$	5.5	2 ± 2	$a_{fK^0K^0} = 0.578g$
$f(1253) \to \eta\eta$	88	$\frac{1}{2}$	$-\frac{2}{\sqrt{30}}\left(\cos\theta_2 - \frac{\alpha}{2}\sin\theta_2\right)$ for $\theta_0 = 0$ † for $\theta_0 \neq 0$		Small	
$f^*(1500) \to \pi\pi$	5330	2	$\frac{2}{\sqrt{30}}(-\sin\theta_2 + \frac{1}{2}\alpha\cos\theta_2)$	0^a	0 ± 6	$a_{f^*\pi^+\pi^-} = 0$
$f^*(1500) \to K\bar{K}$	1355	2	$-\frac{1}{\sqrt{30}}(-\sin\theta_2 - \alpha\cos\theta_2)$	32.4	51 ± 25	$a_{f^*K^0K^0} = 1.37g$
$f^*(1500) \to \eta\eta$	850	$\frac{1}{2}$	$-\frac{2}{\sqrt{30}}(-\sin\theta_2 - \frac{1}{2}\alpha\cos\theta_2)$ for $\theta_0 = 0$ ‡ for $\theta_0 \neq 0$	9.0	Small	

† $-\frac{2}{\sqrt{30}}\left[\cos^2\theta_0(\cos\theta_2 - \frac{1}{2}\alpha\sin\theta_2) - \alpha'\cos\theta_0\sin\theta_0\cos\theta_2 - \frac{\alpha''}{2}\sin^2\theta_0\sin\theta_2\right].$

‡ $-\frac{2}{\sqrt{30}}\left[\cos^2\theta_0(-\sin\theta_2 - \frac{1}{2}\alpha\cos\theta_2) + \alpha'\cos\theta_0\sin\theta_0\sin\theta_2 - \frac{\alpha''}{2}\sin^2\theta_0\cos\theta_2\right].$

[a] Input is meant here.

and between $\langle K^0 K^0|$ and $|f^1\rangle$, leading to

$$-4a_{f^1 K^0 K^0} + a_{f^1 \pi^0 \pi^0} + 3a_{f^1 \eta^8 \eta^8} = 0. \tag{190}$$

In each of these expressions we can use Eqs. (152) and (157) to find the corresponding expressions in terms of the f, f^*, η, and X.

In order to deal with decays $M_{JP}^N \to M_{1^-}^{N'} + M_{0^-}^8$ for $J^P = 1^-, 2^+, 3^-, \ldots$, consider the matrix element (not the most general unless the 1^- particle is a photon)

$$\mathscr{M} = \frac{a_{\nu_1 \nu_2 \nu_3}}{(2M)^J} q_{\alpha_2} q_{\alpha_3} \cdots q_{\alpha_J} \varphi^{\alpha_1 \cdots \alpha_J} \epsilon_{\alpha_1 \beta \mu \nu} k_\beta (q_{2\mu} \varphi_\nu - q_{2\nu} \varphi_\mu) \tag{191}$$

where $q = q_1 - q_2$, $k = q_1 + q_2$, and q_1 and q_2 are four-momenta of $M_{0^-}^8$ and $M_{1^-}^{N'}$, respectively. The arbitrary mass M makes $a_{\nu_1 \nu_2 \nu_3}$ dimensionless and the $\varphi^{\alpha_1 \cdots \alpha_J}$ and φ_ν satisfy the usual subsidiary conditions to make them pure spin states. The decay rate following from this matrix element is

$$\Gamma = |a_{\nu_1 \nu_2 \nu_3}|^2 \frac{M}{8\pi} \left|\frac{\mathbf{q}}{M}\right|^{2J+1} \frac{(J+1)(J-1)!}{(2J+1)!!}. \tag{192}$$

For example, for the $M_{2^+}^8$ and $M_{2^+}^1$ decays we have

$$\Gamma = \frac{1}{40\pi} |a_{\nu_1 \nu_2 \nu_3}|^2 \frac{|\mathbf{q}|^5}{M^4}. \tag{193}$$

In Table VII are listed the predictions and experimental results for Γ. We note that there is only one $\mathscr{C}$-invariant three-field coupling for this case (i.e., f coupling, since $\langle \rho^0 \pi^0 | f^8 \rangle = 0$ by $\mathscr{C}$-invariance) and that there are mixing effects in the $K^{**}(1405) \to \omega K$ and $f^*(1500) \to K^* K$ decays (*32*, *36*). We also note that $\langle \omega^1 \eta^8 | f^8 \rangle = 0$, $\langle \omega^8 \eta^1 | f^8 \rangle = 0$, and $\langle \omega^1 \eta^1 | f^1 \rangle = 0$ by $\mathscr{C}$-invariance so that there is no $1 \boxtimes 8$ or $1 \boxtimes 1$ coupling. Moreover, $\langle \omega^8 \eta^8 | f^1 \rangle = 0$ for the same reason, so that f^1 cannot decay in this channel.

We proceed as before to include symmetry breaking to first order. Namely, we take the matrix element of Eq. (184) between $\langle \bar{K}^{*0} \pi^- |$ and $|K^{**+}\rangle$ and between the states $\langle \bar{K}^{*+} \pi^- |$ and $|K^{**0}\rangle$ and combine the two results such that the constant a_{AK^*K} is eliminated. The result is

$$\sqrt{2} a_{A^0 \rho^+ \pi^-} - 2\sqrt{6} a_{f^8 K^{*0} K^0} = 3a_{K^{**+} \rho^+ K^0} + \sqrt{6} a_{K^{**+} \omega^8 K^+} - 2a_{K^{**+} K^{*0} \pi^+}. \tag{194}$$

TABLE VII

DECAY WIDTHS FOR $M_{2^+} \to M_{1^-} + M_{1^-}$

Decay	$\lvert\mathbf{q}\rvert$ (MeV)	$\lvert\mathbf{q}\rvert^5/m_{\pi^0}^4 100$ (MeV)	Mult.	$a^0_{\nu_1\nu_2\nu_3}$	$\Gamma(a^0)$	Γ_{exp}	$a_{\nu_1\nu_2\nu_3}/g$
$A2(1324) \to \rho\pi$	426	426	2	$a^0_{A^0\rho^+\pi^-} = \frac{g}{\sqrt{3}} \simeq 0.58g$	80[a]	80 ± 14	0.58[a]
$K^{**}(1405) \to K^*\pi$	403	321	$\frac{3}{2}$	$a^0_{K^{**+}K^{*0}\pi^+} = -\frac{g}{\sqrt{6}} \simeq -0.41g$	23	43 ± 15	−0.57
$K^{**}(1405) \to \rho K$	303	77	$\frac{3}{2}$	$a^0_{K^{**+}\rho^+K^0} = \frac{g}{\sqrt{6}} \simeq 0.41g$	5.4	14 ± 5	0.66
$K^{**}(1405) \to \omega K$	283	54	1	$a^0_{K^{**+}K^+\omega} = \frac{1}{2}g\cos\theta_1$	1.4	7 ± 4	0.68
$f^*(1500) \to K^*\bar{K}$	274	47	4	$a^0_{f^8K^{*0}K^0} = \frac{1}{2}g\sin\theta_2$	9.6	34 ± 15	0.81

[a] Input is meant here.

Since neither ω^1 nor f^1 is coupled in this channel, we may use Eqs. (156) and (157) to rewrite this

$$\sqrt{2}a_{A^0\rho^+\pi^-} + 2\sqrt{6}\csc\theta_2\, a_{f^*K^{*0}K^0}$$
$$= 3a_{K^{**+}\rho^+K^0} + \sqrt{6}\sec\theta_1\, a_{K^{**+}\omega K^+} - 2a_{K^{**+}K^{*0}\pi^+}. \quad (195)$$

From the central experimental values, the two sides of this equation are 5.48 and 5.86, about a 7% discrepancy. Alternatively, we could use four of the experimental results to predict the fifth via this equation. The result is $\Gamma(K^{**+} \to \omega K^+) \simeq 5.2$.

Let us consider the decays $\pi^0 \to 2\gamma$, $\eta \to 2\gamma$, and $X \to 2\gamma$. The matrix elements for the decays will be proportional to $a_{M^8\to 2\gamma} \propto \langle \mathbf{0}|\mathbf{j}^2|\mathbf{M}^8\rangle$. But again $\mathbf{j}^2$ (the square of the em current) will be a tensor operator transforming like Q^2. By using $(E_3, Q'^2) = 0$, we find

$$0 = \langle 0|(E_3; Q'^2)|\bar{K}^0\rangle = \langle 0|Q'^2|\pi^0 - \sqrt{3}\eta^8\rangle$$
$$= \langle 0|Q'^2|\pi^0\rangle - \sqrt{3}\langle 0|Q'^2|\cos\theta_0\,\eta - \sin\theta_0\,X\rangle,$$

or the relation (*17, 37*)

$$\frac{1}{\sqrt{3}}a_{\pi^0\to 2\gamma} = \cos\theta_0\, a_{\eta\to 2\gamma} - \sin\theta_0\, a_{X\to 2\gamma}. \quad (196)$$

We can consider the decays $M^N_{JP} \to M^{N'}_{0^-} + \gamma$. The most general matrix element is given in Eq. (191) and the rate in Eq. (192). The matrix element for the decay is proportional to the matrix element

$$\langle \mathbf{M}^{N'}_{0^-}(\nu_2)|\mathbf{Q}'|\mathbf{M}^N_{JP}(\nu_1)\rangle \propto a_{\nu_2\nu_1}.$$

Specifically, for the decays of the $J^P = 1^-$ mesons, we find, to zero order in $\mathscr{H}_{\text{SB}}$ and all orders in $\mathscr{H}_{\text{em}}$,

$$a^0_{K^0K^{*0}} = a^0_{\pi^0\rho^0} - \sqrt{3}a^0_{\pi^0\omega^8} = -\frac{1}{\sqrt{3}}a^0_{\eta^8\rho^0} + a^0_{\eta^8\omega^8};$$

$$a^0_{\eta^8\rho^0} = a^0_{\pi^0\omega^8}; \qquad a^0_{K^+K^{*+}} = a^0_{\pi^+\rho^+}; \qquad a^0_{\eta^1\rho^0} = \sqrt{3}a^0_{\eta^1\omega^8}; \qquad a^0_{\pi^0\omega^1} = \sqrt{3}a^0_{\eta^8\omega^1};$$

by use of $(E_3, Q') = 0$. By restricting ourselves further to first order in $\mathscr{H}_{\text{em}}$, we find from $(E_1, (E_1, Q')) = 0$ the relation $a^0_{\pi^+\rho^+} + a^0_{\pi^-\rho^-} = 2a^0_{\pi^0\rho^0}$ and from $S_1Q'S_1^\dagger + S_2Q'S_2^\dagger = -Q'$ taken between $\langle\pi^-|$ and $|\rho^-\rangle$ we find $2a^0_{\pi^0\rho^0} = -a^0_{K^0K^{*0}}$. Invariance under $\mathscr{C}$ implies the equality of the $a_{\nu_2\nu_1}$ for particle and antiparticle decays. In terms of the physically observed states and mixing angles and for the presently feasible experimental decays (i.e., eliminating $a^0_{X\varphi}$ and $a^0_{X\omega}$) (*17, 37–39*)

$$a^0_{K^0K^{*0}}\cos\theta_0 = a^0_{\eta\omega}\cos\theta_1 - a^0_{\eta\varphi}\sin\theta_1 - \frac{1}{\sqrt{3}}a^0_{\eta\rho^0}$$

$$a^0_{\pi^0\rho^0} = \frac{1}{\sqrt{3}}a^0_{\pi^0\omega}\cos\theta_1 - \frac{1}{\sqrt{3}}a^0_{\pi^0\varphi}\sin\theta_1 \tag{197}$$

$$a^0_{\eta\rho^0}\cos\theta_0 - a^0_{X\rho^0}\sin\theta_0 = a^0_{\pi^0\omega}\cos\theta_1 - a^0_{\pi^0\varphi}\sin\theta_1$$

$$a^0_{K^+K^{*+}} = a^0_{\pi^+\rho^+} = a^0_{\pi^0\rho^0} = -\tfrac{1}{2}a^0_{K^0K^{*0}}.$$

To first order in $\mathscr{H}_{\text{em}}$ and to all orders in $\mathscr{H}_{\text{SB}}$, we find from

$$(E_1, (E_1, Q' \sum_{n=0} a_n Y'^n)) = 0$$

and $\mathscr{C}$-invariance

$$a_{\pi^+\rho^+} = a_{\pi^0\rho^0}. \tag{198}$$

To all orders in $\mathscr{H}_{\text{em}}$ and up to first order in $\mathscr{H}_{\text{SB}}$, the equation

$$(E_3, (E_3, \Sigma[a_{0l} + a_{1l}Y']Q'^{2l+1})) = 0$$

gives us the one relation

$$\begin{aligned}4a_{K^0K^{*0}} = a_{\pi^0\rho^0} &- \sqrt{3}(a_{\eta\rho^0}\cos\theta_0 - a_{X\rho^0}\sin\theta_0) - \sqrt{3}(a_{\pi^0\omega}\cos\theta_1 - a_{\pi^0\varphi}\sin\theta_1)\\ &+3(a_{\eta\omega}\cos\theta_0\cos\theta_1 - a_{\eta\varphi}\cos\theta_0\sin\theta_1 - a_{X\omega}\sin\theta_0\cos\theta_1\\ &+a_{X\varphi}\sin\theta_0\sin\theta_1).\end{aligned} \tag{199}$$

In the limit of no $\eta^1\eta^8$ mixing, that is, $\theta_0 \to 0$, the terms involving the X meson drop out of the second relation (*17*).

The decays of the $M^N_{2^+}$ mesons into $M^{N'}_{0^-}$ and a photon are forbidden by charge conjugation, while the decays into $M^{N'}_{1^-}$ and a photon are allowed. It is straightforward to modify Eqs. (197)–(199) to these decays.

IX. Weak Interactions

A. Semileptonic Decays

In our discussion of the weak interactions, we will begin with the decays in which leptons are present. The interaction Lagrangian density responsible for weak decays involving leptons is assumed to be of the form (*40*)

$$\mathscr{L}_{\mathrm{w}} = \frac{G}{\sqrt{2}} [J_\alpha(x) + l_\alpha(x)]^\dagger [J_\alpha(x) + l_\alpha(x)] \tag{200}$$

where l_α is the leptonic invariant: $l_\alpha^\dagger = \bar{e}\gamma_\alpha(1+\gamma_5)\nu_e + \bar{\mu}\gamma_\alpha(1+\gamma_5)\nu_\mu$. The constant G is determined from μ-decay, $\mu \to e + \bar{\nu}_e + \nu_\mu$, and is $G = 1.022 \times 10^{-5}/m_{\mathrm{p}}^2$ where m_{p} is the mass of the proton and J_α is a covariant made up only of hadronic fields.

For the β-decay of baryons (e.g., $B_1 \to B_2 + e + \nu$) the matrix element will be

$$\mathscr{M} = \frac{G}{\sqrt{2}} \langle \mathbf{B}_2 | \mathbf{J}_\alpha(0) | \mathbf{B}_1 \rangle \, \bar{u}_e \gamma_\alpha (1+\gamma_5) u_\nu \left(\frac{p_{10}\, p_{20}}{m_1 m_2} \right)^{1/2} \tag{201}$$

where the u_ν and u_e are plane-wave spinors. For the baryons, we assume that the current is essentially of a nonderivative VA type and that the induced couplings are small. That is, that the main contribution is accounted for by writing

$$\langle \mathbf{B}_2 | \mathbf{J}_\alpha(0) | \mathbf{B}_1 \rangle = \bar{u}_2 \gamma_\alpha (g_1 + g_3 \gamma_5) u_1 \left(\frac{m_1 m_2}{p_{10}\, p_{20}} \right)^{1/2} \tag{202}$$

where g_1 and g_3 are functions of the masses and $q^2 = (p_1 - p_2)^2$. By assuming g_1 and g_3 are constant (not dependent on q^2), we can calculate the decay from this matrix element. By defining $\omega \equiv \ln(m_1/m_2)$ and noting that $\omega \ll 1$ is a very good approximation in most cases, we can write the decay as (*41*)

$$\Gamma \simeq \frac{G^2 m_1 m_2^4}{(2\pi)^3} \omega^5 \tfrac{2}{15} [g_1^2 + 3g_3^2 + \omega^2 (\tfrac{29}{42} g_1^2 + \tfrac{17}{14} g_3^2)]. \tag{203}$$

In a similar way we can consider the β-decay of a meson. For the matrix element (neglecting the electron mass)

$$\mathscr{M}(M_1 \to M_2 + e + \bar{\nu}) = \frac{G}{\sqrt{2}} \langle \mathbf{M}_2 | \mathbf{J}_\alpha(0) | \mathbf{M}_1 \rangle \, \bar{u}_e \gamma_\alpha (1+\gamma_5) u_\nu (4 q_{10} q_{20})^{1/2} \tag{204}$$

$$\simeq 2f \frac{G}{\sqrt{2}} q_{1\alpha} \bar{u}_e \gamma_\alpha (1+\gamma_5) u_\nu$$

where q_1 is the four-momentum of M_1, we obtain a rate

$$\Gamma = \frac{m_1 m_2^4}{12(2\pi)^3} f^2 G^2 [\cosh \omega (2 \cosh^2 \omega - 5) \sinh \omega + 3\omega] \tag{205}$$

which, when ω [$\equiv \ln(m_1/m_2)$] $\ll 1$ may be written (*44*)

$$\Gamma \simeq \frac{G^2 m_1 m_2^4}{(2\pi)^3} \omega^5 \tfrac{2}{15} f^2 [1 + \tfrac{10}{21}\omega^2]. \tag{206}$$

Next, we consider the decay of a meson into just leptons. For the matrix element

$$\begin{aligned} \mathscr{M}(M \to \mu + \bar{\nu}) &= \frac{G}{\sqrt{2}} \langle \mathbf{0} | \mathbf{J}_\alpha(0) | \mathbf{M} \rangle \bar{u}_\mu \gamma_\alpha (1 + \gamma_5) u_\nu (2q_{10})^{1/2} \\ &= \frac{Gf}{\sqrt{2}} m q_\alpha \bar{u}_\mu \gamma_\alpha (1 + \gamma_5) u_\nu \end{aligned} \tag{207}$$

where q_α is the four-momentum of the meson and m is a "typical" mass that makes f a dimensionless coupling constant, we obtain the rate

$$\Gamma = \frac{G^2 m^2 f^2}{8\pi} m_\mu^2 m_M \left[1 - \frac{m_\mu^2}{m_M^2}\right]^2. \tag{208}$$

In Table VIII, for illustrative purposes we list the various rates that follow from Eqs. (203), (206), and (207) for the various baryon and meson β-decays.

Let us now turn our attention to the J_α. It is assumed that the space-time vector parts of J_α are conserved in the presence of the $SU(3)$-symmetric strong interaction (*1*). We shall label these charged currents $j_\alpha^{(1,1)}$ and $s_\alpha^{(1/2,1/2)}$ where the superscript is (ι, ι_3). We note that since they are the conserved currents,

$$I_+ = \sqrt{6} E_1 = \int d^3x j_0^{(1,1)}(x); \qquad \sqrt{6} E_2 = \int d^3x s_0^{(1/2,1/2)}(x) \tag{209}$$

where E_1 and E_2 are the $SU(3)$ generators. The vector part of J_α, call it J_α^{v}, can be written in the following suggestive manner (*42*)

$$J_\alpha^{\text{v}} = \cos\theta_c j_\alpha^{(1,1)} + \sin\theta_c s_\alpha^{(1/2,1/2)}, \tag{210}$$

which by Eq. (29) is just a rotation of $2\theta_c$ around the second axis in U-spin

TABLE VIII

DECAY RATES FROM EQS. (203), (206), AND (208)[a]

$\Gamma(\Lambda \to \mathrm{p}e\nu) = 0.433 \times 10^{8}[g_{3\Lambda\mathrm{p}}^2 + 0.336 g_{1\Lambda\mathrm{p}}^2]$	$\Gamma(\Sigma^- \to \mathrm{n}e\nu) = 0.261 \times 10^{9}[g_{3\Sigma^-\mathrm{n}}^2 + 0.339 g_{1\Sigma^-\mathrm{n}}^2]$
$\Gamma(\Xi^- \to \Lambda e\nu) = 0.927 \times 10^{8}[g_{3\Xi^-\Lambda}^2 + 0.336 g_{1\Xi^-\Lambda}^2]$	$\Gamma(\Xi^- \to \Sigma^0 e\nu) = 0.950 \times 10^{7}[g_{3\Xi^-\Sigma^0}^2 + 0.334 g_{1\Xi^-\Sigma^0}^2]$
$\Gamma(\Sigma^+ \to \Lambda e\nu) = 0.642 \times 10^{6} g_{3\Sigma^+\mathrm{n}}^2$	$\Gamma(\Xi^0 \to \Sigma^+ e\nu) = 0.877 \times 10^{7}[g_{3\Xi^0\Sigma^+}^2 + 0.334 g_{1\Xi^0\Sigma^+}^2]$
$\Gamma(\Sigma^- \to \Lambda e\nu) = 1.06 \times 10^{6} g_{3\Sigma^-\mathrm{n}}^2$	$\Gamma(K \to \pi e\nu) = 1.45 \times 10^{8} f_{K\pi}^2$
$\Gamma(\pi^+ \to \mu^+ \nu) = 1.79 \times 10^{15}(mh_\pi)^2$	$\Gamma(K^+ \to \mu^+ \nu) = 3.08 \times 10^{16}(mh_K)^2$

[a] Decay rate per second is given in each case.

TABLE IX

WEAK COUPLING CONSTANTS IN THE LIMIT OF $SU(3)$ SYMMETRY

$g_{1\mathrm{pn}}$	$g_{1\mathrm{p}\Lambda}$	$g_{1\mathrm{n}\Sigma^-}$	$g_{1\Sigma^0\Xi^-}$	$g_{1\Sigma^+\Xi^0}$	$g_{1\Lambda\Xi^-}$	$g_{1\Lambda\Sigma^\pm}$
$\cos\theta_c$	$(\frac{3}{2})^{1/2}\sin\theta_c$	$\sin\theta_c$	$\frac{1}{\sqrt{2}}\sin\theta_c$	$-\sin\theta_c$	$(\frac{3}{2})^{1/2}\sin\theta_c$	0
$g_{3\mathrm{pn}}$	$g_{3\mathrm{p}\Lambda}$	$g_{3\mathrm{n}\Sigma^-}$	$g_{3\Sigma^0\Xi^-}$	$g_{3\Sigma^+\Xi^0}$	$g_{3\Lambda\Xi^-}$	$g_{3\Lambda\Sigma^\pm}$
$(f+d)\cos\theta_c$	$(\frac{3}{2})^{1/2}(f+\frac{1}{3}d)\sin\theta_c$	$(f-d)\sin\theta_c$	$\frac{1}{\sqrt{2}}(f+d)\sin\theta_c$	$-(f+d)\sin\theta_c$	$(\frac{3}{2})^{1/2}(f-\frac{1}{3}d)\sin\theta_c$	$(\frac{2}{3})^{1/2} d\cos\theta_c$

space [we use θ_c to distinguish this angle from previous angles we have used; c is for Cabibbo (*42*)].

For the axial vector currents, it is assumed that they also transform as members of an eight-dimensional representation (*42*). We shall label these charged currents $j_{5\alpha}^{(1,1)}$ and $s_{5\alpha}^{(1/2,1/2)}$. Further, the spatial integrals will transform under $SU(3)$ as tensors

$$\int d^3x\, j_{50}^{(1,1)}(x) = \sqrt{6}T_{110}^8; \qquad \int d^3x\, s_{50}^{(1/2,1/2)}(x) = \sqrt{6}T_{1/2,1/2,1}^8. \tag{211}$$

Thus J_α^{A} can be written

$$J_\alpha^{\mathrm{A}} = \cos\theta_c\, j_{5\alpha}^{(1,1)} + \sin\theta_c\, s_{5\alpha}^{(1/2,1/2)} \tag{212}$$

where, in fact, we have used the same angle θ_c as in the vector case (*42*). In Table IX we have listed the symmetric constants.

From just this general form of J_α we can already make some rather strong predictions. From the $SU(3)$ transformation properties of the tensor operators, we may infer the commutation relations

$$\begin{gathered}(I_3, j^{(1,1)}) = j^{(1,1)}, \qquad (Y, s^{(1/2,1/2)}) = s^{(1/2,1/2)}, \\ (I_3, s^{(1/2,1/2)}) = \tfrac{1}{2}s^{(1/2,1/2)}, \qquad (Q, J_\alpha) = J_\alpha, \\ (Y, j^{(1,1)}) = 0, \qquad (B, J_\alpha) = 0.\end{gathered} \tag{213}$$

Consider an arbitrary matrix element of the current. It can be written

$$\langle \boldsymbol{\mu}'\, \boldsymbol{\nu}' | \mathbf{J}_\alpha(0) | \boldsymbol{\mu}\boldsymbol{\nu} \rangle = \langle \Psi_{\nu'}^{\mu'} | V^\dagger J_\alpha(0)\, V | \Psi_\nu^\mu \rangle. \tag{214}$$

Since $\mathscr{H}_{\mathrm{em}}$ transforms under $SU(3)$ like Q and $\mathscr{H}_{\mathrm{SB}}$ like the hypercharge Y, then $(Y, V) = 0$, $(Q, V) = 0$, $(I_3, V) = 0$, $(B, V) = 0$. We can then show *to all orders* in both $\mathscr{H}_{\mathrm{em}}$ and $\mathscr{H}_{\mathrm{SB}}$

$$\langle \boldsymbol{\mu}'\, \boldsymbol{\nu}' | \cos\theta_c(\mathbf{j}_\alpha^{(1,1)} + \mathbf{j}_{5\alpha}^{(1,1)}) | \boldsymbol{\mu}\boldsymbol{\nu} \rangle$$

$$= \langle \Psi_{\nu'}^{\mu'} | \cos\theta_c \left(\sum_{\iota''} a_\alpha^{(\iota'',1)} + \sum_{\iota''} a_{5\alpha}^{(\iota'',1)} \right) | \Psi_\nu^\mu \rangle\, \delta_{\iota_3', \iota_3+1}\, \delta_{yy'} \tag{215}$$

$$\langle \boldsymbol{\mu}'\, \boldsymbol{\nu}' | \sin\theta_c(\mathbf{s}_\alpha^{(1/2,1/2)} + \mathbf{s}_{5\alpha}^{(1/2,1/2)}) | \boldsymbol{\mu}\boldsymbol{\nu} \rangle$$

$$= \langle \Psi_{\nu'}^{\mu'} | \sin\theta_c \left(\sum_{\iota''} b_\alpha^{(\iota'',1/2)} + \sum_{\iota''} b_{5\alpha}^{(\iota'',1/2)} \right) | \Psi_\nu^\mu \rangle\, \delta_{\iota_3', \iota_3+1/2}\, \delta_{y', y+1}$$

by use of commutation relations like $(I_3, V^\dagger j_\alpha^{(1,1)} V) = V^\dagger j_\alpha^{(1,1)} V$. The quantities $a^{(\iota'',1)}$ and $b^{(\iota'',1/2)}$ no longer have any definite transformation properties under $SU(3)$ and the other isotopic spins ι'' occur because $\mathscr{H}_{\text{em}}$ contains an $\iota = 1$ part.

These two relations immediately tell us that, *to all orders* in both $\mathscr{H}_{\text{em}}$ and $\mathscr{H}_{\text{SB}}$, transitions can occur only between states that have the same hypercharge or that differ by one unit in hypercharge, that is, $\Delta y = 0, \pm 1$. Since baryon number is conserved, this means that strangeness also satisfies the same selection rule $|\Delta s| \leqq 1$. Thus $\Delta s = 2$ decays (such as $\Xi^- \to n + e^- + \bar{\nu}$) and $\Delta s = 2$ transitions (such as $K^0 \leftrightarrow \bar{K}^0$) are forbidden to all orders in both $\mathscr{H}_{\text{em}}$ and $\mathscr{H}_{\text{SB}}$ and to first order in $\mathscr{H}_{\text{w}}$.

Moreover, from these matrix elements for $\Delta s = 1$ transitions, we have the rules $\Delta \iota_3 = \frac{1}{2}$ and $\Delta q = 1$. Similarly, for decays proceeding through $J_\alpha^\dagger$, we have for $\Delta s = -1$ transitions the rules $\Delta \iota_3 = -\frac{1}{2}$ and $\Delta q = -1$. These rules can be written $\Delta s = 2\Delta \iota_3 = \Delta q$. Thus, *to all orders* in $\mathscr{H}_{\text{em}}$ and $\mathscr{H}_{\text{SB}}$, decays having $\Delta q = -\Delta s$, such as $K^0 \to \pi^+ l^- \bar{\nu}$, $\Sigma^+ \to n l^+ \nu$, $\Xi^0 \to \Sigma^- l^+ \nu$, are forbidden. By writing K^0 in terms of the short- and long-lived components, as, $|K^0\rangle = \frac{1}{\sqrt{2}} |K_1^0 + iK_2^0\rangle$, and noting that the matrix element for $K^0 \to \pi^+ l^- \bar{\nu}$ is zero, we find for the rates *(43)*

$$\frac{R(K_1^0 \to \pi^+ l^- \bar{\nu})}{R(K_2^0 \to \pi^+ l^- \bar{\nu})} = 1. \tag{215}$$

Let us now make a further approximation. Consider the matrix elements of the current to all orders in $\mathscr{H}_{\text{SB}}$ but to zero order in $\mathscr{H}_{\text{em}}$. Then, since $\mathscr{H}_{\text{SB}}$ commutes with I^2, all the $a^{(\iota'', 1)}$ in Eq. (215) are zero except $a^{(1,1)}$ and all the $b^{(\iota'', 1/2)}$ are zero except $b^{(1/2, 1/2)}$. Since for $\Delta y = 0$ transitions, one unit of isotopic spin is carried by the current, we often call this the $|\Delta \iota| = 1$ rule *(44)*. Similarly, for the $|\Delta y| = 1$ transitions we have the $|\Delta \iota| = \frac{1}{2}$ rule for leptonic modes of hadron decay *(43)*.

Consider the decay $K^+ \to \pi^0 l^+ \nu$. The matrix element of the current is to zero order in $\mathscr{H}_{\text{em}}$ and all orders in $\mathscr{H}_{\text{SB}}$

$$\begin{aligned}
\langle \boldsymbol{\pi}^0 | \mathbf{J}_\alpha^\dagger(0) | \mathbf{K}^+ \rangle &= \sin\theta_c \langle \boldsymbol{\pi}^0 | b_\alpha^{(1/2, 1/2)\dagger} | \mathbf{K}^+ \rangle \\
&= \frac{1}{\sqrt{2}} \sin\theta_c \langle \boldsymbol{\pi}^- | I_- b_\alpha^{(1/2, 1/2)\dagger} | \mathbf{K}^+ \rangle \\
&= \frac{1}{\sqrt{2}} \sin\theta_c \langle \boldsymbol{\pi}^- | b_\alpha^{(1/2, 1/2)\dagger} | \mathbf{K}^0 \rangle \\
&= \frac{1}{\sqrt{2}} \langle \boldsymbol{\pi}^- | \mathbf{J}_\alpha^\dagger(0) | \mathbf{K}^0 \rangle
\end{aligned} \tag{216}$$

where we used $(I_-, b^{(1/2,1/2)\dagger}) = 0$. In terms of the K_2^0, this gives for the rates the $|\Delta\iota| = \frac{1}{2}$ prediction (*43*)

$$\frac{R(K^+ \to \pi^0 l^+ \nu)}{R(K_2^0 \to \pi^- l^+ \nu)} = 1. \tag{217}$$

By the same method we can relate the $\Xi^- \to \Sigma^0 l^- \bar{\nu}$ and $\Xi^0 \to \Sigma^+ l^- \bar{\nu}$ decays. The resulting $|\Delta\iota| = \frac{1}{2}$ prediction is (*43*) $\mathscr{M}(\Xi^0 \to \Sigma^+ e^- \bar{\nu}) = -\sqrt{2}\mathscr{M}(\Xi^- \to \Sigma^0 e^- \bar{\nu})$ or

$$\frac{R(\Xi^- \to \Sigma^0 e^- \bar{\nu})}{R(\Xi^0 \to \Sigma^+ e^- \bar{\nu})} = \frac{1}{2.17}. \tag{218}$$

Also, consider the decay $\Sigma^- \to \Lambda e^- \bar{\nu}$. The most general form, from Lorentz covariance, of the matrix element of $J_\alpha^{\text{v}}(\mathbf{x}, 0)$ is

$$\langle \mathbf{\Lambda} | \mathbf{J}_\alpha^{\text{v}}(\mathbf{x}, 0) | \mathbf{\Sigma}^- \rangle = \bar{u}_\Lambda(\mathbf{p}_2)\,[a\gamma_\alpha + bq_\alpha + c\sigma_{\alpha\beta} q_\beta]\, u_{\Sigma^-}(\mathbf{p}_1) \exp(-i\mathbf{q}\cdot\mathbf{x}) \left(\frac{m_1 m_2}{p_{10} p_{20}}\right)^{1/2} \tag{219}$$

where $q = p_1 - p_2$ and a, b, and c are invariant functions of q^2. But

$$\langle \mathbf{\Lambda} | \mathbf{J}_\alpha^{\text{v}}(\mathbf{x}, 0) | \mathbf{\Sigma}^- \rangle = \cos\theta_c \langle \Lambda | V^\dagger j_\alpha^{(1,1)}(\mathbf{x}, 0)\, V | \Sigma^- \rangle. \tag{220}$$

Thus, considering only the $\alpha = 0$ component and integrating over d^3x, we find

$$\begin{aligned} \langle \mathbf{\Lambda}, \mathbf{p}_2 | \int d^3x \mathbf{J}_0^{\text{v}}(x, 0) | \mathbf{\Sigma}^-, \mathbf{p}_1 \rangle &= \cos\theta_c \langle \Lambda | V^\dagger I_+ V | \Sigma^- \rangle \\ &= \cos\theta_c \langle \Lambda | I_+ | \Sigma^- \rangle \\ &= 0, \end{aligned} \tag{221}$$

since $(I_+, V) = 0$ to zero order in $\mathscr{H}_{\text{em}}$. But from Eq. (219) this means

$$\bar{u}_\Lambda(\mathbf{p}_2)\,[a\gamma_4 + bq_4 + c\sigma_{4i} q_i]\, u_{\Sigma^-}(\mathbf{p}_1)\, \delta^3(\mathbf{q}) = 0 \tag{222}$$

or $a(q^2) = b(q^2) = 0$. Thus for small values of $|\mathbf{q}|/m_{\Sigma^-}$, which is indeed the case over the entire spectrum, the decay proceeds predominantly through the axial vector coupling. It is also immediately apparent by use of the Weyl reflection S_1 that, also to zero order in $\mathscr{H}_{\text{em}}$ and all orders in $\mathscr{H}_{\text{SB}}$, we have the $|\Delta\iota| = 1$ prediction $\mathscr{M}(\Sigma^- \to \Lambda e^- \bar{\nu}) = \mathscr{M}(\Sigma^+ \to \Lambda e^+ \nu)$ or $R(\Sigma^- \to \Lambda e^- \bar{\nu})/R(\Sigma^+ \to \Lambda e^+ \nu) = 1.6$.

Let us consider the vector part of the hadronic current for a strangeness-changing decay*; for example,

$$\begin{aligned}\int d^3x\langle \boldsymbol{\mu}'\,\boldsymbol{\nu}'|\mathbf{J}_0^{\mathrm{V}}(\mathbf{x},0)|\boldsymbol{\mu\nu}\rangle &= \sqrt{6}\sin\theta_c\langle\Psi_{\nu'}^{\mu'}|V^\dagger E_{-2}V|\Psi_\nu^\mu\rangle\\ &= \sqrt{6}\sin\theta_c[\langle\Psi_{\nu'}^{\mu'}|E_{-2}|\Psi_\nu^\mu\rangle\\ &\quad+\langle\Psi_{\nu'}^{\mu'}|V^\dagger(E_{-2},V)|\Psi_\nu^\mu\rangle]\\ &\simeq \sqrt{6}\sin\theta_c\left[\begin{pmatrix}\mu & 8_1 & \mu\\ \nu' & \tfrac{1}{2},-\tfrac{1}{2},-1 & \nu\end{pmatrix}\delta_{\mu\mu'}\,\delta^3(\mathbf{p}-\mathbf{p}')\right.\\ &\quad\left.+\langle\Psi_{\nu'}^{\mu'}|(E_{-2},V)|\Psi_\nu^\mu\rangle\right]\end{aligned} \tag{223}$$

retaining terms to first order in $\mathscr{H}_{\mathrm{SB}}$ (since V is a power series expansion in $\mathscr{H}_{\mathrm{SB}}$ starting with 1). But for the second term,

$$(E_{-2},V)\simeq \sum_b{}_{\mathrm{P}}\,|b\rangle\langle b|\,(E_{-2},\mathscr{H}_{\mathrm{SB}})(H_0-\mathscr{E}_{0b})^{-1} \tag{224}$$

where the symbol $\sum_{\mathrm{P}}$ means to take the principal value when acting on a state. Thus, states with energy $\mathscr{E}_{0b}$ are excluded or, specifically, the initial and final states $|\Psi^\mu\rangle$ and $|\Psi^{\mu'}\rangle$ cannot belong to the same $SU(3)$ multiplet. But in the weak leptonic decays we are primarily interested in transitions between members of the same multiplet; that is, $\mathrm{n}\to\mathrm{p}$, $\Sigma^-\to\mathrm{n}$, $K^+\to\pi^0$, and so on. Thus, including corrections to first order in $\mathscr{H}_{\mathrm{SB}}$, we have (*45*)

$$\int d^3x\langle\boldsymbol{\mu\nu}'|\mathbf{J}_0^{\mathrm{V}}(\mathbf{x},0)|\boldsymbol{\mu\nu}\rangle\simeq\sqrt{6}\sin\theta_c\begin{pmatrix}\mu & 8_1 & \mu\\ \nu' & \tfrac{1}{2},-\tfrac{1}{2},-1 & \nu\end{pmatrix}\delta^3(\mathbf{p}-\mathbf{p}'). \tag{225}$$

For baryon transition, the most general form is ($q=p_1-p_2$)

$$\langle\mathbf{B}_2|\mathbf{J}_\alpha^{\mathrm{V}}(\mathbf{x},0)|\mathbf{B}_1\rangle=\bar{u}_2(\mathbf{p}_2)\,[a\gamma_\alpha+bq_\alpha+c\sigma_{\alpha\beta}q_\beta]\,u_1(\mathbf{p}_1)\exp(-i\mathbf{q}\cdot\mathbf{x})\left(\frac{m_1m_2}{p_{10}\,p_{20}}\right)^{1/2}, \tag{226}$$

which, when the $\alpha=0$ component is integrated over all space, gives

$$\int d^3x\langle\mathbf{B}_2|\mathbf{J}_0^V(\mathbf{x},0)|\mathbf{B}_1\rangle=\bar{u}_2(\mathbf{p}_2)\,[a\gamma_0+bq_0]\,u_1(\mathbf{p}_1)\left(\frac{m_1m_2}{p_{10}\,p_{20}}\right)^{1/2}\delta^3(\mathbf{q}). \tag{227}$$

* The proof of the following theorem on the nonrenormalization to first order in $\mathscr{H}_{\mathrm{SB}}$ of the form factors in the physical region of decay was done in collaboration with D. Schiff.

In the limit of the symmetry, $q_0 \to 0$, so that we find upon comparison that

$$a^{(0)}(q^2=0) = \sqrt{6}\sin\theta_c \begin{pmatrix} \mu & 8_1 & \mu \\ \nu' & \frac{1}{2}, -\frac{1}{2}, -1 & \nu \end{pmatrix}.$$

Note that to first order in $\mathscr{H}_{SB}$

$$\bar{u}_2 u_1 \simeq 1, \qquad \left(\frac{m_1 m_2}{p_{10} p_{20}}\right)^{1/2} \simeq \frac{q_0}{m_1 - m_2}$$

and so

$$a^{(1)} + b^{(0)} \frac{q_0^2}{m_1 - m_2} \simeq 0$$

by Eq. (225). Moreover, when all the particles are on the mass shell one may easily show that

$$m_l^2 \leqslant q^2 \leqslant (m_1 - m_2)^2 = O\,(f^2).$$

Therefore to first order in $\mathscr{H}_{SB}$ we may set $a^{(1)} \simeq b^{(0)} \simeq 0$ and use just the symmetric $a^{(0)}(q^2=0)$.

For meson transitions, the most general form is $(q = q_1 - q_2)$

$$\langle \mathbf{M}_2 | \mathbf{J}_\alpha^\nu(\mathbf{x}, 0) | \mathbf{M}_1 \rangle = [F_+(q_{1\alpha} + q_{2\alpha}) + F_-(q_{1\alpha} - q_{2\alpha})] \frac{\exp(-i\mathbf{q}\cdot\mathbf{x})}{2(q_{10}\, q_{20})^{1/2}}. \quad (228)$$

Proceeding as with the baryons, we find

$$\int d^3x \langle \mathbf{M}_2 | \mathbf{J}_0^\nu(\mathbf{x}, 0) | \mathbf{M}_1 \rangle = [F_+(q_{10} + q_{20}) + F_-(q_{10} - q_{20})]\,\tfrac{1}{2}(q_{10} q_{20})^{-1/2}\,\delta^3(\mathbf{q}). \quad (229)$$

In the limit of the symmetry, $q_{10} \to q_{20}$, so that we find

$$F_+^{(0)}(q^2=0) = \sqrt{6}\sin\theta_c \begin{pmatrix} \mu & 8_1 & \mu \\ \nu' & \frac{1}{2}, -\frac{1}{2}, -1 & \nu \end{pmatrix}.$$

Note again that to first order in $\mathscr{H}_{SB}$,

$$(q_{10} + q_{20})/(4 q_{10} q_{20})^{1/2} \simeq 1,$$

and so

$$F_+^{(1)} + F_-^{(0)} \frac{q_0}{2(q_{10} q_{20})^{1/2}} \simeq 0$$

by Eq. (225). But again, $m_l^2 \leqslant q^2 \leqslant (m_1 - m_2)^2$. Therefore to first order in $\mathscr{H}_{SB}$, we may set $F_+^{(1)} \simeq F_-^{(0)} \simeq 0$ and use just the symmetric $F_+^{(0)}(q^2 = 0)$.

Because of these results, the following predictions (*42*, *46*) involving only the vector strangeness-changing currents hold up to first order in $\mathscr{H}_{SB}$.

$$R(K^+ \to \pi^0 e^+ \nu) = 0.72 \sin^2 \theta_c \times 10^8 \text{ sec}^{-1}$$

$$\frac{R(K^+ \to \pi^0 e^+ \nu)}{R(K^+ \to \pi^0 \mu^+ \nu)} = 1.55. \tag{230}$$

Similarly, the vector contribution to the baryon decays also holds to this order. From the analog of Eq. (223) in the case of neutron β-decay, we have the generator E_1 which, when we neglect $\mathscr{H}_{em}$ in V, commutes with V, thus showing that in β-decay there is no renormalization to all orders in $\mathscr{H}_{SB}$.

It is interesting to note that if we take the matrix element of the equal-time commutation relation at $t = 0$

$$(\mathbf{E}_2(0), \mathbf{E}_{-2}(0)) = \frac{1}{2\sqrt{3}} \mathbf{H}_1(0) + \tfrac{1}{2}\mathbf{H}_2(0)$$

[the $SU(3)$ analog of Eq. (9)] between the states $\langle \boldsymbol{\pi}^+ |$ and $| \boldsymbol{\pi}^+ \rangle$, for example, we find

$$\langle \boldsymbol{\pi}_2^+ | (E_2, E_{-2}) | \boldsymbol{\pi}_1^+ \rangle = \langle \boldsymbol{\pi}_2^+ | \frac{1}{2\sqrt{3}} H_1 + \tfrac{1}{2} H_2 | \boldsymbol{\pi}_1^+ \rangle$$
$$= \langle \pi_2^+ | V^\dagger \left(\frac{1}{2\sqrt{3}} H_1 + \tfrac{1}{2} H_2 \right) V | \pi_1^+ \rangle.$$

If we neglect $\mathscr{H}_w$ in V, then H_1 and H_2 will commute with V. Thus (*3*)

$$\langle \boldsymbol{\pi}_2^+ | (E_2, E_{-2}) | \boldsymbol{\pi}_1^+ \rangle = \langle \boldsymbol{\pi}_2^+ | \boldsymbol{\pi}_1^+ \rangle = \delta^3(\mathbf{p}_1 - \mathbf{p}_2). \tag{231}$$

In the commutator we may insert a complete set of physical states, explicitly separating the complete set into one-particle and many-particle states, the one-particle states belonging in the symmetric limit to the same representation of $SU(3)$ as the π^+. The one-particle state contribution will involve $\langle \boldsymbol{\pi}_2^+ | E_2 | \bar{\boldsymbol{K}}^0 \rangle$, which by Eq. (229) is related to the observed form factor at zero momentum transfer (i.e., coupling constant). The many-particle state contribution will involve $\langle \boldsymbol{\pi}_2^+ | E_2 | \mathbf{m} \rangle$ where $| \mathbf{m} \rangle$ is the many-particle state vector.

But the total Hamiltonian $\mathscr{H}$ will not commute with $\mathbf{E}_2$. From Eqs. (8) and (209)

$$(\mathscr{H}, \mathbf{E}_2(t)) = -i\frac{d}{dt}\mathbf{E}_2(t) = -\frac{i}{\sqrt{6}}\int d^3x \frac{\partial}{\partial t}\mathbf{s}_0^{(1/2,1/2)}(x)$$

$$= \frac{i}{\sqrt{6}}\int d^3x\mathbf{D}(\mathbf{x}, t),$$

where $\mathbf{D}(x) = \partial_\mu \mathbf{s}_\mu^{(1/2,1/2)}$ is a measure of the symmetry-breaking effect, since in the limit of the symmetry $\mathscr{H}$ would commute with $\mathbf{E}_2$ and hence $\mathbf{D}$ would be zero (*3*). By taking the matrix element of the equation, we see that

$$\langle \boldsymbol{\pi}_2^+ | E_2 | \mathbf{m} \rangle = (\mathscr{E}_\pi - \mathscr{E}_m)^{-1}\frac{i}{\sqrt{6}}\int d^3x \langle \boldsymbol{\pi}_2^+ | D(\mathbf{x}, 0) | \mathbf{m} \rangle.$$

Thus relation (231) with a complete set of states inserted in the commutator gives us a relation in which the deviation from unity of the square of the observed coupling constant is proportional to the second order in D, that is, to second order in symmetry breaking (*3*, *45*). This is another proof of the nonrenormalization of the vector coupling constant to first order in symmetry breaking [Eq. (225)]. But now we can assume that $\langle \boldsymbol{\pi}_2^+ | D(0) | \mathbf{m} \rangle$ has the proper analyticity properties required by unitarity and can be related, by the usual dispersive techniques and approximations, to certain observable scattering processes. Thus, by using the experimental results from the pertinent scattering

TABLE X

COMPARISON OF SEMILEPTONIC DECAY EXPERIMENTS AND THEORETICAL PREDICTIONS FOR $\theta_c = 0.264$, $f = 0.437$, AND $d = 0.742$

	Theoretical prediction	Experimental result	$(g_3/g_1)_{\text{th}}$	$(g_3/g_1)_{\text{exp}}$
$g_{3\text{pn}}/g_{1\text{pn}}$	1.18	1.18		
$g_{1\text{pn}}/g_{1\mu e}$	0.965	0.974 ± 0.010		
$B(\Sigma^- \to \Lambda e\nu)$	5.72×10^{-5}	$(7.5 \pm 0.28) \times 10^{-5}$	~8	
$B(\Sigma^- \to \text{n}e\nu)$	1.21×10^{-3}	$(1.2 \pm 0.2) \times 10^{-3}$	−0.305	
$B(\Lambda \to \text{p}e\nu)$	0.925×10^{-3}	$(0.88 \pm 0.08) \times 10^{-3}$	+0.684	$0.9^{+0.3}_{-0.25}$
$B(\Xi^- \to \Lambda e\nu)$	0.615×10^{-3}	$\leqq 1.7 \times 10^{-3}$	+0.190	
$R(K^+ \to \mu^+\nu)$	$\frac{1}{2.03 \times 10^{-8}}$	$\frac{1}{(1.94 \pm 0.03) \times 10^{-8}}$		

processes, we can evaluate the corrections and determine the observed form factor at zero momentum transfer.

With respect to axial vector currents, we are unable, without introducing further assumptions, to make any statements similar to those we have just made for the vector currents. Since our purpose was only to examine $SU(3)$ with symmetry breaking, we shall not examine these other assumptions here. As a result, we shall simply use the $SU(3)$-symmetric axial vector couplings, understanding, of course, that symmetry-breaking effects should be important. To illustrate the kind of agreement (*42, 47*) obtained in this case, we have listed the presently known experimental results and the theoretical predictions for $\theta_c = 0.264, f = 0.437, d = 0.742$ in Table X.

B. Nonleptonic Decays

The weak-interaction Lagrangian of Eq. (200) also gives rise (*40*) to weak nonleptonic decays through the term $(G/\sqrt{2})J_\alpha^\dagger(x)J_\alpha(x)$. Whether or not this is the only term that contributes to such decays has not been definitely established (*48*). On the other hand, as we shall discuss shortly, there are two experimental rules that seem to indicate the existence of other terms. For the sake of our discussion, therefore, we shall allow for this possibility by not restricting ourselves to Eq. (200). We call the weak-interaction Hamiltonian responsible for nonleptonic decays $\mathscr{H}_{\mathrm{Wnl}}$.*

The nonleptonic decays that are observed experimentally are:

$$\Sigma^+ \to \mathrm{p} + \pi^0, \quad \Sigma^+ \to \mathrm{n} + \pi^+, \quad \Sigma^- \to \mathrm{n} + \pi^-, \quad \Lambda \to \mathrm{p} + \pi^-, \quad \Lambda \to \mathrm{n} + \pi^0,$$
$$\Xi^0 \to \Lambda + \pi^0, \quad \Xi^- \to \Lambda + \pi^-, \quad K^+ \to \pi^+ + \pi^0, \quad K^+ \to \pi^+ + \pi^+ + \pi^-,$$
$$K^+ \to \pi^+ + \pi^0 + \pi^0, \quad K_1^0 \to \pi^+ + \pi^-, \quad K_1^0 \to \pi^0 + \pi^0, \quad K_2^0 \to 3\pi^0,$$
$$K_2^0 \to \pi^+ + \pi^- + \pi^0, \quad K_2^0 \to \pi^+ + \pi^-.$$

The last decay listed is distinguished from all the others in that it violates $\mathscr{CP}$-invariance. Since the branching ratio of this mode of K_2^0 decay is so small ($\simeq 2.1 \times 10^{-3}$), we might conjecture that $\mathscr{CP}$ violation is not a property of $\mathscr{H}_{\mathrm{Wnl}}$ but arises from another part of the total Hamiltonian [see Lee (*50*) and references therein]. We shall make this conjecture and assume $\mathscr{H}_{\mathrm{Wnl}}$ to be invariant under $\mathscr{CP}$.

Nonleptonic decays that are *not* observed are the $\Delta s = 2$ transitions $\Xi^- \to \mathrm{n} + \pi^-$, $\Xi^0 \to \mathrm{p} + \pi^-$, and $\Xi^0 \to \mathrm{n} + \pi^0$. Equation (200) is consistent

* A simple and elegant form for $\mathscr{H}_{\mathrm{Wnl}}$ (*49*) involves three currents (two neutral and one charged, forming the fundamental representation of U_3) each coupled to itself such that $\mathscr{H}_{\mathrm{Wnl}}$ transforms like $1 \boxtimes 8$.

with such results. We can easily see this in the following way. From Eq. (213) we see that $(Y, j^{(1,1)\dagger} j^{(1,1)}) = 0$, $(Y, j^{(1,1)\dagger} s^{(1/2,1/2)}) = j^{(1,1)\dagger} s^{(1/2,1/2)}$ and $(Y, s^{(1/2,1/2)\dagger} s^{(1/2,1/2)}) = 0$. By taking the matrix elements of these equations, we find the selection rule $|\Delta s| \leqq 1$. In adding extra terms to Eq. (200) as discussed earlier, we may, therefore, forbid the unobserved transitions by requiring the new terms to give rise to a $|\Delta s| \leqq 1$ rule also.

Note that for all the observed decays listed earlier, $|\Delta s| = 1$. Insofar as Eq. (200) is concerned, the $\Delta s = 1$ decays should proceed through the term $j^{(1,1)\dagger} s^{(1/2,1/2)}$. Now, experimentally, what is observed is a selection rule $|\Delta \iota| = \frac{1}{2}$ for these decays. Specifically, this rule (*51*) means that the $\Delta s = 1$ nonleptonic-decay Hamiltonian transforms under isotopic spin transformations like the $\iota_3 = -\frac{1}{2}$ component of an $\iota = \frac{1}{2}$ spinor, call it $\mathscr{H}_{\mathrm{Wnl}}^{(1/2,-1/2,1)}$ (the superscript is $\nu = \{\iota, \iota_3, y\}$). But the term $j^{(1,1)\dagger} s^{(1/2,1/2)}$ transforms like a linear combination of the $\iota_3 = -\frac{1}{2}$ components of an $\iota = \frac{1}{2}$ and an $\iota = \frac{3}{2}$ spinor. Therefore, barring some dynamical accident, Eq. (200) would not lead to a $|\Delta \iota| = \frac{1}{2}$ rule. This is the first experimental rule that indicates the existence, in $\mathscr{H}_{\mathrm{Wnl}}^{(1/2,-1/2,1)}$, of terms other than those of Eq. (200) (*52*).

The predictions of the $|\Delta \iota| = \frac{1}{2}$ rule can be obtained easily by use of

$$(I_-, \mathscr{H}_{\mathrm{Wnl}}^{(1/2,-1/2,1)}) = 0.$$

For example,

$$\begin{aligned}
\langle \mathbf{n}\boldsymbol{\pi}^- | \mathscr{H}_{\mathrm{Wnl}}^{(1/2,-1/2,1)} | \boldsymbol{\Sigma}^- \rangle &= -\tfrac{1}{2} \langle \mathbf{n}\boldsymbol{\pi}^- | \mathscr{H}_{\mathrm{Wnl}}^{(1/2,-1/2,1)} I_-^2 | \boldsymbol{\Sigma}^+ \rangle \\
&= -\tfrac{1}{2} \langle \mathbf{n}\boldsymbol{\pi}^- | I_-^2 \mathscr{H}_{\mathrm{Wnl}}^{(1/2,-1/2,1)} | \boldsymbol{\Sigma}^+ \rangle \\
&= -\sqrt{2} \langle \mathbf{p}\boldsymbol{\pi}^0 | \mathscr{H}_{\mathrm{Wnl}}^{(1/2,-1/2,1)} | \boldsymbol{\Sigma}^+ \rangle \\
&\quad + \langle \mathbf{n}\boldsymbol{\pi}^+ | \mathscr{H}_{\mathrm{Wnl}}^{(1/2,-1/2,1)} | \boldsymbol{\Sigma}^+ \rangle .
\end{aligned} \tag{232}$$

Another example is

$$\begin{aligned}
0 &= \langle \boldsymbol{\pi}^- \boldsymbol{\pi}^- | (I_-, \mathscr{H}_{\mathrm{Wnl}}^{(1/2,-1/2,1)}) | \bar{\boldsymbol{K}}^+ \rangle \\
&= \langle \boldsymbol{\pi}^- \boldsymbol{\pi}^0 + \boldsymbol{\pi}^0 \boldsymbol{\pi}^- | \mathscr{H}_{\mathrm{Wnl}}^{(1/2,-1/2,1)} | \bar{\boldsymbol{K}}^+ \rangle .
\end{aligned} \tag{233}$$

But in the rest system of the $\bar{K}^+$, angular momentum conservation implies that the pions are in an S state and because of Bose statistics they therefore are in a state that is symmetric under interchange. Thus the $|\Delta \iota| = \frac{1}{2}$ rule forbids $\bar{K}^+ \to \pi^- + \pi^0$.

Another relation (*53*) that seems to hold rather well experimentally is

$$2\langle \boldsymbol{\Lambda}\boldsymbol{\pi}^- | \mathscr{H}_{\mathrm{Wnl}}^{(1/2,-1/2,1)} | \boldsymbol{\Xi}^- \rangle = \langle \mathbf{p}\boldsymbol{\pi}^- | \mathscr{H}_{\mathrm{Wnl}}^{(1/2,-1/2,1)} | \boldsymbol{\Lambda} \rangle - \sqrt{3} \langle \mathbf{p}\boldsymbol{\pi}^0 | \mathscr{H}_{\mathrm{Wnl}}^{(1/2,-1/2,1)} | \boldsymbol{\Sigma}^+ \rangle . \tag{234}$$

Just as the isotopic spin transformation properties of $\mathscr{H}_{\mathrm{Wnl}}^{(1/2,-1/2,1)}$ led to the relationship (232) among the decays of the members of the same isotopic spin multiplet, so we might expect that this relation (234) among the decays of the members of the same octet may arise from the transformation property of $\mathscr{H}_{\mathrm{Wnl}}^{(1/2,-1/2,1)}$ under $SU(3)$ transformations (*48*, *54*). That is, since in general we can write this Hamiltonian as a linear combination of $SU(3)$ tensors, $\mathscr{H}_{\mathrm{Wnl}}^{(1/2,-1/2,1)} = \sum_\mu a(\mu) T^\mu_{1/2,-1/2,1}$, the relationship (234) might follow from just one or two representations in this sum.

In fact, by noting that the total Hamiltonian must be Hermitian, relation (234) can be derived from the assumption that $\mathscr{H}_{\mathrm{Wnl}}^{(1/2,-1/2,1)} + \mathscr{H}_{\mathrm{Wnl}}^{(1/2,-1/2,1)\dagger} \equiv \mathscr{H}_{\mathrm{Wnl}}^{(1/2)}$ is invariant under the transformation $G_U \equiv \mathscr{C} S_3$ (G_U is to U-spin as the G-parity transformation is to ι-spin) (*55*)

$$G_U \mathscr{H}_{\mathrm{Wnl}}^{(1/2)} G_U^\dagger = \mathscr{H}_{\mathrm{Wnl}}^{(1/2)} \tag{235}$$

Given the isotopic spin form of $\mathscr{H}_{\mathrm{Wnl}}^{(1/2)}$, this condition requires $\mathscr{H}_{\mathrm{Wnl}}^{(1/2,-1/2,1)}$ to be an eight-dimensional tensor. Since under this transformation [from Eqs. (30), (317), (44), (209), and (211)]

$$\begin{aligned} G_U j_\alpha^{(1,1)} G_U^\dagger &= -\mathscr{C} s_\alpha^{(1/2,1/2)} \mathscr{C}^\dagger = s_\alpha^{(1/2,1/2)\dagger}, \\ G_U s_\alpha^{(1/2,1/2)} G_U^\dagger &= -j_\alpha^{(1,1)\dagger}, \\ G_U j_{5\alpha}^{(1,1)} G_U^\dagger &= -s_{5\alpha}^{(1/2,1/2)\dagger}, \\ G_U s_{5\alpha}^{(1/2,1/2)} G_U^\dagger &= j_{5\alpha}^{(1,1)\dagger}, \end{aligned} \tag{236}$$

only the parity-nonconserving current $\times$ current terms like $j_{5\alpha}^{(1,1)\dagger} s_\alpha^{(1/2,1/2)}$, $j_\alpha^{(1,1)\dagger} s_{5\alpha}^{(1/2,1/2)}$, and so on in Eq. (200) will satisfy such a symmetry; the parity-conserving terms will not. By adding appropriate terms to Eq. (200), however, we could bring $\mathscr{H}_{\mathrm{Wnl}}^{(1/2)}$ into a form such that it is invariant under G_U.

To derive relation (234) under assumption (235), we proceed as follows. First

$$-\sqrt{3}\langle \mathrm{p}\pi^0 | \mathscr{H}_{\mathrm{Wnl}}^{(1/2)} | \Sigma^+ \rangle + \langle \mathrm{p}\pi^- | \mathscr{H}_{\mathrm{Wnl}}^{(1/2)} | \Lambda \rangle = \langle \mathrm{p}\pi^- | \mathscr{H}_{\mathrm{Wnl}}^{(1/2)} | \sqrt{3}\Sigma^0 + \Lambda \rangle,$$

since

$$\langle \mathrm{p}\pi^- | \mathscr{H}_{\mathrm{Wnl}}^{(1/2)} | \Sigma^0 \rangle = -\frac{1}{\sqrt{2}} \langle \mathrm{p}\pi^- | \mathscr{H}_{\mathrm{Wnl}}^{(1/2,-1/2,1)} I_- | \Sigma^+ \rangle = -\langle \mathrm{p}\pi^0 | \mathscr{H}_{\mathrm{Wnl}}^{(1/2,-1/2,1)} | \Sigma^+ \rangle.$$

Further

$$\begin{aligned}\langle p\pi^-|\mathscr{H}_{\text{Wnl}}^{(1/2)}|\sqrt{3}\Sigma^0+\Lambda\rangle &= \langle p\pi^-|G_U^\dagger \mathscr{H}_{\text{Wnl}}^{(1/2)} G_U|\sqrt{3}\Sigma^0+\Lambda\rangle \\ &= -\langle \Sigma^+ \bar{K}^+|\mathscr{C}^\dagger \mathscr{H}_{\text{Wnl}}^{(1/2)}\mathscr{C}|\sqrt{3}\Sigma^0+\Lambda\rangle \\ &= \sqrt{2}\langle \Sigma^0 \bar{K}^0|\mathscr{C}^\dagger \mathscr{H}_{\text{Wnl}}^{(1/2)}\mathscr{C}|\Lambda\rangle \\ &\quad +\sqrt{3}\langle \Sigma^0 \bar{K}^+|\mathscr{C}^\dagger \mathscr{H}_{\text{Wnl}}^{(1/2)}\mathscr{C}|\Sigma^-\rangle \\ &= \sqrt{2}\langle \Sigma^0 \bar{K}^0|\mathscr{C}^\dagger \mathscr{H}_{\text{Wnl}}^{(1/2)}\mathscr{C}|\Lambda\rangle \\ &\quad -\sqrt{2}\langle \Lambda \bar{K}^0|\mathscr{C}^\dagger \mathscr{H}_{\text{Wnl}}^{(1/2)}\mathscr{C}|\Sigma^0\rangle \\ &\quad +\langle(\sqrt{3}\Sigma^0-\Lambda)\bar{K}^+|\mathscr{C}^\dagger \mathscr{H}_{\text{Wnl}}^{(1/2)}\mathscr{C}|\Sigma^-\rangle \\ &= \sqrt{2}\langle \Sigma^0 K^0|G_U^\dagger \mathscr{H}_{\text{Wnl}}^{(1/2)} G_U|\Lambda\rangle \\ &\quad -\sqrt{2}\langle \Lambda K^0|G_U^\dagger \mathscr{H}_{\text{Wnl}}^{(1/2)} G_U|\Sigma^0\rangle \\ &\quad +2\langle \Lambda\pi^-|G_U^\dagger \mathscr{H}_{\text{Wnl}}^{(1/2)} G_U|\Xi^-\rangle.\end{aligned}$$

But, in the reference frame where the Σ^0 and Λ have opposite momenta and neglecting final state interactions (*56*), we can write

$$\begin{aligned}\langle \Sigma^0 K^0|G_U^\dagger \mathscr{H}_{\text{Wnl}}^{(1/2)} G_U|\Lambda\rangle - \langle \Lambda K^0|G_U^\dagger \mathscr{H}_{\text{Wnl}}^{(1/2)} G_U|\Sigma^0\rangle \\ = \langle K^0|G_U^\dagger \mathscr{H}_{\text{Wnl}}^{(1/2)} G_U|\bar{\Sigma}^0\Lambda-\bar{\Lambda}\Sigma^0\rangle \\ = 0,\end{aligned}$$

since $G_U|K^0\rangle = -|K^0\rangle$, $G_U|\bar{\Sigma}^0\Lambda-\bar{\Lambda}\Sigma^0\rangle = |\bar{\Sigma}^0\Lambda-\bar{\Lambda}\Sigma^0\rangle$. We thus have derived relation (234).

Let us also consider $K_1^0 \to \pi^+ + \pi^-$ or, because of invariance under $\mathscr{CP}$, just $K^0 \to \pi^+ + \pi^-$ (since, then, this mode is forbidden to the K_2^0). The matrix element is $\langle \pi^+\pi^-|\mathscr{H}_{\text{Wnl}}^{(1/2)}|K^0\rangle$. But

$$\begin{aligned}(I_+, \mathscr{H}_{\text{Wnl}}^{(1/2,1/2,-1)}) = 0 = (I_+, G_U \mathscr{H}_{\text{Wnl}}^{(1/2,1/2,-1)} G_U^\dagger) \\ = G_U(\sqrt{6}E_{-2}, \mathscr{H}_{\text{Wnl}}^{(1/2,1/2,-1)}) G_U^\dagger, \qquad (237)\end{aligned}$$

so that the matrix element can be written

$$\langle\pi^+\pi^-|\mathscr{H}^{(1/2,1/2,-1)}_{\text{Wnl}}|K^0\rangle = -\sqrt{6}\langle\bar{K}^0\pi^-|E_{-2}\mathscr{H}^{(1/2,1/2,-1)}_{\text{Wnl}}|K^0\rangle + \langle\bar{K}^0K^0|\mathscr{H}^{(1/2,1/2,-1)}_{\text{Wnl}}|K^0\rangle$$

$$= -\langle\bar{K}^0\pi^-|\mathscr{H}^{(1/2,1/2,-1)}_{\text{Wnl}}|\pi^-\rangle + \langle\bar{K}^0K^0|\mathscr{H}^{(1/2,1/2,-1)}_{\text{Wnl}}|K^0\rangle.$$

The second term on the right is zero by invariance under G_U since $G_U|K^0\rangle = -|K^0\rangle$. In the reference system in which the K^0 and π^+ have the opposite momenta, the first term on the right can be written as the negative of the original matrix element. Thus the K_1^0 is forbidden to decay into 2π (*57*). Although there is no quantitative estimate of the ratio $R(K_1^0 \to 2\pi)/R(K^+ \to \pi^+ + \pi^0)$, the forbiddenness of the 2π mode to both the K_1^0 and K^+ makes more plausible (*57*) the argument that only electromagnetic effects contribute to the violation of the $|\varDelta\iota| = \frac{1}{2}$ rule and hence to the decay $K^+ \to \pi^+ + \pi^0$.

X. Appendix

We demonstrate here the technique of using spin-projection operators in the calculation of the rate of decay of high-spin particles. As an example we consider the decay $B_{JP} \to B_{1/2^+} + M_{0^-}$. The rate is

$$\Gamma = \frac{|\mathbf{q}| \sum |\mathscr{M}|^2}{8\pi m_1^2(2J+1)} \tag{A1}$$

where $\mathbf{q}$ is the three-momentum of one of the final particles in the center-of-mass system, $\mathscr{M}$ is the matrix element Eq. (163), and p_1, p_2, and $q = p_1 - p_2$ are the four-momenta of the initial and final baryon and of the meson, respectively. Specifically,

$$\mathscr{M} = \frac{1}{M^{J-1/2}}\bar{u}_2 a_{\nu_1\nu_2\nu_3} \mathcal{O} u_{1\alpha_1\alpha_2\cdots\alpha_{J-1/2}} q^{\alpha_1}\cdots q^{\alpha_{J-1/2}}. \tag{A2}$$

We take the square of this matrix element and sum over spins. By use of the relation

$$\sum_{\text{spins}} u_{\alpha_1\cdots\alpha_{J-1/2}}\bar{u}^{\beta_1\cdots\beta_{J-1/2}} = \Theta^{\beta_1\cdots\beta_{J-1/2}}_{\alpha_1\cdots\alpha_{J-1/2}}\left(\frac{p_1 + im_1}{2im_1}\right) \tag{A3}$$

we obtain

$$\Sigma\,|\mathscr{M}|^2 = -\frac{|a_{\nu_1\nu_2\nu_3}|^2}{M^{2J-1}}\,\mathrm{Tr}\,(\boldsymbol{p}_2 + im_2)\,\mathscr{O}\Theta^{\beta_1\cdots\beta_{J-1/2}}_{\alpha_1\cdots\alpha_{J-1/2}}(\boldsymbol{p}_1 + im_1)$$
$$\times\gamma_4\,\mathscr{O}^\dagger\,\gamma_4 q^{\alpha_1}\cdots q^{\alpha_{J-1/2}} q_{\beta_1}\cdots q_{\beta_{J-1/2}} \tag{A4}$$

where $\Theta^{\beta_1\cdots\beta_{J-1/2}}_{\alpha_1\cdots\alpha_{J-1/2}}$ is the spin-projection operator for the free field and $\boldsymbol{p} = \gamma_\alpha p_\alpha$. It is completely symmetric separately in the superscripts and subscripts and satisfies

$$p_1^{\alpha_1}\,\Theta^{\beta_1\cdots\beta_{J-1/2}}_{\alpha_1\cdots\alpha_{J-1/2}} = 0, \qquad \gamma^{\alpha_1}\,\Theta^{\beta_1\cdots\beta_{J-1/2}}_{\alpha_1\cdots\alpha_{J-1/2}} = 0, \tag{A5}$$

in order that the particle have unique spin J. We use the following properties of this projection operator

$$\Theta^{\beta_1\cdots\beta_{J-1/2}}_{\alpha_1\cdots\alpha_{J-1/2}}(J) = \frac{J+\frac{1}{2}}{2J+2}\gamma^\alpha\gamma_\beta\,\Theta^{\beta\beta_1\cdots\beta_{J-1/2}}_{\alpha\alpha_1\cdots\alpha_{J-1/2}}(J+\tfrac{1}{2}); \tag{A6}$$

$$\Theta^{\alpha\beta_1\cdots\beta_{J-1/2}}_{\alpha\alpha_1\cdots\alpha_{J-1/2}}(J+\tfrac{1}{2}) = \frac{J+1}{J}\,\Theta^{\beta_1\cdots\beta_{J-1/2}}_{\alpha_1\cdots\alpha_{J-1/2}}(J-\tfrac{1}{2}); \tag{A7}$$

$$q^{\alpha_1}\cdots q^{\alpha_{J-1/2}} q_{\beta_1}\cdots q_{\beta_{J-1/2}}\,\Theta^{\beta_1\cdots\beta_{J-1/2}}_{\alpha_1\cdots\alpha_{J-1/2}}(J-\tfrac{1}{2}) = \left[q^2 - \frac{(p_1\cdot q)^2}{p_1^2}\right]^{J-1/2}\frac{(J-\frac{1}{2})!}{(2J-2)!!}$$
$$= |\mathbf{q}|^{2J-1}\frac{(J-\frac{1}{2})!}{(2J-2)!!}; \tag{A8}$$

where the last line holds in the rest system of particle one.

By use of (A6) in (A4), we find

$$\Sigma\,|\mathscr{M}|^2 = -\frac{|a_{\nu_1\nu_2\nu_3}|^2}{M^{2J-1}}\,q^{\alpha_1}\cdots q^{\alpha_{J-1/2}} q_{\beta_1}\cdots q_{\beta_{J-1/2}}\,\Theta^{\beta\beta_1\cdots\beta_{J-1/2}}_{\alpha\alpha_1\cdots\alpha_{J-1/2}}(J+\tfrac{1}{2})$$
$$\times\frac{J+\frac{1}{2}}{2J+2}\,\mathrm{Tr}\,(\boldsymbol{p}_2 + im_2)\,\mathscr{O}\gamma^\alpha\gamma_\beta(\boldsymbol{p}_1 + im_1)\,\gamma_4\,\mathscr{O}^\dagger\,\gamma_4. \tag{A9}$$

The trace may be evaluated in the standard manner. The result, after using Eq. (A5) is

$$\Sigma\,|\mathscr{M}|^2 = \frac{|a_{\nu_1\nu_2\nu_3}|^2}{M^{2J-1}}\,q^{\alpha_1}\cdots q^{\alpha_{J-1/2}} q_{\beta_1}\cdots q_{\beta_{J-1/2}}\,\Theta^{\alpha\beta_1\cdots\beta_{J-1/2}}_{\alpha\alpha_1\cdots\alpha_{J-1/2}}(J+\tfrac{1}{2})$$
$$\times\frac{2J+1}{J+1}(-p_1\cdot p_2 \pm m_1 m_2) \tag{A10}$$

where the + or − is for $\mathcal{O} = 1$ or γ_5, respectively. If we now employ Eqs. (A7) and (A8), this may be written, in the center-of-mass system, as

$$\Sigma\,|\mathcal{M}|^2 = |a_{\nu_1\nu_2\nu_3}|^2 \left|\frac{\mathbf{q}}{M}\right|^{2J-1} 2m_1(\mathscr{E}_2 \pm m_2)\frac{(J-\frac{1}{2})!\,(2J+1)}{(2J)!!}. \tag{A11}$$

Upon substitution into (A1), we find Eq. (164)

$$\Gamma = \frac{|a_{\nu_1\nu_2\nu_3}|^2}{4\pi}\frac{(\mathscr{E}_2 \pm m_2)}{m_1}\frac{|\mathbf{q}|^{2J}}{M^{2J-1}}\frac{(J-\frac{1}{2})!}{(2J)!!}.$$

Acknowledgments

The author is indebted to Dr. L. F. Landovitz for numerous discussions and suggestions. He also thanks Dr. D. C. Choudhury for helpful suggestions, and Dr. R. G. Sachs and Dr. K. C. Wali for the gracious hospitality proffered at Argonne National Laboratory, where part of this work was done.

REFERENCES

1. M. Gell-Mann, Cal-Tech. Rept. CTSL-20, 1961, unpublished; *Phys. Rev.* **125**, 1067 (1962); Y. Ne'eman, *Nuclear Phys.* **26**, 222 (1961).
2. R. E. Behrends, J. Dreitlein, C. Fronsdal, and B. W. Lee, *Rev. Mod. Phys.* **34**, 1 (1962).
3. S. Fubini and G. Furlan, *Physics* **4**, 229 (1965); S. Fubini, G. Furlan, and C. Rossetti, *Nuovo Cimento* **40**, 1171 (1965); G. Furlan, F. Lannoy, C. Rossetti and G. Segré, *ibid.* **40**, 597 (1965).
4. G. Racah, *Ergeb. exakt. Naturwiss.* **37**, 28 (1965).
5. S. Meshkov, C. A. Levinson, and H. J. Lipkin, *Phys. Rev. Lett.* **10**, 361 (1963).
6. See, e.g., L. C. Biedenharn, "Lectures in Theoretical Physics," Vol. v, p. 258. Wiley (Interscience), New York, 1963.
7. G. E. Baird and L. C. Biedenharn, *J. Mathematical Phys.* **6**, 1847 (1965) and references therein.
8. E. U. Condon and G. H. Shortley, "Theory of Atomic Spectra." Cambridge Univ. Press, London and New York, 1935.
9. J. J. De Swart, *Rev. Mod. Phys.* **35**, 916 (1963).
10. G. Racah, *in* "Group Theoretical Concepts and Methods in Elementary Particle Physics —Istanbul Summer School, 1962" (F. Gürsey, ed.), p. 22. Gordon and Breach, New York, 1964.
11. D. Speiser, *in* "Group Theoretical Concepts and Methods in Elementary Particle Physics—Istanbul Summer School, 1962" (F. Gürsey, ed.), p. 240. Gordon and Breach, New York, 1964.
12. L. C. Biedenharn, *Phys. Lett.* **3**, 254 (1962).
13. A. H. Rosenfeld *et al.*, *Rev. Mod. Phys.* **37**, 633 (1965).
14. S. Okubo, *Progr. Theoret. Phys.* **27**, 949 (1962).

15. S. Coleman and S. L. Glashow, *Phys. Rev. Lett.* **6**, 423 (1961).
16. S. L. Glashow, *in* "Group Theoretical Concepts and Methods in Elementary Particle Physics—Istanbul Summer School, 1962" (F. Gürsey, ed.), p. 303. Gordon and Breach, New York, 1964.
17. S. Okubo, *Phys. Lett.* **4**, 14 (1963).
18. R. Marshak, S. Okubo, and E. C. G. Sudarshan, *Phys. Rev.* **106**, 599 (1957).
19. M. Gell-Mann, *Proc. Intern. Conf. High Energy Phys.* p. 805. CERN, Geneva, 1962.
20. S. P. Rosen, *Phys. Rev. Lett.* **11**, 100 (1963); R. J. Oakes, *Phys. Rev.* **132**, 2349 (1963).
21. A. J. MacFarlane and E. C. G. Sudarshan, *Nuovo Cimento* **31**, 1176 (1964).
22. S. Weinberg and S. B. Treiman, *Phys. Rev.* **116**, 465 (1959).
23. S. Okubo, *J. Phys. Soc. Japan* **19**, 1507 (1964).
24. A. J. MacFarlane and R. H. Socolow, *Phys. Rev.* **144,** 1194 (1966).
25. J. J. Sakurai, *Phys. Rev. Lett.* **9**, 472 (1962).
26. L. Michel, *in* "Group Theoretical Concepts and Methods in Elementary Particle Physics—Istanbul Summer School, 1962" (F. Gürsey, ed.), p. 135. Gordon and Breach, New York, 1964.
27. R. E. Cutkowsky, *Ann. Rev. Nuclear Sci.* **14**, 175 (1964).
28. R. E. Behrends and C. Fronsdal, *Phys. Rev.* **106**, 345 (1957); C. Fronsdal, *Nuovo Cimento Supp.* **9**, 416 (1958).
29. M. Gell-Mann, *Phys. Lett.* **8**, 214 (1964).
30. J. J. Sakurai, *Ann. Physics* **11**, 1 (1960).
31. R. E. Behrends and L. F. Landovitz, *Phys. Rev. Lett.* **11**, 296 (1963).
32. Cf. S. L. Glashow and A. H. Rosenfeld, *Phys. Rev. Lett.* **10**, 192 (1963); M. Goldberg, J. Leitner, R. Musto, and L. O'Raifeartaigh, *Nuovo Cimento* **45,** A169 (1966).
33. V. Gupta and V. Singh, *Phys. Rev.* **135**, B1442 (1964); C. Becchi, E. Eberle, and G. Morpurgo, *ibid.* **136**, B808 (1964); M. Konuma and Y. Tomozawa, *Phys. Lett.* **10,** 347 (1964).
34. C. A. Levinson, H. J. Lipkin, and S. Meshkov, *Phys. Lett.* **7**, 81 (1963).
35. B. Barrett and K. Tanaka, *Nuovo Cimento* **36**, 965 (1965).
36. S. L. Glashow and R. H. Socolow, *Phys. Rev. Lett.* **15**, 329 (1965).
37. R. H. Dalitz and D. G. Sutherland, *Nuovo Cimento* **37**, 1777 (1965).
38. N. Cabibbo and R. Gatto, *Nuovo Cimento* **21**, 872 (1961).
39. S. L. Glashow, *Phys. Rev. Lett.* **11**, 48 (1963).
40. R. P. Feynman and M. Gell-Mann, *Phys. Rev.* **109**, 193 (1958).
41. R. E. Behrends and A. Sirlin (unpublished).
42. N. Cabibbo, *Phys. Rev. Lett.* **10**, 531 (1964).
43. S. Okubo, R. E. Marshak, E. C. G. Sudarshan, W. B. Teutsch, and S. Weinberg, *Phys. Rev.* **112**, 665 (1958).
44. T. D. Lee and C. N. Yang, *Phys. Rev.* **119**, 1410 (1960).
45. C. Bouchiat and Ph. Meyer, *Nuovo Cimento* **34**, 1122 (1964); M. Ademollo and R. Gatto, *Phys. Rev. Lett.* **13**, 264 (1964).
46. M. Sugawara, *Phys. Rev.* **112**, 2128 (1958).
47. W. Willis *et al.*, *Phys. Rev. Lett.* **13**, 291 (1964).
48. M. Gell-Mann, *Phys. Rev. Lett.* **12**, 155 (1964).
49. B. d'Espagnat and Y. Villachon, *Nuovo Cimento* **33**, 948 (1964).
50. T. D. Lee, *Phys. Rev.* **139**, B1415 (1965).
51. M. Gell-Mann and A. Pais, *Proc. 1954 Glasgow Conf. Nuclear and Meson Phys.*, p. 342. Pergamon, London, 1955.
52. S. B. Treiman, *Nuovo Cimento* **15**, 916 (1960); T. D. Lee and C. N. Yang, *Phys. Rev.* **119**, 1410 (1960).

53. B. W. Lee, *Phys. Rev. Lett.* **12**, 83 (1964); H. Sugawara, *Progr. Theoret. Phys.* **31**, 213 (1964).
54. B. W. Lee and A. R. Swift, *Phys. Rev.* **136**, B228 (1964); S. P. Rosen, *Phys. Rev. Lett.* **12**, 408 (1964); B. Sakita, *ibid.* **12**, 379 (1964).
55. S. P. Rosen, *Phys. Rev.* **137**, B431 (1965); *ibid.* **140**, B326 (1965).
56. S. B. Treiman, *Nuovo Cimento* **15**, 916 (1960); A. Pais, *Phys. Rev.* **122**, 317 (1961).
57. N. Cabibbo, *Phys. Rev. Lett.* **12**, 62 (1964).

De Sitter Space and Positive Energy

T. O. PHILIPS
BELL TELEPHONE LABORATORIES, INC.
WHIPPANY, NEW JERSEY
and
E. P. WIGNER
PRINCETON UNIVERSITY, PRINCETON, NEW JERSEY

I. Introduction and Summary

Even though the unitary representations of the pseudo-orthogonal groups $O(p, q)$ (that is, of the groups of transformations that leave the form $x_1^2 + x_2^2 + \cdots + x_p^2 - x_{p+1}^2 - x_{p+2}^2 - \cdots - x_{p+q}^2$ invariant) are known in principle,*

* The representations of $O(4,1)$ (i.e., of the ordinary de Sitter group) were first determined by Thomas (*1*). Corrections of this article were given by Newton (*2*) and by Dixmier (*3*). The last article also gives a rigorous foundation to the earlier work. The first mathematically rigorous treatment of the unitary representations of $O(2,1)$ is due to Bargmann (*4*), of $O(3,1)$ to Bargmann (*4*) and Gelfand and Naimark (*5*), Kihlberg (*6*), and Kihlberg and Ström (*7*). These last articles, including that of Bargmann, remain interesting and illuminating reading to this day. See also the review by Gelfand *et al.* (*8*) and the articles by Biedenharn *et al.* (*9*), Takahashi (*10*), and Pukanszky (*56*).

Concerning the more general $O(p, q)$ groups, see Harish-Chandra (*11*). For $O(3, 2)$ (the "infinite de Sitter group") see Ehrman (*12*). More complete descriptions were given by Berezini *et al.* (*13*). A very elegant method to determine the unitary representations of $O(p, q)$ successively was devised by Rosen and Roman (*14*). This is based on a property of the Lie algebra of the inhomogeneous groups $IO(p, q)$, first discovered, apparently, by Melvin (*15*) and subsequently discovered independently by several others (including the present writers). See also Sharp (*16*), Robinson (*17*), Levy-Nahas (*18*), Berendt (*19*), Rosen (*20*), and Esteve and Sona (*21*).

the physical interpretation of the most important of them, of the ordinary de Sitter group $O(4, 1)$, has not been adequately elucidated. The principal purpose of the present chapter is to contribute toward such elucidation, in particular, toward the understanding of how the positive nature of the energy can be incorporated into the interpretation. No attempt will be made at full generality nor at complete mathematical rigor. Nevertheless, a few problems of mathematical pathology will have to be discussed.

The second section of this chapter contains a proof that all classes of the de Sitter group $O(4, 1)$ are ambivalent, that is, that every element is in the same class as its reciprocal. It then follows that every infinitesimal element N' can be transformed into its negative, that is, an S can be found so that $SN'S^{-1} = -N'$. It then follows that no infinitesimal element's representative can be positive definite. The third section reproduces a somewhat modified version of Melvin's observation (*15*). This observation leads to an expression for the infinitesimal elements of the unitary representations of the groups $O(m, 1)$. In the fourth section, the finite elements of these representations will be determined. These two sections contain no fundamentally new material but establish the connection between Melvin's observation and the work based thereupon, on the one hand, and the work of Bargmann and the Russian school, on the other. In particular, our Eq. (27) is essentially the same as the equations given by these authors. In the case of $O(2, 1)$ (that is, only one spacelike dimension of the underlying space) the calculations do give all those unitary representations that describe particles with a real mass.

The fifth section deals with spatial and time reflections. Since, as a result of the absence of a positive definite energy operator, the usual argument for the antiunitary nature of the time reflection operator is not valid, the possibility of a unitary time reflection operator is kept open. The determination of the reflection operators is, as far as we know, new, but it is also entirely straightforward.

The sixth section determines the localized states for the unitary representations of $O(2, 1)$. It turns out that a postulate that played only a subordinate role in the Minkowski (flat) case assumes a decisive role here. As a result, the state vector of the localized state depends on the validity of the reflection operator; that is, if the localized state is assumed to be reflection invariant, its state vector is different from that arrived at without the assumption of reflection invariance. We know that the reflection symmetry, in the real world, is only approximate. No set of postulates for the state localized at a certain point differs from the postulates for the state vector localized at the antipode of that point. Hence, two (orthogonal) state vectors (or, rather, distributions) satisfy the postulates for localization at any point. The choice between these will be made in Section VIII.

No complete mathematical theory of the process of contraction of representations is developed.* However, three ways of contracting are enumerated. In the first, or "straight," type of contraction, the correspondence of representatives to group elements is left unchanged. Since, in the directions of the contraction of the group space, every element approaches, in the limit, the unit element infinitely closely, the representatives of these elements become the representative of the unit element, that is, the unit operator. The resulting representation is not a faithful representation of the contracted group: all the elements of the Abelian invariant subgroup formed by the contraction process are represented by the unit element. This type of contraction is possible for any representation, finite- or infinite-dimensional.

In the second type of contraction, simultaneously with the approach of some of the group elements to the unit element, a transition to another representation of the original group occurs. More precisely, if $g(\varphi)$ is an element of an Abelian subgroup $g(\varphi)g(\varphi') = g(\varphi + \varphi')$ that is contracted, so that the contracted group elements are $g(\epsilon\varphi) = g_\epsilon(\varphi)$, the representative of this element becomes $D^{l(\epsilon)}(\epsilon\varphi)$ where $D^l(\varphi)$ is the representative of $g(\varphi)$ in the representation l. Simultaneously with this change of the representation, the underlying representation space may also be changed. Of particular interest is the case in which the dimensionality of $D^{l(\epsilon)}$ increases as ϵ decreases so that the representation space becomes, in the limit $\epsilon \to 0$, an infinite-dimensional Hilbert space. In order to assure that the representatives $D^{l(\epsilon)}(\epsilon\varphi)$ of the subgroups undergoing contraction, as well as the representatives $D^{l(\epsilon)}(s)$ of the elements of the subgroup with respect to which the contraction is undertaken, converge to definite operators in the resulting Hilbert space, the representations $D^{l(\epsilon)}$ must be properly chosen and assumed to be transformed into a suitable form.

The last type of contraction—which is appropriate for the contraction of the representations of the $O(m, 1)$ groups—differs from the second type principally because the original representation spaces are already infinite-dimensional Hilbert spaces. In this case, too, the contraction may be coupled with a change of the representation. It is also coupled with a modification of the representation space: the limiting forms of the representatives $D^{l(\epsilon)}$ are applied not to the vectors ψ_i of the original Hilbert space but to vectors ψ_i^ϵ, which converge, as $\epsilon \to 0$, to distributions in, rather than vectors of, the original Hilbert space. The distributions to which the ψ_i^ϵ converge span only

* The process of the contraction of groups has, by now, an extensive literature. A generalized contraction process was proposed by Segal (*22*). The more specific concept was proposed by Inönü and Wigner (*23*). This article also discusses the problems of the contraction of representations. See also Inönü (*24*, *25*). Cf. also Saletan (*26*). The process of avoiding to obtain the non-faithful representations given by straight contraction is called "saving" of the representation in this article. Bacry and Lévy-Leblond (*57*) have recently investigated all the contractions of the de Sitter groups which preserve the rotation subgroup.

a subspace of the original Hilbert space, that is, the space orthogonal to all the distributions to which the ψ_i^ϵ converge is not empty. The last step in the contraction process is a change in the magnitude of the inner product as a result of which the distributions in the original Hilbert space become vectors in a new Hilbert space. Naturally, there is a problem of convergence, just as in the case considered before.

The first kind of straight contraction is a trivial operation. The second type, if applied to the ordinary group of rotations in n-dimensional space, can give the representations of the inhomogeneous (Euclidean) group in $(n-1)$-dimensional space. It is, however, the last type of contraction that has to be applied in the case of the de Sitter group to yield a faithful representation of the Poincaré group. The contraction process must be equivalent to an increase of the radius R of the universe and, if the mass of the particle is to be held constant, this entails an increase in one of the characteristics of the representation. At the same time, the representation space must be restricted so that its vectors correspond to states localized within a decreasing fraction of the total de Sitter space. This may be called the retained region; in the limit it is the neighborhood of a single vector $x_1, x_2, \ldots, x_m, x_t$, infinitely small if measured in terms of the solid angle that it subtends over the origin of the coordinate system but—because of the infinitely large R—infinitely large in actual dimensions. The contracted group contains, in addition to the transformations that leave the vector $x_1, x_2, \ldots, x_m, x_t$ invariant, only transformations that leave this vector in the retained region, and products of all such transformations. The picture that has just been projected is not precise mathematically but is the natural one physically. It also explains how the distributions that form the basis of the new Hilbert space were arrived at; they are based on the state localized in the retained region. Since the angular spread of this region, as viewed from the center of the de Sitter space, is in the limit infinitely small, the corresponding state vectors become distributions in the limit.

The calculations sketched in the preceding paragraph are carried out in detail in Section VIII for the de Sitter space with one spatial direction, that is, for the space with $O(2,1)$ symmetry. If the contraction is based on the localized states that show reflection symmetry, the expected representation of the Poincaré group, describing the states of a particle with a finite mass, is obtained. The energy is positive if the contraction is based on one of the localized states, negative if it is based on its antipode. If reflection symmetry is not used for the specification of the localized states, the contraction process becomes ambiguous and the most natural way to carry it out yields a representation of the Poincaré group that corresponds to zero rest mass. (This is foreshadowed in Section III.) The situation appears to be even more complex in de Sitter spaces of higher dimensionalities. As is evident on the basis of the ambivalent nature of the classes of the de Sitter groups, proved in Section II, the role of the requirement of positive energy is entirely different in de Sitter space and in flat Minkowski space. In the latter case, it gives an added condition for the physical realizability of a representation; in the de Sitter case it eliminates an ambiguity in the definition of the localized state. In de Sitter space, the positive nature of the energy has no purely invariant theoretic meaning; that is, it plays no role in determining whether a representation may or may not be realized physically.

Let us, finally, state the commutation relations between the infinitesimal operators of our $O(m, 1)$ group. These will be assumed in the form

$$[N_{ab}, N_{cd}] = g_{ad}N_{bc} - g_{ac}N_{bd} + g_{bc}N_{ad} - g_{bd}N_{ac}. \tag{1}$$

N_{ab} refers to the transformation in the ab plane, a and b can be any of the coordinates $x_1, x_2, \ldots, x_m$; t and $g_{aa} = -1$ if a refers to one of the spatial coordinates $x_1, \ldots, x_m$, whereas $g_{tt} = 1$, the g_{ab} with $a \neq b$ being zero.

II. Ambivalent Nature of the Classes of de Sitter Groups

It is well known that all classes of the proper rotation group in n dimensions are ambivalent unless n has the form $4k + 2$ with an integer k. (A class is called ambivalent if it contains, with every element, its reciprocal as well. Actually, each class contains the reciprocal of each of its elements if it contains the reciprocal of any.) Let us denote by $\omega_1, \omega_1^{-1}, \omega_2, \omega_2^{-1}, \ldots$ the characteristic values of a rotation in n dimensions, with all $|\omega_i| = 1$ and the series ending with $(\omega_{n/2})^{-1}$ or 1 depending on whether n is even or odd, and denote the corresponding characteristic vectors by $\mathbf{v}_1, \mathbf{v}_1^*, \mathbf{v}_2, \mathbf{v}_2^*, \ldots$, the series again ending with $(\mathbf{v}_{n/2})^*$ or a real $\mathbf{v}$, depending on whether n is even or odd. As is well known, the complex $\mathbf{v}_i$ have all length 0; that is, the sum of the squares of their components is 0. Hence, the two real vectors $\mathbf{v}_j + \mathbf{v}_j^*$ and $i(\mathbf{v}_j - \mathbf{v}_j^*)$ have equal length and are perpendicular to each other. They span a two-dimensional manifold and these two-dimensional manifolds are perpendicular to each other and, in case of odd n, perpendicular to the real $\mathbf{v}$. The whole rotation is a product of rotations in the two-dimensional manifolds spanned by the vectors $\mathbf{v}_j + \mathbf{v}_j^*$ and $i(\mathbf{v}_j - \mathbf{v}_j^*)$; the angle of rotation in this manifold is the argument of the corresponding ω_i. This rotation can be transformed into its reciprocal by the transformation

$$\mathbf{v}_j + \mathbf{v}_j^* \rightarrow i(\mathbf{v}_j - \mathbf{v}_j^*); \qquad i(\mathbf{v}_j - \mathbf{v}_j^*) \rightarrow \mathbf{v}_j + \mathbf{v}_j^*. \tag{2}$$

The real $\mathbf{v}$ (in case of odd n) can be left unchanged or transformed into $-\mathbf{v}$. The last choice renders it always possible, in case of odd n, to make the determinant of the transformation 1. If n is a multiple of 4, the transformation (2) is automatically unimodular. This proves at least that all classes are ambivalent in the groups of rotations in n dimensions as long as n is odd or a multiple of 4. The proof that some (in fact, most) classes are not ambivalent in the rotation groups with $n = 4k + 2$ will not be carried out in detail. The proof is not difficult, but the result can be inferred from the fact that these groups have representations with not-real characters.

Let us now consider the de Sitter groups. The theory of the characteristic values and characteristic vectors of all de Sitter groups ($O(m, m')$ groups) was developed by Zassenhaus (*27*) but we shall restrict ourselves to the case of only one dimension having a different signature from the rest, that is, $m' = 1$. In this case, actually, the results obtained by one of us at an earlier date suffice (*28*).

There are two types of group elements. The matrices of the first type are fully reducible (that is, they can be brought into diagonal form). Two characteristic values are real: λ and λ^{-1}; the corresponding characteristic vectors $\mathbf{w}$ and $\mathbf{w}'$ are real and have zero length

$$\{\mathbf{w}, \mathbf{w}\} = \{\mathbf{w}', \mathbf{w}'\} = 0 \tag{3}$$

where the symbol $\{\mathbf{v}, \mathbf{w}\}$ is the invariant, in general, Hermitian, scalar product

$$\{\mathbf{v}, \mathbf{w}\} = \sum_{ab} g_{ab}(v^a)^* w^b, \tag{4}$$

v^a being the components of the vector $\mathbf{v}$. We shall choose them so that their time component w^t and $(w')^t$ are positive and normalize them in such a way that

$$\{\mathbf{w}, \mathbf{w}'\} = \tfrac{1}{2}. \tag{5}$$

Then, $\mathbf{w} + \mathbf{w}'$ is a timelike vector, with positive length, whereas $\mathbf{w} - \mathbf{w}'$ is a spacelike vector, and the two are perpendicular to each other

$$\{\mathbf{w}+\mathbf{w}', \mathbf{w}+\mathbf{w}'\} = 1, \qquad \{\mathbf{w}-\mathbf{w}', \mathbf{w}-\mathbf{w}'\} = -1, \qquad \{\mathbf{w}+\mathbf{w}', \mathbf{w}-\mathbf{w}'\} = 0. \tag{6}$$

There are, then, $n - 2$ or $n - 3$ characteristic values $\omega_1, \omega_1^{-1}, \omega_2, \omega_2^{-1}, \ldots$ of modulus 1, depending on whether $n = m + 1$ is even or odd. The corresponding characteristic vectors $\mathbf{v}_1, \mathbf{v}_1^*, \mathbf{v}_2, \mathbf{v}_2^*, \ldots$ are pairwise conjugate complex, perpendicular in the sense of

$$\{\mathbf{v}_j, \mathbf{w}\} = \{\mathbf{v}_j, \mathbf{w}'\} = 0 \tag{7a}$$

to the aforementioned characteristic null vectors, also mutually perpendicular

$$\{\mathbf{v}_j, \mathbf{v}_l\} = \{\mathbf{v}_j^*, \mathbf{v}_l\} = 0 \qquad \text{for} \quad j \neq l,$$
$$\{\mathbf{v}_j^*, \mathbf{v}_j\} = 0. \tag{7b}$$

They are spacelike, that is, can be normalized to -1,

$$\{\mathbf{v}_j, \mathbf{v}_j\} = -1. \tag{7c}$$

Finally, in case of odd n there is always a characteristic value 1 with a real spacelike characteristic vector $\mathbf{v}$, perpendicular to all other characteristic vectors

$$\{\mathbf{v}, \mathbf{w}\} = \{\mathbf{v}, \mathbf{w}'\} = 0, \tag{8}$$

$$\{\mathbf{v}, \mathbf{v}_j\} = \{\mathbf{v}, \mathbf{v}_j^*\} = 0, \qquad \{\mathbf{v}, \mathbf{v}\} = -1. \tag{8a}$$

The preceding characterization assumes, implicitly, that there is no degeneracy; that is, $\lambda \neq 1$ and none of the ω, ω^* are either equal or real. The preceding statements concerning the characteristic vectors then are consequences of the character of the de Sitter transformations. If these assumptions are not valid, that is, if either $\lambda = 1$ or some of the ω, ω^* are real or equal, there is more freedom in the choice of the characteristic vectors. However, they can always be chosen in such a way that Eqs. (5), (6), (7), and (8) may be valid.

The preceding characterization of the first type of de Sitter transformations can be expressed somewhat more geometrically by observing that $\mathbf{w}$, $\mathbf{w}'$ define a real plane (two-space) in which the signature of the metric is 1, -1. The vectors $\mathbf{v}$ lie in the $(n-2)$-space perpendicular to the two-space of $\mathbf{w}$, $\mathbf{w}'$. The whole transformation is the product of a Lorentz transformation in the two-space,

$$(\mathbf{w} + \mathbf{w}') = \lambda\mathbf{w} + \lambda^{-1}\mathbf{w}' = \tfrac{1}{2}(\lambda + \lambda^{-1})(\mathbf{w} + \mathbf{w}') + \tfrac{1}{2}(\lambda - \lambda^{-1})(\mathbf{w} - \mathbf{w}'),$$
$$(\mathbf{w} - \mathbf{w}') = \lambda\mathbf{w} - \lambda^{-1}\mathbf{w}' = \tfrac{1}{2}(\lambda - \lambda^{-1})(\mathbf{w} + \mathbf{w}') + \tfrac{1}{2}(\lambda + \lambda^{-1})(\mathbf{w} - \mathbf{w}'), \tag{9}$$

and a rotation in the $(n-2)$-space perpendicular to it. The signature of the metric in this latter space is negative throughout, which is the same thing as if it were positive.

The transformation that converts the de Sitter transformation just considered into the reciprocal transformation is the product of the transformation in the two-space

$$\mathbf{w} \to \mathbf{w}', \qquad \mathbf{w}' \to \mathbf{w} \tag{10}$$

and a transformation in the $(n-2)$-space. Since the determinant of (10) is -1, the determinant of the latter transformation must also be -1. This can be achieved if n is odd—in this case we can choose between $\mathbf{v} \to \mathbf{v}$ and $\mathbf{v} \to -\mathbf{v}$ to give any sign to the second transformation. It is naturally so if $n-2$ has the form $4k+2$, because in that case the determinant of the transformation (2) is -1. Hence, we again arrive at the conclusion that at least the group elements of the first type form ambivalent classes if n is either odd (as in our case) or a multiple of 4.

The group elements of the second type cannot be brought to diagonal form. They form a manifold of lower dimensionality than that of the elements of the first type and we could avoid analyzing them for the purpose at hand. For the sake of completeness, however, we shall describe them rather thoroughly.

Each element S of the second type defines three vectors $\mathbf{v}_e$, $\mathbf{w}_e$, $\mathbf{z}_e$ such that the group element applied to it gives

$$S\mathbf{v}_e = \mathbf{v}_e, \qquad S\mathbf{w}_e = \mathbf{w}_e + \mathbf{v}_e, \qquad S\mathbf{z}_e = \mathbf{z}_e + \mathbf{w}_e + \tfrac{1}{2}\mathbf{v}_e \tag{11}$$

where $\mathbf{v}_e$ and $\mathbf{z}_e$ are null vectors, $\mathbf{w}_e$ spacelike and perpendicular to them:

$$\begin{gathered}\{\mathbf{v}_e, \mathbf{v}_e\} = \{\mathbf{v}_e, \mathbf{w}_e\} = \{\mathbf{z}_e, \mathbf{w}_e\} = \{\mathbf{z}_e, \mathbf{z}_e\} = 0, \\ -\{\mathbf{w}_e, \mathbf{w}_e\} = \{\mathbf{z}_e, \mathbf{v}_e\} = 1.\end{gathered} \tag{11a}$$

What is remarkable, of course, is that the multiple characteristic value with only one characteristic vector has necessarily the value 1 and that it is exactly threefold (*28*). There can be only one such anomalous characteristic value, that is, only one set of three vectors satisfying Eq. (11). There are, in addition, $n-3$ other characteristic values, ω_1, ω_1^*, ω_2, ω_2^*, …, ending on $\omega_{(n-3)/2}^*$ if n is odd, on 1 if n is even. The corresponding characteristic vectors are $\mathbf{v}_1$, $\mathbf{v}_1^*$, $\mathbf{v}_2$, $\mathbf{v}_2^*$, …, the last one being $\mathbf{v}_{(n-3)/2}^*$ or a real $\mathbf{v}$, depending on whether n is odd or even (the reverse of the situation for the first type). These are all spacelike, can be normalized to -1, and can be assumed to be orthogonal to $\mathbf{v}_e$, $\mathbf{w}_e$, $\mathbf{z}_e$

$$\{\mathbf{v}_j, \mathbf{v}_e\} = \{\mathbf{v}_j, \mathbf{w}_e\} = \{\mathbf{v}_j, \mathbf{z}_e\} = 0. \tag{11b}$$

The same equations hold if, in case of even n, $\mathbf{v}$ is substituted for $\mathbf{v}_j$; they hold, naturally, for the $\mathbf{v}_j^*$ as well. In addition, (7b) and (8a) hold for the $\mathbf{v}_j$, $\mathbf{v}_j^*$ and, if n is even, for $\mathbf{v}$.

Again, the group elements of the second type can be described more geometrically. There is a three-space, spanned by the vectors $\mathbf{v}_e$. $\mathbf{w}_e$, $\mathbf{z}_e$, with signature $--+$, in which the effect of S is given by Eq. (11). S is then a product of this transformation and a rotation in the $(n-3)$-space perpendicular to the three-space, with totally negative signature.

S will be transformed into its reciprocal by a product of two transformations. The transformation in the three-space is

$$\mathbf{v}_e \rightarrow \mathbf{v}_e, \qquad \mathbf{w}_e \rightarrow -\mathbf{w}_e, \qquad \mathbf{z}_e \rightarrow \mathbf{z}_e; \tag{12}$$

the transformation in the $(n-3)$-space converts the rotation therein into its reciprocal; it is given by (2). The determinant of the transformation (12) is -1, and the determinant of (2) must be -1 also. This can always be accomplished if $n-3$ is odd, that is, if n is even. If $n-3$ is even, the determinant of the transformation (2) will be -1 if $n-3$ has the form $4k-2$. It follows that n, if odd, must have the form $4k+1$ if the S of the second type are to be in the class with their reciprocals. We note that for $n=5$ both types of group elements form ambivalent classes.

It should be observed that the ambivalent nature of some classes is only a sufficient condition for the corresponding infinitesimal element to have oppositely equal characteristic values. This condition is fulfilled for $n=5$ so that there are no pairs of representations such that the characteristic values of one of the infinitesimal operators be different and oppositely equal in the two. However, even if there are not-ambivalent classes, such infinitesimal elements need not exist—they do not for any odd n.

III. The Infinitesimal Elements of Unitary Representations of the de Sitter Group

The infinitesimal elements of unitary representations of $O(m, m')$ have been given in numerous forms (see footnote on p. 631). Nevertheless, we shall give a modified form here for *some* representations of the groups $O(m, 1)$, because the particular form to be given permits determination of the finite elements of the representations with relative ease and in a compact form. In the case of the group $O(2, 1)$, that is, the finite de Sitter group with one spatial and one timelike dimension, all the single-valued representations with positive mass will be obtained.

We use as Hilbert space the square-integrable functions on a sphere in Euclidean m-dimensional space. We introduce a rectangular coordinate system the axes of which will correspond to the spatial axes of the de Sitter space. We define infinitesimal operators N_{ab} satisfying the relations (1) for spatial a and b (that is, $g_{ab} = -\delta_{ab}$):

$$N_{ab} = \xi_b \frac{\partial}{\partial \xi_a} - \xi_a \frac{\partial}{\partial \xi_b}. \tag{13}$$

These indeed satisfy the relations $[N_{ab}, N_{bc}] = N_{ca}$ for $c \neq a$, at least formally; they are skew-Hermitian, and two N with no common indices commute. Even though they are defined in terms of the m coordinates of m-space, it is clear that they can also be defined for functions on the surface of a sphere therein, the sphere being centered at the origin of the coordinate system. A particularly simple way to verify this is to use, instead of the aforementioned Hilbert space, the Hilbert space of all functions in m-space that have the form

$$f(\rho)\,\psi(\Omega) \tag{14}$$

where $f(\rho)$ is a fixed function of the radius ρ, which is smooth and square-integrable in m-space (for example, $f(\rho) = \exp(-\rho^2)$), whereas the $\psi(\Omega)$ are square-integrable functions of the direction Ω in m-space. The operators (13) transform the functions (14) into similar functions *with the same f*. Hence, they are transformations within the Hilbert space of the functions (14).

We need operators N_{at} where a is a spatial and t the timelike axis. The commutation relations to be satisfied are

$$\begin{aligned} &[N_{ab}, N_{at}] = N_{bt}, \\ &[N_{ab}, N_{ct}] = 0 \qquad \text{for} \quad c \neq a, b, \\ &[N_{at}, N_{bt}] = -N_{ab} \qquad (a \neq b). \end{aligned} \tag{15}$$

These are satisfied, again at least formally, by the operators*

$$N_{at} = \frac{1}{2\rho} \sum_{c \neq a} (N_{ac}\,\xi_c + \xi_c\,N_{ac}) + \frac{i}{\rho}\,\mu\xi_a. \tag{16}$$

μ is an arbitrary real number and the operators are skew-Hermitian and transform functions of the form (14) into functions of the same form. The summation over c in (16) omits $c = a$ but goes over all other spatial dimensions. Alternatively, the N with two equal indices can be set equal to 0. It is useful to remember that all N commute with $1/\rho$; that

$$[N_{ab}, \xi_c] = \delta_{ac}\,\xi_b - \delta_{bc}\,\xi_a; \tag{17}$$

and, of course, that

$$[\xi_a, \xi_b] = 0, \qquad \Sigma\, \xi_a^2 = \rho^2. \tag{17a}$$

* Essentially, this is the content of Melvin's observation (*15*). See also Takabayasi (*29*). Actually, the expressions (16) are somewhat more general than those given by these authors.

Hence, (16) can be given the forms

$$N_{at} = \frac{1}{\rho} \sum_{c \neq a} N_{ac} \xi_c + \frac{\nu}{\rho} \xi_a = \frac{1}{\rho} \sum_{c \neq a} \xi_c N_{ac} + \frac{\nu'}{\rho} \xi_a \tag{16a}$$

where

$$\nu = i\mu + \frac{m-1}{2}, \qquad \nu' = i\mu - \frac{m-1}{2}. \tag{16b}$$

This simplifies the verification of Eqs. (15).

Such verifications are, in our experience, more readily carried out by the reader alone than under the guidance of some printed calculation. We reproduce, therefore, only the verification of the first of Eqs. (15). We have

$$\begin{aligned}
[N_{ab}, N_{at}] &= \frac{1}{\rho} \sum_{c \neq a} \left\{ [N_{ab}, N_{ac}] \xi_c + N_{ac}[N_{ab}, \xi_c] + \frac{\nu}{\rho} [N_{ab}, \xi_a] \right\} \\
&= \frac{1}{\rho} \sum_{c \neq a,b} \{ N_{bc} \xi_c - N_{ac} \delta_{bc} \xi_a \} + \frac{\nu}{\rho} \xi_b \\
&= \frac{1}{\rho} \sum_{c \neq b} N_{bc} \xi_c + \frac{\nu}{\rho} \xi_b = N_{bt}.
\end{aligned} \tag{15a}$$

It is probably not necessary to remark that the verification of Eqs. (15) uses only the commutation relations between the N_{ab} and the commutation relations (17) between the N_{ab} and the ξ, or rather, the ξ/ρ, together with the relations $[\xi_a, \xi_b] = 0$, $\sum (\xi_a/\rho)^2 = 1$. Hence, any other operators with the same commutation relations could be used to define the N_{at} in Eq. (16). However, the special forms (13), (16) of these operators will render it particularly easy to determine the finite group operators.

Before going on to the determination of the finite group operators, let us calculate the first invariant of the Lie algebra of the N, that is, the first Casimir operator

$$C = \tfrac{1}{2} \sum_{a \neq b} N_{ab}^2 - \sum_{a} N_{at}^2 \tag{18}$$

For this purpose, let us first calculate, by means of (16a),

$$\begin{aligned}
\sum_a \left(N_{at} - \frac{\nu}{\rho} \xi_a \right) \left(N_{at} - \frac{\nu'}{\rho} \xi_a \right) &= \sum_a \sum_c N_{ac} \xi_c \sum_d \xi_d N_{ad} \\
&= \sum_{acd} \left(\frac{\partial}{\partial \xi_a} \xi_c - \frac{\partial}{\partial \xi_c} \xi_a \right) \xi_c \frac{1}{\rho^2} \xi_d \left(\xi_d \frac{\partial}{\partial \xi_a} - \xi_a \frac{\partial}{\partial \xi_d} \right).
\end{aligned} \tag{18a}$$

Since the N_{ac}, N_{ad} with two equal indices are evidently zero for the N defined by (13), the restriction $c, d \neq a$ can be dropped in this case. The $1/\rho$ was shifted to be the last factor of $N_{ac}\xi_c$, which is permissible since it commutes with N_{ac} and ξ_c.

Every one of the four terms in the last member of (18a) has a sum over ξ_a^2, ξ_c^2, or ξ_d^2 to cancel the $1/\rho^2$. If this cancellation is carried out and a and c are used for the remaining summation variables, two terms drop out and we obtain

$$\sum_a \left(N_{at} - \frac{\nu}{\rho}\xi_a\right)\left(N_{at} - \frac{\nu'}{\rho}\xi_a\right) = \sum_{a,c}\left[-\frac{\partial}{\partial \xi_c}\xi_a\xi_c\frac{\partial}{\partial \xi_a} + \frac{\partial}{\partial \xi_a}\xi_c^2\frac{\partial}{\partial \xi_a}\right]. \tag{18b}$$

On the other hand,

$$\sum_{ab}\tfrac{1}{2}N_{ab}^2 = \tfrac{1}{2}\sum_{ab}\left(\frac{\partial}{\partial \xi_a}\xi_b - \frac{\partial}{\partial \xi_b}\xi_a\right)\left(\xi_b\frac{\partial}{\partial \xi_a} - \xi_a\frac{\partial}{\partial \xi_b}\right)$$

$$= \sum_{ab}\left[\frac{\partial}{\partial \xi_a}\xi_b^2\frac{\partial}{\partial \xi_a} - \frac{\partial}{\partial \xi_b}\xi_a\xi_b\frac{\partial}{\partial \xi_a}\right]. \tag{18c}$$

In two of the terms, the roles of a and b were interchanged. Hence,

$$\sum_a \left(N_{at} - \frac{\nu}{\rho}\xi_a\right)\left(N_{at} - \frac{\nu'}{\rho}\xi_a\right) - \tfrac{1}{2}\sum_{ab} N_{ab}^2 = 0, \tag{19}$$

a relation that may be known to some of the readers. Adding (19) to (18), we obtain

$$C = -\frac{1}{\rho}\sum_a (\nu\xi_a N_{at} + N_{at}\nu'\xi_a) + \frac{\nu\nu'}{\rho^2}\sum \xi_a^2$$

$$= -\frac{1}{\rho}\sum_{ac}[\nu\xi_a(\xi_c N_{ac} + \nu'\xi_a) + (N_{ac}\xi_c + \nu\xi_a)\nu'\xi_a] + \frac{\nu\nu'}{\rho^2}\sum_a \xi_a^2. \tag{20}$$

The sums over $\xi_a\xi_c N_{ac}$ and $N_{ac}\xi_a\xi_c$ vanish because N is antisymmetric in its indices and the ξ commute. The sums over ξ_a^2 just cancel the ρ^2 and we obtain

$$C = -\nu\nu' = \mu^2 - \tfrac{1}{4}(m-1)^2. \tag{21}$$

We are naturally tempted to interpret Eq. (21) by considering a state vector ψ such that all $N_{ab}\psi = 0$, that is, the system at rest. Then, (21) shows that the sum of the squares of iN_{at} is $\mu^2 - \frac{1}{4}(m-1)^2$, which would have to be interpreted as $(RMc/\hbar)^2$ where R is the radius of the universe, M the rest mass of the system. This is a tremendously large number, and it should be possible to relax the condition $N_{ab}\psi = 0$ without giving the system any appreciable kinetic energy. This relaxation should render it possible to restrict the position of the particle to a relatively small part of space and should render one of the iN_{at} much larger than the others. Since the total velocities are still very small, the large iN_{at} should be, essentially, the energy operator. However, because of the ambivalent nature of all classes, the spectrum of this operator is symmetric about 0 so that, apparently, negative energy values cannot be avoided.

We shall see that the resolution of this paradox revolves about the location of the system. The states with positive and with negative energy values are located antipodally, so that the same N_{at} that advances the time at one location turns it back at the other. However, the actual situation is more complex (and, in our view, more interesting, too) than this resolution of the positive-negative energy paradox might indicate.

IV. Finite Elements of the Unitary Representations of Section III

The advantage of the form (13), (16) of the infinitesimal operators is that they permit the rather easy calculation of the finite operators. This is because they are first-order differential operators. That the operators obtained this way are unitary proves that the infinitesimal operators are self-adjoint. We can also verify the group relations on the finite group elements.

The finite group elements can be obtained as products of the one-parametric subgroups formed by the exponentials $e^{\varphi N}$ of the infinitesimal elements N. We write

$$U(\varphi) = e^{\varphi N} \tag{22}$$

with proper indices on both the N and U; the latter satisfy the equations

$$\frac{dU(\varphi)}{d\varphi} = NU(\varphi) = U(\varphi)N. \tag{22a}$$

As far as spatial rotations are concerned, the solution of Eq. (22a),

$$\frac{dU_{ab}(\varphi)\,\psi}{d\varphi}=\left(\xi_b\frac{\partial}{\partial\xi_a}-\xi_a\frac{\partial}{\partial\xi_b}\right)U_{ab}(\varphi)\,\psi, \tag{23}$$

is well known. If ψ is a suitable vector in Hilbert space, that is, a differentiable function of the variables ξ, we have, for $a=1$, $b=2$,

$$U_{12}\,\psi(\xi_1,\xi_2,\ldots)=\psi(\xi_1\cos\varphi+\xi_2\sin\varphi,\ \xi_2\cos\varphi-\xi_1\sin\varphi,\ldots). \tag{24}$$

The variable φ of U_{ab} is suppressed and the variables $\xi_3,\ldots,\xi_m$ are not written out on either side; they are identical. To verify (23) for the operator defined by (24), we calculate

$$\frac{\partial}{\partial\varphi}U_{12}\,\psi(\xi_1,\xi_2,\ldots)=(-\xi_1\sin\varphi+\xi_2\cos\varphi)\,\psi_1+(-\xi_1\cos\varphi-\xi_2\sin\varphi)\,\psi_2 \tag{24a}$$

where ψ_1 and ψ_2 are the derivatives of ψ with respect to the first and second variables and the arguments of both are as on the right side of (24). On the other hand, applying $N_{12}=\xi_2\,\partial/\partial\xi_1-\xi_1\,\partial/\partial\zeta_2$ to (24) gives

$$N_{12}\,U_{12}\,\psi(\xi_1,\xi_2,\ldots)=\xi_2(\cos\varphi\,\psi_1-\sin\varphi\,\psi_2)-\xi_1(\sin\varphi\,\psi_1+\cos\varphi\,\psi_2) \tag{24b}$$

and this is identical with (24a). The rotations in the general ab plane are obtained by an obvious generalization of (24).

Let us now calculate $U_{1t}(\varphi)$. From (22a) and (16a), (13), we have,

$$\frac{\partial\Psi}{\partial\varphi}=\frac{1}{\rho}\left[\sum_{c\neq1}\xi_c\left(\xi_c\frac{\partial}{\partial\xi_1}-\xi_1\frac{\partial}{\partial\xi_c}\right)+\nu'\,\xi_1\right]\Psi \tag{25}$$

where $\Psi=U_{1t}(\varphi)\,\psi(\xi_1,\ldots,\xi_m)$ is a function of the ξ and of φ. This is a linear first-order partial differential equation that can be solved by standard methods. Since $\xi_c\,\partial/\partial\xi_1-\xi_1\,\partial/\partial\xi_c$ gives 0 if applied to a function of ρ, and since this commutes with the ξ, it can be treated as a constant in the solution. We find

$$\Psi=F\left[\frac{\rho+\xi_1}{\rho-\xi_1}e^{2\varphi},\ \frac{\xi_2}{(\rho^2-\xi_1^2)^{1/2}},\ \frac{\xi_3}{(\rho^2-\xi_1^2)^{1/2}},\ldots\right]\left(\cosh\varphi+\frac{\xi_1}{\rho}\sinh\varphi\right)^{\nu'} \tag{26}$$

where F is an arbitrary function. We can introduce new symbols

$$v_1 = \frac{\rho + \xi_1}{\rho - \xi_1} e^{2\varphi}, \qquad v_i = \frac{\xi_i}{(\rho^2 - \xi_1^2)^{1/2}}, \qquad (i \neq 1) \tag{26a}$$

for the variables of F, and then obtain the combinations of these variables, which are, for $\varphi = 0$, equal to $\xi_1, \xi_2, \ldots$. These are

$$\rho \frac{v_1 - 1}{v_1 + 1} = \rho \frac{\xi_1 \cosh \varphi + \rho \sinh \varphi}{\rho \cosh \varphi + \xi_1 \sinh \varphi} \tag{26b}$$

$$\frac{2\rho v_1^{1/2} v_i}{v_1 + 1} = \frac{\rho \xi_i}{\rho \cosh \varphi + \xi_1 \sinh \varphi} \qquad (i = 2, 3, \ldots, m); \tag{26c}$$

F can be considered, as well, an arbitrary function of these variables. The new function can be denoted by ψ since, for $\varphi = 0$, the function $\Psi = U_{1t}(\varphi)\psi$ should be equal to ψ. Hence,*

$$\begin{aligned} \Psi &= U_{1t}(\varphi)\psi(\xi_1, \ldots, \xi_m) \\ &= \psi\left(\frac{\xi_1 \rho \operatorname{Ch} \varphi + \rho^2 \operatorname{Sh} \varphi}{\rho \operatorname{Ch} \varphi + \xi_1 \operatorname{Sh} \varphi}, \frac{\rho \xi_2}{\rho \operatorname{Ch} \varphi + \xi_1 \operatorname{Sh} \varphi}, \frac{\rho \xi_3}{\rho \operatorname{Ch} \varphi + \xi_1 \operatorname{Sh} \varphi}, \ldots\right) \\ &\quad \times \left(\operatorname{Ch} \varphi + \frac{\xi_1}{\rho} \operatorname{Sh} \varphi\right)^{-(m-1)/2 + i\mu} \end{aligned} \tag{27}$$

In order to render this equation somewhat more compact, the symbols Ch and Sh were used instead of cosh and sinh. The expressions for the other U_{at} are the analogues of (27). Actually, (27) has a very simple geometrical description. In order to obtain it, let us first convert the vector $\xi_1, \xi_2, \ldots, \xi_m$ into a null vector in $(m+1)$-dimensional space. Its components will be

$$\xi_1, \xi_2, \xi_3, \ldots, \xi_m, \rho. \tag{27a}$$

Such a vector transforms under transformations affecting only the spatial coordinates as indicated by (24). Let us apply a Lorentz transformation in

* Equation (27) is essentially identical with formulas given, simultaneously, by Bargmann (*4*) and Gel'fand and Naimark (*5*).

the $1t$ plane to (27a). This yields the vector with the components

$$\xi_1 \operatorname{Ch} \varphi + \rho \operatorname{Sh} \varphi,\ \xi_2,\ \xi_3,\ \ldots,\ \xi_m,\ \rho \operatorname{Ch} \varphi + \xi_1 \operatorname{Sh} \varphi. \tag{27b}$$

If we now reduce this vector in length so that the length of its spatial part again becomes the original ρ, we divide every component by the square root of

$$\begin{aligned}(\xi_1 \operatorname{Ch} \varphi + \rho \operatorname{Sh} \varphi)^2 &+ \xi_2^2 + \xi_3^2 + \cdots + \xi_m^2 \\ &= \xi_1^2(1 + \operatorname{Sh}^2 \varphi) + 2\xi_1 \rho \operatorname{Ch} \varphi \operatorname{Sh} \varphi + \rho^2(\operatorname{Ch}^2 \varphi - 1) + \xi_2^2 + \cdots + \xi_m^2 \\ &= \xi_1^2 + \xi_2^2 + \cdots + \xi_m^2 - \rho^2 + (\xi_1 \operatorname{Sh} \varphi + \rho \operatorname{Ch} \varphi)^2 \\ &= (\xi_1 \operatorname{Sh} \varphi + \rho \operatorname{Ch} \varphi)^2. \end{aligned} \tag{27c}$$

This is just what appears in the denominators of the variables on the right side of (27). Hence, we can say that the variable of ψ is an equivalence class of null vectors, in the $(m + 1)$-dimensional de Sitter space, all vectors of the class having the same direction. Since all the transformations of the de Sitter group are linear and homogeneous, such equivalence classes are transformed into equivalence classes and, naturally, null vectors are transformed by de Sitter transformations into null vectors. It is necessary to use equivalence classes of null vectors as variables because vectors of any other length in the same direction do not all have the same length. The last factor of (27) restores unitarity to the transformation.

If φ is very large, the values of $U_{1t}(\varphi)\psi$ are determined, except in the neighborhood of $\xi_1 \approx -\rho$, essentially by the value of ψ at $\xi_1 \approx \rho$, the other $\xi_a \ll \rho$. Unless ψ fluctuates violently in this region, $U_{1t}(\varphi)\psi$ will approach the product of this value and the factor $(\operatorname{Ch} \varphi + (\xi_1/\rho) \operatorname{Sh} \varphi)^{-(1/2)m+1/2+i\mu}$. The values of ψ elsewhere affect the values of $U_{1t}(\varphi)\psi$ only at $\xi_1 \approx -\rho$; more precisely, the values of ψ at $\xi_1 < \rho(1 - \epsilon)$ affect only the values of $U_{1t}(\varphi)\psi$ at $\xi_1 < -\rho + (4\rho/\epsilon)e^{-2\varphi}$. In the region concerned, $\operatorname{Ch} \varphi + (\xi_1/\rho) \operatorname{Sh} \varphi$ is smaller than $e^{-\varphi}(1 + 2/\epsilon)$ so that, unless ϵ is very small, the last factor of (27) increases the absolute value of $U_{1t}(\varphi)\psi$ greatly over the value of ψ from which it is derived. This is, naturally, a necessary consequence of the unitary nature of U_{1t}.

The fact that $U_{1t}(\varphi)\psi$, at a given set of values of its variables, depends on the value of ψ only at a given point, is quite surprising. Such behavior could be expected, at best, for the $(2 + 1)$-dimensional de Sitter group; that is, the de Sitter group with a single spacelike coordinate. In fact, the interpretation of the representation will turn out to be simplest in that case. Before turning to the subject of interpretation, however, the representation considered will be extended to a representation of the full de Sitter group, including reflections.

V. Spatial and Time Reflections

There are two types of postulates on the basis of which the reflection operators can be determined. Those of the first type are concerned with the relation of the reflection operators to the other symmetry operations and to each other. One such relation is that the square of every reflection operator is either unity or, at worst, multiplication with a number. Another relation is, in Minkowski space, that spatial reflections and time displacement commute and that time inversion Θ transforms the time displacement operator T_t into $\Theta^{-1}T_t\Theta = T_{-t} = T_t^{-1}$. The conditions on the various reflection operators are different in de Sitter space, but they are equally stringent. These relations are ordinarily* used to determine the reflection operators and they suffice to do this, leaving only a few alternatives open. We shall use the analogous relations in de Sitter space in a similar way to obtain the possible reflection operators.

The second type of postulate refers to the relation of the inversion operators to other physical observables. Thus, operators of positional coordinates commute with time inversion, those of momentum coordinates anticommute. Again, there is a large number of such relations that will not be enumerated in detail.† What we do wish to remind the reader of is that the possibility of satisfying these relations, together with those of the first type, is equivalent with the existence of the corresponding reflection symmetry. Hence, if no such reflection symmetry exists, as seems to be generally admitted,‡ the operators that we shall determine on the basis of the first set of postulates (such determination will turn out to be possible) will not satisfy the second set of postulates. Putting this slightly differently, we can say that the operators of observables determined under the assumption of the validity of the second set of postulates will not be the true operators for the observable in question.

Let us now proceed to the determination of reflection operators that satisfy the first set of relations. These will be formulated in some cases without regard for the possibility that geometrical relations are satisfied by the corresponding operators only up to a factor: we shall postulate for the reflection operators the same relations that the corresponding geometrical operations satisfy. We shall note, though, the extent to which these relations can be shown to be essentially satisfied, if the a priori indeterminate numerical multiplicative factors in the reflection operators are properly chosen (see Ref. 30, Sects. 6–9).

* This is the method used by Wigner (*30*, Sects. 6–9). See also Tarimer (*31*).

† In earlier determinations of the reflection operators, extensive use was made of these relations. See e.g., Wigner (*32*, *33*).

‡ The basic experiment is the well-known one of Christenson *et al.* (*34*). See also Treiman (*35*).

We consider first a spatial reflection operator T_1, that is, the unitary operator that corresponds to the transformation $x_1 \to -x_1$. By multiplying it with a suitable factor, we can render its square to be unity. It further follows, because T_1 satisfies the group relations up to a factor, that

$$T_1 U(S) = \omega(S) U(t_1 S t_1) T_1 \tag{28}$$

where t_1 is the transformation $x_1 \to -x_1$ of de Sitter space; $\omega(S)$ is the factor that we wish to show to be equal to 1. Multiplying (28) by $U(S')$ where S' is another element of the restricted de Sitter group and applying (28) to the result with S replaced by S', we obtain

$$\begin{aligned} T_1 U(S) U(S') &= \omega(S) U(t_1 S t_1) T_1 U(S') \\ &= \omega(S) \omega(S') U(t_1 S t_1) U(t_1 S' t_1) T_1. \end{aligned} \tag{28a}$$

Since the U do form a representation of the restricted de Sitter group, and since $t_1 S t_1$ and $t_1 S' t_1$ are elements of this group, (28a) is equivalent to

$$T_1 U(SS') = \omega(S) \omega(S') U(t_1 SS' t_1) T_1. \tag{28b}$$

Comparison of this with (28), in which S is replaced by SS', gives

$$\omega(S) \omega(S') = \omega(SS'); \tag{29}$$

that is, that $\omega(S)$ is a one-dimensional representation of the restricted de Sitter group. The only such representation* is $\omega(S) = 1$.

We can infer equally easily that T_1 can be identified with the operator

$$T_1 \psi(\xi_1, \xi_2, \ldots) = \psi(-\xi_1, \xi_2, \ldots) \tag{30}$$

or with

$$T_1 \psi(\xi_1, \xi_2, \ldots) = -\psi(-\xi_1, \xi_2, \ldots). \tag{30a}$$

Actually, the two possibilities are physically equivalent, since they differ only in a constant factor that has no physical significance.

In order to prove that one of the preceding alternatives is valid, we first verify that the T_1 of (30) does satisfy the group relations [that is, it satisfies (28)

* If (29) had a nontrivial solution (i.e., a solution different from $\omega(S) = 1$), the restricted de Sitter group would have to have an invariant subgroup with an Abelian factor group. This is not the case, however. In fact, all $O(m, 1)$ groups are simple.

with $\omega(S) = 1$]. The same will then be true of (30a). To verify this, we decompose S into a product of $U_{ab}(\varphi)$ and of $U_{at}(\varphi)$ and show (28) for each of the factors. This will be true, then, for the product S of the factors, also.

The validity of

$$T_1 U_{ab}(\varphi) = U_{ab}(\pm\varphi) T_1 \tag{31}$$

where the $-$ or $+$ applies, depending on whether one or none of the indices a, b is 1, is immediately evident. Let us verify, therefore, $T_1 U_{1t}(\varphi) = U_{1t}(-\varphi) T_1$. We have, by (30) and (27),

$$\begin{aligned} T_1 U_{1t}(\varphi)\psi(\xi_1, \xi_2, \ldots) &= U_{1t}(\varphi)\psi(-\xi_1, \xi_2, \ldots) \\ &= \psi\left(\rho\frac{-\xi_1 \operatorname{Ch}\varphi + \rho \operatorname{Sh}\varphi}{\rho \operatorname{Ch}\varphi - \xi_1 \operatorname{Sh}\varphi}, \frac{\rho\xi_2}{\rho \operatorname{Ch}\varphi - \xi_1 \operatorname{Sh}\varphi}, \ldots\right) \\ &\quad \times \left(\operatorname{Ch}\varphi - \frac{\xi_1}{\rho}\operatorname{Sh}\varphi\right)^{-(m-1)/2+i\mu} \end{aligned} \tag{31a}$$

whereas, since $\operatorname{Ch}(-\varphi) = \operatorname{Ch}\varphi$, $\operatorname{Sh}(-\varphi) = -\operatorname{Sh}\varphi$

$$\begin{aligned} &U_{1t}(-\varphi) T_1 \psi(\xi_1, \xi_2, \ldots) \\ &T_1 \psi\left(\rho\frac{\xi_1 \operatorname{Ch}\varphi - \rho \operatorname{Sh}\varphi}{\rho \operatorname{Ch}\varphi - \xi_1 \operatorname{Sh}\varphi}, \frac{\rho\xi_2}{\rho \operatorname{Ch}\varphi - \xi_1 \operatorname{Sh}\varphi}, \ldots\right)\left(\operatorname{Ch}\varphi - \frac{\xi_1}{\rho}\operatorname{Sh}\varphi\right)^{-(m-1)/2+i\mu} \\ &\quad = \psi\left(\rho\frac{-\xi_1 \operatorname{Ch}\varphi + \rho \operatorname{Sh}\varphi}{\rho \operatorname{Ch}\varphi - \xi_1 \operatorname{Sh}\varphi}, \frac{\rho\xi_2}{\rho \operatorname{Ch}\varphi - \xi_1 \operatorname{Sh}\varphi}, \ldots\right) \\ &\quad \times \left(\operatorname{Ch}\varphi - \frac{\xi_1}{\rho}\operatorname{Sh}\varphi\right)^{-(m-1)/2+i\mu}, \end{aligned} \tag{31b}$$

so that the proper commutation relation is valid in this case also. We can verify in a similar way that $U_{at}(\varphi)$ commutes with T_1 for $a \neq 1$. Hence, (30) and (30a) define possible T_1 operators as far as the first type of postulate is concerned.

Conversely, it can be shown that in an irreducible representation of the de Sitter group that contains spatial reflections and that contains our representation of the restricted de Sitter group [that is, contains vectors ψ for which (24) and (27) are valid], the reflection operator that corresponds to t_1 is necessarily given by (30) or (30a). First, we observe that the restricted de Sitter group is an invariant subgroup of the spatially extended group.

Let us denote the reflection operator that corresponds to t_1 by Q_1; we then have to prove that $Q_1 = \pm T_1$. The vectors $Q_1 \psi$, resulting from the application of Q_1 to the basis vectors ψ of the original representation of the restricted group, also form a basis for the representation of this group. This representation is equivalent to the one in which $U(t_1 S t_1)$ corresponds to the element S of the restricted group. As (28) [with $\omega(S) = 1$] shows, however, this representation is equivalent to the representation in which $U(S)$ corresponds to the element S. We can, therefore, find a linear operator T_1' in the Hilbert space of the original functions ψ such that the $Q_1(T_1'\psi)$ are transformed, under the operators that correspond to the elements of the restricted group, just as the ψ are transformed by these elements. Furthermore, $(T_1')^2 = 1$. It then follows that the linear manifold of the vectors $\psi + Q_1 T_1' \psi$ is invariant under the operators that correspond to S; in fact, these have the same effect on $\psi + Q_1 T_1' \psi$ as on the ψ themselves. They are also invariant under Q_1: this carries, because of $Q_1^2 = 1$, the vector $\psi + Q_1 T_1' \psi$ into $Q_1 \psi + T_1' \psi = T_1' \psi + Q_1 T_1'(T_1' \psi)$. The same applies to the linear manifold of the vectors $\psi - Q_1 T_1' \psi$. Hence, unless the vectors of one of these manifolds are zero, the representation of the extended group that we obtained is reducible. On the other hand, unless the vectors $\psi + Q_1 T_1' \psi$ are zero, they do generate an irreducible representation of the group extended by spatial reflections, which is, however, equivalent to the representation in which the operators of the restricted group are given by (24) and (27), the operator of the reflection of x_1 by (30). The manifold of basic states is the same as for the representation of the restricted group. Similarly, if the vectors $\psi - Q_1 T_1' \psi$ are not zero, they generate an irreducible representation of the extended group; the operators that correspond to the restricted group are again equivalent to those of (24) and (27), the operator of the reflection of x_1 being given by (30a). Again the manifold of basic states for the representation of the extended group is the same as for the restricted group.

It follows that we can assume that the operator Q_1 that corresponds to t_1, the reflection of x_1, operates within the manifold of the original $\psi(\xi_1, \xi_2, \ldots, \xi_m)$. If it were different from the T_1 defined by (30), $T_1^{-1} Q_1$ would commute with all operators $U(S)$ of the restricted group. Hence, $T_1^{-1} Q_1$ is a constant, $Q_1 = c T_1$, and it follows from $Q_1^2 = 1$ and $T_1^2 = 1$ that $c = \pm 1$, so that we are brought back to either (30) or the physically equivalent (30a). The authors realize that the consideration just presented is not new and that it should be possible to condense it into a few lines, but they have not succeeded in doing so.

Let us now consider the time inversion operator Θ. In the theory of the representations of the Poincaré group, the positive definite energy operator forces us to assume Θ to be antiunitary. There is no such operator in the de Sitter group and we shall consider both unitary and antiunitary time inversion operators. The postulates of the first type now read

$$U_{ab}(\varphi)\,\Theta = \Theta U_{ab}(\varphi) \tag{32}$$

$$U_{at}(\varphi)\,\Theta = \Theta U_{at}(-\varphi). \tag{32a}$$

Again, these equations need be valid only up to a factor, but this factor can be shown again, by means of the same argument that led to (29), to be equal to 1. The relation between time and space inversions is (again apart from a multiplicative factor)

$$T_a\Theta = \Theta T_a. \tag{32b}$$

Even though the multiplicative factor in this case (*30*) cannot be shown to be equal to 1, this will be assumed.

If Θ is assumed to be unitary, $\Theta = \Theta_u$, its square can be normalized to 1. The relations (32), (32a), and (32b) then can be satisfied by either

$$\Theta_u\psi(\xi_1, \ldots, \xi_m) = \psi(-\xi_1, \ldots, -\xi_m) \tag{33}$$

or

$$\Theta_u\psi(\xi_1, \ldots, \xi_m) = -\psi(-\xi_1, \ldots, -\xi_m). \tag{33a}$$

A unitary Θ can be shown to be given by either (33) or (33a) by means of the same argument that established (30) or (30a) for the spatial inversion T_1. It may be observed that, in case of even m, the transformation (30) is the same as the $U(S)$ that corresponds to reversing the sign of all spatial coordinates. This is, in case of even m, an element of the restricted group. The representative of this element and Θ_u can be equal because their product, together with the unit element, forms an Abelian center of the full group.

Let us now determine the antiunitary Θ_a that satisfy Eqs. (32). We can write for $\Theta_a = \vartheta K$ where K is the transition to the conjugate complex and, if we introduce this into (32), (32b) and the infinitesimal form of (32a), we obtain

$$U_{ab}(\varphi)\,\vartheta = \vartheta U_{ab}(\varphi) \tag{34}$$

$$N_{at}\vartheta = -\vartheta N_{at}^* \tag{34a}$$

$$T_a\vartheta = \vartheta T_a. \tag{34b}$$

We shall not give the solution of these equations for arbitrary dimension $m + 1$ of the de Sitter space, but only for the lowest nontrivial dimension, 3. In this case, the Hilbert space is the space of square-integrable functions in the plane, of the form (14). This form is best assured if we introduce polar coordinates ρ, φ' in the plane; φ' then replaces the Ω of (14). The operator $U_{12}(\varphi)$ of (24) becomes, if we define the polar coordinates ρ, φ' so that $\xi_1 = \rho\cos\varphi'$, $\xi_2 = \rho\sin\varphi'$,

$$U_{12}(\varphi)\,\psi(\rho, \varphi') = \psi(\rho, \varphi' - \varphi). \tag{35}$$

The operators ϑ that commute with these have kernels $\vartheta(\varphi', \varphi'')$ that depend only on the difference $\varphi' - \varphi''$ so that

$$\vartheta\psi(\rho, \varphi') = \int \vartheta(\varphi' - \varphi'')\,\psi(\rho, \varphi'')\,d\varphi''.$$

The operator T_1 becomes

$$T_1\,\psi(\rho, \varphi') = \psi(\rho, \pi - \varphi')$$

and (33b) will be satisfied if

$$\begin{aligned} T_1\,\vartheta\psi(\rho, \varphi') &= \vartheta\psi(\rho, \pi - \varphi') = \int \vartheta(\pi - \varphi' - \varphi'')\,\psi(\rho, \varphi'')\,d\varphi'' \\ &= \vartheta T_1\,\psi(\rho, \varphi') = \int \vartheta(\varphi' - \varphi'')\,T_1\,\psi(\rho, \varphi'')\,d\varphi'' = \int \vartheta(\varphi' - \varphi'')\,\psi(\rho, \pi - \varphi'')\,d\varphi''. \end{aligned}$$

If this is to be valid for all ψ, we must have

$$\begin{aligned} \int \vartheta(\pi - \varphi' - \varphi'')\,\psi(\rho, \varphi'')\,d\varphi'' &= \int \vartheta(\varphi' - \varphi'')\,\psi(\rho, \pi - \varphi'')\,d\varphi'' \\ &= \int \vartheta(\varphi' + \varphi'' - \pi)\,\psi(\rho, \varphi'')\,d\varphi'' \end{aligned}$$

or

$$\vartheta(\varphi) = \vartheta(-\varphi);$$

that is ϑ must be an even function. Since T_2 is obtained from T_1 by transforming it with $U_{12}(\frac{1}{2}\pi)$, Eq. (34b) for $a = 2$ is now automatically satisfied. It is apparent from (35) that $N_{12} = -d/d\varphi'$. Hence, by (16a),

$$N_{1t} = -\sin\varphi'\,\frac{d}{d\varphi'} + (i\mu - \tfrac{1}{2})\cos\varphi' \tag{35a}$$

and (34a) becomes

$$\int\left[-\sin\varphi'\frac{d}{d\varphi'}+(i\mu-\tfrac{1}{2})\cos\varphi'\right]\vartheta(\varphi'-\varphi'')\,\psi(\rho,\varphi'')\,d\varphi''$$
$$=-\int\vartheta(\varphi'-\varphi'')\left[-\sin\varphi''\frac{d}{d\varphi''}-(i\mu+\tfrac{1}{2})\cos\varphi''\right]\psi(\rho,\varphi'')\,d\varphi''.$$

Partial integration of the right side gives, since all functions are periodic in the angular variable,

$$\int[\sin\varphi''\,\vartheta'(\varphi'-\varphi'')-\cos\varphi''\,\vartheta(\varphi'-\varphi'')+(i\mu+\tfrac{1}{2})\cos\varphi'']\,\psi(\rho,\varphi'')\,d\varphi''.$$

If the resulting equation is to be valid for all ψ, we must have

$$(\sin\varphi'+\sin\varphi'')\,\vartheta'(\varphi'-\varphi'')=(i\mu-\tfrac{1}{2})(\cos\varphi'-\cos\varphi'')\,\vartheta(\varphi'-\varphi'')\qquad(36)$$

or

$$\frac{\vartheta'(\varphi'-\varphi'')}{\vartheta(\varphi'-\varphi'')}=(i\mu-\tfrac{1}{2})\frac{\cos\varphi'-\cos\varphi''}{\sin\varphi'+\sin\varphi''}=-(i\mu-\tfrac{1}{2})\tan\tfrac{1}{2}(\varphi'-\varphi'')$$

so that

$$\vartheta(\varphi'-\varphi'')=c\cos^{2i\mu-1}\tfrac{1}{2}(\varphi'-\varphi'').\qquad(36a)$$

The constant c has to be determined from the condition that the kernel represent a unitary operator. This gives

$$\int\vartheta(\varphi-\varphi')\,\vartheta(\varphi-\varphi'')^*\,d\varphi\,d\varphi''=1\qquad(36b)$$

or

$$\left|\int\vartheta(\varphi)\,d\varphi\right|=1.$$

Since

$$\int_0^{(1/2)\pi}\cos^{2i\mu-1}\zeta\,d\zeta=\tfrac{1}{2}\pi^{1/2}\frac{\Gamma(i\mu)}{\Gamma(i\mu+\tfrac{1}{2})},$$

we obtain, except for a phase factor,

$$c=\left|\left(\frac{\mu}{4\pi}\right)\mathrm{Th}\,\pi\mu\right|^{1/2},\qquad(36c)$$

where Th $\equiv$ tanh.

The argument of c is meaningless physically and indeterminate mathematically but it is simplest to assume, as was done in (36c), that c is real and positive.

A second way to calculate ϑ, which resembles more its determination for de Sitter spaces of higher dimensionalities, starts with an expansion of ϑ into a Fourier series

$$\vartheta(\varphi - \varphi') = \sum a_\lambda \exp[i\lambda(\varphi - \varphi')]. \tag{37}$$

The condition that ϑ be unitary reduces in this case to

$$|a_\lambda| = \frac{1}{2\pi}\cdot \tag{38}$$

Since ϑ must be even, we further have

$$a_\lambda = a_{-\lambda}. \tag{39}$$

Finally, (36) now reads

$$\sum_\lambda (\sin\varphi + \sin\varphi')\, i\lambda a_\lambda \exp[i\lambda(\varphi - \varphi')]$$
$$= \sum_\lambda (i\mu - \tfrac{1}{2})(\cos\varphi - \cos\varphi')\, a_\lambda \exp[i\lambda(\varphi - \varphi')].$$

We obtain from this

$$\frac{a_{\lambda+1}}{a_\lambda} = -\frac{\lambda + \frac{1}{2} - i\mu}{\lambda + \frac{1}{2} + i\mu} \tag{40}$$

or

$$\frac{a_{-\lambda-1}}{a_{-\lambda}} = -\frac{-\lambda - \frac{1}{2} + i\mu}{-\lambda - \frac{1}{2} - i\mu} \tag{40a}$$

so that (38) is satisfied if $a_0 = 1/2\pi$ and (39) is automatically satisfied. It follows that (37), with the a_λ of (40), also satisfies all equations (30) and must be identical with (36a) with c being given by (36c).

If we again disregard the possibility that the square of $\Theta = \vartheta K$ may be -1 and the possibility that Θ and T_1 commute only apart from a factor, the Θ just determined is (apart from a phase factor) uniquely defined. This can be demonstrated in the same way in which the essential uniqueness of T_1 was proved.

Let us repeat, finally, that the possibility of determining the T_a and Θ so as to satisfy the first type of postulate of this section in no way guarantees that the T and Θ determined this way will also satisfy the second type of postulate. The question whether or not this is the case is synonymous with the question whether the corresponding reflection symmetry is a valid symmetry operation. This point will play a major role in the analysis of the next section, where we shall attempt to determine the position operators. The validity of the reflection operators limits the freedom we have for defining the position operators.

It is well to recall, once more, that our discussion and determination of the reflection operators was not based on first principles; that we have, in particular, disregarded the complications that arise from the fact that the reflection operators need to satisfy the group relations only apart from numerical factors. A similar departure from first principles will be made in the next section, where the existence of position operators, operating within the Hilbert space of irreducible representations, will be assumed.

VI. The Position Operators

Two types of position operators* (or, equivalently, localized states) have been considered in the literature. The first type consists, in Minkowski space, of four commuting operators X_μ, corresponding to the four space-time coordinates. They have the character of a vector operator, that is, their commutation relations with the angular momenta are the same as those of the linear momenta; their commutation relations with the linear momenta are $[p_\mu, X_\nu] = g_{\mu\nu}$. The physical interpretation of these position operators is not entirely clear even though it has been considerably clarified lately (*37*, *38*). We are used to thinking about a characteristic vector ψ with the characteristic values a_μ, that is, of the ψ for which $X_\mu \psi = a_\mu \psi$, as a state localized at the point a_1, a_2, a_3 at time a_0. However, the probability is zero that the particle represented by ψ will be at *any* place a_1', a_2', a_3' at a time $a_0' \neq a_0$. This follows from the fact that ψ is orthogonal to characteristic vectors ψ' for which $X_0 \psi' = a_0' \psi'$ as soon as $a_0' \neq a_0$. It appears that the particle is nowhere at times $a_0' \neq a_0$. Expressed in terms of classical physics, the particle occupies a *point* of space-time rather than a line, the world line, therein.

As was mentioned before, ideas have been proposed to interpret the commuting position operators differently. Nevertheless, we shall use the type of position operator† that is most appropriate for our purposes. We define only operators for the spatial position and these will be functions of time. Actually,

* This is the subject of the doctoral dissertation of Philips (*36*), and the following discussion freely borrows from that thesis.

† See Newton and Wigner (*39*), Mackey (*40*), and Loomis (*41*). A review with further literature and mathematically rigorous discussion of the subject has been given by Wightman (*42*).

we will be more interested in the characteristic vectors (or, rather, distributions) of these operators. If one such distribution—for example, the one that specifies the position $x_1 = 0$, $x_2 = R$ at $t = 0$—is known, the others, corresponding to any other position at any other time, can be obtained by the group operations. Hence, what we shall determine is the spectral decomposition of the position operators, the localized states, rather than the operators themselves.

It will turn out that the state, localized at a point at a given time, is so localized only when viewed from a definite coordinate system; but it is not localized at the corresponding point and the corresponding time if viewed from a moving coordinate system. We are driven to this conclusion by the mathematical framework and the postulates adopted*; it is not a conclusion at which we intended to arrive.

The postulates for localized states are easier to formulate than those for the position operators. The formulation of the postulates that follows will not be rigorous because the localized states are not vectors in Hilbert space but "distributions" or "elements of a continuous spectrum," and we shall not deal with them with mathematical rigor. Since the object described by the representation of de Sitter space that we now consider has no spin, we expect that, in a given coordinate system, there will be only one state localized at a given time at a definite position. The postulates, then, are as follows.

(a) The state shall be invariant with respect to rotations and reflections (if the theory admits such) that leave the point of localization unchanged. As was implied in the preceding paragraph, this postulate speaks only about rotations and reflections in the narrower sense, not about transitions to a moving coordinate system. As a result of postulate (a), the localized state will be different depending on whether or not we assume the validity of space and time reflection operators.

(b) Any displacement of a localized state by a finite distance creates a new state, localized at the displaced point, which is, therefore, orthogonal to the original state.

(c) The state obtained from the original state by giving it a small velocity should differ from the original state as little as possible. Expressed more mathematically, postulate (c) states that a homogeneous Lorentz transformation that leaves invariant the point of space-time where the object was localized should change the state vector as little as possible.

Evidently, postulate (c) will have to be formulated more precisely. Its

* The attempt of the first author to define relativistically invariant localized states (*36*, *43*) had to abandon the postulate that a state localized at a point at a definite time is orthogonal to every state localized at any other point at the same time [assumption (b)]. The postulates proposed in these considerations would lead, however, to the same conclusions as those adopted here.

significance is increased, as compared with the Minkowski case, because condition (b) is less restrictive in a finite universe than it is in Minkowski space. Let us verify this in the case of a single spatial dimension; the only displacement operator in our case is then that of Eq. (35), namely, the substitution $\varphi' \to \varphi' - \varphi$. If the range of φ' is infinite, the condition that $\psi(\varphi' - \varphi)$ be orthogonal to $\psi(\varphi')$ for all φ implies that the support of ψ be restricted to a single point*; that is, that ψ be zero everywhere except at one point. If, on the other hand, φ' is a periodic variable, such as our φ' is, ψ can be different from zero at one point, say $\varphi' = 0$, and have *ic* times this value at the φ' that is half a period larger (that is, at $\varphi' = \pi$ in our case); *c* can be any real number. There are even more possibilities if we assume that there are several points at which ψ is different from zero, if these points are evenly spaced. This would mean, in our case, that ψ is different from zero at $\varphi_0' + 2\pi k/n$ where n is an integer and k assumes the values 0, 1, 2, ..., $n-1$. The situation is quite different if there are more spatial coordinates (that is, if $m > 2$) but the restrictive power of postulate (b) seems to be, in any case, smaller than in an infinite universe.

It is, evidently, sufficient to determine one localized state; the others can be obtained from this by means of the displacement operators in Minkowski space, by means of operators of the restricted group in de Sitter space. We choose for the localized state the one localized at $x_1 = 0$ at $t = 0$; its state vector will be denoted by $\psi_1(\varphi')$. We first assume that both spatial and time reflections are valid symmetry operations as far as the position of the particle is concerned; these are the only symmetry operations in our universe with only one spatial dimension to which postulate (a) can be applied. In particular, the state ψ_1 is invariant under T_1 and under time inversion operator Θ_u or Θ_a, depending on which we assume to be valid.

The invariance of ψ_1 under T_1 means

$$T_1 \psi_1(\varphi') = \epsilon_1 \psi_1(\varphi'), \qquad \epsilon_1 = \pm 1, \tag{41}$$

so that we have, because of (34b),

$$\psi_1(\pi - \varphi') = \epsilon_1 \psi_1(\varphi') \tag{41a}$$

or, if ψ_1 is expanded into a Fourier series

$$\psi_1(\varphi') = \sum l_\lambda e^{i\lambda\varphi'}, \tag{42}$$

* We are much indebted to Dr. Lars Hörmander of the Institute for Advanced Study for a discussion on this point.

that

$$l_{-\lambda} = \epsilon_1 (-)^\lambda l_\lambda. \tag{42a}$$

The value of ϵ_1 in (41) can be only ± 1 because $T_1^2 = 1$.

To express the postulate that ψ_1 is invariant under time inversion, let us assume, first, that Θ is unitary; it is given, then, by (33). Thus

$$\Theta_u \psi_1(\varphi') = \psi_1(\pi + \varphi') = \epsilon_t \psi_1(\varphi'), \qquad \epsilon_t = \pm 1 \tag{43}$$

means, in terms of the l_λ, that

$$\begin{aligned} l_\lambda &= 0 \qquad \text{for odd } \lambda \text{ if} \quad \epsilon_t = 1 \\ l_\lambda &= 0 \qquad \text{for even } \lambda \text{ if} \quad \epsilon_t = -1. \end{aligned} \tag{44}$$

It will follow from this, by means of postulate (b), that there are no states satisfying our postulates. Although this fact does not imply that the unitary Θ is not the proper time inversion operator—there need be no localized states—it makes this at least plausible and we shall, in fact, adopt the anti-unitary Θ_a.

If ψ_1 is invariant under Θ_a,

$$\Theta_a \psi_1 = \omega \psi_1 \qquad |\omega| = 1, \tag{45}$$

we can replace it by $\omega' \psi_1$ and have

$$\Theta_a(\omega' \psi_1) = (\omega')^* \Theta_a \psi_1 = (\omega')^{-1} \omega \psi_1 = (\omega')^{-2} \omega (\omega' \psi_1) \tag{45a}$$

so that, if $(\omega')^{-2} \omega = 1$,

$$\Theta_a \psi_1 = \psi_1 \tag{45b}$$

holds for the new ψ_1. We shall adopt the normalization implied by (45b). Hence, if we again use the expansion (42) for ψ_1, and (37) for the kernel ϑ in $\Theta_a = \vartheta K$, we have

$$\begin{aligned} \Theta_a \psi_1(\varphi') &= \int \vartheta(\varphi' - \varphi'') K \psi_1(\varphi'') \, d\varphi'' \\ &= \int \sum_\lambda a_\lambda \exp[i\lambda(\varphi' - \varphi'')] \sum_\mu l_\mu^* \exp(-i\mu\varphi'') \, d\varphi'' \\ &= 2\pi \sum a_\lambda l_{-\lambda}^* \exp(i\lambda\varphi'). \end{aligned}$$

If this is to be equal to $\psi_1(\varphi')$, we must have

$$2\pi a_\lambda l_{-\lambda}^* = l_\lambda \tag{46}$$

or, with (42a),

$$2\pi a_\lambda = \frac{l_\lambda}{l_{-\lambda}^*} = \frac{l_\lambda}{\epsilon_1(-)^\lambda l_\lambda^*}. \tag{46a}$$

If we substitute $\lambda + 1$ for λ in this equation, divide it by (46a), and use (40) for $a_{\lambda+1}/a_\lambda$, we obtain

$$\frac{l_{\lambda+1}/l_\lambda}{l_{\lambda+1}^*/l_\lambda^*} = \frac{\lambda + \frac{1}{2} - i\mu}{\lambda + \frac{1}{2} + i\mu}, \tag{46b}$$

whence

$$\frac{l_{\lambda+1}}{l_\lambda} = \zeta_{\lambda+(1/2)} \frac{\lambda + \frac{1}{2} - i\mu}{((\lambda + \frac{1}{2})^2 + \mu^2)^{1/2}} \tag{47}$$

where the ζ are arbitrary real numbers, subject only to the condition, resulting from (42a), that

$$\zeta_{\lambda+(1/2)}\,\zeta_{-\lambda-(1/2)} = 1. \tag{47a}$$

Let us now apply postulate (b). It means that $\psi_1(\varphi')$ and $\psi_1(\varphi' - \varphi)$ are orthogonal for all $0 < \varphi < 2\pi$. This is, of course, not a rigorous formulation of the postulate because ψ_1 is a distribution rather than a vector. It is customary to infer from the postulate that $|l_\lambda|^2$ is independent of λ so that it can be set equal to 1. This is not a correct inference (*16*)—$|l_\lambda|^2$ could yet be any polynomial of λ corresponding to ψ_1 being a linear combination of the δ function and of its derivatives. It will turn out, however, that condition (c) will entail $|l_\lambda|^2 = 1$; that is, all $\zeta_{\lambda+(1/2)} = \pm 1$. For the time being, we can infer only, since (44) cannot be satisfied if $|l_\lambda|^2$ is a polynomial, that postulates (a) and (b) are not compatible if the time inversion operator is given by the unitary Θ_u of (33).

(c) The natural expression for the postulate that ψ_1 should differ as little as possible from $U_{1t}(\varphi)\psi_1$, in which it has been given a small velocity $c\tanh\varphi$, is that the rays of ψ_1 and $U_{1t}(\varphi)\psi_1$ be as nearly the same as possible. Since ψ_1 and $U_{1t}\psi_1$ have the same length, this means that, for given length of ψ_1, $|(\psi_1, U_{1t}(\varphi)\psi_1)|^2$ are as large as possible. Since our ψ_1 is not normalized, we have to ask that

$$M = (\psi_1, \psi_1)^{-1}\,|(\psi_1, U_{1t}(\varphi)\psi_1)| \tag{48}$$

be as large as possible, consistent with the restrictions (42a), (47) derived earlier.

It is reasonable to substitute

$$U_{1t}(\varphi)\psi_1 = (1 + N_{1t}\varphi + \tfrac{1}{2}N_{1t}^2\varphi^2)\psi_1 \tag{49}$$

and neglect the higher powers of φ (that is, to restrict ourselves to very small velocities). Then

$$(\psi_1, U_{1t}(\varphi)\psi_1) = (\psi_1, \psi_1) + \varphi(\psi_1, N_{1t}\psi_1) - \tfrac{1}{2}\varphi^2(N_{1t}\psi_1, N_{1t}\psi_1). \tag{49a}$$

The skew-Hermitian nature of N_{1t} was used to transform the last term.

In order to evaluate (49a) we apply the N_{1t}, given by (34a), to the series expansion (42) for ψ_1. If we again expand $N_{1t}\psi_1$ into a series

$$N_{1t}\psi_1(\varphi') = \sum k_\lambda e^{i\lambda\varphi'}, \tag{50}$$

the coefficients will be given in terms of the expansion coefficients l_λ of ψ_1

$$k_\lambda = \tfrac{1}{2}[(-\lambda + \tfrac{1}{2} + i\mu)\, l_{\lambda-1} + (\lambda + \tfrac{1}{2} + i\mu)\, l_{\lambda+1}]. \tag{50a}$$

We may note that it follows from (42a) that $k_{-\lambda} = \epsilon_1(-)^\lambda k_\lambda$. We can further express, by means of (47), $l_{\lambda-1}$ and $l_{\lambda+1}$ in terms of l_λ to obtain

$$\begin{aligned} k_\lambda &= \tfrac{1}{2}l_\lambda\left[(-\lambda + \tfrac{1}{2} + i\mu)\frac{l_{\lambda-1}}{l_\lambda} + (\lambda + \tfrac{1}{2} + i\mu)\frac{l_{\lambda+1}}{l_\lambda}\right] \\ &= \tfrac{1}{2}l_\lambda\{-\zeta_{\lambda-(1/2)}^{-1}[(\lambda - \tfrac{1}{2})^2 + \mu^2]^{1/2} + \zeta_{\lambda+(1/2)}[(\lambda + \tfrac{1}{2})^2 + \mu^2]^{1/2}\}. \end{aligned} \tag{50b}$$

Since the ζ are all real, it now follows that

$$(\psi_1, N_{1t}\psi_1) = \sum l_\lambda^* k_\lambda \tag{51}$$

is real. Since, on the other hand, it is the Hermitian form of a skew-Hermitian operator, it is also imaginary. It follows that it vanishes. This can be verified, of course, also by direct calculation.

The quantity M of (48) that we want to make a maximum now reduces to

$$\begin{aligned} M &= 1 - \tfrac{1}{2}\varphi^2\frac{(N_{1t}\psi_1, N_{1t}\psi_1)}{(\psi_1, \psi_1)} \\ &= 1 - \tfrac{1}{2}\varphi^2\frac{\sum |k_\lambda|^2}{\sum |l_\lambda|^2}. \end{aligned} \tag{52}$$

It follows that, in order to increase M, we have to make the $|k_\lambda|$ as small as possible. This implies, first, that the ζ have all the same sign. Furthermore, since $|l_\lambda|^2$ is proportional to a polynomial of λ, the ratio $|l_{\lambda+1}/l_\lambda| = |\zeta_\lambda|$ approaches 1 from above with increasing λ. Hence, the absolute value of the second term of (50b) is larger than that of the first term and the difference, the absolute value of the expression in the braces, will be smallest if the $|\zeta|$ exceed 1 as little as possible. This will be the case if $|l_\lambda|^2 = 1$, whence $|\zeta| = 1$ and, since they all have the same sign, we can have

$$\zeta = 1 \qquad \text{or} \qquad \zeta = -1 \tag{53}$$

and, by (47),

$$l_\lambda = \zeta^\lambda \frac{(\frac{1}{2} - i\mu)(\frac{3}{2} - i\mu)\cdots(\lambda - \frac{1}{2} - i\mu)}{|(\frac{1}{2} - i\mu)(\frac{3}{2} - i\mu)\cdots(\lambda - \frac{1}{2} - i\mu)|} \qquad \lambda > 0, \tag{54a}$$

$$l_0 = 1, \tag{54b}$$

$$l_{-\lambda} = \zeta^\lambda \frac{(-\frac{1}{2} + i\mu)(-\frac{3}{2} + i\mu)\cdots(-\lambda + \frac{1}{2} + i\mu)}{|(-\frac{1}{2} + i\mu)(-\frac{3}{2} + i\mu)\cdots(-\lambda + \frac{1}{2} + i\mu)|}. \tag{54c}$$

Equation (42a) is automatically satisfied for $\epsilon_1 = 1$; $\epsilon_1 = -1$ is excluded. We note that we have obtained two states that satisfy our postulates equally, and that they are orthogonal to each other. It is not difficult to guess that the two states are localized at diagonally opposite points $x_1 = 0$, $x_2 = R$, and $x_1 = 0$, $x_2 = -R$. We shall find, in the next section, that $\zeta = -1$ corresponds to the first, $\zeta = 1$ to the second of these points.

It would have been possible to derive both Eq. (42a) (with $\epsilon_1 = 1$) and Eq. (47), which follow from the symmetry postulate (a), the orthogonality postulate (b), and the postulate (c) of minimum change of a localized state when given a low velocity, using only the real character of k_λ/l_λ. The close connection between postulates (c) and (a) is not surprising, perhaps, since postulate (c) is invariant under the symmetry operations of postulate (a). The preceding calculation could have been simplified somewhat had we transformed our representation into the form in which N_{1t} is real. However, the present form of the calculation appears to be more instructive.

We can, finally, calculate the quantity M of (48), or rather its value for very small φ. This is given by (52), for which we have to calculate $\sum |l_\lambda|^2$ and $\sum |k_\lambda|^2$. To do this, we replace the l_λ of (54a) by $l_\lambda \exp(-\frac{1}{2}\epsilon\lambda^2)$. We then have, for very small ϵ,

$$\sum |l_\lambda|^2 = \sum \exp(-\epsilon\lambda^2) = \left(\frac{\pi}{\epsilon}\right)^{1/2}. \tag{55}$$

The calculation of the sum $\sum |k_\lambda|^2$ on the basis of (50a) or (50b) is somewhat more laborious but straightforward. It gives $\frac{1}{2}(\pi/\epsilon)^{1/2}$. Hence,

$$M = 1 - \tfrac{1}{2}\varphi^2 \frac{\sum |k_\lambda|^2}{\sum |l_\lambda|^2} = 1 - \tfrac{1}{4}\varphi^2. \tag{56}$$

It is worth noting that this result is different from that which seems to follow from the asymptotic ratio $k_\lambda/l_\lambda \to \frac{1}{2}$. This would give $M = 1 - \varphi^2/8$. However, $k_\lambda/l_\lambda \to \frac{1}{2}$ only as long as $\epsilon\lambda^2 \ll 1$, and the region $\epsilon\lambda^2 \sim 1$ contributes significantly to both sums. The situation is the same for the localized states in Minkowski space: the absolute value of $N_{1t}\psi_1 = (p_0 d/dp)p_0^{1/2} = \frac{1}{2}p/p_0^{1/2}$ seems to be, asymptotically, one half of the absolute value of $\psi_1 = p_0^{1/2}$. If, however, we write $\psi_1 = p_0^{1/2}\exp(-\frac{1}{2}\epsilon p^2)$, we calculate the same

$$\frac{(N_{1t}\psi_1, N_{1t}\psi_1)}{(\psi_1, \psi_1)} = \frac{\int |p_0\, d/dp\, \psi_1|^2\, dp/p_0}{\int |\psi_1|^2\, dp/p_0} = \tfrac{1}{2} \tag{56a}$$

that we obtained for the de Sitter ψ_1.

Let us observe, finally, that if we completely disregard postulate (a) for the determination of the localized state, the result can be entirely different. In fact, Eq. (27) and the discussion following it suggest that we consider the state concentrated in the ξ_1 direction [that is, $\tilde{\psi}_1 = \delta(\xi_1 - \rho)$ or $\delta(\xi_1 + \rho)$] as localized at $x_1 = 0$ (and $x_2 = R$). This would violate (47), in particular, but would give the same M as our ψ_1. It is, furthermore, apparently invariant under $U_{1t}(\varphi)$, though not truly, just as the apparently invariant $\tilde{\psi}_1 = p_0$ in Minkowski space is not truly invariant. This means that $U_{1t}(\varphi)\tilde{\psi}_1 = U_{1t}(\varphi)\exp[-\frac{1}{2}(\rho^2 + (\xi_1 - \rho)^2/\epsilon)]$ does not converge to $\tilde{\psi}_1 = \exp[-\frac{1}{2}(\rho^2 + (\xi_1 - \rho)^2/\epsilon)]$ as $\epsilon \to 0$, so that the situation is the same as in Minkowski space.* However, and this differs from the situation in Minkowski space, the time development $U_{2t}(\varphi)\tilde{\psi}_1$ is such that it remains pseudo-localized: it moves, in fact, with light velocity along the de Sitter hyperboloid. That it does so is not surprising, in view of the observations at the end of Section IV, but it shows that the interpretation of the representation given by (24), (27) is far from unique.

To present this last point in somewhat greater detail, we start with a $\tilde{\psi}$ that is zero unless $\xi_1 = \rho\cos\varphi_i'$, $\xi_2 = \rho\sin\varphi_i'$ (i stands for *initial*). According to the interpretation of the last paragraph, such a wave function would represent a state localized, at time zero, at the point

$$x_{1i} = R\sin\varphi_i', \qquad x_{2i} = R\cos\varphi_i' \tag{57}$$

where R is the radius of the universe.

* This is discussed in Newton and Wigner (*39*).

If we apply the operator $U_{1t}(\varphi)$ to this wave function, we obtain, according to (27), a wave function that vanishes unless

$$\frac{\xi_1 \operatorname{Ch}\varphi + \rho \operatorname{Sh}\varphi}{\xi_1 \operatorname{Sh}\varphi + \operatorname{Ch}\varphi} = \cos\varphi_i', \qquad \frac{\xi_2}{\xi_1 \operatorname{Sh}\varphi + \rho \operatorname{Ch}\varphi} = \sin\varphi_i'. \tag{58}$$

Such a wave function represents a state localized at $x_{1f}' = R\sin\varphi_f'$, $x_{2f}' = R\cos\varphi_f'$ where φ_f' is determined by setting $\xi_1 = \rho\cos\varphi_f'$, $\xi_2 = \rho\sin\varphi_f'$ into (58) and solving for $\cos\varphi_f'$ and $\sin\varphi_f'$. This gives, for the coordinates of the point at which the particle is localized at zero time in the new coordinate system,

$$x_{1f}' = R\sin\varphi_f' = R\frac{\sin\varphi_i'}{\operatorname{Ch}\varphi - \cos\varphi_i' \operatorname{Sh}\varphi} \tag{58a}$$

$$x_{2f}' = R\cos\varphi_f' = R\frac{\cos\varphi_i' \operatorname{Ch}\varphi - \operatorname{Sh}\varphi}{\operatorname{Ch}\varphi - \cos\varphi_i' \operatorname{Sh}\varphi}. \tag{58b}$$

The point with the coordinates $x_1' = x_{1f}'$, $x_2' = x_{2f}'$, $t' = 0$ in the coordinate system obtained by the transformation $U_{1t}(\varphi)$ is the point

$$x_{1f} = x_{1f}' \operatorname{Ch}\varphi, \qquad x_{2f} = x_{2f}', \qquad t_f = x_{1f}' \operatorname{Sh}\varphi \tag{59}$$

in the original coordinate system. The space-time distance of this point from the initial point of localization is

$$t_f^2 - (x_{1f} - x_{1i})^2 - (x_{2f} - x_{2i})^2 = 0 \tag{60}$$

and a short calculation verifies that this is 0. Admittedly, this calculation cannot be extended to $m > 2$, that is, to several spatial dimensions. Nevertheless, the interpretation of our representation, given at the end of Section IV, shows that the representation space can be interpreted as the space of states of a particle with zero mass. It is evident, however, that the interpretation just considered violates reflection symmetry grossly, inasmuch as the particles localized at a given point necessarily move in one, rather than in the opposite, direction. Thus, the initial localization $x_{1i} = R$, $x_{2i} = 0$, at $t = 0$ goes over into $x_{1f} = R$, $x_{2f} = -R\operatorname{Th}\varphi$ at $t_f = R\operatorname{Th}\varphi$, rather than into the point $x_{1f} = R$, $x_{2f} = +R\operatorname{Th}\varphi$. Inversion symmetry could be restored by doubling the number of states, similar to that considered in Wigner (*30*) and Tarimer (*31*). Nevertheless, the interpretation just considered will not be pursued further and we return to the localizations given by (42) and Eqs. (54). The connection between the positive nature of the energy and the operation of contraction will be demonstrated on the basis of that localization.

VII. General Remarks about Contraction of Groups and Their Representations

We shall give, first, a short review of the process of contraction. Intuitively, contraction of a group consists in the restriction of the group space to that of a subgroup and its infinitely close neighborhood. The subgroup in question is fundamental to the process of contraction; one speaks of the subgroup with respect to which the group is contracted. It may be any continuous subgroup of the original group.

The multiplication laws of the elements of the subgroup with respect to which the original group is contracted remain unaltered. The general element of the contracted group is a product of an element of this subgroup and an element of an Abelian group. This Abelian group is formed by equivalence classes of the infinitesimal elements of the original group, all infinitesimal elements that differ by an infinitesimal element of the subgroup being in the same equivalence class. If the original group has p parameters and the subgroup with respect to which the contraction is undertaken q parameters, the equivalence classes can be characterized by $p-q$ parameters. These parameters can be defined by choosing a set of infinitesimal elements of the original group that are linearly independent of each other and of the infinitesimal elements of the subgroup. Each equivalence class then contains one and only one linear combination of the infinitesimal elements of the set chosen, and the coefficients of the elements of the set then characterize the equivalence class uniquely and completely. The coefficients in question can be considered as the components of a vector $\mathbf{v}$; this vector characterizes the equivalence class, and will be used to denote it. The element of the Abelian group that it characterizes will be denoted by $\langle\mathbf{v}\rangle$.

The product of all the elements of one equivalence class with all the elements of another equivalence class results in the elements of a single equivalence class. The vector characterizing the equivalence class of the product is the sum of the vectors characterizing the equivalence classes of the factors

$$\langle\mathbf{v}_1\rangle\langle\mathbf{v}_2\rangle=\langle\mathbf{v}\rangle \qquad \text{if} \quad \mathbf{v}_1+\mathbf{v}_2=\mathbf{v}. \tag{61}$$

Further, if we transform the elements E of an equivalence class by an element s of the subgroup, that is, form the elements sEs^{-1}, these are again the elements of an equivalence class. Finally, the components of the vector characterizing the equivalence class of sEs^{-1} will depend linearly on the components of the vector that characterized the equivalence class of E. Hence, the correspondence

$$\langle\mathbf{w}\rangle=s\langle\mathbf{v}\rangle s^{-1} \tag{62a}$$

defines a matrix $\mathbf{M}(s)$ for every element s of the subgroup so that (62a) is equivalent with

$$\mathbf{w} = \mathbf{M}(s)\,\mathbf{v}. \tag{62b}$$

The matrices $\mathbf{M}(s)$ then give a representation of the subgroup

$$\mathbf{M}(s_1)\,\mathbf{M}(s_2) = \mathbf{M}(s_1\,s_2). \tag{63}$$

The elements of the contracted group are products of an element of the Abelian group defined in the foregoing, and specified by a vector $\mathbf{v}$, and an element of the subgroup s. The dimensionality of the contracted group is the same as that of the group from which it is contracted. The multiplication law of the contracted group is obtained from

$$\langle\mathbf{v}_1\rangle\, s_1 \cdot \langle\mathbf{v}_2\rangle\, s_2 = \langle\mathbf{v}_1\rangle \cdot s_1\langle\mathbf{v}_2\rangle\, s_1^{-1} \cdot s_1\, s_2. \tag{64}$$

The first two factors on the right side are elements of the Abelian group; because of (61) and (62) we have

$$\langle\mathbf{v}_1\rangle \cdot s_1\langle\mathbf{v}_2\rangle\, s_1^{-1} = \langle\mathbf{v}_1 + \mathbf{M}(s_1)\,\mathbf{v}_2\rangle; \tag{64a}$$

the last factor of (64) is an element of the subgroup. It is evident from this discussion that all contracted groups are "inhomogeneous groups"; their elements are products of a "translation" $\langle\mathbf{v}\rangle$ and a homogeneous transformation s. The former constitute an invariant Abelian subgroup of the contracted group; the group of the latter, the subgroup with respect to which we contracted, is isomorphic to the factor group of this invariant subgroup. If the representation $\mathbf{M}(s)$ of this factor group is faithful, (64) and (64a) are the usual equations of an inhomogeneous group*

$$(\mathbf{v}_1,\, \mathbf{M}(s_1))\,(\mathbf{v}_2,\, \mathbf{M}(s_2)) = (\mathbf{v}_1 + \mathbf{M}(s_1)\,\mathbf{v}_1,\, \mathbf{M}(s_1)\,\mathbf{M}(s_2)). \tag{65}$$

If the $\mathbf{M}(s)$ of (64a) are not faithful, (65) does not reproduce the group Eq. (64). In order to reproduce the full group equations, we can replace the $\mathbf{M}(s)$ in (65) by a faithful representation $\mathbf{F}(s)$ of the subgroup. This can be the direct sum of the representation $\mathbf{M}(s)$ and of a faithful representation of the subgroup. If the components of the vectors $\mathbf{v}$ that correspond to this

* The construction of the contracted group here described gives, for the contracted group, Rosen's general form of inhomogeneous groups. Cf. Rosen (*44*).

additional representation are all set equal to zero, (65), with $\mathbf{M}(s)$ replaced by $\mathbf{F}(s)$, will reproduce the group equations fully.

It follows from the preceding discussion (the last paragraph is, in fact, not necessary thereto) that the representations of the contracted group can be obtained by Frobenius's method (*45, 46*)* if the representations of the subgroup and, a fortiori, the representations of the group to be contracted are known. Our purpose, however, will not be the determination of the representations of the contracted de Sitter groups, which are known anyway, but to obtain that representation (or those representations) of the contracted group into which the contraction process transforms a given representation.

If we carry out the contraction in a straightforward way and use a fixed set of vectors ψ_i in the representation space, the representatives of the elements of the Abelian invariant subgroup will all converge to the unit operator. This follows, simply, from the continuity of the representation, as a consequence of which $U(g)\psi_i \to \psi_i$ as g converges to the unit element. Hence, the straight contraction process does not give faithful representations of the contracted group, but only representations of the factor group of the Abelian group, the factor group that is isomorphic to the subgroup with respect to which the contraction was undertaken. In the case of compact groups and finite-dimensional unitary representations, the result of the contraction is always such a not-faithful representation. In such a case $U(g)\psi$ converges to ψ uniformly in ψ as g converges to the unit element. Hence, in order to obtain faithful representations of the contracted group, we must couple the contraction process with a change of the representation (*23*). In case of the contraction of the de Sitter groups this follows also from the fact that the contracted groups (which are never compact) have no faithful unitary representations in finite dimensions, so that if we wish to obtain a faithful representation, we must proceed, in the course of the contraction process, to representations of increasingly high dimensions.

As Inönü's observation already indicates, the situation is different if the group to be contracted is itself noncompact. In this case, $U(g)\psi$ does not converge uniformly in ψ to ψ itself and we can couple the contraction process with transitions to new coordinate systems in Hilbert space. The states that form the new axes of the Hilbert space will increasingly approach the states localized at the point that is left invariant by the transformations of the subgroup with respect to which the contraction is undertaken, and at points nearby The resulting representation of the contracted group (the inhomogeneous Lorentz group) will be faithful. The question whether this is the only way to contract fixed representations of the de Sitter groups in order to obtain faithful representations of the contracted (inhomogeneous Lorentz) group will be left open. We do not know the answer.

* See also Seitz (*47*).

VIII. Contraction of the Representations of the 2 + 1 de Sitter Group

We wish to contract the representations of the 2 + 1 de Sitter group with respect to the transformations in the $x_1 t$ plane. The contracted group is the inhomogeneous Lorentz group with one spatial and one timelike dimension. First we establish the results of the straightforward contraction. For this, $U_{12}(\varphi)$ and $U_{2t}(\varphi)$ are replaced by

$$\lim_{\epsilon\to 0} U_{12}(\epsilon\varphi) = 1 \tag{66a}$$

and

$$\lim_{\epsilon\to 0} U_{2t}(\epsilon\varphi) = 1, \tag{66b}$$

whereas $U_{1t}(\varphi)$, given by (27), remains unchanged. The factor group that is represented by the operators $U_{1t}(\varphi)$ is the noncompact one-parametric group of homogeneous Lorentz transformations in the $x_1 t$ plane. The representation $U_{1t}(\varphi)$ of this group can be decomposed into its irreducible parts either by solving the characteristic value equation

$$N_{1t}\psi_s = is\psi_s \tag{67}$$

with the N_{1t} given by (35a) or, equivalently, by postulating

$$U_{1t}(\varphi)\psi_s = e^{is\varphi}\psi_s \tag{67a}$$

and using (27) with $m = 2$ for U_{1t}. This last equation yields, with $\xi_1 = \rho\cos\varphi'$, $\xi_2 = \rho\sin\varphi'$,

$$\psi_s\left(\rho\frac{\cos\varphi' \operatorname{Ch}\varphi + \operatorname{Sh}\varphi}{\operatorname{Ch}\varphi + \cos\varphi' \operatorname{Sh}\varphi}, \frac{\rho\sin\varphi'}{\operatorname{Ch}\varphi + \cos\varphi' \operatorname{Sh}\varphi}\right)(\operatorname{Ch}\varphi + \cos\varphi' \operatorname{Sh}\varphi)^{i\mu-(1/2)}$$
$$= e^{is\varphi}\psi_s(\rho\cos\varphi', \rho\sin\varphi'). \tag{68}$$

One can obtain ψ_s as function of φ' from this by setting $\cos\varphi' = -\operatorname{Th}\varphi$ so that the arguments of ψ_s on the left side become 0 and ρ; that is, they become independent of φ'. Since, then, $\operatorname{Ch}\varphi = 1/\sin\varphi'$, $\operatorname{Sh}\varphi = -\cot\varphi'$, the expression in the braces is simply $\sin\varphi'$ and we have, if we suppress the dummy dependence on ρ, apart from a constant

$$\psi_s(\varphi') = (\sin\varphi')^{i\mu-(1/2)}\exp(-is\ln\tan\tfrac{1}{2}\varphi'). \tag{69}$$

We can convince ourselves by direct calculation that this ψ_s satisfies (68) for arbitrary φ and φ'. It can be brought into a more familiar form by the substitution $\ln\tan\frac{1}{2}\varphi' = q$; this variable then increases from $-\infty$ to ∞ as φ' increases from 0 to π. If we wish to use q as a variable and straight integration over q for the scalar product, ψ_s must be multiplied by $(dq/d\varphi')^{-1/2} = \sin^{1/2}\varphi'$. Hence, the characteristic functions ψ_s assume, when considered to be functions of q, the well-known form

$$\psi_s(\varphi') \to (\sin\varphi')^{i\mu} e^{-isq} = (\mathrm{Ch}\, q)^{-i\mu} e^{-isq}. \tag{69a}$$

These form a complete continuous spectrum as q changes from $-\infty$ to ∞ and hence the $\psi_s(\varphi')$ with the value given by (69) for $0 < \varphi' < \pi$ and the value 0 for negative φ' form a similar continuous spectrum. There is a second essentially identical continuous spectrum formed by the functions $\psi_s'(\varphi')$ that have the values given by (69) for $-\pi < \varphi' < 0$ and the value 0 for positive φ'.

The preceding calculation shows what must have been well known to most who have contributed to the theory of the representations of quasi-orthogonal groups, in particular the $O(2,1)$ group; if we restrict this representation to a Lorentzian subgroup $O(1,1)$, it becomes not the sum of irreducible representations, but an integral over such representations in the sense of von Neumann (*48*) and Mautner (*49*).* In fact, it is the sum of two such integrals. This last point has an interesting reason, closely related to, though somewhat more subtle than, the one to which Fronsdal has pointed (*52*). His L and K are

$$L = -iN_{yt}, \qquad K = -i(N_{xy} + N_{xt}). \tag{70}$$

To these can be added

$$M = -i(N_{xy} - N_{xt}), \tag{70a}$$

so that the commutation relations become

$$[L, K] = -iK, \qquad [L, M] = iM, \qquad [K, M] = 2iL. \tag{70b}$$

The reader will note that we use Hermitian infinitesimal elements when the present observation is presented. Fronsdal then assumes that ψ is a characteristic vector of L with characteristic value λ so that $L\psi = \lambda\psi$. It then follows from the first of Eqs. (70b) that

$$LK\psi = KL\psi - iK\psi = \lambda K\psi - iK\psi = (\lambda - i)\, K\psi, \tag{71}$$

* See also Dixmier (*50*) and Naimark (*51*).

so that $K\psi$ is a characteristic function of L, with characteristic value $\lambda - i$. This contradicts the self-adjoint nature of L so that it appears impossible to satisfy the first commutation relation (70b) by means of self-adjoint operators and this would then appear a fortiori for all three Eqs. (70b). The conclusion is, however, erroneous: the operators

$$Lf(q) = -i\left(\frac{d}{dq}\right) f(q), \qquad Kf(q) = e^q f(q) \tag{71a}$$

satisfy the relation $[L, K] = -iK$. The corresponding finite operators are

$$\begin{aligned} L(\varphi)f(q) &= \exp(i\varphi L)f(q) = f(q-\varphi) \\ K(\varphi')f(q) &= \exp(i\varphi' K)f(q) = \exp[i\varphi' \exp(q)]f(q). \end{aligned} \tag{71b}$$

We can verify that these satisfy the relations

$$K(\varphi')\,L(\varphi) = L(\varphi)\,K(\varphi' e^{\varphi}) \tag{71c}$$

characteristic of the subgroup spanned by L and K. This group is isomorphic to that of the matrices

$$\begin{pmatrix} e^{\varphi} & \varphi' \\ 0 & 1 \end{pmatrix}.$$

It follows that the calculation presented in (71) cannot be valid. In fact, the characteristic functions ψ of L are $\exp(i\lambda q)$ and these are not in the definition domain of K, so that K cannot be formed.

In order to satisfy all three commutation relations (70b), we need slightly more complicated expressions than (71a)

$$\begin{aligned} L &= -i\frac{d}{dq}, \\ K &= e^q\left(-i\frac{d}{dq} + \mu - \tfrac{1}{2}i\right), \\ M &= e^{-q}\left(-i\frac{d}{dq} - \mu + \tfrac{1}{2}i\right); \end{aligned} \tag{72}$$

L, which has the same spectrum as $-iN_{1t}$, has now a single continuous spectrum rather than the double one obtained before. The resolution of this paradox is similar to that of Fronsdal. If we form the operator $\frac{1}{2}(K+M) = -iN_{xy}$ and determine its spectrum, we find that the characteristic functions are square-integrable, so that the spectrum must be discrete. We find further that the characteristic vectors are orthogonal only if the corresponding characteristic values differ by an even integer. Hence, in order to make the operator self-adjoint, its spectrum must be restricted to a set of numbers such that the difference of any two is an even integer. However, the operators K and M produce from each characteristic vector a sum of two characteristic vectors with characteristic values differing by ± 1 from the characteristic value of the vector to which K or M was applied. Hence, the operators (72), if restricted so as to be self-adjoint, satisfy the commutation relations only apparently.

Let us consider, next, the contraction in the more extended sense discussed at the end of the preceding section. Whereas in the straight contraction process just considered it was quite conceivable that the vectors of the irreducible representations of the contracted group were bona fide vectors in the original representation space as well (though in the preceding example this did not turn out to be the case), such a situation can never be present for the contraction process in the extended sense. For any definite vector ψ of the original representation space, $U(g)\psi$ does converge to ψ as g approaches the unit element. Hence, the vectors of the representation space of the contracted group will be distributions rather than vectors in the original space and, from the point of view of purely mathematical representation theory, there may be a great deal of freedom in the choice of these distributions. In the present case, however, there is no such ambiguity: the localized state ψ_1 of (42) must be a limiting case of the new representation space as it was of the original Hilbert space. Hence, we shall first construct states that are localized within a short interval, though not at a point. We shall then guess at an invariant extension of these states—invariant under all $U_{1t}(\varphi)$, but only under infinitesimal $U_{2t}(\epsilon\varphi)$ and $U_{12}(\epsilon\varphi)$. Finally, we shall verify that the states so obtained form an irreducible representation space of the contracted group, that is, the $2+1$ Poincaré group.

In order to form normalizable states from the localized states ψ_1, we form the states $U_{12}(\varphi)\psi_1$ localized at displaced points $x_1 = R\sin\varphi$, $x_2 = R\cos\varphi$ (at time 0) and integrate with respect to φ over a narrow range, small compared with $1/R$. Integration of the series (42) from $-\epsilon$ to ϵ, term by term, gives

$$\psi_{1\epsilon}(\varphi') = \sum 2l_\lambda e^{i\lambda\varphi'}\left(\frac{\sin \epsilon\lambda}{\lambda}\right). \tag{73}$$

Since all $|l_\lambda| = 1$, this is indeed normalizable. Had we used, instead of the step function, some other factor, such as $\exp(-\varphi^2/\epsilon^2)$, with which to weight $U_{12}(\varphi)\psi_1$, the result would have been similar to (73) except that the convergence factor in the parentheses would have been different. The important point about this factor is that it changes very little if λ is replaced by $\lambda \pm 1$. Such a change corresponds to a change in the momentum p by $\hbar/R$ and the momentum interval in which ψ must change significantly if the position is to be within a distance Δx_1 from $x_1 = 0$ is $\hbar/\Delta x_1$. Hence, the interval over which λ can change appreciably, if $|x_1|$ is not to be larger than Δx_1, is $R/\Delta x_1$. We shall tentatively assume, therefore, that the ψ of the contracted representation space have the form

$$\psi(\varphi') = \Sigma\, l_\lambda f\left(\frac{\lambda}{R}\right) e^{i\lambda\varphi'} \tag{74}$$

where $f(k)$ is a differentiable function of k. If it is also normalizable and $\int |f(k)|^2\, dk = 1$, the function

$$\psi(\varphi') = (2\pi R)^{-1/2} \int l_{kR} f(k)\, e^{ikR\varphi'}\, dk \tag{74a}$$

will be a normalized function of φ'.

Because of the factor l_λ in (74), the additional factor f has the same phase that the Fourier transform of $\psi(\varphi')$ would have had, had we adopted the usual form [for example, that used by Philips (*36*)] of the representation. We may note that the functions of the form (74a) span, in the limit $R \to \infty$, only an infinitely small part of the function space. The functions

$$\psi_\varphi(\varphi') = (2\pi R)^{-1/2} \int l_{kR} f(k) \exp[ikR(\varphi' - \varphi)]\, dk \tag{74b}$$

with any $\varphi > 0$, $\varphi < 2\pi$, are orthogonal to them. They correspond to states localized near $x_1 = R\sin\varphi$, $x_2 = R\cos\varphi$, within a distance $\Delta x \ll R$ from this point. However, these spaces do not correspond to a reduction of the original representation into representations of the contracted group. Except for the functions of the form (74), they are not invariant under the operators $U_{1t}(\varphi)$. It is, in fact, as far as we can see, open to question whether there is a limiting set of Hilbert spaces into which the original Hilbert space can be decomposed, similar to the decomposition into the ψ_s of (69), obtained by straightforward contraction.

Let us verify now that the set of functions (74) is invariant under the operators $U_{1t}(\varphi)$ and the operators $U_{12}(\varphi/R)$ and $U_{2t}(\varphi/R)$ as $R \to \infty$. Again, the calculation can be carried out by means of either the finite operators or the infinitesimal ones. The latter method is somewhat simpler in this case.

Let us calculate, first [compare (35a) and (74)],

$$N_{1t}\psi(\varphi') = \left[-\sin\varphi' \frac{d}{d\varphi'} + (i\mu - \tfrac{1}{2})\cos\varphi'\right] \Sigma\, l_\lambda f\left(\frac{\lambda}{R}\right) e^{i\lambda\varphi'}$$

$$= \Sigma\, \tfrac{1}{2}\left[(-\lambda + \tfrac{1}{2} + i\mu)\, l_{\lambda-1} f\left(\frac{\lambda-1}{R}\right)\right.$$

$$\left. + (\lambda + \tfrac{1}{2} + i\mu)\, l_{\lambda+1} f\left(\frac{\lambda+1}{R}\right)\right] e^{i\lambda\varphi'}. \tag{75}$$

If we consider $\Psi = U_{1t}(\varphi)\psi(\varphi')$ as a function of both φ' and φ, the left side gives $\partial\Psi/\partial\varphi$. Assuming that Ψ has an expansiòn such as (74), we must consider the f to be functions of both λ/R and φ. The right side can be brought into a more suitable form by placing l_λ outside the brackets and using (47) to express $l_{\lambda+1}/l_\lambda$ and $l_{\lambda-1}/l_\lambda$. Hence, we obtain

$$\frac{\partial\Psi}{\partial\varphi} = \tfrac{1}{2}\Sigma\, l_\lambda \zeta \left\{-[(\lambda - \tfrac{1}{2})^2 + \mu^2]^{1/2} f\left(\frac{\lambda-1}{R}\right)\right.$$

$$\left. + [(\lambda + \tfrac{1}{2})^2 + \mu^2]^{1/2} f\left(\frac{\lambda+1}{R}\right)\right\} e^{i\lambda\varphi'}. \tag{75a}$$

Since, on the other hand,

$$\frac{\partial\Psi}{\partial\varphi} = \Sigma\, l_\lambda \frac{\partial f_\lambda}{\partial\varphi} e^{i\lambda\varphi'}, \tag{75b}$$

We can equate the coefficients of the $e^{i\lambda\varphi'}$ of both sides.

$$\frac{\partial f_\lambda}{\partial\varphi} = \tfrac{1}{2}\zeta\left\{[(\lambda + \tfrac{1}{2})^2 + \mu^2]^{1/2} f\left(\frac{\lambda+1}{R}\right) - [(\lambda - \tfrac{1}{2})^2 + \mu^2]^{1/2} f\left(\frac{\lambda-1}{R}\right)\right\}, \tag{75c}$$

and if R is large, we can express $f[(\lambda+1)/R]$ and $f[(\lambda-1)/R]$ by means of $f(\lambda/R)$ and its first derivative. This gives (if we neglect $\tfrac{1}{4}$, as compared with λ),

$$\frac{\partial f}{\partial\varphi} = \tfrac{1}{2}\zeta\left[\frac{1}{R}(\lambda^2 + \mu^2)^{1/2} f' + \lambda(\lambda^2 + \mu^2)^{-1/2} f\right]. \tag{75d}$$

We can finally introduce $k = \lambda/R$ into this equation, recall that $\mu^2 = R^2 M^2 c^2/\hbar^2$, and obtain

$$\frac{\partial f}{\partial\varphi} = \tfrac{1}{2}\zeta\left[\left(k^2 + \frac{M^2c^2}{\hbar^2}\right)^{1/2} \frac{\partial f}{\partial k} + k\left(k^2 + \frac{M^2c^2}{\hbar^2}\right)^{-1/2} f\right]. \tag{76}$$

This is a first-order partial differential equation for f that can be solved, in fact rather easily, if, for $\varphi = 0$, f is differentiable with respect to k. The solution, when reinserted into

$$\Psi = \Sigma\, l_\lambda f\left(\frac{\lambda}{R}\right) e^{i\lambda\varphi'} \tag{76a}$$

then gives $U_{1t}(\varphi)\psi(\varphi')$. Since f, as function of k, remains differentiable for arbitrary φ if it was differentiable for $\varphi = 0$, the set of functions of the form (74) is indeed invariant under the operators $U_{1t}(\varphi)$.

It may be worth observing that the possibility of expressing the coefficients of the differential equation (75d) in terms of k depends essentially on the approximate cancellation of the two terms of (75c). This, in its turn, was the consequence of the fact that the λ dependence of the coefficient of $e^{i\lambda\varphi'}$ in (74) or (76a) deviates little from the λ dependence of the coefficient l_λ of the localized state $\psi_1(\varphi')$ of (42). In fact, the coefficients l_λ were determined by the postulate that $N_{1t}\psi_1$ be as small as possible. It is further worth observing that the conclusion we arrived at is independent of whether $\zeta = 1$ or $\zeta = -1$.

In case of $U_{12}(\varphi/R)$ we may apply, as well, the finite operator. This replaces φ' by $\varphi' - \varphi/R$; that is, it replaces

$$f\left(\frac{\lambda}{R}\right) \rightarrow f\left(\frac{\lambda}{R}\right) \exp\left(\frac{-i\lambda\varphi}{R}\right) = f(k)\exp(-ik\varphi) \tag{77}$$

so that $f(k)$ remains differentiable with respect to k if $U_{12}(\varphi/R)$ is applied to it. We note, incidentally, that in order to be in accord with the conventional interpretation of k, we should have substituted $-k$ rather than k for λ/R. Again, it makes no difference whether $\zeta = 1$ or $\zeta = -1$ and no choice on the alternative in (54) is indicated.

Let us consider, finally, the operator $U_{2t}(\varphi/R)$. It is useful, in this case, to use the infinitesimal operator N_{2t}, which can be calculated as was N_{1t} for (35a)

$$N_{2t} = \cos\varphi' \frac{\partial}{\partial\varphi'} + (i\mu - \tfrac{1}{2})\sin\varphi. \tag{78}$$

Applying this to (74) as before, we obtain, for the $g(\lambda/R)$ of

$$R^{-1} N_{2t}\psi = R^{-1} N_{2t} \Sigma\, l_\lambda f\left(\frac{\lambda}{R}\right) e^{i\lambda\varphi'} = \Sigma\, l_\lambda g\left(\frac{\lambda}{R}\right) e^{i\lambda\varphi'}, \tag{79}$$

the expression

$$g\left(\frac{\lambda}{R}\right) = \tfrac{1}{2}R^{-1}\,\zeta i\left\{[(\lambda-\tfrac{1}{2})^2+\mu^2]^{1/2} f\left(\frac{\lambda-1}{R}\right) + [(\lambda+\tfrac{1}{2})^2+\mu^2]^{1/2} f\left(\frac{\lambda+1}{R}\right)\right\},$$

$$\approx R^{-1}\, i\zeta(\lambda^2+\mu^2)^{1/2} f\left(\frac{\lambda}{R}\right). \tag{79a}$$

Hence, $f(\lambda/R)$ is replaced in $U_{2t}(\varphi/R)\psi$ by

$$f\left(\frac{\lambda}{R}\right) \to f\left(\frac{\lambda}{R}\right)\exp\left[i\zeta\left(\left(\frac{\lambda}{R}\right)^2+\frac{M^2c^2}{\hbar^2}\right)^{1/2}\right] = f(k)\exp\left[i\zeta\left(k^2+\frac{M^2c^2}{\hbar^2}\right)^{1/2}\right]. \tag{80}$$

As was to be anticipated, the operations implied by (77) and (80) commute: they represent elements of the invariant Abelian subgroup of the contracted group. Equations (76), (77), and (80) give, therefore, the transformations of the contracted representation for the three subgroups: Lorentz transformations, spatial displacements, and time displacements.* We also note that to remain in accord with the usual sign convention, we have to set $\zeta = -1$ for the state localized at $x_1 = 0$, $x_2 = R$, and $\zeta = 1$ for the state localized at $x_1 = 0$, $x_2 = -R$.

That the contraction of the de Sitter group in the extended sense did give the expected representation of the corresponding Poincaré group with a single sign of the energy should not obscure the fact that the respective roles of positive and negative energy states differ in the de Sitter groups from their roles in the Poincaré groups. There corresponds to every real rest mass in our $2+1$ de Sitter group, and to every rest mass and spin in the $4+1$ de Sitter group, only one irreducible representation. The distinction between the representations of the contracted groups is based on the difference of the choice of the contracted states, and this difference was dictated by the ambiguity (54) in the definition of the position operator. Physically, the difference exists only because we always deal with states with a coherence length very small as compared with the size of the universe. If a state with a truly sharply defined momentum, such as any $e^{i\lambda\varphi'}$ state in the $(2+1)$-space, or any analogous state in the $(4+1)$-space, were realizable, the distinction between positive and negative energy states would disappear. Although we consider this an interesting observation, its significance is not yet fully clear.

* Among previous investigations of our problem, the point of view of Gürsey is closest to ours. Cf. Gürsey (*53*). See also Roman and Aghassi (*54*) and Roman and Koh (*55*).

Acknowledgment

We are much indebted to Dr. L. C. Biedenharn for having drawn our attention to a number of important publications. As a result of his help, our References are much less deficient than they would have been otherwise.

REFERENCES

1. L. H. Thomas, *Ann. of Math.* **42**, 113 (1941).
2. T. D. Newton, *Ann. of Math.* **51**, 730 (1950).
3. J. Dixmier, *Bull. Soc. Math. France* **89**, 9 (1961).
4. V. Bargmann, *Ann. of Math.* **48**, 568 (1947).
5. I. M. Gel'fand and M. A. Naimark, *J. Phys. USSR* **10**, 93 (1946); *Izv. Akad. Nauk SSSR* **11**, 411 (1947); *Uspehi Mat. Nauk* **9**, 19 (1954).
6. A. Kihlberg, *Ark. Fys.* **30**, 121 (1965).
7. A. Kihlberg and S. Ström, *Ark. Fys.* **31**, 491 (1966).
8. I. M. Gel'fand, R. A. Minlos, and Z. Ya Shapiro, "Representations of the Rotation and Lorentz Groups." Pergamon Press, London, 1963.
9. L. C. Biedenharn, J. Nuyts, and N. Straumann, *Ann. Inst. H. Poincaré* **A3**, 13 (1965).
10. R. Takahashi, *Bull. Soc. Math. France* **91**, 289 (1963).
11. Harish-Chandra, *Proc. Nat. Acad. Sci. U.S.A.* **37**, 170, 362, 366, 691 (1951); *Trans. Amer. Math. Soc.* **75**, 185 (1953); **76**, 26, 234, 485 (1954); *Proc. Nat. Acad. Sci. U.S.A.* **40**, 200, 1076, 1078 (1954).
12. J. B. Ehrman, Princeton Dissertation, 1954; *Proc. Cambridge Philos. Soc.* **53**, 290 (1957).
13. F. A. Berezini, I. M. Gel'fand, M. I. Graev, and M. A. Naimark, *Uspehi Mat. Nauk* **11**, 13 (1956).
14. J. Rosen and P. Roman, *J. Mathematical Phys.* **7**, 2072 (1966).
15. M. A. Melvin, *Bull. Amer. Phys. Soc.* **7**, 493 (1962); **8**, 356 (1963).
16. W. T. Sharp, Rept. 933, Atomic Energy of Canada, 1960.
17. D. W. Robinson, *Helv. Phys. Acta* **35**, 98 (1962).
18. M. Levy-Nahas, *J. Mathematical Phys.* **8**, 1211 (1967).
19. G. Berendt, *Acta Phys. Austriaca* **25**, 207 (1967).
20. J. Rosen, *Nuovo Cimento* **35**, 1234 (1965).
21. A. Esteve and P. G. Sona, *Nuovo Cimento* **32**, 473 (1964).
22. I. E. Segal, *Duke Math. J.* **18**, 221 (1951).
23. E. Inönü and E. P. Wigner, *Proc. Nat. Acad. Sci. U.S.A.* **39**, 510 (1953).
24. E. Inönü, *Comm. Fac. Sci. Univ. Ankara Ser. A* **8**, 83 (1956).
25. E. Inönü, *in* "Group Theoretical Concepts and Methods in Elementary Particle Physics" (F. Gürsey, ed.), p. 365. Gordon and Breach, New York, 1964.
26. E. J. Saletan, *J. Mathematical Phys.* **2**, 1 (1961).
27. H. Zassenhaus, *Canad. Math. Bull.* **1**, 31, 101, 183 (1958).
28. E. P. Wigner, *Ann. of Math.* **40**, 149 (1939).
29. T. Takabayasi, *Progr. Theoret. Phys.* **36**, 1074 (1966).
30. E. P. Wigner, *in* "Group Theoretical Concepts and Methods in Elementary Particle Physics" (F. Gürsey, ed.), p. 37. Gordon and Breach, New York, 1964.
31. N. Tarimer, *Phys. Rev.* **140B**, 977 (1965).
32. E. P. Wigner, *Gött. Nachr.* p. 546 (1932).
33. E. P. Wigner, "Group Theory and Its Application to the Quantum Mechanics of Atomic Spectra," pp. 329–333. Academic Press, New York, 1959.
34. J. H. Christenson, J. W. Cronin, V. L. Fitch, and R. Turlay, *Phys. Rev.* **140B**, 74 (1965).

35. S. Treiman, *Comments on Nuclear and Particle Physics* **1**, 89 (1967).
36. T. O. Philips, Localized States in de Sitter Space, Doctoral Dissertation, Princeton University, 1963.
37. A. Sankaranarayanan and R. H. Good, *Phys. Rev.* **140B**, 509 (1965).
38. H. Bacry, *Phys. Lett.* **5**, 37 (1963).
39. T. D. Newton and E. P. Wigner, *Rev. Mod. Phys.* **21**, 400 (1949).
40. G. W. Mackey, *Proc. Nat. Acad. Sci. U.S.A.* **35**, 537 (1949).
41. L. H. Loomis, *Duke Math. J.* **27**, 569 (1960).
42. A. S. Wightman, *Rev. Mod. Phys.* **34**, 845 (1962).
43. T. O. Philips, *Phys. Rev.* **136B**, 893 (1964).
44. J. Rosen, *Nuovo Cimento* **35**, 1234 (1965).
45. G. Frobenius, *Sitz. d. Kön. Preuss. Akad.* p. 501 (1898).
46. I. Schur, *Sitz. d. Kön. Preuss. Akad.* p. 164 (1906).
47. F. Seitz, *Ann. of Math.* **37**, 17 (1936).
48. J. von Neumann, *Ann. of Math.* **50**, 401 (1949).
49. F. I. Mautner, *Ann. of Math.* **51**, 1 (1950); **52**, 528 (1950); *Proc. Amer. Math. Soc.* **2**, 490 (1951).
50. J. Dixmier, "Les Algèbres d'Operateurs dans l'Espace Hilbertien," Chap. 2. Gauthier-Villars, Paris, 1957.
51. M. Naimark, "Normed Rings" (translated by L. F. Boron and P. Noordhoff), Sec. 41. Groningen, 1964.
52. C. Fronsdal, *Rev. Mod. Phys.* **37**, 221 (1965).
53. F. Gürsey, *in* "Group Theoretical Concepts and Methods in Elementary Particle Physics" (F. Gürsey, ed.), p. 365. Gordon and Breach, New York, 1964.
54. P. Roman and J. J. Aghassi, *Nuovo Cimento* **42**, 193 (1966).
55. P. Roman and C. J. Koh, *Nuovo Cimento* **45A**, 268 (1966).
56. L. Pukanszky, *Math. Ann.* **156**, 96 (1964).
57. H. Bacry and J.-M. Lévy-Leblond, *J. Mathematical Phys.*, to be published.

Author Index

Numbers in parentheses are reference numbers and indicate that an author's work is referred to, although his name is not cited in the text. Numbers in italics show the page on which the complete reference is listed.

W

Y

Z

Subject Index

H

I

J

K

L

M

N

O

P

Q

R